Stanley Gib

STAMP CATAL

C000257784

PART 21

South-East Asia

Fourth Edition, 2004

Stanley Gibbons Ltd
London and Ringwood

By Appointment to Her Majesty The Queen
Stanley Gibbons Ltd., London
Philatelists

Published by **Stanley Gibbons Ltd.**
Publications Editorial, Sales Offices and
Distribution Centre:
Parkside, Christchurch, Ringwood,
Hants, BH24 3SH

1st Edition in this form - July 1980
2nd Edition - August 1983
3rd Edition - November 1986
4th Edition - August 2004

' Stanley Gibbons Ltd. 2004

ISBN: 0-85259-563-8

. **Item No. 2850 (04)**

Printed and bound by Polestar Wheatons Ltd, Exeter

Stanley Gibbons Foreign Catalogue Parts 2–22

Edward Stanley Gibbons published his first catalogue of postage stamps from Plymouth in November 1865. Its unillustrated twenty pages listed stamps and postal stationery from Antigua to Wurttemburg with price columns provided for unused or used, either as singles or by the dozen.

Since 1865 the catalogue range has grown to over forty current titles, all profusely illustrated and reflecting current research and price information.

The foreign listings, of which this volume forms a part, were published as Part II of the Stanley Gibbons catalogue from 1897 to 1945. Circumstances were difficult in the austerity period following the Second World War so the foreign listings were split into seven smaller catalogues. From 1951 to 1970 these were consolidated into Part II Europe and Colonies and Part III America, Asia and Africa.

Collecting patterns do change, however, so in 1970—71 an experimental series of Sectional catalogues appeared which were, in turn, replaced by a series of three alphabetical volumes covering Europe and four covering Overseas.

The present system of twenty-one catalogues, covering individual countries or collecting groups, was initiated in 1979. Full details of each volume and its contents are provided on the back cover. The scheme has the advantage of allowing flexibility in response to changing collecting habits with the listings being continually improved, currently by notes covering certain postal history aspects and by the addition of stamp booklet listings.

About this edition

This new edition, the first since 1995, contains a considerable amount of revision in addition to the updating of prices and the provision of new issue listings.

This catalogue also includes for the first time complete listings for Burma taken from the *Part 1* catalogue, Netherlands Indies and Timor taken from *Part 9 (Portugal and Spain)* and also Philippines taken from *Parts 9* and *22 (United States)*. The complete listing for Indo-China has also been included, taken from the *Part 6 (France)* catalogue, to bring the countries of Cambodia, Laos and Vietnam up to date.

The opportunity has also been taken to revise the listings of those sets in double-price columns.

Considerable research has been undertaken into current market prices and we would like to thank Mr. Ron Bentley for his considerable help with the listing of Laos. Addresses of specialist societies for the areas covered in this catalogue can be found on page iv.

Hugh Jefferies
Clare de la Feuillade
Colin Mount
Geoff Wilson

Stamps added to this edition

Items added to this catalogue, not previously published in *Gibbons Stamp Monthly* supplements:

Cambodia:	810a
	810b
	1170a/g
Indonesia:	J15a
Myanmar:	171a
	309a
	334a
Vietnam:	638
	639
	641

New Issues

The first supplement to this catalogue appeared in *Gibbons Stamp Monthly* for July 2004.

Stanley Gibbons Holdings Plc.

HEAD OFFICE, 399 STRAND, LONDON WC2R 0LX
Telephone 020 7836 8444 and **Fax** 020 7836 7342
Website: www.stanleygibbons.com for all departments.

Stanley Gibbons Ltd, Stanley Gibbons Auctions.
Auction Room and Specialist Stamp Departments: Open Monday-Friday,
9.30 a.m. to 5 p.m.
Shop: Open Monday-Friday 9 a.m. to 5.30 p.m. and Saturday 9.30 a.m. to 5.30 p.m.
E-mail: enquiries@stanleygibbons.co.uk

Fraser's. Autographs, photographs, letters, documents. Open Monday-Friday 9 a.m. to 5.30 p.m.
and
Saturday 10 a.m. to 4 p.m.
Website: www.frasersautographs.com **E-mail:** info@frasersautographs.co.uk

RINGWOOD OFFICE, PARKSIDE, CHRISTCHURCH ROAD, RINGWOOD, HANTS BH24 3SH
Telephone 01425 472363 (24 hour answer phone service), **Fax** 01425 470247.
Website: www.stanleygibbons.com **E-mail:** info@stanleygibbons.co.uk

Stanley Gibbons Publications.
Publications Mail Order: FREEPHONE 0800 611 622 Monday-Friday 8.30 a.m. to 5 p.m.

Stanley Gibbons Publications has overseas licensees and distributors for Australia, Belgium, Canada, Denmark, Finland, France, Hong Kong, Israel, Italy, Japan, Luxembourg, Netherlands, New Zealand, Norway, Singapore, Sweden and Switzerland. Please contact the Ringwood address for details.

Specialist Societies

Society of Indo-China Philatelists
Executive Secretary: Ron Bentley
2600 North 24th Street, Arlington
Virginia 22207, U.S.A.
E-mail: ron.bentley@verizon.net
Website: www.sicp-online.org

Burma Philatelic Study Circle
A new society is being formed, for the time
being anyone seeking up to date information is
welcome to contact Mr. G. M. Rosamond, 35
Church Hill, Winchmore Hill, London N21 1LN

Nepal and Tibet Philatelic Study Circle
Secretary: Mr. Colin Hepper
C72 Calle Miguel Angel, El Sueno - Fase 1
El Chaparral, 03180 Torreveja, Alicante, Spain
E-mail: hepper@terra.es
Website: fuchs-online.com/ntpsc

Philippine Philatelic Society
Hon Secretary: Alan C. Walder
82 Waterloo Road, Crowthorne
Berks RG45 7NW
and Don Peterson, 7408 Alaska Avenue NW
Washington DC 20012, U.S.A.
E-mail: ppsuk@f2s.com

International Philippine Philatelic Society
Bob Yacano, International Philippines Philatelic
Society (IPPS), PO Box 100, Toast, NC 27049
E-mail: ryacano@triad.rr.com

Thailand Philatelic Society
Membership Secretary: Rory Morrisey
56 Rowley Furrows, Leighton Buzzard,
Bedfordshire LU7 2SH, UK
E-mail: MemSec@ThailandPhilSoc.org.uk
Website: www.ThailandPhilSoc.org.uk

General Philatelic Information
and Guidelines to the Scope of the Foreign Catalogue

The notes which follow seek to reflect current practice in compiling the Foreign Catalogue.

It scarcely needs emphasising that the *Stanley Gibbons Stamp Catalogue* has a very long history and that the vast quantity of information it contains has been carefully built up by successive generations through the work of countless individuals. Philately itself is never static and the Catalogue has evolved and developed during this long time-span. Thus, while these notes are important for today s criteria, they may be less precise the farther back in the listings one travels. They are not intended to inaugurate some unwanted series of piecemeal alterations in a widely respected work, but it does seem to us useful that Catalogue users know as exactly as possible the policies currently in operation.

THE CATALOGUE IN GENERAL

Contents. The Catalogue is confined to adhesive postage stamps, including miniature sheets. For particular categories the rules are

(*a*) Revenue (fiscal) stamps or telegraph stamps are listed only where they have been expressly authorised for postal duty.

(*b*) Stamps issued only precancelled are included, but normally issued stamps available additionally with precancel have no separate precancel listing unless the face value is changed.

(*c*) Stamps prepared for use but not issued, hitherto accorded full listing, are nowadays footnoted with a price (where possible).

(*d*) Bisects (trisects, etc.) are only listed where such usage was officially authorised.

(*e*) Stamps issued only on first day covers and not available separately are not listed but priced (on the cover) in a footnote.

(*f*) New printings, as such, are not listed, though stamps from them may qualify under another category, e.g. when a prominent new shade results.

(*g*) Official and unofficial reprints are dealt with by footnote.

(*h*) Stamps from imperforate printings of modern issues which also occur perforated are covered by footnotes or general notes, but are listed where widely available for postal use.

Exclusions. The following are excluded: (a) non-postal revenue or fiscal stamps; (b) postage stamps used fiscally; (c) local carriage labels and private local issues; (d) telegraph stamps; (e) bogus or phantom stamps; (f) railway or airline letter fee stamps, bus or road transport company labels; (g) cut-outs; (h) all types of non-postal labels; (i) documentary labels for the postal service, e.g. registration, recorded delivery, airmail etiquettes, etc.; (j) privately applied embellishments to official issues and privately commissioned items generally; (k) stamps for training postal officers; (l) specimen stamps.

Full listing. Full listing confers our recognition and implies allotting a catalogue number and (wherever possible) a price quotation.

In judging status for inclusion in the catalogue broad considerations are applied to stamps. They must be issued by a legitimate postal authority, recognised by the government concerned, and must be adhesives valid for proper postal use in the class of service for which they are inscribed. Stamps, with the exception of such categories as postage dues and officials, must be available to the general public, at face value, in reasonable quantities without any artificial restrictions being imposed on their distribution.

We record as abbreviated, Appendix entries, without catalogue numbers or prices, stamps from countries which either persist in having far more issues than can be justified by postal need or have failed to maintain control over their distribution so that they have not been available to the public in reasonable quantities at face value. Miniature sheets and imperforate stamps are not mentioned in these entries.

The publishers of this catalogue have observed, with concern, the proliferation of artificial stamp-issuing territories. On several occasions this has resulted in separately inscribed issues for various component parts of otherwise united states or territories.

Stanley Gibbons Publications have decided that where such circumstances occur, they will not, in the future, list these items in the SG catalogue without first satisfying themselves that the stamps represent a genuine political, historical or postal division within the country concerned. Any such issues which do not fulfil this stipulation will be recorded in the Catalogue Appendix only.

For errors and varieties the criterion is legitimate (albeit inadvertent) sale over a post office counter in the normal course of business. Details of provenance are always important; printers waste and fraudulently manufactured material is excluded.

Certificates. In assessing unlisted items due weight is given to Certificates from recognised Expert Committees and, where appropriate, we will usually ask to see them.

New Issues. New issues are listed regularly in the Catalogue Supplement published in *Gibbons Stamp Monthly*, whence they are consolidated into the next available edition of the Catalogue.

Date of Issue. Where local issue dates differ from dates of release by agencies, date of issue is the local date. Fortuitous stray usage before the officially intended date is disregarded in listing.

Catalogue numbers. Stamps of each country are catalogued chronologically by date of issue. Subsidiary classes (e.g. postage due stamps) are integrated into one list with postage and commemorative stamps and distinguished by a letter prefix to the catalogue number.

The catalogue number appears in the extreme left column. The boldface Type numbers in the next column are merely cross-references to illustrations. Catalogue numbers in the *Gibbons Stamp Monthly* Supplement are provisional only and may need to be altered when the lists are consolidated. Miniature sheets only purchasable intact at a post office have a single **MS** number; sheetlets — individual stamps available — number each stamp separately. The catalogue no longer gives full listing to designs, originally issued in normal sheets, which subsequently appear in sheetlets showing changes of colour, perforation, printing process or face value. Such stamps will be covered by footnotes.

Information (contd.)

Once published in the Catalogue, numbers are changed as little as possible; really serious renumbering is reserved for the occasions when a complete country or an entire issue is being rewritten. The edition first affected includes cross-reference tables of old and new numbers.

Our catalogue numbers are universally recognised in specifying stamps and as a hallmark of status.

Illustrations. Stamps are illustrated at three-quarters linear size. Stamps not illustrated are the same size and format as the value shown unless otherwise indicated. Stamps issued only as miniature sheets usually have the stamp alone illustrated but sheet size is also quoted. Overprints, surcharges, watermarks and postmarks are normally actual size. Illustrations of varieties are often enlarged to show the detail.

CONTACTING THE CATALOGUE EDITOR

The editor is always interested in hearing from people who have new information which will improve or correct the Catalogue. As a general rule he must see and examine the actual stamps before they can be considered for listing; photographs or photocopies are insufficient evidence. Neither he nor his staff give opinions as to the genuineness of stamps.

Submissions should be made in writing to the Catalogue Editor, Stanley Gibbons Publications, 7 Parkside, Christchurch Road, Ringwood, Hants BH24 3SH. The cost of return postage for items submitted is appreciated, and this should include the registration fee if required.

Where information is solicited purely for the benefit of the enquirer, the editor cannot undertake to reply if the answer is already contained in these published notes or if return postage is omitted. Written communications are greatly preferred to enquiries by telephone and the editor regrets that he or his staff cannot see personal callers without a prior appointment being made.

The editor welcomes close contact with study circles and is interested, too, in finding reliable local correspondents who will verify and supplement official information in overseas countries where this is deficient.

We regret we do not give opinions as the genuine-ness of stamps, nor do we identify stamps or number them by our Catalogue.

TECHNICAL MATTERS

The meanings of the technical terms used in the Catalogue will be found in Stanley Gibbons *Philatelic Terms Illustrated* by James Mackay (price £14/€95 plus postage).

1. Printing

Printing errors. Errors in printing are of major interest to the Catalogue. Authenticated items meriting consideration would include background, centre or frame inverted or omitted; centre or subject transposed; error of colour; error or omission of value; double prints and impressions; printed both sides; and so on. Designs *tête-bêche*, whether intentionally or by accident, are listable. *Se-tenant* arrangements of stamps are recognised in the listings or footnotes. Gutter pairs (a pair of stamps separated by blank margin) are excluded unless they have some philatelic importance. Colours only partially omitted are not listed, neither are stamps printed on the gummed side.

Printing Varieties. Listing is accorded to major changes in the printing base which lead to completely new types. In recess-printing this could be a design re-engraved, in photogravure or photolithography a screen altered in whole or in part. It can also encompass flat-bed and rotary printing if the results are readily distinguishable.

To be considered at all, varieties must be constant.

Early stamps, produced by primitive methods, were prone to numerous imperfections; the lists reflect this, recognising re-entries, retouches, broken frames, mis-shapen letters, and so on. Printing technology has, however, radically improved over the years, during which time photogravure and lithography have become predominant. Varieties nowadays are more in the nature of flaws and these, being too specialised for a general catalogue, are almost always outside the scope. We therefore do not list such items as dry prints, kiss prints, doctor-blade flaws, blanket set-offs, doubling through blanket stretch, plate cracks and scratches, registration flaws (leading to colour shifts), lithographic ring flaws, and so on. Neither do we recognise fortuitous happenings like paper creases or confetti flaws.

Overprints (and surcharges). Overprints of different types qualify for separate listing. These include overprints in different colours; overprints from different printing processes such as litho and typo; overprints in totally different typefaces, etc.

Overprint errors and varieties. Major errors in machine-printed overprints are important and listable. They include overprint inverted or omitted; overprint double (treble, etc); overprint diagonal; overprint double, one inverted; pairs with one overprint omitted, e.g. from a radical shift to an adjoining stamp; error of colour; error of type fount; letters inverted or omitted, etc. If the overprint is handstamped, few of these would qualify and a distinction is drawn.

Varieties occurring in overprints will often take the form of broken letters, slight differences in spacing, rising spacers, etc. Only the most important would be considered for footnote mention.

Sheet positions. If space permits we quote sheet positions of listed varieties, and authenticated data is solicited for this purpose.

2. Paper

All stamps listed are deemed to be on ordinary paper of the wove type and white in colour; only departures from this are mentioned.

Types. Where classification so requires we distinguish such other types of paper as, for example, vertically and horizontally laid; wove and laid b tonn ; card(board); carton; cartridge; enamelled; glazed; GC (Grande Consommation); granite; native; pelure; porous; quadrill ; ribbed; rice; and silk thread.

Our chalky (chalk-surfaced) paper is specifically one which shows a black mark when touched with a silver wire. This and other coatings are easily lost or damaged through immersion in water.

The various makeshifts for normal paper are listed as appropriate. They include printing on: unfinished banknotes, war maps, ruled paper, Post Office forms, and the unprinted side of glossy magazines.

Descriptive terms. The fact that a paper is handmade (and thus probably of uneven thickness) is mentioned where necessary. Such descriptive terms as hard and soft ; smooth and rough ; thick , medium and thin are applied where there is philatelic merit in classifying papers.

Coloured, very white and toned papers. A coloured paper is one that is coloured right through (front and back of the stamp). In the Catalogue the colour of the paper is given in *italics*, thus

black/*rose* = black design on rose paper.

Papers have been made specially white in recent years by, for example, a very heavy coating of chalk. We do not classify shades of whiteness of paper as distinct varieties. There does exist, however, a type of paper from early days called toned. This is off-white, often brownish or buffish, but it cannot be assigned any definite colour. A toning effect brought on by climate, incorrect storage or gum staining is disregarded here, as this was not the state of the paper when issued.

Safety devices. The Catalogue takes account of such safety devices as varnish lines, grills, burelage or imprinted patterns on the front or moire on the back of stamps.

Modern Developments. Two modern developments also affect the listings, printing on self-adhesive paper and the tendency, philatelic in origin, for conventional paper to be reinforced or replaced by different materials. Some examples are the use of foils in gold, silver, aluminium, palladium and steel; application of an imitation wood veneer; printing on plastic moulded in relief; and use of a plastic laminate to give a three-dimensional effect. Examples also occur of stamps impregnated with scent; printed on silk; and incorporating miniature gramophone records.

3. Perforation and Rouletting

Perforation gauge. The gauge of a perforation is the number of holes in a length of 2 cm. For correct classi-fication the size of the holes (large or small) may need to be distinguished; in a few cases the actual number of holes on each edge of the stamp needs to be quoted.

Measurement. The Gibbons *Instanta* gauge is the standard for measuring perforations. The stamp is viewed against a dark background with the transparent gauge put on top of it. Though the gauge measures to decimal accuracy, perforations read from it are generally quoted in the Catalogue to the nearest half. For example:

Just over perf. $12^3/4$ to just under perf. $13^1/4$ = perf. 13
Perf. $13^1/4$ exactly, rounded up = perf. $13^1/2$
Just over perf. $13^1/4$ to just under perf. $3^3/4$ = perf. $13^1/2$
Perf. $13^3/4$ exactly, rounded up = perf. 14

However, where classification depends on it, actual quarter-perforations are quoted.

Notation. Where no perforation is quoted for an issue it is imperforate. Perforations are usually abbreviated (and spoken) as follows, though sometimes they may be spelled out for clarity. This notation for rectangular stamps (the majority) applies to diamond shapes if top is read as the edge to the top right.

P 14: perforated alike on all sides (read: perf.14).

P 14x15: the first figure refers to top and bottom, the second to left and right sides (read: perf. 14 by 15). This is a compound perforation. For an upright triangular stamp the first figure refers to the two sloping sides and the second to the base. In inverted triangulars the base is first and the second figure refers to the sloping sides.

P 14—15: perforation measuring anything between 14 and 15: the holes are irregularly spaced, thus the gauge may vary along a single line or even along a single edge of the stamp (read: perf. 14 to 15).

P 14 *irregular*: perforated 14 from a worn perforator, giving badly aligned holes irregularly spaced (read: irregular perf. 14).

P comp(ound) 14x15: two gauges in use but not necessarily on opposite sides of the stamp. It could be one side in one gauge and three in the other, or two adjacent sides with the same gauge (Read: perf. compound of 14 and 15). For three gauges or more, abbreviated as *P* 14, $14^1/2$, 15 or *compound* for example.

P 14, $14^1/2$: perforated approximately $14^1/2$ (read: perf. 14 or $14^1/2$). It does *not* mean two stamps, one perf. 14 and the other perf. $14^1/2$. This obsolescent notation is gradually being replaced in the Catalogue.

Imperf: imperforate (not perforated).

ImperfxP 14: imperforate at top and bottom and perf 14 at sides.

P 14x*imperf*: perf 14 at top and bottom and imperforate at sides.

Such headings as *P* 13x14 (*vert*) and *P* 14x13 (*horiz*) indicate which perforations apply to which stamp format — vertical or horizontal.

Some stamps are additionally perforated so that a label or tab is detachable; others have been perforated suitably for use as two halves. Listings are normally for whole stamps, unless stated otherwise.

Other terms. Perforation almost always gives circular holes; where other shapes have been used they are specified, e.g. square holes; lozenge perf. Interrupted perfs are brought about by the omission of pins at regular intervals. Perforations have occasionally been simulated by being printed as part of the design. With few exceptions, privately applied perforations are not listed.

Perforation errors and varieties. Authenticated errors, where a stamp normally perforated is accidentally issued imperforate, are listed provided no traces of perforation (blind holes or indentations) remain. They must be provided as pairs, both stamps wholly imperforate, and are only priced in that form.

Stamps merely imperforate between stamp and margin (fantails) are not listed.

Imperforate-between varieties are recognised, where one row of perfs has been missed. They are listed and priced in pairs:

Imperf between (horiz pair): a horizontal pair of stamps with perfs all around the edges but none between the stamps.

Imperf between (vert pair): a vertical pair of stamps with perfs all around the edges but none between the stamps.

Where several of the rows have escaped perforation the resulting varieties are listable. Thus:

Imperf vert (horiz pair): a horizontal pair of stamps perforated top and bottom; all three vertical directions are imperf — the two outer edges and between the stamps.

Imperf horiz (vert pair): a vertical pair perforated at left and right edges; all three horizontal directions are imperf — the top, bottom and between the stamps.

Straight edges. Large sheets cut up before issue to post offices can cause stamps with straight edges, i.e. imperf on one side or on two sides at right angles. They are not usually listable in this condition and are worth less than corresponding stamps properly perforated all round.

This does not, however, apply to certain stamps, mainly from coils and booklets, where straight edges on various sides are the manufacturing norm affecting every stamp. The listings and notes make clear which sides are correctly imperf.

Information (contd.)

Malfunction. Varieties of double, misplaced or partial perforation caused by error or machine malfunction are not listable, neither are freaks, such as perforations placed diagonally from paper folds. Likewise disregarded are missing holes caused by broken pins, and perforations fading out down a sheet, the machinery progressively disengaging to leave blind perfs and indentations to the paper.

Centring. Well-centred stamps have designs surrounded by equal opposite margins. Catalogue prices are for stamps with fine centring; poorly centred stamps should usually be available at a lower price.

Types of perforating. Where necessary for classification, perforation types are distinguished. These include:

Line perforation from one line of pins punching single rows of holes at a time.

Comb perforation from pins disposed across the sheet in comb formation, punching out holes at three sides of the stamp a row at a time.

Harrow perforation applied to a whole pane or sheet at one stroke.

Rotary perforation from the toothed wheels operating across a sheet, then crosswise.

Sewing-machine perforation. The resultant condition, clean-cut or rough, is distinguished where required.

Pin-perforation is the commonly applied term for pin-roulette in which, instead of being punched out, round holes are pricked by sharp-pointed pins and no paper is removed.

Punctured stamps. Perforation holes can be punched into the face of the stamp. Patterns of small holes, often in the shape of initial letters, are privately applied devices against pilferage. These perfins are outside the scope. Identification devices, when officially inspired, are listed or noted; they can be shapes, or letters or words formed from holes, sometimes converting one class of stamp into another.

Rouletting. In rouletting the paper is cut, for ease of separation, but none is removed. The gauge is measured, when needed, as for perforations. Traditional French terms descriptive of the type of cut are often used and types include:

Arc roulette (percé en arc). Cuts are minute, spaced arcs, each roughly a semicircle.

Cross roulette (percé en croix). Cuts are tiny diagonal crosses.

Line roulette (percé en ligne or en ligne droite). Short straight cuts parallel to the frame of the stamp. The commonest basic roulette. Where not further described, roulette means this type.

Rouletted in colour or coloured roulette (percé en lignes colorées or en lignes de couleur). Cuts with coloured edges, arising from notched rule inked simultaneously with the printing plate.

Saw-tooth roulette (percé en scie). Cuts applied zigzag fashion to resemble the teeth of a saw.

Serpentine roulette (percé en serpentin). Cuts as sharply wavy lines.

Zigzag roulettes (percé en zigzags). Short straight cuts at angles in alternate directions, producing sharp points on separation. U.S. usage favours serrate(d) roulette for this type.

Pin-roulette (originally *percé en points* and now *perforés trous d'epingle*) is commonly called pin-perforation in English.

4. Gum

All stamps listed are assumed to have gum of some kind; if they were issued without gum this is stated. Original gum (o.g.) means that which was present on the stamp as issued to the public. Deleterious climates and the presence of certain chemicals can cause gum to crack and, with early stamps, even make the paper deteriorate. Unscrupulous fakers are adept in removing it and regumming the stamp to meet the unreasoning demand often made for full o.g. in cases where such a thing is virtually impossible.

Until recent times the gum used for stamps has been gum arabic, but various synthetic adhesives — tinted or invisible-looking — have been in use since the 1960s. Stamps existing with more than one type of gum are not normally listed separately, though the fact is noted where it is of philatelic significance, e.g. in distinguishing reprints or new printings.

The distinct variety of grilled gum is, however, recognised. In this the paper is passed through a gum breaker prior to printing to prevent subsequent curling. As the patterned rollers were sufficient to impress a grill into the paper beneath the gum we can quote prices for both unused and used examples.

Self-adhesive stamps are issued on backing paper from which they are peeled before affixing to mail. Unused examples are prices as for backing paper intact. Used examples are best kept on cover or on piece.

5. Watermarks

Stamps are on unwatermarked paper except where the heading to the set says otherwise.

Detection. Watermarks are detected for Catalogue description by one of four methods: (1) holding stamps to the light; (2) laying stamps face down on a dark background; (3) adding a few drops of petroleum ether 40/60 to the stamp laid face down in a watermark tray; or (4) by use of the Morley-Bright Detector, or other equipment, which works by revealing the thinning of the paper at the watermark. (Note that petroleum ether is highly inflammable in use and can damage photogravure stamps.)

Listable types. Stamps occurring on both watermarked and unwatermarked papers are different types and both receive full listing.

Single watermarks (devices occurring once on every stamp) can be modified in size and shape as between different issues; the types are noted but not usually separately listed. Fortuitous absence of watermark from a single stamp or its gross displacement would not be listable.

To overcome registration difficulties the device may be repeated at close intervals (a *multiple watermark*), single stamps thus showing parts of several devices. Similarly a large sheet watermark (or *all-over watermark*) covering numerous stamps can be used. We give informative notes and illustrations for them. The designs may be such that numbers of stamps in the sheet automatically lack watermark; this is not a listable variety. Multiple and all-over watermarks sometimes undergo modifications, but if the various types are difficult to distinguish from single stamps, notes are given but not separate listings.

Papermakers' watermarks are noted where known but not listed separately, since most stamps in the sheet will lack them. Sheet watermarks which are nothing more than officially adopted papermakers watermarks are, however, given normal listing.

Marginal watermarks, falling outside the pane of stamps, are ignored except where misplacement causes the adjoining row to be affected, in which case they may be footnoted.

Watermark errors and varieties. Watermark errors are recognised as of major importance. They comprise stamps intended to be on unwatermarked paper but issued watermarked by mistake, or stamps printed on paper with the wrong watermark. Watermark varieties, on the other hand, such as broken or deformed bits on the dandy roll, are not listable.

Watermark positions. Paper has a side intended for printing and watermarks are usually impressed so that they read normally when looked through from that printed side.

Illustrations in the Catalogue are of watermarks in normal positions (from the front of the stamps) and are actual size where possible.

Differences in watermark position are collectable as distinct varieties. In this Catalogue, however, only normal and sideways watermarks are listed (and sideways inverted is treated as sideways). Inverted and reversed watermarks have always been outside its scope: in the early days of flat-bed printing, sheets of watermarked paper were fed indiscriminately through the press and the resulting watermark positions had no particular philatelic significance. Similarly, the special make-up of sheets for booklets can in some cases give equal quantities of normal and inverted watermarks.

6. Colours

Stamps in two or three colours have these named in order of apearance, from the centre moving outwards. Four colours or more are usually listed as multicoloured.

In compound colour names the second is the predominant one, thus:

orange-red = a red tending towards orange;

red-orange = an orange containing more red than usual.

Standard colours used. The 200 colours most used for stamp identification are given in the Stanley Gibbons Colour Key. The Catalogue has used the Key as a standard for describing new issues over some years. The names are also introduced as lists are rewritten, though exceptions are made for those early issues where traditional names have become universally established.

Determining colours. When comparing actual stamps with colour samples in the Key, view in a good north daylight (or its best substitute: fluorescent colour-matching light). Sunshine is not recommended. Choose a solid portion of the stamp design; if available, marginal markings such as solid bars of colour or colour check dots are helpful. Shading lines in the design can be misleading as they appear lighter than solid colour. Postmarked portions of a stamp appear darker than normal. If more than one colour is present, mask off the extraneous ones as the eye tends to mix them.

Errors of colour. Major colour errors in stamps or overprints which qualify for listing are: wrong colours; one colour inverted in relation to the rest; albinos (colourless impressions), where these have Expert Committee certificates; colours completely omitted, but only on unused stamps (if found on used stamps the information is footnoted).

Colours only partially omitted are not recognised. Colour shifts, however spectacular, are not listed.

Shades. Shades in philately refer to variations in the intensity of a colour or the presence of differing amounts of other colours. They are particularly significant when they can be linked to specific printings. In general, shades need to be quite marked to fall within the scope of this Catalogue; it does not favour nowadays listing the often numerous shades of a stamp, but chooses a single applicable colour name which will indicate particular groups of outstanding shades. Furthermore, the listings refer to colours as issued: they may deteriorate into something different through the passage of time.

Modern colour printing by lithography is prone to marked differences of shade, even within a single run, and variations can occur within the same sheet. Such shades are not listed.

Aniline colours. An aniline colour meant originally one derived from coal-tar; it now refers more widely to colour of a particular brightness suffused on the surface of a stamp and showing clearly on the back.

Colours of overprints and surcharges. All overprints and surcharges are in black unless stated otherwise in the heading or after the description of the stamp.

7. Luminescence

Machines which sort mail electronically have been introduced in recent years. In consequence some countries have issued stamps on fluorescent or phosphorescent papers, while others have marked their stamps with phosphor bands.

The various papers can only be distinguised by ultra-violet lamps emitting particular wavelengths. They are separately listed only when the stamps have some other means of distinguishing them, visible without the use of these lamps. Where this is not so, the papers are recorded in footnotes or headings. (Collectors using the lamps, nevertheless, should exercise great care in their use as exposure to their light is extremely dangerous to the eyes.)

Phosphor bands are listable, since they are visible to the naked eye (by holding stamps at an angle to the light and looking along them, the bands appear dark). Stamps existing with and without phosphor bands or with differing numbers of bands are given separate listings. Varieties such as double bands, misplaced or omitted bands, bands printed on the wrong side, are not listed.

8. Coil Stamps

Stamps issued only in coil form are given full listing. If stamps are issued in both sheets and coils the coil stamps are listed separately only where there is some feature (e.g. perforation) by which singles can be distinguished. Coil strips containing different stamps *se-tenant* are also listed.

Coil join pairs are too random and too easily faked to permit of listing; similarly ignored are coil stamps which have accidentally suffered an extra row of perforations from the claw mechanism in a malfunctioning vending machine.

9. Booklet Stamps

Single stamps from booklets are listed if they are distinguishable in some way (such as watermark or perforation) from similar sheet stamps. Booklet panes, provided they are distinguishable from blocks of sheet stamps, are listed for most countries; booklet panes containing more than one value *se-tenant* are listed under the lowest of the values concerned.

Lists of stamp booklets are given for certain countries and it is intended to extend this generally.

10. Forgeries and Fakes

Forgeries. Where space permits, notes are considered if they can give a concise description that will permit unequivocal detection of a forgery. Generalised warnings, lacking detail, are not nowadays inserted since their value to the collector is problematic.

Fakes. Unwitting fakes are numerous, particularly new shades which are colour changelings brought about by exposure to sunlight, soaking in water contaminated with dyes from adherent paper, contact with oil and dirt from a pocketbook, and so on. Fraudulent operators, in addition, can offer to arrange: removal of hinge marks; repairs of thins on white or coloured papers; replacement of missing margins or perforations; reperforating in true or false gauges; removal of fiscal cancellations; rejoining of severed pairs, strips and blocks; and (a major hazard) regumming. Collectors can only be urged to purchase from reputable sources and to insist upon Expert Committee certification where there is any kind of doubt.

The Catalogue can consider footnotes about fakes where these are specific enough to assist in detection.

PRICES

Prices quoted in this Catalogue are the selling prices of Stanley Gibbons Ltd at the time when the book went to press. They are for stamps in fine condition; in issues where condition varies they may ask more for the superb and less for the sub-standard.

All prices are subject to change without prior notice and Stanley Gibbons Ltd may from time to time offer stamps at other than catalogue prices in consequence of special purchases or particular promotions.

No guarantee is given to supply all stamps priced, since it is not possible to keep every catalogued item in stock. Commemorative issues may, at times, only be available in complete sets and not as individual values.

Quotations of prices. The prices in the left-hand column are for unused stamps and those in the right-hand column are for used.

Prices are expressed in pounds and pence sterling. One pound comprises 100 pence (£1 = 100p).

The method of notation is as follows: pence in numerals (e.g. 10 denotes ten pence); pounds and pence up to £100, in numerals (e.g. 4Æ25 denotes four pounds and twenty-five pence); prices above £100 expressed in whole pounds with the £ sign shown.

Unused stamps. Prices for stamps issued up to the end of the Second World War (1945) are for lightly hinged examples and more may be asked if they are in unmounted mint condition. Prices for all later unused stamps are for unmounted mint. Where not available in this condition, lightly hinged stamps supplied are often at a lower price.

Used stamps. The used prices are normally for stamps postally used but may be for stamps cancelled-to-order where this practice exists.

A pen-cancellation on early issues can sometimes correctly denote postal use. Instances are individually noted in the Catalogue in explanation of the used price given.

Prices quoted for bisects on cover or on large piece are for those dated during the period officially authorised.

Stamps not sold unused to the public but affixed by postal officials before use (e.g. some parcel post stamps) are priced used only.

Minimum price. The minimum catalogue price quoted is 10p. For individual stamps prices between 10p and 95p are provided as a guide for catalogue users. The lowest price *charged* for individual stamps purchased from Stanley Gibbons Ltd. is £1.

Set Prices. Set prices are generally for one of each value, excluding shades and varieties, but including major colour changes. Where there are alternative shades, etc, the cheapest is usually included. The number of stamps in the set is always stated for clarity.

Where prices are given for se-tenant blocks or strips, any mint set price quoted for such an issue is for the complete se-tenant strip plus any other stamps included in the set. Used set prices are always for a set of single stamps.

Repricing. Collectors will be aware that the market factors of supply and demand influence the prices quoted in this Catalogue. Whatever the scarcity of a particular stamp, if there is no one in the market who wishes to buy it, it cannot be expected to achieve a high price. Conversely, the same item actively sought by numerous potential buyers may cause the price to rise.

All the prices in this Catalogue are examined during the preparation of each new edition by expert staff of Stanley Gibbons and repriced as necessary. They take many factors into account, including supply and demand, and are in close touch with the international stamp market and the auction world.

GUARANTEE

All stamps are guaranteed genuine originals in the following terms:

If not as described, and returned by the purchaser, we undertake to refund the price paid to us in the original transaction. If any stamp is certified as genuine by the Expert Committee of the Royal Philatelic Society, London, or by B.P.A. Expertising Ltd, the purchaser shall not be entitled to make claim against us for any error, omission or mistake in such certificate. Consumers statutory rights are not affected by this guarantee.

The established Expert Committees in this country are those of the Royal Philatelic Society, 41 Devonshire Place, London W1G 6JY, and B.P.A. Expertising Ltd, P.O. Box 137, Leatherhead, Surrey, KT22 0RG. They do not undertake valuations under any circumstances and fees are payable for their services.

International Philatelic Glossary

English	French	German	Spanish	Italian
Agate	Agate	Achat	Agata	Agata
Air stamp a rienne	Timbre de la poste	Flugpostmarke	Sello de correo a reo	Francobollo per posta aerea
Apple Green	Vert-pomme	Apfelgr n	Verde manzana	Verde mela
Barred	Annul par barres	Balkenentwertung	Anulado con barras	Sbarrato
Bisected	Timbre coup	Halbiert	Partido en dos	Frazionato
Bistre	Bistre	Bister	Bistre	Bistro
Bistre-brown	Brun-bistre	Bisterbraun	Casta o bistre	Bruno-bistro
Black	Noir	Schwarz	Negro	Nero
Blackish Brown	Brun-noir	Schw rzlichbraun	Casta o negruzco	Bruno nerastro
Blackish Green	Vert fonc	Schw rlichgr n	Verde negruzco	Verde nerastro
Blackish Olive	Olive fonc	Schw rlicholiv	Oliva negruzco	Oliva nerastro
Block of four	Bloc de quatre	Viererblock	Bloque de cuatro	Bloco di quattro
Blue	Bleu	Blau	Azul	Azzurro
Blue-green	Vert-bleu	Blaugr n	Verde azul	Verde azzuro
Bluish Violet	Violet bleu tre	Bl ulichviolett	Violeta azulado	Violtto azzurrastro
Booklet	Carnet	Heft	Cuadernillo	Libretto
Bright Blue	Bleu vif	Lebhaftblau	Azul vivo	Azzurro vivo
Bright Green	Vert vif	Lebhaftgr n	Verde vivo	Verde vivo
Bright Purple	Mauve vif	Lebhaftpurpur	P rpura vivo	Porpora vivo
Bronze Green	Vert-bronze	Bronzegr n	Verde bronce	Verde bronzo
Brown	Brun	Braun	Casta o	Bruno
Brown-lake	Carmin-brun	Braunlack	Laca casta o	Lacca bruno
Brown-purple	Pourpre-brun	Braunpurpur	P rpura casta o	Porpora bruno
Brown-red	Rouge-brun	Braunrot	Rojo casta o	Rosso bruno
Buff	Chamois	S misch	Anteado	Camoscio
Cancellation	Oblit ration	Entwertung	Cancelaci n	Annullamento
Cancelled	Annul	Gestempelt	Cancelado	Annullato
Carmine	Carmin	Karmin	Carm n	Carminio
Carmine-red	Rouge-carmin	Karminrot	Rojo carm n	Rosso carminio
Centred	Centr	Zentriert	Centrado	Centrato
Cerise	Rouge-cerise	Kirschrot	Color de ceresa	Color Ciliegia
Chalk-surfaced paper	Papier couch	Kreidepapier	Papel estucado	Carta gessata
Chalky Blue	Bleu terne	Kreideblau	Azul turbio	Azzurro smorto
Charity stamp	Timbre de bienfaisance	Wohlt tigkeitsmarke	Sello de beneficenza	Francobollo di beneficenza
Chestnut	Marron	Kastanienbraun	Casta o rojo	Marrone
Chocolate	Chocolat	Schokolade	Chocolate	Cioccolato
Cinnamon	Cannelle	Zimtbraun	Canela	Cannella
Claret	Grenat	Weinrot	Rojo vinoso	Vinaccia
Cobalt	Cobalt	Kobalt	Cobalto	Cobalto
Colour	Couleur	Farbe	Color	Colore
Comb-perforation	Dentelure en peigne	Kammz hnung, Reihenz hnung	Dentado de peine	Dentellatura e pettine
Commemorative stamp	Timbre comm moratif	Gedenkmarke	Sello conmemorativo	Francobollo commemorativo
Crimson	Cramoisi	Karmesin	Carmes	Cremisi
Deep Blue	Blue fonc	Dunkelblau	Azul oscuro	Azzurro scuro
Deep bluish Green	Vert-bleu fonc	Dunkelbl ulichgr n	Verde azulado oscuro	Verde azzurro scuro
Design	Dessin	Markenbild	Dise o	Disegno
Die	Matrice	Urstempel. Type, Platte	Cu o	Conio, Matrice

English	French	German	Spanish	Italian
Double	Double	Doppelt	Doble	Doppio
Drab	Olive terne	Tr boliv	Oliva turbio	Oliva smorto
Dull Green	Vert terne	Tr bgr n	Verde turbio	Verde smorto
Dull purple	Mauve terne	Tr bpurpur	P rpura turbio	Porpora smorto
Embossing	Impression en relief	Pr gedruck	Impresi n en relieve	Impressione a relievo
Emerald	Vert-em raude	Smaragdgr n	Esmeralda	Smeraldo
Engraved	Grav	Graviert	Grabado	Inciso
Error	Erreur	Fehler, Fehldruck	Error	Errore
Essay	Essai	Probedruck	Ensayo	Saggio
Express letter stamp	Timbre pour lettres par expr s	Eilmarke	Sello de urgencia	Francobollo per espresso
Fiscal stamp	Timbre fiscal	Stempelmarke	Sello fiscal	Francobollo fiscale
Flesh	Chair	Fleischfarben	Carne	Carnicino
Forgery	Faux, Falsification	F lschung	Falsificaci n	Falso, Falsificazione
Frame	Cadre	Rahmen	Marco	Cornice
Granite paper	Papier avec fragments de fils de soie	Faserpapier	Papel con filamentos	Carto con fili di seta
Green	Vert	Gr n	Verde	Verde
Greenish Blue	Bleu verd tre	Gr nlichblau	Azul verdoso	Azzurro verdastro
Greenish Yellow	Jaune-vert	Gr nlichgelb	Amarillo verdoso	Giallo verdastro
Grey	Gris	Grau	Gris	Grigio
Grey-blue	Bleu-gris	Graublau	Azul gris	Azzurro grigio
Grey-green	Vert gris	Graugr n	Verde gris	Verde grigio
Gum	Gomme	Gummi	Goma	Gomma
Gutter	Interpanneau	Zwischensteg	Espacio blanco entre	Ponte dos grupos
Imperforate	Non-dentel	Geschnitten	Sin dentar	Non dentellato
Indigo	Indigo	Indigo	Azul indigo	Indaco
Inscription	Inscription	Inschrift	Inscripci n	Dicitura
Inverted	Renvers	Kopfstehend	Invertido	Capovolto
Issue	mission	Ausgabe	Emisi n	Emissione
Laid	Verg	Gestreift	Listado	Vergato
Lake	Lie de vin	Lackfarbe	Laca	Lacca
Lake-brown	Brun-carmin	Lackbraun	Casta o laca	Bruno lacca
Lavender	Bleu-lavande	Lavendel	Color de alhucema	Lavanda
Lemon	Jaune-citron	Zitrongelb	Lim n	Limone
Light Blue	Bleu clair	Hellblau	Azul claro	Azzurro chiaro
Lilac	Lilas	Lila	Lila	Lilla
Line perforation	Dentelure en lignes	Linienz hnung	Dentado en linea	Dentellatura lineare
Lithography	Lithographie	Steindruck	Litograf a	Litografia
Local	Timbre de poste locale	Lokalpostmarke	Emisi n local	Emissione locale
Lozenge roulette	Perc en losanges	Rautenf rmiger Durchstich	Picadura en rombos	Perforazione a losanghe
Magenta	Magenta	Magentarot	Magenta	Magenta
Margin	Marge	Rand	Borde	Margine
Maroon	Marron pourpr	Dunkelrotpurpur	P rpura rojo oscuro	Marrone rossastro
Mauve	Mauve	Malvenfarbe	Malva	Malva
Multicoloured	Polychrome	Mehrfarbig	Multicolores	Policromo
Myrtle Green	Vert myrte	Myrtengr n	Verde mirto	Verde mirto
New Blue	Bleu ciel vif	Neublau	Azul nuevo	Azzurro nuovo
Newspaper stamp	Timbre pour journaux	Zeitungsmarke	Sello para peri dicos	Francobollo per giornali

English	French	German	Spanish	Italian
Obliteration	Oblit ration	Abstempelung	Matasello	Annullamento
Obsolete	Hors (de) cours	Ausser Kurs	Fuera de curso	Fuori corso
Ochre	Ocre	Ocker	Ocre	Ocra
Official stamp	Timbre de service	Dienstmarke	Sello de servicio	Francobollo di servizio
Olive-brown	Brun-olive	Olivbraun	Casta o oliva	Bruno oliva
Olive-green	Vert-olive	Olivgr n	Verde oliva	Verde oliva
Olive-grey	Gris-olive	Olivgrau	Gris oliva	Grigio oliva
Olive-yellow	Jaune-olive	Olivgelb	Amarillo oliva	Giallo oliva
Orange	Orange	Orange	Naranja	Arancio
Orange-brown	Brun-orange	Orangebraun	Casta o naranja	Bruno arancio
Orange-red	Rouge-orange	Orangerot	Rojo naranja	Rosso arancio
Orange-yellow	Jaune-orange	Orangegelb	Amarillo naranja	Giallo arancio
Overprint	Surcharge	Aufdruck	Sobrecarga	Soprastampa
Pair	Paire	Paar	Pareja	Coppia
Pale	P le	Blass	P lido	Pallido
Pane	Panneau	Gruppe	Grupo	Gruppo
Paper	Papier	Papier	Papel	Carta
Parcel post stamp	Timbre pour colis postaux	Paketmarke	Sello para paquete postal	Francobollo per pacchi postali
Pen-cancelled	Oblit r plume	Federzugentwertung	Cancelado a pluma	Annullato a penna
Perc en arc	Perc en arc	Bogenf rmiger Durchstich	Picadura en forma de arco	Perforazione ad arco
Perc en scie	Perc en scie	Bogenf rmiger Durchstich	Picado en sierra	Foratura a sega
Perforated	Dentel	Gez hnt	Dentado	Dentellato
Perforation	Dentelure	Z hnung	Dentar	Dentellatura
Photogravure	Photogravure, Heliogravure	Rastertiefdruck	Fotograbado	Rotocalco
Pin perforation	Perc en points	In Punkten durchstochen	Horadado con alfileres	Perforato a punti
Plate	Planche	Platte	Plancha	Lastra, Tavola
Plum	Prune	Pflaumenfarbe	Color de ciruela	Prugna
Postage Due stamp	Timbre-taxe	Portomarke	Sello de tasa	Segnatasse
Postage stamp	Timbre-poste	Briefmarke, Freimarke, Postmarke	Sello de correos	Francobollo postale
Postal fiscal stamp	Timbre fiscal-postal	Stempelmarke als Postmarke verwendet	Sello fiscal-postal	Fiscale postale
Postmark	Oblit ration postale	Poststempel	Matasello	Bollo
Printing	Impression, Tirage	Druck	Impresi n	Stampa, Tiratura
Proof	preuve	Druckprobe	Prueba de impresi n	Prova
Provisionals	Timbres provisoires	Provisorische Marken. Provisorien	Provisionales	Provvisori
Prussian Blue	Bleu de Prusse	Preussischblau	Azul de Prusia	Azzurro di Prussia
Purple	Pourpre	Purpur	P rpura	Porpora
Purple-brown	Brun-pourpre	Purpurbraun	Casta o p rpura	Bruno porpora
Recess-printing	Impression en taille douce	Tiefdruck	Grabado	Incisione
Red	Rouge	Rot	Rojo	Rosso
Red-brown	Brun-rouge	Rotbraun	Casta o rojizo	Bruno rosso
Reddish Lilac	Lilas rouge tre	R tlichlila	Lila rojizo	Lilla rossastro
Reddish Purple	Poupre-rouge	R tlichpurpur	P rpura rojizo	Porpora rossastro
Reddish Violet	Violet rouge tre	R tlichviolett	Violeta rojizo	Violetto rossastro
Red-orange	Orange rouge tre	Rotorange	Naranja rojizo	Arancio rosso
Registration stamp	Timbre pour lettre charg e (recommand e)	Einschreibemarke	Sello de certificado lettere	Francobollo per raccomandate

English	French	German	Spanish	Italian
Reprint	R impression	Neudruck	Reimpresi n	Ristampa
Reversed	Retourn	Umgekehrt	Invertido	Rovesciato
Rose	Rose	Rosa	Rosa	Rosa
Rose-red	Rouge ros	Rosarot	Rojo rosado	Rosso rosa
Rosine	Rose vif	Lebhaftrosa	Rosa vivo	Rosa vivo
Roulette	Percage	Durchstich	Picadura	Foratura
Rouletted	Perc	Durchstochen	Picado	Forato
Royal Blue	Bleu-roi	K nigblau	Azul real	Azzurro reale
Sage green	Vert-sauge	Salbeigr n	Verde salvia	Verde salvia
Salmon	Saumon	Lachs	Salm n	Salmone
Scarlet	carlate	Scharlach	Escarlata	Scarlatto
Sepia	S pia	Sepia	Sepia	Seppia
Serpentine roulette	Perc en serpentin	Schlangenliniger Durchstich	Picado a serpentina	Perforazione a serpentina
Shade	Nuance	T nung	Tono	Gradazione de colore
Sheet	Feuille	Bogen	Hoja	Foglio
Slate	Ardoise	Schiefer	Pizarra	Ardesia
Slate-blue	Bleu-ardoise	Schieferblau	Azul pizarra	Azzurro ardesia
Slate-green	Vert-ardoise	Schiefergr n	Verde pizarra	Verde ardesia
Slate-lilac	Lilas-gris	Schierferlila	Lila pizarra	Lilla ardesia
Slate-purple	Mauve-gris	Schieferpurpur	P rpura pizarra	Porpora ardesia
Slate-violet	Violet-gris	Schieferviolett	Violeta pizarra	Violetto ardesia
Special delivery stamp	Timbre pour expr s	Eilmarke	Sello de urgencia	Francobollo per espressi
Specimen	Sp cimen	Muster	Muestra	Saggio
Steel Blue	Bleu acier	Stahlblau	Azul acero	Azzurro acciaio
Strip	Bande	Streifen	Tira	Striscia
Surcharge	Surcharge	Aufdruck	Sobrecarga	Soprastampa
T te-b che	T te-b che	Kehrdruck	T te-b che	T te-b che
Tinted paper	Papier teint	Get ntes Papier	Papel coloreado	Carta tinta
Too-late stamp	Timbre pour lettres en retard	Versp tungsmarke	Sello para cartas retardadas	Francobollo per le lettere in ritardo
Turquoise-blue	Bleu-turquoise	T rkisblau	Azul turquesa	Azzurro turchese
Turquoise-green	Vert-turquoise	T rkisgr n	Verde turquesa	Verde turchese
Typography	Typographie	Buchdruck	Tipografia	Tipografia
Ultramarine	Outremer	Ultramarin	Ultramar	Oltremare
Unused	Neuf	Ungebraucht	Nuevo	Nuovo
Used	Oblit r , Us	Gebraucht	Usado	Usato
Venetian Red	Rouge-brun terne	Venezianischrot	Rojo veneciano	Rosso veneziano
Vermilion	Vermillon	Zinnober	Cinabrio	Vermiglione
Violet	Violet	Violett	Violeta	Violetto
Violet-blue	Bleu-violet	Violettblau	Azul violeta	Azzurro violetto
Watermark	Filigrane	Wasserzeichen	Filigrana	Filigrana
Watermark sideways	Filigrane couch liegend	Wasserzeichen	Filigrana acostado	Filigrana coricata
Wove paper	Papier ordinaire, Papier uni	Einfaches Papier	Papel avitelado	Carta unita
Yellow	Jaune	Gelb	Amarillo	Giallo
Yellow-brown	Brun-jaune	Gelbbraun	Casta o amarillo	Bruno giallo
Yellow-green	Vert-jaune	Gelbgr n	Verde amarillo	Verde giallo
Yellow-olive	Olive-jaun tre	Gelboliv	Oliva amarillo	Oliva giallastro
Yellow-orange	Orange jaun tre	Gelborange	Naranja amarillo	Arancio giallastro
Zig-zag roulette	Perc en zigzag	S gezahnartiger	Picado en zigzag	Perforazione a zigzag

Bhutan

1955. 16 Annas = 1 Rupee
1957. 100 Chetrum = 1 Ngultrum

Bhutan is a kingdom in the eastern Himalayas guided by India in external affairs under a treaty of August 1949. It joined the U.P.U. on 7 March 1969.

King Jigme Dorji Wangchuk
March 1952–21 July 1972

F **1** "Dorje" (Thunderbolt)

1955 (1 Jan). *POSTAL FISCAL. Litho.* No wmk. P 12½.

F1	F **1**	1(= ¼r.) blue		1·00	3·75
F2		2(= ½r.) carmine-red		2·75	3·75
F3		4(= 1r.) green		4·50	6·25
F4		8(= 2 or 5r.) orange		12·50	15·00
F1/4	*Set of* 4			19·00	26·00

On 1 January 1955 the Bhutan Government decreed that these fiscal stamps could be used for postage on domestic mail. They are denominated in local currency (the shiki) for which however no coins existed. Until 1965 (when Bhutan produced its own coinage) Indian or Tibetan money was used. The equivalent in Indian rupees is given; prior to decimalisation in 1957 the "8" value was sold at 2r., after 1957 at 5r.

The "1" blue exists handstamped "10 NP." or "25 N.P."; these were not official issues.

DATES OF ISSUE. Wherever possible we have quoted the dates when the stamps were placed on sale in Bhutan but these sometimes differ considerably from the dates of release by the agency in the Bahamas.

1 Postal Runner

2 "Uprooted Tree" Emblem and Crest of Bhutan

(Litho Harrison)

1962 (10 Oct). *T* **1** *and similar designs.* P 14 × 14½ (vert) or 14½ × 14 (horiz).

1		2ch. brown-red and grey		15	15
2		3ch. rose-red and violet-blue		25	25
3		5ch. bistre-brown and blue-green		80	80
4		15ch. orange-yellow, black and brown-red		15	30
5		33ch. blue-green and bright reddish violet		25	25
6		70ch. ultramarine and turquoise blue		50	35
7		1n.30 black and new blue		1·40	1·40
1/7	*Set of* 7			3·25	3·25

Designs. *Vert*—2, 33ch. Type **1**.*Horiz*—3, 70th., Archer; 5ch., 1n.30, Yak; 15ch. Map of Bhutan, Maharaja Druk Gyalpo and Pare Dzong (fortress and monastery).

(Litho Harrison)

1962 (10 Oct). *World Refugee Year.* P 14½ × 14.

8	**2**	1n. carmine and dull ultramarine		2·75	2·75
9		2n. reddish violet and apple-green		2·50	2·50

3 Accoutrements of Ancient Warrior

4 "Boy filling box" (with grain)

(Litho Harrison)

1962 (5 Dec). *Membership of Colombo Plan.* P 14 × 14½.

10	**3**	33ch. red, sepia, yellow and green		25	25
11		70ch. red, sepia, yellow and slate-blue		50	50
12		1n.30 red, sepia and yellow		75	75

(Litho De La Rue)

1963 (15 July). *Freedom from Hunger.* P 13½ × 14.

13	**4**	20ch. red-brown, lt blue & greenish yell		25	25
14		1n.50 brt purple, red-brown & lt blue		65	65

(5)

6 Dancer with upraised Hands

1964 (7 Apr). *Winter Olympic Games, Innsbruck, and Bhutanese Winter Sports Committee Fund.* Nos. 10/12 *such as T* **5**.

15	**3**	33ch.+50ch.		2·40	2·40
16		70ch.+50ch.		2·40	2·40
17		1n.30+50ch.		2·40	2·40

IMPERFORATE STAMPS. Many issues from No. 18 exist imperforate from limited printings but most of these were not put on sale in Bhutan.

(Photo Harrison)

1964 (16 Apr). *Bhutanese Dancers. T* **6** *and similar multicoloured designs.* P 14½ × 14 (vert) or 14 × 14½ (horiz).

18		2ch. Standing on one leg (*vert*)		10	10
19		3ch. Type **6**		10	10
20		5ch. Dancer with tambourine (*vert*)		10	10
21		20ch. As 2ch.		10	10
22		33ch. Type **6**		10	10
23		70ch. Dancer with sword		15	15
24		1n. Dancer with tasselled hat (*vert*)		35	35
25		1n.30 As 5ch.		65	65
26		2n. As 70ch.		1·10	1·10
18/26	*Set of* 9			2·50	2·50

7 Bhutanese Athlete

1964 (10 Oct). *Olympic Games, Tokyo. T* **7** *and similar vert designs. Multicoloured. Litho.* P 14½.

27	2ch. Type **7**		15	10
28	5ch. Boxing		10	10
29	15ch. Type **7**		10	10
30	33ch. As 5ch.		15	15
31	1n. Archery		35	35
32	2n. Football		70	70
33	3n. As 1n.		1·30	1·30
27/33 *Set of 7*			2·50	2·50
MS33*a* 85 × 118 mm. Nos. 31/2			10·00	10·00

8 Flags at Half-mast

1964 (22 Nov). *President Kennedy Commemoration. Litho.* P 14½.

34	**8**	33ch. multicoloured	25	25
35		1n. multicoloured	60	60
36		3n. multicoloured	90	90
MS36*a* 82 × 119 mm. Nos. 35/6			3·75	3·75

9 Primula

WINSTON CHURCHILL

1874   1965

(**10**)

(Des F. Ludlow. Litho De La Rue)

1965 (6 Jan). *Bhutan Flowers. T* **9** *and similar vert designs. Multicoloured.* P 13.

37	2ch. Type **9**		10	10
38	5ch. Gentian		10	10
39	15ch. Type **9**		10	10
40	33ch. As 5 ch.		15	15
41	50ch. Rhododendron		25	25
42	75ch. Peony		35	35
43	1n. As 50ch.		35	35
44	2n. As 75ch.		85	85
37/44 *Set of 8*			2·00	2·00

1965 (27 Feb). *Churchill Commemoration. Nos. 5, 35/6 and 43/4 optd as T* **10**.

45	–	33ch. blue-green & reddish lilac (No. 5)	35	35
46	**8**	1n. multicoloured	55	55
47	–	1n. multicoloured (No. 43)	50	50

48	–	2n. multicoloured (No. 44)	85	85
49	**8**	3n. multicoloured	1·30	1·30
45/49 *Set of 5*			3·25	3·25

The overprint on Nos. 45, 47/8 is in smaller sans-serif type, set in three lines.

11 Pavilion and Skyscrapers

1965 (21 Apr). *New York World's Fair. T* **11** *and similar horiz designs. Multicoloured. Litho.* P 14½.

50	1ch. Type **11**		10	10
51	10ch. Buddha and Michelangelo's "Pieta"		10	10
52	20ch. Bhutan houses and New York skyline		10	10
53	33ch. Bhutan and New York bridges		10	10
54	1n.50 Type **11**		50	50
55	2n. As 10ch.		80	80
50/55 *Set of 6*			1·50	1·50
MS55*a* 120 × 86 mm. Nos. 54/5			3·50	3·50

(**12**)

1965–67. *Various stamps surch as T* **12**.

56	**2**	5ch.on 1n. (No. 8) (1967)	28·00	28·00
57		5ch.on 2n. (No. 9)	28·00	28·00
58	–	10ch.on 70ch. (No. 23) (1.66)	7·75	7·75
59	–	10ch.on 2n. (No. 26)	7·75	7·75
60	–	15ch.on 70ch. (No. 6)	6·50	6·50
61	–	15ch.on 1n.30 (No. 7)	6·50	6·50
62	–	20ch.on 1n. (No. 24) (1.66)	9·25	9·25
63	–	20ch.on 1n.30 (No. 25)	9·25	9·25
56/63 *Set of 8*			90·00	90·00

13 "Telstar" and Portable Transmitter

1966 (2 Mar). *Centenary of International Telecommunications Union. T* **13** *and similar horiz designs. Multicoloured. Photo.* P 14½.

64	35ch. Type **13**		15	15
65	2n. "Telstar" and morse key		40	40

66	3n. "Relay" and headphones		75	75
MS67	118 × 78 mm. Nos. 65/6		4·25	4·25

14 Asiatic Black Bear   **15** Simtoka Dzong (fortress)

1966 (24 Mar). *Animals. T* **14** *and similar vert designs. Multicoloured. Litho. P* 13½.

68	1ch. Type **14**		10	10
69	2ch. Snow leopard		10	10
70	4ch. Pygmy hog		10	10
71	8ch. Tiger		10	10
72	10ch. Dhole		10	10
73	75ch. As 8ch.		25	25
74	1n. Takin		40	40
75	1n.50 As 10ch.		55	55
76	2n. As 4ch.		70	70
77	3n. As 2ch.		1·00	1·00
78	4n. Type **14**		1·40	1·40
79	5n. As 1n.		2·00	2·00
68/79	*Set of* 12		6·00	6·00

(Photo Security Printing Press, Nasik, India)

1966 (12 May)–**67**. *T* **15** *and similar horiz design. P* 14½ × 14.

80	–	5ch. chestnut (2.5.67)	15	10
81	**15**	15ch. brown	15	15
82		20ch. yellow-green	25	25

Design:—5ch. Rinpung Dzong (fortress).

16 King Jigme Dorji Wangchuk
(obverse of 50n.p. coin)

(Des and embossed Walsall Lithographic Co, Ltd)

1966 (8 July). 40*th Anniv of King Jigme Wangchuk's Accession (father of King Jigme Dorji Wangchuk). Circular designs, embossed on gold foil, backed with multicoloured patterned paper. Imperf. Sizes:—*

(a) Diameter 38 mm; (b) Diameter 50 mm; (c) Diameter 63 mm.

(i) 50n.p. Coin

83	10ch. emerald (a)		15	15

(ii) 1r. Coin.

84	25ch. emerald (b)		25	25

(iii) 3r. Coin.

85	50ch. emerald (c)		45	45

(iv) 1 sertum Coin.

86	1n. carmine (a)		80	80
87	1n.30 carmine (a)		1·20	1·20

(v) 2 sertum Coin.

88	2n. carmine (b)		1·80	1·80
89	3n. carmine (b)		2·50	2·50

(vi) 5 sertum Coin.

90	4n. carmine (c)		3·25	3·25
91	5n. carmine (c)		3·75	3·75
83/91	*Set of* 9		13·00	13·00

The 10, 25, 50ch., 1, 2, 4n. each show the obverse side of the coins as T **16**. The remainder show the reverse side of the coins (Symbol).

17 "Abominable Snowman"

(Photo Heraclio Fournier, S.A., Vitoria, Spain)

1966 (10 Oct)–**67**. *"Abominable Snowman". Various triangular designs as T* **17**. *P* 13.

92	1ch. multicoloured		10	10
93	2ch. multicoloured		10	10
94	3ch. multicoloured		10	10
95	4ch. multicoloured		10	10
96	5ch. multicoloured		10	10
97	15ch. multicoloured		10	10
98	30ch. multicoloured		10	10
99	40ch. multicoloured (15.11.66)		15	15
100	50ch. multicoloured		15	15
101	1n.25 multicoloured (15.11.66)		30	30
102	2n.50 multicoloured (15.11.66)		50	50
103	3n. multicoloured (15.11.66)		60	60
104	5n. multicoloured (15.11.66)		85	85
105	6n. multicoloured (4.3.67)		85	85
106	7n. multicoloured (4.3.67)		95	95
92/106	*Set of* 15		4·50	4·50

AIR MAIL
(18)   (19)

1967 (10 Jan). *AIR. Various stamps overprinted.*

(a) Type 18

107A	**6**	33ch. (No. 22)	10	15
108A	–	50ch. (No. 41)	25	25
109A	–	70ch. (No. 23)	30	30
		a. Opt inverted	30·00	30·00
110A	–	75ch. (No. 42)	25	25
111A	–	1n. (No. 24)	35	35
112A	–	1n.50 (No. 75)	55	55
113A	–	2n. (No. 76)	80	80
114A	–	3n. (No. 77)	1·20	1·20

115A	**14**	4n. (No. 78)		1·80	1·80
116A	–	5n. (No. 79)		2·30	2·30
107A/116A		Set of 10		7·00	7·00

(b) Type **19**

107B	**6**	33ch. (No. 22)		10	10
108B	–	50ch. (No. 41)		25	25
109B	–	70ch. (No. 23)		30	30
110B	–	75ch. (No. 42)		25	25
111B	–	1n. (No. 24)		35	35
112B	–	1n.50 (No. 75)		55	55
113B	–	2n. (No. 76)		80	80
114B	–	3n. (No. 77)		1·20	1·20
115B	**14**	4n. (No. 78)		1·80	1·80
116B	–	5n. (No. 79)		2·30	2·30
107B/116B		Set of 10		7·00	7·00

All values exist in *se-tenant* pairs showing both types of overprint.

20 *Lilium sherriffiae*

(Designs from watercolours selected by F. Ludlow, Natural History Museum, London. Litho)

1967 (9 Feb). *Flowers. T* **20** *and similar multicoloured designs.* P 13½.

117	3ch. Type **20**		10	10
118	5ch. *Meconopsis*		10	10
119	7ch. *Rhododendron dhwoju*		10	10
120	10ch. *Pleione hookeriana*		10	10
121	50ch. Type **20**		15	15
122	1n. As 5ch.		30	30
123	2n.50 As 7ch.		75	75
124	4n. As 10ch.		1·00	1·00
125	5n. *Rhododendron giganteum*		1·30	1·30
117/125	Set of 9		3·50	3·50

21 Scouts planting a Sapling

1967 (28 Mar). *Bhutanese Boy Scouts. T* **21** *and similar multicoloured designs. Photo.* P 13½.

126	5ch. Type **21**		10	10
127	10ch. Scouts preparing meal		10	10
128	15ch. Scout mountaineering		15	15
129	50ch. Type **21**		25	25

130	1n.25 As 10ch.		70	70
131	4n. As 15ch.		1·70	1·70
126/131	Set of 6		2·75	2·75
MS132	93 × 93 mm. Nos. 130/1		6·25	6·25

(**22**)

1967 (15 May). *World Fair, Montreal. Nos. 53/5 and* **MS**55a *optd with T* **22**.

133	33ch. multicoloured		30	30
134	1n.50 multicoloured		40	40
135	2n. multicoloured		45	45
MS136	120 × 86 mm. Nos. 134/5		2·00	2·00

23 Avro Type 683 Lancaster Bomber

1967 (25 July). *Churchill and Battle of Britain Commemoration. T* **23** *and similar horiz designs. Multicoloured. Litho.* P 13½.

137	45ch. Type **23**		20	20
138	2n. Supermarine Spitfire Mk IIB fighter		45	45
139	4n. Hawker Hurricane Mk IIC fighter		90	90
MS140	118 × 75 mm. Nos. 138/9		2·40	2·40

It is understood that the miniature sheet was not issued in Bhutan.

WORLD JAMBOREE IDAHO, U.S.A. AUG. 1-9/67
(**24**)

1967 (8 Aug). *World Scout Jamboree, Idaho. Nos. 126/31 and* **MS**132 *optd with T* **24**.

141	5ch. multicoloured		15	15
142	10ch. multicoloured		20	20
143	15ch. multicoloured		25	25
144	50ch. multicoloured		35	35
145	1n.25 multicoloured		70	70
146	4n. multicoloured		1·80	1·80
141/146	Set of 6		3·00	3·00
MS147	93 × 93 mm. Nos. 145/6		3·75	3·75

A second setting of the overprint is known with the "I" of "IDAHO" below "OR" of "WORLD".

25 Painting

1967 (28 Sept). *Bhutan Girl Scouts. T 25 and similar multicoloured designs. Photo.* P 13½.

148	5ch. Type **25**	10	10
149	10ch. Playing musical instrument	10	10
150	15ch. Picking fruit	10	10
151	1n.50 Type **25**	45	45
152	2n.50 As 10ch.	1·10	1·10
153	5n. As 15ch.	2·50	2·50
148/153 *Set of 6*		4·00	4·00
MS154 93 × 93 mm. Nos. 152/3		5·50	5·50

26 Astronaut in Space

1967 (30 Oct). *Space Achievements. T 26 and similar horiz designs. Multicoloured. Litho with laminated prismatic-ribbed plastic surface.* Imperf.

(a) POSTAGE.

155	3ch. Type **26**	25	25
156	5ch. Space vehicle and astronaut	25	25
157	7ch. Astronaut and landing vehicle	45	45
158	10ch. Three astronauts in space	50	50
159	15ch. Type **26**	75	75
160	30ch. As 5ch.	90	90
161	50ch. As 7ch.	1·30	1·30
162	1n.25 As 10ch.	2·75	2·75

(b) AIR.

163	2n.50 Type **26**	1·90	1·90
164	4n. As 5ch.	2·75	2·75
165	5n. As 7ch.	3·75	3·75
166	9n. As 10ch.	6·50	6·50
155/166 *Set of 12*		20·00	20·00
MS167 Three sheets, each 130 × 111 mm.			
Nos. 155/8, 159/62 and 163/6. Imperf		29·00	29·00

The laminated plastic surface gives the stamps a three-dimensional effect.

APPENDIX. Further commemorative issues which appeared during 1968–74 will be found recorded in the Appendix to this country.

27 Tashichho Dzong

(Des from photos by L. Wangchuck. Photo Security Printing Press, Nasik, India)

1968 (29 Feb). P 13.

168	**27**	10ch. purple and bronze-green	20	10

28 Elephant

1968 (14 Mar). *Mythological Creatures. T 28 and similar diamond-shaped designs. Photo.* P 12½.

(a) POSTAGE.

169	2ch. carmine-lake, blue & orange-brown	10	10
170	3ch. bright rose, dp blue & turq-grn	10	10
171	4ch. dull orange, grey-olive & deep blue	10	10
172	5ch. deep blue, yellow and bright rose	10	10
173	15ch. yellowish green, purple & dp blue	10	10
174	20ch. brown, black and salmon	10	10
175	30ch. yellow, black and violet-blue	15	15
176	50ch. bistre, deep emerald and black	15	15
177	1n.25 black, emerald and red	15	15
178	2n. bistre-yellow, reddish violet & black	30	30

(b) AIR. Inscr "AIR MAIL".

179	1n.50 myrtle grn, dull pur & yell-ochre	25	25
180	2n.50 red, black and blue	35	35
181	4n. red-orange, emerald and black	60	60
182	5n. agate, slate and red-orange	80	80
183	10n. reddish violet, olive-grey and black	1·50	1·50
169/183 *Set of 15*		4·50	4·50

Designs:—2, 20ch., 1n.50, Type **28**; 3, 30ch., 2n.50, Garuda; 4, 50ch., 4n. Tiger; 5ch., 1n.25, 5n. Wind horse; 15ch., 2, 10n. Snow lion.

29 Tongsa Dzong

30 Ward's Trogon

(Photo Security Ptg Press, Nasik, India)

1968 (30 Oct)–**70.** *T* **29** *and similar horiz designs.* P 13½ × 13.

184	50ch. deep bluish green		30	15
185	75ch. olive-brown & dp ultram (2.5.70)		35	20
186	1n. ultramarine and violet (2.5.70)		40	25

Designs:—75ch. Daga Dzong; 1n. Lhuntsi Dzong.

1968 (7 Dec)–**69.** *Rare Birds. T* **30** *and similar multicoloured designs. Photo.* P 12½.

(a) POSTAGE.

187	2ch. Red-faced liocichla (inscr "Crimson-winged laughing thrush") (*horiz*)		10	10
188	3ch. Type **30**		10	10
189	4ch. Burmese (inscr "Grey") peacock-pheasant (*horiz*)		10	10
190	5ch. Rufous-necked hornbill		10	10
191	15ch. Fire-tailed myzornis (*horiz*)		15	15
192	20ch. As No. 187		20	20
193	30ch. Type **30**		20	20
194	50ch. As No. 189		25	25
195	1n.25 As No. 190		35	35
196	2n. As No. 191		45	45

(b) AIR. Inscr "AIR MAIL" (29.1.69).

197	1n.50 As No. 187		50	50
198	2n.50 Type **30**		60	55
199	4n. As No. 189		90	90
200	5n. As No. 190		1·20	1·20
201	10n. As No. 191		1·80	1·80
187/201 *Set of* 15			6·25	6·25

31 Mahatma Gandhi

(Photo Security Ptg Press, Nasik, India)

1969 (2 Oct). *Birth Centenary of Mahatma Gandhi.* P 13 × 13½.

202	**31**	20ch. sepia and light new blue	15	15
203		2n. olive-brown and olive-yellow	75	75

(**32**)

(Surch by Security Ptg Press, Nasik, India)

1970 (June). *Provisionals. Various stamps surch as T* **32.**

I. 1966 Animals issue (Nos. 77/9).

204	–	20ch.on 3n. multicoloured	2·10	2·10
205	**14**	20ch.on 4n. multicoloured	2·10	2·10
206	–	20ch.on 5n. multicoloured	2·10	2·10

II. 1966–67 Abominable Snowmen issue (Nos. 103/6).

207		20ch.on 3n. multicoloured	1·90	1·90
208	–	20ch.on 5n. multicoloured	2·10	2·10
209	–	20ch.on 6n. multicoloured	2·75	2·75
210	–	20ch.on 7n. multicoloured	2·75	2·75

III. 1967 Flowers issue (Nos. 124/5).

211	–	20ch.on 4n. multicoloured	2·10	2·10
212	–	20ch.on 5n. multicoloured	2·50	2·50

IV. 1967 Boy Scouts issue (No. 131).

213	–	20ch.on 4n. multicoloured	17·00	17·00

V. 1968 Pheasants issue (Appendix).

214	–	20ch.on 4n. multicoloured	2·10	2·10

VI. 1968 Mythological Creatures issue (Nos. 178, 182/3).

(a) POSTAGE.

215	–	20ch.on 2n. bistre-yellow, reddish violet and black	3·75	3·75

(b) AIR.

216		20ch.on 5n. agate, slate and red-orange	2·40	2·40
217	–	20ch.on 10n. reddish violet, olive-grey and black	2·10	2·10

VII. 1968–69 Rare Birds issue (Nos. 196, 198/201).

(a) POSTAGE.

218	–	20ch.on 2n. multicoloured	2·75	2·75

(b) AIR.

219	**30**	20ch.on 2n.50 multicoloured	2·75	2·75
220	–	20ch.on 4n. multicoloured	2·10	2·10
221	–	20ch.on 5n. multicoloured	2·50	2·50
222	–	20ch.on 10n. multicoloured	3·50	3·50
204/222 *Set of* 19			55·00	55·00

See also Nos. 223/245, 253/65 and 385/410.

(Surch by Security Ptg Press, Nasik, India)

1970 (2 Nov). *Provisionals. Various stamps surch similar to T* **32.**

I. 1963 Freedom from Hunger issue (No. 14).

223	**4**	20ch.on 1n.50 bright purple, red brown and light blue	2·75	2·75

II. 1965 Animals issue (Nos. 75/6).

224	–	20ch.on 1n.50 multicoloured	2·75	2·75
225	–	20ch.on 2n. multicoloured	2·75	2·75

III. 1966–67 Abominable Snowmen issue (Nos. 101/2).

226	–	20ch.on 1n.25 multicoloured	2·75	2·75
227	**17**	20ch.on 2n.50 multicoloured	2·75	2·75

IV. 1967 Boy Scouts issue (No. 130).

228	–	20ch.on 1n.25 multicoloured	2·75	2·75

V. 1967 Churchill issue (Nos. 138/9).

229	–	20ch.on 2n. multicoloured	2·75	2·75
230	–	20ch.on 4n. multicoloured	2·75	2·75

VI. 1968 Pheasants issue (Appendix).

231	–	20ch.on 2n. multicoloured	3·75	3·75
232	–	20ch.on 7n. multicoloured	3·75	3·75

VII. 1968 Mythological Creatures issue (Nos. 175/80).

(a) POSTAGE.

233	–	5ch.on 30ch. yellow, black & vio-bl	85	85
234	–	5ch.on 50ch. bistre, dp emer & blk	85	85
235	–	5ch.on 1n.25 black, emerald and red	85	85
236	–	5ch.on 2n. bistre-yellow, reddish violet and black	85	85

(b) AIR.

237	**28**	5ch.on 1n.50 myrtle-green, dull purple and yellow-ochre	85	85
238	–	5ch.on 2n.50 red, black and blue	85	85

VIII. 1968–69 Rare Birds issue (Nos. 193/5, 197).

(a) POSTAGE.

239	**30**	20ch.on 30ch. multicoloured	3·75	3·75
240	–	20ch.on 50ch. multicoloured	3·75	3·75
241	–	20ch.on 1n.25 multicoloured	3·75	3·75

(b) AIR.

242	–	20ch.on 1n.50 multicoloured	3·75	3·75

IX. 1969 U.P.U. issue (Appendix).

243	–	20ch.on 1n.05 multicoloured	2·75	2·75
244	–	20ch.on 1n.40 multicoloured	2·75	2·75
245	–	20ch.on 4n. multicoloured	2·75	2·75
223/245 *Set of* 23			40·00	40·00

33 Wangdiphodrang Dzong and Bridge

34 Book Year Emblem

(Photo Security Ptg Press, Nasik, India)

1971 (22 Feb)–**72**. P 14 × 13½
246	**33**	2ch. grey (1972)		25	10
247		3ch. deep mauve (1972)		35	15
248		4ch. bluish violet (1972)		35	25
249		5ch. yellow-green		10	10
250		10ch. orange-brown		15	10
251		15ch. blue		20	15
252		20ch. reddish purple		30	15
246/252 *Set of 7*				1·50	1·00

King Jigme Singye Wangchuk, 21 July 1972

35 Dochi

1972 (5 Oct). *Dogs. T* **35** *and similar multicoloured designs. Photo.* P 13½.
270	5ch. Apsoo standing on hind legs (*vert*)		10	10
271	10ch. Type **35**		10	10
272	15ch. Brown and white damci		10	10
273	25ch. Black and white damci		10	10
274	55ch. Apsoo lying down		10	10
275	8n. Two damci		1·40	1·40
270/275 *Set of 6*			1·70	1·70
MS276 100 × 119 mm. Nos. 274/5			40	1·40

1971 (1 July). *Provisionals. Various stamps surch similar to T* **32** (*No. 235 handstamped*).
		I. 1964 Dancers issue (Nos. 25/6).		
253	–	55ch.on 1n.30 multicoloured	85	85
254	–	90ch.on 2n. multicoloured	85	85
		II. 1966 Animals issue (Nos. 77/8).		
255	–	55ch.on 3n. multicoloured	85	85
256	**14**	90ch.on 4n. multicoloured	85	85
		III. 1967 Boy Scouts issue (No. 131).		
257	–	90ch.on 4n. multicoloured	1·60	1·60
		IV. 1967 Pheasants issue (Appendix).		
258	–	55ch.on 5n. multicoloured	3·00	3·00
259	–	90ch.on 9n. multicoloured	3·00	3·00
		V. 1968 Mythological Creatures issue (No. 181). AIR.		
260	–	55ch.on 4n. red-orange, emer & blk	55	55
		VI. 1968 Mexico Olympics issue (Appendix).		
261	–	90ch.on 1n.05 multicoloured	1·40	1·40
		VII. 1968–69 Rare Birds issue (No. 196).		
262	–	90ch.on 2n. multicoloured	3·00	3·00
		VIII. 1969 U.P.U. Issue (Appendix).		
263	–	55ch.on 60ch. multicoloured	85	85
		IX. 1970 New U.P.U. Headquarters issue (Appendix).		
264	–	90ch.on 2n.50 gold and lake	2·75	2·75
		X. 1971 Moon Vehicles (plastic-surfaced) issue (Appendix).		
265	–	90ch.on 1n.70 multicoloured (Y.)	4·00	4·00
253/265 *Set of 13*			21·00	21·00

36 King and Royal Crest

37 Mail Delivery by Horse

(Des G. L. Vasarhelyi. Litho Format)

1974 (2 June). *Coronation of King Jigme Singye Wangchuk. T* **36** *and similar horiz designs, showing king and national emblems. Multicoloured. P* 13½.
277	10ch. Type **36**	10	10
278	25ch. Bhutan flag	15	15
279	1n.25 Good Luck signs	30	30
280	2n. Punakha Dzong	45	45
281	3n. Royal Crown	60	60
277/281 *Set of 5*		1·40	1·40
MS282 Two sheets each 177 × 127 mm. (a) 5ch. As 10ch.; 5n. As 3n.; (b) 90ch. As 1n.25; 4n. As 2n. Perf or imperf		4·75	4·75

(Des G. Vasarhelyi. Litho Format)

1974 (9 Oct). *Centenary of Universal Postal Union. T* **37** *and similar vert designs. Multicoloured. P* 14½.

(a) POSTAGE.
283	1ch. Type **37**	10	10
284	2ch. Early and modern locomotives	10	10
285	3ch. *Hindoostan* (paddle-steamer) and *Iberia* (liner)	10	10
286	4ch. Vickers FB-27 Vimy and Concorde aircraft	10	10
287	25ch. Mail runner and jeep	10	10

1972 (15 May). *International Book Year. Photo.* P 13½ × 13.
266	**34**	2ch. deep green and turquoise-blue	10	10
267		3ch. purple-brown and yellow	10	10
268		5ch. chocolate, salmon and orange-red	10	10
269		20ch. red-brown and turquoise-blue	10	10
266/269 *Set of 4*			35	35

(b) AIR. Inscr "AIR MAIL".

288	1n. As 25ch.	20	20
289	1n.40 As 2ch.	45	45
290	2n. As 4ch.	80	80
283/290	Set of 8	1·80	1·80
MS291	91 × 78 mm. 10n. As 4ch.	3·75	3·75

38 Family and W.P.Y. Emblem

(Des G. Vasarhelyi. Litho Format)

1974 (17 Dec). *World Population Year.* P 13½.

292	**38**	25ch. multicoloured	10	10
293		50ch. multicoloured	10	10
294		90ch. multicoloured	25	25
295		2n.50 multicoloured	55	55
292/295		Set of 4	90	90
MS296	116 × 79 mm. **38** 10n. multicoloured		2·10	2·10

39 Eastern Courtier (*Sephisa chandra*)

(Des Waddington Studios. Litho Format)

1975 (15 Sept). *Butterflies.* T **39** *and similar horiz designs. Multicoloured.* P 14½.

297	1ch. Type **39**	10	10
298	2ch. Bamboo forester (*Lethe kansa*)	10	10
299	3ch. Tailed labyrinth (*Neope bhadra*)	10	10
300	4ch. Blue duchess (*Euthalia duda*)	10	10
301	5ch. Cruiser (*Vindula erota*)	10	10
302	10ch. Bhutan glory (*Bhutanitis lidderdalei*)	10	10
303	3n. Bi-coloured commodore (*Limenitis zayla*)	65	65
304	5n. Red-breasted jezebel (*Delias thysbe*)	1·40	1·40
297/304	Set of 8	2·40	2·40
MS305	116 × 91 mm. 10n. *Meandrusa scrion* (*Dabasa gyas*)	2·75	2·75

40 King Jigme Singye Wangchuk

(Litho and embossed on foil by Walsall Lithographic Co. Ltd)

1975 (11 Nov). *King's 20th Birthday.* T **40** *and similar circular design. Imperf.*

(a) Diameter 39 mm.

306	**40**	15ch. bright emerald/*gold*	10	10
307		1n. carmine-red/*gold*	25	25
308	–	1n.30 carmine-red/*gold*	25	25

(b) Diameter 50 mm.

309	**40**	25ch. bright emerald/*gold*	10	10
310		2n. carmine-red/*gold*	45	45
311	–	3n. carmine-red/*gold*	70	70

(c) Diameter 63 mm.

312	**40**	90ch. bright emerald/*gold*	75	75
313		4n. carmine-red/*gold*	1·40	1·40
314	–	5n. carmine-red/*gold*	1·70	1·70
306/314		Set of 9	5·00	5·00

Design:—1n.30, 3, 5n. Decorative motif.

41 "Apollo"

(Des G. Vasarhelyi. Litho Format)

1975 (1 Dec). *"Apollo"–"Soyuz" Space Link.* T **41** *and similar horiz design. Multicoloured.* P 14 × 13½.

315	10n. Type **41**	2·40	2·40
	a. Horiz pair Nos. 315/16	5·00	5·00
316	10n. "Soyuz"	2·40	2·40
MS317	130 × 89 mm. 15n. Type **41**; 15n. As No. 316	6·75	6·75

Nos. 315/16 were issued together in *se-tenant* pairs within the sheet, each pair forming a composite design.

42 Jewellery   **43** *Rhododendron cinnabarinum*

(Des G. Vasarhelyi. Litho Format)

1975 (17 Dec). *Handicrafts and Craftsmen.* T **42** *and similar horiz designs. Multicoloured.* P 14½.

318	1ch. Type **42**	10	10
319	2ch. Coffee pot, hand bell and sugar dish	10	10
320	3ch. Powder horns	10	10
321	4ch. Pendants and inlaid box	10	10
322	5ch. Painter	10	10
323	15ch. Silversmith	10	10
324	20ch. Wood carver with tools	10	10
325	1n.50 Textile printer	40	40
326	10n. Printer	1·90	1·90
318/326	Set of 9	1·80	1·80
MS327	105 × 79 mm. 5n. As No. 326	1·70	1·70

(Des G. Vasarhelyi. Litho Format)

1976 (15 Feb). *Rhododendrons.* T **43** *and similar vert designs. Multicoloured.* P 15.

328	1ch. Type **43**	10	10
329	2ch. *R. campanulatum*	10	10
330	3ch. *R. fortunei*	10	10

331	4ch. *R. arboreum*		10	10
332	5ch. *R. arboreum (different)*		25	10
333	1n. *R. falconeri*		20	40
334	3n. *R. hodgsonii*		55	55
335	5n. *R. keysii*		1·10	1·10
328/335 *Set of 8*			2·00	2·30
MS336 105 × 79 mm. 10n. *R. cinnabarinum (different)*			2·75	2·75

44 Skiing

(Des J. Waddington Studios. Litho Format)

1976 (29 Mar). *Winter Olympic Games, Innsbruck. T* **44** *and similar horiz designs. Multicoloured.* P 14 × 13½.

337	1ch. Type **44**		10	10
338	2ch. Bobsleighing		10	10
339	3ch. Ice hockey		10	10
340	4ch. Cross-country skiing		10	10
341	5ch. Individual figure skating		10	10
342	2n. Downhill skiing		25	25
343	4n. Speed skating		60	55
344	10n. Pairs figure skating		1·90	1·70
337/344 *Set of 8*			3·00	2·75
MS345 78 × 104 mm. 6n. Ski jumping			1·60	1·60

45 Dragon Mask

(Litho Dai Nippon Ptg Co, Japan)

1976 (23 Apr). *Ceremonial Masks. T* **45** *and similar designs showing different masks. Laminated prismatic-ribbed plastic surface.* Imperf.

(a) POSTAGE.

346	5ch. multicoloured		10	10
347	10ch. multicoloured		10	10
348	15ch. multicoloured		10	10
349	20ch. multicoloured		10	10
350	25ch. multicoloured (*horiz*)		10	10
351	30ch. multicoloured (*horiz*)		10	10
352	35ch. multicoloured (*horiz*)		10	10

(b) AIR. Inscr "AIR MAIL".

353	1n. multicoloured (*horiz*)		25	25
354	2n. multicoloured (*horiz*)		45	45

355	2n.50 multicoloured (*horiz*)		75	75
356	3n. multicoloured (*horiz*)		90	90
346/356 *Set of 11*			2·75	2·75
MS357 Two sheets, each 119 × 160 mm. (a) 5n. As No. 348; (b) 10n. As No. 351			4·00	4·00

46 Orchid

(Litho Format)

1976 (29 May). *Flowers. T* **46** *and similar horiz designs. Multicoloured.* P 15.

358	1ch. Type **46**		10	10
359	2ch. Orchid (*different*)		10	10
360	3ch. Orchid (*different*)		10	10
361	4ch. *Primula denticulata*		10	10
362	5ch. Arum		10	10
363	2n. Orchid (*different*)		35	35
364	4n. *Leguminosa*		80	80
365	6n. Rhododendron		1·20	1·20
358/365 *Set of 8*			2·50	2·50
MS366 106 × 80 mm. 10n. Arum (*different*)			3·75	3·75

47 Double Carp Emblem

(Litho Format)

1976 (1 July). *25th Anniv of Colombo Plan. T* **47** *and similar square designs showing various motifs. Multicoloured.* P 15.

367	3ch. Type **47**		10	10
368	4ch. Vase emblem		10	10
369	5ch. Geometric design		10	10
370	25ch. Design incorporating animal's face		10	10
371	1n.25 Ornamental design		25	25
372	2n. Floral design		40	35
373	2n.50 Carousel design		50	45
374	3n. Wheel design		70	65
367/374 *Set of 8*			2·00	1·90

48 Bandaranaike Conference Hall   **49** Liberty Bell

(Litho Format)

1976 (16 Aug). *Fifth Non-aligned Countries Summit Conference, Colombo.* P 14 × 13½.

375	**48**	1n.25 multicoloured	35	35
376		2n.50 multicoloured	75	65

(Des J. Waddington Studios. Litho Questa)

1978 (15 Nov). *Anniversaries.* T **49** *and similar vert designs. Multicoloured.* P 14½.

377	20n. Type **49** (bicentenary of U.S. independence)	4·00	4·00
378	20n. Alexander Graham Bell and early telephone (telephone centenary)	4·00	4·00
379	20n. Archer (Olympic Games, Montreal)	4·00	4·00
380	20n. Alfred Nobel (75th anniv of Nobel Prizes)	4·00	4·00
381	20n. Ryan NYP *Spirit of St. Louis* (50th anniv of Lindbergh's transatlantic flight)	4·00	4·00
382	20n. Airship LZ3 (75th anniv of Zeppelin)	4·50	4·50
383	20n. Queen Elizabeth II (25th anniv of Coronation)	4·00	4·00
377/383	*Set of 7*	26·00	26·00

MS384 Seven sheets, each 103 × 79 mm. (a) 25n. Flags of Bhutan and United States; (b) 25n. "Syncom II" communications satellite; (c) 25n. Shot putter; (d) 25n. Nobel medal; (e) 25n. *Spirit of St. Louis* landing at Le Bourget; (f) 25n. Airship *Viktoria Luise*; (g) 25n. Westminister Abbey . . . . 42·00   42·00

1978 (15 Dec). *Provisionals. Various stamps surch similar to T* **32**.

I. 1967 Girl Scouts issue (No. 153).

385	–	25ch.on 5n. multicoloured	12·50	10·00

II. 1968 Mythological Creatures issues (Nos. 181, 183).

386	–	25ch.on 4n. red-orange, emer & blk	2·50	2·10
387	–	25ch.on 10n. reddish violet, olive-grey and black	2·50	2·10

III. 1971 Admission to United Nations Issue (Appendix).

(a) POSTAGE.

388	–	25ch.on 3n. multicoloured	2·10	1·70

(b) AIR.

389	–	25ch.on 5n. multicoloured	2·10	1·70
390	–	25ch.on 6n. multicoloured	2·10	1·70

IV. 1971 Boy Scout Anniv issue (Appendix).

391	–	25ch.on 6n. multicoloured	13·00	11·00

V. 1972 Dogs issue (No. 275).

392	–	25ch.on 8n. multicoloured	3·75	3·25

VI. 1973 Dogs issue (Appendix).

393	–	25ch.on 4n. multicoloured	3·75	3·25

VII. 1973 "Indipex 73" issue (Appendix).

(a) POSTAGE.

394	–	25ch.on 3n. multicoloured	3·25	3·00

(b) AIR.

395	–	25ch.on 5n. multicoloured	3·25	3·00
396	–	25ch.on 6n. multicoloured	3·25	3·00

VIII. 1974 U.P.U. issue (Nos. 289/90).

397	–	25ch.on 1n.40 multicoloured	3·00	2·50
398	–	25ch.on 2n. multicoloured	3·00	2·50

IX. 1974 World Population Year issue (No. 295).

399	–	25ch.on 2n.50 multicoloured	5·00	4·25

X. 1975 Butterflies issue (Nos. 299, 301).

400	–	25ch.on 3n. multicoloured	5·00	4·25
401	–	25ch.on 5n. multicoloured	5·00	4·25

XI. 1975 "Apollo-Soyuz" issue (Nos. 315/6).

402	**41**	25ch.on 10n. multicoloured	12·50	10·00
403	–	25ch.on 10n. multicoloured	12·50	10·00

XII. 1975 Handicrafts issue (No. 326).

404	–	25ch.on 10n. multicoloured	2·50	2·10

XIII. 1976 Rhododendrons issue (No. 335).

405	–	25ch.on 5n. multicoloured	4·25	3·50

XIV. 1976 Winter Olympic Games issue (Nos. 343/4).

406	–	25ch.on 4n. multicoloured	5·75	5·00
407	–	25ch.on 10n. multicoloured	5·75	5·00

XV. 1976 Flowers issue (Nos. 364/5).

408	–	25ch.on 4n. multicoloured	2·10	1·80
409	–	25ch.on 6n. multicoloured	2·10	1·80

XVI. 1976 Colombo Plan issue (No. 373).

410	–	25ch.on 2n.50 multicoloured	2·50	2·10
385/410		*Set of 26*	£110	95·00

50 Mother and Child

(Litho Questa)

1979 (28 July). *International Year of the Child.* T **50** *and similar horiz designs. Multicoloured.* P 14 × 13½.

411		2n. Type **50**	50	50
412		5n. Mother carrying two children	1·10	95
413		10n. Children at school	1·60	1·50
MS414		131 × 103 mm. Nos. 411/3	3·25	2·75

51 Conference Emblem and Dove

1979 (3 Sept). *Sixth Non-aligned Countries Summit Conference, Havana.* T **51** *and similar horiz design. Multicoloured. Litho.* P 14 × 13½.

415		25ch. Type **51**	15	15
416		10n. Conference emblem and Bhutanese symbols	2·50	2·20

52 Dorji (rattle)

1979 (17 Dec). *Antiquities.* T **52** *and similar multicoloured designs. Litho.* P 14 × 13½ (horiz) or 13½ × 14 (vert).

417		5ch. Type **52**	10	10
418		10ch. Dilbu (hand bell) (*vert*)	10	10
419		15ch. Jadum (cylindrical pot) (*vert*)	10	10
420		25ch. Jamjee (teapot)	10	10
421		1n. Kem (cylindrical container) (*vert*)	35	30
422		1n.25 Jamjee (*different*)	40	40
423		1n.70 Sangphor (ornamental vessel)	60	60
424		2n. Jamjee (*different*) (*vert*)	75	70
425		3n. Yangtho (pot with lid) (*vert*)	95	90

426	4n. Battha (circular case)	1·20	1·20
427	5n. Chhap (ornamental flask) (*vert*)	1·70	1·60
417/427	*Set of* 11	5·75	5·50

53 Rinpiang Dzong, Bhutan Stamp and Rowland Hill Statue

1980 (6 May). *Death Centenary of Sir Rowland Hill. T 53 and similar horiz designs. Multicoloured. Litho.* P 13½.

428	1n. Type **53**	45	40
429	2n. Dzong, Bhutan stamp and statue	80	75
430	5n. Ounsti Dzong, Bhutan stamp and statue	1·30	1·20
431	10n. Lingzi Dzong and British 1d. stamp of 1912	2·75	2·50
428/431	*Set of* 4	4·75	4·25
MS432	102 × 103 mm. 20n. Rope bridge, British 1d. black stamp and statue	9·50	9·50

54 Dungtse Lhakhang, Paro

55 St. Paul's Cathedral

(Litho Format)

1981 (11 July). *Monasteries. T 54 and similar multicoloured designs.* P 13½ × 14 (vert) or 14 × 13½ (horiz).

433	1n. Type **54**	20	15
434	2n. Kichu Lhakhang, Paro (*horiz*)	40	35
435	2n.25 Kurjey Lhakhang, Kurjey (*horiz*)	55	50
436	3n. Tangu, Thimphu (*horiz*)	70	65
437	4n. Cheri, Thimphu (*horiz*)	95	85
438	5n. Chorten, Kora (*horiz*)	1·50	1·30
439	7n. Tak-Tsang, Paro	2·10	1·90
433/439	*Set of* 7	5·75	5·25

(Des R. Granger Barrett. Litho Format)

1981 (10 Sept). *Wedding of Prince of Wales. T 55 and similar vert designs. Multicoloured.* P 14½.

440	1n. Type **55**	10	10
441	5n. Type **55**	90	75
442	20n. Prince Charles and Lady Diana Spencer	3·25	2·75
443	25n. As No. 442	4·00	3·75
440/443	*Set of* 4	7·50	6·75
MS444	69 × 90 mm. 20n. Wedding Procession	4·00	3·50

Nos. 440 and 443 were each issued in sheets of 30 stamps and five labels, Nos. 441/2 each in sheetlets of 5 stamps and one label.

56 Orange-bellied Leafbird (*Chloropsis hardwickii*)

57 Footballers

(Des G. Drummond. Litho Questa)

1982 (19 Apr). *Birds. T 56 and similar vert designs. Multicoloured.* P 14.

445	2n. Type **56**	70	65
446	3n. Himalayan monal pheasant (*Lophorus impeyanus*)	1·00	95
447	5n. Ward's trogon (*Harpactes wardi*)	2·00	1·80
448	10n. Mrs Gould's sunbird (*Aethopyga gouldiae*)	3·25	3·00
445/448	*Set of* 4	6·25	5·75
MS449	96 × 101 mm. 25n. Maroon oriole (*Oriolus trailli*)	6·75	6·00

(Des Clover Mill. Litho Format)

1982 (25 June). *World Cup Football Championship, Spain. T 57 and similar designs showing football scenes.* P 15 × 14½.

450	1n. multicoloured	20	15
451	2n. multicoloured	45	40
452	3n. multicoloured	65	60
453	20n. multicoloured	3·75	3·25
450/453	*Set of* 4	4·50	4·00
MS454	79 × 108 mm. 25n. multicoloured (*horiz*). P 15	6·75	5·25

No. **MS**454 exists in two versions, differing in the list of qualifying countries in the border.

58 St. James's Palace

59 Lord Baden-Powell (founder)

(Des PAD Studios. Litho Questa)

1982 (1 July–24 Aug). *21st Birthday of Princess of Wales. T 58 and similar vert designs. Multicoloured.* P 14½.

455	1n. Type **58**	40	35
456	10n. Prince and Princess of Wales (24.8)	2·20	2·00
457	15n. Windsor Castle (24.8)	3·75	4·00
458	25n. Princess in wedding dress	5·75	5·25
455/458	*Set of* 4	11·00	10·50
MS459	102 × 76 mm. 20n. Princess of Wales	5·00	4·50

Nos. 456/7 were each issued in sheetlets of five stamps and one label.

(Des Artists International. Litho Questa)

1982 (23 Aug). *75th Anniv of Boy Scout Movement. T* **59** *and similar horiz designs. Multicoloured.* P 14.

460	3n. Type **59**		55	50
461	5n. Scouts around campfire		1·10	95
462	15n. Map reading		2·75	2·50
463	20n. Pitching tents		4·00	3·75
460/463 *Set of 4*			7·50	7·00
MS464 91 × 70 mm. 25n. Scout			5·25	4·75

ROYAL BABY 21.6.82
(61)

60 Rama finds Mowgli

(Des Walt Disney Productions. Litho Format)

1982 (1 Sept). *The Jungle Book (cartoon film). T* **60** *and similar horiz designs. Multicoloured.* P 11.

465	1ch. Type **60**		10	10
466	2ch. Bagheera leading Mowgli to Man-village		10	10
467	3ch. Kaa planning attack on Bagheera and Mowgli		10	10
468	4ch. Mowgli and elephants		10	10
469	5ch. Mowgli and Baloo		10	10
470	10ch. Mowgli and King Louie		10	10
471	30ch. Kaa and Shere Khan		10	10
472	2n. Mowgli, Baloo and Bagheera		45	35
473	20n. Mowgli carrying jug for girl		4·00	3·50
465/473 *Set of 9*			4·50	4·00
MS474 Two sheets, each 127 × 102 mm. (a) 20n. Mowgli and Baloo; (b) 20n. Mowgli and Baloo floating down river. P 14			8·75	7·75

1982 (3 Nov). *Birth of Prince William of Wales. Nos.* 455/MS459 *optd with T* **61**.

475	1n. multicoloured		40	40
476	10n. multicoloured		1·40	1·20
477	15n. multicoloured		2·75	2·50
478	25n. multicoloured		4·50	4·00
475/478 *Set of 4*			8·25	7·25
MS479 102 × 76 mm. 20n. multicoloured			5·00	4·75

Druk Air

62 Washington Surveying   **(63)**

(Des R. Vigurs. Litho Format)

1982 (15 Nov). *250th Birth Anniv of George Washington and Birth Centenary of Franklin D. Roosevelt. T* **62** *and similar multicoloured designs.* P 14½.

480	50ch. Type **62**		10	10
481	1n. Roosevelt and Harvard University		10	10
482	2n. Washington at Valley Forge		30	30
483	3n. Roosevelt's mother and family		45	40
484	4n. Washington at Battle of Monmouth		55	50
485	5n. Roosevelt and the White House		80	75

486	15n. Washington and Mount Vernon		2·40	2·20
487	20n. Churchill, Roosevelt and Stalin at Yalta		3·25	3·00
480/487 *Set of 8*			7·25	6·75
MS488 Two sheets, each 102 × 73 mm. (a) 25n. Washington (*vert*); (b) 25n. Roosevelt (*vert*)			8·00	7·25

1983 (11 Feb). *"Druk Air" Bhutan Air Service. Various stamps optd with T* **63** *or similar types, No. 489 additionally surcharged.*

(a) POSTAGE.

489	30ch.on 1ch. multicoloured (No. 318)		1·30	1·30
490	6n. multicoloured (Scouts, Appendix)		2·40	2·10
491	8n. multicoloured (No. 275)		2·50	2·20

(b) AIR. Inscr "AIR MAIL".

492	5n. multicoloured ("Indipex 73", Appendix)		3·75	3·50
493	7n. multicoloured (Munich Olympics, Appendix)		3·75	3·50
489/493 *Set of 5*			12·50	11·50

On No. 491 the overprint is in capital letters, on Nos. 490 and 492/3 as Type **63** but smaller. On the 5n. the overprint is sideways.

500th ANNIVERSARY BIRTH OF RAPHAEL
BHUTAN འབྲུག

64 "Angelo Doni"

65 Ta-Gyad-Boom-Zu (the eight luck-bringing symbols)

(Des Design Images. Litho Format)

1983 (23 Mar). *500th Death Anniv of Raphael (artist). T* **64** *and similar multicoloured designs.* P 13½ × 14.

494	1n. Type **64**		15	10
495	4n. "Maddalena Doni"		70	60
496	5n. "Baldassare Castiglione"		1·00	85
497	20n. "Woman with Veil"		4·00	3·50
494/497 *Set of 4*			5·25	4·50
MS498 Two sheets, each 127 × 101 mm. (a) 25n. Self-portrait (detail from "Mass of Bolsena"); (b) 25n. Self-portrait (detail from "Expulsion of Heliodorus")			10·50	9·75

(Des K. Sugiura, S. Sugiura, H. Suzuki, Litho Toppan Ptg Co,Tokyo)

1983 (11 Aug). *Religious Offerings. T* **65** *and similar multicoloured designs.* P 13½.

499	25ch. Type **65**		10	10
500	50ch. Doeyun Nga (the five sensory symbols)		15	15
501	2n. Norbu Chadun (the seven treasures) (47 × 41 *mm*)		35	35
502	3n. Wangpo Nga (the five sensory organs)		60	55

503	8n. Sha Nga (the five kinds of flesh)	1·30	1·10
504	9n. Men-Ra-Tor Sum (the sacrificial		
	cake) (47 × 41 mm)	1·60	1·60
499/504	Set of 6	3·75	3·50
MS505	180 × 135 mm. Nos. 499/504	4·50	4·25

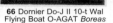

66 Dornier Do-J II 10-t Wal Flying Boat O-AGAT *Boreas*

67 Mickey Mouse as Caveman

(Des Artists International. Litho Format)

1983 (15 Aug). *Bicentenary of Manned Flight. T* **66** *and similar horiz designs. Multicoloured.* P 15.

506	50ch. Type **66**	10	10
507	3n. Savoia-Marchetti S-66 flying boat	60	55
508	10n. Hawker Osprey biplane	2·00	1·90
509	20n. Astra airship *Ville de Paris*	4·00	3·75
506/509	Set of 4	6·00	5·70
MS510	106 × 80 mm. 2n. Henri Giffard's balloon *Le Grand Ballon Captif*	5·00	4·50

(Des Walt Disney Productions. Litho Questa)

1984 (10 Apr). *World Communications Year. T* **67** *and similar multicoloured designs.* P 13½ × 14.

511	4ch. Type **67**	10	10
512	5ch. Goofy as printer	10	10
513	10ch. Chip 'n' Dale with morse key	10	10
514	20ch. Pluto talks to girlfriend on telephone	10	10
515	25ch. Minnie Mouse pulling record from bulldog	10	10
516	50ch. Morty and Ferdie with microphone and loudhailers	10	10
517	1n. Huey, Dewey and Louie listening to radio	30	30
518	5n. Donald Duck watching television on buffalo	1·10	1·10
519	20n. Daisy Duck with computers and abacus	4·25	4·00
511/519	Set of 9	5·75	5·50
MS520	Two sheets, each 127 × 102 mm. P 14 × 13½. (a) 20n. Mickey Mouse on television (*horiz*); (b) 20n. Donald Duck and satellite (*horiz*)	8·75	8·25

68 Golden Langur (*Presbytis geei*)

69 Downhill Skiing

(Des J. Iskowitz. Litho Format)

1984 (10 June). *Endangered Animals. T* **68** *and similar multicoloured designs.* P 15.

521	50ch. Type **68**	20	20
522	1n. Golden langur family in tree (*horiz*)	30	30
523	2n. Male and female golden langurs with young (*horiz*)	70	70
524	4n. Group of langurs	1·40	1·30
521/524	Set of 4	2·30	2·30
MS525	Three sheets. (a) 88 × 121 mm. 20n. Snow leopard (*Panthera uncia*) (*horiz*); (b) 121 × 88 mm. 25n. Yak (*Bos grunniens*); (c) 121 × 88 mm. 25n. Bharal (*Pseudois nayaur*) (*horiz*)	14·50	12·00

(Des S. Karp Studio. Litho)

1984 (16 June). *Winter Olympic Games, Sarajevo. T* **69** *and similar vert designs. Multicoloured.* P 14.

526	50ch. Type **69**	10	10
527	1n. Cross-country skiing	20	15
528	3n. Speed skating	70	65
529	20n. Four-man bobsleigh	3·50	3·25
526/529	Set of 4	4·00	3·75
MS530	108 × 76 mm. 25n. Ice hockey	4·75	4·00

70 *Sans Pareil*, 1829

71 Riley "Sprite", 1936

(Des C. Lundgren. Litho Format)

1984 (16 July). *Railway Locomotives. T* **70** *and similar multicoloured designs.* P 15.

531	50ch. Type **70**	10	10
532	1n. *Planet*, 1830	15	15
533	3n. *Experiment*, 1832	65	60
534	4n. *Black Hawk*, 1835	85	80
535	5n.50 *Jenny Lind*, 1847 (*horiz*)	1·10	1·10
536	8n. *Bavaria*, Semmering line, 1851 (*horiz*)	1·60	1·50
537	10n. Great Northern No 1, 1870 (*horiz*)	2·10	1·90
538	25n. Steam locomotive Type 110, Prussia, 1880 (*horiz*)	5·00	4·50
531/538	Set of 8	10·50	9·50
MS539	Four sheets, each 92 × 65 mm. (a) 20n. Crampton's locomotive, 1846 (*horiz*); (b) 20n. *Erzsebet*, 1870 (*horiz*); (c) 20n. Sondermann freight, 1896 (*horiz*); (d) 20n. Darjeeling – Himalaya railway (*horiz*)	16·00	14·50

(Des R. Sauber. Litho Questa)

1984 (29 Aug). *Cars. T* **71** *and similar horiz designs. Multicoloured.* P 14.

540	50ch. Type **71**	10	10
541	1n. Lanchester, 1919	15	15
542	3n. Itala, 1907	55	50
543	4n. Morris "Oxford (Bullnose)", 1913	80	70
544	5n.50 Lagonda "LG6", 1939	1·10	95
545	6n. Wolseley, 1903	1·30	1·10

546	8n. Buick "Super", 1952	1·50	1·40
547	20n. Maybach "Zeppelin", 1933	4·00	3·50
540/547	Set of 8	8·50	7·50

MS548 Two sheets, each 126 × 99 mm. (a) 25n.
Renault, 1901; (b) 25n. Simplex, 1912 . . . . 8·00 7·25

72 Women's Archery   **73** Domkhar Dzong

(Des S. Karp. Litho Questa)

1984 (27 Oct). *Olympic Games, Los Angeles.* *T* **72** *and similar multicoloured designs.* P 14.

549	15ch. Type **72**	10	10
550	25ch. Men's archery	15	10
551	2n. Table tennis	40	35
552	2n.25 Basketball	50	45
553	5n.50 Boxing	1·00	95
554	6n. Running	1·20	1·10
555	8n. Tennis	1·70	1·60
549/555	Set of 7	4·50	4·25

MS556 115 × 82 mm. 25n. Couple practising archery (72 × 43 *mm*) . . . . 4·50 4·00

(Litho State Ptg Wks, Moscow)

1984 (1 Dec). *Monasteries.* *T* **73** *and similar horiz designs.* P 12.

557	10ch. deep violet-blue	10	10
558	25ch. Venetian red	10	10
559	50ch. deep reddish violet	10	10
560	1n. brown	20	20
561	2n. red	35	35
562	5n. olive-green	85	85
557/562	Set of 6	1·50	1·50

Designs:—25ch. Shemgang Dzong; 50ch. Chapcha Dzong; 1n. Tashigang Dzong; 2n. Pungthang Dzong; 5n. Dechhenphoda Dzong.

74 *Magician Mickey*   **(75)**

(Des Walt Disney Productions. Litho Questa)

1984 (10 Dec). *50th Anniv of Donald Duck.* *T* **74** *and similar vert designs showing scenes from films. Multicoloured.* P 13½ × 14.

563	4ch. Type **74**	10	10
564	5ch. *Slide, Donald, Slide*	10	10
565	10ch. *Donald's Golf Game*	10	10
566	20ch. *Mr. Duck steps Out*	10	10
567	25ch. *Lion Around*	10	10
568	50ch. *Alpine Climbers*	10	10
569	1n. *Flying Jalopy*	10	10

570	5n. *Frank Duck brings 'Em Back Alive*	55	45
571	20n. *Good Scouts*	2·20	1·80
563/571	Set of 9	3·00	2·75

MS572 Two sheets, each 128 × 101 mm. (a)
20n. *Sea Scouts*; (b) 20n. *The Three Caballeros* . . . . 9·00 8·25

1985 (Jan–June). *Various stamps surch as T* **75**.

(a) World Cup Football Championship, Spain (Nos. 450/MS454) (20.6).

573	5n.on 1n. multicoloured	1·60	1·40
574	5n.on 2n. multicoloured (Sil.)	1·60	1·40
575	5n.on 3n. multicoloured	1·60	1·40
576	5n.on 20n. multicoloured	1·60	1·40

MS577 79 × 108 mm. 20n. on 25n.
multicoloured . . . . 6·25 6·25
No. **MS**577 exists in two versions, differing in the list of qualifying countries in the border.

(b) 21st Birthday of Princess of Wales (Nos. 455/MS459) (28.2).

578	5n.on 5n. multicoloured	1·40	1·30
579	5n.on 10n. multicoloured	1·40	1·30
580	5n.on 15n. multicoloured	1·40	1·30
581	40n.on 25n. multicoloured	11·00	10·00

MS582 102 × 76 mm. 25n. on 20n.
multicoloured . . . . 7·50 7·50

(c) Birth of Prince William of Wales (Nos. 475/MS479) (28.2)

583	5n.on 1n. multicoloured	1·30	1·30
584	5n.on 5n. multicoloured	1·30	1·30
585	5n.on 15n. multicoloured	1·30	1·30
586	40n.on 25n. multicoloured	11·00	10·50

MS587 102 × 76 mm. 25n. on 20n.
multicoloured . . . . 10·00 10·00

(d) Wedding of Prince of Wales (Nos. 440/MS444) (28.2)

588	10n.on 1n. multicoloured	2·40	2·20
589	10n.on 5n. multicoloured	2·40	2·20
590	10n.on 10n. multicoloured	2·40	2·20
591	10n.on 25n. multicoloured	2·40	2·20

MS592 69 × 90 mm. 30n. on 20n.
multicoloured . . . . 10·00 10·00
On Nos. 588/**MS**592 the new value is surcharged twice.

(e) 75th Anniv of Boy Scout Movement (Nos. 460/MS464) (20.1).

593	10n.on 3n. multicoloured (Sil.)	2·40	2·20
594	10n.on 5n. multicoloured	2·40	2·20
595	10n.on 15n. multicoloured	2·40	2·20
596	10n.on 20n. multicoloured	2·40	2·20

573/6, 578/81, 583/6, 588/91, 593/6 *Set of*
20 . . . . 50·00 47·00

MS597 91 × 70 mm. 20n. on 25n.
multicoloured . . . . 10·00 10·00

76 Shinje Choegyel   **77** Bhutan and U.N. Flags

(Des K. Sugiura. Litho Toppan Ptg Co, Tokyo)

1985 (27 Apr). *Judgement of Death Mask Dance.* *T* **76** *and similar vert designs. Multicoloured.* P 13½.

598	5ch. Type **76**	10	10
599	35ch. Raksh Lango	10	10
600	50ch. Druelgo	10	10
601	2n.50 Pago	40	35
602	3n. Telgo	55	50
603	4n. Due Nakcung	75	70
604	5n. Lha Karpo	90	85

605	5n.50 Nyalbum	1·00	95
606	6n. Khimda Pelkyi	1·10	1·10
598/606 *Set of 9*		4·50	4·25
MS607 90 × 135 mm. Nos. 598/9 and 603/4		2·30	2·20

(Des B. Grout. Litho Questa)

1985 (24 Oct). *40th Anniv of United Nations Organization. T* **77** *and similar designs.* P 14.

608	50ch. multicoloured	20	20
609	15n. multicoloured	2·00	1·70
610	20n. black and new blue	3·00	2·50
MS611 65 × 80 mm. 25n. black, yellow & scarlet		3·75	3·25

Designs: *Vert*—15n. U.N. building, New York; 25n. 1945 charter. *Horiz*—20n. Veterans' War Memorial Building, San Francisco (venue of signing of charter, 1945).

78 Mickey Mouse tramping through Black Forest   **79** Prince sees Rapunzel

(Des Walt Disney Studios. Litho Questa)

1985 (15 Nov). *150th Birth Anniv of Mark Twain (writer) and International Youth Year. T* **78** *and similar vert designs showing scenes from A Tramp Abroad (cartoon film of Twain novel).* P 12 × 12½ (9n.) or 13½ × 14 (others).

612	50ch. Type **78**	10	10
613	2n. Mickey Mouse, Donald Duck and Goofy on steamboat trip on Lake Lucerne	35	30
614	5n. Mickey Mouse, Donald Duck and Goofy climbing Rigi-Kulm	85	75
615	9n. Mickey Mouse and Goofy rafting to Heidelberg on River Neckar	1·60	1·40
616	20n. Mickey Mouse leading Donald Duck on horseback up the Riffelberg	3·50	3·25
612/616 *Set of 5*		5·75	5·25
MS617 126 × 101 mm. 25n. Mickey Mouse and Goofy		4·75	4·25

(Des Walt Disney Studios. Litho Questa)

1985 (15 Nov). *Birth Bicentenaries (1985 and 1986) of Grimm Brothers (folklorists). T* **79** *and similar vert designs. Multicoloured.* P 12 × 12½ (8n.) or 13½ × 14 (others).

618	1n. Type **79**	10	10
619	4n. Rapunzel (Minnie Mouse) in tower	50	45
620	7n. Mother Gothel calling to Rapunzel to let down her hair	1·10	95

621	8n. Prince climbing tower using Rapunzel's hair	1·40	1·30
622	15n. Prince proposing to Rapunzel	2·40	2·10
618/622 *Set of 5*		5·00	4·50
MS623 126 × 101 mm. 25n. Prince riding away with Rapunzel		5·00	4·75

80 "Brewers Duck" (mallard)

1985 (29 Nov–6 Dec). *Birth Bicentenary of John J. Audubon (ornithologist). T* **80** *and similar horiz designs showing Audubon illustrations. Multicoloured.* P 14.

624	50ch. Type **80** (6.12)	10	10
625	1n. "Willow Ptarmigan" (willow/red grouse)	15	15
626	2n. "Mountain Plover" (6.12)	35	30
627	3n. "Red-throated Loon" (red-throated diver) (6.12)	50	50
628	4n. "Spruce Grouse"	80	70
629	5n. "Hooded Merganser"	95	90
630	15n. "Trumpeter Swan" (whooper swan)	2·75	2·50
631	20n. "Common Goldeneye" (6.12)	3·75	3·25
624/631 *Set of 8*		8·50	7·50
MS632 75 × 105 mm. 25n. "Sharp-shinned Hawk"		4·50	4·00
MS633 75 × 105 mm. 25n. "Tufted Titmouse" (6.12)		4·50	4·00

81 Members' Flags around Buddhist Design   **82** Precious Wheel

(Litho Format)

1985 (8 Dec). *South Asian Regional Co-operation Summit, Dhaka, Bangladesh.* P 13½ × 14.

634	**81** 50ch. multicoloured	15	15
635	5n. multicoloured	95	85

(Litho Format)

1986 (12 Feb). *The Precious Symbols. T* **82** *and similar vert designs. Multicoloured.* P 12½.

636	30ch. Type **82**	10	10
637	50ch. Precious Gem	10	10
638	1n.25 Precious Queen	15	15
639	2n. Precious Minister	30	30
640	4n. Precious Elephant	55	55
641	6n. Precious Horse	80	80
642	8n. Precious General	1·10	1·10
636/642 *Set of 7*		2·75	2·75

GOLD
HYANG SOON SEO
SOUTH KOREA
(83)

(84)

1986 (5 May). *Olympic Games Gold Medal Winners. Nos. 549/50 and 552/MS556 optd as T 83.*

643	15ch. Type **83**	10	10
644	25ch. "GOLD / DARRELL PACE / USA"	10	10
645	2n.25 "GOLD MEDAL / USA"	35	35
646	5n.50 "GOLD / MARK BRELAND / USA"	70	70
647	6n. "GOLD / DALEY THOMPSON / ENGLAND"	80	80
648	8n. "GOLD / STEFAN EDBERG / SWEDEN"	1·10	1·10
643/648 *Set of 6*		2·75	2·75

MS649 Two sheets, each 115 × 82 mm. (a) 25n. "HYANG SOON SEO, SOUTH KOREA"; (b) 25n. "DARRELL PACE, USA" ..... 7·50 6·25

1986 (16 June). *"Ameripex 86" International Stamp Exhibition, Chicago. Various stamps optd with T 84.*

(a) Nos. 615/MS617.

650	9n. multicoloured	2·20	1·80
651	20n. multicoloured	3·25	3·00
MS652 126 × 101 mm. 25n. multicoloured		4·00	3·50

(b) Nos. 621/MS623

653	8n. multicoloured	1·40	1·20
654	15n. multicoloured	1·90	1·70
650/651, 653/654 *Set of 4*		7·75	7·00
MS655 126 × 101 mm. 25n. multicoloured		4·00	3·50

On No. 653 the overprint is sideways.

85 Mandala of Phurpa (Ritual Dagger)

75th ANNIVERSARY GIRL GUIDES (86)

(Des K. Sugiura. Litho Toppan Ptg Co, Tokyo)

1986 (17 June). *Kilkhor Mandalas of Mahayana Buddhism. T 85 and similar vert designs. Multicoloured. P 13½.*

656	10ch. Type **85**	10	10
657	25ch. Mandala of Amitayus in Wrathful Form	10	10
658	50ch. Mandala of Overpowering Deities	10	10
659	75ch. Mandala of the Great Wrathful One	10	10
660	1n. Type **85**	15	15
661	3n. As No. 657	45	45
662	5n. As No. 658	65	65
663	7n. As No. 659	85	85
656/663 *Set of 8*		2·25	2·25

1986 (23 July). *75th Anniv of Girl Guides. Nos. 460/MS464 optd with T 86.*

664	3n. multicoloured	40	40
665	5n. multicoloured	1·00	1·00

666	15n. multicoloured	3·00	3·00
667	20n. multicoloured	4·00	4·00
664/667 *Set of 4*		7·50	7·50
MS668 91 × 70 mm. 25n. multicoloured		5·50	5·50

87 Babylonian Tablet and Comet over Noah's Ark

(Litho Format)

1986 (4 Nov). *Appearance of Halley's Comet. T 87 and similar horiz designs. Multicoloured. P 15.*

669	50ch. Type **87**	10	10
670	1n. 17th-century print	10	10
671	2n. 1835 French silhouette	25	25
672	3n. Bayeux tapestry	40	35
673	4n. Woodblock from *Nuremburg Chronicle*	60	50
674	5n. Illustration of Revelation 6, 12-13 from 1650 Bible	80	75
675	15n. Comet in constellation of Cancer	2·30	2·10
676	20n. Decoration on Delft plate	3·25	2·75
669/676 *Set of 8*		7·00	6·25

MS677 Two sheets, each 109 × 79 mm. (a) 25n. Comet over dzong in Himalayas; (b) 25n. Comet over shrine ..... 8·00 7·25

88 Statue and *Libertad* (Argentine full-rigged cadet ship)

89 *Santa Maria*

(Litho Format)

1986 (4 Nov). *Centenary of Statue of Liberty. T 88 and similar multicoloured designs. P 15.*

678	50ch. Type **88**	10	10
679	1n. *Shalom* (Israeli liner)	10	10
680	2n. *Leonardo da Vinci* (Italian liner)	25	25
681	3n. *Mircea* (Rumanian cadet barque)	40	35
682	4n. *France* (French liner)	55	50
683	5n. *United States* (American liner)	80	75
684	15n. *Queen Elizabeth 2* (British liner)	2·30	2·10
685	20n. *Europa* (West German liner)	3·25	2·75
678/685 *Set of 8*		7·00	6·25

MS686 Two sheets, each 114 × 83 mm. (a) Statue (27 × 41 *mm*); (b) Statue and tower blocks (27 × 41 *mm*) ..... 7·50 6·75

The descriptions of the ships on Nos. 678 and 681 were transposed in error.

(Des Mary Walters. Litho Questa)

1987 (25 May). *500th Anniv (1992) of Discovery of America by Columbus. T 89 and similar multicoloured designs. P 14.*

687	20ch. Type **89**	25	30
688	25ch. Queen Isabella of Spain	25	25
689	50ch. Flyingfish	25	25
690	1n. Columbus's coat of arms	50	40

691	2n. Christopher Columbus	85	70
692	3n. Columbus landing with Spanish soldiers	1·10	1·10
687/692	Set of 6	3·00	2·75

MS693 7 sheets, each 97 × 65 mm. (a) 20ch. Pineapple; (b) 25ch. Indian hammock (*horiz*); (c) 50ch. Tobacco plant; (d) 1n. Greater flamingo; (e) 2n. Astrolabe; (f) 3n. Lizard (*horiz*); (g) 5n. Iguana (*horiz*) . . . . 11·50 11·50

MS694 170 × 144 mm. As Nos. 687/92 but with white backgrounds . . . . . 23·00 23·00

714	12n. "Bouquet with Flying Lovers"	2·30	2·30
715	20n. "In the Sky of the Opera"	4·00	4·00
704/715	Set of 12	15·00	15·00

MS716 12 sheets, each 95 × 110 mm (e) or 110 × 95 mm (others). Imperf. (a) 25n. "The Red Gateway"; (b) 25n. "Romeo and Juliet"; (c) 25n. "Maternity"; (d) 25n. "The Carnival for Aleko, Scene II"; (e) 25n. "Magician of Paris"; (f) 25n. "Visit to the Grandparents"; (g) 25n. "Cow with Parasol"; (h) 25n. "Russian Village"; (i) 25n. "Still Life"; (j) 25n. "Composition with Goat"; (k) 25n. "The Smolensk Newspaper"; (l) 25n. "The Concert" . . . . 47·00 47·00

92 Goofy (slalom)

(Des Walt Disney Co. Litho Questa)

1988 (15 Feb). *Winter Olympic Games, Calgary. T* **92** *and similar horiz designs. Multicoloured.* P 14 × 13½.

717	50ch. Type **92**	10	10
718	1n. Donald Duck pushing Goofy at start (downhill skiing)	15	15
719	2n. Goofy in goal (ice hockey)	25	25
720	4n. Goofy (biathlon)	55	50
721	7n. Goofy and Donald Duck (speed skating)	1·10	95
722	8n. Minnie Mouse (figure skating)	1·30	1·20
723	9n. Minnie Mouse (free-style skating)	1·50	1·30
724	20n. Goofy and Mickey Mouse (two-man bobsleigh)	3·00	2·75
717/24	Set of 8	7·25	6·50

MS725 Two sheets, each 127 × 101 mm. (a) 25n. Goofy (ski jumping); (b) 25n. Donald and Daisy Duck (ice dancing) . . . . 7·00 7·00

90 Canadian National Class "U1-f" Steam Locomotive No. 6060

91 "Two Faces" (sculpture)

(Des W. Wright. Litho Questa)

1987 (15 June). *"Capex '87" International Stamp Exhibition, Toronto. Canadian Railways. T* **90** *and similar multicoloured designs.* P 14.

695	50ch. Type **90**	10	10
696	1n. Via Rail "L.R.C." electric locomotive No. 6903	10	10
697	2n. Canadian National GM "GF30t" diesel locomotive No. 5341	35	30
698	3n. Canadian National steam locomotive No. 6157	45	40
699	8n. Canadian Pacific steam locomotive No. 2727	1·30	1·20
700	10n. Via Express diesel locomotive No. 6524	1·60	1·40
701	15n. Canadian National "Turbotrain"	2·40	2·10
702	20n. Canadian Pacific diesel-electric locomotive No. 1414	3·00	2·75
695/702	Set of 8	8·50	7·50

MS703 Two sheets, each 102 × 75 mm. (a) 25n. Cab and tender of "Royal Hudson" steam locomotive No. 2860 (27 × 41 *mm*); (b) Canadian National steam locomotive No. 6402 (27 × 41 *mm*) . . . . 7·50 6·75

93 Stephenson's Railway Locomotive *Rocket*, 1829

(Des W. Wright. Litho Questa)

1988 (31 Mar). *Transport. T* **93** *and similar multicoloured designs.* P 14.

726	50ch. Pullman "Pioneer" sleeper, 1865	10	10
727	1n. Type **93**	15	15
728	2n. Pierre Lallement's "Velocipede", 1866	25	25
729	3n. Benz "Patent Motor Wagon", 1886	45	35
730	4n. Volkswagen "Beetle"	55	50
731	5n. Mississippi paddle-steamers *Natchez* and *Robert E. Lee*, 1870	65	60
732	6n. American "La France" motor fire engine, 1910	80	75
733	7n. Frigate U.S.S. *Constitution*, 1797 (*vert*)	95	85

(Litho Questa)

1987 (17 Dec). *Birth Centenary of Marc Chagall (artist). T* **91** *and similar vert designs. Multicoloured.* P 13½ × 14.

704	50ch. Type **91**	15	15
705	1n. "At the Barber's"	25	25
706	2n. "Old Jew with Torai"	40	40
707	3n. "Red Maternity"	65	65
708	4n. "Eve of Yom Kippur"	1·00	1·00
709	5n. "The Old Musician"	1·20	1·20
710	6n. "The Rabbi of Vitebsk"	1·30	1·30
711	7n. "Couple at Dusk"	1·50	1·50
712	9n. "The Artistes"	1·80	1·80
713	10n. "Moses breaking the Tablets"	2·00	2·00

734	9n. Bell rocket belt, 1961 (*vert*)		1·20	1·10
735	10n. Trevithick's railway locomotive, 1804		1·30	1·20
726/735	*Set of* 10		5·75	5·25

MS736 Four sheets, each 118 × 89 mm. (a) 25n. Steam locomotive *Mallard* (27 × 41 *mm*); (b) 25n. French "TGV" express train (41 × 27 *mm*); (c) 25n. Japanese Shinkansen "Tokaido" bullet train (41 × 27 *mm*); (d) 25n. Concorde supersonic airplane (41 × 27 *mm*) . . . . . 17·00   17·00

No. 731 is wrongly inscribed "Natches" and No. 733 is wrongly dated "1787".

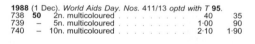

WORLD AIDS DAY
(95)

94 Dam and Pylon

1988 (20 Oct). *Chhukha Hydro-electric Project. Litho.* P 13½.
737	**94**	50ch. multicoloured	30	30

1988 (1 Dec). *World Aids Day. Nos.* 411/13 *optd with T* **95**.
738	**50**	2n. multicoloured	40	35
739	–	5n. multicoloured	1·00	90
740	–	10n. multicoloured	2·10	1·90

BHUTAN 2NU
96 "Diana and Actaeon" (detail)

97 Volleyball

(Litho Questa)

1989 (15 Feb). *500th Birth Anniv of Titian (painter). T* **96** *and similar multicoloured designs.* P 13½ × 14.
741	50ch. "Gentleman with a Book"	10	10
742	1n. "Venus and Cupid with a Lute Player" (detail)	15	15
743	2n. Type **96**	30	30
744	3n. "Cardinal Ippolito dei Medici"	50	45
745	4n. "Sleeping Venus" (detail)	75	70
746	5n. "Venus risen from the Waves" (detail)	90	85
747	6n. "Worship of Venus" (detail)	1·20	1·10
748	7n. "Fête Champêtre" (detail)	1·40	1·30
749	10n. "Perseus and Andromeda" (detail)	1·80	1·70
750	15n. "Danaë" (detail)	2·75	2·50

751	20n. "Venus at the Mirror" (detail)	3·75	3·50
752	25n. "Venus and the Organ Player" (detail)	4·50	4·25
741/752	*Set of* 12	16·00	15·00

MS753 12 sheets, each 109 × 94 mm (a/d) or 94 × 109 mm (others). (a) 25n. "Bacchus and Ariadne". (b) 25n. "Danaë with the Shower of Gold" (*horiz*); (c) 25n. "The Pardo Venus" (*horiz*); (d) 25n. "Venus and Cupid, with an Organist"; (e) 25n. "Diana and Callisto"; (f) 25n. "Mater Dolorosa with Raised Hands"; (g) 25n. "Miracle of the Irascible Son"; (h) 25n. "Portrait of Johann Friedrich"; (i) 25n. "Portrait of Laura Dianti"; (j) 25n. "St. John the Almsgiver"; (k) 25n. "Venus blindfolding Cupid"; (l) 25n. "Venus of Urbino" . . . . 47·00   47·00

(Litho Questa)

1989 (15 Feb). *Olympic Games, Seoul (1988). T* **97** *and similar multicoloured designs.* P 14.
754	50ch. Gymnastics	10	10
755	1n. Judo	10	10
756	2n. Putting the Shot	25	25
757	4n. Type **97**	55	50
758	7n. Basketball (*vert*)	95	85
759	8n. Football (*vert*)	1·10	95
760	9n. High jumping (*vert*)	1·30	1·10
761	20n. Running (*vert*)	2·75	2·50
754/761	*Set of* 8	6·50	5·75

MS762 Two sheets. (a) 109 × 79 mm. 25n. Fencing; (b) 79 × 109 mm. 25n. Archery (*vert*) . . . . . 7·00   7·00

ASIA-PACIFIC EXPOSITION
FUKUOKA '89

(98)

99 Mickey Mouse

1989 (17 Feb). *"Fukuoka '89" Asia-Pacific Exhibition. Nos.* 598/606 *optd with T* **98** *in silver.*
763	5ch. multicoloured	10	10
764	35ch. multicoloured	10	10
765	50ch. multicoloured	10	10
766	2n.50 multicoloured	25	25
767	3n. multicoloured	40	35
768	4n. multicoloured	50	45
769	5n. multicoloured	60	55
770	5n.50 multicoloured	75	65
771	6n. multicoloured	85	80
763/771	*Set of* 9	3·25	2·00

(Des Walt Disney Studio. Litho Questa)

1989 (20 June). *60th Anniv of Mickey Mouse. T* **99** *and similar vert designs showing film posters. Multicoloured.* P 13½ × 14.
772	1ch. Type **99**	15	15
773	2ch. *Barnyard Olympics*	15	15
774	3ch. *Society Dog Show*	15	15
775	4ch. *Fantasia*	15	15
776	5ch. *The Mad Dog*	15	15
777	10ch. *A Gentleman's Gentleman*	15	15
778	50ch. *Symphony hour*	15	15
779	10n. *The Moose Hunt*	1·50	1·50
780	15n. *Wild Waves*	2·30	2·30
781	20n. *Mickey in Arabia*	3·25	3·25

782	25n. *Tugboat Mickey*	3·75	3·75
783	30n. *Building a Building*	4·75	4·75
772/783	*Set of 12*	15·00	15·00

MS784 12 sheets, each 127 × 101 mm. (a) 25n. *The Klondike Kid*; (b) 25n. *The Mad Doctor*; (c) 25n. *The Meller Drammer*; (d) 25n. *Mickey's Good Deed*; (e) 25n. *Mickey's Nightmare*; (f) 25n. *Mickey's Pal Pluto*; (g) 25n. *Steamboat Willie*; (h) 25n. *Touchdown Mickey*; (i) 25n. *Trader Mickey*; (j) 25n. *The Wayward Canary*; (k) 25n. *The Whoopee Party*; (l) 25n. *Ye Olden Days* . . . . . . 42·00 42·00

100 *Tricholoma pardinum* (*Tricholoma pardalotum*)

(Des L. Nelson. Litho Questa)

1989 (22 Aug). *Fungi. T **100** and similar horiz designs. Multicoloured.* P 14.

785	50ch. Type **100**	10	10
786	1n. *Suillus placidus*	10	10
787	2n. Royal boletus (*Boletus regius*)	25	25
788	3n. *Gomphidius glutinosus*	45	35
789	4n. Scarlet-stemmed boletus (*Boletus calopus*)	55	50
790	5n. Elegant Boletus (*Suillus grevillei*)	70	65
791	6n. *Boletus appendiculatus*	85	80
792	7n. Griping toadstool (*Lactarius torminosus*)	1·10	95
793	10n. *Macrolepiota rhacodes*	1·40	1·30
794	15n. The blusher (*Amanita rubescens*)	2·10	1·90
795	20n. Death cap (*Amanita phalloides*)	2·75	2·50
796	25n. False death cap (*Amanita citrina*)	3·50	3·25
785/796	*Set of 12*	12·50	11·50

MS797 12 sheets, each 97 × 68 mm. (a) 25n. *Boletus rhodoxanthus*; (b) 25n. Chanterelle (*Cantharellus cibarius*); (c) 25n. *Dentinum repandum*; (d) 25n. Chestnut boletus (*Gyroporus castaneus*); (e) 25n. Indigo boletus (*Gyroporus cyanescens*); (f) 25n. *Hydnum imbricatum*; (g) 25n. Blue leg (*Lepista nuda*); (h) 25n. *Lepista saeva*; (i) 25n. Brown roll-rim (*Paxillus involutus*); (j) 25n. Golden russula (*Russula aurata*); (k) 25n. *Russula olivacea*; (l) 25n. Downy boletus (*Xerocomus subto-mentosus*) . . . . . . 42·00 42·00

101 *La Reale* (Spanish galley), 1680

102 Nehru

(Des J. Batchelor. Litho Questa)

1989 (24 Aug). *30th Anniv of International Maritime Organization. T **101** and similar horiz designs. Multicoloured.* P 14.

798	50ch. Type **101**	10	10
799	1n. *Turtle* (submarine), 1776	15	15
800	2n. *Charlotte Dundas* (steamship), 1802	30	30
801	3n. *Great Eastern* (paddle-steamer), 1858	50	45
802	4n. H.M.S. *Warrior* (armoured ship), 1862	65	60
803	5n. Mississippi river steamer, 1884	85	75
804	6n. *Preussen* (full-rigged ship) 1902	1·00	90
805	7n. U.S.S. *Arizona* (battleship), 1915	1·20	1·10
806	10n. *Bluenose* (fishing schooner), 1921	1·60	1·50
807	15n. Steam trawler, 1925	2·50	2·20
808	20n. "Liberty" freighter, 1943	3·25	3·00
809	25n. *United States* (liner), 1952	4·00	3·50
798/809	*Set of 12*	14·00	13·00

MS810 12 sheets, each 100 × 70 mm. (a) 25n. Chinese junk, 1988; (b) 25n. U.S.S. *Constitution* (frigate); (c) 25n. VIIC type U-boat, 1942; (d) 25n. *Cutty Sark* (clipper), 1869, (e) 25n. H.M.S. *Dreadnought* (battleship), 1906; (f) U.S.S. *Monitor* (ironclad), 1862; (g) Moran Company tug, 1950; (h) 25n. *Normandie* (French liner), 1933; (i) 25n. H.M.S. *Resolution* (Cook); (j) 25n. *Titanic* (liner), 1912; (k) 25n. H.M.S. *Victory* (ship of the line), 1805; (l) 25n. *Yamato* (Japanese battleship), 1944 . . . . . . 42·00 42·00

1989 (14 Nov). *Birth Centenary of Jawaharlal Nehru (Indian statesman). Photo.* P 14.

811	**102** 1n. bistre-brown	30	30

No. 811 is erroneously inscribed "ch".

103 Greater Flame-backed Woodpecker

104 *Best Friend of Charleston* (USA, 1830)

(Des Jennifer Toombs. Litho Questa)

1989 (22 Nov). *Birds. T **103** and similar multicoloured designs.* P 14.

812	50ch. Type **103**	10	10
813	1n. Black-naped blue monarch	15	15
814	2n. White-crested laughing thrush	30	30
815	3n. Blood pheasant	50	45
816	4n. Plum-headed (inscr "Blossom-headed") parakeet	65	60
817	5n. Rosy minivet	85	75
818	6n. Chestnut-headed fulvetta (inscr "Tit-Babbler") (*horiz*)	1·00	90
819	7n. Blue pitta (*horiz*)	1·20	1·10
820	10n. Black-naped oriole (*horiz*)	1·60	1·50
821	15n. Green magpie (*horiz*)	2·50	2·20

822	20n. Three-toed kingfisher (*horiz*)		3·25	3·00
823	25n. Ibis bill (*horiz*)		4·00	3·50
812/823	*Set of 12*		14·50	13·00

MS824 12 sheets, each 76 × 104 mm (vert designs) or 104 × 76 mm (horiz). (a) 25n. Fire-tailed sunbird; (b) 25n. Crested tree swift (inscr "Indian Crested Swift"); (c) 25n. Greater (inscr "Large") racket-tailed drongo; (d) 25n. Little spiderhunter; (e) 25n. Blue-backed fairy bluebird (*horiz*); (f) 25n. Great Indian (inscr "Pied") hornbill (*horiz*); (g) 25n. Collared (inscr "Himalayan Redbreasted") falconet (*horiz*); (h) 25n. Lammergeier (*horiz*); (i) 25n. Satyr tragopan (*horiz*); (j) 25n. Spotted forktail (*horiz*); (k) 25n. Wallcreeper (*horiz*); (l) 25n. White eared-pheasant (wrongly inscr "White-eared") (*horiz*) ... 42·00 42·00

(Des T. Agans. Litho Questa)

1990 (30 Jan). *Steam Railway Locomotives. T* **104** *and similar multicoloured designs.* P 14.

825	50ch. Type **104**		10	10
826	1n. Class U (France, 1948)		10	10
827	2n. Lehigh Valley Railroad Consolidation (USA, 1866)		25	25
828	3n. Newcastle & Berwick railway luggage engine (Great Britain, 1843)		45	35
829	4n. Class 60-3 Shay No. 18 (USA, 1913)		55	50
830	5n. Camden & Amboy railroad *John Bull* (USA, 1831)		70	65
831	6n. *Hercules* (USA, 1837)		85	80
832	7n. North Eastern Railway locomotive (Great Britain, 1874)		1·10	95
833	10n. *Illinois* (USA, 1852)		1·40	1·30
834	15n. Class 05 steam locomotive No. 947 (1935)		2·10	1·90
835	20n. Rogers standard (1865)		2·75	2·50
836	25n. Southern Railway Class Ps-4 (USA, 1926)		3·50	3·25
825/836	*Set of 12*		12·50	11·50

MS837 12 sheets, each 74 × 100 mm (horiz designs) or 100 × 74 mm (vert). (a) 25n. Baltimore & Ohio Railroad *Cumberland* (USA, 1845); (b) 25n. Billerica & Bedford Railroad *Ariel* (USA, 1877); (c) 25n. Baldwin locomotive *Hiawatha* (USA, 1873); (d) 25n. Baltimore & Potomac Railroad Class A No. 22 (USA, 1935) (*vert*); (e) 25n. St. Paul & Pacific Railroad Class K-36 (USA, 1923); (f) 25n. No. 999 "Empire State Express" (USA, 1893); (g) 25n. Camden & Amboy Railroad *John Stevens* (USA, 1849) (*vert*); (h) 25n. LNER Class A4 No. 4479 (Great Britain, 1935) (*vert*); (i) 25n. *Puffing Billy* (Great Britain, 1814) (*vert*); (j) 25n. *The Rocket* (Great Britain, 1829) (*vert*); (k) 25n. Wabash Railroad Class P1 (USA, 1943) (*vert*); (l) 25n. Webb compound engine No. 1301 (Great Britain, 1889) ... 42·00 42·00

(Des Susan Johnston. Litho Questa)

1990 (30 Jan). *Butterflies. T* **105** *and similar multicoloured designs.* P 14.

838	50ch. Type **105**		10	10
839	1n. *Prioneris thestylis*		10	10
840	2n. Eastern courtier (*Sephisa chandra*)		25	25
841	3n. *Penthema lisarda* (*horiz*)		45	35
842	4n. Golden birdwing (*Troides aecus*)		55	50
843	5n. Great nawab (*Polyura eudamippus*)		70	65
844	6n. *Polyura dolon* (*horiz*)		85	80
845	7n. Tailed labyrinth (*Neope bhadra*) (*horiz*)		1·10	95
846	10n. *Delias descombesi*		1·40	1·30
847	15n. *Childreni childrena* (*horiz*)		2·10	1·90
848	20n. Leaf butterfly (*Kallima inachus*) (*horiz*)		2·75	2·50
849	25n. *Elymnias malelas* (*horiz*)		3·50	3·25
838/849	*Set of 12*		12·50	11·50

MS850 12 sheets, each 111 × 80 mm. (a) 25n. Bhutan glory; (b) 25n. Blue (inscr "Blue Banded") peacock; (c) 25n. Camberwell beauty; (d) 25n. Chequered swallowtail; (e) 25n. Chestnut tiger; (f) 25n. Common birdwing; (g) 25n. Common map butterfly; (h) 25n. Common (inscr "Great") eggfly; (i) 25n. Jungle glory; (j) 25n. Kaiser-i-hind; (k) 25n. Red lacewing; (l) 25n. Swallowtail ... 42·00 42·00

(Des W. Wright. Litho Questa)

1990 (6 Apr). *"Expo '90" International Garden and Greenery Exposition, Osaka. Orchids. T* **106** *and similar vert designs. Multicoloured.* P 14.

851	10ch. Type **106**		10	10
852	50ch. *Vanda coerulea*		10	10
853	1n. *Phalaenopsis violacea*		15	15
854	2n. *Dendrobium nobile*		30	25
855	5n. *Vandopsis lissochiloides*		60	55
856	6n. *Paphiopedilum rothschildianum*		85	75
857	7n. *Phalaenopsis schilleriana*		1·00	90
858	9n. *Paphiopedilum insigne*		1·30	1·10
859	10n. *Paphiopedilum bellatulum*		1·40	1·30
860	20n. *Doritis pulcherrima*		2·75	2·50
861	25n. *Cymbidium giganteum*		4·25	3·25
862	35n. *Phalaenopsis mariae*		5·00	4·75
851/862	*Set of 12*		16·00	14·00

MS863 12 sheets, each 111 × 84 mm. (a) 30n. *Dendrobium aphyllum*; (b) 30n. *Dendrobium loddigesii*; (c) 30n. *Dendrobium margaritaceum*; (d) 30n. *Paphiopedilum haynaldianum*; (e) 30n. *Paphiopedilum niveum*; (f) 30n. *Phalaenopsis amabilis*; (g) 30n. *Phalaenopsis cornu-cervi*; (h) 30n. *Phalaenopsis equestris*; (i) 30n. *Vanda alpina*; (j) 30n. *Vanda coerulescens*; (k) 30n. *Vanda cristata*; (l) 30n. *Vandopsis parishi* ... 50·00 50·00

105 *Charaxes harmodius*

106 *Renanthera monachica*

107 "Plum Estate, Kameido"

(Litho Questa)

1990 (21 May). *Death of Emperor Hirohito and Accession of Emperor Akihito of Japan. "100 Famous Views of Edo" by Ando Hiroshige.* **T 107** *and similar vert designs. Multicoloured.* P 13½ × 14.

864	10ch.	Type **107**	10	10
865	20ch.	"Yatsumi Bridge"	10	10
866	50ch.	"Ayase River and Kanegafuchi"	10	10
867	75ch.	"View of Shiba Coast"	10	10
868	1n.	"Grandpa's Teahouse, Meguro"	15	15
869	2n.	"Inside Kameido Tenjin Shrine"	25	25
870	6n.	"Yoroi Ferry, Koami-cho"	90	80
871	7n.	"Sakasai Ferry"	1·10	95
872	10n.	"Fukagawa Lumberyards"	1·50	1·40
873	15n.	"Suido Bridge and Surugadai"	2·40	2·10
874	20n.	"Meguro Drum Bridge and Sunset Hill"	3·00	2·75
875	25n.	"Atagoshita and Yabu Lane"	3·75	3·25
864/875 *Set of 12*			12·00	11·00

MS876 12 sheets, each 102 × 76 mm. (a) 25n. "The City Flourishing, Tanabata Festival"; (b) 25n. "Fukagawa Susaki and Jumantsubo"; (c) 25n. "Horikiri Iris Garden"; (d) 25n. "Komakata Hall and Azuma Bridge"; (e) 25n. "Minowa, Kanasugi, Mikawashima"; (f) 25n. "New Year's Eve Foxfires at the Changing Tree, Oji"; (g) 25n. "Nihonbashi, Clearing after Snow"; (h) 25n. "Sudden Shower over Shin-Ohashi Bridge and Atake"; (i) 25n. "Suijin Shrine and Massaki on the Sumida River"; (j) 25n. "Suruga-cho"; (k) 25n. "Towboats along the Yotsugi-dori Canal"; (l) 25n. "View to the North from Asukayama"   42·00 38·00

108 Thimphu Post Office   **109** Giant Panda

1990 (29 May). *Photo.* P 14.

877	**108**	1n. multicoloured	15	15

(Des S. Barlowe. Litho Questa)

1990 (11 July). *Mammals.* **T 109** *and similar multicoloured designs.* P 14.

878	50ch.	Type **109**	10	10
879	1n.	Giant panda in tree	15	15
880	2n.	Giant panda with cub	30	30
881	3n.	Giant panda (*horiz*)	50	45
882	4n.	Giant panda eating (*horiz*)	65	60
883	5n.	Tiger (*horiz*)	85	75
884	6n.	Giant pandas pulling up bamboo (*horiz*)	1·00	90
885	7n.	Giant panda and cub resting (*horiz*)	1·20	1·10
886	10n.	Indian elephant (*horiz*)	1·60	1·50
887	15n.	Giant panda beside fallen tree	2·50	2·20

888	20n.	Indian muntjac (inscr "Barking deer") (*horiz*)	3·25	3·00
889	25n.	Snow leopard (*horiz*)	4·00	3·50
878/889 *Set of 12*			14·50	13·00

MS890 12 sheets, each 100 × 73 mm. (a) 25n. Asiatic black bear; (b) 25n. Dhole (inscr "Asiatic wild dog"); (c) 25n. Clouded leopard; (d) 25n. Gaur; (e) 25n. Giant panda; (f) 25n. Golden cat; (g) 25n. Siberian (inscr "Himalayan") musk deer; (h) 25n. Red deer (inscr "Himalayan shou"); (i) 25n. Pygmy hog; (j) 25n. Indian rhinoceros; (k) 25n. Sloth bear; (l) 25n. Wolf   45·00 45·00

110 Roim

(Des K. Sugiura. Litho Toppan Ptg Co, Tokyo)

1990 (29 Sept). *Religious Musical Instruments.* **T 110** *and similar horiz designs. Multicoloured.* P 13½.

891	10ch.	Dungchen (large trumpets)	10	10
892	20ch.	Dungkar (conch shell)	10	10
893	30ch.	Type **110**	10	10
894	50ch.	Tinchag (cup cymbals)	10	10
895	1n.	Dradu and drilbu (pellet drum and hand bell)	10	10
896	2n.	Gya-ling (oboes)	20	15
897	2n.50	Nga (drum)	30	25
898	3n.50	Kang-dung (trumpets)	35	35
891/898 *Set of 8*			1·20	1·10

MS899 Two sheets, each 92 × 135 mm. (a) Nos. 891, 893, 895 and 898; (b) Nos. 892, 894 and 896/7   1·75 1·75

111 Penny Black and Bhutan 1962 2ch. Stamp

112 Girls

(Des William R. Hanson Studios. Litho Questa)

1990 (9 Oct). *"Stamp World London 90" International Stamp Exhibition. 150th Anniv of the Penny Black.* **T 111** *and similar horiz designs, each showing the Penny Black. Multicoloured.* P 14.

900	50ch.	Type **111**	10	10
901	1n.	Oldenburg 1852 ⅓oth. stamp	15	15
902	2n.	Bergedorf 1861 1½s. stamp	25	25
903	4n.	German Democratic Republic 1949 50pf. stamp	50	45
904	5n.	Brunswick 1852 1sgr. stamp	60	55
905	6n.	Basel 1845 2½r. stamp	85	75
906	8n.	Geneva 1843 5c.+5c. stamp	1·10	1·00
907	10n.	Zürich 1843 4r. stamp	1·40	1·30
908	15n.	France 1849 20c. stamp	2·10	1·90
909	20n.	Vatican City 1929 5c. stamp	2·75	2·50

910	25n. Israel 1948 3m. stamp	3·50	3·25
911	30n. Japan 1871 48m. stamp	4·25	3·75
900/911	Set of 12	16·00	14·00

MS912 12 sheets, each 106 × 76 mm. (a) 15n.
Baden 1851 1k. stamp, 15n. Württemberg
1851 1k. stamp; (b) 15n. Germany 1872 3k.
and 2g. stamps, 15n. Prussia 1850 6pf.
stamp; (c) 15n. Hamburg 1859 ½s. stamp,
15n. North German Confederation 1868 ¼g.
and 1k. stamps; (d) 15n. Heligoland 1867
½sch. stamp, 15n. Hanover 1850 1ggr. stamp;
(e) 15n. Schleswig-Holstein 1850 1s. stamp,
15n. Lübeck 1859 4s. stamp; (f) 15n.
Mecklenburg-Schwerin 1856 ⅘s. stamp, 15n.
Mecklenburg-Strelitz 1864 ¼sgr. stamp; (g)
15n. Thurn and Taxis (Northern District) 1852
½sgr. stamp, 15n. Thurn and Taxis (Southern
District) 1852 1k. stamp; (h) 30n. Bavaria
1849 1k. stamp; (i) 30n. West Berlin 1948
2pf. stamp; (j) 30n. Great Britain 1840 Penny
Black; (k) 30n. Saxony 1850 3pf. stamp; (l)
30n. United States 1847 5c. stamp ..... 48·00 48·00
No. 901 is wrongly inscribed "Oldenberg".

1990 (8 Dec). *South Asian Association for Regional Co-operation Girl Child Year. T* **112** *and similar vert design. Multicoloured. Litho.* P 14.

913	50ch. Type **112**	20	20
914	20n. Girl	2·75	2·40

113 Temple of Artemis, Ephesus

114 "Atalanta and Meleager" (detail)

(Des Walt Disney Co. Litho Questa)

1991 (28 Jan). *Wonders of the World. T* **113** *and similar multicoloured designs featuring Walt Disney cartoon characters.* P 13½ × 14 (vert) or 14 × 13½ (horiz).

915	1ch. Type **113**	10	10
916	2ch. Statue of Zeus, Olympia	10	10
917	3ch. Pyramids of Egypt	10	10
918	4ch. Lighthouse of Alexandria, Egypt	10	10
919	5ch. Mausoleum, Halicarnassus	10	10
920	10ch. Colossus of Rhodes	10	10
921	50ch. Hanging Gardens of Babylon	10	10
922	5n. Mauna Loa Volcanoes, Hawaii (horiz)	70	65
923	6n. Carlsbad Caverns, New Mexico (horiz)	90	80
924	10n. Rainbow Bridge National Monument, Utah (horiz)	1·50	1·40
925	15n. Grand Canyon, Colorado (horiz)	3·25	1·90
926	20n. Old Faithful, Yellowstone National Park, Wyoming (horiz)	2·75	2·50

927	25n. Sequoia National Park, California (horiz)	3·75	3·25
928	30n. Crater Lake and Wizard Island, Oregon (horiz)	4·50	4·00
915/928	Set of 14	16·00	14·00

MS929 14 sheets, each 127 × 101 mm. (a) 25n.
Alcan Highway, Alaska and Canada (horiz);
(b) 25n. Catacombs of Alexandria; (c) 25n.
Sears Tower, Chicago, Illinois (horiz); (d) 25n.
Great Wall of China (horiz); (e) 25n.
St. Sophia'a Mosque, Constantinople; (f) 25n.
Porcelain Tower, Nanking, China (horiz); (g)
25n. Hoover Dam, Nevada; (h) 25n. Empire
State Building, New York City; (i) 25n.
Panama Canal (horiz); (k) 25n. Leaning Tower
of Pisa; (k) 25n. Colosseum, Rome; (l) 25n.
Gateway Arch, St. Louis, Missouri; (m) 25n.
Golden Gate Bridge, San Francisco (horiz);
(n) 25n. Stonehenge ..... 42·00 42·00

(Litho Questa)

1991 (20 Feb). *350th Death Anniv (1990) of Peter Paul Rubens (painter). T* **114** *and similar multicoloured designs.* P 13½ × 14 (vert) or 14 × 13½ (horiz).

930	10ch. Type **114**	10	10
931	50ch. "The Fall of Phaëton" (detail)	10	10
932	1n. "Feast of Venus Verticordia" (detail)	15	15
933	2n. "Achilles slaying Hector" (detail)	35	30
934	3n. "Arachne punished by Minerva" (detail)	50	35
935	4n. "Jupiter receives Psyche on Olympus" (detail)	75	55
936	5n. "Atalanta and Meleager" (different detail)	90	85
937	6n. "Atalanta and Meleager" (different detail)	1·10	1·00
938	7n. "Venus in Vulcan's Furnace" (detail)	1·30	1·20
939	10n. "Atalanta and Meleager" (different detail)	1·70	1·60
940	20n. "Briseis returned to Achilles" (detail)	3·50	3·25
941	30n. "Mars and Rhea Sylvia" (detail)	5·00	4·50
930/941	Set of 12	14·00	12·50

MS942 12 sheets, each 72 × 101 mm (a/e) or
101 × 72 mm (f/l). (a) 25n. "Atalanta and
Meleager"; (b) 25n. "Feast of Venus
Verticordia"; (c) 25n. "Ganymede and the
Eagle"; (d) 25n. "Jupiter receives Psyche on
Olympus"; (e) 25n. "Venus shivering"; (f) 25n.
"Adonis and Venus" (horiz); (g) 25n.
"Arachne punished by Minerva" (horiz); (h)
25n. "Briseis returned to Achilles" (horiz); (i)
25n. "The Fall of the Titans" (horiz); (j) 25n.
"Hero and Leander" (horiz); (k) 25n. "Mars
and Rhea Sylvia" (horiz); (l) 25n. "The Origin
of the Milky Way" (horiz) ..... 48·00 48·00

115 "Cottages, Reminiscence of the North"

(Litho Walsall Security Printers Ltd)

1991 (22 July). *Death Centenary (1990) of Vincent van Gogh (painter).* T **115** *and similar multicoloured designs.* P 13½.

943	10ch.	Type **115**	10	10
944	50ch.	"Head of a Peasant Woman with Dark Cap"	10	10
945	1n.	"Portrait of a Woman in Blue"	15	15
946	2n.	"Head of an Old Woman with White Cap (the Midwife)"	45	35
947	8n.	"Vase with Hollyhocks"	1·20	1·10
948	10n.	"Portrait of a Man with a Skull Cap"	1·40	1·30
949	12n.	"Agostina Segatori sitting in the Café du Tambourin"	1·80	1·60
950	15n.	"Vase with Daisies and Anemones"	2·20	2·00
951	18n.	"Fritillaries in a Copper Vase"	2·75	2·40
952	20n.	"Woman sitting in the Grass"	3·00	2·75
953	25n.	"On the Outskirts of Paris" (*horiz*)	3·50	3·25
954	30n.	"Chrysanthemums and Wild Flowers in a Vase"	4·25	3·75
943/954	*Set of 12*		19·00	16·00

MS955 12 sheets, each 76 × 101 mm (a/h) or 101 × 76 mm (i/l). Imperf. (a) 30n. "Le Moulin de Blute-Fin"; (b) 30n. "Le Moulin de la Galette"; (c) 30n. "Le Moulin de la Galette" (with man in foreground); (d) 30n. "Poppies and Butterflies"; (e) 30n. "Trees in the Garden of St.-Paul Hospital"; (f) 30n. "Vase with Peonies"; (g) 30n. "Vase with Red Poppies"; (h) 30n. "Vase with Zinnias"; (i) 30n. "Bowl with Sunflowers, Roses and Other Flowers" (*horiz*); (j) 30n. "Fishing in the Spring, Pont de Clichy" (*horiz*); (k) 30n. "Vase with Zinnias and other Flowers" (*horiz*); (l) 30n. "Village Street in Auvers" (*horiz*) .... 48·00 | 48·00

116 Winning Uruguay Team, 1930

(Litho Questa)

1991 (1 Aug). *World Cup Football Championship.* T **116** *and similar multicoloured designs.* P 14 × 13½.

956	50ch.	Type **116**	10	10
957	1n.	Italy, 1934	15	15
958	2n.	Italy, 1938	25	20
959	3n.	Uruguay, 1950	45	30
960	5n.	West Germany, 1954	70	65
961	10n.	Brazil, 1958	1·40	1·30
962	20n.	Brazil, 1962	2·75	2·50
963	25n.	England, 1966	3·50	3·25
964	29n.	Brazil, 1970	4·00	3·50
965	30n.	West Germany, 1974	4·25	3·75
966	31n.	Argentina, 1978	4·25	3·75
967	32n.	Italy, 1982	4·50	4·00
968	33n.	Argentina, 1986	4·50	4·00
969	34n.	West Germany, 1990	4·50	4·00
970	35n.	Stadium, Los Angeles (venue for 1994 World Cup)	4·50	4·00
956/970	*Set of 15*		36·00	32·00

MS971 6 sheets, each 105 × 120 mm. P 13½ × 14. (a) 30n. Roberto Baggio, Italy (*vert*); (b) 30n. Claudio Canniggia, Argentina (*vert*); (c) 30n. Paul Gascoigne, England (*vert*); (d) 30n. Lothar Matthäus, West Germany (*vert*); (e) 30n. Salvatore Schillaci, Italy (*vert*); (f) 30n. Peter Shilton, England .. 24·00 | 24·00

117 Bhutan and Japan State Flags

118 Teachers, Pupils and Hemisphere

1991 (16 Nov). *"Phila Nippon '91" International Stamp Exhibition, Tokyo.* Litho. P 13.

972	**117**	15n. multicoloured	2·10	1·80

1992 (5 Mar). *"Education for All by Year 2000".* Photo. P 13½.

973	**118**	1n. multicoloured	10	10

119 Hurdler   **120** Santa Maria

1992 (24 July). *Olympic Games, Barcelona.* T **119** *and similar vert designs. Multicoloured.* Litho. P 12.

974	25n.	Type **119**	3·25	3·25
		a. Horiz pair. Nos. 974/5	6·75	6·75
975	25n.	Body of hurdler	3·25	3·25
MS976	110 × 75 mm. 25n. Archery		4·75	4·75

Nos. 974/5 were issued together in horizontal *se-tenant* pairs within the sheet, each pair forming a composite design.

1992 (18 Sept). *500th Anniv of Discovery of America by Columbus.* T **120** *and similar vert design. Multicoloured.* Litho. P 12.

977	15n.	Type **120**	1·10	1·10
978	20n.	Columbus	1·40	1·40
MS979	78 × 118 mm. 25n. As No. 978 but without inscription at top (27 × 43 mm)		2·00	2·00

121 Brandenburg Gate and rejoicing Couple

1992 (3 Oct). *Second Anniv of Reunification of Germany.* Litho. P 12.

980	**121**	25n. multicoloured	1·80	1·80
MS981	110 × 82 mm. 25n. As No. 980 but without inscription at top (43 × 27 mm)		1·80	1·80

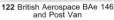

122 British Aerospace BAe 146 and Post Van

123 Industry and Agriculture

1992 (9 Oct). *30th Anniv of Bhutan Postal Organization. T* **122** *and similar horiz designs. Multicoloured. Litho.* P 12.

982	1n. Type **122**	10	10
983	3n. Rural letter carrier	25	25
984	5n. Emptying post box	40	40

1992 (11 Nov). *20th Anniv of Accession of King Jigme Singye Wangchuk. T* **123** *and similar multicoloured designs. Litho.* P 12.

985	1n. Type **123**	15	15
	a. Block of 4. Nos. 985/8	2·00	
986	5n. British Aerospace RJ70 of National Airline	35	35
987	10n. House with water-pump	65	65
988	15n. King Jigme Singye Wangchuk	1·20	1·20
985/988 *Set of* 4		2·10	2·10
MS989 94 × 62 mm. 20n. King, flag and Bhutanese people (43 × 26 *mm*)		1·70	1·70

Nos. 985/8 were issued together in *se-tenant* blocks of four stamps within the sheet, each horizontal pair within the block forming a composite design.

124 Dragon

125 *Meconopsis grandis*

1992 (5 Dec). *International Volunteer Day. Litho.* P 13½ × 14.

990	**124** 1n.50 multicoloured	15	15
	a. Block. Nos. 990/2 plus label	2·00	
991	9n. multicoloured	65	65
992	15n. multicoloured	1·20	1·20

Nos. 990/2 were issued together in *se-tenant* blocks of three stamps and a label showing the Posts and Telegraphs emblem.

1993 (1 Jan). *Medicinal Flowers. T* **125** *and similar vert designs showing varieties of the Asiatic Poppy. Multicoloured.* P 12.

993	1n.50 Type **125**	15	15
994	7n. Meconopsis sp.	60	60
995	10n. Meconopsis wallichii	75	75

996	12n. *Meconopsis horridula*	1·00	1·00
997	20n. *Meconopsis discigera*	1·70	1·70
993/997 *Set of* 5		3·75	3·75
MS998 74 × 107 mm. 25n. *Meconopsis horridula (different)* (27 × 43 *mm*)		2·00	2·00

126 Rooster and Chinese Signs of the Zodiac

1993 (22 Feb). *New Year. Year of the Water Rooster. Sheet* 89 × 89 *mm. Litho.* P 14.

MS999 **126** 25n. multicoloured		1·90	1·90

127 "The Love Letter" (Jean Honoré Fragonard)

128 Lesser Panda

1993 (2 May). *Paintings. T* **127** *and similar vert designs. Multicoloured. Litho.* P 13½.

(a) POSTAGE.

1000	1ch. Type **127**	15	15
1001	2ch. "The Writer" (Vittore Carpaccio)	15	15
1002	3ch. "Madamoiselle Lavergne" (Jean Étienne Liotard)	15	15
1003	5ch. "Portrait of Erasmus" (Hans Holbein)	15	15
1004	10ch. "Woman writing a Letter" (Gerard Terborch)	15	15
1005	15ch. Type **127**	15	15
1006	25ch. As No. 1001	15	15
1007	50ch. As No. 1002	15	15
1008	60ch. As No. 1003	15	15
1009	80ch. As No. 1004	15	15
1010	1n. Type **127**	15	15
1011	1n.25 As No. 1001	15	15

(b) AIR. Inscr "AIR MAIL".

1012	2n. As No. 1002	15	15
1013	3n. As No. 1003	15	15
1014	6n. As No. 1004	15	15
1000/1014	*Set of 15*	2·00	2·00

MS1015 135 × 97 mm. As Nos. 1012/14 but
with copper borders . . . . 1·70 1·70
Nos. 1000/1014 were prepared in 1974 but not issued in Bhutan until the above date.

1993 (1 July). *Environmental Protection. T* **128** *and similar vert designs. Multicoloured.* P 14.

1016	7n. Type **128**	60	60
	a. Sheetlet. Nos. 1016/19	4·25	
1017	10n. One-horned rhinoceros	85	85
1018	15n. Black-necked crane and blue poppy	1·20	1·20
1019	20n. Takin	1·50	1·50
1016/1019	*Set of 4*	3·75	3·75

Nos. 1016/19 were issued together in *se-tenant* sheetlets of four stamps, each sheetlet forming a composite design.

TAIPEI '93

NU 30

(129)

1993 (14 Aug). *"Taipei '93" International Stamp Exhibition, Taiwan. No.* **MS**999 surch with *T* **129** *in silver and black.*
MS1020 **126** 30n. on 25n. multicoloured . . . . 2·40 2·40

1·5
BHUTAN Nu
130 Namtheo-say

131 *Rhododendron mucronatum*

1993 (17 Dec). *Door Gods. T* **130** *and similar vert designs. Litho.* P 12.

1021	1n.50 Type **130**	10	15
1022	5n. Pha-ke-po	40	40
1023	10n. Chen-mi Jang	80	80
1024	15n. Yul-khor-sung	1·20	1·20
1021/1024	*Set of 4*	2·25	2·25

1994 (1 Jan). *Flowers. T* **131** *and similar multicoloured designs. Litho.* P 13.

1025	1n. Type **131**	15	15
	a. Horiz strip of 10. Nos. 1025/34	4·25	
1026	1n.50 *Anemone rupicola*	15	15
1027	2n. *Polemonium coeruleum*	15	15
1028	2n.50 *Rosa marophylla*	15	15
1029	4n. *Paraquilegia microphylla*	35	35
1030	5n. *Aquilegia nivalis*	40	40
1031	6n. *Geranium wallichianum*	50	50

1032	7n. *Rhododendron campanulatum* (wrongly inscr "Rhododendron")	60	60
1033	9n. *Viola suavis*	75	75
1034	10n. *Cyananthus lobatus*	90	90
1025/1034	*Set of 10*	3·75	3·75

MS1035 126 × 86 mm. 13n. Lily (*horiz*) . . . 1·00 1·00
Nos. 1024/33 were issued together in horizontal *se-tenant* strips of ten stamps within the sheet.

1994 WOOD DOG YEAR NU 11·50
132 Dog

15 NU BHUTAN
133 Trophy and Mascot

1994 (11 Feb). *New Year. Year of the Dog. "Hong Kong '94" International Stamp Exhibition.* P 14.

1036	**132** 11n.50 multicoloured	80	80

MS1037 118 × 178 mm. **132** 20n. multicoloured . . . . 1·50 1·50

(Des. T. Chhetri. Litho)

1994 (17 July). *World Cup Football Championship, U.S.A.* P 12.

1038	**133** 15n. multicoloured	80	80

134 Tagtshang Monastery (⅓-*size illustration*)

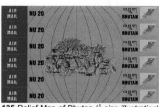

135 Relief Map of Bhutan (⅓-*size illustration*)

(Des T. Chhetri. Litho PostLine Security Printing, Sweden)

1994 (15 Aug). *AIR. Self-adhesive. Rouletted.*

1039	**134** 16n. multicoloured	85	85
	a. Card No. 1039 × 6	5·25	
1040	**135** 20n. multicoloured	1·00	1·00
	a. Card No. 1040 × 6	6·25	

The individual stamps are peeled directly from the card backing. Each card contains six different designs with the same face value forming the composite designs illustrated. Each stamp is a horizontal strip with a label indicating the main class of mail cover by the rate at the left, separated by a vertical line of rouletting. The outer edges of the cards are imperforate.

136 Tower Bridge, London (centenary)

137 Astronaut on Moon

(Des T. Chhetri. Litho Secura, Singapore)

1994 (11 Nov). *Bridges. Sheet* 160 × 101 *mm containing T* **136** *and similar horiz design. Multicoloured.* P 12.
MS1041 15n. Type **136**; 16n. "Wangdue Bridge, Bhutan" (Samuel Davis) (250th anniv) . . . . 1·60   1·60

(Litho and holography Walsall Security Printers Ltd)

1994 (11 Nov). *25th Anniv of First Manned Moon Landing. Sheet* 114 × 57 *mm containing T* **137** *and similar horiz design. Multicoloured.* P 14.
MS1042 30n. Type **137**; 36n. Space shuttle   . .   3·50   3·50

138 Horseman with raised Sword

139 Paro Valley

(Litho Courvoisier)

1994 (17 Dec). *350th Anniv of Victory over Tibet–Mongol Army. T* **138** *and similar vert designs. Multicoloured.* P 12½.
1043   15n. Type **138** 80   80
     a. Sheetlet of 4. Nos. 1043/6   . . . .
1044   15n. Archers and hand-to-hand sword
     fighting 80   80
1045   15n. Horseman with insignia on helmet
     amongst infantry 80   80
1046   15n. Drummer, piper and troops   80   80
1043/1046 *Set of 4* . . . . 2·75   2·75
     Nos. 1043/6 were issued together in *se-tenant* sheetlets of four stamps and one label, forming a composite design of a battle scene and the Drugyel Dzong.

1995 (1 Jan). *World Tourism Year. Sheet* 111 × 92 *mm containing T* **139** *and similar horiz designs. Multicoloured. Litho.* P 12.
MS1047 1n.50, Type **139**; 5n. Chorten Kora; 10n. Thimphu Tshechu; 15n. Wangdue
Tshechu   . . . . 2·40   2·40

140 Lunar Rat

141 *Pleione praecox*

1995 (2 Mar). *New Year. Year of the Boar. T* **140** *and similar horiz designs. Multicoloured. Litho.* P 12.
1048   10ch. Type **140** 15   15
     a. Sheetlet of 12. Nos. 1048/59   . . . 2·10   2·10
1049   20ch. Lunar ox 15   15
1050   30ch. Lunar tiger   15   15
1051   40ch. Lunar rabbit   15   15
1052   1n. Lunar dragon 15   15
1053   2n. Lunar snake 15   15
1054   4n. Lunar horse 15   15
1055   4n. Lunar sheep   15   15
1056   5n. Lunar monkey   15   15
1057   7n. Lunar rooster   25   25
1058   8n. Lunar dog 35   35
1059   8n. Lunar boar 40   40
1048/1059 *Set of 12* . . . . 2·10   2·10
MS1060 111 × 92 mm. 10n. Wood hogs   . . . 55   55
     Nos. 1048/59 were issued together in *se-tenant* sheetlets of 12 stamps.

1995 (2 May). *Flowers. T* **141** *and similar vert designs. Multicoloured. Litho.* P 12.
1061   9n. Type **141** 50   50
1062   10n. *Primula calderina*   60   60
1063   16n. *Primula whitei*   . . . . . . 1·00   1·00
1064   18n. *Notholirion macrophyllum* . . . . 1·10   1·10
1061/1064 *Set of 4*   . . . . 2·75   2·75

142 Human Resources Development

143 Greater Pied Kingfisher (Himalayan Pied Kingfisher)

1995 (26 June). *50th Anniv of United Nations Organization. T* **142** *and similar square designs. Multicoloured. Litho.* P 14.
1065   1n.50 Type **142** 15   15
     a. Horiz strip of 7. Nos. 1065/71 . . . 3·75   3·75
1066   5n. Transport and Communications . . 35   35
1067   9n. Health and Population   50   50
1068   10n. Water and Sanitation   60   60
1069   11n.50 U.N. in Bhutan   65   65
1070   16n. Forestry and Environment   . . . 90   90
1071   18n. Peace and Security   . . . . . 1·00   1·00
1065/1071 *Set of 7* . . . . 3·75   3·75
     Nos. 1065/71 were issued together in horizontal *se-tenant* strips of seven stamps within the sheet.

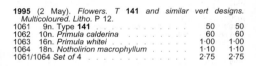

(Des T. Chhetri. Litho)

1995 (1 Sept). *"Singapore'95" International Stamp Exhibition. Birds.* T **143** *and similar vert designs. Multicoloured.* P 12.
1072	1n. Type **143**		15	15
	a. Sheetlet of 6. Nos. 1072/7 plus 3 labels		3·00	
1073	2n. Blyth's tragopan		15	15
1074	3n. Long-tailed minivets		15	15
1075	10n. Red junglefowl		60	60
1076	15n. Black-capped sibia		85	85
1077	20n. Red-billed chough		1·00	1·00
1072/1077 *Set of* 6			2·75	2·75
MS1078 73 × 97 mm. 20n. Black-necked crane			1·10	1·10

Nos. 1072/7 were issued together in *se-tenant* sheetlets of six stamps and three labels.

144 Making Paper   **145** Golden Langur

(Des Jacqueline Shearman. Litho Secura, Singapore)

1995 (17 Dec). *Traditional Crafts.* T **144** *and similar square designs. Multicoloured.* P 14.
1079	1n. Type **144**		15	15
1080	2n. Religious painting		15	15
1081	3n. Clay sculpting		15	15
1082	10n. Weaving		60	60
1083	15n. Making boots		85	85
1084	20n. Carving wooden bowls		1·00	1·00
1079/1084 *Set of* 6			2·50	2·50
MS1085 121 × 82 mm. 20n. Decorative carvings on wooden buildings			1·00	1·00

1996 (1 Jan). *New Year. Year of the Rat. Sheet* 111 × 176 *mm containing* T **145** *and similar square designs. Multicoloured.* P 14.
MS1086 10n. Type **145**; 10n. Rat; 10n. Dragon		1·60	1·60

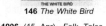 

146 The White Bird   **147** Blue Pansy

1996 (15 Apr). *Folk Tales.* T **146** *and similar vert designs. Multicoloured. Litho.* P 12.
1087	1n. Type **146**		15	15
	a. Sheetlet of 6. Nos. 1087/92		2·75	
1088	2n. *Sing Sing Lhamo and the Moon*		15	15
1089	3n. The Hoopoe		15	15
1090	5n. *The Cloud Faries*		35	35
1091	10n. *The Three Wishes*		60	60
1092	20n. *The Abominable Snowman*		1·10	1·10
1087/1092 *Set of* 6			2·25	2·25
MS1093 109 × 75 mm. 25n. As No. 1090			1·70	1·70

Nos. 1087/92 were issued together in *se-tenant* sheetlets of six stamps.

1996 (2 May). *Butterflies.* T **147** *and similar square designs. Multicoloured. Litho.* P 14.
1094	2n. Type **147**		15	15
	a. Sheetlet of 6. Nos. 1094/9		3·50	
1095	3n. Blue peacock		15	15
1096	5n. Great mormon		25	25
1097	10n. Fritillary		60	60
1098	15n. Blue duke		85	85
1099	25n. Brown gorgon		1·30	1·30
1094/1099 *Set of* 6			3·00	3·00
MS1100 Two Sheets, each 108 × 75 mm. (a) 30n. Fivebar swordtail; (b) 30n. Xanthomelas			3·00	3·00

Nos. 1094/9 were issued together in *se-tenant* sheetlets of six stamps.

148 300n. Football coin   **149** Standard Goods Locomotive, India

1996 (15 June). *Olympic Games, Atlanta.* T **148** *and similar square designs. Multicoloured.* P 13½ × 14.
1101	5n. Type **148**		25	25
1102	7n. basketball coin		40	40
1103	10n.5s. judo coin		60	60
MS1104 102 × 80 mm.15n. Archery			85	85

(Des H. Friedman. Litho. Questa)

1996 (11 Nov). *Trains.* T **149** *and similar horiz. designs. Multicoloured.* P 14.
1105	20n. Type **149**		1·00	1·00
	a. Sheetlet of 6. Nos 1105/10		5·50	
1106	20n. Diesel-electric locomotive, Finland		1·00	1·00
1107	20n. Shunting tank locomotive, Russia		1·00	1·00
1108	20n. Alco PA-1 diesel-electric locomotive, U.S.A.		1·00	1·00
1109	20n. Class C11 passenger tank locomotive, Japan		1·00	1·00
1110	20n. Settebello high speed electric train, Italy		1·00	1·00
1111	20n. Tank locomotive No. 191, Chile		1·00	1·00
	a. Sheetlet of 6. Nos. 1111/16		5·50	
1112	20n. Pacific locomotive, France		1·00	1·00
1113	20n. Steam locomotive No. 10, Norway		1·00	1·00
1114	20n. Atlantic express locomotive, Germany		1·00	1·00
1115	20n. Express steam locomotive, Belgium		1·00	1·00
1116	20n. Type 4 diesel-electric locomotive, England		1·00	1·00
1105/1116 *Set of* 12			11·00	11·00
MS1117 Two sheets, each 96 × 66 mm. (a) 70n. "Hikari" express train, Series 200, Japan; (b) Class KD steam goods locomotive, Sweden			7·25	7·25

150 Penny Black

151 Vegard Ulvang, Norway

(Embossed and litho Cartor)

1996 (17 Dec). P 13½.
1118 **150** 140n. gold and black . . . . . 7·25 7·25

(Des Román Compañy. Litho Quest)

1997 (1 Jan). *Winter Olympic Gold Medallists. Mulicoloured.* P 14.

(a) T **151** *and similar vert designs.*
1119 10n. Type **151** (30 km. cross-country
skiing, 1992) 60 60
1120 15n. Kristi Yamaguchi, U.S.A. (women's
figure skating, 1992) 85 85
1121 25n. Markus Wasmeier, Germany (men's
super giant slalom, 1994) . . . 1·50 1·50
1122 30n. Georg Hackl, Germany (luge,
1992) . . . . 1·70 1·70

(b) As T **151** *but with black frame around design.*
1123 15n. Andreas Ostler, West Germany
(two-man bobsleighing, 1952) . . 80 80
a. Horiz strip of 4. Nos. 1123/6 . . 3·25 3·25
1124 15n. East German team (four-man
bobsleighing, 1984) 80 80
1125 15n. Stein Eriksen, Norway (men's giant
slalom, 1952) 80 80
1126 15n. Alberto Tomba, Italy (men's giant
slalom, 1988) 80 80
1119/1126 *Set of 8* . . . . . . 7·00 7·00
MS1127 Two sheets, each 106 × 76 mm. (a)
70n. Henri Oreiller, France (men's downhill
skiing, 1948); (b) 70n. Swiss team (four-man
boblesighing, 1924) . . . . 7·50 7·50
Nos. 1124/7 were issued together in horizontal *se-tenant* strips
within sheetlets of eight stamps.

152 Bee (*Apis
laboriosa*)

153 Polar Bear (*Thalarctos
maritumus*)

1997 (15 Jan). *Insects and Arachnidae. T* **152** *and similar vert
designs. Multicoloured. Litho.* P 13.
1128 1ch. Type **152** 10 10
a. Sheetlet of 25. Nos. 1128/52 . 2·20 2·20
1129 2ch. *Neptunides polychromus*
(beetle) 10 10
1130 3ch. *Conocephalus* sp. (beetle) . . 10 10
1131 4ch. *Blattidae* sp. (beetle) . . . 10 10
1132 5ch. Great diving beetle (*Dytiscus
marginalis*) 10 10
1133 10ch. Hercules beetle (*Dynastes
hercules*) 10 10
1134 15ch. Ladybird (*Hippodamia* sp.) . 10 10
1135 20ch. *Sarcophaga haemorrhoidalis*
(fly) 10 10
1136 25ch. Stag beetle (*Lucanus cervus*) . 10 10
1137 30ch. Caterpillar 10 10
1138 35ch. *Lycia hirtaria* (moth) . . . 10 10
1139 40ch. *Clytarius pennatus* (beetle) . . 10 10
1140 45ch. *Ephemera denica* (mayfly) . . 10 10
1141 50ch. European field cricket (*Gryllus
campestris*) 10 10
1142 60ch. Elephant hawk moth (*Deilephila
elpenor*) 10 10
1143 65ch. *Gerris* sp. (beetle) . . . 10 10
1144 70ch. Banded agrion (*Agrion
splendens*) 10 10
1145 80ch. *Tachyta nana* (beetle) . . . 10 10
1146 90ch. *Eurydema pulchra* (shieldbug) . 10 10
1147 1n. *Hadrurus hirsutus* (scorpion) . . 10 10
1148 1n.50 *Vespa germanica* (wasp) . . 10 10
1149 2n. *Pyrops* sp. (beetle) . . . 10 10
1150 2n.50 Praying mantis (*Mantis
religiosa*) 10 10
1151 3n. *Araneus diadematus* (spider) . . 10 10
1152 3n.50 *Atrophaneura* sp. (butterfly) . 10 10
1128/1152 *Set of 25* . . . . . 2·20 2·20
MS1153 76 × 111 mm. 15n. Cockchafer
(*Melolontha* sp.) . . . . . 1·00 1·00
Nos. 1128/52 were issued together in *se-tenant* sheetlets of 25
stamps.

1997 (1 Feb). *"Hong Kong '97" International Stamp
Exhibition. T* **153** *and similar square designs. Multicoloured.
Litho.* P 14.
1154 10n. Type **153** 55 55
a. Sheetlet of 4. Nos. 1154/7 . . 2·00 2·00
1155 10n. Koalas (*Phascolarctos
cinereus*) 55 55
1156 10n. Asatic black bear (*Selenarctos
thibetanus*) 55 55
1157 10ch. Lesser panda (*Ailurus fulgens*) . 55 55
1154/1157 *Set of 4* . . . . . 2·00 2·00
MS1158 107 × 75 mm. 20n. Giant panda
(*Ailuropoda melanoleuca*) . . . 1·30 1·30
Nos. 1154/7 were issued together in *se-tenant* sheetlets of four
stamps.

154 Rat

155 Lynx (*Felis lynx*)

1997 (8 Feb). *New Year. Year of the Ox. T* **154** *and similar square
designs. Multicoloured. Litho.* P 14.
1159 1ch. Type **154** 15 15
a. Sheetlet of 12. Nos. 1159/70 plus
label . . . . . . 4·75
1160 2ch. Ox 15 15
1161 3ch. Tiger 15 15
1162 4ch. Rabbit 15 15
1163 90ch. Monkey 15 15
1164 5n. Dragon 25 25
1165 6n. Snake 35 35
1166 7n. Horse 40 40

1167	8n. Ram	50	50
1168	10n. Cock	65	65
1169	11n. Dog	75	75
1170	12n. Boar	85	85
1159/1170	*Set of 12*	4·00	4·00
MS1171	70 × 66 mm. 20n. Ox	2·75	2·75

Nos. 1159/70 were issued together in *se-tenant* sheetlets of 12 stamps and one central label depicting an ox and a verse by Theodora Lau.

(Des D. Burkhart. Litho Questa)

1997 (24 Apr). *Endangered Species. T* **155** *and similar horiz designs. Multicoloured.* P 14.

1172	10n. Type **155**	55	55
	a. Sheetlet of 9. Nos. 1172/80	6·50	
1173	10n. Lesser ("Red") panda (*Ailurus fulgens*)	55	55
1174	10n. Takin (*Budorcas taxicolor*)	55	55
1175	10n. Forest musk deer (*Moschus chrysogaster*)	55	55
1176	10n. Snow leopard (*Panthera uncia*)	55	55
1177	10n. Golden langur (*Presbytis geei*)	55	55
1178	10n. Tiger (*Panthera tigris*)	55	55
1179	10n. Indian muntjac (*Muntiacus muntjak*)	55	55
1180	10n. Bobak marmot (*Marmota bobak*)	55	55
1181	10n. Dhole (*Cuon alpinis*) running	55	55
	a. Horiz strip of 4. Nos. 1181/4	2·30	
1182	10n. Dhole walking	55	55
1183	10n. Mother dhole nursing cubs	55	55
1184	10n. Two dhole	55	55
1172/1184	*Set of 13*	6·50	6·50
MS1185	Two sheets, each 106 × 76 mm. (a)		

70n. Bharal (*Pseudois nayaur*); (b) 70n. Asiatic black bear (*Ursus thibetanus*) . . . . 7·50 7·50

Nos. 1172/80 were issued together in *se-tenant* sheetlets of nine stamps. Nos. 1181/4, which also show the WWF emblem, were issued together in horizontal *se-tenant* strips within sheetlets of 12 stamps.

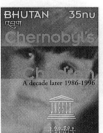

156 Child's Face and UNESCO Emblem

157 Mount Huangshah, China

(Des R. Sauber. Litho Questa)

1997 (2 May). *Tenth Anniv of Chernobyl Nuclear Disaster.* P 13½ × 14.
1186	**156**	35n. multicoloured	1·90	1·90

(Des M. Friedman and Dena Rubin. Litho Questa)

1997 (15 May). *50th Anniv of United Nations Educational, Scientific and Cultural Fund. World Heritage Sites. T* **157** *and similar multicoloured designs.* P 13½ × 14.

1187	10n. Type **157**	65	65
	a. Sheetlet of 8. Nos. 1187/94 plus label	5·25	
1188	10n. Staute of Emperor Qin, China	65	65
1189	10n. Imperial bronze dragon, China	65	65
1190	10n. Pyamids, Tikal National Park, Guatemala	65	65
1191	10n. Fountain, Évora, Portugal	65	65
1192	10n. Forest path, Shirakami-Sanchi, Japan	65	65
1193	10n. View from Eiffel Tower, Paris, France	65	65

1194	10n. Wooden walkway, Valley Below the Falls, Croatia	65	65
1195	15n. Bamberg Cathedral, Germany	1·00	1·00
	a. Sheetlet of 8. Nos. 1195/1202	7·25	
1196	15n. Aerial view of Bamberg	1·00	1·00
1197	15n. St. Michael's Church, Hildesheim, Germany	1·00	1·00
1198	15n. Potsdam Palace, Germany	1·00	1·00
1199	15n. Church, Potsdam	1·00	1·00
1200	15n. Waterfront, Lübeck, Germany	1·00	1·00
1201	15n. Quedlinberg, Germany	1·00	1·00
1202	15n. Benedictine church, Lorsch, Germany	1·00	1·00
1187/1202	*Set of 16*	11·00	11·00
MS1203	Two sheets, each 126 × 102 mm. (a)		

60n. House, Goslar, Germany (horiz); (b) 60n. Comenzada Cathedal, Portugal (horiz). P 14 × 13½. . . . . 6·25 6·25

Stamps of the same value were issued together in *se-tenant* sheetlets of eight stamps and one central label showing the UNESCO and World Heritage Site emblems.

158 Turkish Angora

159 Stuart Pearce (England)

(Des M. Lebouff. Litho Questa)

1997 (15 July). *Domestic Animals. T* **158** *and similar vert designs. Multicoloured.* P 14.

(a) Cats.

1204	10n. Type **158**	65	65
1205	15n. Oriental shorthair	90	90
1206	15n. Japanese bobtail	85	85
	a. Sheetlet of 6. Nos. 1206/11	5·00	
1207	15n. Ceylon	85	85
1208	15n. Exotic	85	85
1209	15n. Rex	85	85
1210	15n. Ragdoll	85	85
1211	15n. Russian blue	85	85
1212	20n. British shorthair	1·20	1·20
1213	25n. Burmese	1·40	1·40

(b) Dogs.

1214	10n. Dalmatian	65	65
1215	15n. Siberian husky	90	90
1216	20n. Saluki	1·20	1·20
1217	20n. Dandie Dinmont terrier	1·20	1·20
	a. Sheetlet of 6. Nos. 1217/22	7·25	
1218	20n. Chinese crested	1·20	1·20
1219	20n. Norwich terrier	1·20	1·20
1220	20n. Basset hound	1·20	1·20
1221	20n. Cardigan Welsh corgi	1·20	1·20
1222	20n. French bulldog	1·20	1·20
1223	25n. Shar-Pei	1·40	1·40
1204/1223	*Set of 20*	19·00	19·00
MS1224	Two sheets, each 76 × 106 mm. (a)		

60n. Tokinese (cat); (b) 60n. Hovawart (dog) . . . . 6·75 6·75

Nos. 1206/11 and 1217/22 respectively were issued together in *se-tenant* sheetlets of six stamps, each sheetlet forming a composite design.

(Litho Questa)

1997 (9 Oct). *World Cup Football Championship, France (1998). T* **159** *and similar designs. Black (Nos. 1225, 1231, 1235, 1237, 1241, 1243) or multicoloured (others).* P 13½ × 14 (vert) or 14 × 13½ (horiz).

1225	5n. Type **159** (black)	35	35
1226	10n. Paul Gascoigne (England)	65	65
1227	10n. Diego Maradona (Argentina 1986) *(horiz)*	65	65
	a. Sheetlet of 8. Nos. 1227/34 plus label	5·25	
1228	10n. Carlos Alberto (Brazil 1970) *(horiz)*	65	65
1229	10n. Dunga (Brazil 1994) *(horiz)*	65	65
1230	10n. Bobby Moore (England 1966) *(horiz)*	65	65
1231	10n. Fritz Walter (West Germany 1954) (black) *(horiz)*	65	65
1232	10n. Lothar Matthäus (Germany 1990) *(horiz)*	65	65
1233	10n. Franz Beckenbauer (West Gernany 1974) *(horiz)*	65	65
1234	10n. Daniel Passarella (Argentina 1978) *(horiz)*	65	65
1235	10n. Italy team, 1938 (black) *(horiz)*	65	65
	a. Sheetlet of 9. Nos. 1235/43	6·00	
1236	10n. West Germany team, 1954 *(horiz)*	65	65
1237	10n. Uruguay team, 1950 (black) *(horiz)*	65	65
1238	10n. England team, 1966 *(horiz)*	65	65
1239	10n. Argentina team, 1978 *(horiz)*	65	65
1240	10n. Brazil team, 1962 *(horiz)*	65	65
1241	10n. Italy team, 1934 (black) *(horiz)*	65	65
1242	10n. Brazil team, 1970 *(horiz)*	65	65
1243	10n. Uruguay team, 1930 (black) *(horiz)*	65	65
1244	15n. David Beckham (England)	1·00	1·00
1245	20n. Steve McManaman (England)	1·20	1·20
1246	25n. Tony Adams (England)	1·50	1·50
1247	30n. Paul Ince (England)	1·90	1·90
1225/1247 *Set of 23*		15·00	15·00

MS1248 Two sheets, each 102 × 127 mm. (a) 35n. Salvatore "Toto" Schillaci (Italy) (horiz); (b) 35n. Philippe Albert (Belgium)   4·75   4·75

Nos. 1227/34 were issued together in *se-tenant* sheetlets of eight stamps and one label showing a football and the French flag; Nos. 1235/43 were issued in *se-tenant* sheetlets of nine stamps. No. 1237 is inscribed 1958 in error.

160 Buddha in Lotus Position

161 Jawaharlal Nehru and King Jigme Dorji Wangchuk

(Des T. Chhetri. Litho Secura, Singapore)

1997 (15 Dec). *"Indepex '97" International Stamp Exhibition, New Delhi. 50th Anniv of Independence of India. T* **160** *and similar vert designs. Multicoloured.* P 13½ × 13.

1249	5n. Type **160**	15	15
	a. Sheetlet of 4. Nos. 1249/52	1·70	
1250	7n. Mahatma Gandhi with hands together	35	35
1251	10n. Gandhi (three-quarter face portrait)	50	50
1252	15n. Buddha with feet on footstall	65	65
1249/1252 *Set of 4*		1·50	1·50

MS1253 Two sheets, each 75 × 106 mm. (a) 15n. Buddha with right hand raised; (b) 15n. Gandhi carrying stick   1·70   1·70

1997 (15 Dec). *International Friendship between India and Bhutan. T* **161** *and similar horiz designs. Litho.* P 13 × 13½.

1254	3n. black and pink	15	15
1255	10n. multicoloured	55	55

MS1256 100 × 70 mm. 20n. multicoloured. P 13½ × 13   2·30   2·30

Designs: As T **161**—10n. Prime Minister Rajiv Gandhi of India and King Jigme Singye Wangchuck. 76 × 34 mm—20n. President R. Venkataraman of India and King Jigme Singye Wangchuck.

162 Tiger

1998 (27 Dec). *New Year. Year of the Tiger. T* **162** *and similar square designs. Multicoloured. Litho.* P 14.

1257	3n. Type **162**	10	10

MS1258 Two sheets. (a) 95 × 95 mm. 3n. Type **162**; 5n. Lying down; 15n. Hunting; 17n. On rocky outcrop; (b) 114 × 81 mm. 20n. Head of tiger   2·75   2·75

163 Safe Motherhood and Anniversary Emblem

164 Mother Teresa

1998 (7 Apr). *50th Anniv of World Health Organization. Litho.* P 13½.

1259	**163** 3n. multicoloured	10	10
1260	10n. multicoloured	50	50

MS1261 100 × 60 mm. 15n. Safe Motherhood emblem (134 × 34 mm). P 14   75   75

1998 (25 May). *Mother Teresa (founder of the Missionaries of Charity) Commemoration. T* **164** *and similar vert designs. Multicoloured. Litho.* P 13½.

1262	10n. Type **164**	50	50
	a. Sheetlet of 9. Nos. 1262/70	4·50	
1263	10n. With Diana, Princess of Wales	50	50
1264	10n. Holding child	50	50
1265	10n. Holding baby	50	50
1266	10n. With Sisters	50	50
1267	10n. Smiling	50	50
1268	10n. Praying	50	50
1269	10n. With Pope John Paul II	50	50
1270	10n. Close-up of face	50	50
1262/1270 *Set of 9*		4·00	4·00

MS1271 150 × 122 mm. 25n. As No. 1263 but 39 × 46 mm; 25n. As No. 1269 but different colour background and 39 × 46 mm

Nos. 1262/70 were issued together in *se-tenant* sheetlets of nine stamps.

165 Red-billed Chough   **166** Rabbit

1998 (28 July). *Birds. T* **165** *and similar horiz designs. Multicoloured.* P 13 × 13½.

1272	10ch. Type **165**	15	15
	a. Sheetlet of 12. Nos. 1272/83	1·60	
1273	30ch. Greater Indian hornbill ("Great Hornbill")	15	15
1274	50ch. Western singing bush lark ("Singing Lark")	15	15
1275	70ch. Chestnut-flanked white-eye	15	15
1276	90ch. Magpie robin ("Magpie-robin")	15	15
1277	1n. Mrs Gould's sunbird	15	15
1278	2n. Long-tailed tailor bird ("Tailorbird")	15	15
1279	3n. Mallard ("Duck")	15	15
1280	5n. Great spotted cuckoo ("Spotted Cuckoo")	15	15
1281	7n. Severtzov's tit warbler ("Goldcrest")	15	15
1282	9n. Common mynah	15	15
1283	10n. Green cochoa	15	15
1272/1283 *Set of 12*		1·60	1·60
MS1284 75 × 118 mm. 15n. Turtle dove (40 × 29 mm). P 13.		90	90

Nos. 1272/83 were issued together in *se-tenant* sheetlets of 12 stamps. No. 1272/7 were also issued in separate sheets.

168 King Wangchuk

1999 (2 June). *25th Anniv of Coronation of King Jigme Singye Wangchuck. T* **168** *and similar vert designs. Multicoloured. Litho.* P 12.

1289	25n. Type **168**	1·20	1·20
	a. Sheetlet of 4. Nos. 1289/92	5·00	
1290	25n. Facing left (yellow background)	1·20	1·20
1291	25n. Facing forwards (orange background)	1·20	1·20
1292	25n. With arm raised (green background)	1·20	1·20
1289/1292 *Set of 4*		4·50	4·50
MS1293 180 × 140 mm. 25n. King Wangchuk (magenta background)		4·25	4·25

Nos. 1289/92 were issued together in *se-tenant* sheetlets of four stamps with enlarged illustrated margins.

1999 (1 Jan). *New Year. Year of the Rabbit. T* **166** *and similar multicoloured design. Litho.* P 12½.

1285	4n. Type **166**	20	20
1286	16n. Rabbit on hillock	70	70
MS1287 83 × 114 mm. 20n. Rabbit beneath tree (34 × 34 *mm*). P 13½		1·00	1·00

169 Early German Steam Locomotive   **170** "Festive Dancers"

1999 (21 July). *Trains. T* **169** *and similar horiz designs. Multicoloured. Litho.* P 14.

1294	5n. Type **169**	25	25
1295	10n. Electric locomotive	65	65
1296	10n. "Hikari" express train, Japan	60	60
	a. Sheetlet of 12. Nos. 1296/1307	6·50	
1297	10n. Steam locomotive, South Africa, 1953	60	60
1298	10n. Super Chief locomotive, U.S.A., 1946	60	60
1299	10n. Magleus Magnet train, Japan, 1991	60	60
1300	10n. Flying Scotsman, Great Britain, 1992	60	60
1301	10n. Kodama locomotive, Japan, 1958	60	60
1302	10n. "Blue Train", South Africa, 1969	60	60
1303	10n. Intercity train, Germany, 1960	60	60
1304	10n. ET 403 high speed electric locomotive, Germany, 1973	60	60

167 Nuremberg

1999 (27 Apr). *"iBRA '99" International Stamp Exhibition, Nuremberg. Sheet 75 × 94 mm containing T* **167** *and similar square design. Multicoloured. Litho.* P 14.

MS1288 35n. Type **167**; 40n. Exhibition emblem		1·00	1·00

1305	10n. 4-4-0 steam locomotive, U.S.A., 1855	60	60
1306	10n. Beyer-Garratt steam locomotive, South Africa, 1954 (wrongly inscr "BAYER GARRATT")	60	60
1307	10n. Settebello locomotive, Italy, 1953	60	60
1308	15n. Pacific Class 01 steam locomotive, Germany	85	85
	a. Sheetlet of 9. Nos. 1308/16	7·00	
1309	15n. Neptune Express, Germany	85	85
1310	15n. 4-6-0 steam locomotive, Great Britain	85	85
1311	15n. Shovelnose Streamliner diesel locomotive, U.S.A.	85	85
1312	15n. Electric locomotive, Germany	85	85
1313	15n. Early steam locomotive, Germany	85	85
1314	15n. Union Pacific diesel locomotive, U.S.A.	85	85
1315	15n. 1881 Borsig steam locomotive, Germany	85	85
1316	15n. Borsig 4-6-4 diesel locomotive, Germany	85	85
1317	15n. Diesel-electric locomotive, France	85	85
	a. Sheetlet of 9. Nos. 1317/25	7·00	
1318	15n. Pennsylvania Railroad locomotive, U.S.A.	85	85
1319	15n. Steam locomotive, Germany	85	85
1320	15n. Amtrak locomotive, U.S.A.	85	85
1321	15n. 2-2-2 steam locomotive, Great Britain	85	85
1322	15n. P class steam locomotive, Denmark	85	85
1323	15n. Electric locomotive, France	85	85
1324	15n. First Japanese locomotive	85	85
1325	15n. 2-8-2 steam locomotive, Germany	85	85
1326	20n. Steam locomotive	1·20	1·20
1327	30n. Electric locomotive	1·70	1·70
1294/1327	*Set of 34*	24·00	24·00

MS1328 Two sheets, each 110 × 85 mm. (a) 80 n. City of Los Angeles, U.S.A.; (b) 80 n. Great Northern diesel-electric Streamliner locomotive, U.S.A. ... 9·75 9·75

Nos. 1296/1307, 1308/16 and 1317/25 respectively were issued together in *se-tenant* sheetlets of 12 (1296/1307) or nine (others).

1999 (27 July). *150th Death Anniv of Katsushika Hokusai (artist).* T **170** *and similar multicoloured designs. Litho.* P 13½ × 14 (vert) or 14 × 13½ (horiz).

1329	15n. Type **170**	75	75
	a. Sheetlet of 6. Nos. 1329/34	4·50	
1330	15n. "Drawings of Women" (woman reading)	75	75
1331	15n. "Festive Dancers" (man wearing pointed hat)	75	75
1332	15n. "Festive Dancers" (man looking up)	75	75
1333	15n. "Drawings of Women" (woman sitting on ground)	75	75
1334	15n. "Festive Dancers" (woman)	75	75
1335	15n. "Suspension Bridge between Hida and Etchu"	75	75
	a. Sheetlet of 6. Nos. 1335/40	4·50	
1336	15n. "Drawings of Women" (woman dressing hair)	75	75
1337	15n. "Exotic Beauty"	75	75
1338	15n. "The Poet Nakamaro in China"	75	75
1339	15n. "Drawings of Women" (woman rolling up sleeve)	75	75
1340	15n. "Chinese Poet in Snow"	75	75
1341	15n. "Mount Fuji seen above Mist on the Tama River" (horiz)	75	75
	a. Sheetlet of 6. Nos. 1341/6	4·50	
1342	15n. "Mount Fuji seen from Shichirigahama" (horiz)	75	75
1343	15n. "Sea Life" (turtle) (horiz)	75	75
1344	15n. "Sea Life" (fish) (horiz)	75	75
1345	15n. "Mount Fuji reflected in a Lake" (horiz)	75	75
1346	15n. "Mount Fuji seen through the Piers of Mannenbashi" (horiz)	75	75
1329/1346	*Set of 18*	12·50	12·50

MS1347 Three sheets (a) 100 × 71 mm. 80n. "Peasants leading Oxen"; (b) 71 × 100 mm. 80n. "The Lotus Pedestal". (c) 71 × 100 mm. 80n. "Kusunoki Masashige" ... 15·00 15·00

Nos. 1329/34, 1335/40 and 1341/6 respectively were issued together in *se-tenant* sheetlets of six stamps.

171 Tyrannosaurus Rex

172 Siberian Musk Deer (*Moschus moschiferus*)

1999 (10 Aug). *Prehistoric Animals.* T **171** *and similar multicoloured designs. Litho.* P 14.

1348	10n. Type **171**	60	60
	a. Sheetlet of 12. Nos. 1348/59	6·50	
1349	10n. Dimorphodon	60	60
1350	10n. Diplodocus	60	60
1351	10n. Pterodaustro	60	60
1352	10n. Tyrannosaurus rex (*different*)	60	60
1353	10n. Edmontosaurus	60	60
1354	10n. Apatosaurus	60	60
1355	10n. Deinonychus	60	60
1356	10n. Hypsilophodon	60	60
1357	10n. Oviraptor	60	60
1358	10n. Stegosaurus beside lake	60	60
1359	10n. Head of Triceratops	60	60
1360	10n. Pterodactylus and Brachiosaurus	60	60
	a. Sheetlet of 12. Nos. 1360/71	6·50	
1361	10n. Pteranodon	60	60
1362	10n. Anurognathus and Tyrannosaurus rex	60	60
1363	10n. Brachiosaurus	60	60
1364	10n. Corythosaurus	60	60
1365	10n. Iguanodon	60	60
1366	10n. Lesothosaurus	60	60
1367	10n. Allosaurus	60	60
1368	10n. Velociraptor	60	60
1369	10n. Triceratops in water	60	60
1370	10n. Stegosaurus in water	60	60
1371	10n. Compsognathus	60	60
1372	20n. Moeritherium	90	90
	a. Sheetlet of 8. Nos. 1372/79	6·50	
1373	20n. Platybelodon	90	90
1374	20n. Woolly mammoth	90	90
1375	20n. African elephant (*Loxodonta africana*)	90	90
1376	20n. Deinonychus	90	90
1377	20n. Dimorphodon	90	90
1378	20n. Archaeopteryx	90	90
1379	20n. Ring-necked pheasant (*Phasianus colchicus*)	90	90
1348/1379	*Set of 32*	19·00	19·00

MS1380 Four sheets, each 110 × 85 mm. (a) 80n. Hoatzin (*vert*); (b) 80n. Ichthyosaurus (wrongly inscr "Present Day Dolphin") (*vert*); (c) 80n. Triceratops (*vert*); 80n. Pteranodon (wrongly inscr "Triceratops") ... 18·00 18·00

Nos. 1348/59 and 1360/71 respectively were issued together in *se-tenant* sheetlets of twelve stamps, the backgrounds forming a composite design. Nos. 1372/9 were issued together in sheetlets of eight stamps separated by an inscribed gutter margin. The horizontal rows depict the evolution of the African elephant and modern birds.

1999 (21 Aug). *"China '99" World Philatelic Exhibition, Peking. Animals. T **172** and similar vert designs. Multicoloured. Litho.* P 13.

1381	20n. Type **172**		1·00	1·00
	a. Sheetlet of 5. Nos. 1381/5, plus label		5·00	
1382	20n. Takin (*Budorcas taxicolor*)		1·00	1·00
1383	20n. Bharal ("Blue sheep") (*Pseudois nayur*) (wrongly inscr "nayour")		1·00	1·00
1384	20n. Yak (*Bos gunniens*)		1·00	1·00
1385	20n. Common goral (*Nemorhaedus goral*)		1·00	1·00
1381/1385 *Set of 5*			4·50	4·50

Nos. 1381/5 were issued together in *se-tenant* sheetlets of five stamps and one label showing the exhibition emblem.

173 Sara Orange-tip

(Litho Questa)

1999 (4 Oct). *Butterflies. T **173** and similar multicoloured designs.* P 14.

1386	5n. Type **173**		35	35
1387	10n. Pipe-vine swallowtail		60	60
1388	15n. Longwings		85	85
1389	20n. Viceroy		1·10	1·10
1390	20n. Frosted skipper		1·20	1·20
	a. Sheetlet of 6. Nos. 1390/5		7·25	
1391	20n. Fiery skipper		1·20	1·20
1392	20n. Banded hairstreak		1·20	1·20
1393	20n. Cloudless ("Clouded") sulphur		1·20	1·20
1394	20n. Milbert's tortoiseshell		1·20	1·20
1395	20n. Eastern tailed blue		1·20	1·20
1396	20n. Jamaican kite ("Zebra") swallowtail		1·20	1·20
	a. Sheetlet of 6. Nos. 1396/1401		7·25	
1397	20n. Colorado hairstreak		1·20	1·20
1398	20n. Pink-edged sulphur		1·20	1·20
1399	20n. Barred sulphur (wrongly inscr "Fairy Yellow")		1·20	1·20
1400	20n. Red-spotted purple		1·20	1·20
1401	20n. Aphrodite		1·20	1·20
1402	25n. Silver-spotted skipper (*vert*)		1·40	1·40
1403	30n. Great spangled fritillary (*vert*)		1·70	1·70
1404	35n. Little copper (vert)		2·00	2·00
1386/1404 *Set of 19*			20·00	20·00

MS1405 Four sheets, each 98 × 68 mm. (a) 80n. Monarch (*vert*); (b) 80n. Checkered white; (c) 80n. Gulf fritillary (*vert*); (d) 80n. Grey hairstreak (*vert*) ..... 14·50 14·50

Nos. 1390/95 and 1396/1401 respectively were issued in *se-tenant* sheetlets of six stamps, each sheetlet forming a composite design.

174 Chestnut Bellied Chlorophonia

175 Yuri Gagarin (first person in space, 1961)

1999 (17 Oct). *Birds. T **174** and similar multicoloured designs. Litho.* P 14.

1406	15n. Type **174**		65	65
	a. Sheetlet of 9. Nos. 1406/14		6·00	
1407	15n. Yellow-faced amazon parrot		65	65
1408	15n. White ibis		65	65
1409	15n. Caique		65	65
1410	15n. Green jay		65	65
1411	15n. Tufted coquette		65	65
1412	15n. Troupial		65	65
1413	15n. Purple gallinule		65	65
1414	15n. Copper-rumped hummingbird		65	65
1415	15n. Common egret		65	65
	a. Sheetlet of 9. Nos. 1415/23		6·00	
1416	15n. Rufous-browed pepper shrike		65	65
1417	15n. Glittering-throated emerald		65	65
1418	15n. Great kiskadee		65	65
1419	15n. Cuban green woodpecker		65	65
1420	15n. Scarlet ibis		65	65
1421	15n. Belted kingfisher		65	65
1422	15n. Barred antshrike		65	65
1423	15n. Brown-throated conure ("Caribbean parakeet")		65	65
1424	15n. Rufous-tailed jacamar (*vert*)		65	65
	a. Sheetlet of 9. Nos. 1424/32		6·00	
1425	15n. Scarlet macaw (*vert*)		65	65
1426	15n. Channel-billed toucan (*vert*)		65	65
1427	15n. Louisiana heron ("Tri-colored heron") (*vert*)		65	65
1428	15n. St. Vincent amazon ("St. Vincent parrot") (*vert*)		65	65
1429	15n. Blue-crowned motmot (*vert*)		65	65
1430	15n. Horned screamer (*vert*)		65	65
1431	15n. Grey plover ("Black-billed plover") (*vert*)		65	65
1432	15n. Eastern meadowlark ("Common meadowlark") (*vert*)		65	65
1406/1432 *Set of 27*			16·00	16·00

MS1433 Three sheets, each 85 × 110. (a) 80n. Military macaw (*vert*); (b) 80n. Toco toucan; (c) 80n. Red-billed scythebill (*vert*) ..... 11·00 11·00

Nos. 1406/14, 1415/23 and 1424/32 respectively were issued together in *se-tenant* sheetlets of nine stamps, each sheetlet forming a composite design.

1999 (1 Nov). *30th Anniv of First Manned Moon Landing. T **175** and similar multicoloured designs. Litho.* P 14.

1434	20n. Type **175**		90	90
	a. Sheetlet of 6. Nos. 1434/9		5·50	
1435	20n. Alan Shepard (first American in space, 1961)		90	90
1436	20n. John Glenn (first American to orbit Earth, 1962)		90	90
1437	20n. Valentina Tereshkova (first woman in space, 1963)		90	90
1438	20n. Edward White (first American to walk in space, 1965)		90	90
1439	20n. Neil Armstrong (first person to set foot on Moon, 1969)		90	90
1440	20n. Neil Armstrong (wearing N.A.S.A. suit)		90	90
	a. Sheetlet of 6. Nos. 1440/5		5·50	
1441	20n. Michael Collins		90	90
1442	20n. Edwin (Buzz) Aldrin		90	90
1443	20n. *Columbia* (pointing upwards)		90	90
1444	20n. *Eagle* on lunar surface		90	90
1445	20n. Edwin Aldrin on lunar surface		90	90
1446	20n. N.A.S.A. X-15 rocket (1960)		90	90
	a. Sheetlet of 6. Nos. 1446/51		5·50	
1447	20n. Gemini 8 (1966)		90	90
1448	20n. Saturn V rocket (1969)		90	90
1449	20n. Columbia (pointing downwards)		90	90
1450	20n. Eagle above Moon		90	90
1451	20n. Edwin Aldrin descending ladder		90	90
1434/1451 *Set of 18*			15·00	15·00

MS1452 Three sheets. (a) 111 × 85 mm. 80n. Neil Armstrong (*different*); (b) 111 × 85 mm. 80n. Gemini 8 docking with Agena target vehicle (56 × 41 *mm*); (c) 85 × 111 mm. 80n. Apollo 11 command module landing in Pacific Ocean (*vert*) ..... 11·00 11·00

Nos. 1434/9, 1440/5 and 1446/51 respectively were issued in *se-tenant* sheetlets of six stamps, each sheetlet forming a composite design.

176 Tortoiseshell Cat   **177** Bharal

(Litho Questa)

1999 (15 Nov). *Animals. T* **176** *and similar horiz designs. Multicoloured.* P 14.

1453	5n. Type **176**	75	75
1454	5n. Girl and blue and white cat	75	75
1455	10n. Chinchilla golden longhair adult and kittens	1·40	1·40
1456	12n. Russian blue adult and kitten	65	65
	a. Sheetlet of 9. Nos. 1456/64	6·00	
1457	12n. Birman	65	65
1458	12n. Devon rex	65	65
1459	12n. Pewter longhair	65	65
1460	12n. Bombay	65	65
1461	12n. Sorrel somali	65	65
1462	12n. Red tabby manx	65	65
1463	12n. Blue smoke longhair	65	65
1464	12n. Oriental tabby shorthair adult and kitten	65	65
1465	12n. Australian silky terrier	65	65
	a. Sheetlet of 9. Nos. 1465/73	6·00	
1466	12n. Samoyed	65	65
1467	12n. Basset bleu de Gascogne	65	65
1468	12n. Bernese mountain dog	65	65
1469	12n. Pug	65	65
1470	12n. Bergamasco	65	65
1471	12n. Basenji	65	65
1472	12n. Wetterhoun	65	65
1473	12n. Drever	65	65
1474	12n. Przewalski horse	65	65
	a. Sheetlet of 9. Nos. 1474/82	6·00	
1475	12n. Shetland pony	65	65
1476	12n. Dutch gelderlander horse	65	65
1477	12n. Shire horse	65	65
1478	12n. Arab	65	65
1479	12n. Boulonnais	65	65
1480	12n. Falabella	65	65
1481	12n. Orlov trotter	65	65
1482	12n. Suffolk punch	65	65
1483	15n. Lipizzaner	65	65
1484	20n. Andalusian	1·20	1·20
1485	25n. Weimaraner (dog)	1·70	1·70
1486	30n. German shepherd dog	3·00	3·00
1453/1486 *Set of 34*		24·00	24·00

MS1487 Three sheets, each 115 × 91 mm. (a) 70n. Labrador retriever; (b) 70n. Norwegian forest cat; (c) 70n. Connemara horse .... 9·75 9·75
Nos. 1456/64 (cats), 1465/73 (dogs) and 1474/82 (horses) respectively were issued in *se-tenant* sheetlets of nine stamps. No. 1488 is vacant.

(Des A. Toht. Litho Questa)

1999 (24 Nov–17 Dec). *Animals and Birds of the Himalayas. T* **177** *and similar vert designs. Multicoloured.* P 13½ × 14.

(a) Animals.

1489	20n. Type **177**	90	90
	a. Sheetlet of 6. Nos. 1489/94	5·50	
1490	20n. Lynx	90	90
1491	20n. Rat snake	90	90
1492	20n. Indian elephant	90	90
1493	20n. Langur	90	90
1494	20n. Musk deer	90	90
1495	20n. Otter	90	90
	a. Sheetlet of 6. Nos. 1495/1500	5·50	

1496	20n. Tibetan wolf	90	90
1497	20n. Himalayan black bear	90	90
1498	20n. Snow leopard	90	90
1499	20n. Flying squirrel	90	90
1500	20n. Red fox	90	90
1501	20n. Ibex	90	90
	a. Sheetlet of 6. Nos. 1501/6	5·50	
1502	20n. Takin	90	90
1503	20n. Agama lizard	90	90
1504	20n. Marmot	90	90
1505	20n. Red panda	90	90
1506	20n. Leopard cat	90	90
1489/1506 *Set of 18*		13·50	13·50

MS1507 Three sheets, each 78 × 118 mm. (a) 100n. Cobra; (b) 100n. Tiger; (c) 100n. Rhinoceros (wrongly inscr "Rhinocerous") .. 16·00 16·00

(b) Birds (17.12).

1508	20n. Red-crested pochard	90	90
	a. Sheetlet of 6. Nos. 1508/13	5·50	
1509	20n. Satyr tragopan	90	90
1510	20n. Lammergeier vulture	90	90
1511	20n. Kalij pheasant	90	90
1512	20n. Great Indian hornbill	90	90
1513	20n. Stork	90	90
1514	20n. Rufous-necked hornbill (wrongly inscr "Rofous")	90	90
	a. Sheetlet of 6. Nos. 1514/19	5·50	
1515	20n. Drongo	90	90
1516	20n. Himalayan monal pheasant	90	90
1517	20n. Black-necked crane	90	90
1518	20n. Little green bee-eater	90	90
1519	20n. Oriental ibis ("Ibis")	90	90
1520	20n. Crested lark	90	90
	a. Sheetlet of 6. Nos. 1520/5	5·50	
1521	20n. Ferruginous duck	90	90
1522	20n. Blood pheasant	90	90
1523	20n. Laughing thrush	90	90
1524	20n. Golden eagle	90	90
1525	20n. Siberian rubythroat	90	90
1508/1525 *Set of 18*		15·00	15·00

MS1526 Three sheets, each 78 × 118 mm. (a) 100n. Siberian rubythroat (*different*); (b) 100n. Black-naped monarch; (c) 100n. Mountain peacock pheasant; .... 16·00 16·00
Nos. 1489/94, 1495/1500, 1501/6, 1508/13, 1514/19 and 1520/5 respectively were issued together in *se-tenant* sheetlets of six stamps.

178 Elephant, Monkey, Rabbit and Bird (Four Friends)   **179** Elegant Stink Horn (*Mutinus elegans*)

1999 (15 Dec). *Year 2000.* P 14.

1527	**178**	10n. multicoloured	60	60
1528		20n. multicoloured	1·10	1·10

(Des A. Toht. Litho Questa)

1999 (19 Dec). *Fungi. T* **179** *and similar vert designs. Multicoloured.* P 13½ × 14.

1529	20n. Type **179**	1·20	1·20
	a. Sheetlet of 6. Nos. 1529/34	7·25	
1530	20n. Pholiota squarrosoides	1·20	1·20
1531	20n. Scaly inky cap (*Coprinus quadrifidus*)	1·20	1·20

1532	20n.	Golden spindles (*Clavulinopsis fusiformis*)	1·20	1·20
1533	20n.	*Spathularia velutipes*	1·20	1·20
1534	20n.	*Ganoderma lucidum*	1·20	1·20
1535	20n.	*Microglossum rufum*	1·20	1·20
	a.	Sheetlet of 6. Nos. 1535/40	7·25	
1536	20n.	*Lactarius hygrophoroides*	1·20	1·20
1537	20n.	*Lactarius speciosus* complex	1·20	1·20
1538	20n.	*Calostoma cinnabarina*	1·20	1·20
1539	20n.	*Clitocybe clavipes*	1·20	1·20
1540	20n.	*Microstoma floccosa*	1·20	1·20
1541	20n.	Frost's bolete (*Boletus frostii*)	1·20	1·20
	a.	Sheetlet of 6. Nos. 1541/6	7·25	
1542	20n.	Common morel (*Morchella esculenta*) (wrongly inscr "estculenta")	1·20	1·20
1543	20n.	*Hypomyces lactifuorum*	1·20	1·20
1544	20n.	*Polyporus auricularius*	1·20	1·20
1545	20n.	*Cantharellus lateritius*	1·20	1·20
1546	20n.	*Volvariella pusilla*	1·20	1·20
1529/1546		*Set of 18*	20·00	20·00

MS1547 Three sheets, each 78 × 118 mm. (a) 100n. *Pholiota aurivella*; (b) 100n. *Ramaria grandis*; (c) 100n. *Oudemansiella lucidum* . . . 16·00 16·00
Nos. 1529/34, 1535/40 and 1541/6 respectively were issued together in *se-tenant* sheetlets of six stamps.

180 Green Dragon with Red Flames

181 LZ-1 (first flight), 1900

2000 (1 Jan). *New Year. Year of the Dragon.* T **180** *and similar multicoloured designs.* Litho. P 13 (**MS**1553) or 14 (others).

1548	3n.	Type **180**	15	15
1549	5n.	Green dragon encircling moon	25	25
1550	8n.	Dragon and symbols of Chinese zodiac	50	50
1552	12n.	Brown dragon encircling moon	75	75
1548/1552		*Set of 4*	1·50	1·50

MS1553 90 × 130 mm. 15n. Dragon head (29 × 40 *mm*) . . . 85 85

(Des G. Capasso. Litho Questa)

2000 (15 May). *Centenary of First Zeppelin Flight.* T **181** *and similar multicoloured designs.* P 14.

1554	25n.	Type **181**	1·30	1·30
	a.	Sheetlet of 6. Nos. 1554/9	8·00	
1555	25n.	LZ-2, 1906	1·30	1·30
1556	25n.	LZ-3 over hills (first flight, 1906)	1·30	1·30
1557	25n.	LZ-127 *Graf Zeppelin* (first flight, 1928)	1·30	1·30
1558	25n.	LZ-129 *Hindenberg* (first flight, 1936)	1·30	1·30
1559	25n.	LZ-130 *Graf Zeppelin II* (first flight, 1938)	1·30	1·30
1560	25n.	LZ-1 over hill with tree	1·30	1·30
	a.	Sheetlet of 6. Nos. 1560/5	8·00	
1561	25n.	LZ-2 over mountains	1·30	1·30
1562	25n.	LZ-3 against sky	1·30	1·30
1563	25n.	LZ-4 (first flight, 1908)	1·30	1·30
1564	25n.	LZ-5 (first flight, 1909)	1·30	1·30
1565	25n.	LZ-6 (formation of Deutsche Liftschiffahrts Aktien Gesallschaft (DELAG) (world's first airline), 1909)	1·30	1·30
1566	25n.	LZ-1 over grassy hills, 1900	1·30	1·30
	a.	Sheetlet of 6. Nos. 1566/71	8·00	
1567	25n.	Z11 *Ersatz*, 1913	1·30	1·30
1568	25n.	LZ-6 exiting hangar, 1909	1·30	1·30
1569	25n.	LZ-10 *Schwaben* (first flight, 1911)	1·30	1·30
1570	25n.	LZ-7 *Deutschland* (inscr "Ersatz Deutschland")	1·30	1·30
1571	25n.	LZ-11 *Viktoria Luise*	1·30	1·30
1554/1571		*Set of 18*	21·00	21·00

MS1572 Three sheets, each 106 × 80 mm. (a) 80n. Ferdinand von Zeppelin wearing white cap (*vert*); (b) 80n. Zeppelin wearing black cap (*vert*); (c) 80n. Zeppelin (*vert*) . . . 12·50 12·50
Nos. 1554/9, 1560/5 and 1566/71 respectively were issued in *se-tenant* sheetlets of six stamps.

182 Lunix III

183 Trashigang Dzong

(Des Lollini. Litho Questa)

2000 (15 May). *"WORLD STAMP EXPO 2000" International Stamp Exhibition, Anaheim, California. Space.* T **182** *and similar multicoloured designs.* P 14.

1573	25n.	Type **182**	1·30	1·30
	a.	Sheetlet of 6. Nos. 1573/8	8·00	
1574	25n.	Ranger 9	1·30	1·30
1575	25n.	Lunar Orbiter	1·30	1·30
1576	25n.	Lunar Prospector spacecraft	1·30	1·30
1577	25n.	Apollo 11 spacecraft	1·30	1·30
1578	25n.	Selene satellite	1·30	1·30
1579	25n.	Space shuttle *Challenger*	1·30	1·30
	a.	Sheetlet of 6. Nos. 1579/84	8·00	
1580	25n.	North American X-15 experimental rocket aircraft	1·30	1·30
1581	25n.	Space shuttle *Buran*	1·30	1·30
1582	25n.	Hermes (experimental space plane)	1·30	1·30
1583	25n.	X-33 Venturi Star (re-usable launch vehicle)	1·30	1·30
1584	25n.	Hope (unmanned experimental spacecraft)	1·30	1·30
1585	25n.	Victor Patsayev (cosmonaut)	1·30	1·30
	a.	Sheetlet of 6. Nos. 1585/90	8·00	
1586	25n.	Yladisloav Volkov (cosmonaut)	1·30	1·30
1587	25n.	Georgi Dobrvolski (cosmonaut)	1·30	1·30
1588	25n.	Virgil Grissom (astronaut)	1·30	1·30
1589	25n.	Roger Chaffee (astronaut)	1·30	1·30
1590	25n.	Edward White (astronaut)	1·30	1·30
1573/1590		*Set of 18*	31·00	31·00

MS1591 Three sheets. (a) 76 × 111 mm. 80n. Launch of space shuttle *Challenger* (*vert*); (b) 76 × 111 mm. 80n. Launch of space shuttle *Buran* (*vert*); (c) 116 × 85 mm. 80n. Edwin E. Aldrin on moon (first manned Moon landing, 1969) (*vert*) . . . 12·50 12·50
Nos. 1573/8, 1579/84 and 1585/90 respectively were issued in *se-tenant* sheetlets of six stamps.

(Des G. Capasso. Litho Questa)

2000 (1 June). *"EXPO 2000" World's Fair, Hanover, Germany (1st issue). Monasteries.* T **183** *and similar multicoloured designs.* Litho. P 13 (**MS**1598) or 13 × 13½ (others).

1592	3n.	Type **183**	15	15
	a.	Sheetlet of 6. Nos. 1592/7	2·10	
1593	4n.	Lhuentse Dzong	15	15
1594	6n.	Gasa Dzong	25	25
1595	7n.	Punakha Dzong	35	35
1596	10n.	Trashichhoe Dzong	40	40
1597	20n.	Paro Dzong	85	85
1592/1597		*Set of 6*	1·90	1·90

MS1598 157 × 98 mm. 15n. Roof (29 × 40 *mm*) . . . 65 65
Nos. 1592/7 were issued together in *se-tenant* sheetlets of six stamps.

184 Snow Leopard

185 Jesse Owens (U.S.A.) (Berlin, 1936)

2000 (1 June). *"EXPO 2000" World's Fair, Hanover, Germany (2nd issue). Wildlife.* T **184** *and similar vert designs. Multicoloured. Litho.* P 13.

1599	10n. Type **184**		40	40
	a. Sheetlet of 6. Nos. 1599/1604		2·40	
1600	10n. Raven		40	40
1601	10n. Golden langur		40	40
1602	10n. Rhododendron		40	40
1603	10n. Black-necked crane		40	40
1604	10n. Blue poppy		40	40
1559/1604 *Set of 6*			2·20	2·20

Nos. 1599/1604 were issued together in *se-tenant* sheetlets of six stamps.

(Litho Walsall Security Printers)

2000 (24 July). *Olympic Games, Sydney.* T **185** *and similar horiz designs. Multicoloured.* P 14.

1605	20n. Type **185**		1·00	1·00
	a. Sheetlet of 4. Nos. 1605/8		4·00	
1606	20n. Kayaking (modern games)		1·00	1·00
1607	20n. Fulton County Stadium, Atlanta, Georgia (1996 games)		1·00	1·00
1608	20n. Ancient Greek athlete		1·00	1·00
1605/1608 *Set of 4*			3·75	3·75

Nos. 1605/8 were issued together in *se-tenant* sheetlets of four stamps.

186 G. and R. Stephenson's Rocket (first steam locomotive)

(Des R. Sauber. Litho Walsall Security Printers)

2000 (31 July). *175th Anniv of Opening of Stockton and Darlington Railway.* T **186** *and similar horiz designs. Multicoloured.* P 14.

1609	20n. Type **186**		2·50	2·50
	a. Sheetlet of 3. Nos. 1609/11		7·50	
1610	20n. Steam locomotive (opening of London and Birmingham railway, 828)		2·50	2·50
1611	20n. Northumbrian locomotive, 1825		2·50	2·50
MS1612 118 × 79 mm. 100n. Inaugural run on Stockton and Darlington Railway, 1825 (56 × 42 *mm*)			4·00	4·00

Nos. 1609/11 were issued together in *se-tenant* sheetlets of three stamps.

187 Laird Commercial (biplane), 1929

(Des M. Miller. Litho Questa)

2000 (7 Aug). *Airplanes.* T **187** *and similar horiz designs. Multicoloured.* P 14.

1613	25n. Type **187**		1·20	1·20
	a. Sheetlet of 6. Nos. 1613/18		7·25	
1614	25n. Ryan B-5 Brougham, 1927 (wrongly inscr "Broughm")		1·20	1·20
1615	25n. Cessna AW, 1928		1·20	1·20
1616	25n. Travel Air 4000 biplane, 1927		1·20	1·20
1617	25n. Fairchild F-71, 1927		1·20	1·20
1618	25n. Command Aire biplane, 1928		1·20	1·20
1619	25n. Waco YMF biplane, 1935		1·20	1·20
	a. Sheetlet of 6. Nos. 1619/24		7·25	
1620	25n. Piper J-4 Cub Coupe, 1938		1·20	1·20
1621	25n. Ryan ST-A, 1937		1·20	1·20
1622	25n. Spartan Executive, 1939		1·20	1·20
1623	25n. Luscombe 8, 1939		1·20	1·20
1624	25n. Stinson SR5 Reliant seaplane, 1935		1·20	1·20
1625	25n. Cessna 195 seaplane, 1949		1·20	1·20
	a. Sheetlet of 6. Nos. 1625/30		7·25	
1626	25n. Waco SRE biplane, 1940		1·20	1·20
1627	25n. Erco Ercope, 1948		1·20	1·20
1628	25n. Boeing Stearman biplane, 1941		1·20	1·20
1629	25n. Beech Staggerwing biplane, 1944		1·20	1·20
1630	25n. Republic Seabee, 1947		1·20	1·20
1613/1630 *Set of 18*			20·00	20·00
MS1631 Three sheets, each 77 x 108 mm. (a) 100n. Waco CSO seaplane, 1929; (b) 100n. Curtiss-Wright 19W, 1936; (c) 100n. Grumman G-44 Widgeon flying boat, 1941			12·00	12·00

Nos. 1613/18, 1619/24 and 1625/30 respectively were issued in *se-tenant* sheetlets of six stamps.

MS1631 each have a description of the aircraft inscribed in the margin.

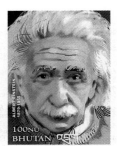

188 *A Kind of Loving,* 1962

189 Einstein

(Des R. Sauber. Litho Walsall Security Printers Ltd)

2000 (15 Aug). *Berlin Film Festival. Winners of Golden Bear Award.* T **188** *and similar vert designs. Multicoloured.* P 14.

1632	25n. Type **188**		1·20	1·20
	a. Sheetlet of 6. Nos. 1632/7		7·25	
1633	25n. *Bushido Zankoku Monogatari,* 1963		1·20	1·20
1634	25n. *Hobson's Choice,* 1954		1·20	1·20
1635	25n. *El Lazarillo de Tormes,* 1960		1·20	1·20

1636   25n. *In the Name of the Father*, 1997 . .   1·20   1·20
1637   25n. *Les Cousins*, 1959 . . . . .   1·20   1·20
1632/1637 *Set of 6* . . . . . .   6·50   6·50
MS1638 96 × 102 mm.100n. *Die Ratten*,
  1962 . . . .   4·00   4·00
  Nos. 1632/7 were issued together in *se-tenant* sheetlets of six stamps within an enlarged inscribed margin at left.

(Des R. Sauber. Litho Walsall Security Printers Ltd)
2000 (15 Aug). *Albert Einstein—Time Magazine Man of the Century. Sheet* 113 × 83mm. P 12.
MS1639 **189** 100n. multicoloured . . . .   4·50   4·50

190 Aquinas   **191** Pierre de Coubertin

(Litho B.D.T. International Security Ptg Ltd, Dublin, Ireland)
2000 (18 Sept). *775th Birth Anniv of Thomas Aquinas (Catholic philosopher and theologian). Sheet* 136 × 76 mm. P 14 × 14½.
MS1640 **190** 25n. × 4 multicoloured . . .   4·00   4·00

(Des E. Moreiro. Litho B.D.T. International Security Ptg Ltd, Dublin, Ireland)
2000 (18 Sept). *New Millennium. T* **191** *and similar horiz designs. Multicoloured.* P 14.

  (a) Centenary of the Modern Olympic Games.
1641   25n. Type **191** (founder of modern
     games) . . . . . .   1·20   1·20
    a. Sheetlet of 6. Nos. 1641/6 . .   7·25
1642   25n. Hand holding baton (first modern
     Games, Athens, 1896) . .   1·20   1·20
1643   25n. Jesse Owen (Berlin, 1936) . .   1·20   1·20
1644   25n. Handprint and white dove (Munich,
     1972) . . . . .   1·20   1·20
1645   25n. Sydney Opera House (Sydney,
     2000) . . . . .   1·20   1·20
1646   25n. Children wearing T-shirts (Greece,
     2004) . . . . .   1·20   1·20

  (b) Breakthroughs in Modern Medicine.
1647   25n. Albert Calmette (bacteriologist, joint
     discoverer of B.C.G. vaccine) . .   1·20   1·20
    a. Sheetlet of 6. Nos. 1647/52 . .   7·25
1648   25n. Camillo Colgi and S. Ramón y
     Cajal (discovery of the neurone) .   1·20   1·20
1649   25n. Alexander Fleming (bacteriologist,
     discoverer of penicillin) . .   1·20   1·20
1650   25n. Jonas Salk (virologist, developer of
     polio vaccine) . . . .   1·20   1·20
1651   25n. Christiaan Barnard (surgeon,
     performed first human heart
     transplant) . . . .   1·20   1·20
1652   25n. Luc Mantagnier (A.I.D.S.
     research) . . . .   1·20   1·20
1641/1652 *Set of 12* . . . .   13·00   13·00
  Nos. 1641/6 and 1647/52 respectively were each issued together in *se-tenant* sheetlets of six stamps with an enlarged illustrated margin at foot.

192 Paro Taktsang   **193** Christopher
                      Columbus

2000 (18 Sept). *Sheet* 86 × 49 *mm.Litho.* P 14.
MS1653 **192** 100n. multicoloured . . . .   4·00   4·00

(Des H. Friedman. Litho B.D.T. International Security Ptg Ltd, Dublin, Ireland)
2000 (18 Sept). *Explorers. T* **193** *and similar vert design. Two sheets each* 66 × 83 *mm. Multicoloured.* P 14.
MS1654 (a) 100n. Type **193**; (b) 100n. Captain
    James Cook . . . . .   8·00   8·00

194 Crinum amoenum   **195** "The Duke and
                         Duchess of Osuna with
                         their Children" (detail,
                         Francisco de Goya)

(Des Y. Lee. Litho Questa)
2000 (5 Oct). *Flowers of the Himalayan Mountains. T* **194** *and similar multicoloured designs.* P 14½.
1655   25n. Type **194** . . . .   1·20   1·20
    a. Sheetlet of 6. Nos. 1655/60 .   7·25
1656   25n. *Beaumontia grandiflora* . .   1·20   1·20
1657   25n. *Trachelospermum lucidum* . .   1·20   1·20
1658   25n. *Curcuma aromatica* . . .   1·20   1·20
1659   25n. *Barleria cristata* . . .   1·20   1·20
1660   25n. *Holmskioldia sanguinea* . .   1·20   1·20
1661   25n. *Meconopsis villosa* . . .   1·20   1·20
    a. Sheetlet of 6. Nos. 1661/6 .   7·25
1662   25n. *Salva hians* . . . .   1·20   1·20
1663   25n. *Caltha palustris* . . .   1·20   1·20
1664   25n. *Anemone polyanthes* . .   1·20   1·20
1665   25n. *Cypripedium cordigerum* . .   1·20   1·20
1666   25n. *Cryptochilus luteus* . . .   1·20   1·20
1667   25n. *Androsace globifera* . .   1·20   1·20
    a. Sheetlet of 6. Nos. 1667/72 .   7·25
1668   25n. *Tanacetum atkinsonii* . .   1·20   1·20
1669   25n. *Aster stracheyi* . . .   1·20   1·20
1670   25n. *Arenaria glanduligera* . .   1·20   1·20
1671   25n. *Sibbaldia purpurea* . .   1·20   1·20
1672   25n. *Saxifraga parnassifolia* . .   1·20   1·20
1655/1672 *Set of 18* . . . .   20·00   20·00
MS1673 Three sheets, each 68 × 98 mm. (a)
  100n. *Dendrobium densiflorum* (vert); (b)
  100n. *Rhododendron arboreum* (vert); (c)
  100n. *Gypsophila cerastioides* . .   14·50   14·50
  Nos. 1655/60, 1661/6 and 1667/72 respectively were issued together in *se-tenant* sheetlets of six stamps, each sheetlet forming a composite design.

(Litho Walsall Security Printers Ltd)

2000 (6 Oct). *"Espana 2000" International Stamp Exhibition, Madrid. Prado Museum Exhibits. T* **195** *and similar vert designs. Multicoloured.* P 12 × 12½.

1674	25n. Type **195**		1·50	1·50
	a. Sheetlet of 6. Nos. 1674/9		9·00	
1675	25n. Young child (detail from "The Duke and Duchess of Osuna with their Children")		1·50	1·50
1676	25n. Duke (detail from "The Duke and Duchess of Osuna with their Children")		1·50	1·50
1677	25n. "Isidoro Maiquez" (Francisco de Goya)		1·50	1·50
1678	25n. "Doña Juana Galarza de Goicoechea" (Francisco de Goya)		1·50	1·50
1679	25n. "Ferdinand VII in an Encampment" (Francisco de Goya)		1·50	1·50
1680	25n. "Portrait of an Old Man" (Joos van Cleve)		1·50	1·50
	a. Sheetlet of 6. Nos. 1680/5		9·00	
1681	25n. "Mary Tudor" (Anthonis Mor)		1·50	1·50
1682	25n. "Portrait of a Man" (Jan van Scorel)		1·50	1·50
1683	25n. "The Court Jester Pejerón" (Anthonis Mor)		1·50	1·50
1684	25n. "Elizabeth of France" (Frans Pourbus the Younger)		1·50	1·50
1685	25n. "King James I" (Paul van Somer)		1·50	1·50
1686	25n. "The Empress Isabella of Portugal" (Titian)		1·50	1·50
	a. Sheetlet of 6. Nos. 1686/91		9·00	
1687	25n. "Lucrecia di Baccio del Fede, the Painter's Wife" (Andrea del Sarto)		1·50	1·50
1688	25n. "Self-Portrait" (Titian)		1·50	1·50
1689	25n. "Philip II" (Sofonisba Anguisciola)		1·50	1·50
1690	25n. "Portrait of a Doctor" (Lucia Anguisciola)		1·50	1·50
1691	25n. "Anna of Austria" (Sofonisba Anguisciola)		1·50	1·50
1674/1691 *Set of 18*			25·00	25·00

MS1692 Three sheets. (a) 90 × 110 mm. 100n. Duchess and Duke (detail from "The Duke and Duchess of Osuna with their Children" (Francisco de Goya) (*horiz*); (b) 90 × 110 mm. 100n. "Charles V at Mühlberg" (Titian); (c) 110 × 90 mm. 100n. "The Relief of Genoa" (Antonio de Pereda) . . . . . 13·50 13·50

Nos. 1674/9, 1680/5 and 1686/91 respectively were issued together in *se-tenant* sheetlets of six stamps.

196 Butterfly

197 Snake

2000 (7 Dec). *"Indepex Asiana 2000" International Stamp Exhibition, Calcutta. T* **196** *and similar vert designs. Multicoloured. Litho.* P 14.

1693	5n. Type **196**		15	15
	a. Sheetlet of 4. Nos. 1693/6		1·70	
1694	8n. Red jungle fowl		40	40
1695	10n. Zinnia elegans		50	50
1696	12n. Tiger		60	60
1693/1696 *Set of 4*			1·50	1·50

MS1697 144 × 84 mm. 15n. Spotted deer (28 × 34 *mm*). P 13½ 65 65

Nos. 1693/6 were issued together in *se-tenant* sheetlets of four stamps.

(Des B. Tamang. Litho)

2001 (1 Jan). *New Year. Year of the Snake. T* **197** *and similar vert designs. Multicoloured.* P 13.

1698	3n. Type **197**		15	15
1699	20n. Snake		1·10	1·10

MS1700 135 × 135 mm. 3, 10n. As Type **197**; 15n., 20n. As No. 1699 . . . . . 2·00 2·00

198 Snow Leopard (*Uncia uncia*)

199 Working in Fields

2001 (1 Feb). *"Hong Kong 2001" International Stamp Exhibition. Nature Protection. Sheet* 195 × 138 *mm containing T* **198** *and similar horiz designs. Multicoloured.* P 13.
MS1701 15n. Type **198**; 15n. Rufous-necked hornbill (*Aceros nipalensis*); 15n. Black-necked crane (*Grus nigricollis*); 15n. Tiger (*Panthera tigris*) . . . . . 2·75 2·75

(Des B. Tamang. Litho)

2001 (1 Mar). *International Year of Volunteers. T* **199** *and similar horiz designs. Multicoloured.* P 13.

1702	3n. Type **199**		15	15
1703	4n. Planting crops		25	25
1704	10n. Children and bucket		50	50
1705	15n. Planting seeds and making compost		75	75
1702/1705 *Set of 4*			1·50	1·50

MS1706 170 × 120 mm. Nos. 1705/8 . . . . 1·30 1·30

200 Chenrezig

(Des B. Tamang. Litho

2001 (23 Sept). *Buddhist Art, Taksang Monastery. Sheet* 120 × 147 *mm containing T* **200** *and similar vert designs. Multicoloured.* P 13 × 13½.
MS1707 10n. Type **200**; 15n. Guru Rimpoche; 20n. Sakyamuni . . . . . 2·10 2·10

Nu4

(201)

2001 (9 Oct). *Nos. 557/60 surch as T* **201**.

1708	4n.on 10ch. deep violet-blue		40	40
1709	10n.on 25ch. Venetian red		50	50

1710	15n.on 50ch. deep reddish violet	70	70
1711	20n.on 1n. brown	95	95
1708/1711 Set of 4	2·30	2·30

202 Snow Leopard's Head

(Des B. Pearce. Litho BDT Security Printing, Dublin, Ireland)

2001 (17 Dec). *Snow Leopard (Uncia uncia). Sheet 172 × 140 mm containing T 202 and similar multicoloured design.* P 14.
MS1712 10n. × 4, each × 2, Type **202**; Two
adults; Three juveniles; Crouched adult . .   4·00   4·00
MS1712 contains four 10n. stamps, each × 2, arranged diagonally around a central label.

203 Horse carrying Treasure Vase (Buddhist symbol)

204 Teri gang

(Des B. Tamang. Litho Secura, Singapore)

2002 (1 Jan). *Year of the Horse. T 203 and similar multicoloured designs.* P 13.
1713	20n. Type **203**	1·00	1·00
	a. Pair. Nos. 1713/14	2·00	2·00
1714	20n. White horse	1·00	1·00
MS1715 94 × 94mm. 25n.Horse and Dharma
Wheel (*horiz*) . . . .   1·20   1·20
Nos. 1713/14 were issued together in *se-tenant* pairs, each pair forming a composite design.

(Des B. Tamang. Litho Secura, Singapore)

2002 (5 Feb). *International Year of Mountains. Sheet 144 × 105 mm containing T 204 and similar horiz designs. Multicoloured.* P 13.
MS1716 Type **204**; 20n. Tsenda gang; 20n.
Jomolhari; 20n. Gangeheytag; 20n.
Jitchudrake; 20n. Tse-rim gang . . . . . .   5·75   5·75

205 *Rhomboda lanceolata*

206 *Rhododendron niveum*

(Des Hemlata Pradhan. Litho)

2002 (3 Apr). *Orchids. Sheet 162 × 131 mm containing T 205 and similar vert designs. Multicoloured.* P 13½.
MS1717 10n. Type **205**; 10n. *Odontochilus lanceolatus*; 10n. *Zeuxine glandulosa*; 10n. *Goodyera schlechtendaliana*; 10n. *Anoectochilus lanceolatus*; 10n. *Goodyera hispida* . . . .   3·00   3·00

(Des Nancy Tichborne. Litho Secura, Singapore)

2002 (1 May). *Rhododendrons. Sheet 132 × 132 mm containing T 206 and similar square designs. Multicoloured.* P 14.
MS1718 15n. Type **206**; 15n. *Rhododendron glaucophyllum*; 15n. *Rhododendron arboreum*; 15n. *Rhododendron grande*; 15n. *Rhododendron dalhousiae*; 15n. *Rhododendron barbatum* . . . .   4·00   4·00
No. **MS**1718 was issued with a central label inscribed "RHODODENDRONS Our Nations wealth" in gold.

207 Kapok Tree (*Bombax ceiba*)

208 Fireman and Flags

(Des B. Tamang. Litho Secura, Singapore)

2002 (2 June). *Medicinal Plants. T 207 and similar vert designs. Multicoloured.* P 13.
1719	10n. Type **207**	25	25
1720	10n. Angel's trumpet (*Brugmansia suaveolens*)	25	25
1721	10n. Himalayan mayapple (*Podophyllum hexandrum*)	25	25
1722	10n. Himalayan pokeberry (*Photlacca acinosa*)	25	25
1719/1722 Set of 4	90	90
MS1723 85 × 106 mm. 10n. × 4,
Nos. 1719/22 . . . .   1·20   1·20

2002 (16 Sept). *"United We Stand". Litho.* P 14.
| 1724 | **208** | 25n. multicoloured . . . . . . | 60 | 60 |
No. 1724 was issued in sheetlets of four stamps.

209 Zinedine Zidane

210 Queen Elizabeth

2002 (16 Sept). *World Cup Football Championship, Japan and South Korea. Two sheets containing T* **209** *and similar vert designs. Multicoloured. Litho.* P. 14.
MS1725 (a) 167 × 118 mm. 25n. Type **209**; 25n. Michael Owen; 25n. Miyagi stadium, Japan; 25n. Cuauhtemoc Blanco (inscr "Cuahutemoc"); 25n. Gabriel Batistuta; 25n. Incheon stadium, South Korea; (b) 97 × 112 mm. 150n. Roberto Carlos . . . . . 7·00   7·00

2002 (16 Sept). *Golden Jubilee of Queen Elizabeth II. Two sheets containing T* **210** *and similar square designs. Multicoloured. Litho.* P 14½.
MS1726 (a) 133 × 101 mm. 40n. Type **210**; 40n. Wearing green floral hat; 40n. With Duke of Edinburgh; 40n. Wearing white hat; (b) 79 × 108 mm. 90n. Wearing tiara . . . . . . 6·00   6·00

211 Ski Jumping   **212** Lotus Flower

(Litho Questa)

2002 (16 Sept). *Winter Olympic Games, Salt Lake City, USA. Sheet 89 × 120 mm containing T* **211** *and similar vert design. Multicoloured.* P 14.
MS1727 50n. Type **211**; 50n. Cross country skiing . . . . 2·40   2·40

2002 (14 Oct). *United Nations Year of Eco-Tourism. Two sheets containing T* **212** *and similar vert designs. Multicoloured. Litho.* P 14.
MS1728 (a) 117 × 75 mm. 50n. Type **212**; 50n. Northern Jungle queen butterfly; 50n. Bengal Tiger; (b) 72 × 95 mm. 90n. Peacock . . . . 5·75   5·75

213 Cub Scout   **214** Charles Lindbergh and The Spirit of St Louis

2002 (14 Oct). *World Scout Jamboree, Thailand. Two sheets containing T* **213** *and similar multicoloured designs. Litho.* P 14.
MS1729 (a) 182 × 142 mm. 50n. Type **213**; 50n. Scouts of different nationalities; 50n. 1908 Scout; (b) 90 × 120 mm. 90n. Dan Beard (founder of American Boy Scouts) (*vert*) . . . 5·75   5·75

2002 (14 Oct). *75th Anniv of First Solo Trans-Atlantic Flight. Two sheets containing T* **214** *and similar vert designs. Multicoloured. Litho.* P 14.
MS1730 (a) 171 × 134 mm. 75n. Type **214**; 75n. Lindbergh; (b) 123 × 89 mm. 90n. Lindbergh (*different*) . . . . 5·75   5·75

215 Guar

(Des Dayna Elefant. Litho Questa)

2002 (16 Dec)–3 Feb **2003** *Flora and Fauna. Twelve sheets containing T* **215** *and similar horiz designs. Multicoloured.* P 14.
MS1731 (a) 132 × 155 mm. 25n. Type **215**; 25n. Hog Badger; 25n. Indian Cobra; 25n. Leopard Gecko; 25n. Gavial; 25n. Hispid Hare (3.2.03); (b) 132 × 155 mm. 25n. Yellow-legged Gull; 25n. Sand Martin; 25n. Asian Open-bill Stork; 25n. White Stork; 25n. Eurasian Oystercatcher; 25n. Indian Pitta (3.2.03); (c) 132 × 155 mm. 25n. Blue Oak-leaf butterfly (inscr "Dead leaf butterfly") (*Kalima horsfieldi*); 25n. Golden Birdwing (*Troides aeacus*); 25n. *Atrophaneura latrellei*; 25n. Kaiser-I-Hind (*Teinopalpus imperialis*); 25n. *Zeuxidia aurelius*; 25n. *Euploea dufresne* (3.2.03); (d) 137 × 158 mm. 25n. *Primula cawdoriana*; 25n. *Meconopsis aculeata*; 25n. *Primula wigramiana*; 25n. *Primula stuartii*; 25n. *Saxifraga andersonii*; 25n. *Rheum nobile*; (e) 133 × 153 mm. 25n. *Russula integra*; 25n. *Hydrophorus marzuolus*; 25n. *Trichloma fulvum*; 25n. *Hypholoma fasciculare*; 25n. *Tricholoma populinum*; 25n. *Cortinarius orellanus*; (f) 136 × 161 mm. 25n. *Coelogyne rhodeana*; 25n. *Coelogyne virescens*; 25n. *Phalanopsis schilleriana*; 25n. *Angraecum eburneum*; 25n. *Dendrobium aureum*; 25n. *Dendrobium ceasar*; (g) 89 × 92 mm. 90n. Esturine Crocodile; (h) 89 × 94 mm. 90n. Mandarin Duck; (i) 93 × 94 mm. 90n. *Portia philota*; (j) 103 × 93 mm. 90n. *Paris polyphylla*; (k) 101 × 101 mm. 90n. *Clathrus archeri*; (l) 99 × 100 mm. 90n. *Dendrobium chrysotoxum* . . . . 35·00   35·00

APPENDIX

The following stamps were either issued in excess of postal needs or were not available to the public in reasonable quantities at face value. Some values from several sets were placed on sale in Bhutan at the time of issue but many examples which were subsequently postally used were purchased outside Bhutan and re-imported, although small quantities could still be obtained from the Post Office. Miniature sheets and imperforate stamps are excluded from this section

1968

Bhutan Pheasants 1, 2, 4, 8, 15ch.., 2, 4, 5, 7, 9n.

Winter Olympic Games, Grenoble, Optd on 1966 *Abominable Snowmen issue.* 40ch., 1n.25, 3, 6n.

Butterflies (plastic-surfaced). Postage 15, 50ch., 1n.25, 2n.; *Air* 3, 4, 5, 6n.

Paintings (relief-printed). Postage 2, 4, 5, 10, 45, 80ch., 1n.05, 1n.40, 2, 3, 4, 5n.; *Air* 1n.50, 2n.50, 6, 8n.

Olympic Games, Mexico. 5, 45, 60, 80ch., 1n.05, 2, 3, 5n.

Human Rights Year. Die-stamped surch on unissued "Coins". 15ch. on 50n.p., 33ch. on 1r., 9n. on 3r.75

Flood Relief. Surch on 1968 *Mexico Olympics issue.* 5ch.+5ch., 80ch.+25ch., 2n.+50ch.

1969

Fish (plastic-surfaced). Postage 15, 20, 30ch.; *Air* 5, 6, 7n.

Insects (plastic-surfaced). Postage 10, 75ch., 1n.25, 2n.; *Air* 3, 4, 5, 6n.

Admission of Bhutan to Universal Postal Union. 5, 10, 15, 45, 60ch., 1n.05, 1n.40, 4n.

5000 Years of Steel Industry. On steel foil. Postage 2, 5, 15, 45, 75ch., 1n.50, 1n.75, 2n.; *Air* 3, 4, 5, 6n.

Birds (plastic-surfaced). Postage 15, 50ch., 1n.25, 2n.; *Air* 3, 4, 5, 6n.

Buddhist Prayer Banners. On silk rayon. 15, 75ch., 2, 5, 6n.

Moon Landing of "Apollo 11" (plastic-surfaced). Postage 3, 5, 15, 20, 25, 45, 50ch., 1n.75; *Air* 3, 4, 5, 6n.

1970

Famous Paintings (plastic-surfaced). Postage 5, 10, 15ch., 2n.75; *Air* 3, 4, 5, 6n.

New U.P.U. headquarters Building, Berne. 3, 10, 20ch., 2n.50.

Flower Paintings (relief-printed). Postage 2, 3, 5, 10, 15, 75ch., 1n., 1n.40,; *Air* 80, 90ch., 1n.10, 1n.40, 1n.60, 1n.70, 3n., 3n.50.

Animals (plastic-surfaced). Postage 5, 10, 20, 25, 30, 40, 65, 75, 85ch.; *Air* 2, 3, 4, 5n.

Conquest of Space (plastic-surfaced). Postage 2, 5, 15, 25, 30, 50, 75ch. 1n.50; *Air* 2, 3, 6, 7n.

1971

History of Sculpture (plastic-moulded). Postage 10, 75ch. 1n.25, 2n.; *Air* 3, 4, 5, 6n.

Moon Vehicles (plastic-surfaced). Postage 10ch., 1n.70; *Air* 2n.50, 4n.

History of the Motor Car (plastic-surfaced). Postage 2, 5, 10, 15, 20, 30, 60, 75, 85ch., 1n., 1n.20, 1n.55, 1n.80, 2n., 2n.50; *Air* 4, 6, 7, 9, 10n.

Bhutan's Admission to United Nations. Postage 5, 10, 20ch., 3n.; *Air* 2n.50, 5, 6n.

60th Anniv of Boy Scout Movement. 10, 20, 50, 75ch., 2, 6n.

World Refugee Year. Optd on 1971 *United Nations issue. Postage* 5, 10, 20ch., 3n.; *Air* 2n.50, 5, 6n.

1972

Famous Paintings (relief-printed). Postage 15, 20, 90ch., 2n.50; *Air* 1n.70, 4n.60, 5n.40, 6n.

Famous Men (plastic-moulded). Postage 10, 15 , 55ch., *Air* 2, 6, 8n.

Olympic Games, Munich. Postage 10, 15, 20, 30, 45ch., *Air* 35ch., 1n.35, 7n.

Space Flight "Apollo 16" (plastic-surfaced). Postage 15, 20, 90ch., 2n.50; *Air* 1n.70, 4n.60, 5n.40, 6n.

1973

Dogs. 2, 3, 15, 20, 30, 99ch., 2n.50, 4n.

Roses (on scent-impregnated paper). Postage 15, 25 30ch., 3n.; *Air* 6, 7n.

Moon Landing of "Apollo 17" (plastic-surfaced). Postage 10, 15, 55ch., 2n.; *Air* 7, 9n.

"Talking Stamps" (miniature records). Postage 10, 25ch., 1n.25, 7, 8n.; *Air* 3, 9n.

Death of King Jigme Dorji Wangchuk. Embossed on gold foil. Postage 10, 25ch., 3n.; *Air* 6, 8n.

Mushrooms. 15, 25, 30ch., 3, 6, 7n.

"Indipex 73" Stamp Exhibition, New Delhi. Postage 5, 10, 15, 25ch., 1n.25, 3n.; *Air* 5, 6n.

Cambodia

1951. 100 Cents = 1 Piastre
1955. 100 Cents = 1 Riel

The land of the Khmer people, called Kambuja in its Indianized form, was originally in the middle Mekong valley. About the year 627 the Khmers conquered the country of Funan to the south, and founded a kingdom, where the temple of Angkor Vat was later built. This kingdom reached the height of its power and civilisation late in the 14th century, before Siamese invasions caused the abandonment of Angkor in 1432. Continual wars with Siam led to a long decline until in 1847 Cambodia accepted the suzerainty both of Siam and Annam.

On 11 August 1863 Cambodia was forced to become a French protectorate, which became part of the Union of Indo-China in 1887 (see Part 6 (*France*) of this catalogue).

In 1941–45 Cambodia was occupied by Japanese forces and on 12 March 1945 King Norodom Sihanouk proclaimed its independence. After the surrender of Japan, French rule was restored. On 8 November 1949 Cambodia became an Associated State of the French Union, and sovereign independence was attained on 9 November 1953 with the transfer of military powers. It left the French Union on 25 September 1955.

INTERNATIONAL COMMISSION. Overprinted Indian stamps were used from field post offices in Cambodia from 1954 to 1958. For details see under INTERNATIONAL COMMISSION IN INDO-CHINA.

PRINTERS. All the stamps of Cambodia (to 1970) and of the Khmer Republic were printed at the Government Printing Works, Paris, *unless otherwise stated*.

IMPERFORATE STAMPS. Many stamps exist imperforate in their issued colours, but these were not valid for postage. Imperforate stamps in other colours are colour trials.

CAMBODIA

KINGDOM

King Norodom Sihanouk

25 April 1941–2 March 1955

1 "Apsara" or
Dancing Nymph

3 King Norodom
Sihanouk

2 Throne Room, Phnom Penh

1951 (3 Nov)–**52**. *Recess.* P 13.

1	1	10c. blue-green and deep blue-green (1.2.52)	50	3·50
2		20c. chestnut and lake (1.2.52)	45	1·50
3		30c. indigo and reddish violet (1.2.52)	55	60
4		40c. turquoise-blue & ultram (1.2.52)	1·10	90
5	2	50c. dull green & deep blue-grn (1.2.52)	95	85
6	3	80c. blue-green and indigo (1.2.52)	1·70	4·25
7	2	1p. reddish violet and indigo (1.2.52)	1·30	45
8	3	1p.10 vermilion and lake (1.2.52)	2·10	4·25
9	1	1p.50 carmine and lake	2·00	1·40
10	2	1p.50 deep blue and indigo (1.2.52)	2·10	2·30
11	3	1p.50 purple-brown & choc (1.2.52)	2·10	1·80
12		1p.90 blue and indigo (1.2.52)	3·75	6·00
13	2	2p. chestnut and lake (1.2.52)	2·75	75
14	3	3p. chestnut and lake (1.2.52)	4·25	2·30
15	1	5p. reddish violet and indigo (1.2.52)	12·50	5·75
16	2	10p. indigo and reddish violet (1.2.52)	13·50	10·50
17	3	15p. reddish violet & dp violet (1.2.52)	28·00	45·00
1/17		Set of 17	70·00	38·00

MS17*a* Three sheets each 130 × 90 mm.
Nos. 15/17 (1.2.52) *Price for three sheets* £120 £100
No **MS**17*a* was issued in a souvenir cover. Price quoted is for the complete "booklet".

+40ᶜ
AIDE A L'ÉTUDIANT
(4)

5 "Kinnari"

1952 (20 Oct). *Students' Aid Fund. Nos. 8, 12, 14 and 15, surch as T **4**.*

18	3	1p.10+40c. vermilion and lake	3·50	13·00
19		1p.90+60c. blue and indigo	3·50	13·00
20		3p.+1p. chestnut and lake	3·50	13·00
21	1	5p.+2p. reddish violet and indigo	3·75	13·00
18/21		Set of 4	13·00	47·00

1953 (16 Apr–1 Oct). *AIR. Recess.* P 13.

22	5	50c. green	1·10	2·10
23		3p. brown-lake (1.7)	2·00	1·80
24		3p.30 reddish violet	2·50	5·25
25		4p. blue and black-brown (1.7)	2·75	1·20
26		5p.10 ochre, red and brown	4·00	6·75
27		6p.50 brt purple & black-brown (1.7)	3·75	8·75
28		9p. emerald and magenta (1.7)	5·00	13·00
29		11p.50 orange, red, magenta, emerald and black (1.7)	9·75	18·00
30		30p. ochre, brown and deep blue-green	16·00	26·00
22/30		Set of 9	42·00	75·00

MS30*a* Three sheets each 129 × 100 mm.
Nos. 22, 24, 26 and 30 (sold at 50p.);
Nos. 23, 25 and 29 (sold at 25p.); Nos. 27/8
(sold at 20p.). (1.10.53). *Price for three sheets* £180 £160

6 Arms of Cambodia   **7** "Postal Transport"

1954 (24 Sept)–**55**. *Inscr* "ROYAUME DE CAMBODGE". *Recess.*
P 13.

31	–	10c. carmine-red	1·20	1·80
32	–	20c. deep green	1·40	50
33	–	30c. indigo	1·40	2·10
34	–	40c. deep violet	1·40	85
35	–	50c. brown-purple	1·40	25
36	–	70c. chocolate (10.12.54)	1·60	3·25
37	–	1p. red-violet (10.12.54)	1·70	1·80
38	–	1p.50 red (10.12.54)	1·70	60
39	6	2p. red (30.10.54)	1·30	45
40		2p.50 deep green (30.10.54)	1·60	60
41	7	2p.50 green (9.11.54)	2·50	2·10
42	6	3p. deep bright blue (30.10 54)	2·10	1·70
43	7	4p. black-brown (9.11.54)	3·25	2·75
44	6	4p.50 deep violet (30.10.54)	2·75	1·80
45	7	5p. rose-red (9.11.54)	3·50	2·50
46	6	6p. chocolate (30.10.54)	3·00	2·50
47	7	10p. deep violet (9.11.54)	4·00	2·75
48		15p. blue (9.11.54)	5·00	5·00
49	–	20p. ultramarine (10.12.54)	11·50	5·75
50	–	30p. blue-green (10.12.54)	18·00	9·75
31/50 *Set of 20*			60·00	41·00

MS50*a* Three sheets each 120 × 120 mm.
Nos. 31/5 (sold at 2p.); Nos. 39/40, 42, 44
and 46 (sold at 20p.); Nos. 41, 43, 45 and
47/8 (sold at 40p.) and one sheet
160 × 92 mm containing Nos. 36/8 and 49/50
(sold at 60p.). (13.4.55). *Price for four
sheets* £150   £140
Designs: *Vert*—10 to 50c. View of Phnom Daun Penh. *Horiz*—
70c., 1p., 1p.50, 20, 30p. East Gate, Temple of Angkor.

King Norodom Suramarit

2 March 1955–3 April 1960

King Norodom Sihanouk abdicated in favour of his father, but
continued in power as president of the Council of Ministers

8 King Norodom   **9** King and Queen of
   Suramarit   Cambodia

1955 (24 Nov). *New Currency. T* **8** *and similar portrait. Recess.*
P 14 × 13.

51	–	50c. indigo	25	20
52	8	50c. violet	35	30
53		1r. carmine-red	40	30
54		2r. deep blue	70	45
55	–	2r.50 chocolate	1·00	35
56		4r. slate-green	1·40	45
57	–	6r. carmine-lake	1·90	1·20
58	8	7r. blackish brown	2·30	1·40
59	–	15r. deep lilac	3·25	1·20
60	8	20r. deep bluish green	4·75	4·25
51/60 *Set of 10*			15·00	9·25

Portrait: *Vert*—50c., 2r.50, 4r., 6r., 15r. Queen Kossamak.
For stamps as Nos. 58 and 60, but with black border, see
Nos. 101/2.

1955 (24 Nov). *Coronation (1st issue). Recess.* P 13.

61	9	1r.50 sepia and blackish brown	75	45
62		2r. black and indigo	75	55
63		3r. scarlet and brown-orange	95	30
64		5r. black and slate-green	1·50	55
65		10r. brown-purple and violet	2·50	55
61/65 *Set of 5*			5·75	2·20

10 King Norodom   **11** Prince   **12**
   Suramarit   Sihanouk, Flags
              and Globe

1956 (3 Mar). *Coronation (2nd issue). T* **10** *and similar vert design.
Recess.* P 13.

66	10	2r. red	1·10	2·30
67	–	3r. deep blue	1·60	3·25
68	–	5r. yellow-green	2·40	4·50
69	10	10r. deep myrtle-green	6·25	9·25
70		30r. deep violet	13·00	22·00
71	–	50r. bright reddish purple	25·00	25·00
66/71 *Set of 6*			45·00	60·00

Portraits:—3r., 5r., 50r. Queen of Cambodia.

(Des L. Sinh. Eng A. Frères. Recess)

1957 (1 Mar). *First Anniv of Admission of Cambodia into United
Nations Organization.* P 13.

72	11	2r. red, deep blue and blue-green	1·20	90
73		4r.50 ultramarine	1·20	90
74		8r.50 carmine-red	1·20	90

(Des and eng L. Sinh. Recess)

1957 (15 Mar–May). *2,500th Anniv of Buddhism.* P 13.

(a) With premiums (15 March).

75	12	1r.50+50c. bistre, red and deep blue	1·40	1·80
76		6r.50+1r.50 bistre, red & bright purple	2·10	2·75
77		8r.+2r. bistre, red and blue	3·50	4·50

(b) Colours changed and premiums omitted (12 May).

78	12	1r.50 red	1·30	1·00
79		6r.50 blue-violet	1·50	1·20
80		8r. deep bluish green	1·50	1·50
75/80 *Set of 6*			10·00	11·50

D 13   **13** Mythological Bird

1957 (3 May). *POSTAGE DUE. Typo.* P 13½ × 14.

D81	D 13	10c. red, pale blue and black	20	20
D82		50c. red, pale blue and black	55	45
D83		1r. red, pale blue and black	85	75
D84		3r. red, pale blue and black	1·10	90
D85		5r. red, pale blue and black	1·80	1·60
D81/85 *Set of 5*			4·00	3·50

1957 (11 Dec)–**58**. *AIR. Recess.* P 13.

81	13	50c. brown-red	35	10
82		1r. emerald	60	10
83		4r. ultramarine	1·80	45

84		50r. carmine		7·50	2·75
85		100r. red, deep green and blue		13·00	5·00
81/85 *Set of 5*				21·00	7·50

MS85a 160 × 92 mm. Nos. 81/5 (sold at 160r.)
(3.3.58) . . . . 13·00 28·00

14 King Ang Duong

15 King Norodom I

(Des and eng L. Sinh. Recess)

1958 (4 Mar)—**59**. *King Ang Duong Commemoration*. P 13.

86	**14**	1r.50 brown and reddish violet		55	45
87		5r. bistre and black		70	65
88		10r. sepia and brown-purple		1·40	90

MS88a 156 × 92 mm. Nos. 86/8 (sold at 25r.)
(31.1.59) . . . . 6·00 5·00

(Des L. Sinh. Eng C. Mazelin. Recess)

1958 (3 Nov)—**59**. *King Norodom I Commemoration*. P 12½ × 13.

89	**15**	2r. olive-brown and ultramarine		60	35
90		6r. deep bronze-green & yellow-			
		orge		85	55
91		15r. deep olive-brown and green		1·70	1·10

MS91a 156 × 92 mm. Nos. 89/91 (sold at 32r.)
(31.1 59) . . . . 6·00 4·50

16 Children

(17)

(Recess Govt Ptg Bureau, Tokyo)

1959 (9 Dec). *Children's World Friendship*. P 13.

92	**16**	20c. purple		25	35
93		50c. Prussian blue		45	45
94		80c. carmine-lake		90	85

1959 (9 Dec). *Red Cross Fund. Nos. 92/4 surch as Type 17 in red.*

95	**16**	20c.+20c. purple		30	45
96		50c.+30c. Prussian blue		65	65
97		80c.+50c. carmine-lake		1·30	1·20

18 Prince Sihanouk, Plan of
Port and Freighter

(18a
"20r.")

19 Sacred Plough in
Procession

1960 (2 Apr). *Inauguration of Sihanoukville Port. Recess.*
P 13 × 12½.

98	**18**	2r. sepia and rose-red (6.4)		55	55
		a. Type **18a**		1·70	1·70
99		5r. chocolate and blue (6.4)		55	65
		a. Type **18a**		2·50	2·50
100		20r. blue and reddish violet		2·00	2·00

Several thousand copies of Nos. 98a and 99a (with incorrect
Cambodian figures of value in the lower left-hand corner) were
sold, prior to the receipt of corrected supplies.

1960 (30 Apr). *King Norodom Suramarit Mourning issue. Nos. 58
and 60 reissued with black border.*

101	**8**	7r. blackish brown and black		3·00	4·25
102		20r. deep bluish green and black		3·00	4·25

(Des and eng L. Sinh. Recess Govt Ptg Bureau. Tokyo)

1960 (14 May). *Festival of the Sacred Furrow.* P 12.

103	**19**	1r. reddish purple		60	45
104		2r. sepia		75	65
105		3r. deep turquoise-green		1·20	90

Prince Norodom Sihanouk, Chief of State
14 June 1960–18 March 1970

On the death of his father, Prince Norodom Sihanouk refused
to resume the crown, but ruled as Chief of State. His mother,
Queen Kossamak, symbolised the throne.

20 Child and Book
("Education")

21 Flag and Dove
of Peace

1960 (1 Sept–5 Dec). *"Works of the Five-Year Plan". T **20** and
similar designs. Recess.* P 13.

106		2r. red-brown, blue and deep green		50	30
107		3r. deep green and chocolate		65	35
108		4r. violet, blue-green and rose		65	45
109		6r. red-brown, red-orange & deep			
		green		75	55
110		10r. ultramarine, blue-green and bistre		1·80	1·10
111		25r. red and lake		3·75	2·20
106/111 *Set of 6*				7·25	4·50

MS111a Two sheets each 150 × 100 mm.
Nos. 106, 109 and 111 (sold at 42r.);
Nos. 107/8 and 110 (sold at 23r.) (5.12).
Price for two sheets . . . . 5·25 6·50
Designs: *Horiz*—3r. Chhouksar Barrage ("Irrigation"); 6r.
Carpenter and huts ("Construction"); 10r. Rice-field
("Agriculture"). *Vert*—4r. Industrial scene and books ("National
balance-sheet"); 25r. Anointing children ("Child welfare").

1960 (24 Dec)—**61**. *Peace. Recess.* P 13.

112	**21**	1r.50 red, blue, blue-grn &			
		chocolate		30	45
113		5r. red, blue and orange-red		45	65
114		7r. red, blue and blue-green		60	90

MS114a 147 × 93 mm. Nos. 112/14 (sold at
16r.) (16.3.61) . . . . 20·00 11·00
MS114b as **MS**114a but stamps in new colours
(sold at 20r.) (16.3.61) . . . . 4·00 11·00

23 Jasmine   **24** "Rama" (from temple door, Baphoun)

27 Power Station (Czech Aid)   **28** Campaign Emblem

(Eng J. Pheulpin. Recess)

1961 (1 July). *Cambodian Flowers. T* **23** *and similar vert designs.*
P 13.
115	2r. yellow, green and magenta	. . .	50	55
116	5r. magenta, green and bright blue	. .	80	1·10
117	10r. rose-red, green and violet-blue	. .	2·30	2·00
MS117a	130 × 100 mm. Nos. 115/17 (sold at 20r.)	. . . . . .	7·00	7·00

Flowers:—5r. Lavender; 10r. Rose lily.

1961 (1 Nov)–**63**. *Cambodian Soldiers Commemoration. Typo.*
P 14 × 13½.
118	**24**	1r. bright mauve	50	20
118a		2r. new blue (1.7.63)	1·90	1·80
119		3r. emerald	85	30
120		6r. orange	1·00	45
118/120 Set of 4		. . . . . .	3·75	2·50
MS120a	150 × 85 mm. Nos. 118, 119/20 (sold at 12r.)	. . . .	3·25	3·25

25 Prince Norodom Sihanouk and Independence Monument

VIe CONFERENCE MONDIALE BOUDDHIQUE
12 - 11 - 1961
(26)

(Eng C. Mazelin. Recess)

1961 (9 Nov). *Independence Monument.* P 13 × 12½.

(a) POSTAGE.
121	**25**	2r. green	80	35
122		4r. deep sepia	80	45

(b) AIR.
123	**25**	7r. chestnut, bright purple, deep bluish green and sepia	75	75
124		30r. rose-carmine, bright blue & green	2·30	2·30
125		50r. deep violet-black, bluish green, yellow-green and brown	3·50	3·75
121/125 Set of 5		. . . . . .	7·25	6·75
MS125a	Two sheets each 150 × 85 mm. Nos. 121/2 (sold at 10r.); Nos. 123/5 (sold at 100r.). *Price for two sheets*	15·00	11·00

1961 (12 Nov). *Sixth World Buddhist Conference. Nos. 40, 44 optd with T* **26** *in red.*
126	**6**	2p.50 (2r.50) deep green	90	55
127		4p.50 (4r.50) deep violet	1·40	85

1962 (1 Feb). *Foreign Aid Programme. T* **27** *and similar horiz designs. Recess.* P 13.
128	2r. carmine-lake and orange-red	. . .	30	20
129	3r. orange-brown, blue-green and blue	. .	35	20
130	4r. orange-brown, carm-lake & greenish bl	. . .	35	30
131	5r. bright purple and blue-green	. .	55	35
132	6r. orange-brown and blue	. .	1·00	35
128/132 Set of 5			2·25	1·25
MS132a	150 × 85 mm. Nos. 128/32 (sold at 25r.)	. . .	7·50	5·00

Designs:—3r. Motorway (American Aid); 4r. Textile factory (Chinese Aid); 5r. Friendship Hospital, Khmero (Soviet Aid); 6r. Phnom Penh Airport (French Aid).

(Eng J. Combet. Recess)

1962 (7 Apr). *Malaria Eradication.* P 13.
133	**28**	2r. bright purple and red-brown	. . .	35	30
134		4r. deep bluish green and chocolate	. .	40	35
135		6r. violet and bistre	. .	35	45

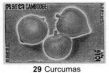   **0$50**

29 Curcumas   **(30)**

(Eng C. Durrens. Recess)

1962 (4 June). *Cambodian Fruits (1st issue). T* **29** *and similar horiz designs.* P 13.
136	2r. yellow-orange and olive-brown	. .	45	45
137	4r. blackish olive and deep turquoise	. .	65	55
138	6r. carmine-lake, green and blue	. .	75	85
MS138a	150 × 85 mm. Nos. 136/8 (sold at 15r.)	. . .	6·00	3·75

Designs:—4r. Lychees; 6r. Mangosteens.

(Eng C. Haley (2r., 5r.); P. Béquet (9r.). Recess)

1962 (3 Sept). *Cambodian Fruits, etc. (2nd issue). Designs as T* **29** *but vert.* P 13.
139	2r. yellow-brown and deep blue-green	. .	75	35
140	5r. green and brown	. . .	1·10	55
141	9r. brown and deep blue-green	. .	1·30	75

Designs:—2r. Pineapples; 5r. Sugar-cane; 9r. "Bread" trees.

1962 (6 Nov). *No. 94 surch with T* **30**.
142	**16**	50c. on 80c. carmine-lake	. . .	55	35

INAUGURATION DU MONUMENT
(31)

32 Campaign Emblem, Corn and Maize

1962 (9 Nov). *Inauguration of Independence Monument. Optd with T 31 in black, and surch with new value in red.*

(a) POSTAGE.

143	25	3r. on 2r. green (No. 121)		55	35

(b) AIR.

144	25	12r. on 7r. (No. 123)		1·50	1·00

1963 (21 Mar). *Freedom from Hunger. Recess.* P 13.

145	32	3r. chestnut, yellow-brown & lt blue	50	45
146		6r. chestnut, yellow-brown & ultram	50	45

33 Temple, Preah Vihear

= (34) **=**

3^f

(Des and eng G. Bétemps. Recess)

1963 (15 June). *Reunification of Preah Vihear Temple with Cambodia.* P 12½ × 13.

147	33	3r. brown, purple & dp bluish green	40	35
148		6r. bronze-green, orange and turquoise-blue	70	55
149		15r. chocolate, blue and green	1·10	90

1963 (1 July). *No. 55 surch with T 34.*

150	3r. on 2r.50 chocolate	75	45

1863 1963

CENTENAIRE
DE LA
CROIX-ROUGE

35 Kep sur Mer

+ 0.40

(36)

(Photo Delrieu)

1963 (1 Aug). *Cambodian Resorts. Multicoloured.* P 12½ × 12 (20r.) or 12 × 12½ (others).

151	3r. Koh Tonsay (vert)	40	30
152	7r. Popokvil (waterfall) (vert)	65	35
153	20r. Type 35	2·10	90

1963 (1 Oct). *Red Cross Centenary. Malaria Eradication stamps surch as T 36, in red.*

154	28	4r.+40c. dp bluish green & chocolate	65	75
155		6r.+60c. violet and bistre	1·00	1·10

37 Scales of Justice

38 Kouprey

1963 (10 Dec). *15th Anniv of Declaration of Human Rights. Recess.* P 13.

156	37	1r. green, crimson and ultramarine	40	45
157		3r. crimson, ultramarine and green	70	55
158		12r. ultramarine, green and crimson	1·30	1·30

1964 (2 Mar). *Wild Animal Protection. Recess.* P 13.

159	38	50c. brown, emerald-green & orge-brn	85	35
160		3r. brown, orange-brown & yell-grn	1·20	55
161		6r. brown, blue and green	1·80	1·10

39 Black-billed Magpie

40 "Hanuman"

12^f

JEUX
OLYMPIQUES
TOKYO-1964

(41)

(Des and eng G. Aufschneider (12r.), R. Cottet (others). Recess)

1964 (2 May). *Birds. T 39 and similar vert designs.* P 13.

162		3r. blue, yellow-green and indigo	1·10	65
163		6r. orange, maroon and slate-blue	1·80	1·00
164		12r. turquoise-green and purple-brown	3·25	2·00

Birds:—6r. River kingfisher; 12r. Grey heron.

(Eng C. Durrens. Recess)

1964 (1 Sept). *AIR.* P 13.

165	40	5r. magenta, sepia and blue	65	45
166		10r. bistre, magenta and deep green	1·00	55
167		20r. bistre, reddish violet and blue	1·70	1·10
168		40r. bistre, deep turquoise-blue and lake	3·75	2·00
169		80r. orange, green and reddish purple	6·00	5·00
165/169		Set of 5	12·00	8·25

1964 (10 Oct). *AIR. Olympic Games, Tokyo. Nos. 165/8 surch as T 41, in red.*

170	40	3r.on 5r. magenta, sepia and blue	60	35
171		6r.on 10r. bistre, magenta & dp green	1·00	55
172		9r.on 20r. bistre, reddish violet & blue	1·10	90
173		12r.on 40r. bistre, dp turquoise-bl & lake	2·30	1·40
170/173		Set of 4	4·50	2·75

42 Airline Emblem

43 Prince Norodom Sihanouk

(Des and eng R. Fenneteaux. Recess)

1964 (15 Oct). *Eighth Anniv of Royal Air Cambodia.* P 13 × 12½.
174	**42**	1r.50 red and deep reddish violet	25	20
175		3r. vermilion and deep blue	45	30
176		7r.50 carmine and ultramarine	90	45

(Des and eng J. Piel. Recess)

1964 (31 Oct). *10th Anniv of Foundation of Sangkum (Popular Socialist Community).* P 12½ × 13.
177	**43**	2r. deep reddish violet	45	30
178		3r. red-brown	60	35
179		10r. deep blue	1·20	75

CONFERENCE DES PEUPLES INDOCHINOIS

44 Weaving

(45)

1965 (1 Feb). *Native Handicrafts.* T **44** and similar horiz designs. Recess. P 13.
180	1r. violet, red-brown and yellow-bistre	30	30
181	3r. yellow-brown, light bronze-green and bright purple	55	35
182	5r. carmine, brown-purple and green	85	75

Designs:—3r. Engraving; 5r. Basket-making.

1965 (1 Mar). *Indo-Chinese People's Conference.* Nos. 178/9 optd with T **45**.
183	**43**	3r. red-brown	45	45
184		10r. deep blue (R.)	70	65

In 1965 a set of three values commemorating International Co-operation Year, showing clasped hands, were prepared but not issued.

46 I.T.U. Emblem and Symbols

47 Cotton

1965 (17 May). *Centenary of International Telecommunications Union.* Recess. P 13.
185	**46**	3r. bistre and bluish green	35	35
186		4r. blue and vermilion	45	55
187		10r. bright purple and bluish violet	75	75

1965 (2 Aug). *Industrial Plants.* T **47** and similar vert designs. Multicoloured. Recess. P 12½ × 13.
188		1r.50 Type **47**	45	30
189		3r. Groundnuts	70	35
190		7r.50 Coconut palms	1·10	75

48 Preah Ko

(Des and eng J. Pheulpin (3r.), C. Hertenberger (5r.), J. Gauthier (7r.), M. Monvoisin (9r.), C. Mazelin (12r.). Recess)

1966 (1 Feb). *Cambodian Temples.* T **48** and similar horiz designs. P 13.
191		3r. bronze-green, bluish green & orge-brn	75	45
192		5r. purple-brown, bluish green & bt pur	95	55
193		7r. purple-brown, bronze-green & ochre	1·30	65
194		9r. plum, myrtle-green and violet-blue	2·20	90
195		12r. rose-carmine, myrtle-green & verm	2·75	1·60
191/195		*Set of 5*	7·00	3·75

Temples:—5r, Baksei Chamkrong; 7r. Banteay Srei; 9r. Angkor Vat; 12r. Bayon.

49 W.H.O. Building

50 Tree-planting

(Photo So.Ge.Im)

1966 (1 July). *Inauguration of World Health Organization Headquarters, Geneva.* P 12½ × 13.
196	**49**	2r. black, yellow, blue and pale pink	30	20
197		3r. black, yellow, blue & lt yellow-grn	35	30
198		5r. black, yellow, blue and light blue	60	45

1966 (22 July). *Tree Day.* Recess. P 12½ × 13.
199	**50**	1r. bistre-brown, blue-green & brown	25	30
200		3r. bistre-brown, blue-green & orange	40	35
201		7r. bistre-brown, blue-green & ol-grey	70	45

51 U.N.E.S.C.O. Emblem

52 Stadium

(Photo So.Ge.Im)

1966 (4 Nov). *20th Anniv of United Nations Children's Fund.* P 13.
202	**51**	3r. multicoloured		35	30
203		7r. multicoloured		45	55

(Des and eng C. Bétemps. Recess)

1966 (25 Nov). *"Ganefo" Games, Phnom Penh.* T **52** *and similar horiz designs.* P 13 × 12½.
204	3r. royal blue		15	20
205	4r. bottle green		20	35
206	7r. crimson		30	55
207	10r. chocolate		40	75
204/207 *Set of* 4			95	1·60

Designs:—4, 7, 10r. Various bas-reliefs of ancient sports from Angkor Vat.

53 Wild Boar

MILLENAIRE DE BANTEAY SREI 967-1967

(55)

ANNEE INTERNATIONALE DU TOURISME 1967

(54)

1967 (20 Feb). *Fauna.* T **53** *and similar designs. Recess.* P 12½ × 13 (5r.) or 13 × 12½ (others).
208	3r. black, yellow-green and new blue		70	45
209	5r. brown, yellow-green, blackish green and new blue		80	75
210	7r. black, new blue, red-orange & dp brn		1·30	1·10

Fauna: *Vert*—5r. Hog-deer. *Horiz*—7r. Indian elephant.

1967 (27 Apr). *International Tourist Year. Nos. 191/2, 194/5 and 149 variously optd as* T **54** *in red.*
211	3r. bronze-green, bluish green & orge-brn		65	45
212	5r. purple-brown, bluish green & bt pur		75	45
213	9r. plum, myrtle-green and violet-blue		1·10	75
214	12r. rose-carmine, myrtle-green & verm		1·30	90
215	15r. chocolate, blue and green		1·60	1·10
211/215 *Set of* 5			4·75	3·25

The overprint on the 5 and 15r. is in four lines, on the 12r. in three lines and on the 9r. in two lines but differently arranged from Type **54**.

1967 (27 Apr). *Millenary of Banteay Srei Temple. No. 193 optd with* T **55**, *in red.*
216	7r. purple-brown, bronze-green & ochre		1·10	45

56 Ballet Dancer

(57)

Journée Internationale de l'Alphabétisation 8-9-67

(Eng J. Combet (1r., 10r.), M. Monvoisin (3r., 7r.), P. Gandon (5r.). Recess)

1967 (30 May). *Cambodian Royal Ballet.* T **56** *and various vert designs showing ballet dancers.* P 13.
217	1r. yellow-orange		30	35
218	3r. greenish blue		65	35
219	5r. ultramarine		85	45
220	7r. carmine		1·30	65
221	10r. multicoloured		1·70	90
217/221 *Set of* 5			4·25	2·40

1967 (8 Sept). *International Literacy Day. Nos. 158 and 91 surch as* T **57** *in red.*
222	**37**	6r. on 12r. ultramarine, grn & crimson		70	35
223	**15**	7r. on 15r. deep olive-brown and green		85	55

58 Decade Emblem

59 Royal University of Kompong-Cham

1967 (1 Nov). *International Hydrological Decade. Typo.* P 13 × 14.
224	**58**	1r. orange, blue and black	20	20
225		6r. orange, light blue and violet	40	35
226		10r. orange, lt blue-green & blue-grn	60	55

1968 (1 Mar). *Cambodian Universities and Institutes.* T **59** *and similar horiz designs. Recess.* P 13.
227	4r. brown-purple, ultramarine & olive-brn		40	30
228	6r. lt brown, myrtle-green & slate-blue		55	35
229	9r. bistre-brown, yell-grn & greenish bl		75	45

Designs:—6r. "Khmero-Soviet Friendship" Higher Technical Institute; 9r. Sangkum Reaster Niyum University Centre.

60 Doctor tending Child

61 Stadium

(Des Nhek Dim. Eng J. Miermont (3r.), C. Jumelet (7r.). Recess)

1968 (8 July). *20th Anniv of World Health Organization.* T **60** *and similar horiz design.* P 13.
230	3r. ultramarine		45	30
231	7r. blue		65	45

Design:—7r. Man using insecticide.

(Des Nhek Dim. Eng C. Guillame (1r.), P. Forget (2r., 7r.50),
anon (3r.), N. Hanniquet (5r.). Recess)

1968 (12 Oct). *Olympic Games, Mexico. T **61** and similar designs.*
P 13.
232   1r. bistre-brown, It emerald & brown-
        red   40   30
233   2r. brown, crimson and blue   45   35
234   3r. brown, greenish blue and purple . . .   55   35
235   5r. reddish violet   60   35
236   7r.50 chocolate, emerald and red   85   45
232/236 *Set of 5* . . . .   2·50   1·60
    Designs: *Horiz*—2r. Wrestling; 3r. Cycling. *Vert*—5r. Boxing;
7r.50. Runner with torch.

62 Stretcher-party   **63** Prince Norodom
                           Sihanouk

1968 (1 Nov). *Cambodian Red Cross Fortnight. Recess.* P 13.
237   **62**   3r. red, green and light blue   70   30

1968 (9 Nov). *15th Anniv of Independence. T **63** and similar horiz
design. Recess.* P 13.
238   7r. dp reddish violet, emerald & ultram . .   45   45
239   8r. chocolate, myrtle-green and blue . . .   45   65
    Design:—8r. Soldiers wading through stream.

64 Human Rights Emblem   **65** I.L.O. Emblem
and Prince Norodom
Sihanouk

(Des Lim Sinh. Eng P. Béquet. Recess)

1968 (10 Dec). *Human Rights Year.* P 13.
240   **64**   3r. blue   30   20
241   5r. bright purple   65   30
242   7r. black, red-orange and emerald . .   95   45

1969 (1 May). *50th Anniv of International Labour Organization.
Recess.* P 13.
243   **65**   3r. ultramarine   25   20
244   6r. carmine-red   40   30
245   9r. blue-green   65   45

66 Red Cross Emblems   **67** *Troides aeacus* (*Papilio
around Globe   oeacus*)

(Des Lim Sinh. Eng C. Jumelet. Recess)

1969 (8 May). *50th Anniv of League of Red Cross Societies.* P 13.
246   **66**   1r. multicoloured   30   20
247   3r. multicoloured   40   30
248   10r. multicoloured   85   45

(Des and eng Lim Sinh. Recess)

1969 (10 Oct). *Butterflies. T **67** and similar horiz designs.* P.13.
249   3r. black, yellow and light violet . . . . .   1·40   55
250   4r. black, green and vermilion . . . . .   1·40   85
251   8r. black, red-orange and yellow-green . .   1·80   1·40
    Designs:—4r. *Graphium agamemnon* (*Papilio agamenon*); 8c.
Danaus genutia (wrongly inscr "Danaus plexippus").

68 Diesel Train and Route Map

(Des and eng C. Thourk (3, 9r.), Lim Sinh (others). Recess)

1969 (27 Nov). *Opening of Phnom Penh-Sihanoukville
Railway. T **68** and similar horiz designs.* P 13.
252   3r. multicoloured   30   30
253   6r. orange-brn, blackish brn & myrtle-
        grn   45   30
254   8r. black   75   35
255   9r. deep blue, greenish blue and light
        green   85   45
252/255 *Set of 4* . . . .   2·10   1·25
    Designs:—6r. Phnom Penh Station; 8r. Diesel locomotive and
Kampot Station; 9r. Steam locomotive at Sihanoukville Station.

69 Siamese Tigerfish   **70** Vat Tepthidaram

(Des C. Thourk. Photo)

1970 (29 Jan). *Fishes. T **69** and similar horiz designs.
Multicoloured.* P 13.
256   3r. Type **69**   75   65
257   7r. Marbled sleeper . . . .   1·50   1·10
258   9r. Chevron snakehead . . . .   2·40   1·50

1970 (29 Apr). *Buddhist Monasteries in Cambodia. T **70** and
similar multicoloured designs. Photo.* P 13.
259   2r. Type **70**   40   30
260   3r. Vat Maniratanaram (*horiz*)   45   30
261   6r. Vat Patumavati (*horiz*)   85   35
262   8r. Vat Unnalom (*horiz*) . . . .   1·60   45
259/262 *Set of 4* . . . .   3·00   1·25

71 Dish Aerial and   **73** *Nelumbium speciosum*
Open Book

72 New Headquarters Building

1970 (17 May). *World Telecommunications Day. Photo.* P 13.
263	**71**	3r. multicoloured		15	20
264		4r. multicoloured		25	20
265		9r. multicoloured		40	35

1970 (20 May). *Opening of New Universal Postal Union Headquarters Building, Berne. Photo.* P 13.
266	**72**	1r. multicoloured		20	10
267		3r. multicoloured		30	10
268		4r. multicoloured		55	10
269		10r. multicoloured		1·10	35
266/269		Set of 4		1·90	60

Two types of 3r.:—

I   II

In Type II the Cambodian and English sections of the value tablet are transposed.

1970 (17 Aug). *Aquatic Plants.* T **73** *and similar square designs. Multicoloured. Photo.* P 13.
270	3r. Type **73** (I)		40	55
	a. Value tablet as Type II		3·50	
271	4r. *Eichhornia crassipes*		60	55
272	13r. *Nymphea lotus*		1·10	85

74 "Banteay-srei" (bas-relief)

(Des Nhek Dim. Eng J. Miermont. Recess)

1970 (21 Sept). *World Meteorological Day.* P 13.
273	**74**	3r. crimson and myrtle-green	30	10
274		4r. crimson, myrtle-grn & greenish bl	45	30
275		7r. myrtle-green, greenish blue & black	60	55

KHMER REPUBLIC

Prince Norodom Sihanouk was deposed on 18 March 1970, whilst in Peking. There he announced on 5 May an alliance between his followers and the communist "Khmer Rouge" forces in Cambodia. On 9 October 1970 the Khmer Republic was proclaimed by prime minister Lon Nol, who had deposed the Prince, and the constitution was ratified on 1 November.

75 Rocket, Dove and Globe   **76** I.E.Y. Emblem

(Photo Delrieu)

1970 (24 Oct). *25th Anniv of United Nations.* P 12½ × 12.
276	**75**	3r. multicoloured	25	20
277		5r. multicoloured	45	35
278		10r. multicoloured	65	55

(Des and eng Svay Teng. Recess)

1970 (9 Nov). *International Education Year.* P 13 × 12½.
279	**76**	1r. blue	15	10
280		3r. bright purple	20	10
281		8r. blue-green	50	35

77 Samdech Chuon-Nath

(Des O. Sokhon. Photo)

1971 (27 Jan). *Second Death Anniv of Samdech Chuon-Nath (Khmer language scholar).* P 13.
282	**77**	3r. multicoloured	25	10
283		8r. multicoloured	60	30
284		9r. multicoloured	75	45

78 "Attack"   **79** "World Races" and U. N. Emblem

1971 (18 Mar). *Defence of Khmer Territory. Photo.* P 13.
285	**78**	1r. multicoloured	15	10
286		3r. multicoloured	15	15
287		10r. multicoloured	50	25

(Des Nhek Dim. Photo)

1971 (21 Mar). *Racial Equality Year.* P 13.
288	**79**	3r. multicoloured	25	15
289		7r. multicoloured	40	25
290		8r. multicoloured	60	40

80 General Post Office, Phnom Penh

1971 (19 Apr). *Photo.* P 13.
291	**80**	3r. multicoloured	15	10
292		9r. multicoloured	50	35
293		10r. multicoloured	60	40

81 Global Emblem   **82** Indian Coral Bean
(*Erythrina indica*)

1971 (17 May). *World Telecommunications Day. T* **81** *and similar horiz design. Photo.* P 13.

294	**81**	3r. multicoloured	25	15
295		4r. multicoloured	35	15
296	—	7r. multicoloured	40	25
297	—	8r. vermilion, black and salmon	50	25
294/297 *Set of 4*			1·30	75

Design:—7, 8r. International Telecommunications Union emblem.

1971 (5 July). *Flowers. T* **82** *and similar multicoloured designs. Photo.* P 12½ × 13 (10c.) or 13 × 12½ (others).

298	2r. Type **82**		40	15
299	3r. Orchid tree (*Bauhinia variegata*)		50	40
300	6r. Flame-of-the-forest (*Butea frondosa*)		1·00	40
301	10r. Malayan crape myrtle (*Lagerstroemia floribunda*) (*vert*)		1·20	65
298/301 *Set of 4*			2·75	1·40

83 Arms of the   **84** Monument and   **85** U.N.I.C.E.F.
Republic   Flag   Emblem

(Des and eng O. Sokhon. Recess)

1971 (9 Oct). *First Anniv of Republic.* P 13.

302	**83**	3r. olive-bistre and emerald	25	10
303	**84**	3r. multicoloured	25	10
304		4r. multicoloured	35	15
305	**83**	8r. olive-bistre and red-orange	40	15
306		10r. olive-bistre and orange-brown	60	25
307	**84**	10r. multicoloured	50	35
302/307 *Set of 6*			2·10	1·00

MS308 Two sheets each 130 × 100 mm. (a) Nos. 302 and 305/6 (sold for 25r.); (b) Nos. 303/4 and 307 (sold at 20r.) . . . . . . 4·75   4·00

(Des and eng E. Lacaque. Recess)

1971 (11 Dec). *25th Anniv of United Nations Children's Fund.* P 13.

309	**85**	3r. blackish maroon	25	15
310		5r. bright blue	35	25
311		9r. carmine and reddish violet	65	40

86 Book Year Emblem

1972 (3 Jan). *International Book Year. Recess.* P 13.

312	**86**	3r. yellow-green, purple and new blue	25	15
313		8r. new blue, yellow-green and purple	40	25
314		9r. bistre, new blue and yellow-green	60	40
MS315 160 × 100 mm. Nos. 312/14 (sold at 25r.)			2·10	1·80

87 Lion of St. Mark's   **88** U.N. Emblem

1972 (7 Feb). *U.N.E.S.C.O. "Save Venice" Campaign. T* **87** *and similar designs. Recess.* P 13.

316		3r. orange-brown, buff & dp reddish pur	35	15
317		5r. orange-brown, buff and green	60	25
318		10r. red-brown, blue and yellow-green	75	40
MS319 160 × 100 mm. Nos. 316/18 (sold at 23r.)			3·00	2·50

Designs: *Horiz*—5r. St. Mark's Basilica. *Vert*—10r. Bridge of Sighs.

1972 (28 Mar). *25th Anniv of Economic Commission for Asia and the Far East (C.E.A.E.O.). Recess.* P 13.

320	**88**	3r. carmine	25	15
321		6r. blue	40	25
322		9r. orange-red	60	40
MS323 141 × 101 mm. Nos. 320/2 (sold at 23r.)			1·90	1·70

89 Dancing   **90** "UIT" on T.V. Screen
Apsaras (relief),
Angkor

1972 (5 May). *Recess.* P 13.

324	**89**	1r. yellow-brown	25	15
325		3r. bluish violet	25	15
326		7r. claret	40	25
327		8r. olive-brown	40	25
328		9r. turquoise-green	50	25
329		10r. bright blue	65	25
330		12r. plum	90	35
331		14r. turquoise-blue	1·20	40
324/331 *Set of 8*			4·00	1·90

1972 (17 May). *World Telecommunications Day. Photo.* P 13.

332	**90**	3r. black, greenish blue and lemon	25	15
333		9r. black, greenish blue and cerise	50	25
334		14r. black, greenish blue & yellow-brn	75	40

91 Conference Emblem

92 Javan Rhinoceros

SECOURS AUX
VICTIMES DE GUERRE
(95)

96 Garuda

1972 (5 June). *United Nations Environment Conservation Conference, Stockholm. Recess.* P 13.

335	**91**	3r. bronze-green, reddish violet and yellow-brown	25	15
336		12r. reddish violet and turquoise-green	40	25
337		15r. turquoise-green and reddish violet	60	40
MS338	131 × 100 mm. Nos. 335/7 (sold at 35r.)		2·75	2·30

(Des Ouk Sokhon. Eng R. Fenneteaux (3, 4r.), J. Miermont (6, 8r.), M. Monvoisin (7r.), C. Guillame (10r.). Recess)

1972 (1 Aug). *Wild Animals. T* **92** *and similar horiz designs.* P 13.

339		3r. black, brown-red and reddish violet	40	15
340		4r. slate-violet, bistre and purple	50	15
341		6r. brown, dull green and light blue	90	35
342		7r. ochre, green and bistre-brown	1·30	35
343		8r. black, yellow-green and light blue	1·50	40
344		10r. black, ultramarine and deep green	2·00	60
339/344	*Set of 6*		5·75	1·80

Designs:—4r. Mainland serow; 6r. Thamin; 7r. Banteng; 8r. Water buffalo; 10r. Gaur.

XXe JEUX OLYMPIQUES
MUNICH 1972
(93)

94 Hoisting Flag

1972 (9 Sept). *Olympic Games, Munich. Various stamps optd with T* **93**, *in red.*

345	**83**	3r. olive-bistre and emerald	35	35
346		10r. olive-bistre and orange-brown	1·20	65
347	—	12r. turquoise-green and purple-brown (No. 164)	1·40	85
348	**91**	12r. reddish violet and turquoise-green	1·40	85
349		15r. turquoise-green and reddish violet	1·70	1·10
345/349	*Set of 5*		5·50	3·50

No. 335 was similarly overprinted but was not issued.

APPENDIX. Further commemorative issues are recorded in the Appendix to this country.

(Des Nhek Dim. Photo)

1972 (9 Oct). *Second Anniv of Republic.* P 12½ × 13.

350	**94**	3r. multicoloured	15	10
351		5r. multicoloured	25	15
352		9r. multicoloured	60	40

1972 (15 Nov). *Red Cross Aid for War Victims. Various stamps surch as T* **95**, *in red.*

353	**83**	3r.+2r. olive-bistre and emerald	25	25
354		10r.+6r. olive-bistre and orange-brown	65	65
355	—	12r.+7r. turquoise-green and purple brown (No. 164)	75	65
356	**91**	12r.+7r. reddish violet & turquoise-grn	75	75
357		15r.+8r. turquoise-green & reddish vio	1·30	1·30
353/357	*Set of 5*		3·25	3·25

(Des Ouk Sokhon. Eng J. Miermont. Recess)

1973 (18 Jan). *AIR.* P 13.

358	**96**	3r. rosine	25	15
359		30r. royal blue	1·80	1·00
360		50r. deep reddish lilac	3·25	1·80
361		100r. deep dull green	4·50	2·75
358/361	*Set of 4*		8·75	5·00

97 Crest and Temple

98 Apsara

99 Interpol Emblem

1973 (12 May). *New Constitution. Recess.* P 13.

362	**97**	3r. multicoloured	15	10
363		12r. multicoloured	25	15
364		14r. multicoloured	40	35
MS365	130 × 100 mm. Nos. 362/4 (sold at 34r.)		1·60	1·40

(Des Ouk Sokhon. Eng J. Miermont (10r.), R. Fenneteaux (others). Recess)

1973 (23 July). *Angkor Sculptures. T* **98** *and similar vert designs.* P 13.

366		3r. black	25	15
367		8r. turquoise-blue	40	25
368		10r. light bistre-brown	50	40
MS369	130 × 100 mm. Nos. 366/8 (sold at 25r.)		2·30	2·00

Designs:—8r. Devata (12th century). 10r. Devata (10th century).

1973 (2 Oct). *50th Anniv of International Criminal Police Organization (Interpol). Recess.* P 13.

370	**99**	3r. blackish green and blue-green	25	15
371		7r. blackish green and brown-red	35	25

372　　10r. blackish green and light bistre
　　　　brown　　　　　　　　　　　　40　　40
MS373 130 × 100 mm. Nos. 370/2 (sold at
　30r.)　. . . . .　2·75　2·30

100 Marshal Lon Nol

D **101** Frieze, Angkor
Vat

(Des and eng E. Lacaque. Recess)

1973 (9 Oct). *Honouring Marshal Lon Nol, First President of the
　Republic.* P 12½ × 13.
374　**100**　3r. black, orange-brown and bright
　　　　　　green　. . . . .　15　15
375　　　　　8r. black, red-brown and blackish
　　　　　　olive　. . . . .　25　25
376　　　　　14r. black, red-brown and brownish
　　　　　　black　. . . . .　40　25
MS377 130 × 100 mm. Nos. 374/6, but
　background colours changed (sold at 50r.)　. .　4·75　4·25

1974 (18 Feb). *POSTAGE DUE. Recess.* P 12½ × 13.
D378　D **101**　2r. orange-brown　. . . . .　25　25
D379　　　　　6r. emerald　. . . . .　35　35
D380　　　　　8r. carmine-lake　. . . . . .　50　50
D381　　　　　10r. deep ultramarine　. . . . .　65　75
D378/381 *Set of 4*　. . . . .　1·60　1·70

102 Copernicus and Space Rocket

1974 (10 Sept). *500th Birth Anniv of Nicolas Copernicus
　(astronomer). T **102** and similar horiz designs. Multicoloured.
　Litho.* P 13½.

(a) POSTAGE.
382　　1r. Type **102**　. . . . .　20　20
383　　5r. Copernicus and "Mariner II"　. . . .　20　20
384　　10r. Copernicus and "Apollo"　. . . .　50　25
385　　25r. Copernicus and "Telstar"　. . . . .　1·10　55
386　　50r. Copernicus and space-walker　. . .　2·00　1·00
387　　100r. Copernicus, and spaceship landing
　　　　　on Moon　. . . . .　4·75　2·50
388　　150r. Copernicus, and Moon-landing craft
　　　　　leaving "Apollo"　. . . . . . .　7·00　4·00

(b) AIR. Inscr "POSTE AERIENNE".
389　　200r. Copernicus and "Skylab III"　. . . .　8·50　4·00
390　　250r. Copernicus and Concorde　. . . . .　14·00　7·50
382/390 *Set of 9*　. . . . .　35·00　18·00

4ᴱ ANNIVERSAIRE DE LA
REPUBLIQUE
(103)　　　　**104** Xylophone

1974 (9 Oct). *Fourth Anniv of Republic. Various stamps optd
　with T **103** or similar surch.*
391　**78**　10r. multicoloured (No. 287) (R.)　. .　90　85
392　**77**　50r.on 3r. multicoloured (No. 282)
　　　　　(Sil.)　. . . . .　3·00　2·10
393　**94**　100r.on 5r. multicoloured (No. 351)
　　　　　(Sil.)　. . . . .　5·75　5·50
　No. 392 is additionally optd "REPUBLIQUE KHMERE" in
French and Cambodian.

1975 (26 Mar). *Unissued stamps of Cambodia as T **104**, showing
　musical instruments, locally optd "REPUBLIQUE KHMERE" in
　French and Cambodian and surch also, in silver on brown
　panels. Multicoloured. Photo.* P 13.
394　　5r.on 8r. Type **104**　. . . .
395　　20r.on 1r. So (two-stringed violin)　. . . .
396　　160r.on 7r. Khoung vong (bronze
　　　　　gongs)　. . . . .
397　　180r.on 14r. Two drums　. . . . .
398　　235r.on 12r. Barrel-shaped drum　. . . .
399　　500r.on 9r. Xylophone (different)　. . . .
400　　1000r.on 10r. Boat-shaped xylophone　. . .
401　　2000r.on 3r. Twenty-stringed guitar on
　　　　　legs　. . . . .
394/401 *Set of 8*　. . . . .　£250

DEMOCRATIC KAMPUCHEA

The Khmer Rouge forces intensified their operations early in
1975 and on 1 April Marshal Lon Nol went into exile. On 17 April
1975 the Khmer Rouge army captured the capital, Phnom Penh,
and the Khmer Republic came to an end.

The subsequent period of total isolation from the outside world
began to be relaxed from September 1977. The policies of the
new state of Democratic Kampuchea were seen to have included
emptying cities of inhabitants, reversion to barter by the abolition
of money, the suspension of public transport and the
discontinuance of postal and telegraphic services.

In these circumstances no stamps were issued. Five pictorial
stamps inscribed "Kampuchéa" without indication of currency
were publicised early in 1978; if they exist their status would be
propaganda labels.

PEOPLE'S REPUBLIC OF KAMPUCHEA

After border fighting in the autumn, Vietnamese forces invaded
Kampuchea on 25 December 1978. Phnom Penh fell on 7 January
1979 and the People's Republic of Kampuchea was proclaimed
on 10 January 1979. The policies of the preceding regime began
to be reversed; the riel, equivalent to one kilogram of rice, was
reintroduced in the spring of 1980 and postal services were
resumed.

105 Soldiers with
Flag and
Independence
Monument, Phnom
Penh

106 Moscow Kremlin and
Globe

1980 (10 Apr). *T **105** and similar horiz designs. Multicoloured.
　Litho. Without gum.* P 11.
402　0.1r. Type **105**　. . . . .　4·50　4·50
403　0.2r. Khmer people and flag　. . . . .　7·25　7·25

404	0.5r. Fishermen pulling in nets	11·00	11·00
405	1r. Armed forces and Kampuchean flag	18·00	18·00
402/405 Set of 4		37·00	37·00

Various stamps of the previous regimes exist overprinted "RPK". These were sold in Phnom Penh, mainly on covers cancelled with datestamps between 15 August 1979 and 22 June 1981. It is believed they were not available for postal use.

PRINTERS. From No. 406 all stamps of Kampuchea and Cambodia were printed by the National Printing Works, Havana, Cuba, *unless otherwise stated.*

1982 (10 Dec). *60th Anniv of U.S.S.R. T **106** and similar vert design. Multicoloured. Litho.* P 12 × 12½.

| 406 | 50c. Type **106** | 35 | 20 |
| 407 | 1r. Industrial complex and map of U.S.S.R. | 55 | 25 |

107 Arms of Kampuchea

108 Runner with Olympic Torch

1983 (7 Jan). *Fourth Anniv of People's Republic of Kampuchea. T **107** and similar multicoloured designs. Litho.* P 12½.

408	50c. Type **107**	55	10
409	1r. Open book illustrating national flag and arms (*horiz*)	90	20
410	3r. Stylized figures and map	2·50	65
MS411	90 × 109 mm. 6r. Temple, Phnom Penh (28 × 35 mm). P 13	4·75	90

1983 (20 Jan). *Olympic Games, Los Angeles (1984) (1st issue). T **108** and similar multicoloured designs. Litho.* P 12½.

412	20c. Type **108**	25	10
413	50c. Javelin throwing	35	10
414	80c. Pole vaulting	45	10
415	1r. Discus throwing	55	10
416	1r.50 Relay (*horiz*)	90	20
417	2r. Swimming (*horiz*)	1·30	20
418	3r. Basketball	2·00	20
412/418 Set of 7		5·25	90
MS419	92 × 64 mm. 6r. Football (31 × 39 mm). P 13	4·25	90

See also Nos. 526/**MS**533.

1983 (18 Feb). *Butterflies. T **109** and similar multicoloured designs. Litho.* P 13.

420	20c. Type **109**	20	10
421	50c. Euploea althaea	25	10
422	80c. Byasa polyeuctes (*horiz*)	35	10
423	1r. Stichophthalma howqua (*horiz*)	55	10
424	1r.50 Leaf butterfly (*Kallima inachus*)	1·20	20
425	2r. Blue argus (*Precis orithya*)	1·30	20
426	3r. Lemon migrant (*Catopsilia pomona*)	2·00	20
420/426 Set of 7		5·25	90

1983 (15 Mar). *Khmer Culture. T **110** and similar multicoloured designs. Litho.* P 13.

427	20c. Type **110**	20	10
428	50c. Bakong	25	10
429	80c. Ta Som (*vert*)	35	10
430	1r. North Gate, Angkor Thom (*vert*)	55	20
431	1r.50 Kennora (winged figures) (*vert*)	1·20	25
432	2r. Apsara (carved figures), Angkor (*vert*)	1·30	35
433	3r. Banteai Srei (goddess), Tevoda (*vert*)	2·00	55
427/433 Set of 7		5·25	1·50

111 Dancers with Castanets

112 Detail of Fresco

1983 (17 Apr). *Folklore. T **111** and similar vert designs. Multicoloured. Litho.* P 13.

434	50c. Type **111**	25	20
435	1r. Dancers with grass headdresses	90	25
436	3r. Dancers with scarves	2·00	65
MS437	94 × 63 mm. 6r. Warrior with blowpipe (31 × 39 mm)	4·00	90

1983 (10 May). *500th Birth Anniv of Raphael (artist). T **112** and similar vert designs showing details of frescoes by Raphael. Litho.* P 12½ × 13.

438	20c. multicoloured	20	10
439	50c. multicoloured	25	10
440	80c. multicoloured	35	10
441	1r. multicoloured	80	20
442	1r.50 multicoloured	1·30	25
443	2r. multicoloured	1·60	35
444	3r. multicoloured	2·20	55
438/444 Set of 7		4·00	1·25
MS445	97 × 75 mm. 6r. multicoloured (39 × 31 mm). P 13	6·00	1·60

109 Orange Tiger (*Salatura genutia*)

110 Srah Srang

113 Montgolfier Balloon

114 Cobra

CAMBODIA Kampuchea

1983

1983 (3 June). *Bicentenary of Manned Flight. T* **113** *and similar multicoloured designs. Litho.* P 12½.

446	20c. Type **113**	20	10
447	30c. *La Ville d'Orleans*, 1870	25	10
448	50c. Charles's hydrogen balloon	35	10
449	1r. Blanchard and Jeffries crossing Channel, 1785	65	20
450	1r.50 Salomon Andrée's balloon flight over Arctic	90	25
451	2r. Auguste Piccard's stratosphere balloon *F.N.R.S.*	1·30	35
452	3r. Hot-air balloon race	1·80	70
446/452 *Set of 7*		4·75	1·60

MS453 75 × 67 mm. 6r. Balloons over European town (*vert*). P 13 . . . . . 5·75 1·10

1983 (28 June). *Reptiles. T* **114** *and similar multicoloured designs. Litho.* P 12½.

454	20c. Crested lizard (*horiz*)	20	10
455	30c. Type **114**	25	20
456	80c. Trionyx turtle (*horiz*)	45	20
457	1r. Chameleon	70	25
458	1r.50 Boa constrictor	1·30	45
459	2r. Crocodile (*horiz*)	1·60	65
460	3r. Turtle (*horiz*)	2·10	90
454/460 *Set of 7*		6·00	2·50

115 Rainbow Lory **116** Sunflower

1983 (20 Sept). *Birds. T* **115** *and similar multicoloured designs. Litho.* P 12½ × 13 (vert) or 13 × 12½ (horiz).

461	20c. Type **115**	20	10
462	50c. Barn swallow	25	10
463	80c. Golden eagle (*horiz*)	45	10
464	1r. Griffon vulture (*horiz*)	90	10
465	1r.50 Javanese collared dove (*horiz*)	1·60	20
466	2r. Magpie	2·00	20
467	3r. Great Indian hornbill	3·50	20
461/467 *Set of 7*		8·00	90

1983 (18 Oct). *Flowers. T* **116** *and similar vert designs. Multicoloured. Litho.* P 12½ × 13.

468	20c. Type **116**	20	10
469	50c. *Caprifoliaceae*	25	10
470	80c. Bougainvillea	35	10
471	1r. *Ranunculaceae*	65	20
472	1r.50 *Nyctagynaeceae*	1·30	20
473	2r. Cockscomb	1·60	25
474	3r. Roses	2·00	45
468/474 *Set of 7*		6·00	1·30

117 Luge

1983 (10 Nov). *Winter Olympic Games, Sarajevo (1984) (1st issue). T* **117** *and similar horiz designs. Multicoloured. Litho.* P 12½.

475	1r. Type **117**	65	10
476	2r. Biathlon	1·40	20
477	4r. Ski-jumping	2·75	25
478	5r. Two-man bobsleigh	3·25	35
479	7r. Ice hockey	4·75	45
475/479 *Set of 5*		11·50	1·20

MS480 81 × 68 mm. 6r. Skiing (35 × 28 mm) . . 5·25 90
See also Nos. 496/**MS**503.

118 Cyprinidae

1983 (16 Nov). *Fishes. T* **118** *and similar horiz designs. Multicoloured. Litho.* P 13.

481	20c. Type **118**	20	10
482	50c. Trout	25	10
483	80c. Catfish	35	10
484	1r. Moray eel	70	10
485	1r.50 *Cyprinidae* (*different*)	1·30	20
486	2r. *Cyprinidae* (*different*)	1·80	20
487	3r. *Cyprinidae* (*different*)	2·20	20
481/487 *Set of 7*		6·00	90

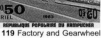

119 Factory and Gearwheel **120** Red Cross and Sailing Ship

1983 (2 Dec). *Festival of Rebirth. T* **119** *and similar multicoloured designs. Litho.* P 13 × 12½ (1r.) or 12½ × 13 (others).

488	50c. Type **119**	25	20
489	1r. Tractor and cow (*horiz*)	90	20
490	3r. Bulk carrier, diesel locomotive, car and bridge	2·00	55

MS491 65 × 85 mm. 6r. Radio signal (31 × 39 mm). P 13 . . . . 5·25 1·10

1984 (7 Jan). *5th Anniv of Liberation. T* **120** *and similar vert designs. Multicoloured. Litho.* P 13.

492	50c. Type **120**	25	20
493	1r. Three soldiers, flags and temple	65	20
494	3r. Crowd surrounding temple	1·80	55

MS495 91 × 60 mm. 6r. Man carrying containers (31 × 39 mm) . . . . 5·25 1·10

121 Speed Skating   **122** Ilyushin Il-62M over Angkor Vat

1984 (20 Jan). *Winter Olympic Games, Sarajevo (2nd issue). T* **121** *and similar vert designs. Multicoloured. Litho.* P 13.

496	20c. Type **121**	20	10
497	50c. Ice hockey	25	10
498	80c. Skiing	35	10
499	1r. Ski jumping	65	20
500	1r.50 Skiing (*different*)	1·30	20
501	2r. Cross-country skiing	1·60	25
502	3r. Ice skating (pairs)	2·00	45
496/502 *Set of 7*		5·75	1·30
MS503 120 × 80 mm. 6r. Ice skating (individual) (31 × 29 mm)		5·25	1·10

1984 (1 Feb). *AIR. Litho.* P 12½.

504	**122**	5r. multicoloured	4·00	20
505		10r. multicoloured	7·50	35
506		15r. multicoloured	11·00	45
507		25r. multicoloured	18·00	80
504/507 *Set of 4*			37·00	1·50

For same design but inscribed "R.P. DU KAMPUCHEA" see Nos. 695/8.

123 Cattle Egret (*Bubulcus ibis*)   **124** Doves and Globe

1984 (2 Feb). *Birds. T* **123** *and similar vert designs. Multicoloured. Litho.* P 13.

508	10c. Type **123**	20	10
509	40c. Black-headed shrike (*Lanius schach*)	65	10
510	80c. Slaty-headed parakeet (*Psittacula himalayana*)	1·20	20
511	1r. Golden-fronted leafbird (*Chloropsis aurifrons*)	1·60	20
512	1r.20 Red-winged crested cuckoo (*Clamator coromandus*)	1·80	25
513	2r. Grey wagtail (*Motacilla cinerea*)	3·50	35
514	2r.50 Forest wagtail (*Dendronanthus indicus*)	3·75	45
508/514 *Set of 7*		11·50	1·50

1984 (25 Feb). *International Peace in South-East Asia Forum, Phnom Penh. Multicoloured, background colour given. Litho.* P 13 × 12½.

515	**124**	50c. blue-green	25	20
516		1r. new blue	65	20
517		3r. reddish violet	1·80	55

125 "Luna 2"

1984 (8 Mar). *Space Research. T* **125** *and similar multicoloured designs. Litho.* P 12½.

518	10c. "Luna 1"	20	10
519	40c. Type **125**	25	10
520	80c. "Luna 3"	35	10
521	1r. "Soyuz 6" and cosmonauts (*vert*)	65	10
522	1r.20 "Soyuz 7" and cosmonauts (*vert*)	90	20
523	2r. "Soyuz 8" and cosmonauts (*vert*)	1·30	20
524	2r.50 Book, rocket and S. P. Korolev (Russian spaceship designer) (*vert*)	1·80	20
518/524 *Set of 7*		5·00	90
MS525 81 × 80 mm. 6r. "Soyuz"–"Salyut" space complex and Earth (39 × 31 mm)		5·25	90

126 Throwing the Discus   **127** Hispano-Suiza "K6", 1933

1984 (20 Apr). *Olympic Games, Los Angeles (2nd issue). T* **126** *and similar vert designs. Multicoloured. Litho.* P 13.

526	20c. Type **126**	20	10
527	50c. Long jumping	25	10
528	80c. Hurdling	35	10
529	1r. Relay	90	20
530	1r.50 Pole vaulting	1·20	20
531	2r. Throwing the javelin	1·40	25
532	3r. High jumping	2·00	45
526/532 *Set of 7*		5·75	1·30
MS533 79 × 59 mm. 76r. Sprinting		5·25	90

1984 (27 Apr). *"España 84" International Stamp Exhibition, Madrid. Sheet 71 × 58 mm. Litho.* P 12½.
MS534 **127** 5r. multicoloured . . . . . 5·25   1·80

128 Coyote (*Canis latrans*)

1984 (5 May). *Dog Family. T* **128** *and similar multicoloured designs. Litho.* P 13.

535	10c. Type **128**	20	10
536	40c. Dingo (*Canis dingo*)	25	10
537	80c. Hunting dog (*Lycaon pictus*)	45	10
538	1r. Golden jackal (*Canis aureus*)	90	10
539	1r.20 Red fox (*Vulpes vulpes*)	1·10	20

540	2r. Maned wolf (*Chrysocyon brachyurus*) (*vert*)	2·00	20
541	2r.50 Wolf (*Canis lupus*)	3·00	20
535/541	*Set of 7*	7·00	90

129 French "BB-1002" Type Diesel, 1966

130 Magnolia

1984 (15 June). *Railway Locomotives. T* **129** *and similar horiz designs. Multicoloured. Litho.* P 12½.

542	10c. Type **129**	20	10
543	40c. French "BB-1052" type diesel, 1966	25	10
544	80c. Franco-Belgian steam locomotive, 1945	35	10
545	1r. Franco-Belgian "231-505" type steam, 1929	80	10
546	1r.20 German "803" type railcar, 1968	1·30	20
547	2r. French "BDE-405" type diesel, 1957	1·60	20
548	2r.50 French "DS-01" type diesel railcar, 1929	2·75	20
542/548	*Set of 7*	6·50	90

1984 (10 July). *Flowers. T* **130** *and similar vert designs. Multicoloured. Litho.* P 13.

549	10c. Type **130**	20	10
550	40c. *Plumeria* sp.	25	10
551	80c. *Himenoballis* sp.	45	10
552	1r. *Pelophorum roxburghii*	1·10	20
553	1r.20 *Couroupita guianensis*	1·30	20
554	2r. *Lagerstroemia* sp.	2·20	20
555	2r.50 *Thevetia perubiana*	3·50	25
549/555	*Set of 7*	8·00	1·00

131 Mercedes Benz

132 Sra Lai (rattle)

1984 (15 Sept). *Cars. T* **131** *and similar horiz designs. Multicoloured. Litho.* P 13 × 12½.

556	20c. Type **131**	20	10
557	50c. Bugatti	25	20
558	80c. Alfa Romeo	45	20
559	1r. Franklin	1·00	25
560	1r.50 Hispano-Suiza	1·40	35
561	2r. Rolls Royce	2·00	45
562	3r. Tatra	2·75	70
556/562	*Set of 7*	7·25	2·00
MS563	68 × 70 mm. 6r. Mercedes Benz (39 × 31 *mm*). P 12½	5·75	1·10

1984 (10 Oct). *Musical Instruments. T* **132** *and similar multicoloured designs. Litho.* P 13.

564	10c. Type **132**	20	10
565	40c. Skor drum (*horiz*)	25	10
566	80c. Skor drums (*different*)	35	10
567	1r. Thro khmer (stringed instrument) (*horiz*)	65	20
568	1r.20 Raneat ek (xylophone) (*horiz*)	1·30	35
569	2r. Raneat kong (bells) (*horiz*)	1·40	35
570	2r.50 Thro khe (stringed instrument) (*horiz*)	2·20	65
564/570	*Set of 7*	5·75	1·70

133 Gazelle

134 "Madonna and Child"

1984 (11 Nov). *Mammals. T* **133** *and similar multicoloured designs. Litho.* P 13.

571	10c. Type **133**	20	10
572	40c. Roe deer (*Capreolus capreolus*)	25	10
573	80c. Hare (*horiz*)	35	10
574	1r. Red deer (*Cervus elaphus*)	65	20
575	1r.20 Indian elephant (*Elephas maximus*)	1·30	20
576	2r. Genet (*horiz*)	1·40	20
577	2r.50 Kouprey (*Bibos sauveli*) (*horiz*)	2·20	25
571/577	*Set of 7*	5·75	1·00

1984 (10 Dec). *450th Death Anniv of Correggio (artist). T* **134** *and similar multicoloured designs. Litho.* P 12½ × 13.

578	20c. Type **134**	20	10
579	50c. Detail showing man striking monk	25	10
580	80c. "Madonna and Child" (*different*)	35	10
581	1r. "Madonna and Child" (*different*)	70	20
582	1r.50 "Mystical Marriage of St. Catherine"	1·30	20
583	2r. "Pietà"	1·50	20
584	3r. Detail showing man descending ladder	2·00	25
578/584	*Set of 7*	3·25	1·75
MS585	91 × 64 mm. 6r. "Coronation of the Virgin" (39 × 31 *mm*). P 12½	5·50	95

135 Bullock Cart

136 Footballers

1985 (7 Jan). *National Festival (Sixth Anniv of People's Republic). T* **135** *and similar multicoloured designs. Litho.* P 12½.

586	50c. Type **135**	45	20
587	1r. Horse-drawn passenger cart	90	25
588	3r. Elephants	2·75	45
MS589	85 × 64 mm. 6r. Bullock-drawn passenger cart (31 × 39 *mm*)	5·75	90

1985 (4 Feb). *World Cup Football Championship, Mexico (1986) (1st issue). T* **136** *and similar designs showing footballers. Litho. P* 13.

590	20c. multicoloured	20	10
591	50c. multicoloured	25	10
592	80c. multicoloured	35	10
593	1r. multicoloured (*horiz*)	65	20
594	1r.50 multicoloured (*horiz*)	1·10	20
595	2r. multicoloured	1·30	20
596	3r. multicoloured	2·00	25
590/596 *Set of 7*		5·25	1·00

MS597 94 × 57 mm. 6r. multicoloured
(39 × 31 *mm*) . . . . . 5·25   90

See also Nos. 680/**MS**687.

137 Eska-Mofa Motor Cycle, 1939

138 Glistening Ink Cap (*Coprinus micaceus*)

1985 (8 Mar). *Centenary of Motor Cycle. T* **137** *and similar horiz designs. Multicoloured Litho. P* 13.

598	20c. Type **137**	20	10
599	50c. Wanderer, 1939	25	10
600	80c. Premier, 1929	35	20
601	1r. Ardie, 1939	70	20
602	1r.50 Jawa, 1932	1·30	45
603	2r. Simson, 1983	1·50	70
604	3r. "CZ 125", 1984	2·00	90
598/604 *Set of 7*		5·75	2·40

MS605 100 × 68 mm. 6r. MBA, 1984
(39 × 31 *mm*) . . . . . 5·75   90

1985 (4 Apr). *Fungi. T* **138** *and similar multicoloured designs. Litho. P* 13.

606	20c. Gymnopilus spectabilis (*horiz*)	20	10
607	50c. Type **138**	35	10
608	80c. Panther cap (*Amanita panterina*)	70	10
609	1r. Fairy cake mushroom (*Hebelona crustuliniforme*)	1·00	10
610	1r.50 Fly agaric (*Amanita muscaria*)	2·00	20
611	2r. Shaggy ink cap (*Coprinus comatus*)	2·75	20
612	3r. Caesar's mushroom (*Amanita caesarea*)	3·00	20
606/612 *Set of 7*		9·00	90

139 "Sputnik 1"

1985 (12 Apr). *Space Exploration. T* **139** *and similar horiz designs. Multicoloured. Litho. P* 13.

613	20c. Type **139**	20	10
614	50c. Rocket on transporter and Yury Gagarin (first man in space)	25	20
615	80c. "Vostok 6" and Valentina Tereshkova (first woman in space)	35	20
616	1r. Space walker	65	25
617	1r.50 "Salyut"–"Soyuz" link	1·10	35

618	2r. "Lunokhod 1" (lunar vehicle)	1·30	45
619	3r. "Venera" (Venus probe)	2·00	70
613/619 *Set of 7*		5·25	2·00

MS620 94 × 59 mm., 6r. "Soyuz" preparing to dock with "Salyut" space station
(39 × 31 *mm*) . . . . . 5·25   1·40

140 Absara Dancer

140a Captured Nazi Standards, Red Square, Moscow

1985 (13 Apr). *Traditional Dances. T* **140** *and similar multicoloured designs. Litho. P* 12½.

621	50c. Absara group (*horiz*)	45	10
622	60c. Tepmonorom dance (*horiz*)	90	25
623	3r. Type **140**	1·80	70

(Litho State Ptg Wks, Moscow)

1985 (9 May). *40th Anniv of End of Second World War. T* **140a** *and similar vert designs. Multicoloured. P* 12 × 12½.

623a	50c. Rejoicing soldiers in Berlin	35	10
623b	1r. Type **140a**	80	25
623c	3c. Tank battle	2·40	70

141 Tortoiseshell Cat

142 "Black Dragon" Lily

1985 (16 May). *Domestic Cats. T* **141** *and similar vert designs. Multicoloured. Litho. P* 12½.

624	20c. Type **141**	20	10
625	50c. Tortoiseshell (*different*)	25	20
626	80c. Tabby	45	20
627	1r. Long-haired Siamese	1·00	25
628	1r.50 Sealpoint Siamese	1·40	35
629	2r. Grey cat	2·00	45
630	3r. Black cat	2·75	70
624/630 *Set of 7*		7·25	2·00

1985 (5 June). *Flowers. T* **142** *and similar vert designs. Multicoloured. Litho. P* 13.

631	20c. Type **142**	20	10
632	50c. Iris delavayi	25	10
633	80c. Crocus aureus	35	10
634	1r. Cyclamen persicum	70	20

635   1r.50 Fairy primrose (*Primula*
       malacoides) . . . . 1·30   25
636   2r. Pansy (*Viola tricolor*) "Ullswater" . . 1·80   35
637   3r. *Crocus purpureus grandiflorus* . . . 2·10   55
631/637 *Set of 7* . . . . 6·00   1·50

654   3r. Rufous-bellied thrush (*Turdus*
       rufiventris) . . . . 2·10   55
648/654 *Set of 7* . . . . 6·00   1·50
       No. 652 is wrongly inscribed "Chiloroceryle".

143 "Per Italiani"   **144** Lenin and Arms
(Antoine Watteau)

1985 (13 June). *International Music Year. T* **143** *and similar multicoloured designs. Multicoloured. Litho.* P 13.
638   20c. Type **143** 20   10
639   50c. "St. Cecilia" (Carlos Saraceni) . . 25   10
640   80c. "Still Life with Violin" (Jean Baptiste
       Oudry) (*horiz*) 55   10
641   1r. "Three Musicians" (Fernand
       Léger) 65   20
642   1r.50 Orchestra 90   25
643   2r. "St. Cecilia" (Bartholomeo
       Schedoni) . . . . 1·30   35
644   3r. "Harlequin with Violin" (Christian
       Caillard) . . . . 1·80   55
638/644 *Set of 7* . . . . 5·00   1·50
MS645 55 × 89 mm. 6r. "The Fifer" (Edouard
       Manet) (31 × 39 *mm*) . . . . 6·50   1·40

1985 (20 June). *115th Birth Anniv of Lenin. T* **144** *and similar vert design. Multicoloured. Litho.* P 13.
646   1r. Type **144** . . . . 1·10   35
647   3r. Lenin on balcony and map . . . . . 2·10   70

145 Saffron-cowled Blackbird (Xanthopsar
flavus)

1985 (5 July). *"Argentina '85" International Stamp Exhibition, Buenos Aires. Birds. T* **145** *and similar multicoloured designs.* Litho. P 13 × 12½ (horiz) or 12½ × 13 (vert).
648   20c. Type **145** 20   10
649   50c. Saffron finch (*Sicalis flaveola*)
       (*vert*) 25   10
650   80c. Blue and yellow tanager (*Thraupis*
       bonariensis) (*vert*) 35   10
651   1r. Scarlet-headed blackbird
       (*Amblyramphus holosericeus*) 70   20
652   1r.50 Amazon kingfisher (*Chloroceryle*
       amazona) (*vert*) . . . . 1·30   25
653   2r. Toco toucan (*Ramphastos toco*)
       (*vert*) . . . . 1·80   35

146 River Launch, Cambodia, 1942

1985 (8 Aug). *Water Craft. T* **146** *and similar horiz designs. Multicoloured. Litho.* P 13.
655   10c. Type **146** 20   10
656   40c. River launch, Cambodia, 1948 . . 25   10
657   80c. Tug, Japan, 1913 35   10
658   1r. Dredger, Holland 65   20
659   1r.20 Tug, U.S.A. 90   25
660   2r. River freighter . . . . 1·30   35
661   2r.50 River tanker, Panama . . . . . . 1·80   55
655/661 *Set of 7* . . . . 5·00   1·50

147 "The Flood"   **148** Son Ngoc Minh
(Michelangelo)

1985 (25 Oct). *"Italia '85" International Stamp Exhibition, Rome. Paintings. T* **147** *and similar vert designs. Multicoloured. Litho.* P 12½.
662   20c. Type **147** 20   10
663   50c. "The Virgin of St. Marguerite"
       (Mazzola) 25   10
664   80c. "The Martyrdom of St. Peter"
       (Zampieri Domenichino) 35   10
665   1r. "Allegory of Spring" (detail) (Sandro
       Botticelli) 70   10
666   1r.50 "The Sacrifice of Abraham"
       (Caliari) . . . . 1·30   20
667   2r. "The Meeting of Joachim and Anne"
       (Giotto) . . . . 1·80   20
668   3r. "Bacchus" (Michel Angelo
       Carravaggio) . . . . 2·10   20
662/668 *Set of 7* . . . . 6·00   90
MS669 94 × 64 mm. 6r. Early steam locomotive,
       Berlin (31 × 39 *mm*). P 13 . . . . . . 6·50   1·40

1985 (2 Dec). *Festival of Rebirth. Litho.* P 12½.
670   **148** 50c. multicoloured 35   20
671   1r. multicoloured 55   25
672   3r. multicoloured . . . . 1·30   45

149 Damsel Barbs (*Barbus tetrazona*)   **150** Footballers

1985 (28 Dec). *Fishes. T* **149** *and similar horiz designs. Multicoloured. Litho.* P 13.

673	20c. Type **149**	20	10
674	50c. *Ophiocephalus micropeltes*	25	10
675	80c. Goldfish (*Carassius auratus*)	35	10
676	1r. Pearl gourami (*Trichogaster leeri*)	65	20
677	1r.50 Black-banded barbs (*Puntius hexazona*)	1·10	25
678	2r. Siamese fighting fish (*Betta splendens*)	1·30	35
679	3r. *Datnioides microlepis*	2·00	55
673/679	*Set of 7*	5·25	1·50

1986 (29 Jan). *World Cup Football Championship, Mexico (2nd issue). T* **150** *and similar vert designs showing various footballing scenes. Litho.* P 13.

680	20c. multicoloured	20	10
681	50c. multicoloured	25	10
682	80c. multicoloured	35	10
683	1r. multicoloured	65	20
684	1r.50 multicoloured	90	25
685	2r. multicoloured	1·30	35
686	3r. multicoloured	1·80	55
680/686	*Set of 7*	5·00	1·50
MS687	95 × 92 mm. 6r. multicoloured (31 × 39 mm)	5·25	90

151 Cob   **152** "Mir" Space Station and Spacecraft

1986 (15 Feb). *Horses. T* **151** *and similar horiz designs. Multicoloured. Litho.* P 13.

688	20c. Type **151**	20	10
689	50c. Arab	25	10
690	80c. Australian pony	35	10
691	1r. Appaloosa	70	20
692	1r.50 Quarter horse	1·30	20
693	2r. Vladimir heavy draught horse	1·50	20
694	3r. Andalusian	2·00	25
688/694	*Set of 7*	5·75	1·00

(Litho State Ptg Wks, Moscow)

1986 (25 Feb). *27th Russian Communist Party Congress. T* **152** *and similar vert designs. Multicoloured.* P 12 × 12½.

694a	50c. Type **152**	25	10
694b	1r. Lenin	80	35
694c	5r. Statue and launch of space rocket	3·00	65

1986 (4 Mar). *AIR. As Nos.* 504/7 *but inscr* "R.P. DU KAMPUCHEA". *Litho.* P 12½.

695	**122**	5r. multicoloured	3·50	20
696		10r. multicoloured	7·25	35
697		15r. multicoloured	9·00	45
698		25r. multicoloured	16·00	80
695/698	*Set of 4*		32·00	1·60

153 Edaphosaurus

1986 (20 Mar). *Prehistoric Animals. T* **153** *and similar multicoloured designs. Litho.* P 12½.

699	20c. Type **153**	35	10
700	50c. Sauroctonus	45	10
701	80c. Mastodonsaurus	90	10
702	1r. Rhamphorhynchus (*vert*)	1·60	20
703	1r.50 Brachiosaurus brancai (*vert*)	2·50	25
704	2r. Tarbosaurus bataar (*vert*)	3·25	35
705	3r. Indricotherium (*vert*)	4·50	70
699/705	*Set of 7*	12·00	1·60

154 "Luna 16"

1986 (12 Apr). *25th Anniv of First Man in Space. T* **154** *and similar horiz designs. Multicoloured. Litho.* P 13 × 12½.

706	10c. Type **154**	20	10
707	40c. "Luna 3"	25	10
708	80c. "Vostok"	35	10
709	1r. Cosmonaut Leonov on space walk	65	20
710	1r.20 "Apollo" and "Soyuz" preparing to dock	1·10	20
711	2r. "Soyuz" docking with "Salyut" space station	1·30	20
712	2r.50 Yury Gagarin (first man in space) and spacecraft	2·00	25
706/712	*Set of 7*	5·25	1·00

155 Baksei Chmkrong Temple, 920   **156** Tricar, 1885

1986 (12 Apr). *Khmer Culture. T* **155** *and similar vert designs. Multicoloured. Litho.* P 13.

713	20c. Type **155**	20	10
714	50c. Buddha's head	25	10

715	80c. Prea Vihear monastery, Dangrek	35	10
716	1r. Fan with design of man and woman	45	20
717	1r.50 Fan with design of men fighting	65	25
718	2r. Fan with design of dancer	1·10	35
719	3r. Fan with design of dragon-drawn chariot	1·50	70
713/719	Set of 7	4·00	1·70

1986 (14 May). *Centenary (1985) of Motor Car. T 156 and similar horiz designs showing various Mercedes Benz models. Multicoloured. Litho* P 13 × 12½.

720	20c. Type **156**	20	10
721	50c. Limousine, 1935	25	10
722	80c. Open tourer, 1907	35	10
723	1r. Light touring car, 1920	65	20
724	1r.50 Cabriolet, 1932	1·10	25
725	2r. "SKK" tourer, 1938	1·30	35
726	3r. "190", 1985	2·00	70
720/726	Set of 7	5·25	1·60

157 Orange Tiger   **158** English Kogge of Richard
(*Danaus genutia*)   II's Reign

1986 (19 June). *Butterflies. T 157 and similar vert designs. Multicoloured. Litho.* P 13.

727	20c. Type **157**	20	10
728	50c. Five-bar swallowtail (*Graphium amtiphates*)	25	10
729	80c. Chequered swallowtail (*Papilio demoleus*)	35	10
730	1r. Chestnut tiger (*Danaus sita*)	70	20
731	1r.50 *Idea blanchardi*	1·30	25
732	2r. Common mormon (*Papilio polytes*)	1·50	35
733	3r. *Dabasa payeni*	2·00	55
727/733	Set of 7	5·50	1·50

1986 (7 July). *Medieval Ships. T 158 and similar horiz designs. Litho.* P 13.

734	20c. Type **158**	20	10
735	50c. Kogge	25	10
736	80c. Knarr	35	10
737	1r. Galley	65	20
738	1r.50 Norman ship	90	25
739	2r. Mediterranean usciere	1·30	35
740	3r. French kogge	1·80	55
734/740	Set of 7	5·00	1·50

159 Solar System,   **160** Ruy Lopez
Copernicus, Galileo
and Tycho Brahe
(astronomers)

1986 (21 July). *Appearance of Halley's Comet. T 159 and similar vert designs. Multicoloured. Litho.* P 12½.

741	10c. Type **159**	20	10
742	20c. "Nativity" (Giotto) and comet from Bayeux Tapestry	20	10
743	50c. Comet, 1910, and Mt. Palomar observatory, U.S.A.	25	10
744	80c. Edmond Halley and "Planet A" space probe	45	20
745	1r.20 Diagram of comet's trajectory and "Giotto" space probe	70	25
746	1r.50 "Vega" space probe and camera	90	35
747	2r. Thermal pictures of comet	1·30	55
741/747	Set of 7	3·50	1·50
MS748	87 × 56 mm. 6r. "Vega" space probe (31 × 39 mm). P 13	4·25	1·10

1986 (28 Aug). *"Stockholmia 86" International Stamp Exhibition. Chess. T 160 and similar horiz designs. Multicoloured. Litho.* P 12½.

749	20c. Type **160**	20	10
750	50c. Fran ois-André Philidor	25	10
751	80c. Karl Anderssen and Houses of Parliament, London	35	10
752	1r. Wilhelm Steinitz and Charles Bridge, Prague	70	20
753	1r.50 Emanuel Lasker and medieval knight	1·30	25
754	2r. José Raúl Capablanca and Morro Castle, Cuba	1·80	35
755	3r. Aleksandr Alekhine	2·10	70
749/755	Set of 7	6·00	1·60
MS756	62 × 72 mm. 6r. Chess pieces (39 × 31 mm). P 13	6·50	1·40

No. 751 is wrongly inscribed "Andersen".

161 *Parodia maassii*   **162** Bananas

1986 (25 Sept). *Cacti. T 161 and similar vert designs. Multicoloured. Litho.* P 13.

757	20c. Type **161**	20	10
758	50c. *Rebutia marsoneri*	25	10
759	80c. *Melocactus evae*	35	10
760	1r. *Gymnocalycium valnicekianum*	70	20
761	1r.50 *Discocactus silichromus*	1·30	25
762	2r. *Neochilenia simulans*	1·50	35
763	3r. *Weingartia chiquichuquensis*	2·00	55
757/763	Set of 7	5·75	1·50

1986 (4 Oct). *Fruit. T 162 and similar multicoloured designs. Litho.* P 12½.

764	10c. Type **162**	20	10
765	40c. Papaya	25	20
766	80c. Mangoes	35	20
767	1r. Breadfruit	45	20
768	1r.20 Lychees	65	35
769	2r. Pineapple	1·10	55
770	2r.50 Grapefruit (*horiz*)	1·50	70
764/770	Set of 7	4·00	2·10

163 Concorde

1986 (21 Nov). *Aircraft. T* **163** *and similar horiz designs. Multicoloured. Litho.* P 12½.
771	20c. Type **163** (wrongly inscr "Concord")	20	10
772	50c. Douglas DC-10	25	10
773	80c. Boeing 747SP	35	10
774	1r. Ilyushin Il-62M	65	20
775	1r.50 Ilyushin Il-86	90	25
776	2r. Antonov An-24 (wrongly inscr "AN-124")	1·30	35
777	3r. Airbus Industrie A300	1·80	70
771/777 *Set of 7*		5·00	1·60

164 Elephant and Silver Containers on Tray

1986 (2 Dec). *Festival of Rebirth. Silverware. T* **164** *and similar horiz designs. Multicoloured. Litho.* P 13.
778	50c. Type **164**	35	20
779	1r. Tureen	70	25
780	3r. Dish on stand	2·10	45

165 Kouprey

166 Tou Samuth (revolutionary)

1986. *Endangered Animals. Cattle. T* **165** *and similar horiz designs. Multicoloured. Litho.* P 13.
781	20c. Type **165**	1·10	20
782	20c. Gaur	1·60	25
783	80c. Banteng cow and calf	4·00	35
784	1r.50 Asiatic water buffalo	6·75	55
781/784 *Set of 4*		12·00	1·20

1987 (7 Jan). *National Festival. Eighth Anniv of People's Republic.* P 13.
785	**166**	50c. multicoloured	25	20
786		1r. multicoloured	45	25
787		3r. multicoloured	1·10	45

167 Biathlon

1987 (14 Jan). *Winter Olympic Games, Calgary* (1988) *(1st issue). T* **167** *and similar horiz designs. Multicoloured. Litho.* P 13 × 12½.
788	20c. Type **167**	20	10
789	50c. Figure skating	25	10
790	80c. Speed skating	35	10
791	1r. Ice hockey	65	20
792	1r.50 Two-man luge	90	25
793	2r. Two-man bobsleigh	1·30	35
794	3r. Cross-country skiing	1·80	70
788/794 *Set of 7*		5·00	1·60

MS795 91 × 65 mm. 6r. Skiing (39 × 31 *mm*).
P 12½	4·25	1·10

See also Nos. 864/**MS**871.

168 Weightlifting

1987 (2 Feb). *Olympic Games, Seoul* (1988) *(1st issue). T* **168** *and similar multicoloured designs showing ancient Greek and modern athletes. Litho.* P 12½ × 13 (vert) or 13 × 12½ (horiz).
796	20c. Type **168**	20	10
797	50c. Archery (*horiz*)	25	10
798	80c. Fencing (*horiz*)	35	20
799	1r. Gymnastics	65	20
800	1r.50 Throwing the discus (*horiz*)	90	20
801	2r. Throwing the javelin	1·30	25
802	3r. Hurdling	1·85	35
796/802 *Set of 7*		5·00	1·30

MS803 93 × 63 mm. 6r. Wrestling (39 × 31 *mm*).
P 13	4·25	1·10

See also Nos. 875/**MS**882.

169 Papillon   **170** "Sputnik 1"

1987 (3 Mar). *Dogs. T* **169** *and similar horiz designs. Multicoloured. Litho.* P 13.
804	20c. Type **169**	20	10
805	50c. Greyhound	25	10

806	80c. Great dane	35	10
807	1r. Dobermann	70	20
808	1r.50 Samoyed	1·30	25
809	2r. Borzoi	1·80	35
810	3r. Rough collie	2·10	55
804/810	Set of 7	6·00	1·40

1987 (Mar). *Nos. 492 and 497 handstamped with new values.*
810a	35r.on 50c. (No. 492)	
810b	50r.on 50c. (No. 497)	

1987 (12 Apr). *Space Exploration. T* **170** *and similar vert designs. Multicoloured. Litho.* P 13.
811	20c. Type **170**	20	10
812	50c. "Meteor"	25	10
813	80c. "Proton"	35	10
814	1r. "Vostok 1"	65	20
815	1r.50 "Elektron 2"	90	25
816	2r. "Kosmos"	1·30	35
817	3r. "Luna 2"	1·80	70
811/817	Set of 7	5·00	1·60
MS818	71 × 48 mm. 6r. "Elektron 4" (39 × 31 *mm*)	4·25	1·10

171 Flask   **172** Carmine Bee Eater (*Merops nubicus*)

1987 (13 Apr). *Metalwork. T* **171** *and similar multicoloured designs. Litho.* P 13.
819	50c. Type **171**	25	20
820	1r. Repoussé box (*horiz*)	70	25
821	1r.50 Teapot and cups on tray (*horiz*)	1·10	35
822	3r. Ornamental sword (*horiz*)	2·00	55
819/822	Set of 4	3·75	1·20

1987 (5 May). *"Capex'87" International Stamp Exhibition, Toronto. Birds. T* **172** *and similar multicoloured designs. Litho.* P 13 × 12½ (horiz) or 12½ × 13 (vert).
823	20c. Type **172**	20	10
824	50c. Hoopoe (*Upupa epops*) (*vert*)	25	10
825	80c. South African crowned crane (wrongly inscr "Balearica pavonina") (*vert*)	35	10
826	1r. Barn owl (*Tyto alba*) (*vert*)	65	20
827	1r.50 Grey-headed kingfisher (*Halcyon leucocephala*) (*vert*)	1·10	25
828	2r. Red-whiskered bulbul (*Pycnonotus jocosus*)	1·30	35
829	3r. Purple heron (*Ardea purpurea*) (*vert*)	2·00	55
823/829	Set of 7	5·25	1·50
MS830	70 × 94 mm. 6r. Asiatic paradise flycatcher (*Terpsiphone paradisi*) (28 × 39 *mm*). P 13	6·50	90

173 Horatio Phillips's "Multiplane" Model, 1893

1987 (7 Aug). *Experimental Aircraft Designs. T* **173** *and similar multicoloured designs. Litho.* P 13.
831	20c. Type **173**	25	10
832	50c. John Stringfellow's steam-powered model, 1848	25	10
833	80c. Thomas Moy's model *Aerial Steamer*, 1875	35	10
834	1r. Leonardo da Vinci's "ornithopter" design, 1490	65	20
835	1r.50 Sir George Cayley's "convertiplane", 1843	1·10	20
836	2r. Sir Hiram Maxim's "Flying Test Rig", 1894	1·30	20
837	3r. William Henson's *Aerial Steam Carriage*, 1842	2·00	25
831/837	Set of 7	5·25	1·00
MS838	98 × 83 mm. 6r. Leonardo da Vinci's drawing of "Flying Man" (31 × 39 *mm*). P 12½	4·25	90

No. 835 is wrongly dated "1840".

174 Giant Tortoise (*Testudo gigantea*)

1987 (9 Sept). *Reptiles. T* **174** *and similar horiz designs. Multicoloured. Litho.* P 13.
839	20c. Type **174**	20	10
840	50c. African spiny-tailed lizard (*Uromastix acanthinuros*)	25	10
841	80c. Iguana (*Cyclura macleayi*)	35	10
842	1r. Coast horned lizard (*Phrynosoma coronatum*)	65	20
843	1r.50 Northern chuckwalla (*Sauromalus obesus*)	90	25
844	2r. Glass lizard (*Ophisaurus apodus*)	1·30	35
845	3r. Common garter snake (*Thamnophis sirtalis*)	1·80	55
839/845	Set of 7	5·00	1·50

175 Kamov Ka-15

1987 (16 Oct). *"Hafnia 87" International Stamp Exhibition, Copenhagen. Helicopters. T* **175** *and similar horiz designs. Multicoloured. Litho.* P 12½.
846	20c. Type **175**	20	10
847	50c. Kamov Ka-18	25	10
848	80c. Westland Lynx	35	10
849	1r. Sud Aviation Gazelle	65	20
850	1r.50 Sud Aviation SA 330E Puma	90	20
851	2r. Boeing-Vertol CH47 Chinook	1·30	20
852	3r. Boeing UTTAS	1·80	25
846/852	Set of 7	5·00	1·00
MS853	65 × 85 mm. 6r. Fairey rotodyne	4·25	1·10

176 Revolutionaries   **177** Magirus-Deutz No. 21

(Litho State Ptg Wks, Moscow)

1987. *70th Anniv of Russian October Revolution. T* **176** *and similar multicoloured designs.* P 12 × 12½ (3r.) or 12½ × 12 (others).

853a	2r. Revolutionaries on street corner *(horiz)*		1·10	20
853b	3r. Type **176**		1·30	45
853c	5r. Lenin receiving ticker-tape message *(horiz)*		3·00	70

1987 (24 Nov). *Fire Engines. T* **177** *and similar horiz designs. Multicoloured. Litho.* P 13.

854	20c. Type **177**		20	10
855	50c. "SIL-131" rescue vehicle		25	10
856	80c. "Cas-25" fire pump		35	10
857	1r. Sirmac Saab "424"		70	20
858	1r.50 Rosenbaum-Falcon		1·30	25
859	2r. Tatra "815-PRZ"		1·80	35
860	3r. Chubbfire "C-44-20"		2·10	55
854/860	*Set of 7*		6·00	1·50

178 Earth Station Dish Aerial   **179** Speed Skating

1987 (2 Dec). *Telecommunications. T* **178** *and similar multicoloured designs. Litho.* P 13 (50c.) or 12½ (others).

861	50c. Type **178**		35	20
862	1r. Technological building with radio microwave aerial (27 × 44 mm)		70	25
863	3r. Intersputnik programme earth station (44 × 27 mm)		1·60	65

No. 863 was issued with *se-tenant* half stamp-size label showing a satellite.

1988 (7 Jan). *Winter Olympic Games, Calgary (2nd issue). T* **179** *and similar multicoloured designs. Litho.* P 12½.

864	20c. Type **179**		20	10
865	50c. Ice hockey		25	10
866	80c. Slalom		35	10
867	1r. Ski jumping		65	10
868	1r.50 Biathlon		90	20
869	2r. Ice dancing		1·30	20
870	3r. Cross-country skiing		1·80	20
864/870	*Set of 7*		5·00	90
MS871	66 × 89 mm. 6r. Four-man bobsleigh (31 × 39 mm). P 13		4·25	90

180 Irrigation Canal Bed

1988 (7 Jan). *Irrigation Projects. T* **180** *and similar horiz designs. Multicoloured.* P 13.

872	50c. Type **180**		35	20
873	1r. Dam construction		70	25
874	3r. Dam and bridge		1·60	45

181 Beam Exercise   **182** Abyssinian

1988 (2 Feb). *Olympic Games, Seoul (2nd issue). Women's Gymnastics. T* **181** *and similar multicoloured designs.* P 12½ × 13 (vert) or 13 × 12½ (horiz).

875	20c. Type **181**		20	10
876	50c. Bar exercise *(horiz)*		25	10
877	80c. Ribbon exercise		35	10
878	1r. Hoop exercise		55	10
879	1r.50 Baton exercise		70	20
880	2r. Ball exercise *(horiz)*		1·20	20
881	3r. Floor exercise *(horiz)*		1·60	20
875/881	*Set of 7*		4·25	80
MS882	84 × 59 mm. 6r. Ball exercise *(different)* (28 × 36 mm). P 12½		4·25	90

1988 (15 Mar). *"Juvalux 88" Ninth Youth Philately Exhibition, Luxembourg. Cats. T* **182** *and similar multicoloured designs. Litho.* P 12½.

883	20c. White long-haired *(horiz)*		20	10
884	50c. Type **182**		25	10
885	80c. Ginger and white long-haired		35	10
886	1r. Tortoiseshell queen and kitten *(horiz)*		65	20
887	1r.50 Brown cat		1·10	25
888	2r. Black long-haired cat		1·30	35
889	2r. Grey cat		2·00	55
883/889	*Set of 7*		5·25	1·50
MS890	61 × 50 mm. 6r. Kittens (39 × 31 mm). P 13		7·00	90

183 *Emerald Seas* (liner)

1988 (14 Apr). *"Essen 88" International Stamp Fair. Ships. T* **183** *and similar horiz designs. Multicoloured. Litho.* P 12½.

891	20c. Type **183**		20	10
892	50c. Car ferry		25	10
893	80c. Freighter		35	10

894	1r. *Kosmonavt Yury Gagarin* (research ship)	65	20
895	1r.50 Tanker	1·10	25
896	2r. Hydrofoil	1·30	35
897	3r. Hovercraft	2·00	55
891/897	*Set of 7*	5·25	1·50

MS898 95 × 70 mm. 6r. Hydrofoil (*different*)
(39 × 31 *mm*). P 13 . . . . . . 4·75 90

184 Satellite

1988 (24 Apr). *Space Exploration. T* **184** *and similar designs showing different satellites.* Litho. P 12½ × 13 (vert) or 13 × 12½ (horiz).

899	20c. multicoloured (*vert*)	20	10
900	50c. multicoloured (*vert*)	25	10
901	80c. multicoloured (*vert*)	35	10
902	1r. multicoloured	55	10
903	1r.50 multicoloured	80	20
904	2r. multicoloured	1·20	20
905	3r. multicoloured	1·60	20
899/905	*Set of 7*	4·50	90

MS906 103 × 63 mm. 6r. multicoloured
(39 × 31 *mm*). P 13 . . . . . . 4·25 90

185 *Xiphophorus helleri*   **186** *Helicostyla florida*

1988 (10 June). *"Finlandia 88" International Stamp Exhibition, Helsinki. Tropical Fish. T* **185** *and similar multicoloured designs.* Litho. P 13 × 12½.

907	20c. Type **185**	20	10
908	50c. Head- and tail-light tetra (*Hemigrammus ocellifer*)	25	10
909	80c. Paradise fish (*Macropodus opercularis*)	35	20
910	1r. Goldfish (*Carassius auratus*)	65	20
911	1r.50 Tetra (*Hyphessobrycon ineai*)	1·10	20
912	2r. *Corynopoma riisei*	1·30	25
913	3r. Sailfin molly (*Mollienisia latipinna*)	2·00	35
907/913	*Set of 7*	5·25	1·25

MS914 62 × 72 mm. 6r. Angel fish (*Pterophyllum scalare*) (31 × 39 *mm*).
P 12½ . . . . . . 5·75 90

1988 (5 Aug). *Sea Shells. T* **186** *and similar vert designs. Multicoloured.* Litho. P 13 × 12½.

915	20c. Type **186**	20	10
916	50c. *Helicostyla marinduquensis*	25	10
917	80c. *Helicostyla fulgens*	35	10
918	1r. *Helicostyla woodiana*	65	10
919	1r.50 *Chloraea sirena*	1·10	20
920	2r. *Helicostyla mirabilis*	1·30	20
921	3r. *Helicostyla limansauensis*	2·00	20
915/921	*Set of 7*	5·25	90

187 Seven-spotted Ladybird

1988 (6 Sept). *Insects. T* **187** *and similar horiz designs. Multicoloured.* Litho. P 13 × 12½.

922	20c. Type **187**	20	10
923	50c. *Zonabride geminata* (blister beetle)	25	10
924	80c. *Carabus auronitens* (ground beetle)	35	10
925	1r. Honey bee (*Apis mellifera*)	65	10
926	1r.50 Praying mantis	1·10	20
927	2r. Dragonfly	1·30	20
928	3r. Soft-winged flower beetle (*Malachius aeneus*)	2·00	20
922/928	*Set of 7*	5·25	90

188 *Cattleya aclandiae*   **189** Egyptian Banded Cobra (*Naja haje*)

1988 (10 Oct). *Orchids. T* **188** *and similar multicoloured designs.* Litho. P 12½ × 13.

929	20c. Type **188**	20	10
930	50c. *Odontoglossum* "Royal Sovereign"	25	10
931	80c. *Cattleya labiata*	35	10
932	1r. Bee orchid (*Ophrys apifera*)	65	10
933	1r.50 *Laelia anceps*	90	20
934	2r. *Laelia pumila*	1·30	20
935	3r. *Stanhopea tigrina* (horiz)	1·80	20
929/935	*Set of 7*	5·00	90

1988 (7 Nov). *Reptiles. T* **189** *and similar multicoloured designs.* Litho. P 12½.

936	20c. Type **189**	20	10
937	50c. Common iguana (*Iguana iguana*)	25	10
938	80c. Long-nosed vine snake (*Dryophis nasuta*) (horiz)	35	10
939	1r. Common box turtle (*Terrapene carolina*) (horiz)	65	10
940	1r.50 Iguana (*Cyclura macleayi*) (horiz)	1·10	20
941	2r. Viper (*Bothrops bicolor*) (horiz)	1·30	20
942	3r. Common cobra (*Naja naja*)	2·00	20
936/942	*Set of 7*	5·25	90

190 Walking Dance   **191** Bridge

194 Train   **195** Fidel Castro

1988 (2 Dec). *Festival of Rebirth. Khmer Culture.* T **190** and *similar multicoloured designs. Litho.* P 13.

943	50c. Type **190**	35	20
944	1r. Peacock dance (*horiz*)	80	25
945	3r. Kantere dance (*horiz*)	2·00	65

1989. T **191** *and similar horiz designs. Multicoloured. Litho.* P 13 × 12½.

946	50c. Type **191**	25	10
947	1r. More distant view of bridge	65	35
948	3r. Closer view of bridge	1·60	90

1989. *Trains.* T **194** *and similar horiz designs showing various trains. Litho.* P 13.

960	2r. multicoloured	25	10
961	3r. multicoloured	35	10
962	5r. multicoloured	45	10
963	10r. multicoloured	80	10
964	15r. multicoloured	1·20	20
965	20r. multicoloured	1·60	20
966	35r. multicoloured	3·00	20
960/966 Set of 7		7·00	90
MS967 85 × 55 mm. 45r. multicoloured			
(39 × 31 *mm*). P 12½		5·25	90

1989. *30th Anniv of Cuban Revolution. Litho.* P 13.

968	**195** 12r. multicoloured	1·10	55

192 Cement Works   **193** Footballers

1989. *National Festival. Tenth Anniv of People's Republic of Kampuchea.* T **192** *and similar multicoloured designs. Litho.* P 12½ × 13 (30r.) or 13 × 12½ (others).

949	3r. Bayon Earth Station (*horiz*)	25	10
950	12r. Electricity generating station 4 (*horiz*)	70	35
951	30r. Type **192**	2·00	90

1989. *World Cup Football Championship, Italy (1990) (1st issue).* T **193** *and similar vert designs showing various footballing scenes. Litho.* P 12½ × 13.

952	2r. multicoloured	20	10
953	3r. multicoloured	25	10
954	5r. multicoloured	35	10
955	10r. multicoloured	80	10
956	15r. multicoloured	1·20	20
957	20r. multicoloured	1·60	20
958	35r. multicoloured	2·75	20
952/958 Set of 7		6·50	90
MS959 92 × 54 mm. 45r. multicoloured			
(goalkeeper) (31 × 39 *mm*). P 13		4·25	90

See also Nos. 1042/**MS**1049.

196 Scarlet Macaw (*Ara macao*)

1989. *Parrots.* T **196** *and similar multicoloured designs. Litho.* P 13.

969	20c. Type **196**	20	10
970	80c. Sulphur-crested cockatoo (*Kakatoe galerita triton*)	25	10
971	3r. Rose-ringed parakeet (*Psittacula krameri*)	35	10
972	6r. Blue and yellow macaw (*Ara ararauna*)	70	10
973	10r. Cape parrot (*Poicephalus robustus*)	90	20
974	15r. Blue-fronted amazon (*Amazona aestiva*)	1·40	20
975	25r. White-capped parrot (*Pionus senilis*) (*horiz*)	2·00	20
969/975 Set of 7		5·25	90
MS976 65 × 75 mm 45r. Red-fronted parakeet (*Cyanoramphus novaezelandiae*)			
(31 × 39 *mm*). P 12½		6·50	90

197 Skiing   **198** *Nymphaea capensis* (pink)

1989. *Winter Olympic Games, Albertville (1992). 1st issue. T* **197** *and similar vert designs. Multicoloured Litho.* P 13.

977	2r. Type **197**		20	10
978	3r. Biathlon		25	10
979	5r. Cross-country skiing		35	10
980	10r. Ski jumping		80	10
981	15r. Speed skating		1·10	20
982	20r. Ice hockey		1·30	20
983	35r. Two-man bobsleighing		2·75	20
977/983 *Set of 7*			6·00	90

MS984 75 × 89 mm. 45r. Figure skating (31 × 39 *mm*). P 12½ . . . . 4·25   90

See also Nos. 1069/**MS**1076 and 1152/**MS**1159.

1989. *Water Lilies. T* **198** *and similar multicoloured designs. Litho.* P 12½ × 13.

985	20c. Type **198**		20	10
986	80c. *Nymphaea capensis* (mauve)		20	10
987	3r. *Nymphaea lotus dentata*		25	10
988	6r. "Dir. Geo. T. Moore"		45	10
989	10r. "Sunrise"		65	20
990	15r. "Escarbonclé"		1·30	20
991	25r. "Cladstoniana"		2·00	20
985/991 *Set of 7*			4·50	90

MS992 59 × 79 mm. 45r. "Paul Hariot" (31 × 39 *mm*). P 12½ . . . . 4·25   90

199 Wrestling   **200** Downy Boletus (*Xerocomus subtomentosus*)

1989. *Olympic Games, Barcelona (1992). (1st issue). T* **199** *and similar multicoloured designs. Litho.* P 13.

993	2r. Type **199**		20	10
994	3r. Gymnastics (*vert*)		25	10
995	5r. Putting the shot		35	10
996	10r. Running (*vert*)		70	10
997	15r. Fencing		1·10	20
998	20r. Canoeing (*vert*)		1·30	20
999	35r. Hurdling (*vert*)		2·75	20
993/999 *Set of 7*			6·00	90

MS1000 62 × 87 mm. 45r. Weightlifting (31 × 39*mm*). P 12½ . . . . 4·25   90

See also Nos. 1061/**MS**1068, 1163/**MS**1170, 1208/**MS**1213 and 1241/**MS**1246.

1989. *Fungi. T* **200** *and similar vert designs. Multicoloured. Litho.* P 13.

1001	20c. Type **200**		20	10
1002	80c. Red-staining inocybe (*Inocybe patouillardii*)		25	10
1003	3r. Honey fungus (*Armillaria mellea*)		35	10
1004	6r. Field mushroom (*Agaricus campestris*)		70	10
1005	10r. Brown roll-rim (*Paxillus involutus*)		90	20
1006	15r. Shaggy ink cap (*Coprinus comatus*)		1·40	20
1007	25r. Parasol mushroom (*Lepiota procera*)		2·00	20
1001/1007 *Set of 7*			5·25	90

201 Shire Horse

1989. *Horses. T* **201** *and similar designs. Multicoloured. Litho.* P 12½.

1008	2r. Type **201**		20	10
1009	3r. Brabant		25	10
1010	8r. Bolounais		35	10
1011	10r. Breton		80	10
1012	15r. Vladimir heavy draught horse		1·20	20
1013	20r. Italian heavy draught horse		1·60	20
1014	35r. Freiberger		2·75	20
1008/1014 *Set of 7*			6·50	90

MS1015 77 × 56 mm. 45r. Team of four white horses (39 × 31 *mm*) . . . . 5·25   90

Nos. 1008/14 were each issued with *se-tenant* half stamp-size label depicting a carriage.

CAMBODIA

The last Vietnamese forces withdrew from Kampuchea in September 1989 and it was announced that the country's name would revert to Cambodia. In August 1990 a Supreme National Council, consisting of members from the various factions, was set up with the major ministries under United Nations control until elections could be held.

203 17th-century Coach

1989. *Coaches. T* **203** *and similar multicoloured designs. Litho.* P 13.

1020	2r. Type **203**		10	10
1021	3r. Paris-Lyon coach, 1720		15	10
1022	5r. Mail coach, 1793		25	10
1023	10r. Light mail coach, 1805		55	20
1024	15r. Royal mail coach		80	30
1025	20r. Russian mail coach		95	35
1026	35r. Paris-Lille coupé, 1837 (*vert*)		1·90	55
1020/1026 *Set of 7*			4·25	1·50

MS1027 60 × 84 mm. 45r. Royal messenger coach, 1815 (31 × 39 *mm*). P 12½ . . . . 4·25   90

No. **MS**1027 commemorates "Philexfrance '89" International Stamp Exhibition, Paris.

ETAT DU CAMBODGE
204 *Papilio zagreus*

3ª POSTES ETAT DU CAMBODGE 1989
205 Pirogue

1989. *"Brasiliana 89" International Stamp Exhibition, Rio de Janeiro. Butterflies. T **204** and similar multicoloured designs. Litho.* P 13.

1028	2r. Type **204**		10	10
1029	3r. *Morpho catenarius*		15	10
1030	5r. *Morpho aega*		25	10
1031	10r. *Callithea sapphira* (wrongly inscr "saphhira")		50	10
1032	15r. *Catagramma sorana*		75	20
1033	20r. *Pierella nereis*		95	20
1034	35r. *Papilio brasiliensis*		1·90	20
1028/1034 *Set of 7*			4·25	90
MS1035 100 × 66 mm. 45r. *Thecla marsyas* (39 × 31 *mm*)			5·25	90

1989. *Khmer Culture. T **205** and similar horiz designs. Multicoloured. Litho.* P 12½.

1036	3r. Type **205**		20	10
1037	12r. Pirogue (two sets of oars)		80	35
1038	30r. Pirogue with cabin		2·10	90

206 "Youth"

207 Goalkeeper

1989. *National Development. T **206** and similar multicoloured designs. Litho.* P 13.

1039	3r. Type **206**		20	10
1040	12r. Trade unions emblem (*horiz*)		60	20
1041	30r. National Front emblem (*horiz*)		1·70	75

1990 (5 Jan). *World Cup Football Championship, Italy (2nd issue). T **207** and similar vert designs. Multicoloured. Litho.* P 13.

1042	2r. Type **207**		10	10
1043	3r. Dribbling ball		15	10
1044	5r. Controlling ball with thigh		25	10
1045	10r. Running with ball		55	10
1046	15r. Shooting		80	20
1047	20r. Tackling		95	20
1048	35r. Tackling (*different*)		1·90	20
1042/1048 *Set of 7*			4·25	90
MS1049 94 × 75 mm. 45r. Players (31 × 39 *mm*)			4·25	90

The issue of handstamped surcharges on this issue has been reported but has not been verified by us.

208 Two-horse Postal Van

1990. *"Stamp World London 90" International Stamp Exhibition. Royal Mail Horse-drawn Transport. T **208** and similar horiz designs. Multicoloured. Litho.* P 12½.

1050	2r. Type **208**		10	10
1051	3r. One-horse cart		10	10
1052	5r. Rural post office cart		15	10
1053	10r. Rural post office van		25	10
1054	15r. Local post office van		40	20
1055	20r. Parcel-post cart		55	20
1056	35r. Two-horse wagon		1·10	20
1050/1056 *Set of 7*			2·40	90
MS1057 69 × 80 mm. 45r. Rural one-horse van (39 × 31 *mm*). P 13			4·25	90

Nos. 1050/6 were each issued with *se-tenant* half stamp-size label showing the rear view of the vehicle depicted on the stamp.

209 Rice Grains

210 Shooting

1990. *Cultivation of Rice. T **209** and similar multicoloured designs. Litho.* P 13.

1058	3r. Type **209**		20	10
1059	12r. Transporting rice (*horiz*)		80	35
1060	30r. Threshing rice		2·10	90

1990. *Olympic Games, Barcelona (1992) (2nd issue). T **210** and similar vert designs. Multicoloured. Litho.* P 13.

1061	2r. Type **210**		10	10
1062	3r. Putting the shot		15	10
1063	5r. Weightlifting		25	10
1064	10r. Boxing		55	10
1065	15r. Pole vaulting		80	20
1066	20r. Basketball		1·10	20
1067	36r. Fencing		1·90	20
1061/1067 *Set of 7*			4·25	90
MS1068 83 × 70 mm. 45r. Gymnastics (31 × 37 *mm*)			4·25	90

211 Four-man Bobsleighing

212 Fa ade of Banteay Srei

1990. *Winter Olympic Games, Albertville (1992) (2nd issue). T* **211** *and similar vert designs. Multicoloured. Litho.* P 13.

1069	2r. Type **211**	10	10
1070	3r. Speed skating	15	10
1071	5r. Figure skating	20	10
1072	10r. Ice hockey	45	10
1073	15r. Biathlon	70	20
1074	20r. Lugeing	90	20
1075	35r. Ski jumping	1·70	20
1069/1075 *Set of 7*		3·75	90

MS1076 64 × 104 mm. 45r. Ice hockey goalkeeper (31 × 38 *mm*) . . . . . . 4·25 90

1990. *Khmer Culture. T* **212** *and similar horiz designs. Multicoloured. Litho.* P 12½ × 13 (30r.) or 12½ (others).

1077	3r. Type **212**	20	10
1078	12r. Ox-carts (12th-century relief)	80	35
1079	30r. Banon ruins (36 × 21 *mm*)	2·10	90

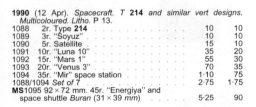

213 *Zizina oxleyi*   214 "Vostok"

1990. *"New Zealand 1990" International Stamp Exhibition, Auckland. Butterflies. T* **213** *and similar horiz designs. Multicoloured. Litho.* P 13.

1080	2r. Type **213**	10	10
1081	3r. *Cupha prosope*	10	10
1082	5r. *Heteronympha merope*	15	10
1083	10r. *Dodonidia helmsi*	30	20
1084	15r. *Argirophenga antipodum*	55	20
1085	20r. *Tysonotis danis*	80	20
1086	35r. *Pyrameis gonnarilla*	1·20	30
1080/1086 *Set of 7*		3·00	1·10

MS1087 76 × 65 mm 45r. *Pyrameis itea* (39 × 31 *mm*). P 12½ . . . . . . 5·75 1·10

1990 (12 Apr). *Spacecraft. T* **214** *and similar vert designs. Multicoloured. Litho.* P 13.

1088	2r. Type **214**	10	10
1089	3r. "Soyuz"	10	10
1090	5r. Satellite	15	10
1091	10r. "Luna 10"	35	20
1092	15r. "Mars 1"	55	30
1093	20r. "Venus 3"	70	35
1094	35r. "Mir" space station	1·10	75
1088/1094 *Set of 7*		2·75	1·75

MS1095 92 × 72 mm. 45r. "Energiya" and space shuttle *Buran* (31 × 39 *mm*) . . . . 5·25 90

215 Poodle

1990. *Dogs. T* **215** *and similar horiz designs. Multicoloured.* P 13.

1096	20c. Type **215**	20	10
1097	80c. Shetland sheepdog	20	10
1098	3r. Samoyede	45	10
1099	6r. Springer spaniel	85	10
1100	10r. Wire-haired fox terrier	1·10	20
1101	15r. Afghan hound	1·70	20
1102	25r. Dalmatian	2·30	20
1096/1102 *Set of 7*		6·00	90

MS1103 95 × 83 mm. 45r. Bernese mountain dog (39 × 31 *mm*) . . . . . . 4·25 90

216 *Cereus hexagonus*   217 Learning to Write

1990. *Cacti. T* **216** *and similar vert designs. Multicoloured. Litho.* P 13.

1104	20c. Type **216**	10	10
1105	80c. *Arthrocereus rondonianus*	10	10
1106	3r. *Matucana multicolor*	15	10
1107	6r. *Hildewintera aureispina*	25	10
1108	10r. *Opuntia retrosa*	50	20
1109	15r. *Erdisia tenuicula*	75	20
1110	25r. *Mamillaria yaquensis*	1·10	20
1104/1110 *Set of 7*		2·75	90

1990. *International Literacy Year. Litho.* P 13.

1111	**217**	3r. black and pale blue	15	10
1112		12r. black and greenish yellow	1·10	35
1113		30r. black and rose	3·50	90

218 English Nef, 1200

1990. *Ships. T* **218** *and similar multicoloured designs. Litho.* P 13.

1114	20c. Type **218**	20	10
1115	80c. 16th-century Spanish galleon	30	10
1116	3r. Dutch jacht, 1627	45	10
1117	6r. *La Couronne* (French galleon), 1638	85	10
1118	10r. Dumont d'Urville's ship *L' Astrolabe*, 1826	1·10	20
1119	15r. *Louisiane* (French steamer), 1864	1·90	20
1120	25r. Clipper, 1900 (*vert*)	2·30	20
1114/1120 *Set of 7*		6·25	90

MS1121 97 × 80 mm. 45r. 19th-century merchant brig (31 × 39 *mm*). P 12½ . . . . 4·75 90

No. 1118 is wrongly inscribed "d'Üville".

219 Phnom-Penh-Kampong Som Railway

220 Sacré-Coeur de Montmartre and White Bishop

1990. *National Development. T* **219** *and similar horiz designs. Multicoloured. Litho.* P 13.

1122	3r. Type **219**	30	10
1123	12r. Port, Kampong Som	1·30	35
1124	30r. Fishing boats, Kampong Som	3·75	90

1990. *"Paris '90" World Chess Championship, Paris. T* **220** *and similar multicoloured designs. Litho.* P 13.

1125	2r. Type **220**	20	10
1126	3r. "The Horse Trainer" (statue) and white knight	30	10
1127	5r. "Victory of Samothrace" (statue) and white queen	45	10
1128	10r. Azay-le-Rideau Chateau and white rook	95	20
1129	15r. "The Dance" (statue) and white pawn	1·40	30
1130	20r. Eiffel Tower and white king	1·90	35
1131	35r. Arc de Triomphe and black chessmen	3·25	55
1125/1131 *Set of 7*		7·50	1·50
MS1132 91 × 58 mm. 45r. White chessmen (39 × 31 *mm*)		5·25	1·10

221 Columbus

222 Tyre Factory

1990 (12 Oct). *500th Anniv (1992) of Discovery of America by Columbus (1st issue). T* **221** *and similar vert designs. Multicoloured Litho.* P 13.

1133	2r. Type **221**	30	10
1134	3r. Queen Isabella's jewel-chest	45	10
1135	5r. Queen Isabella the Catholic	55	10
1136	10r. *Santa Maria* (flagship)	95	10
1137	15r. Juan de la Cosa	1·40	10
1138	20r. Monument to Columbus	1·90	20
1139	35r. Devin Pyramid, Yucatán	3·50	20
1133/1139 *Set of 7*		8·00	80
MS1140 79 × 60 mm. 45r. Christopher Columbus (31 × 39 *mm*)		5·25	90

See also Nos. 1186/**MS**1193.

1991 (7 Jan). *National Festival. T* **222** *and similar multicoloured designs. Litho.* P 13 (500r.) or 12½ (others).

1141	100r. Type **222**	55	20
1142	300r. Rural hospital	2·10	90
1143	500r. Freshwater fishing (27 × 40 *mm*)	3·25	1·20

223 Tackle

224 Speed Skating

1991 (15 Feb). *World Cup Football Championship, U.S.A. (1994) (1st issue). T* **223** *and similar vert designs showing different footballing scenes. Litho.* P 13.

1144	5r. multicoloured	15	10
1145	25r. multicoloured	15	10
1146	70r. multicoloured	35	10
1147	100r. multicoloured	40	10
1148	200r. multicoloured	75	20
1149	400r. multicoloured	1·50	20
1150	1000r. multicoloured	3·50	20
1144/1150 *Set of 7*		6·25	90
MS1151 85 × 93 mm. 900r. multicoloured (31 × 39 *mm*)		5·25	90

See also Nos. 1220/**MS**1225, 1317/**MS**1322 and 1381/**MS**1386.

1991 (30 Mar). *Winter Olympic Games, Albertville (1992) (3rd issue). T* **224** *and similar vert designs. Multicoloured. Litho.* P 12½.

1152	5r. Type **224**	20	10
1153	25r. Slalom skiing	30	10
1154	70r. Ice hockey	55	10
1155	100r. Bobsleighing	65	10
1156	200r. Freestyle skiing	1·30	20
1157	400r. Ice skating	2·50	20
1158	1000r. Downhill skiing	3·75	20
1152/1158 *Set of 7*		8·25	90
MS1159 87 × 62 mm. 900r. Ski jumping (31 × 39 *mm*). P 13		5·25	90

225 "Torso of Vishnu Reclining" (11th century)

226 Pole Vaulting

1991 (13 Apr). *Sculpture. T* **225** *and similar horiz designs. Multicoloured. Litho.* P 12½.

1160	100r. "Garuda" (Koh Ker, 10th century)	35	20
1161	300r. Type **225**	1·10	90
1162	500r. "Reclining Nandin" (7th century)	1·90	1·10

1991 (25 Apr). *Olympic Games, Barcelona (1992) (3rd issue). T* **226** *and similar vert designs. Multicoloured. Litho.* P 12½ × 13.

1163	5r. Type **226**	20	10
1164	25r. Table tennis	30	10
1165	70r. Running	45	10
1166	100r. Wrestling	55	10
1167	200r. Gymnastics (bars)	95	20

1168	400r. Tennis		1·80	20
1169	1000r. Boxing		4·25	20
1163/1169	Set of 7		7·50	90

MS1170 78 × 73 mm. 900r. Gymnastics (beam)
(31 × 39 mm). P 13 . . . . 5·25   90

1991–92. Nos. 1088/94 handstamped with new values in red.

1170a	100r.on 2r. (No. 1088)	
1170b	150r.on 3r. (No. 1089)	
1170c	200r.on 5r. (No. 1090)	
1170d	300r.on 10r. (No. 1091)	
1170e	500r.on 15r. (No. 1092)	
1170f	1500r.on 20r. (No. 1093)	
1170g	2000r.on 35r. (No. 1094)	

227 Douglas DC-10-30

1991 (15 June). Airplanes. T **227** and similar horiz designs.
Multicoloured. Litho. P 13 × 12½.

1171	5r. Type **227**		15	10
1172	25r. McDonnell Douglas MD-11		20	10
1173	70r. Ilyushin Il-96-300		30	10
1174	100r. Airbus Industrie A310		40	10
1175	200r. Yakovlev Yak-42		80	20
1176	400r. Tupolev Tu-154		1·50	20
1177	1000r. Douglas DC-9		3·75	20
1171/1177	Set of 7		6·50	90

228 Diaguita Funerary
Urn, Catamarca

229 Pinta

1991 (10 July). "Espamer '91" Iberia-Latin America Stamp
Exhibition, Buenos Aires. T **228** and similar multicoloured
designs. Litho. P 13.

1178	5r. Bareales glass pot, Catamarca (horiz)		15	10
1179	25r. Type **228**		20	10
1180	70r. Quiroga urn, Tucumán		30	10
1181	100r. Round glass pot, Santiago del Estero (horiz)		45	10
1182	200r. Pitcher, Santiago del Estero (horiz)		85	20
1183	400r. Diaguita funerary urn, Tucumán		1·60	20
1184	1000r. Bareales funerary urn, Catamarca (horiz)		4·00	20
1178/1184	Set of 7		6·75	90

MS1185 80 × 65 mm. 900r. Funerary urn,
Catamarca (36 × 27 mm). P 12½ . . . . 5·25   90

1991 (12 Oct). 500th Anniv (1992) of Discovery of America by
Columbus (2nd issue). T **229** and similar designs. Each orange-
brown, stone and black. Litho. P 12½ × 13 (vert) or 13 × 12½
(horiz).

1186	5r. Type **229**		20	10
1187	25r. Niña		30	10
1188	70r. Santa Maria		55	10
1189	100r. Landing at Guanahani, 1492 (horiz)		65	10
1190	200r. Meeting of two cultures (horiz)		1·30	20
1191	400r. La Navidad (first European settlement in America) (horiz)		2·50	20
1192	1000r. Amerindian village (horiz)		5·75	20
1186/1192	Set of 7		10·00	90

MS1193 84 × 59 mm. 900r. Columbus
(39 × 31 mm). P 12½ . . . . 5·75   90

230 Neptis pryeri

1991 (16 Nov). "Phila Nippon '91" International Stamp Exhibition,
Tokyo. Butterflies. T **230** and similar horiz designs.
Multicoloured. Litho. P 13.

1194	5r. Type **230**		15	10
1195	25r. Papilio xuthus		15	10
1196	70r. Common map butterfly (Cyrestis thyodamas)		10	10
1197	100r. Argynnis anadiomene		40	10
1198	200r. Lethe marginalis		75	20
1199	400r. Artopoetes pryeri		95	20
1200	1000r. African monarch (Danaus chrysippus)		3·50	20
1194/1200	Set of 7		5·50	90

MS1201 73 × 57 mm. 900r. Ochlodes
subhyalina (39 × 31 mm). P 12½ . . . . . . 5·25   1·10

231 Coastal Fishing Port   **232** Chakdomuk
                                         Costumes

1991 (2 Dec). National Development. Food Industry. T **231** and
similar multicoloured designs. Litho. P 13 (300r.) or 12½ (others).

1202	100r. Type **231**		50	45
1203	300r. Preparing palm sugar (29 × 40 mm)		1·40	90
1204	500r. Picking peppers		2·40	1·20

1992 (7 Jan). National Festival. Traditional Costumes. T **232** and
similar vert designs. Multicoloured. Litho. P 13.

1205	150r. Type **232**		50	20
1206	350r. Longvek		1·40	30
1207	1000r. Angkor		2·50	45

233 Wrestling   **234** Neon Tetra (*Hyphessobrycon innesi*)

1992 (Jan). *Olympic Games, Barcelona (4th issue).* T **233** and similar vert designs. Multicoloured. Litho. P 13.

1208	5r. Type **233**	15	10
1209	15r. Football	15	10
1210	80r. Weightlifting	20	10
1211	400r. Archery	1·00	30
1212	1500r. Gymnastics	3·50	35
1208/1212	*Set of 5*	4·50	85

MS1213 79 × 59 mm. 1000r. Show jumping (31 × 39 *mm*). P 12½ .... 4·25 90

(Des J. Medina. Litho.)

1992 (8 Feb). *Fishes.* T **234** and similar horiz designs. Multicoloured. P 12½.

1214	5r. Type **234**	15	10
1215	15r. Siamese fighting fish (*Betta splendens*)	15	10
1216	80r. Kaiser tetra (*Nematobrycon palmeri*)	20	10
1217	400r. Dwarf gourami (*Colisa lalia*)	1·00	30
1218	1500r. Port hoplo (*Hoplosternum thoracatum*)	3·50	35
1214/1218	*Set of 5*	4·50	90

MS1219 80 × 65 mm. 1000r. Freshwater angelfish (*Pterophyllum scalare*) (39 × 31 *mm*) .... 4·25 90

235 Germany v Columbia   **236** Monument

(Des C. Echenagusia. Litho.)

1992 (6 Mar). *World Cup Football Championship, U.S.A. (1994) (2nd issue).* T **235** and similar multicoloured designs. P 13.

1220	5r. Type **235**	15	10
1221	15r. Netherlands player (*horiz*)	15	10
1222	80r. Uruguay v C.I.S. (ex-Soviet states)	20	10
1223	400r. Cameroun v Yugoslavia	1·00	30
1224	1500r. Italy v Sweden	3·50	35
1220/1224	*Set of 5*	4·50	85

MS1225 76 × 51 mm. 1000r. Shot at goal (39 × 31 *mm*). P 12½ .... 4·25 90

1992 (13 Apr). *Khmer Culture. 19th-century Architecture.* T **236** and similar vest designs. Multicoloured. Litho. P 13.

1226	150r. Type **236**	55	35
1227	350r. Stupa	1·30	85
1228	1000r. Mandapa library	3·50	2·00

237 Motor Car

1992 (15 Apr). *540th Birth Anniv (1992) of Leonardo da Vinci (artist and inventor).* T **237** and similar multicoloured designs. Litho. P 13 × 12 (1500r.) or 12 × 13 (others).

1229	5r. Type **237**	20	10
1230	15r. Container ship	20	10
1231	80r. Helicopter	30	10
1232	400r. Scuba diver	1·50	30
1233	1500r. Parachutists (*vert*)	4·75	35
1229/1233	*Set of 5*	6·25	85

MS1234 79 × 59 mm. 1000r. Da Vinci and drawing of "Flying Man" (31 × 39 *mm*). P 13 .... 4·75 90

Nos. 1229/33 were each issued with *se-tenant* half stamp-size label bearing a related drawing.

238 Juan de la Cierva and Autogyro

1992 (23 Apr). *"Expo '92" World's Fair, Seville. Inventors.* T **238** and similar designs. Multicoloured (except **MS**1240). Litho. P 13.

1235	5r. Type **238**	20	10
1236	15r. Thomas Edison and electric light bulb	20	10
1237	80r. Samuel Morse and Morse telegraph	30	10
1238	400r. Narciso Monturiol and *ktineo* (early submarine)	1·40	30
1239	1500r. Alexander Graham Bell and early telephone	2·75	35
1235/1239	*Set of 5*	4·25	85

MS1240 83 × 62 mm. 1000r. pink and black (Robert Fulton (steamship)) (31 × 39 *mm*) .... 4·75 90

239 Weightlifting

(Des J. Medina. Litho.)

1992 (15 May). *Olympic Games, Barcelona (5th issue).* T **239** and similar horiz designs. Multicoloured. P 13.

1241	5r. Type **239**	20	10
1242	15r. Boxing	20	10
1243	80r. Basketball	30	10
1244	400r. Running	1·40	30
1245	1500r. Water polo	4·75	35
1241/1245	*Set of 5*	6·00	85

MS1246 71 × 75 mm. 1000r. Gymnastics (39 × 31 *mm*). P 12½ .... 4·50 90

240 Palm Trees

241 Louis de Bougainville and *La Boudeuse*

1992 (16 June). *Environmental Protection. T* **240** *and similar horiz designs. Multicoloured. Litho.* P 13.

1247	5r. Couple on riverside		20	10
1248	15r. Pagoda		20	10
1249	80r. Type **240**		30	10
1250	400r. Boy riding water buffalo		1·40	30
1251	1500r. Swimming in river		4·75	35
1247/1251 *Set of 5*			6·25	85
MS1252 100 × 71 mm. 1000r. Angkor Wat (39 × 31 *mm*)			4·50	90

1992 (1 Aug). *"Genova '92" International Thematic Stamp Exhibition, Genoa. T* **241** *and similar vert designs. Multicoloured. Litho.* P 12½.

1253	5r. Type **241**		20	10
1254	15r. James Cook and H.M.S. *Endeavour*		30	10
1255	80r. Charles Darwin and H.M.S. *Beagle*		45	10
1256	400r. Jacques Cousteau and *Calypso*		1·50	30
1257	1500r. Thor Heyerdahl and *Kon Tiki*		5·25	35
1253/1257 *Set of 5*			7·00	85
MS1258 80 × 65 mm. 1000r. Christopher Columbus (28 × 36 *mm*)			4·50	90

242 *Albatrellus confluens*

243 Bellanca Pacemaker Seaplane, 1930

(Des Alvarado. Litho)

1992 (25 Sept). *Fungi. T* **242** *and similar vert designs. Multicoloured.* P 13.

1259	5r. Type **242**		15	10
1260	15r. (*Boletus calopus*)		20	10
1261	80r. (*Stropharia aeruginosa*)		25	10
1262	400r. *Telamonia armillata*		1·00	30
1263	1500r. (*Cortinarius traganus*)		3·75	35
1259/1263 *Set of 5*			4·75	85

(Des A. Franca. Litho)

1992 (16 Oct). *Aircraft. T* **243** *and similar multicoloured designs.* P 12½.

1264	5r. Type **243**		20	10
1265	15r. Canadair CL-215 fire-fighting amphibian, 1965		20	10
1266	80r. Grumman G-21 Goose amphibian, 1937		30	10

1267	400r. Grumman SA-6 Sealand flying boat, 1947		1·30	30
1268	1500r. Short S.23 Empire "C" Class flying boat, 1936		4·50	35
1264/1268 *Set of 5*			5·75	85
MS1269 80 × 60 mm. 1000r. Grumman G-44 Widgeon, 1940 (31 × 39 *mm*). P 13			4·50	90

244 Dish Aerial

245 Sociological Institute

1992 (12 Dec). *National Development. T* **244** *and similar vert designs. Multicoloured. Litho.* P 12½.

1270	150r. Type **244**		55	20
1271	350r. Dish aerial, flags and satellite		1·30	30
1272	1000r. Hotel Cambodiana		4·00	45

1993 (7 Jan). *National Festival. T* **245** *and similar horiz designs. Multicoloured. Litho.* P 13.

1273	50r. Type **245**		45	20
1274	450r. Motel Cambodiana		1·40	30
1275	1000r. Theatre, Bassac		4·00	45

246 Bottle-nosed Dolphin (*Tursiops truncatus*) and Submarine

247 *Datura suaveolens*

(Des J. Medina. Litho)

1993 (5 Feb). *Wildlife and Technology. T* **246** *and similar horiz designs. Multicoloured.* P 13.

1276	150r. Type **246**		55	10
1277	200r. Supersonic jet airplane and Peregrine falcon (*Falco kreyenborgi*)		65	20
1278	250r. Eurasian beaver (*Castor fiber*) and dam		75	20
1279	500r. Satellite and Natterer's bat (*Myotis nattereri*)		2·00	20
1280	900r. Rufous hummingbird (*Selasphorus rufus*) and helicopter		3·00	30
1276/1280 *Set of 5*			6·25	90

(Des F. Glez. Litho)

1993 (15 Mar). *Wild Flowers. T* **247** *and similar multicoloured designs.* P 13.

1281	150r. Type **247**		55	10
1282	200r. *Convolvulus tricolor*		65	20
1283	250r. *Hippeastrum* hybrid		75	20
1284	500r. *Camellia* hybrid		1·90	20
1285	900r. *Lilium speciosum*		3·00	30
1281/1285 *Set of 5*			6·00	90
MS1286 75 × 50 mm. 1000r. Various flowers (39 × 31 *mm*)			4·50	1·10

248 Vihear Temple

1993 (13 Apr). *Khmer Culture. T* **248** *and similar horiz designs. Multicoloured. Litho.* P 13.
1287	50r. Sculpture of ox	45	20
1288	450r. Type **248**	1·30	75
1289	1000r. Offering to Buddha	3·75	1·70

249 Philippine Flying Lemur
(*Cynocephalus volans*)

1993 (4 May). *Animals. T* **249** *and similar horiz designs. Multicoloured. Litho.* P 12½.
1290	150r. Type **249**	55	20
1291	200r. Red giant flying squirrel (*Petaurista petaurista*)	65	20
1292	250r. Fringed gecko (*Ptychozoon homalocephalum*)	75	30
1293	500r. Wallace's flying frog (*Rhacophorus nigropalmatus*)	2·00	35
1294	900r. Flying lizard (*Draco volans*)	3·00	65
1290/1294 *Set of 5*		6·25	1·50

No. 1291 is wrongly inscr "Petuarista petuarista".

250 *Symbrenthia hypselis*

251 Armed
Cambodians reporting
to U.N. Base

1993 (15 June). *"Brasiliana '93" International Stamp Exhibition, Rio de Janeiro. Butterflies. T* **250** *and similar horiz designs. Multicoloured. Litho.* P 12½.
1295	250r. Type **250**	75	20
1296	350r. *Sithon nedymond*	1·30	20
1297	600r. *Geitoneura minyas*	1·90	30
1298	800r. *Argyreus hyperbius*	2·40	35
1299	1000r. *Argyrophenga antipodum*	3·25	65
1295/1299 *Set of 5*		8·50	1·50
MS1300 82 × 52 mm. 1500r. *Pararge schakra* (39 × 31 *mm*)		5·75	1·10

1993 (4 Aug). *United Nations Transitional Authority in Cambodia Pacification Programme. T* **251** *and similar vert designs, each black and bright new blue. Litho.* P 13.
1301	150r. Type **251**	55	10
1302	200r. Military camp	65	20
1303	250r. Surrender of arms	75	20

1304	500r. Vocational training	1·70	20
1305	900r. Liberation	2·75	30
1301/1305 *Set of 5*		5·75	90
MS1306 54 × 84 mm. 1000r. Return to homes (31 × 39 *mm*)		4·75	1·10

252 Venetian Felucca   253 Santos-Dumont,
Eiffel Tower and *Ballon
No. 6,* 1901

1993 (27 Aug). *Sailing Ships. T* **252** *and similar horiz designs. Multicoloured. Litho.* P 13.
1307	150r. Type **252**	40	10
1308	200r. Phoenician galley	50	20
1309	250r. Ancient Egyptian ship	65	20
1310	500r. Genoese medieval sailing merchantman	1·50	20
1311	900r. English medieval kogge	2·40	30
1307/1311 *Set of 5*		5·00	90

(Des J. Medina. Litho)

1993 (10 Sept). *120th Birth Anniv of Alberto Santos-Dumont (aviator). T* **253** *and similar multicoloured designs.* P 13.
1312	150r. Type **253**	55	10
1313	200r. *14 bis* (biplane), 1906 (*horiz*)	65	20
1314	250r. *Demoiselle* (monoplane), 1909 (*horiz*)	75	20
1315	500r. Embraer EMB-201 A (*horiz*)	2·00	20
1316	900r. Embraer EMB-111 (*horiz*)	3·00	30
1312/1316 *Set of 5*		6·25	90

KINGDOM

King Norodom Sihanouk

Following the election of a constituent assembly in May 1993 a new Constitution was promulgated on 23 September by which Cambodia became a parliamentary monarchy. The United Nations mandate was terminated.

254 Footballer

(Des R. Quintana. Litho)

1993 (23 Sept). *World Cup Football Championship, U.S.A.* (1994) (3rd issue). *T* **254** *and similar designs showing various footballing scenes.* P 12½.
1317	250r. multicoloured	75	10
1318	350r. multicoloured	1·30	20
1319	600r. multicoloured	1·90	20
1320	800r. multicoloured	2·40	20
1321	1000r. multicoloured (*vert*)	3·25	30
1317/1321 *Set of 5*		8·50	90
MS1322 60 × 85 mm. 1500r. multicoloured (39 × 31 *mm*)		5·75	1·10

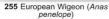

255 European Wigeon (*Anas penelope*)

256 First Helicopter Model, France, 1784

(Des J. Medina. Litho)

1993 (1 Oct). *"Bangkok 1993" International Stamp Exhibition, Thailand. Ducks. T* **255** *and similar horiz designs. Multicoloured.* P 13.

1323	250r. Type **255**	75	20
1324	350r. Baikal teal (*Anas formosa*)	1·30	30
1325	600r. Mandarin (*Aix galericulata*)	1·90	35
1326	800r. Wood duck (*Aix sponsa*)	2·40	65
1327	1000r. Harlequin duck (*Histrionicus histrionicus*)	3·25	85
1323/1327 Set of 5		8·50	2·00
MS1328 63 × 89 mm. 1500r. Head of mandarin (39 × 31 *mm*)		5·75	90

1993 (6 Nov). *Vertical Take-off Aircraft. T* **256** *and similar multicoloured designs. Litho.* P 12½.

1329	150r. Type **256**	55	10
1330	200r. Model of steam helicopter, 1863	65	20
1331	250r. New York-Atlanta-Miami autogyro flight, 1927 (*horiz*)	75	20
1332	500r. Sikorsky helicopter, 1943 (*horiz*)	1·70	20
1333	900r. French vertical take-off jet	3·00	30
1329/1333 Set of 5		6·00	90
MS1334 90 × 49 mm. 1000r. Juan de la Cierva's C.4, 1923 (first practical autogyro) (39 × 31 *mm*)		4·75	90

257 *Cnaphalocrosis medinalis*

258 Ministry of Posts and Telecommunications

(Des F. González. Litho)

1993 (2 Dec). *National Development. Harmful Insects. T* **257** *and similar vert designs. Multicoloured.* P 13.

1335	50r. Type **257**	30	20
1336	450r. Brown leaf-hopper	1·50	20
1337	500r. *Scirpophaga incertulas*	1·70	30
1338	1000r. Stalk-eyed fly (*Diopsis macrophthlalma*)	3·50	30
1335/1338 Set of 4		6·25	90
MS1339 89 × 50 mm. 1000r. *Leptocorisa oratorius* (31 × 39 *mm*). P 12½		4·75	90

1993. *40th Anniv of Independence. T* **258** *and similar designs. Litho.* P 12½.

1340	300r. multicoloured	1·10	30
1341	500r. multicoloured	1·70	65

1342	700r. ultramarine, vermilion and black	2·50	90

Designs: *Vert*—500r. Independence monument. *Horiz*—700r. National flag.

259 Boy with Pony

260 Figure Skating

1993. *Hummel Figurines. T* **259** *and similar vert designs. Multicoloured. Litho.* P 12½.

1343	50r. Type **259**	20	10
1344	100r. Girl and pram	55	10
1345	150r. Girl bathing doll	75	10
1346	200r. Girl holding doll	95	20
1347	250r. Boys playing	1·20	20
1348	300r. Girls pulling boy in cart	1·50	30
1349	350r. Girls playing ring-o-roses	1·70	35
1350	600r. Boys with stick and drum	2·75	55
1343/1350 Set of 8		8·50	1·60

(Des Román Company. Litho)

1994 (23 Jan). *Winter Olympic Games, Lillehammer, Norway. T* **260** *and similar multicoloured designs.* P 13.

1351	150r. Type **260**	45	10
1352	250r. Two-man luge (*horiz*)	75	20
1353	400r. Skiing (*horiz*)	1·30	20
1354	700r. Biathlon (*horiz*)	2·30	20
1355	1000r. Speed skating	3·25	30
1351/1355 Set of 5		7·25	90
MS1356 85 × 60 mm. 1500r. Curling (31 × 39 *mm*)		5·75	90

261 Opel, 1924

262 Gymnastics

(Des A. Franca. Litho)

1994 (20 Feb). *Motor Cars. T* **261** *and similar multicoloured designs.* P 13.

1357	150r. Type **261**	55	10
1358	200r. Mercedes, 1901	65	20
1359	250r. Ford Model "T", 1927	75	20
1360	500r. Rolls Royce, 1907	1·70	20
1361	900r. Hutton, 1908	2·75	30
1357/1361 Set of 5		5·75	90
MS1362 80 × 60 mm. 1000r. Duesenberg, 1931 (31 × 39 *mm*)		4·50	90

(Des J. Medina. Litho)

1994 (20 Mar). *Olympic Games, Atlanta (1996). T* **262** *and similar multicoloured designs.* P 13.

1363	150r. Type **262**	45	10
1364	200r. Football	65	10
1365	250r. Throwing the javelin	75	20
1366	300r. Canoeing	85	20

1367	600r. Running	1·90	20
1368	1000r. Diving (horiz)	3·50	20
1363/1368 Set of 6		7·25	90

MS1369 79 × 63 mm. 1500r. Show jumping
(31 × 39 mm) . . . . 5·75   90

263 Siva and Uma   **264** Olympic Flag
(10th century,
Banteay Srei)

1994 (13 Apr). *Khmer Culture. Statues. T* **263** *and similar vert designs. Multicoloured.* P 13.

1370	300r. Type **263**	1·10	55
1371	500r. Vishnu (6th century, Tvol Dai-Buon)	1·90	90
1372	700r. King Jayavarman VII (12th–13th century, Krol Romeas Angkor)	2·75	1·30

(Des R. Quintana. Litho)

1994 (23 Apr). *Centenary of International Olympic Committee. T* **264** *and similar horiz designs. Multicoloured.* P 12½.

1373	100r. Type **264**	30	10
1374	300r. Flag and torch	1·10	45
1375	600r. Flag and Pierre de Coubertin (reviver of modern Olympic Games)	2·30	85

265 Mesonyx   **266** Players

1994 (10 May). *Prehistoric Animals. T* **265** *and similar horiz designs. Multicoloured. Litho.* P 12½.

1376	150r. Type **265**	55	20
1377	250r. Doedicurus	85	30
1378	400r. Mylodon	1·50	45
1379	700r. Uintatherium	2·50	55
1380	1000r. Hyrachyus	3·50	85
1376/1380 Set of 5		8·00	2·10

1994 (17 June). *World Cup Football Championship, U.S.A.* (4th issue). *T* **266** *and similar vert designs showing different footballing scenes. Litho.* P 12½.

1381	150r. multicoloured	45	10
1382	250r. multicoloured	75	20
1383	400r. multicoloured	1·30	20
1384	700r. multicoloured	2·30	20
1385	1000r. multicoloured	3·25	30
1381/1385 Set of 5		7·25	90

MS1386 58 × 73 mm. 1500r. multicoloured
(31 × 39 mm) . . . . 5·75   90

267 "Soldiers in   **268** *Chlorophanus viridis*
Combat"

1994. *Tourism. Statues in Public Gardens. T* **267** *and similar multicoloured designs. Litho.* P 13.

1387	300r. "Stag and Hind" (horiz)	1·30	45
1388	500r. Type **267**	1·90	90
1389	700r. "Lions"	2·75	1·40

1994 (7 July). *Beetles. T* **268** *and similar horiz designs. Multicoloured. Litho.* P 12½.

1390	150r. Type **268**	55	10
1391	200r. *Chrysochroa fulgidissima*	65	20
1392	250r. *Lytta vesicatoria*	75	20
1393	500r. *Purpuricenus kaehleri*	2·00	45
1394	900r. Hercules beetle (*Dynastes hercules*)	3·00	75
1390/1394 Set of 5		6·25	1·50

MS1395 69 × 50 mm. 1000r. *Timarcha tenebricosa* (39 × 31 mm) . . . . . 4·75   90

269 Halley's Diving-   **270** Francois-André Philidor,
bell, 1690   1795

1994 (12 Aug). *Submarines. T* **269** *and similar multicoloured designs. Litho.* P 13.

1396	150r. Type **269**	55	10
1397	200r. *Gimnote*, 1886 (horiz)	65	20
1398	250r. *Peral* (Spain), 1888 (horiz)	75	20
1399	500r. *Nautilus* (first nuclear-powered submarine), 1954 (horiz)	2·00	20
1400	900r. *Trieste* (bathyscaphe), 1953 (horiz)	3·00	30
1396/1400 Set of 5		6·25	90

MS1401 80 × 70 mm. 1000r. Narciso Monturiol's submarine *Ictineo*, 1885 (39 × 31 mm).
P 12½ . . . . 4·75   90

1994 (20 Sept). *Chess Champions. T* **270** *and similar horiz designs. Multicoloured. Litho.* P 13.

1402	150r. Type **270**	55	10
1403	200r. Mahé de la Bourdonnais, 1821	65	20
1404	250r. Karl Anderssen, 1851	75	20
1405	500r. Paul Morphy, 1858	2·00	45
1406	900r. Wilhelm Steinitz, 1866	3·00	75
1402/1406 Set of 5		6·25	1·50

MS1407 90 × 50 mm. 1000r. Emanuel Lasker, 1894 (31 × 39 mm) . . . . . 4·50   1·10

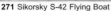

271 Sikorsky S-42 Flying Boat

272 Penduline Tit
(*Remiz pendulinus*)

1994 (6 Oct). *Aircraft. T* **271** *and similar horiz designs. Multicoloured. Litho.* P 13.

1408	150r. Type **271**	55	10
1409	200r. Vought-Sikorsky VS-300A helicopter prototype	65	20
1410	250r. Sikorsky S-37 biplane	75	20
1411	500r. Sikorsky S-35 biplane	2·00	20
1412	900r. Sikorsky S-43 amphibian	3·00	30
1408/1412 *Set of 5*		6·25	90

MS1413 80 × 50 mm. 1000r. Sikorsky Ilya Muromets (80th anniv of first multi-engined airplane) (39 × 31 *mm*). P 12½ . . . . . 4·50 90

1994 (20 Nov). *Birds. T* **272** *and similar multicoloured designs. Litho.* P 12½.

1414	150r. Type **272**	45	10
1415	250r. Bearded reedling (*Panurus biarmicus*) (*horiz*)	75	20
1416	400r. Little bunting (*Emberiza rustica*) (*horiz*)	1·40	20
1417	700r. Cirl bunting (*Emberiza schoeniclus*) (*horiz*)	2·40	45
1418	1000r. Goldcrest (*Regulus regulus*) (*horiz*)	3·50	75
1414/1418 *Set of 5*		7·50	1·50

MS1419 60 × 90 mm. 1500r. African pitta (*Pitta angolensis*) (31 × 39 *mm*). P 13 . . . . . 5·75 1·40

273 Postal Service Float

1994 (9 Dec). *National Independence Festival. T* **273** *and similar horiz designs. Multicoloured. Litho.* P 13.

1420	300r. Type **273**	1·10	45
1421	500r. Soldiers marching	1·60	90
1422	700r. Women's army units on parade	2·50	1·40

274 Chruoi Changwar Bridge

1994 (10 Dec). *National Development. T* **274** *and similar horiz designs. Multicoloured. Litho.* P 14.

1423	300r. Type **274**	85	30
1424	500r. Olympique Commercial Centre	1·50	45
1425	700r. Sakyamony Chedei Temple	1·90	65

275 Psittacosaurus

276 Orange-tip
(*Anthocharis carhdamines*)

1995 (10 Jan). *Prehistoric Animals. T* **275** *and similar horiz designs. Multicoloured. Litho.* P 13.

1426	100r. Type **275**	20	10
1427	200r. Protoceratops	45	20
1428	300r. Montanoceraptors	65	20
1429	400r. Centosaurus	1·40	30
1430	700r. Stytacosaurus	2·30	35
1431	800r. Triceratops	3·00	55
1426/1431 *Set of 6*		7·25	1·50

1995 (12 Feb). *Butterflies. T* **276** *and similar vert designs. Multicoloured. Litho.* P 13.

1432	100r. Type **276**	20	10
1433	200r. Scarce swallowtail (*Iphiclides podalirius*)	65	20
1434	300r. Dark green fritillary (*Mesoacidalia aglaja*)	95	20
1435	600r. Red admiral (*Vanessa atalanta*)	1·40	20
1436	800r. Peacock (*Inachis io*)	2·10	30
1432/1436 *Set of 5*		4·75	90

277 Swimming

278 Amanita phalloides

1995 (9 Mar). *Olympic Games, Atlanta (1996) (2nd issue). T* **277** *and similar multicoloured designs. Litho.* P 13.

1437	100r. Type **277**	30	10
1438	200r. Callisthenics (*vert*)	65	20
1439	400r. Basketball (*vert*)	1·20	20
1440	800r. Football (*vert*)	2·75	20
1441	1000r. Cycling (*vert*)	3·25	30
1437/1441 *Set of 5*		7·25	90

MS1442 48 × 69 mm. 1500r. Running (31 × 39 *mm*) . . . . . 3·75 90

1995 (23 Mar). *Fungi. T* **278** *and similar vert designs. Multicoloured. Litho.* P 13.

1443	100r. Type **278**	30	10
1444	200r. Cantharellus cibarius	75	20
1445	300r. Armillaria mellea	1·10	20
1446	600r. Agaricus campestris	1·80	20
1447	800r. Amanita muscaria	2·40	30
1443/1447 *Set of 5*		6·25	90

279 Kneeling Ascetic

280 Gaur (*Bos gaurus*)

1995 (13 Apr). *Khmer Culture. Statues. T* **279** *and similar vert designs. Multicoloured. Litho.* P 12½.

1448	300r. Type **279**	85	30
1449	500r. Parasurama	1·50	45
1450	700r. Shiva	1·90	65

1995 (5 May). *Protected Animals. T* **280** *and similar multicoloured designs. Litho.* P 13.

1451	300r. Type **280**	85	20
1452	500r. Kouprey (*Bos sauveli*) (*vert*)	1·50	30
1453	700r. Saurus crane (*Grus antigone*) (*vert*)	1·90	45

281 Black-capped Lory (*Lorius lory*)

282 Bird (sculpture)

1995 (23 May). *Parrot Family. T* **281** *and similar vert designs. Multicoloured. Litho.* P 13.

1454	100r. Type **281**	30	10
1455	200r. Princess parrot (*Polytelis alexandrae*)	65	20
1456	400r. Electus parrot (*Eclectus roratus*) (wrongly inscr "voratus")	1·20	20
1457	800r. Scarlet macaw (*Ara macaw*)	2·75	20
1458	1000r. Budgerigar (*Melopsittacus undulatus*)	3·25	30
1454/1458 *Set of 5*		7·25	90

MS1459 52 × 81 mm. 1500r. Yellow-headed amazon (*Amazona ochrocephala*) (30 × 38 mm). P 12½ . . . . 4·75 90

1995 (15 July). *Tourism. Public Gardens. T* **282** *and similar horiz designs. Multicoloured. Litho.* P 12½.

1460	300r. Type **282**	85	30
1461	500r. Water feature	1·50	45
1462	700r. Mythical figures (sculpture)	1·60	65

283 Richard Trevithick's Steam Locomotive, 1804

1995 (17 Aug). *Steam Locomotives. T* **283** *and similar multicoloured designs. Litho.* P 12½.

1463	100r. Type **283**	20	10
1464	200r. G. and R. Stephenson's *Rocket*, 1829	75	20
1465	300r. Stephenson's *Locomotion*, 1825	1·10	20
1466	600r. *Lafayette*, 1837	1·70	45
1467	800r. *Best Friend of Charleston*, 1830	2·10	75
1463/1467 *Set of 5*		5·25	1·50

MS1468 74 × 59 mm. 1000r. George Stephenson (inventor of steam locomotive) (31 × 38 *mm*) . . . . 3·25 1·50

284 Bristol Type 142 Blenheim Mk II Bomber

1995 (15 Sept). *Second World War Planes. T* **284** *and similar multicoloured designs. Litho.* P 12 × 12½ (100r.) or 12½ (others).

1469	100r. Type **284**	20	10
1470	200r. North American B-25B Mitchell bomber (*horiz*)	75	20
1471	300r. Avro Type 652 Anson Mk I general purpose plane (*horiz*)	1·10	20
1472	600r. Avro Manchester bomber (*horiz*)	1·70	20
1473	800r. Consolidated B-24 Liberator bomber (*horiz*)	2·10	30
1469/1473 *Set of 5*		5·25	90

MS1474 81 × 49 mm. 1000r. Boeing B-17 Flying Fortress bomber (31 × 38 *mm*) . . . . . 3·25 90

285 Gathering Crops

286 Bridge

1995 (24 Oct). *50th Anniv of Food and Agriculture Organization. T* **285** *and similar horiz designs. Multicoloured. Litho.* P 13.

1475	300r. Type **285**	55	30
1476	500r. Transplanting crops	1·10	45
1477	700r. Paddy field	1·60	65

1995 (24 Oct). *50th Anniv of United Nations Organization. Preah Kunlorng Bridge. T* **286** *and similar horiz designs. Multicoloured. Litho.* P 12½.

1478	300r. Type **286**	55	30
1479	500r. Bridge (*different*)	1·10	45
1480	700r. Bridge (*different*)	1·60	65

287 Queen Monineath

1995 (9 Nov). *National Independence. T* **287** *and similar vert design. Multicoloured. Litho.* P 12½ × 13.

1481	700r.	Type **287**	2·10	65
1482	800r.	King Norodom Sihanouk	2·75	75

288 Pennant Coralfish (*Heniochus acuminatus*)

1995 (19 Nov). *Fishes. T* **288** *and similar multicoloured designs. Litho.* P 13.

1483	100r.	Type **288**	30	10
1484	200r.	Copper-banded butterflyfish (*Chelmon rostratus*)	65	20
1485	400r.	Clown anemonefish (*Amphiprion percula*)	1·20	20
1486	800r.	Palette surgeonfish (*Paracanthurus hepatus*)	2·75	20
1487	1000r.	Queen angelfish (*Holocanthus ciliaris*) (wrongly inscr "Holocanthus")	2·10	30
1483/1487 *Set of 5*			6·25	90
MS1488 85 × 50 mm. 500r. Twin-spotted wrasse (*Coris angulata*)			4·75	90

289 Post Office Building

1995 (2 Dec). *Centenary of Head Post Office, Phnom Penh. Litho.* P 12½.

1489	**289**	300r. multicoloured	85	30
1490		500r. multicoloured	1·60	45
1491		700r. multicoloured	2·30	65

290 Independence Monument   **291** Tennis

1995 (14 Dec). *40th Anniv of Admission of Cambodia to United Nations Organization. T* **290** *and similar multicoloured designs. Litho.* P 12½ × 13 (800r.) or 13 × 12½ (others).

1492	300r.	Type **290**	55	30
1493	400r.	Angkor Vat	1·10	45
1494	800r.	U.N. emblem and national flag (*vert*)	1·60	65

1996 (10 Jan). *Olympic Games, Atlanta (3rd issue). T* **291** *and similar (vert) designs. Multicoloured. Litho.* P 12½ × 13.

1495	100r.	Type **291**	10	10
1496	200r.	Volleyball	25	10
1497	300r.	Football	45	20
1498	500r.	Running	60	20
1499	900r.	Baseball	1·10	20
1500	1000r.	Basketball	1·10	20
1495/1500 *Set of 6*			3·25	90
MS1501 64 × 94 mm. 1500r. Windsurfing (29 × 38 *mm*). P 13			3·25	90

292 Kep State Chalet   **293** European Wild Cat (*Felis silvestris*)

1996 (30 Jan). *T* **292** *and similar designs. Litho.* P 12½ × 12 (800r.) or 12 × 12½ (others).

1502	50r.	cobalt and black	20	10
1503	100r.	rose and black	20	10
1504	200r.	yellow and black	20	10
1505	500r.	new blue and black	55	20
1506	800r.	magenta and black	95	30
1507	1000r.	orange-yellow and black	1·30	45
1508	1500r.	turquoise-green and black	1·90	65
1502/1508 *Set of 7*			4·75	1·70

Designs: *Horiz*—100r. Power station; 200r. Wheelchair; 500r. Handicapped basketball team; 1000r. Kep beach; 1500r. Serpent Island. *Vert*—800r. Man making crutches.

1996 (8 Feb). *Wild Cats. T* **293** *and similar multicoloured designs. Litho.* P 13.

1509	100r.	*Felis libyca*	20	10
1510	200r.	Type **293**	35	10
1511	300r.	Caracal (*Felis caracal*)	50	20
1512	500r.	Geoffroy's cat (*felis geoffroyi*)	80	20
1513	900r.	Black-footed cat (*Felis nigripes*)	1·20	20
1514	1000r.	Flat-headed cat (*Felis planiceps*)	1·40	20
1509/1514 *Set of 6*			4·50	90

294 Player dribbling Ball   **295** Tusmukh

1996 (5 Mar). *World Cup Football Championship, France (1998) (1st issue).* T **294** *and similar designs showing different players. Litho.* P 13.

1515	100r. multicoloured	30	10
1516	200r. multicoloured	45	10
1517	300r. multicoloured	75	20
1518	500r. multicoloured	1·30	20
1519	900r. multicoloured	2·30	20
1520	1000r. multicoloured (*horiz*)	2·75	20
1515/1520 *Set of 6*		7·00	90

MS1521 65 × 79 mm. 1500r. Players (31 × 38 mm) . . . . 4·75 90

See also Nos. 1613/19 and 1726/32.

1996 (13 Apr). *Khmer Culture.* T **295** *and similar vert designs. Multicoloured. Litho.* P 12½ × 13.

1522	100r. Type **295**	20	10
1523	300r. Ream Iso	1·30	45
1524	900r. Isei	2·20	85

296 Pacific Class Hr-1 Steam Locomotive No. 620, Finland

297 White-rumped Shama (*Kittacinela malabarica*)

1996 (20 Apr). *Railway Locomotives.* T **296** *and similar horiz designs. Multicoloured. Litho.* P 12½.

1525	100r. Type **296**	10	10
1526	200r. Great Northern Railway Atlantic steam locomotive No. 261, Great Britain	10	10
1527	300r. Steam tank locomotive, 1930	30	20
1528	500r. Steam tank locomotive No. 1362, 1914	40	20
1529	900r. LMS Turbomotive No. 6202, 1930, Great Britain	55	20
1530	1000r. Double-Fairlee type locomotive *Snake*, 1884, New Zealand	75	20
1525/1530 *Set of 6*		2·00	90

MS1531 80 × 55 mm. 1500r. Canadian Pacific train with Vistadome observation car (39 × 31 mm) . . . . 4·75 90

No. **MS**1531 commemorates "CAPEX '96" International Stamp Exhibition, Toronto.

1996 (7 May). *Birds.* T **297** *and similar multicoloured designs. Litho.* P 12½.

1532	100r. Type **297**	30	10
1533	200r. Pekin robin (*Leiothris lutea*) (*horiz*)	45	10
1534	300r. Varied tit (*Parus varius*)	75	20
1535	500r. Black-naped oriole (*Oriolus chinensis*) (*horiz*)	1·30	20

1536	900r. Japanese bush warbler (*Cettia diphone*) (*horiz*)	2·30	20
1537	1000r. Blue and white flycatcher (*Cyanoptila cyanomelana*)	2·75	20
1532/1537 *Set of 6*		7·00	90

298 Rhythmic Gymnstics

1996 (14 June). *"Olymphilex '96" Olympic Stamp Exhibition, Atlanta, U.S.A.* T **298** *and similar horiz designs. Multicoloured. Litho.* P 13.

1538	100r. Type **298**	20	10
1539	200r. Judo	30	10
1540	300r. High jumping	55	20
1541	500r. Wrestling	1·10	20
1542	900r. Weightlifting	1·90	20
1543	1000r. Football	2·30	20
1538/1543 *Set of 6*		5·75	90

MS1544 84 × 55 mm. 1500r. Diving (31 × 39 mm). P 13 . . . . 3·75 90

299 Douglas M-2, 1926   **300** Aspara

1996 (5 July). *Biplanes.* T **299** *and similar horiz designs. Multicoloured. Litho.* P 12½.

1545	100r. Type **299**	30	10
1546	200r. Pitcairn PS-5 Mailwing, 1926	45	10
1547	300r. Boeing 40-B, 1928	75	20
1548	500r. Potez 25, 1925	1·30	20
1549	900r. Stearman C-3MB, 1927	2·30	20
1550	1000r. De Havilland D.H.4, 1918	2·75	20
1545/1550 *Set of 6*		6·75	90

MS1551 80 × 60 mm. 1500r. Standar JR-1B, 1918 (39 × 30 mm). P 13 . . . . 4·75 90

1996 (30 July). *Tonle Bati Temple Ruins.* T **300** *and similar designs. Litho.* P 12½.

1552	50r. black and yellow	20	10
1553	100r. black and blue	20	10
1554	200r. black and ochre	45	10
1555	500r. black and bright new blue	75	20
1556	800r. black and bright green	1·10	30
1557	1000r. black and emerald	1·40	45
1558	1500r. black and olive-bistre	2·30	65
1552/1558 *Set of 7*		5·75	1·70

Designs: *Vert*—Aspara (*different*); 200r. Aspara (*different*); 800r. Taprum Temple; 1000r. Grandmother Peou Temple. *Horiz*—500r. Reliefs on wall; 1500r. Overall view of Tonle Bati.

301 Coelophysis

1996 (8 Aug). *Prehistoric Animals. T* **301** *and similar horiz designs. Multicoloured. Litho.* P 13.

1559	50r. Type **301**	10	10
	a. Sheetlet of 4. Nos. 1559/62		
1560	100r. Euparkeria	10	10
1561	150r. Plateosaurus	30	10
1562	200r. Herrerasaurus	50	10
1563	250r. Dilophosaurus	55	10
	a. Sheetlet of 4. Nos. 1563/6		
1564	300r. Tuojangosaurus	70	10
1565	350r. Camarasaurus	1·10	20
1566	400r. Ceratosaurus	1·30	20
1567	500r. Espinosaurio	1·50	30
	a. Sheetlet of 4. Nos. 1567/70		
1568	700r. Ouranosaurus	2·00	35
1569	800r. Avimimus	2·50	55
1570	1200r. Deinonychus	3·50	65
1559/1570 *Set of 12*		12·50	2·50

Nos. 1559/62, 1563/6 and 1567/70 respectively were issued together in *se-tenant* sheetlets of four stamps, each sheetlet containing a composite design of the globe.

302 José Raul Capablanca (1921–27)

303 Brown Bear (*Ursus arctos*)

1996 (10 Sept). *World Chess Champions. T* **302** *and similar vert designs. Multicoloured. Litho.* P 13.

1571	100r. Type **302**	30	10
1572	200r. Aleksandr Alekhine (1927–35, 1937–46)	45	10
1573	300r. Vasily Vasilevich Smyslov (1957–58)	75	20
1574	500r. Mikhail Nekhemyevich Tal (1960–61)	1·30	20
1575	900r. Robert Fischer (1972–75)	2·30	20
1576	1000r. Anatoly Karpov (1975–85)	2·75	20
1571/1576 *Set of 6*		7·00	90
MS1577 70 × 87 mm. 1500r. Garry Kasparov (1985–2000) (31 × 38 *mm*). P 12½		4·75	90

1996 (3 Oct). *Mammals and their Young. T* **303** *and similar multicoloured designs. Litho.* P 13.

1578	100r. Type **303**	30	10
1579	200r. Lion (*Panthera leo*)	45	10
1580	300r. Malayan tapir (*Tapirus indicus*)	65	20
1581	500r. Bactrian camel (*Camelus ferus*)	1·30	20
1582	900r. Ibex (*Capra ibex*) (*vert*)	2·10	20
1583	1000r. Californian sealion (*Zalophus californianus*) (*vert*)	2·75	20
1578/1583 *Set of 6*		6·75	90

1996 (8 Nov). *Dogs. T* **304** *and similar vert designs. Multicoloured. Litho.* P 13.

1584	200r. Type **304**	45	10
1585	300r. Labrador retriever	65	20
1586	500r. Dobermann pinscher	1·30	20
1587	900r. German shepherd	2·10	20
1588	1000r. Boxer	2·40	30
1584/1588 *Set of 5*		6·25	90

1996 (15 Dec). *Ships. T* **305** *and similar horiz designs. Multicoloured. Litho.* P 13.

1589	200r. Type **305**	45	10
1590	300r. Phoenician warship, 1500–1000 B.C.	65	20
1591	500r. Roman war galley, 264–241 B.C.	1·30	20
1592	900r. 19th-century full-rigged ship	2·10	20
1593	1000r. *Siris* (paddle-steamer), 1838	2·40	30
1589/1593 *Set of 5*		6·25	90
MS1594 90 × 60 mm. 1500r. *Great Eastern* (cable ship and paddle-steamer), 1858 (39 × 31 *mm*). P 12½		4·75	90

306 Silver Pagoda, Phnom Penh

307 Ship and Helicopter

1996 (21 Dec). *45th Anniv of Cambodian Membership of Universal Postal Union. Litho.* P 12½.

1595	**306** 200r. multicoloured	55	20
1596	400r. multicoloured	1·10	35
1597	900r. multicoloured	2·10	85

1996 (23 Dec). *25th Anniv of Greenpeace (environmental organization). T* **307** *and similar vert designs. Multicoloured. Litho.* P 13.

1598	200r. Type **307**	75	10
1599	300r. Float-helicopter hovering over ship	1·40	20
1600	500r. Helicopter on deck and motor launches	2·10	30
1601	900r. Helicopter with two barrels suspended beneath	3·75	35
1598/1601 *Set of 4*		7·25	85
MS1602 111 × 90 mm. 1000r. Float-helicopter (31 × 39 *mm*). P 12½		4·75	90

304 Rough Collie

305 Chinese Junk

308 Ox

1996 (28 Dec). *New Year. Year of the Ox. T **308** and similar horiz designs showing details of painting by Han Huang. Multicoloured. Litho.* P 13 × 12½.

1603	500r. Type **308**	65	20
	a. Horiz. strip. Nos. 1603/7 plus label		
1604	500r. Ox with head turned to right (upright horns)	65	20
1605	500r. Brown and white ox with head up ("handlebar" horns)	65	20
1606	500r. Ox with head in bush ("ram's" horns)	65	20
1603/1606 *Set of 4*		2·40	75

Nos. 1603/6 were issued together in horizontal *se-tenant* strips of four stamps with central half stamp-size label showing front-view of an ox.

309 Dam, Phnom Kaun Sat

1996 (30 Dec). *Tenth International United Nations Volunteers Day. T **309** and similar horiz designs. Multicoloured. Litho.* P 13.

1607	100r. Type **309**	30	10
1608	500r. Canal, O Angkrung	1·40	45
1609	900r. Canal, Chrey Krem	2·50	85

310 Architect's Model of Reservoir

311 Players

1996 (30 Dec). *43rd Anniv of Independence. Water Management. T **310** and similar horiz designs. Multicoloured. Litho.* P 13.

1610	100r. Type **310**	30	10
1611	500r. Reservoir	1·40	45
1612	900r. Reservoir (*different*)	2·50	85

1997 (6 Jan). *World Cup Football Championship, France (1998) (2nd issue). T **311** and similar vert designs showing football action. Litho.* P 13.

1613	100r. multicoloured	30	10
1614	200r. multicoloured	45	10
1615	300r. multicoloured	75	20
1616	500r. multicoloured	1·30	20
1617	900r. multicoloured	2·30	20
1618	1000r. multicoloured	2·75	20
1613/1618 *Set of 6*		7·00	90
MS1619 99 × 68 mm. 2000r. multicoloured (39 × 31 *mm*)		4·75	90

312 Two Elephants

E **313** Bohemiam Waxwing (*Bombycilla garrulus*)

(Des G. Vásárhelyi. Litho)

1997 (12 Feb). *The Indian Elephant (Elephas maximus). T **312** and similar horiz designs. Multicoloured.* P 12½.

1620	300r. Type **312**	30	10
	a. Strip of 4. Nos. 1620/3		
1621	500r. Group of three	55	20
1622	900r. Elephants fighting	1·10	30
1623	1000r. Adult and calf	1·30	35
1620/1623 *Set of 4*		3·00	85

Nos. 1620/3 were issued together in *se-tenant* strips of four stamps within the sheet.

1997 (20 Feb). *EXPRESS MAIL SERVICE. Birds. Type* E **313** *and similar vert designs. Multicoloured. Litho.* P 13.

E1624	600r. Type E **313**	1·10	45
E1625	900r. Great grey shrike (*Lanius excubitor*)	1·30	65
E1626	1000r. Eurasian tree sparrow (*Passer montanus*)	1·80	75
E1627	2000r. Black redstart (*Phoenicurus phoenicurus*)	3·50	1·70
E1628	2500r. Reed bunting (*Emberiza schoeniclus*)	4·75	2·00
E1629	3000r. Ortolan bunting (*Emberiza hortulana*)	5·25	2·50
E1624/1629 *Set of 6*		16·00	7·25

314 Horse-drawn Water Pump, 1731

315 Statue on Plinth

1997 (11 Mar). *Fire Engines. T **314** and similar horiz designs. Multicoloured. Litho.* P 13.

1630	200r. Type **314**	30	10
1631	500r. Putnam horse-drawn water pump, 1863	45	10
1632	900r. Merryweather horse-drawn engine, 1894	65	20
1633	1000r. Shand Mason Co horse-drawn water pump, 1901	85	20
1634	1500r. Maxin Motor Co automatic pump, 1949	1·30	20
1635	4000r. Merryweather exhaust pump, 1950	3·50	20
1630/1635 *Set of 6*		6·25	90
MS1636 106 × 87 mm. 5400r. Mack Truck Co mechanical ladder, 1953 (39 × 31 *mm*)		4·75	90

1997 (26 Mar). *Angkor Wat. T **315** and similar designs. Litho.* P 12½.

1637	300r. black and rose-red	30	10
1638	300r. black and light blue	30	10
1639	800r. black and green	65	10
1640	1500r. black and orange-brown	1·30	10

1641	1700r. black and yellow-orange		1·50	20
1642	2500r. black and greenish blue		1·90	20
1643	3000r. black and deep green		2·50	20
1637/1643 *Set of 7*			7·50	90

Designs: *Vert*—No. 1638, Statue in wall recess; 1639, Walled courtyard; 1640, Decorated panel with two figures. *Horiz*—No. 1641, Rectangular gateway; 1642, Statues and arched gateway; 1643, Stupa and ruins.

316 Steller's Eider (*Polysticta stelleri*)

317 Von Stephan

1997 (7 Apr). *Aquatic Birds.* T **316** *and similar horiz designs. Multicoloured. Litho.* P 13.

1644	200r. Type **316**	10	10
1645	500r. Egyptian goose (*Alopochen aegyptiacus*)	25	10
1646	900r. American wigeon (*Anas americana*)	40	20
1647	1000r. Falcated teal (*Anas falcatai*)	45	20
1648	1500r. Surf scotor (*Melanitta perspicillata*)	65	20
1649	4000r. Blue-winged teal (*Anas discors*)	1·90	20
1644/1649 *Set of 6*		3·25	90
MS1650 95 × 75 mm. 5400r. Baikal teal (*Anas formosa*) (31 × 39 *mm*). P 12½		4·75	90

No. 1644 is wrongly inscribed ("polystieta").

1997 (8 Apr). *Death Centenary of Heinrich von Stephan (founder of Universal Postal Union). Litho.* P 13.

1651	**317**	500r. blue and deep violet-blue	45	20
1652		1500r. bright green and deep olive	1·30	30
1653		2000r. chrome yellow and brown-olive	1·80	45

318 Main Entrance

319 Birman

1997 (13 Apr). *Khmer Culture. Banteay Srei Temple.* T **318** *and similar vert designs. Multicoloured. Litho.* P 13.

1654	500r. Type **318**	45	20
1655	1500r. Main and side entrances	1·30	30
1656	2000r. Courtyard	1·80	45

1997 (8 May). *Cats.* T **319** *and similar vert designs. Multicoloured. Litho.* P 13.

1657	200r. Type **319**	30	10
1658	500r. Exotic shorthair	45	10
1659	900r. Persian	65	20
1660	1000r. Turkish van	85	20

1661	1500r. American shorthair	1·30	20
1662	4000r. Scottish fold	3·50	20
1657/1662 *Set of 6*		6·25	90
MS1663 90 × 70 mm. 5400r. Sphinx (31 × 39 *mm*)		3·75	90

320 No. 488

1997 (9 June). *Steam Railway Locomotives.* T **320** *and similar horiz designs. Multicoloured. Litho.* P 12½.

1664	200r. Type **320**	30	10
1665	500r. *Frederick Smith*	45	10
1666	900r. No. 3131	65	20
1667	1000r. London Transport No. L44, Great Britain	85	20
1668	1500r. LNER No. 1711, Great Britain	1·30	20
1669	4000r. No. 60523 *Château du Soleil*	3·50	20
1664/1669 *Set of 6*		6·25	90
MS1670 79 × 60 mm. 5400r. LNER No. 2006, Great Britain. P 13		4·25	90

321 Shar-pei

1997 (4 July). *Dogs.* T **321** *and similar multicoloured designs. Litho.* P 13.

1671	200r. Type **321**	30	10
1672	500r. Chin-chin	45	10
1673	900r. Pekingese	55	20
1674	1000r. Chow-chow (*vert*)	65	20
1675	1500r. Pug (*vert*)	1·30	20
1676	4000r. Akita (*vert*)	3·50	20
1671/1676 *Set of 6*		6·00	90
MS1677 111 × 88 mm. 5400r. Chinese crested (*vert*). P 12½		3·75	90

322 Qunalom Temple

1997 (5 Aug). *30th Anniv of Association of South East Asian Nations.* T **322** *and similar horiz designs. Multicoloured. Litho.* P 13.

1678	500r. Type **322**	45	20
1679	1500r. Royal Palace	1·30	30
1680	2000r. National Museum	1·80	45

323 15th-century Caravel

1997 (10 Sept). *Sailing Ships.* T **323** *and similar horiz designs. Multicoloured. Litho.* P 12½.

1681	200r. Type **323**	30	10
1682	500r. Spanish galleon	45	10
1683	900r. *Great Harry* (British galleon)	65	20
1684	1000r. *La Counronne* (French galleon)	85	20
1685	1500r. 18th-century East Indiaman	1·30	20
1686	4000r. 19th-century clipper	3·50	20
1681/1686 *Set of 6*		6·25	90

MS1687 94 × 68 mm. 5400r. H.M.S. *Victory* (Nelson). P 13 . . . . 4·25 90

324 Public Garden	**325** Satan's Mushroom (*Boletus satanas*)

1997 (30 Sept). *Public Gardens (Nos. 1688/91) and Tuk Chha Canal (others).* T **324** *and similar designs. Litho.* P 12½.

1688	300r. apple-green and black	30	10
1689	300r. deep rose-red and black	30	10
1690	800r. olive-yellow and black	65	10
1691	1500r. dull orange and black	1·30	10
1692	1700r. flesh and black	1·50	20
1693	2500r. turquoise-blue and black	1·90	20
1694	3000r. blue and black	2·50	20
1688/1694 *Set of 7*		7·50	90

Designs: *Horiz*—300r. (No. 1688) Statue at intersection of paths; 300r. (No. 1689) Hedging in triangular bed; 1500r. Tree and statue of lion; 1700r. View along canal; 2500r. View across canal; 3000r. Closed lock gates. *Vert*—800r. Mounted bowl.

1997 (5 Oct). *Fungi.* T **325** *and similar vert designs. Multicoloured. Litho.* P 13.

1695	200r. Type **325**	30	10
1696	500r. *Amanita regalis*	45	10
1697	900r. *Morchella semilibera*	65	20
1698	1000r. *Gomphus clavatus*	85	20
1699	1500r. *Hygrophorus hypothejus*	1·30	20
1700	4000r. *Albatrellus confluens*	3·50	20
1695/1700 *Set of 6*		6·25	90

MS1701 110 × 89 mm. 5400r. Red-cracked boletus (*Boletus chrysenteron*). P 12½ . . . . 4·75 90

326 Peaceful Fightingfish (*Betta imbellis*) and Siamese Fightingfish (*Betta splendens*)

1997 (8 Nov). *Fishes.* T **326** *and similar horiz designs. Multicoloured. Litho.* P 13.

1702	200r. Type **326**	20	10
1703	500r. Banded gourami (*Colisa fasciata*)	25	10
1704	900r. Rosy barbs (*Puntius conchonius*)	40	20
1705	1000r. Paradise fish (*Macropodus concolor*)	55	20
1706	1500r. *Epalzeorhynchos frenatus*	1·00	20
1707	4000r. *Capoeta tetrazona*	2·10	20
1702/1707 *Set of 6*		4·00	90

MS1708 96 × 72 mm. 5400r. Harlequin fish (*Rasbora heteromorpha*) . . . . 4·75 90

327 Kamput Post Office	**328** *Orchis militaris*

1997 (9 Nov). *44th Anniv of Independence.* T **327** *and similar horiz designs. Multicoloured. Litho.* P 13.

1709	1000r. Type **327**	85	30
1710	3000r. Prey Veng Post Office	2·75	65

1997 (7 Dec). *Orchids.* T **328** *and similar vert designs. Multicoloured. Litho.* P 13.

1711	200r. Type **328**	20	10
1712	500r. *Orchiaceras bivonae*	30	10
1713	900r. *Orchiaceras spuria*	50	20
1714	1000r. *Gymnadenia conopsea*	60	20
1715	1500r. *Serapias neglecta*	1·30	20
1716	4000r. *Pseudorhiza bruniana*	2·75	20
1711/1716 *Set of 6*		5·00	90

MS1717 70 × 90 mm. 5400r. *Dactylodenia wintonii* . . . . 4·75 90

329 In Black Jacket	**330** Player with Ball

1997 (15 Dec). *Diana, Princess of Wales Commemoration.* T **329** *and similar vert designs. Multicoloured. Litho.* P 12½.

1718	100r. Type **329**	15	10
	a. Sheetlet. Nos. 1718/25 plus label		
1719	200r. In black dress	15	10
1720	300r. In blue jacket	15	10
1721	500r. Close-up of Princess in visor	30	10
1722	1000r. In mine-protection clothing	50	10
1723	1500r. With Elizabeth Dole	85	10
1724	2000r. Holding landmine	1·20	20
1725	2500r. With Mother Teresa and Sisters of Charity	1·40	20
1718/1725 *Set of 8*		4·25	90

Nos. 1718/25 were issued together in sheetlets of 8 stamps and one label showing a map and a mine warning sign.

1998 (10 Jan). *World Cup Football Championship, France (3rd issue). T* **330** *and similar horiz designs showing footballing scenes. Litho. P* 12.

1726	200r. multicoloured	15	10
1727	500r. multicoloured	25	10
1728	900r. multicoloured	45	20
1729	1000r. multicoloured	55	20
1730	1500r. multicoloured	80	20
1731	4000r. multicoloured	2·30	20
1726/1731 *Set of 6*		4·00	90

MS1732 110 × 90 mm. 5400r. multicoloured (39 × 31 *mm*). P 13 ... 3·25 90

331 Suorprat Gateway

332 Tiger Cub (*Panthera tigris*)

1998 (31 Jan). *Temple Ruins. T* **331** *and similar designs. Litho.* P 12½.

1733	300r. bright orange and black	20	10
1734	500r. rose and black	30	10
1735	1200r. pale orange and black	45	10
1736	1500r. pale orange and black	65	10
1737	1700r. new blue and black	75	20
1738	2000r. light green and black	95	20
1739	3000r. bright lilac and black	1·50	20
1733/1739 *Set of 7*		4·25	90

Designs: *Horiz*—No. 1734, Kumlung wall; 1735, Bapuon entrance; 1737, Prerup; 1738, Preah Khan. *Vert*—No. 1736, Palilai; 1739 Bayon.

1998 (5 Feb). *New Year. Year of the Tiger. T* **332** *and similar multicoloured designs. Litho.* P 13.

1740	200r. Type **332**	20	10
1741	500r. Tiger and cubs	30	10
1742	900r. Tiger on alert	45	20
1743	1000r. Tiger washing itself (*horiz*)	55	20
1744	1500r. Tiger lying in grass (*horiz*)	80	20
1745	4000r. Tiger snarling (*horiz*)	2·30	20
1740/1745 *Set of 6*		4·00	90

MS1746 120 × 90 mm. 5400r. Tiger on rock (31 × 39 *mm*). P 12½ ... 3·25 90

333 Oakland, Antioch and Eastern Electric Locomotive No. 105

1998 (2 Mar). *Railway Locomotives. T* **333** *and similar triangular designs. Multicoloured. Litho.* P 12½.

1747	200r. Type **333**	20	10
	a. Pair. Nos. 1747/8		
1748	500r. New York, Westchester and electric locomotive No. 1	45	10
1749	900r. Spokane and Inland electric locomotive No. MII	55	20
	a. Pair. Nos. 1749/50		
1750	1000r. International Railway electric locomotive	75	20

1751	1500r. British Columbia Electric Railway locomotive No. 823	1·10	20
	a. Pair. Nos. 1751/2		
1752	4000r. Southern Pacific electric locomotive No. 200	3·00	20
1747/1752 *Set of 6*		5·50	90

MS1753 88 × 94 mm. 5400r. Storage battery locomotive (*vert triangle*) ... 3·75 90

Nos. 1747/8, 1749/50 and 1751/2 respectively were issued in *se-tenant* pairs within their sheets.

334 Rottweiler

335 Stag Beetle (*Lucanus cervus*)

1998 (31 Mar). *Dogs. T* **334** *and similar vert designs. Multicoloured. Litho.* P 12½.

1754	200r. Type **334**	15	10
1755	500r. Beauceron	35	10
1756	900r. Boxer	50	20
1757	1000r. Siberian husky	60	20
1758	1500r. Welsh Pembroke corgi	85	20
1759	4000r. Basset hound	2·30	20
1754/1759 *Set of 6*		4·25	90

MS1760 110 × 89 mm. 5400r. Schnauzer (28 × 37½ *mm*) ... 3·75 90

1998 (10 Apr). *Beetles. T* **335** *and similar horiz designs. Multicoloured. Litho.* P 12½.

1761	200r. Type **335**	20	10
1762	500r. *Carabus auronitens* (ground beetle)	45	10
1763	900r. Alpine longhorn beetle (*Rosalia alpina*)	65	20
1764	1000r. *Geotrupes* (dor beetle)	75	20
1765	1500r. *Megasoma elephas*	1·10	20
1766	4000r. *Chalcosoma*	2·75	20
1761/1766 *Set of 6*		5·25	90

MS1767 110 × 90 mm. 5400r. *Leptura rubra* (longhorn beetle). P 13 ... 3·75 90

336 Prerup Temple

1998 (13 Apr). *Khmer Culture. T* **336** *and similar horiz designs. Multicoloured. Litho.* P 13.

1768	500r. Type **336**	30	20
1769	1500r. Bayon Temple	75	30
1770	2000r. Angkor Vat	1·10	45

337 Cutter

1998 (7 May). *Ships. T* **337** *and similar horiz designs. Multicoloured. Litho.* P 13.

1771	200r. Type **337**	20	10
1772	500r. *Britannia* (mail paddle-steamer, 1840)	45	10
1773	900r. *Viking longship, Gokstad*	65	20
1774	1000r. *Great Britain* (steam/sail)	75	20
1775	1500r. Medieval coasting nau	1·10	20
1776	4000r. Full-rigged ship (inscr "Fregate")	2·75	20
1771/1776 *Set of 6*		5·25	90
MS1777 110 × 91 mm. 5400r. *Tartane* (fishing boat) (39 × 31 *mm*)		3·75	90

340 "Baptism of Christ" (Gerard David)   **342** Post Box, 1997

341 *Phyciodes tharos*

338 Scottish Fold   **339** *Petasites japonica*

1998 (8 June). *Domestic Cats. T* **338** *and similar horiz designs. Multicoloured. Litho.* P 13.

1778	200r. Type **338**	15	10
1779	500r. Ragdoll	35	10
1780	900r. Cymric	50	20
1781	1000r. Devon rex	60	20
1782	1500r. American curl	85	20
1783	4000r. Sphinx	2·30	20
1778/1783 *Set of 6*		4·25	90
MS1784 90 × 108 mm. 5400r. Japanese bobtail (39 × 31 *mm*). P 12½		3·75	90

1998 (15 July). *Flowers. T* **339** *and similar vert designs. Multicoloured. Litho.* P 13.

1785	200r. Type **339**	15	10
1786	500r. *Gentiana triflora*	30	10
1787	900r. *Doronicum cordatum*	50	20
1788	1000r. *Scabiosa japonica*	55	20
1789	1500r. *Magnolia sieboldii*	75	20
1790	4000r. *Erythronium japonica*	2·30	20
1785/1790 *Set of 6*		4·00	90
MS1791 90 × 110 mm. China aster (*Callistephus chinensis*) (30 × 36 *mm*)		3·25	90

1998 (5 Sept). *"Italia '98" International Stamp Exhibition, Milan. Paintings. T* **340** *and similar multicoloured designs. Litho.* P 12½ × 13.

1792	200r. Type **340**	20	10
1793	500r. "Madonna of Martin van Nuwenhoven" (Hans Memling)	30	10
1794	900r. "Baptism of Christ" (Hendrich Holtzius)	55	20
1795	1000r. "Christ with the Cross" (Luis de Morales)	65	20
1796	1500r. "Elias in the Desert" (Dirk Bouts)	95	20
1797	4000r. "The Virgin" (Petrus Christus)	2·75	20
1792/1797 *Set of 6*		4·75	90
MS1798 87 × 107 mm. 5400r. "The Immaculate Conception" (Bartolomé Murillo) (39 × 31 *mm*). P 12½		3·75	90

1998 (3 Oct). *Butterflies. T* **341** *and similar horiz designs. Multicoloured. Litho.* P 12½.

1799	200r. Type **341**	20	10
1800	500r. *Pararge megera*	30	10
1801	900r. Monarch (*Danaus plexippus*)	55	20
1802	1000r. Apollo (*Parnassius apollo*)	65	20
1803	1500r. Swallowtail (*Papilio machaon*)	95	20
1804	4000r. *Eumenis semele*	2·75	20
1799/1804 *Set of 6*		4·75	90
MS1805 91 × 110 mm. 5400r. Blur morpho (*Morpho rhetenor*) (39 × 31 *mm*)		3·75	90

1998 (9 Oct). *World Post Day. T* **342** *and similar vert design. Multicoloured. Litho.* P 13.

1806	1000r. Type **342**	55	30
1807	3000r. Wall-mounted post box, 1951	1·40	65

343 Big-Headed Turtle (*Platysternon megacephalum*)

1998 (8 Nov). *Tortoise and Turtles. T* **343** *and similar horiz designs. Multicoloured. Litho.* P 13.

1808	200r. Type **343**	15	10
1809	500r. Green turtle (*Chelonia mydas*)	25	10

1810	900r. American soft-shelled turtle (*Trionyx spiniferus*)	40	20
1811	1000r. Hawksbill turtle (*Eretmochelys imbricata*)	50	20
1812	1500r. Aldabra tortoise (*Megalochelys gigantea*)	70	20
1813	4000r. Leatherback sea turtle (*Dermochelys coriacea*)	2·00	20
1808/1813 *Set of 6*		3·50	90
MS1814 111 × 84 mm. 5400r. Matamata turtle (*Chelus fimbriatus*) (39 × 31 *mm*)		3·25	90

344 Bayon Dance

1998 (9 Nov). *45th Anniv of Independence. T* **344** *and similar horiz designs. Multicoloured. Litho.* P 12½.

1815	500r. Type **344**	35	20
1816	1500r. Bayon dance (*different*)	85	30
1817	2000r. Bayon dance (*different*)	1·20	45

345 Cheetah (*Acinonyx jubatus*)

1998 (4 Dec). *Big Cats. T* **345** *and similar multicoloured designs. Litho.* P 12½.

1818	200r. Type **345**	15	10
1819	500r. Snow leopard (*Panthera uncia*)	25	10
1820	900r. Ocelot (*Felis pardalis*)	40	20
1821	1000r. Leopard (*Panthera pardus*)	50	20
1822	1500r. Serval (*Felis serval*)	70	20
1823	4000r. Jaguar (*Panthera onca*)	2·00	20
1818/1823 *Set of 6*		3·50	90
MS1824 90 × 109 mm. 5400r. Tiger (*Panthera tigris*) (31 × 39 *mm*). P 13		3·25	90

346 Rabbit

1999 (5 Jan). *New Year. Year of the Rabbit. T* **346** *and similar multicoloured designs showing rabbits. Litho.* P 12½.

1825	200r. Type **346**	30	10
1826	500r. Facing left	45	10
1827	900r. Sitting in bush	75	20
1828	1000r. Sitting on rock	85	20
1829	1500r. Sitting upright	1·40	20
1830	4000r. Head looking out from grass (*vert*)	3·75	20
1825/1830 *Set of 6*		6·75	90
MS1831 110 × 84 mm. 5400r. Rabbit (39 × 31 *mm*). P 13		3·75	90

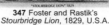

347 Foster and Rastik's Stourbridge Lion, 1829, U.S.A.   **348** Aquamarine

1999 (21 Jan). *Steam Railway Locomotives. T* **347** *and similar horiz designs. Multicoloured. Litho.* P 12½.

1832	200r. Type **347**	20	10
1833	500r. *Atlantic*, 1832	30	10
1834	900r. No. O35, 1934	45	20
1835	1000r. Daniel Gooch's *Iron Duke*, 1847, Great Britain	60	20
1836	1500r. "4-6-0"	95	20
1837	4000r. "4-4-2"	2·50	20
1832/1837 *Set of 6*		4·50	90
MS1838 84 × 109 mm. 5400r. *Fire Fly*, 1840, Great Britain (39 × 31 *mm*)		3·75	90

1999 (28 Jan). *Minerals. T* **348** *and similar multicoloured designs. Litho.* P 12½.

1839	200r. Type **348**	10	10
1840	500r. Cat's eye	20	10
1841	900r. Malachite	35	20
1842	1000r. Emerald	45	20
1843	1500r. Turquoise	65	20
1844	4000r. Ruby	1·80	20
1839/1844 *Set of 6*		3·25	90
MS1845 107 × 88 mm. 5400r. Diamond (39 × 31 *mm*). P 13		3·75	90

349 Alsatian   **350** La Rapide, 1881

1999 (3 Feb). *Dogs. T* **349** *and similar multicoloured designs. Litho.* P 12½.

1846	200r. Type **349**	20	10
1847	500r. Shih tzu (*horiz*)	30	10
1848	900r. Tibetan spaniel (*horiz*)	50	20
1849	1000r. Ainu-ken	55	20
1850	1500r. Lhassa apso (*horiz*)	90	20
1851	4000r. Tibetan terrier (*horiz*)	2·50	20
1846/1851 *Set of 6*		4·50	90
MS1852 109 × 88 mm. 5400r. Tosa inu (31 × 39 *mm*)		3·75	90

1999 (5 Mar). *Cars. T* **350** *and similar horiz designs. Multicoloured. Litho.* P 12½.

1853	200r. Type **350**	15	10
1854	500r. Car designed by Frank Duryea, 1895	25	10
1855	900r. Car designed by Marius Barbarou, 1898	40	20
1856	1000r. Panhard, 1898	50	20

1857	1500r. Mercedes-Benz "Tonneau", 1901	70	20
1858	4000r. Ford, 1915	2·00	20
1853/1858	Set of 6	3·50	90

MS1859 108 × 86 mm. 5400r. Car designed by Siegfried Marcus, 1875 (39 × 31 mm) . . . . 3·75 90

351 Ragdoll   353 *Araschnia levana*

352 Dragon Bridge

1999 (30 Mar). *Cats. T* **351** *and similar vert designs. Multicoloured. Litho.* P 13.

1860	200r. Type 351	20	10
1861	500r. Russian blue	25	10
1862	900r. Bombay	50	20
1863	1000r. Siamese	55	20
1864	1500r. Oriental shorthair	95	20
1865	4000r. Somali	2·50	20
1860/1865	Set of 6	4·50	90

MS1866 84 × 109 mm. 5400r. Egyptian mau (31 × 38 mm) . . . . 3·75 90

1999 (13 Apr). *Khmer Culture. T* **352** *and similar horiz designs. Multicoloured. Litho.* P 13.

1867	500r. Type 352	25	20
1868	1500r. Temple of 100 Columns, Kratié	80	30
1869	2000r. Krapum Chhouk, Kratié	1·20	45

1999 (25 Apr). *Butterflies. T* **353** *and similar multicoloured designs. Litho.* P 13.

1870	200r. Type 353	20	10
1871	500r. Painted lady (*Vanessa cardui*) (horiz)	25	10
1872	900r. *Clossiana euphrosyne*	50	20
1873	1000r. *Coenonympha hero*	55	20
1874	1500r. Apollo (*Parnassius apollo*) (horiz)	90	20
1875	4000r. *Plebejus argus*	2·50	20
1870/1875	Set of 6	3·50	90

MS1876 109 × 90 mm. 5400r. Purple-edged copper (*Palaeochrysophanus hippothoe*) (31 × 39 mm). P 12½ . . . . 3·75 90

354 Saurornitholestes

1999 (10 May). *Prehistoric Animals. T* **354** *and similar horiz designs. Multicoloured. Litho.* P 13.

1877	200r. Type 354	15	10
1878	500r. Prenocephale	20	10
1879	900r. Wuerhosaurus	40	20
1880	1000r. Muttaburrasaurus	45	20
1881	1500r. Shantungosaurus	70	20
1882	4000r. Microceratops	2·10	20
1877/1882	Set of 6	3·50	90

MS1883 111 × 84 mm. 5400r. Daspletosaurus . . . . 3·75 90

355 *Flabellina affinis*   356 "Flowers in a Vase" (Henri Fantin-Latour)

1999 (31 May). *Molluscs. T* **355** *and similar vert designs. Multicoloured. Litho.* P 13.

1884	200r. Type 355	20	10
1885	500r. *Octopus macropus*	30	10
1886	900r. *Helix hortensis*	55	20
1887	1000r. *Lima hians*	65	20
1888	1500r. *Arion empiricorum*	95	20
1889	4000r. Swan mussel (*Anodonta cygnaea*)	2·75	20
1884/1889	Set of 6	4·75	90

MS1890 110 × 84 mm. 5400r. *Eledone aldrovandii.* P 12½ . . . . 3·75 90

1999 (10 June). *"Philexfrance 99" International Stamp Exhibition, Paris. Paintings. T* **356** *and similar horiz designs. Multicoloured. Litho.* P 12½.

1891	200r. Type 356	30	10
1892	500r. "Fruit" (Paul Cézanne)	45	10
1893	900r. "Table and Chairs" (André Derain)	75	20
1894	1000r. "Vase on a Table" (Henri Matisse)	85	20
1895	1500r. "Tulips and Marguerites" (Othon Friesz)	1·40	20
1896	4000r. "Still Life with Tapestry" (Matisse)	3·75	20
1891/1896	Set of 6	6·75	90

MS1897 107 × 84 mm. 5400r. "Still Life with Tapestry" (detail) (Cézanne). P 13 . . . . 3·75 90

357 Prasat Neak Poan   358 Pagoda, Tongzhou

1999 (30 June). *Temples. T* **357** *and similar designs. Litho.* P 12½.

1898	100r. deep ultramarine and black	20	10
1899	300r. bright scarlet and black	20	10
1900	500r. brown-olive and black (vert)	30	10
1901	1400r. emerald and black	85	10
1902	1600r. magenta and black	95	20

1903	1800r. bright violet and black (*vert*)	1·10	20
1904	1900r. deep yellow-brown and black	1·20	20
1898/1904 *Set of 7*		4·25	90

Designs:—300r. Statue, Neak Poan; 500r. Banteay Srey; 1400r. Banteay Samré; 1600r. Banteay Srey; 1800r. Bas-relief, Angkor Vat; 1900r. Brasat Takeo.

1999 (12 July). *"China 1999" International Stamp Exhibition, Peking. T **358** and similar vert designs. Multicoloured. Litho.* P 12½.

1905	200r. Type **358**	20	10
	a. Sheetlet. Nos. 1905/12 plus label		
1906	500r. Pagoda, Tianning Temple	30	10
1907	900r. Pagoda, Summer Palace	75	10
1908	900r. Pagoda, Blue Cloud Temple	75	10
1909	1000r. White pagoda, Bei Hai	75	10
1910	1000r. Pagoda, Scented Hill	75	10
1911	1500r. Pagoda, Yunju Temple	1·30	20
1912	4000r. White pagoda, Miaoying Temple	3·25	20
1905/1912 *Set of 8*		4·50	90

Nos. 1905/12 were issued together in *se-tenant* sheetlets of eight stamps and one inscribed label.

359 *Cymbidium insigne*

361 Emblem

360 Northern Bullfinch (*Pyrrhula pyrrhula*)

1999 (5 Aug). *Orchids. T **359** and similar vert designs. Multicoloured. Litho.* P 13.

1913	200r. Type **359**	20	10
1914	500r. *Papillonanthe teres*	30	10
1915	900r. Panisea uniflora	55	20
1916	1000r. *Euanthe sanderiana*	65	20
1917	1500r. *Dendrobium trigonopus*	95	20
1918	4000r. *Vanda coerulea*	2·75	20
1913/1918 *Set of 6*		4·75	90
MS1919 109 × 80 mm. 5400r. *Paphiopedilum callosum (26 × 36 mm)*. P 12½		3·75	90

1999 (5 Sept). *Birds. T **360** and similar horiz designs. Multicoloured. Litho.* P 13.

1920	200r. Type **360**	30	10
1921	500r. Hawfinch (*Coccothraustes coccothraustes*)	45	10
1922	900r. Western greenfinch (*Carduelis chloris*)	75	20
1923	1000r. Yellow warbler (*Dendroica petechia*)	85	20
1924	1500r. Great grey shrike (*Lanius excubitor*)	1·40	20
1925	4000r. Blue tit (*Parus caeruleus*)	3·75	20
1920/1925 *Set of 6*		6·75	90
MS1926 109 × 85 mm. 5400r. European robin (*Erithacus rubecula*) (39 × 30 mm)		3·75	90

1999 (11 Sept). *46th Anniv of Independence. T **361** and similar horiz designs. Multicoloured. Litho.* P 12½.

1927	500r. Type **361**	30	20
1928	1500r. People with symbols of transport and industry	75	30
1929	2000r. People queueing to vote	1·10	45

362 Tiger Barbs (*Capoeta tetrazona*)

1999 (20 Sept). *Fishes. T **362** and similar horiz designs. Multicoloured. Litho.* P 12½.

1930	200r. Type **362**	30	10
1931	500r. Rainbow shark minnow (*Epalzeorhynchos frenatus*)	45	10
1932	900r. Clown rasbora (*Rasbora kalochroma*)	75	20
1933	1000r. Orange-spotted cichlid (*Etroplus maculatus*)	85	20
1934	1500r. Crescent betta (*Betta imbellis*)	1·40	20
1935	4000r. Honey gourami (*Colisa sota*)	3·75	20
1930/1935 *Set of 6*		6·75	90
MS1936 109 × 84 mm. 5400r. Eyespot pufferfish (*Tetraodon biocellatus*) (39 × 31 mm). P 13		3·75	90

363 Harpy Eagle (*Harpia harpyja*)

1999 (5 Oct). *Birds of Prey. T **363** and similar multicoloured designs. Litho.* P 13.

1937	200r. Type **363**	30	10
1938	500r. Bateleur (*Terathopius ecaudatus*) (*vert*)	45	10
1939	900r. Egyptian vulture (*Neophron percnopterus*) (wrongly inscr "pernopterus") (*vert*)	75	20
1940	1000r. Peregrine falcon (*Falco peregrinus*) (*vert*)	85	20
1941	1500r. Red-tailed hawk (*Buteo jamaicensis*) (*vert*)	1·40	20
1942	4000r. American bald eagle (*Haliaeetus leucocephalus*)	3·75	20
1937/1942 *Set of 6*		6·75	90
MS1943 109 × 85 mm. 5400r. Red kite (*Milvus milvus*) (31 × 39 mm). P 12½		3·75	90

364 Mail Carriage and Globe

1999 (9 Oct). *125th Anniv of Universal Postal Union. Litho.* P 12½.

1944	**364**	1600r. multicoloured	1·60	90

200R
365 Giant Panda
(*Ailuropoda melanoleuca*)

ROYAUME DU CAMBODGE **200R**
367 Dragon

368 Iguanodon (½-size illustration)

2000 (30 Jan). *Dinosaurs. T* **368** *and similar horiz designs. Multicoloured. Litho.* P 13 (**MS**1972) or 12½ (others).

1966	200r. Type **368**	20	10
1967	500r. Euoplocepalus	30	10
1968	900r. Diplosaurus	55	20
1969	1000r. Diplodocus	65	20
1970	1500r. Stegoceras	95	20
1971	4000r. Stegosaurus	2·75	20
1966/1971 Set of 6		4·75	90

MS1972 110 × 85 mm. 4500r. Brachiosaurus (32 × 40 *mm*) . . . . 3·75 90

200R *Posten 1999* **ROYAUME DU CAMBODGE**
366 Coral Snake (*Aspidelaps lubricus*)

369 Ground Beetle (*Calosoma sycophanta*)

1999 (20 Nov). *T* **365** *and similar multicoloured designs. Litho.* P 13.

1945	200r. Type **365** (wrongly inscr "Ailuropada")	20	10
1946	500r. Yak (*Bos mutus*)	30	10
1947	900r. Chinese water deer (*Hydropotes inermis*)	55	20
1948	1000r. Eurasian water shrew (*Neomys fodiens*) (*horiz*)	65	20
1949	1500r. European otter (*Lutra lutra*) (*horiz*)	95	20
1950	4000r. Tiger (*Panthera tigris*) (*horiz*)	2·75	20
1945/1950 Set of 6		4·75	90

MS1951 110 × 81 mm. 5400r. Père David's deer (*Elaphurus davidianus*) (39 × 31 mm). P 12½ . . . . 3·75 90

1999 (6 Dec). *Snakes. T* **366** *and similar horiz designs. Multicoloured. Litho.* P 13.

1952	200r. Type **366**	30	10
1953	500r. Rainbow boa (*Epicrates cenchria*)	45	10
1954	900r. Yellow anaconda (*Eunectes notaeus*)	75	20
1955	1000r. Southern ring-necked snake (*Diadophis punctatus*)	85	20
1956	1500r. Harlequin snake (*Micrurus fulvius*)	1·40	20
1957	4000r. Eastern tiger snake (*Telescopus semiannulatus*)	3·75	20
1952/1957 Set of 6		6·75	90

MS1958 107 × 81 mm. 5400r. Green python (*Chondropython viridis*) (36 × 28 *mm*) . . . . 3·75 90

2000 (5 Feb). *Insects. T* **369** *and similar horiz designs. Multicoloured. Litho.* P 13 (**MS**1979) or 12½ (others).

1973	200r. Type **369**	30	10
1974	500r. European rhinoceros beetle (*Oryctes nasicornis*)	45	10
1975	900r. Diochrysa fastuosa	75	20
1976	1000r. Blaps gigas	85	20
1977	1500r. Green tiger beetle (*Cincindela campestris*)	1·40	20
1978	4000r. Cissistes cephalotes	3·75	20
1973/1978 Set of 6		6·75	90

MS1979 107 × 85 mm. 4500r. Scarab beetle (*Scarabaeus aegyptiorum*) (40 × 32 *mm*) . . . . 3·25 90

370 Box Turtle (*Cuora amboinensis*)

371 Ox-cart carrying Rice

2000 (20 Jan). *New Year. Year of the Dragon. T* **367** *and similar vert designs. Litho.* P 13 (**MS**1965) or 12½ (others).

1959	200r. multicoloured	30	10
1960	500r. vermilion, buff and black	45	10
1961	900r. multicoloured	75	20
1962	1000r. multicoloured	85	20
1963	1500r. multicoloured	1·40	20
1964	4000r. multicoloured	3·75	20
1959/1964 Set of 6		6·75	90

MS1965 86 × 110 mm. 4500r. multicoloured . . . 3·25 90
Designs: As Type **367**—500r. Dragon enclosed in circle; 900r. Green dragon with red flames; 1000r. Heraldic dragon; 1500r. Red dragon with blue extremities; 4000r. Blue dragon with yellow flames—**MS**1965 4500r. Dragon's head (32 × 40 *mm*).

2000 (27 Feb). *"Bangkok 2000" International Stamp Exhibition. Turtles and Tortoise. T* **370** *and similar multicoloured designs. Litho.* P 13 (**MS**1986) or 12½ (others).

1980	200r. Type **370**	30	10
1981	500r. Yellow box turtle (*Cuora flavomarginata*)	45	10
1982	900r. Black-breasted leaf turtle (*Geoemyda spengleri*) (*horiz*)	75	20
1983	1000r. Impressed tortoise (*Manouria (Geochelone) impressa*) (*horiz*)	85	20
1984	1500r. Reeves' turtle (*Chinemys reevesi*) (*horiz*)	1·40	20
1985	4000r. Spiny turtle (*Heosemys spinosa*) (*horiz*)	3·75	20
1980/1985 Set of 6		6·75	90

MS1986 111 × 86 mm. 4500r. Annadal's turtle (*Hieremys annandalei*) (*horiz*) (40 × 32 *mm*) . . . . 3·25 90

2000 (1 Mar). *Rice Cultivation. T* **371** *and similar horiz designs. Litho.* P 12.

1987	100r. bright green and black		20	10
1988	300r. new blue and black		30	10
1989	500r. bright magenta and black		45	10
1990	1400r. orange-brown and black		1·10	10
1991	1600r. bright blue and black		1·50	20
1992	1900r. ochre and black		1·80	20
1993	2200r. vermilion and black		2·10	20
1987/1993 *Set of 7*			6·75	90

Designs:—100r. Type **371**; 300r. Harrowing; 500r. Threshing; 1400r. Winnowing; 1600r. Planting; 1900r. Ploughing; 2200r. Binding sheaves.

372 Jules Petiet Steam Locomotive

2000 (5 Mar). *Locomotives.* "*WIPA 2000*" *International Stamp Exhibition, Vienna* (**MS**2000). *T* **372** *and similar horiz designs. Multicoloured. Litho.* P 13 (**MS**2000) or P 12½ (others).

1994	200r. Type **372**		30	10
1995	500r. Longue Chaudière steam locomotive, 1891		45	10
1996	900r. Glehn du Busquet steam locomotive, 1891		65	20
1997	1000r. Le Grand Chocolats steam locomotive		85	20
1998	1500r. Le Pendule Fran ais diesel locomotive		1·30	20
1999	4000r. TGV 001 locomotive, 1976		3·50	20
1994/1999 *Set of 6*			6·25	90
MS2000 110 × 86 mm. 4500r. "Le Shuttle" in tunnel (80 × 32 *mm*)			3·25	90

373 Fly Agaric (*Amanita muscaria*)

375 Woman in Arched Alcove (stone carving)

374 *Betta unimaculata* and *Betta pugnax* (½-size illustration)

2000 (20 Mar). *Fungi. T* **373** *and similar vert designs. Multicoloured. Litho.* P 13 (**MS**2007) or P 12½ (others).

2001	200r. Type **373**		20	10
2002	500r. Panther cap (*Amanita pantherina*)		30	10
2003	900r. Clitocybe olearia		55	20
2004	1000r. Lactarius scrobiculatus		65	20
2005	1500r. Scleroderma vulgare		95	20
2006	4000r. Amanita verna		2·75	20
2001/2006 *Set of 6*			4·75	90
MS2007 110 × 86 mm. 4500r. Death cap (*Amanita phalloides*) (32 × 40 *mm*)			3·75	90

2000 (10 Apr). *Fighting Fish. T* **374** *and similar horiz designs. Multicoloured. Litho.* P 13 (**MS**2014) or P 12½ (others).

2008	200r. Type **374**		10	10
2009	500r. *Betta macrostoma* and *Betta taeniata*		30	10
2010	900r. *Betta foerschi* and *Betta imbellis*		65	20
2011	1000r. *Betta tessyae* and *Betta picta*		65	20
2012	1500r. *Betta edithae* and *Betta bellica*		95	20
2013	4000r. *Betta smaragdina*		2·75	20
2008/2013 *Set of 6*			4·75	90
MS2014 110 × 85 mm. 4500r. Siamese fighting fish (*Betta splendens*) (40 × 32 *mm*)			3·25	90

2000 (13 Apr). *Khmer Cultural Heritage. T* **375** *and similar vert designs. Each brown and black. Litho.* P 13.

2015	500r. Type **375**		30	20
2016	1000r. Woman in flowered headdress in rectangular bas-relief		75	30
2017	2000r. Woman with right arm raised in arched bas-relief		1·10	45

376 Galapagos Albatross (*Diomedea irrorata*)

2000 (8 May). *Sea Birds. T* **376** *and similar multicoloured designs. Litho.* P 13 (**MS**2024) or 12½ (others).

2018	200r. Type **376**		30	10
2019	500r. Kentish plover (*Charadrius alexandrinus*) (*vert*)		45	10
2020	900r. Blue-footed booby (*Sula nebouxii*)		65	20
2021	1000r. Common tern (*Sterna hirundo*)		85	20
2022	1500r. Herring gull (*Larus argentatus*) (*vert*)		1·30	20
2023	4000r. Whiskered tern (*Chlidonias hybrida*)		3·50	20
2018/2023 *Set of 6*			6·50	90
MS2024 108 × 83 mm. 4500r. Gannet (*Sula* (*Morus*) *bassana*)			3·25	90

377 Cypripedium macranthum

378 Rowers in Large Canoe

2000 (30 May). *Orchids. T* **377** *and similar vert designs. Multicoloured. Litho.* P 13 (**MS**2031) or 12½ × 13 (others).

2025	200r. Type **377**		30	10
2026	500r. Vandopsis gigantea		45	10
2027	900r. Calypso bulbosa		65	20
2028	1000r. Vanda luzonica		85	20
2029	1500r. Paphiopedilum villosum		1·30	20
2030	4000r. Vanda merrillii		3·50	20
2025/2030 *Set of 6*			6·50	90
MS2031 81 × 107 mm. 4500r. Paphiopedilum victoria			3·25	90

2000 (1 June). *Tourism. T* **378** *and similar horiz designs. Multicoloured. Litho.* P 13.

2032	500r. Type **378**	30	20
2033	1500r. Front of decorated canoe	75	30
2034	2000r. Temple, elephant and dancer	1·10	45

379 Weightlifting   380 Metz DLK 23-6

2000 (30 June). *Sports. T* **379** *and similar vert designs. Multicoloured. Litho.* P 12½ (**MS**2041) or 12½ × 13 (others).

2035	200r. Type **379**	20	10
2036	500r. Gymnastics	45	10
2037	900r. Baseball	55	20
2038	1000r. Tennis	65	20
2039	1500r. Basketball	1·10	20
2040	4000r. High jump	2·75	20
2035/2040 *Set of* 6		5·25	90
MS2041 110 × 85 mm. 4500r. Running		3·00	90

2000 (30 July). *Fire Engines. T* **380** *and similar vert designs. Multicoloured. Litho.* P 13 (**MS**2048) or 12½ × 13 (others).

2042	200r. Type **380**	20	20
2043	500r. Iveco-Magirus SLF 24/100	45	35
2044	900r. Metz SLF 7000 WS	55	45
2045	1000r. Iveco-Magirus TLF 24/50	65	55
2046	1500r. Saval-Konenburg RFF-11.000	1·10	90
2047	4000r. Metz TLF 24/50	2·75	2·30
2042/2047 *Set of* 6		5·25	4·25
MS2048 110 × 85 mm. 4500r. Metz TLF 16/25		6·50	5·50

381 Smooth Haired Dachshund

2000 (30 Aug). *Dachshunds. T* **381** *and similar multicoloured designs. Litho.* P 12½ (**MS**2055) or 13 (others).

2049	200r. Type **381**	20	10
2050	500r. Wire haired	45	10
2051	900r. Long haired	55	20
2052	1000r. Two smooth haired	65	20
2053	1000r. Mother and pups	1·10	20
2054	4000r. Two puppies	2·75	20
2049/2054 *Set of* 6		5·25	90
MS2055 117 × 86 mm. 4500r. Head of wire haired (32 × 40 *mm*)		3·00	90

382 Rover 12 C (1912)

2000 (30 Sept). *Cars. Espana* 2000 *International Stamp Exhibition, Madrid.* (**MS**2062). *T* **382** *and similar horiz designs. Multicoloured. Litho.* P 13.

2056	200r. Type **382**	20	10
2057	500r. Austin 30 CV (1907)	45	10
2058	900r. Rolls-Royce Silver Ghost (1909)	55	20
2059	1000r. Graham Paige (1929)	65	20
2060	1500r. Austin 12 (1937)	1·10	20
2061	4000r. Mercedes-Benz 300SL (1957)	2·75	20
2056/2061 *Set of* 6		5·25	90
MS2062 110 × 86 mm. 4500r. MG (1936) (40 × 32 *mm*)		3·00	90

383 18th-century Korean Painting and Two Kittens

2000 (5 Oct). *Cats. T* **383** *and similar horiz designs. Multicoloured. Litho.* P 13 (**MS**2069) or 12½ (others).

2063	200r. Type **383**	20	10
2064	500r. 18th-century Portuguese tiles and Tabby cat	45	10
2065	900r. Satsuma ceramic cat and two cats	55	20
2066	1000r. Goddess Basset (Egyptian) and mother cat and kittens	65	20
2067	1500r. Goddess Freya (engraving) and Tortoiseshell cat	1·10	20
2068	4000r. Japanese painting and Manx cat	2·75	20
2063/2068 *Set of* 6		5·25	90
MS2069 110 × 86 mm. 4500r. Leaping cat (40 × 32 *mm*)		3·00	90

384 Flowers, Monument and Flag   385 The Courageous Little Tailor

2000 (9 Nov). *47th Anniv of Independence. T* **384** *and similar horiz designs. Multicoloured. Litho.* P 13.

2070	500r. Type **384**	30	20
2071	1500r. Dove, monument and flag	75	30
2072	2000r. Flag, monument and crowd	1·10	45

2000 (20 Nov). *Children's Stories. T* **385** *and similar multicoloured designs. Litho.* P 12½.

2073	200r. Type **385**	20	10
2074	500r. Tom Thumb	45	10
2075	900r. Thumbelina	50	20
2076	1000r. Pinocchio (*horiz*)	65	20
2077	1500r. The Crayfish (*horiz*)	1·10	20
2078	4000r. Peter Pan (*horiz*)	2·75	20
2073/2078 *Set of* 6		5·00	90
MS2079 110 × 85 mm. 4500r. Pied Piper of Hamelin (32 × 40 *mm*)		3·00	90

386 Wattled Starling (*Creatophora cinera*)

2000 (10 Dec). *Birds. T* **386** *and similar multicoloured designs. Litho.* P 13.
2080	200r. Type **386**	20	10
2081	500r. Common starling (*Sturnus vulgaris*)	45	10
2082	900r. Pekin robin (*Leiothrix lutea*)	55	20
2083	1000r. Guianan cock of the rock (*Rupicola rupicola*)	85	20
2084	1500r. Alpine accentor (*Prunella collaris*)	1·10	20
2085	4000r. Bearded reedling (*Panurus biarmicus*) (inscr "biarnicus")	2·75	20
2080/2085 *Set of 6*		5·50	90
MS2086 85 × 110 mm. 4500r. Pygmy blue flycatcher (inscr "Muscicapula pallipes") (32 × 40 *mm*)		3·00	90

387 Johannes Gutenberg (invention of printing press)

388 Snake Head

2001 (5 Jan). *Millennium. T* **387** *and similar horiz designs. Multicoloured. Litho.* P 12½.
2087	200r. Type **387**	20	10
2088	500r. Michael Faraday (discovery of electricity)	45	10
2089	900r. Samuel Morse (invention of Morse code)	55	20
2090	1000r. Alexander Bell (invention of telephone)	65	20
2091	1500r. Enrico Fermi (discovery of nuclear fission)	1·10	20
2092	4000r. Edward Roberts (invention of personal computer)	2·75	20
2087/2092 *Set of 6*		5·25	90
MS2093 86 × 112 mm. 5400r. Christopher Columbus (discovery of America) (40 × 32 *mm*); 5400r. Neil Armstrong (first moon walk) (40 × 32 *mm*)		7·50	90

2001 (15 Jan). *Year of the Snake. T* **388** *and similar multicoloured designs. Litho.* P 13 (**MS**2100) or 12½ (others).
2094	200r. Type **388**	20	10
2095	500r. Two snakes entwined	45	10
2096	900r. Snake entwined with moon	55	20
2097	1000r. Entwined snakes (*different*)	65	20
2098	1500r. Snake encircling moon	1·10	20
2099	4000r. Three snakes' heads	2·75	20
2094/2099 *Set of 6*		5·25	90
MS2100 110 × 86 mm. 5400r. Snake head (*different*) (40 × 32 *mm*)		3·75	90

389 Sandou Ladder Transport (1910)

2001 (5 Feb). *Fire Engines. T* **389** *and similar horiz designs. Multicoloured. Litho.* P 13 (**MS**2107) or 12½ (others).
2101	200r. Type **389**	20	10
2102	500r. Gallo ladder transport (1899)	45	10
2103	900r. Merryweather appliance (1950)	55	20
2104	1000r. Merryweather ambulance (1940)	65	20
2105	1500r. Man-Metz appliance (1972)	1·10	20
2106	4000r. Roman diesel appliance (1970)	2·75	20
2101/2106 *Set of 6*		5·25	90
MS2107 111 × 87 mm. 5400r. Metropolitan steam engine (1898) (40 × 32 *mm*)		3·75	90

390 Puff Ball (*Lycoperdon perlatum*)   **391** Preah Vihear

2001 (25 Feb). *Fungi. T* **390** *and similar multicoloured designs. Litho.* P 12½.
2108	200r. Type **390**	20	10
2109	500r. *Trametes versicolor*	45	10
2110	900r. *Hypholoma sublaterium* (inscr "Hipholoma")	55	20
2111	1000r. Fly agaric (*Amanita muscaria*)	65	20
2112	1500r. *Lycoperdon umbrinum*	1·10	20
2113	4000r. *Cortinarius orellanus*	2·75	20
2108/2113 *Set of 6*		5·00	90
MS2114 111 × 84 mm. 5400r. Death cap (*Amanita phalloides*) (32 × 40 *mm*)		3·75	90

2001 (15 Mar). *Temples. T* **391** *and similar horiz designs. Litho.* P 12½.
2115	200r. blue and black	20	10
2116	300r. carmine-rose and black	30	10
2117	600r. bright green and black	45	10
2118	1000r. red-orange and black	65	10
2119	1500r. brown-olive and black	95	20
2120	1700r. violet and black	1·20	20
2121	2200r. purple-brown and black	1·40	20
2115/2121 *Set of 7*		4·75	90

Designs:—300r. Thonmanom; 600r. Tasom; 1000r. Kravan; 1500r. Takeo; 1700r. Mebon; 2200r. Banteay Kdei.

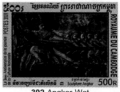

392 Angkor Wat

2001 (3 Apr). *Third Anniv of Day of Khmer Culture. T* **392** *and similar horiz designs showing bas-reliefs. Multicoloured. Litho.* P 13.

2122	500r. Type **392**	30	20
2123	1500r. Bayon Temple	1·10	30
2124	2000r. Bayon Temple (*different*)	1·40	45

393 Large Tortoiseshell (*Nymphalis polychloros*)

394 Gary Cooper

2001 (5 Apr). *Butterflies. Belgica* 2001 *International Stamp Exhibition, Brussels. T* **393** *and similar horiz designs. Multicoloured. Litho.* P 13 (**MS**2131) or 12½ (others).

2125	200r. Type **393**	20	10
2126	500r. *Cethosia hypsea*	45	10
2127	900r. *Papilio palinurus*	55	20
2128	1000r. Lesser purple emperor (*Apatura ilia*)	65	20
2129	1500r. Clipper (*Parthenos Sylvia*)	1·10	20
2130	4000r. *Morpho grandensis*	2·75	20
2125/2130 *Set of 6*		5·25	90
MS2131 111 × 85 mm. 5400r. *Heliconius melpomene* (40 × 32 *mm*)		3·75	90

2001 (25 Apr). *Cinema Actors. T* **394** *and similar vert designs. Multicoloured. Litho.* P 13.

2132	200r. Type **394**	20	10
2133	500r. Marlene Dietrich	45	10
2134	900r. Walt Disney	55	20
2135	1000r. Clark Gable	65	20
2136	1500r. Jeanette Macdonald	1·10	20
2137	4000r. Melvyn Souglas	2·75	20
2132/2137 *Set of 6*		5·25	90
MS2138 86 × 111 mm. 5400r. Rudolf Valentino (32 × 40 *mm*); 5400r. Marilyn Monroe (32 × 40 *mm*)		7·50	90

395 TVR M series (1972)

2001 (5 June). *Cars. T* **395** *and similar horiz designs. Multicoloured. Litho.* P 13.

2139	200r. Type **395**	20	10
2140	500r. Ferrari 410 (1956)	45	10
2141	900r. Peugeot 405 (1995)	55	20
2142	1000r. Fiat 8VZ (1953)	65	20
2143	1500r. Citroën Xsara (1997)	1·10	20
2144	4000r. Renault Espace (1997)	2·75	20
2139/2144 *Set of 6*		5·25	90
MS2145 111 × 85 mm. 5400r. Ferrari 250 GT (1963) (40 × 32 *mm*)		3·75	90

396 Bayon Temple

2001 (25 June). *Tourism. Bayon Temple. T* **396** *and similar horiz designs. Multicoloured. Litho.* P 12½.

2146	500r. Type **396**	30	30
2147	1500r. Faces and monument	1·10	90
2148	2000r. Face and trees	1·40	1·20

397 Steam Locomotive 4-6-0

398 Emperor Penguin (*Aptenodytes forsteri*)

2001 (15 July). *Trains. Philanippon '01 International Stamp Exhibition, Tokyo. T* **397** *and similar horiz designs. Multicoloured. Litho.* P 13 (**MS**2155) or 12½ (others).

2149	200r. Type **397**	20	20
2150	500r. Steam locomotive 4-6-4	45	35
2151	900r. Steam locomotive 4-4-0	55	45
2152	1000r. Steam locomotive 4-6-4	65	55
2153	1500r. Locomotive 4-6-2	1·10	90
2154	4000r. Locomotive 4-8-2	2·75	2·30
2149/2154 *Set of 6*		5·25	4·25
MS2155 110 × 84 mm. 5400r. Steam locomotive 2-8-2 (40 × 32 *mm*). P 13		3·75	3·25

2001 (5 Aug). *Penguins. T* **398** *and similar multicoloured designs. Litho.* P 13 (**MS**2162) or 12½ (others).

2156	200r. Type **398**	20	20
2157	500r. Jackass penguin (*Spheniscus demersus*)	45	35
2158	900r. Humboldt penguin (*Spheniscus humboldti*)	55	45
2159	1000r. Rockhopper penguin (*Eudypes crestatus*) (inscr "cristatus")	65	55
2160	1500r. King penguin (*Aptenodytes patagonica*)	1·10	90
2161	4000r. Bearded penguin (*Pygocelis antarctica*)	2·75	2·30
2156/2161 *Set of 6*		5·25	4·25
MS2162 108 × 83 mm. 5400r. Gentoo penguin (*Pygoscelis papua*) (40 × 32 *mm*)		3·75	3·25

399 Singapura

2001 (25 Aug). *Cats. T* **399** *and similar horiz designs. Multicoloured. Litho.* P 13 (**MS**2169) or 12½ (others).

2163	200r. Type **399**	10	10
2164	500r. Cymric	30	30
2165	900r. Exotic short haired (inscr "shirthair")	65	55

2166	1000r. Ragdoll	65	55
2167	1500r. Manx	1·10	90
2168	4000r. Somali	2·75	2·40
2163/2168	Set of 6	5·00	4·25
MS2169	110 × 85 mm. 5400r. Egyptian mau		
	(40 × 32 *mm*)	3·75	3·25

2189	1500r. Fennec fox (*Vulpes zerda*)	1·10	90
2190	4000r. Arctic fox (*Alopex lagopus*)	2·75	2·30
2185/2190	Set of 6	5·25	4·25
MS2191	112 × 87 mm. 5400r. Iberian wolf		
	(*Canis signatus*) (40 × 32 *mm*)	3·75	3·25

404 *Australopithecus anamensis*

400 Khleng Chak   **401** *Parodia cintiensis*

2001 (7 Sept). *Traditional Kites. T* **400** *and similar multicoloured designs. Litho. P* 12½.

2170	300r. Type **400**	20	20
2171	500r. Khleng Kanton	30	30
2172	1000r. Khleng Phnong	55	45
2173	1500r. Khleng KaunMorn	1·10	90
2174	3000r. Khleng Me Ambao	2·10	1·80
2170/2174	Set of 5	3·75	3·25

2001 (15 Sept). *Cacti. T* **401** *and similar vert designs. Multicoloured. Litho. P* 12½.

2175	200r. Type **401**	10	10
2176	500r. *Astrophytum asterias*	30	30
2177	900r. *Parodia faustiana*	65	55
2178	1000r. *Coryphantha sulcolanata*	65	55
2179	1500r. *Neochilenia hankena*	1·10	90
2180	4000r. *Mammillaria boolii* (inscr "Mamillaria")	2·75	2·40
2175/2180	Set of 6	5·00	4·25
MS2181	110 × 85 mm. 5400r. *Mammillaria* inscr "Mamilleria swinglei" (32 × 40 *mm*)	3·75	3·25

2001 (25 Oct). *Prehistoric Man. T* **404** *and similar horiz designs. Multicoloured. P* 13.

2192	100r. Type **404**	10	10
2193	200r. *Australopithecus afarensis*	20	20
2194	300r. *Australopithecus africanus*	20	20
2195	500r. *Australopithecus rudolfensis*	30	30
2196	500r. *Australopithecus boisei*	30	30
2197	1000r. *Homo habilis*	65	55
2198	1500r. *Homo erectus*	1·10	90
2199	4000r. *Homo sapiens neanderthalensis* (inscr "nesnderthalensis")	2·75	2·40
2192/2199	Set of 8	5·00	4·50
MS2200	110 × 85 mm. 5400r. *Homo sapiens sapiens* (40 × 32 *mm*)	3·75	3·25

APPENDIX

The following stamps have either been issued in excess of postal needs or have not been available to the public in reasonable quantities at face value. Such stamps may later be given full listing if there is evidence of regular postal use. Miniature sheets and imperforate stamps are excluded from this section.

Khmer Republic

1972
Moon Landing of "Apollo 16". Embossed on gold foil. Air 900r. × 2.
Visit of Pres. Nixon to China. Embossed on gold foil. Air 900r. × 2.
Olympic Games, Munich. Embossed on gold foil. Air 900r. × 2.

1973
Gold Medal Winners, Munich Olympics. Embossed on gold foil. Air 900r. × 2.
World Cup Football Championships, West Germany (1974). Embossed on gold foil. Air 900r. × 4.

1974
Pres. Kennedy and "Apollo 11". Embossed on gold foil. Air 1100r. × 2.
500th Birth Anniv of Nicolas Copernicus (astronomer). Embossed on gold foil. Air 1200r.
Centenary of Universal Postal Union. Postage 10, 60r.; Air 700r.; 1200r. embossed on gold foil.

1975
Olympic Games, Montreal (1976). Postage 5, 10, 15, 25r.; Air 50, 100, 150, 200, 250r.; 1200r. embossed on gold foil.
World Cup Football Championship, West Germany (1974). Postage 1, 5, 10, 25r.; Air 50, 100, 150, 200, 250r.; 1200r. embossed on gold foil.
Centenary of Universal Postal Union (2nd issue). Postage 15, 20, 70, 160, 180, 235r.; Air 500, 1000, 2000r.; 2000r. embossed on gold foil.

402 Fishing Dance

2001 (9 Oct). *Dances. T* **402** *and similar horiz designs. Multicoloured. Litho. P* 13.

2182	500r. Type **402**	30	30
2183	1500r. Red fish dance	1·10	90
2184	2000r. Dance of Apsara	1·50	1·30

403 Timber Wolf (*Canis occidentalis*)

2001 (15 Oct). *Wolves and Foxes. T* **403** *and similar multicoloured designs. Litho. P* 12½ (**MS**2191) *or* 13 (*others*).

2185	200r. Type **403**	20	20
2186	500r. Alaska tundra wolf (*Canis tundrorum*)	45	35
2187	900r. Fox (inscr "Vulpes fulvas")	55	45
2188	1000r. Coyote (*Canis latrans*)	65	55

Indo-China

1886. 100 Centimes = 1 Franc
1919. 100 Cents = 1 Piastre

French influence began to grow in Indo-China during the 18th century, receiving an impetus after the loss of French power in India. Missionaries were active in the area and the French bishop Pigneau de Béhaine helped Nguyen Anh to become King of Annam in 1801 and Emperor Gia-Long of Vietnam in 1802. Gia-Long's death was followed by a reaction in favour of the Confucians and French missionaries and their converts were persecuted and killed.

A joint Franco-Spanish punitive expedition under Admiral Rigault de Genouilly took Saigon in 1859, and in 1862 the Emperor Tu Duc ceded the eastern provinces of Cochin China to France. The King of Cambodia accepted a French protectorate in 1863 and in 1867 the remainder of Cochin China was occupied. French sovereignty over all Cochin China was recognised by the Treaty of Saigon in 1874.

China had claims of suzerainty over Annam and Tongking and these, combined with attacks on French ports by Chinese "Black Flag" pirates, led to war in 1884–85. China was defeated, and by the Treaty of Tientsin recognised the French protectorate over Annam and Tongking, which had been established by the Treaty of Hué signed with the Emperor Tu Duc in 1883.

By a decree of 17 October 1887 Cambodia, Cochin China, Annam and Tongking were formed into the Indochinese Union, and Laos was added in 1893, France having forced Siam to relinquish the suzerainty which she had held over parts of the territory.

A. COCHIN CHINA

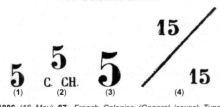

5	**5**	**5**	**15**
(1)	C. CH.	**(3)**	**(4)**
	(2)		

1886 (16 May)–**87**. *French Colonies (General issues) Type* J *surch at Saigon as* T **1**/**3**. P 14 × 13½.

1	**1**	5on 25c. ochre/*yellow*						£160	£110
2	**2**	5on 2c. brown/*buff* (1.87)						14·50	16·00
3		5on 25c. ochre/*yellow* (9.6.86)					20·00	19·00
4	**3**	5on 25c. black/*rose* (2.87)					40·00	34·00
		a. Surch inverted					—	—
		b. Surch double					£1800	
		c. Surch double, T **2**+**3**				£2750	£1500
		d. Surch triple, 2 × T **2**+**3**					£6000	

Nos. 4c/d come from a proof sheet of a 5c. on 25c. black/*rose* surcharge, as Type **2** which was unsatisfactory. This was then further surcharged as Type **3** and issued.

Nos. 1/4 were issued during shortages of the French Colonies (General issues) 5c. values. During 1888 a further surcharge as Type **4** was prepared to meet an expected shortage of the 15c. value. Type **4** was surcharged on Type J 30c. cinnamon, it being intended to bisect the stamps along the diagonal line. Further supplies of the French Colonies (General issues) 15c. were, however, received in time, and the surcharge was not issued (*Price* £42 *un*, £38 *used*).

Postage Due stamps with a diagonal surcharge "COCHIN-CHINE" were never officially issued.

Stamps of the French Colonies (General issues) continued in use until 1892, when they were replaced by Indo-China issues.

B. ANNAM AND TONGKING

A & T	A & T	A - T
1	**5**	**1**
(1)	**(2)**	**(3)**

(Handstamped at Hanoi)

1888 (21 Jan). *French Colonies (General issues) Type* J. P 14 × 13½.

(a) Surch with T **1** *or* **2**.

1	1on 2c. brown/*buff*					38·00	32·00
2	1on 4c. purple-brown/*grey*					32·00	25·00
3	5on 10c. black/*lilac*					38·00	28·00

(b) Surch as T **3**.

4	1on 2c. brown/*buff*					£250	£250
5	1on 4c. purple-brown/*grey*				£375	£425
6	5on 10c. black/*lilac*					£180	£180

Nos. 1/6 were issued during a shortage of French Colonies (General issues) 5c. stamps. A further surcharge as Type **2**, but on the 2c. brown/*buff*, was prepared but not issued.

The surcharges T **1** and **2** were printed from wooden handstamps. Specialists recognise eight different handstamps as Type **1** and four as Type **2**. Because of their construction the handstamps often show signs of wear.

Annam and Tongking continued to use stamps of French Colonies (General issues) until 1892, when they were replaced by Indo-China issues.

C. INDO-CHINA

PRINTERS. All stamps of Indo-China, except Nos. 264 to 327, were printed at the Government Printing Works, Paris, *unless otherwise stated*.

IMPERFORATE STAMPS. Stamps exist imperforate in their issued colours, but these were not valid for postage. Imperforate stamps in other colours are colour trials.

INDO-CHINE 1889	INDO-CHINE 1889	INDO-CHINE 89
5	**5**	**5**
R – D	**R – D**	**R D**
(1)	**(2)**	**(3)**

Figures "1889" 2½ mm (T **1**) or 2 mm high (T **2**)

The letters "R–D" are the initials of Messieurs Richaud, Governor of the Colony, and Démurs, Director of Posts at Saigon.

1889. *Type* J *of French Colonies (General issues) surch at Saigon as* T **1**/**3**. P 14 × 13½.

(a) Surch in red (8 Jan).

1	**1**	5on 35c. black/*orange*					70·00	60·00
		a. Surch inverted					£1100	£1100
		b. Type **2**					£160	£170
		ba. Surch inverted					£2250	£2250
		c. Pair. Nos. 1 and 1b						

(b) Surch in black (10 Jan).

2	**3**	5on 35c. black orange					11·00	9·25
		a. "89" omitted					£190	£170

Type **2** surcharge occurs at three positions in the pane of 25, the remainder being T **1**.

Nos. 1/2 were issued during a shortage of French Colonies (General issues) 5c. stamps.

INDO-CHINE   INDO-CHINE

TIMBRE   TIMBRE

COLIS POSTAUX   COLIS POSTAUX   Colis Postaux
(P **4**)   (P **5**)   (P **6**)

1891. *PARCEL POST. French Colonies (General issues) Type J.*
P 14 × 13½.

    (a) Optd with Type P **4**, *in red at Hanoi.*
P4   10c. black/*lilac* . . . . 15·00   4·25
    (b) Handstamped with Type P **5**, *in red at Hanoi.*
P5   10c. black/*lilac* £600   £500
The lines of type on the handstamp measure 12, 8½ and
16½ mm against similar measurements on Type P **4** of 10½, 6½
and 16 mm.

X "Tablet" type   **(7)**   **8** "Grasset"   (D **9**)
                      type

1892 (Nov)–**96**. *Type X inscr "INDO-CHINE" in red (*1, 5, 15, 25,
75c., 1f.*) or blue (others). P 14 × 13½.*

6	1c. black/*azure*		85	30
	a. Name double			
7	2c. brown/*buff*		1·75	1·75
8	4c. purple-brown/*grey*		1·60	2·25
	a. Name double			
9	5c. green/*pale green*		2·25	20
10	10c. black/*lilac*		3·00	90
11	15c. blue (*quadrillé paper*)		32·00	30
12	20c. red/*green*		8·00	2·25
13	25c. black/*rose*		13·00	1·10
	a. Pair, one with name omitted		£5000	£4750
	b. Grey/*pale rose*		17·00	3·25
14	30c. cinnamon/*drab*		19·00	6·00
15	40c. red/*yellow*		29·00	7·25
16	50c. carmine/*rose*		30·00	9·25
17	75c. brown/*orange*		23·00	17·00
	a. Name inverted (1893)		£4500	£4500
	b. Pair, one with name omitted			
18	1f. olive-green/*toned*		42·00	19·00
	a. Name double		£600	£600
19	5f. mauve/*pale lilac* (1896)		£100	85·00
6/19	Set of 14		£275	£140

1898. *PARCEL POST. No.* 10 *optd at Hanoi with Type* P **6** *in red.*
P20   10c. black/*lilac* . . . . 17·00   26·00

1899–1902. *PARCEL POST. Nos.* 10 *and* 24 *handstamped at
Hanoi as Type* P **5**, *but without "Indo-Chine".*
P21   10c. black/*lilac* . . . . 48·00   23·00
P22   10c. rose-red (1902) . . . . . 40·00   17·00

1900 (Dec)–**01**. *Type X. Colours changed. Inscr in blue (*10c.*) or
red (others). P 14 × 13½.*

23	5c. pale green		3·00	80
	a. Bright yellow-green (1901)		2·50	45
24	10c. rose-red		4·00	35
25	15c. grey		8·00	35
26	25c. blue		23·00	60
27	50c. brown/*azure*		15·00	2·75
23/27	Set of 5		50·00	4·75

1903. *Surch at Hanoi as T* **7**.

28	X	5on 15c. grey (4.12)		45	1·25
29		15on 25c. blue (6.8)		95	65

1904 (Mar)–**06**. *Toned or tinted paper (*1c. on white paper*). Typo.*
P 14 × 13½.

30	**8**	1c. olive-green (6.04)	20	15
31		2c. claret/*yellow* (5.04)	30	15
32		4c. magenta/*azure* (6.04)	30	15
33		5c. deep green (6.04)	1·75	15
34		10c. rose (7.04)	2·50	15
35		15c. brown/*azure*	2·50	20
36		20c. red/*green* (6.04)	3·25	40
37		25c. blue (7.04)	11·50	30
38		30c. brown/*cream* (7.04)	6·75	2·00
39		35c. black/*yellow* (1906)	18·00	1·10
40		40c. black/*greyish* (8.04)	5·00	85
41		50c. brown/*toned* (7.04)	6·75	1·10
42		75c. red/*orange* (7.04)	35·00	19·00
43		1f. pale olive-green (7.04)	21·00	3·50
44		2f. brown/*yellow* (8.04)	45·00	27·00
45		5f. violet (7.04)	£180	£140
46		10f. red/*green* (8.04)	£160	£140
30/46	Set of 17		£450	£300

1904 (26 June). *POSTAGE DUE. French Colonies (General
issues) No.* D79 *surch at Hanoi with Type* D **9**.
D47   5on 60c. brown/*buff* . . . . 8·00   10·00

1905 (22 July). *POSTAGE DUE. French Colonies (General
issues) Nos.* D68/9 *surch at Hanoi as Type* D **9**, *in red.*

D48	5on 40c. black		30·00	11·00
D49	10on 60c. black		30·00	16·00
D50	30on 60c. black		30·00	12·00

10 Annamite   **11** Cambodian   **12** Cambodian

(Des A. Puyplat. Dies eng G. Johannet. Typo)

1907 (July–Oct). *T* **10**, **11** *and vert designs as T* **12** (*Native
women*). *Centre and figures of value in black. P* 14 × 13½ *or*
13½ × 14 (*T* **12**).

51	**10**	1c. sepia (Oct)	55	15
52		2c. brown (Oct)	15	15
53		4c. blue (Oct)	20	55
54		5c. pale green	2·75	20
55		10c. scarlet	2·75	15
		a. Centre and value double		
56		15c. violet	2·75	30
57	**11**	20c. violet	3·25	2·00
58		25c. blue	7·00	15
59		30c. chocolate	9·25	5·75
60		35c. olive-green	3·25	20
61		40c. brown	4·00	2·50
62		45c. orange	12·00	5·25
63		50c. carmine	17·00	1·75
64	**12**	75c. orange	10·00	5·50
65	–	1f. lake (Annamites)	48·00	9·50
66	–	2f. green (Muong)	16·00	16·00
67	–	5f. blue (Laotian)	48·00	28·00
68	–	10f. violet (Cambodian)	85·00	80·00
51/68	Set of 18		£250	£140

These stamps perf 11 are of doubtful status.

D **13** Annamite   **(14)**   **(15)**
      Dragon

(Des and eng A Puyplat. Typo)

1908. *POSTAGE DUE*. P 14 × 13½.

D69	D **13**	2c. black	1·40	45
D70		4c. blue	40	80
D71		5c. green	1·40	25
D72		10c. carmine	3·00	20
D73		15c. violet	2·75	4·00
D74		20c. deep brown	1·75	90
D75		30c. olive-green	2·25	2·75
D76		40c. purple-brown	7·00	8·00
D77		50c. greenish blue	3·50	1·25
D78		60c. yellow	9·00	13·00
D79		1f. grey	19·00	23·00
D80		2f. yellow-brown	19·00	19·00
D81		5f. vermilion	35·00	32·00
D69/81 *Set of* 13			95·00	95·00

1912 (Nov). *Surch as T* **14/15**.

A. *Narrow spacing.*

69A	**8**	05on 4c. magenta/*azure*	4·25	7·25
70A		05on 15c. brown/*azure* (R.)	50	20
71A		05on 30c. brown/*cream*	55	2·25
72A		10on 40c. black/*greyish* (R.)	1·60	3·00
73A		10on 50c. brown/*toned* (R.)	1·10	2·50
74A		10on 75c. red/*orange*	4·00	5·50
69A/74A *Set of* 6			11·00	19·00

B. *Wide spacing.*

69B	**8**	05on 4c. magenta/*azure*	£550	£550
70B		05on 15c. brown/*azure* (R.)	24·00	24·00
71B		05on 30c. brown/*cream*	65·00	65·00
72B		10on 40c. black/*greyish* (R.)	55·00	55·00
73B		10on 50c. brown/*toned* (R.)	55·00	55·00
74B		10on 75c. red/*orange*	80·00	80·00
69B/74B *Set of* 6			£750	£750

In Type A the space between "0" and "5" is 1½ mm and between "1" and "0" 2½ mm. In Type B the spacing is 2 mm and 3 mm respectively.

5
c
5c
INDOCHINE
10 CENTS

(16) (17) (18)

1914 (Nov). *Red Cross. Surch at Hanoi with T* **16**, *in red.*

75	**10**	10c.+5c. black and scarlet	1·25	30

1915 (Feb)–**17**. *Red Cross. Surch in Paris with T* **17**, *in red.*

76	**10**	5c.+5c. black and green (1917)	35	2·50
		a. Surch double	£150	£150
77		10c.+5c. black and scarlet	45	30
78		15c.+5c. black and violet (1917)	1·25	3·00
		a. Surch four times	£150	
		b. Surch three times	£150	

1918 (Nov)–**19**. *Nos.* 76/8 *surch in addition with new value in cents, as in T* **18**.

79	4c.on 5c.+5c. black and green	3·25	5·50
	a. "4" with closed top	£170	
80	6c.on 10c.+5c. black and scarlet	2·75	5·00
81	8c.on 15c.+5c. black and violet (3.19)	10·00	17·00
	a. "8 CENTS" double	£170	

1918 (Nov). *French stamps of War Orphan's Fund (Nos.* 372/7) *surch as T* **18**, *and sold at double the face value.*

82	10c.on 15c.+10c. grey-green	2·50	3·50
	a. "10 CENTS" double	£300	£300
83	16c.on 25c.+15c. blue	5·00	7·00
84	24c.on 35c.+25c. violet and slate	7·00	12·00
	a. Surch double	£600	
	b. "24 CENTS" double	£425	£425
85	40c.on 50c.+50c. brown	14·00	23·00
86	80c.on 1f.+1f. carmine	23·00	35·00
87	4p.on 5f.+5f. blue and black	£225	£225
	a. "4 PIASTRES" double	£3250	£3250
82/87 *Set of* 6		£250	£275

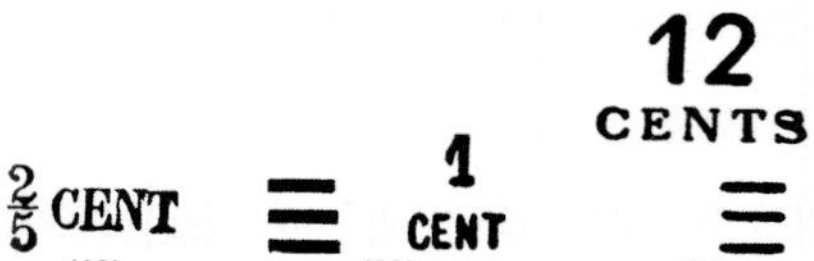
2/5 CENT
1
CENT
12
CENTS

(19) (20) (21)

1919 (Jan). *Stamps of* 1907, *surch as T* **19**.

88	**10**	⅖c.on 1c. black and sepia	1·75	20
89		⅘c.on 2c. black and brown	1·60	35
90		1⅗c.on 4c. black and blue (R.)	3·50	25
91		2c.on 5c. black and pale green	2·50	20
		a. Surch inverted	75·00	
92		4c.on 10c. black and scarlet (B.)	1·25	15
		a. "4" with closed top	10·00	1·60
		b. "4" and "CENTS" widely spaced	20·00	
		c. Surch double	80·00	
93		6c.on 15c. black and violet	3·75	20
		a. Surch inverted	80·00	
94	**11**	8c.on 20c. black and violet	4·00	90
95		10c.on 25c. black and blue	4·00	15
96		12c.on 30c. black and chocolate	6·00	1·00
97		14c.on 35c. black and olive-green	3·25	55
		a. "4" with closed top	10·50	2·75
98		16c.on 40c. black and brown	6·00	45
99		18c.on 45c. black and orange	7·50	2·50
100		20c.on 50c. black and carmine (B.)	10·50	1·10
101	**12**	30c.on 75c. black and orange (B.)	13·00	1·75
102	–	40c.on 1f. black and lake (B.)	18·00	95
103	–	80c.on 2f. black and green (R.)	16·00	6·50
		a. Surch double	£275	£200
104	–	2p.on 5f. black and blue (R.)	85·00	70·00
105	–	4p.on 10f. black and violet (R.)	£120	£120
88/105 *Set of* 18			£275	£190

1919. *POSTAGE DUE. Surch as T* **19**.

D106	D **13**	⅘c.on 2c. black (R.)	1·90	2·75
D107		1⅗c.on 4c. blue (R.)	1·90	3·25
D108		2c.on 5c. green	3·25	1·25
D109		4c.on 10c. carmine (B.)	3·00	25
D110		6c.on 15c. violet (R.)	6·75	3·25
D111		8c.on 20c. deep brown	6·50	1·25
D112		12c.on 30c. olive-green	8·25	2·00
D113		16c.on 40c. purple-brown	6·00	1·90
D114		20c.on 50c. greenish blue	13·50	7·50
D115		24c.on 60c. yellow	3·75	65
		a. Figure "4" with closed top	18·00	14·00
D116		40c.on 1f. grey	4·00	3·25
		a. Figure "4" with closed top	20·00	15·00
D117		80c.on 2f. yellow-brown	25·00	23·00
D118		2p.on 5f. vermilion (B.)	48·00	28·00
		a. Surch double	£140	£140
		b. Surch quadruple	£140	£140
D106/118 *Set of* 13			£120	70·00

A further set of surcharges as Types **20** and **21** on the 1907 issue was produced in Paris during 1922. Although specimens were supplied to the U.P.U., these stamps were not put on sale in Indo-China (*Set of* 6 £9.75 *un*).

1922 (Apr)–**23**. *As T* **10** *and* **11**, *but value in "cents" or "piastres". Head and value in black (except No.* 115). P 14 × 13½.

115	**10**	⅒c. red and grey (6.23)	15	90
116		⅕c. blue (10.22)	15	15
117		⅖c. olive-brown (10.22)	20	1·00
		a. Centre and value double	£170	£170
118		⅘c. cerise/*bluish* (10.22)	25	30
119		1c. brown (10.22)	75	15
120		2c. green (10.22)	30	15
121		3c. violet (10.22)	40	20
122		4c. orange	90	15
		a. Centre and value double	£100	£100
123		5c. carmine	35	15
		a. Centre and value double	£225	£225
124	**11**	6c. red (10.22)	50	20
125		7c. olive-green (10.22)	1·75	20
126		8c. slate/*lilac* (10.22)	1·40	65

127		9c. orange-yellow/*greenish* (10.22)	70	85
128		10c. blue	1·25	20
129		11c. violet	2·00	20
130		12c. deep brown	70	25
		a. Centre and value double (11c.+12c.)	£325	£325
131		15c. orange (10.22)	1·25	20
132		20c. blue/*straw* (10.22)	1·40	1·60
133		40c. scarlet/*bluish* (10.22)	2·25	2·00
134		1p. blue-green/*greenish* (10.22)	6·50	7·25
135		2p. purple/*rose* (10.22)	10·50	11·00
115/135 *Set of 21*			30·00	25·00

Differences in lettering of "CENTS" can be found in printings of the 4, 5, 10, 11 and 12c.

1922 (Oct). *POSTAGE DUE. As Type D* **13**, *but values in* "CENTS" *or* "PIASTRES", *in black.* P 14 × 13½.

D136		⅓c. black	15	85
D137		⅓c. scarlet	15	2·00
D138		1c. buff	40	50
D139		2c. green	1·40	65
D140		3c. violet	2·00	1·90
D141		4c. orange	1·60	2·00
		a. Value double	55·00	55·00
		b. Value omitted	£450	
D142		6c. olive-green	1·75	1·60
D143		8c. black/*lilac*	1·60	90
D144		10c. blue	1·60	1·25
D145		12c. orange/*greenish*	1·75	35
D146		20c. blue/*buff*	1·75	2·25
D147		40c. scarlet/*azure*	1·75	2·00
D148		1p. purple/*rose*	4·25	3·50
D136/148 *Set of 13*			18·00	18·00

22 Ploughman and Tower of Confucius   **23** Bay of Along

24 Ruins of Angkor   **25** Wood-carver

26 Temple, Thuat-Luong   **27** Foundling of Saigon

(T **22**/7 des Yon-Thay, P. Munier, Pham-Thong, N. Dinh Chi, Lecere and Fouqueray respectively. Dies eng A. Del (T **24**, **26**), A. Mignon (others). Typo)

1927 (26 Sept). P 14 × 13½.

136	**22**	½c. olive-green	15	2·75
137		½c. yellow	15	2·50
138		½c. pale blue	20	2·75
139		½c. brown	25	2·00
140		1c. orange	45	15
141		2c. green	60	20
142		3c. indigo	1·40	20
143		4c. pink	2·25	3·00
144		5c. violet	95	15
145	**23**	6c. scarlet	1·50	20
146		7c. blstre-brown	1·25	1·25
147		8c. olive-green	1·75	2·75

148		9c. purple	2·25	2·75
149		10c. pale blue	2·25	40
150		11c. orange	1·75	2·75
151		12c. slate	1·75	2·50
152	**24**	15c. brown and carmine	10·00	9·00
153		20c. slate and bright violet	4·50	65
154	**25**	25c. magenta and red-brown	5·75	6·00
155		30c. olive and blue	3·50	4·00
156	**26**	40c. pale blue and vermilion	5·25	4·25
157		50c. slate and yellow-green	6·25	3·00
158	**27**	1p. black, yellow and blue	12·00	12·00
		a. Yellow omitted	£170	
159		2p. blue, orange and red	22·00	15·00
136/159 *Set of 24*			80·00	75·00

Nos. 144/5 in panes of 10 with inscribed margins are from booklets.

D 28 Mt Còt Pagoda, Hanoi   **D 29** Annamite Dragon

(Des N. Dinh Chi, eng A. Delzers (D **28**); des Ng Thank Oo, eng A. Mignon (D **29**). Typo)

1927 (26 Sept). *POSTAGE DUE.* P 14 × 13½ or 13½ × 14 (D **29**).

D160	D **28**	½c. orange and maroon	15	2·25
D161		½c. black and violet	15	2·25
D162		1c. slate and red	65	1·90
D163		2c. olive and green	1·25	40
D164		3c. pale blue and plum	1·00	2·75
D165		4c. chocolate and slate-blue	1·40	40
D166		6c. red and scarlet	2·50	3·25
D167		8c. violet and olive	2·50	3·00
D168	D **29**	10c. blue	1·60	2·50
D169		12c. olive-brown	4·50	5·00
D170		20c. carmine	3·50	3·00
D171		40c. green	4·00	4·00
D172		1p. orange-red	16·00	19·00
D160/172 *Set of 13*			35·00	45·00

4 C^{TS}   **6**   **C**^{TS}   **10 C**^{TS}

(30)   (31)   (32)

1931 (13 Apr). *International Colonial Exhibition, Paris. As T* **18**/**20** *of French Sudan, inscr* "INDOCHINE" *and surch with T* **30**/**32**.

160		4c.on 50c. mauve	3·00	3·50
161		6c.on 90c. vermilion	3·25	4·25
162		10c.on 1f.50 blue	4·50	3·75

33 Junk   **34** Ruins at Angkor   **35** Rice Fields

36 "Apsara", or dancing Nymph   **D 37**

(Des N. Huu-Dau, G. Barlangue, N. Phan-Chanh and To-Ngoc-Van. Photo Vaugirard, Paris)

1931 (16 Nov)–**41**.

(a) P $13\frac{1}{2} \times 13$.

163	**33**	$\frac{1}{10}$c. greenish blue	15	2·00
164		$\frac{1}{5}$c. deep lake	15	90
165		$\frac{2}{5}$c. brown-orange	15	2·75
166		$\frac{1}{2}$c. red-brown	20	30
167		$\frac{4}{5}$c. violet	20	2·75
168		1c. sepia	20	20
169		2c. green	35	20
170	**34**	3c. brown	20	20
171		3c. green (4.10.34)	6·25	45
172		4c. deep blue	2·50	20
173		4c. blue-green (8.6.38)	1·40	2·50
174		4c. yellow (1940)	15	35
175		5c. purple	20	15
176		5c. green (1941)	45	2·50
177		6c. vermilion	20	20
178		7c. grey-black (8.6.38)	20	20
179		8c. deep lake (8.6.38)	70	1·50
180		9c. black/*yellow* (1941)	20	85
181	**35**	10c. blue	1·10	20
182		10c. blue/*pink* (1941)	35	20
183		15c. sepia	7·25	1·50
184		15c. deep blue (1.7.33)	20	40
185		18c. bright blue (8.6.38)	40	2·50
186		20c. carmine	20	15
187		21c. deep green	35	40
188		22c. blue-green (8.6.38)	50	1·50
189		25c. purple	3·00	1·25
190		25c. deep blue (1941)	85	1·50
191		30c. chestnut (18.7.32)	75	20

(b) P $13\frac{1}{2}$.

192	**36**	50c. sepia	90	15
193		60c. purple (18.7.32)	50	20
194		70c. light blue (1941)	85	1·10
195		1p. bright green	45	40
196		2p. scarlet	55	50
163/196		*Set of* 34	29·00	27·00

Nos. 175 and 177 exist in booklet panes of five stamps plus a label bearing a St. Andrew's Cross.

In 1943 30c., 50c., 1p. and 2p. stamps in these designs, but without "RF", were produced by the Pétain Government in France, but these were not sold in Indo-China (*price* £5 *set of* 4, *unused*).

(Des N. Duc Thuc. Die eng A. Mignon. Typo and photo Vaugirard, Paris)

1931 (16 Nov)–**41**. *POSTAGE DUE. Value in black or blue (1p.).* P $13\frac{1}{2} \times 13$.

D197	D **37**	$\frac{1}{5}$c. red/*yellow* (8.6.38)	15	2·75
D198		$\frac{2}{5}$c. red/*yellow*	15	2·25
D199		$\frac{4}{5}$c. red/*yellow*	20	2·25
D200		1c. red/*yellow*	15	1·75
D201		2c. red/*yellow*	20	50
D202		2,5c. red/*yellow*	35	3·00
D203		3c. red/*yellow* (8.6.38)	35	3·00
D204		4c. red/*yellow*	30	2·50
D205		5c. red/*yellow* (8.6.38)	35	3·00
D206		6c. red/*yellow*	50	1·75
D207		10c. red/*yellow*	50	1·50
D208		12c. red/*yellow*	20	2·50
D209		14c. red/*yellow* (8.6.38)	90	2·75
D210		18c. red/*yellow* (1941)	75	3·00
D211		20c. red/*yellow*	30	2·75
D212		50c. red/*yellow*	70	2·75
D213		1p. red/*yellow*	2·00	3·50
		a. Value in black	5·50	8·75
D197/213		*Set of* 17	12·00	45·00

S
E
R
V
I
C
E
(O **38**)

SERVICE
(O **39**)

SERVICE
(O **40**)

SERVICE
(O **41**)

1933 (27 Feb). *OFFICIAL. Stamps of* 1931–32 *surch.*

(a) With Type O **38**.

O197	**33**	1c. sepia (B.)	2·50	30
O198		2c. green (B.)	2·75	2·75

(b) With Type O **39**.

O199	**34**	3c. brown (B.)	2·50	2·25
		a. Opt inverted	£100	
O200		4c. deep blue (R.)	3·00	2·50
		a. Opt inverted	£100	
O201		5c. purple (B.)	2·75	25
O202		6c. vermilion (B.)	1·50	2·75

(c) With Type O **40**.

O203	**35**	10c. blue (R.)	50	40
O204		15c. sepia (B.)	2·50	85
O205		20c. carmine (B.)	3·00	45
O206		21c. deep green (B.)	1·60	3·25
O207		25c. purple (B.)	1·25	3·50
O208		30c. red-brown (B.)	3·00	2·25

(d) With Type O **41**.

O209	**36**	50c. sepia (B)	14·00	4·75
O210		60c. purple (B.)	1·25	3·00
O211		1p. bright green (B.)	42·00	12·00
O212		2p. scarlet (B.)	10·00	13·00
O197/212		*Set of* 16	85·00	48·00

42 Farman F.190

O **43**

(Des G. Barlangue. Photo Vaugirard, Paris)

1933 (1 June)–**49**. *AIR*. P $13\frac{1}{2}$.

197	**42**	1c. brown	20	1·60
198		2c. myrtle-green	15	1·25
199		5c. yellow-green	70	1·50
200		10c. purple-brown	55	50
201		11c. carmine (8.6.38)	1·60	2·25
202		15c. blue	2·25	1·60
203		16c. cerise (5.2.41)	1·10	2·75
204		20c. grey-green	2·50	1·25
205		30c. red-brown	65	30
206		36c. carmine	3·00	50
207		37c. bronze-green (8.6.38)	80	30
208		39c. olive-green (5.2.41)	65	3·00
209		60c. deep purple	1·60	1·40
210		66c. bronze-green	2·00	1·75
211		67c. light blue (5.10.38)	75	2·75
212		69c. ultramarine (5.2.41)	65	3·00
213		1p. black	30	15
214		2p. orange	60	20
215		5p. bright violet	2·75	95
216		10p. scarlet	4·75	2·75
217		20p. blue-green (13.6.49)	15·00	6·25
218		30p. brown (13.6.49)	17·00	7·25
197/218		*Set of* 22	55·00	38·00

15 values in this design, but without "RF", were produced by the Pétain Government in France during 1942–44, but these were not sold in Indo-China (*price* £10-50 *set unused*).

1934 (4 Oct). *OFFICIAL. As T* **11**, *but value in "CENTS" or "PIASTRES", diagonal opt as in Type* O **43**. P $14 \times 13\frac{1}{2}$.

O219	1c. olive	85	1·40
O220	2c. yellow-brown	1·00	1·75
O221	3c. green	2·25	2·25
O222	4c. rosine	3·50	75
O223	5c. orange	1·00	30
O224	6c. vermilion	5·25	7·25
O225	10c. grey-green (R.)	3·00	4·50
O226	15c. ultramarine	2·50	3·00
O227	20c. slate (R.)	3·25	2·50
O228	21c. bright violet	9·50	11·00
O229	25c. claret	10·00	8·75
O230	30c. slate-violet	3·25	2·75
O231	50c. magenta	8·00	12·00
O232	60c. grey	13·00	13·00

O233   1p. blue (R.) . . . . 28·00   16·00
O234   2p. scarlet . . . . 40·00   35·00
O219/234 Set of 16 . . . . £120   £110

44 Emperor Bao Dai
of Annam

45 King Sisowath
Monivong of
Cambodia

(Eng J. Piel. Recess)

1936 (20 Nov). P 13.
219 **44** 1c. brown 75   2·50
220   2c. bright green . . . . . . 1·00   2·75
221   4c. bright violet . . . . . . 1·25   45
222   5c. brown-lake . . . . 1·60   3·00
223   10c. carmine . . . . 2·50   3·25
224   15c. blue . . . . 3·00   3·25
225   20c. scarlet . . . . 2·75   3·50
226   30c. purple . . . . 2·50   3·25
227   50c. blue-green . . . . . . 3·75   3·75
228   1p. bright magenta . . . . 6·00   6·25
229   2p. black . . . . 6·25   7·25
219/229 Set of 11 . . . . 28·00   35·00

(Eng A. Delzers. Recess)

1936 (20 Nov). P 13.
230 **45** 1c. brown . . . . 1·50   2·25
231   2c. bright green . . . . . . 1·60   2·25
232   4c. bright violet . . . . . . 1·60   2·25
233   5c. brown-lake . . . . 2·25   3·00
234   10c. carmine . . . . 3·25   3·75
235   15c. blue . . . . 3·50   3·75
236   20c. scarlet . . . . 2·75   3·50
237   30c. purple . . . . 3·00   3·50
238   50c. blue-green . . . . . . 3·25   3·00
239   1p. bright magenta . . . . 3·75   3·00
240   2p. black . . . . 3·25   5·25
230/240 Set of 11 . . . . 27·00   32·00
Nos. 219/40 were definitive issues used concurrently throughout India-China.

1937 (15 April). *International Exhibition, Paris. As T* 2/7 *of French Equatorial Africa.*
241   2c. bright violet 65   3·00
242   3c. green 70   2·50
243   4c. carmine 30   1·00
244   6c. brown 50   45
245   9c. scarlet 50   65
246   15c. blue 75   1·25
241/246 Set of 6 . . . . 3·00   8·00
MS246a 120 × 100 mm. 30c. slate-lilac (as **T 7**).
Imperf . . . . 7·50   14·00
    b. Error. Sheet inscription inverted . . . £600

46 President Doumer

47 Mt Côt Pagoda,
Hanoi

(Photo Vaugirard, Paris)

1938 (8 June). *Opening of Trans-Indo-China Railway.* P 13½.
(a) POSTAGE.
247 **46** 5c. carmine 90   40
248   6c. reddish brown . . . . . 1·00   25
249   18c. bright blue . . . . . . 1·75   50
(b) AIR. *Inscr* "POSTE AERIENNE".
250 **46** 37c. red-orange 25   25
247/250 Set of 4 . . . . 3·50   1·25

1938 (24 Oct). *International Anti-Cancer Fund. As T* **14** *of French Equatorial Africa.*
251   18c.+5c. ultramarine . . . . . 3·00   16·00

1939 (10 May). *New York World's Fair. As T* **17** *of French Equatorial Africa.*
252   13c. lake . . . . 1·25   2·25
253   23c. ultramarine . . . . . . 1·75   2·75

(Des E. Feltesse. Eng Cerutti-Maori. Recess)

1939 (12 June). *San Francisco International Exhibition.* P 13.
254 **47** 6c. sepia . . . . 1·50   1·50
255   9c. scarlet 55   50
256   23c. ultramarine 55   1·90
257   39c. purple . . . . 1·90   2·25
254/257 Set of 4 . . . . 4·00   5·50

1939 (5 July). *150th Anniv of French Revolution. As T* **18** *of French Equatorial Africa.*
(a) POSTAGE.
258   6c.+2c. green and black . . . . 7·25   14·00
259   7c.+3c. brown and black . . . . 7·25   14·00
260   9c.+4c. red-orange. and black . . 9·50   14·00
261   13c.+10c. carmine and black . . . 7·75   14·00
262   23c.+20c. blue and black . . . . 7·75   14·00
(b) AIR.
263   39c.+40c. black . . . . 18·00   35·00
258/263 Set of 6 . . . . 50·00   95·00

JAPANESE OCCUPATION

Following the defeat of France in June 1940 Japan forced the Vichy authorities to grant bases for her troops in Indo-China. Following an attack by Thailand on southern Indo-China, during January 1941, Japan "mediated" between the Thai and Vichy French authorities, awarding the Cambodian provinces of Battambang and Siemreap, together with Laotian territory west of the Mekong, to Thailand. These areas were returned to Indo-China in October 1946.

During July 1941 the Japanese army completed the occupation of Indo-China, although the Vichy French administration was allowed to continue as a puppet regime.

A number of issues were prepared in France for Indo-China by the Pétain Government, but none was put on sale there. The stamps were Empire Defence (£3·75 *set of* 3), Pétain and views (60p. *pair*), Pétain surch "OEUVRES COLONIALES" and new value (65p. *pair*), Child Protection (85p. *set of* 3), Imperial Fortnight (20p.) and the definitive and air stamps footnoted below Nos. 196 and 218 (*all prices are for unused stamps*). The Pétain stamps were subsequently issued with "RF" overprint (see Nos. 338/9).

PRINTERS. Nos. 264 to 327 were printed or surcharged by the Imprimerie d'Extrême-Orient, Hanoi.

10
cents
≡
(50)

48 King Sihanouk
of Cambodia

49 Processional
Elephant

56 Kinq Sihanouk
of Cambodia

57 Empress Nam-
Phuong of Annam

58 King Sisavang-
Vong of Laos

1941 (15 Oct). *Coronation of King Sihanouk. Litho. No gum.*
P 11½.

264	**48**	1c. orange-red	60	2·75
265		6c. violet	3·25	4·00
266		25c. blue	24·00	29·00

1942 (29 Mar). *Fêtes of Nam-Giao. Litho. No gum.* P 11½.

267	**49**	3c. brown	2·50	3·25
268		6c. carmine	3·00	3·00

1942. *No. 189 surch with T* **50.**

269	**35**	10c.on 25c. purple	2·00	2·50

10ᶜ   **+2ᶜ**
≡

51 Hanoi University   **(52)**

1942 (1 June)—**44.** *University Fund. Litho. No gum.* P 11½.

(a) Without surcharge.

270	**51**	6c.+2c. carmine	50	3·00
		a. Perf 13½		
271		15c.+5c. purple	55	2·50

(b) No. 270 surch as T **52** *but spacing arranged to fit design.*

272	**51**	10c.+2c. on 6c.+2c. carm (10.6.44)	40	3·00
		a. Perf 13½		

Stamps perf 13½ were a second printing made for surcharging,
but 5,000 were sold without surcharge (No. 270a).

1942 (1 July)—**44.** *Litho. No gum.* P 11½.

273	**53**	1c. brown (4.9.42)	35	2·25
		a. Perf 13½	70	2·75
274		3c. bistre-brown (17.6.43)	1·25	2·50
		a. Perf 13½	2·75	2·75
		b. Perf 11½ × 13½	1·25	2·50
275		6c. carmine	25	1·40
		a. Perf 13½	2·75	1·90
		b. Perf 11½ × 13½	2·75	3·00
276		10c. green (1.12.43)	30	1·60
277		40c. blue (15.1.43)	65	2·50
278		40c. slate (1.4.44)	55	70
273/278	*Set of 6*		3·00	10·00

1942 (1 Aug)—**44.** *National Relief Fund. Litho. No gum.* P 11½.

(a) Without surcharge.

279	**54**	6c.+2c. carmine and blue	85	2·50
280		15c.+5c. violet-black, carmine & blue	45	40
		a. Imperf between (vert pair)		

(b) No. 279 surch as T **52**, *but surch spaced to fit design.*

281	**54**	10c.+2c. on 6c.+2c. carmine and blue (15.3.44)	40	2·75

1942 (1 Sept)—**43.** *Litho. No gum.* P 13½ and (Nos. 283/8) 11½.

282	**55**	½c. purple-brown (1.11.42)	30	3·25
283	**56**	1c. purple-brown (10.3.43)	35	2·50
284	**58**	1c. bistre-brown (10.3.43)	40	2·25
285	**55**	6c. rose	2·00	2·50
286	**56**	6c. carmine (10.5.43)	45	1·90
287	**57**	6c. rose	55	1·10
288	**58**	6c. rose (1.6.43)	35	2·25
282/288	*Set of 7*		4·00	13·00

59 Saigon Fair

1942 (20 Dec). *Saigon Fair. Litho. No gum.* P 11½–13½.

289	**59**	6c. carmine	40	2·75

53 Marshall
Pétain

54 Shield and
Sword

55 Emperor Bao
Dai of Annam

60 Alexandre
Yersin

61 Alexandre de Rhodes

1943 (10 June)**–45**. *As T* **60/1** *(various portraits). Litho. No gum.*
P 11½.

290	**60**	6c. rose (5.10.43)		65	3·00
291		15c. brown-purple (10.12.44)		35	2·25
292	**61**	15c. brown-purple (10.3.45)		35	1·90
293	–	20c. brown-red		60	60
294	**61**	30c. yellow-brown (15.6.43)		35	30
		a. Perf 13½		50	70
		b. Perf 11½ × 13½			
		c. Orange-brown			
295	**60**	$1 green (10.1.45)		40	30
290/295	*Set of 6*			2·40	7·50

Portrait: *Vert*—20c. Pigneau de Behaine, Bishop of Adran.
Nos. 292 and 295 have "EF" replaced by second face value.
No. 294 has "EF" instead of "RF".

D **62**

63 Do-Huu-Vi

(Des T. Chuoc. Litho)

1943–44. *POSTAGE DUE. Type* D **62** *(1c. to 10c.) and similar type with modified background. No gum.* P 11½–13½.

D296	1c. red/*yellow* (10.6.44)		45	3·00
D297	2c. red/*yellow* (15.7.43)		1·00	3·00
D298	3c. red/*yellow* (15.7.43)		80	3·00
D299	4c. red/*yellow* (10.6.44)		40	3·00
D300	6c. red/*yellow* (26.8.43)		90	3·00
D301	10c. red/*yellow* (26.8.43)		1·10	2·75
D302	12c. blue/*salmon* (26.8.43)		40	3·00
D303	20c. blue/*salmon* (26.8.43)		40	2·75
D304	30c. blue/*salmon* (26.8.43)		1·75	3·00
D296/304	*Set of 9*		6·50	24·00

1943 (1 Aug)**–44**. *Famous Airmen. Litho. No gum.* P 12 × 13½ (296) or 11½ (297).

296	**63**	6c.+2c. carmine-red	40	2·75
297	–	6c.+2c. carmine-red (15.11.43)	45	2·50

Nos. 296/7 *surch with T* **52**, *or similarly* (10.2.44).

298	**63**	10c.+2c. on 6c.+2c. carmine-red	20	2·75
299	–	10c.+2c. on 6c.+2c. carmine-red	35	2·25

Design: *Vert* (22 × 30 *mm*)—No. 297, Roland Garros.

64 Doudart de Lagrée

65 La Grandière

1943 (16 Aug)**–45**. *Famous Sailors. As T* **64/5** *(various portraits). Litho. No gum.* P 11½–13½.

300	1c. grey-brown (10.1.45)		15	40
301	1c. olive-bistre (16.9.43)		45	2·00
302	1c. olive-bistre		35	2·50
303	5c. brown (10.1.45)		25	1·60
304	6c. rose (1.9.43)		1·90	70
305	6c. rose (1.9.43)		75	2·50
306	6c. rose (5.10.43)		35	2·50
307	10c. grey-green (10.8.44)		25	2·25
308	15c. purple (10.11.44)		35	2·50
309	20c. brown-red (10.8.44)		35	1·90
310	40c. ultramarine (10.11.44)		25	1·50
311	1p. yellow green (27.7.44)		40	2·75
300/311	*Set of 12*		5·25	21·00

Portraits: *Vert*—1c. (No. 300), 15c., 40c. Type **64**; 6c. (No. 306) Chasseloup Laubat; 10c., 20c., 1p. Charner. *Horiz*—1c. (No. 301), F. Gamier; 1c. (No. 302), 5c. Type **65**; 6c. (No. 304), Courbet; 6c. (No. 305), Rigault de Genouilly.
Similar 3c. and 15c. designs, showing Courbet and Gamier, and a 5c. showing Genouilly were prepared but not issued (*Prices* 3c. £5·75, 5c., 60p., 15c. £6 *unused*).

66 "Family, Homeland and Labour"

1943 (5 Nov). *Third Anniv of National Revolution. Litho. No gum.* P 11½.

312	**66**	6c. rose	40	95

67 De Lanessan

68 Paul Doumer

1944. *Famous Governors. As T* **67/8** *(various portraits). Litho. No gum.* P 11½–13½.

313	1c. olive-brown (10.10)		35	2·50
314	1c. grey-brown (10.12)		35	2·50
315	2c. mauve (15.5)		25	2·25
	a. Imperf between (horiz pair)			
316	4c. yellow-orange (10.2)		20	60
317	4c. brown (15.6)		25	50
318	5c. brown-purple (1.11)		40	2·25
319	10c. grey-green (5.1)		35	1·10
320	10c. grey-green (5.1)		25	2·00
321	10c. grey-green (10.9)		25	1·90
322	10c. grey green (10.10)		45	95
323	15c. purple (16.10)		60	1·25
313/323	*Set of 11*		3·25	16·00

Portraits: *Horiz*—1c. (No. 313), 10c. (No. 322), Van Vollenhoven, 1c. (No. 314), 15c., T **67**; 4c. (No. 316), 10c. (No. 319), Auguste Pavie. *Vert*—2c., 4c. (No. 317), 10c. (No. 320), T **68**; 5c., 10c. (No. 321), Pierre Pasquier.
A 20c. showing Pavie was prepared but not issued. (*Price* £2 *unused*).

69 Athlete

70 Orleans Cathedral

1944 (10 July). *Juvenile Sports. Litho. No gum.* P 11½.

324	**69**	10c. purple and yellow	95	1·10
325		50c. brown-red	90	3·25

1944 (20 Dec). *Martyr Cities. Litho. No gum.* P 11½.

326	**70**	15c.+60c. brown-purple	60	3·25
327		40c.+1p.10 blue	70	3·50

RETURN TO FRENCH CONTROL

On 9 March 1945 the Japanese declared that rule by the Vichy colonial authorities was at an end, and appointed Emperor Bao Dai of Annam head of an autonomous state of Vietnam. Cambodia was declared independent by King Norodom Sihanouk on 12 March 1945. Bao Dai continued in office until after the surrender of Japan, abdicating on 23 August 1945.

During the preceding months the Viet Minh groups of resistance fighters had been formed into a National Liberation Army under Ho Chi Minh. Based in Tongking the Liberation Army seized Hanoi on 17 August and by the end of August had extended their authority into Annam and Cochin China. On 2 September Ho Chi Minh proclaimed the independence of the Democratic Republic of Vietnam (see Part 21 (*South-East Asia*) of this catalogue).

French troops began to arrive in Indo-China during October 1945, replacing the British forces in Cochin China and Annam and Chinese occupation troops in Tongking which had moved into these areas following the Japanese surrender. French authority was quickly re-established over large areas, including Hanoi, and further French issues were released.

INDOCHINE ≡

50 c ✚ 50 c
(71)

IFR
(72)

1945. *Map of French Colonial Empire, as T **149** of France, but with Cross of Lorraine, "1945" and surch as T **71**. P. 13.*
328	50c.+50c. on 2f. olive-green	50	3·00
329	1p.+1p. on 2f. red-brown	60	2·75
330	2p.+2p. on 2f. slate-grey	1·00	3·00

1946 (8 May). *AIR. Victory. As T **32** of French Equatorial Africa.*
331	80c. orange	30	1·10

1946 (6 June). *AIR. From Chad to the Rhine. As Nos. 229/34 of French Equatorial Africa.*
332	50c. emerald-green	2·00	3·25
333	1p. mauve	1·75	3·25
334	1p.50 brown-red	1·50	3·25
335	2p. purple	1·90	3·25
336	2p.50 blue	1·90	3·50
337	5p. brown-red	2·25	3·50
332/337 *Set of 6*		10·00	18·00

1946 (15 Aug). *Unissued stamps similar to T **24** with inset portrait of Marshal Pétain, optd with T **72**. P 12½ × 12.*
338	10c. carmine	40	2·75
339	25c. blue	3·00	3·25

1949 (4 July). *AIR. 75th Anniv of Universal Postal Union. As T **39** of French Equatorial Africa.*
340	3p. blue, violet, olive and red	2·75	3·25

On 14 June 1949 Tongking, Annam and Cochin China were joined as the independent state of Vietnam, within the French Union, with Bao Dai as Head of State. Laos and Cambodia became Associated States within the French Union on 19 July and 9 November 1949 respectively.

STAMP BOOKLETS

The following checklist covers, in simplified form, booklets issued for Indo-China. It is intended to be used in conjunction with the main listings, and full details of stamps listed there are not repeated.

Prices are for complete booklets

Booklet No.	Date	Contents and Cover Price	Price
SB1	1907	*Annamite (T **10**)*	
		4 panes, No. 54 × 10 (2 f.)	£300
SB2	1907	*Annamite (T **10**)*	
		2 panes, No. 55 × 10 (2 f.)	£275
SB3	1919	*Annamite surcharged*	
		4 panes, No. 91 × 10 (80 c.)	£275
SB4	1919	*Annamite surcharged*	
		2 panes, No. 92 × 10 (80 c.)	£275
SB5	1927	*Ploughman (T **22**)*	
		2 panes, No. 144 × 10 (1 p.)	£160
SB6	1927	*Bay of Along (T **23**)*	
		2 panes, No. 145 × 10	
		(a) Cover price 1 p. 20	£160
		(b) Cover price 1 p. 2	£325
SB7	1931	*Angkor Ruins (T **34**)*	
		5 panes, No. 175 × 5 plus label (1 p. 25)	£275
SB8	1931	*Angkor Ruins (T **34**)*	
		5 panes, No. 177 × 5 plus label (1 p. 50)	£325

Indonesia

100 Cents or Sen = 1 Rupiah

The Republic of Indonesia consists of the former Netherlands Indies and West New Guinea, now known as Irian Jaya. It comprises Java and Madura; Sumatra; Sulawesi (formerly Celebes); Kalimantan (formerly Dutch Borneo); the Lesser Sunda islands (Bali, Lombok, Sumbawa, Sumaba, Flores and Timor); the Moluccas; the Riau-Lingga Archipelago; and hundreds of smaller islands.

During the Second World War the Netherlands Indies were occupied by Japan. After their surrender Dutch rule was restored without difficulty in those islands already captured by U.S. and Australian troops, but the Dutch never regained complete control in Java, Madura and Sumatra.

INDONESIAN REPUBLIC, 1945–49

(JAVA, MADURA AND SUMATRA)

An independent republic was proclaimed in Java, Madura and Sumatra on 17 August 1945, after the Japanese surrender. As no Dutch forces were available, British Indian troops were landed in Java and Sumatra in September and October 1945, to receive the Japanese surrender and to maintain order. In November they became involved in heavy fighting with Indonesian Republicans at Soerabaya.

UNLISTED ISSUES. During 1948 and 1949 a number of issues were prepared for the Indonesian Republic, under an agreement between a stamp agency in New York and a New York representative of the republican government. Most of the stamps were photogravure-printed (with the imprint of the State Printing Works, Vienna) but the high values were recess-printed (with the imprint of the E. A. Wright Bank Note Co., Philadelphia). The stamps were inscribed "REPOEBLIK INDONESIA" or "REPUBLIK INDONESIA" and exist with various overprints.

Due to the war between the Dutch and the Indonesian Republic the area for which these issues were intended was under blockade and few of them were received there. They were put on sale from late 1948 but only in limited quantities. Furthermore, due to the blockade, few were used for international mail. The earliest example of their use which we have seen is on a cover addressed to New York and postmarked 10 January 1949 at Lhokseumawe (in the extreme north of Sumatra). On the back of the cover is the rectangular cachet of a blockade-running ship.

From 27 December 1949, when the Dutch relinquished sovereignty over the whole of Indonesia, these issues remained on sale in limited quantities at a few post offices until March 1950. They were apparently valid for postage and we have seen them postally used on cover, the latest being dated 31 July 1951.

We do not list these issues in this catalogue because it is clear that, although some of them (but not those overprinted "RIS") were valid for postage, they were not freely available to the general public in Indonesia.

I. ISSUES FOR JAVA AND MADURA

Before the issue of stamps overprinted "Repoeblik Indonesia", Japanese Occupation issues continued in use. Some local handstamps of "Repoeblik Indonesia" and "Republ. Indonesia", all on Netherlands Indies stamps, were made. Stamps also had manuscript inscriptions of "Republik" or "Rep. Indonesia".

REPOEBLIK
INDONESIA

REPOEBLIK
INDONESIA

‗‗‗‗‗	‗‗‗‗‗
(J 1)	(J 2)

1945 (Oct). *T* **46** *(Rice cultivation) of Netherlands Indies optd at Bandung with Type* J **1**.

J1	**46**	1c. slate-violet (396) (R.)	1·10	1·70
J2		2c. purple (397)	4·50	5·50
J3		3½c. slate (339) (R.)	50·00	55·00

1945 (Oct). *Nos.* 462/5 *(Dancers) of Netherlands Indies optd at Bandung with Type* J **2**.

J4	2½c. claret	1·40	2·30
J5	3c. green (R.)	1·60	2·30
J6	4c. brown-olive (R.)	1·60	2·30
J7	5c. blue (R.)	65·00	75·00
J4/J7	Set of 4	60·00	70·00

1945 (Oct). *Nos.* 2/3 *of Japanese Occupation of Java optd at Bandung as Type* J **1** *but with two bars at left.*

J8	3½s. carmine (Ploughing ricefield)	£275	£375
J9	5s. green (Mt. Soemer)	14·00	9·50

REPOEBLIK
INDONESIA

REPOEBLIK
INDONESIA

‗‗‗	▬▬▬▬ ▬
(J 3)	(J 4)

1945 (Oct). *Nos.* 5/11 *of Japanese Occupation of Java optd at Bandung as Type* J **3**. P 12½.

J10	3½c. carmine (Native head)	38·00	38·00
J11	5s. green (R.) (Puppet)	45	75
J12	10c. blue (R.) (Borobudur Temple)	30	60
	a. Opt inverted	70·00	
	b. Perf 12	3·00	3·75
J13	20c. grey-olive (R.) (Map of Java)	55	85
J14	40c. purple (R.) (Seated dancer and temple)	90	1·20
J15	60c. red-orange (Bird and Mt. Soemer)	1·20	1·40
	a. Opt inverted		
J16	80s. lake-brown (Ploughing)	11·00	15·00
J10/16	Set of 7	45·00	50·00

On the 60c. and 80s. the overprint is spaced out.

1945 (Oct). *Nos.* 396 *(Rice cultivation) and* 461/4 *(Dancers) of Netherlands Indies optd at Djokjakarta with Type* J **4** *(1c.) or similar type with bar* 1½ *mm from name (others).*

J17	**46**	1c. slate-violet (396) (R.)	1·90	2·40
J18		1c. slate-violet (396) (Br.)	8·50	8·50
J19	—	2c. scarlet (461) (R.)	1·10	2·30
J20	—	2½c. claret (462) (R.)	14·00	14·00
J21	—	3c. green (463) (R.)	2·75	2·75
J22	**71**	4c. brown-olive (R.)	2·75	2·75
J17/22	Set of 6	28·00	20·00

Nos. J1/22 are the only official overprints. Unofficial overprints, which may be attempts at forgeries, also exist. They are usually slightly larger than the official overprints, with coarser lettering, sometimes of a different shape and in different colours.

Stamps of the Netherlands Indies and the Japanese Occupation may often be found with the words "Ned. Indie" or Japanese characters obliterated by pen, ink brush or pencil. This was done by official instructions.

J **5** Bull

J **6** Bull and
Indonesian Flag

(Typo at Djokjakarta)

1945 (1 Dec). *Declaration of Independence*. P 11½.
J23	J **5**	10s.(+10s.) chocolate		4·75	6·50
		a. Imperf		38·00	
J24	J **6**	20s.(+10s.) chocolate and red		5·75	6·50
		a. Imperf		75·00	

No. J23a was issued without gum; No. J24 was issued with and without gum.

(J 7)

1946 (Feb). *Handstamp in red, violet, blue-grey or black as Type J 7, covering three stamps, on stamps of Netherlands Indies or Japanese Occupation issues.*

(a) Stamps of Netherlands Indies

(i) Regular issues of 1933–37 (Rice cultivation). No wmk.
J25	**46**	1c. slate-violet (R., Bl-grey, Bk.)	—	1·20
J26		3½c. slate, (R.)	—	1·20

(ii) Regular issues of 1938–40. W **61** *(Circles).*
J27	**46**	1c. slate-violet (R., V., Bl-grey)	—	1·20
J28		2c. purple (R., Bk.)	—	1·20
J29		2½c. olive-bistre (R.)	—	1·20
J30		3c. yellow-green (R., Bk.)	—	1·20

(iii) Dancers issue, Nos. 461/6.
J31	—	2c. scarlet (R., V., Bk.)	—	1·20
J32	—	2½c. claret (R., V., Bk.)	—	1·20
J33	—	3c. green (R., V., Bk.)	—	1·20
J34	**71**	4c. brown-olive (R., V., Bk.)	—	1·20
J35	—	5c. blue (R., Bk.)	—	1·20
J36	—	7½c. violet (R., Bk.)	—	1·20

(iv) Postage Due stamps (inscr "TE BETALEN") of 1913–40 (Typo Enschedé)
J37	D **7**	2½c. salmon (R.)	—	1·50
J38		5c. salmon (R.)	—	1·50
J39		7½c. salmon (R., Bk.)	—	1·50

(v) Postage Due stamps of 1941 (Litho Kolff)
J40	D **7**	1c. pale salmon (R.)	—	1·50
J41		10c. pale salmon (R.)	—	1·50
J42		20c. pale salmon (R., Bk.)	—	1·50
J43		40c. pale salmon (R.)	—	1·50

The overprints on Postage Due stamps were for ordinary postage.

(b) Stamps of Japanese Occupation of Java.

(i) First Anniv of Occupation (Globe showing Eastern Asia).
J44	**1**	2s. red-brown (R., Bk.)		

(ii) Pictorial stamps of 1943 (Nos. 5/8).
J45	—	3½c. carmine (Native head) (Bk.)	—	1·20
J46	**2**	5s. green (Puppet) (Bk.)	—	1·20
J47	—	10c. blue (Borobudur Temple) (R.)	—	3·00
J48	**3**	20c. grey-olive (Map of Java) (R.)	—	3·00

The prices quoted are for single stamps. Strips or pairs (larger stamps) showing the complete overprint are worth considerably more. The handstamp could also be applied to stamps on cover so that most of it struck the envelope. The "NED. INDIE" or Japanese inscriptions on the stamps are usually crossed out.

A similar handstamp, with a box 27 × 12½ mm covering one or two stamps, was not officially authorised but is often found, especially on unused stamps.

J **8** Soldier on Waterfront

J **9** Boat in Storm

(Typo at Djokjakarta)

1946 (1 June–July). *Types J **8/9** and similar designs. No gum.* P 11–11½ and compound.
J49	–	5s. pale blue		75	85
J50	J **8**	20s. brown (*shades*)		85	1·10
J51	J **9**	30s. carmine (1.7)		70	2·75
		a. Imperf		11·50	

Design: *Horiz*—5s. Road and mountains.

J **10** Wayang Puppet	J **11** Kris and Flag	J **12** Temple

(Typo at Djokjakarta)

1946–47. *No gum.* P 11 × 11½ (all), 11½ (50s., 60s.) or 11 (80s.).
J52	J **10**	50s. grey-blue (1.7.46)	14·00	11·00
J53	J **11**	60s. carmine (1.9.46)	4·25	£140
J54	J **12**	80s. dull violet (1.7.47)	52·00	£400

These stamps exist imperforate but do not appear to have been issued thus.

J **13** Buffalo breaking Chains	J **14** Bandung, March, 1946

I	II

I. "SEN" with normal "S".
II. Numerals and value thicker; "S" malformed.

(5, 15, 500 and 1000s. litho; others typo Merdeka Ptg Wks, Djakarta)

1946 (19 Aug)–**47**. *Types J **13/14** and similar designs. No gum.* P 11.
J55		3s. red (*shades*) (1947)	30	3·00
		b. Imperf	10	40
J56		5s. grey-blue (1947)	45	75
		b. Imperf	30	45
J57		10s. greenish black	9·50	8·00
		b. Imperf	9·50	9·50
J58		15s. purple (*shades*) (12.46)	75	1·10
		b. Imperf	75	75
J59		30s. green	1·90	4·50
		b. Imperf	1·40	1·90
J60		40s. violet-blue	75	1·90
		b. Imperf	75	75
J61		50s. black (I)	3·50	4·50
		b. Imperf	2·00	2·50
		c. Type II	3·00	2·30
		cb. Imperf	50	60
J62		60s. slate-lilac	2·75	3·75
		b. Imperf	1·40	1·70
J63		80s. rosine	2·75	6·00
		b. Imperf	£140	
J64		100s. brown-lake	1·40	2·50
		b. Imperf	1·20	1·20
J65		200s. lilac (*shades*)	2·40	1·90
		b. Imperf	1·10	1·90
J66		500s. scarlet (17.2.47)	11·50	19·00
		b. Imperf	7·50	7·50

J67	1000s. emerald (17.2.47)		11·50	22·00
	b. Imperf		5·75	7·50
J55/67a	Set of 13 (50s. Type II)		48·00	70·00
J55b/67b	Set of 13 (50s. Type II)		28·00	28·00

Designs: Vert—40s. Quay at Tandjong Priok, 50s. Type J **13**; 80s. Airman; 500s. Mass meeting with flags, Djakarta. Horiz—10, 15s. Soerabaya, November, 1945; 30s. Anti-aircraft gunners; 60s. Type J **14**; 100s. Ambarawa, November, 1945, 200s. Wonokromo Dam, Soerabaya; 1000s. Cavalryman.

Type I occurs only on Nos. 2 to 5 and 7 to 10 in the top row of the sheet of No. J61.

Dutch troops began to take over the areas held by British troops at Batavia, Bandung, Semarang and Soerabaya early in 1946, and British forces were withdrawn by 29 November. On 25 March 1947 the Linggadjati Agreement was signed by Dutch and Indonesians recognising an Indonesian Republic in Java, Sumatra and Madura, as part of the United States of Indonesia, joined with the Netherlands under the Dutch Crown. Difficulties intensified over the interpretation of the agreement and on 20 July 1947 the Dutch began an offensive which gained them control of the plains of west central Java and the eastern tip of the island. After United Nations intervention brought a cease-fire on 4 August, the Indonesian Republicans still held the east centre of Java, with Djokjakarta as their capital, and also the Bantam area and maintained their postal services. Netherlands Indies stamps were used in the areas taken by the Dutch.

SEGEL

25

sen

PORTO

(J **15**)

J **16** "Labour and Transport"

1948. Netherlands Indies Postage Due stamps of 1941 (Batavia printing), surch with Type J **15** for use as ordinary postage stamps.

| J68 | D **7** | 25s. on 7½s. pale salmon | | 14·00 | 28·00 |
| J69 | | 25s. on 15c. pale salmon | | 9·50 | 24·00 |

The 7½c. value was not issued in Netherlands Indies without surcharge.

(Typo at Djokjakarta)

1948 (17 Aug). Third Anniv of Independence. Wmk in sheet "ARCHIPEL BANK PADALARANG" in double-lined capitals and emblem. No gum. Imperf.

| J70 | J **16** | 50s. blue | | 5·00 | 6·00 |
| J71 | | 100s. red | | 7·00 | 7·00 |

These stamps may be found unofficially perforated.

(J **17**)

1948. POSTAGE DUE. Nos. J67 and J70/1 handstamped as Type J **17** with "DENDA" diag or horiz, in violet or black. (A) "RP 1"; (B) "1—RP".

JD72	50s. blue (Bk.)		—	20·00
JD73	100s. red (Bk.)		—	20·00
JD74	1r. on 50s. blue (A) (Bk.)		—	20·00
JD75	1r. on 50s. blue (B) (V., Bk.)		—	20·00
JD76	1r. on 1000s. blue-green (B) (V.)		—	20·00

U.N. action led to the signature of a truce on U.S.S. Renville on 17 January 1948 but, after further breakdowns of negotiations the Dutch resumed their offensive on 18 December, occupied the major Republican cities and captured Sukarno and half his cabinet ministers. Indonesian resistance continued and on 28 January 1949 the U.N. Security Council called for the release of the Indonesian leaders and the transfer of sovereignty to the United States of Indonesia. The Republican government returned to Djokjakarta on 6 July and the war ended in Java on 10 August. On 2 November a Hague conference reached agreement on the transfer of sovereignty.

J **18** Flag over Waves

(Typo Finance Dept. Press, Djokjakarta)

1949 (20 July). Wmk in Sheet "MADE IN U.S.A." P 11.

J77	J **18**	100s. red		£110	£110
		b. Imperf		5·00	12·00
J78		150s. red		38·00	£110
		b. Imperf		8·00	20·00

For No. J77B surcharged "R 15", see Sumatra No. S179.

II. ISSUES FOR SUMATRA

At the end of 1945 and in 1946, stamps of the Netherlands Indies and the Japanese occupation were handstamped with "Repoeblik Indonesia" (3 types), "Rep. Indonesia" (6 types), "Rep. Ind." (4 types), "P.T.T. Indonesia" (5 types), "P.T.T. R. Indonesia", "P.T.T./N.R.I.", "N.R.I." (6 types), "R.I." (6 types) or "Ind.", for use in North Sumatra, Middle Sumatra, Benkoelen, Lampong or Palembang. These stamps saw much postal use, but as they were of a local nature, they are outside the scope of this catalogue.

British troops, who had occupied Padang, Palembang and part of Medan in 1945, were replaced by Dutch troops in 1946. Here also the Dutch began an offensive on 20 July 1947 and occupied the rubber estates round Medan, the Palembang oilfields, and the ports of Padang and Benkoelen. Netherlands Indies stamps were used here and Indonesian Republican issues in the rest of Sumatra.

USED PRICES. Prices in the used column for Sumatra issues are for postally used copies. Stamps cancelled to order are worth about half these prices.

Repoeblik Indonesia **15** SEN

(S **1**)

Repoeblik Indonesia **40** SEN

(S **2**)

Repoeblik Indonesia **40** SEN

(S **3**)

Repoeblik Indonesia **40** SEN

(S **4**)

(In Type S **4** the value is more to the left than in Type S **3**. The two types occur in alternative vertical rows in the sheet)

Repoeblik

Indonesia

^{1}Roepiah	^{1}Roepiah
(S 5)	(S 6)

1946. *Nos. 339 and 396/9 (Rice cultivation), 429 and 431 (Queen Wilhelmina) and 465 (Dancer) of Netherlands Indies optd at Pematang Siantar with "Repoeblik Indonesia" and surch as Types S 1/6.*

S1	S 1	15s. on 5c. blue (465)		1·50	1·90
S2	S 2	20s. on 3½c. slate (339)		7·50	7·50
S3		30s. on 1c. slate-violet (396)		7·50	7·50
S4		40s. on 2c. purple (397)		25	60
S5	S 3	40s. on 2c. purple (397)		30	1·10
		a. Surch inverted		13·00	14·00
S6	S 4	40s. on 2c. purple (397)		30	1·00
		a. Surch inverted		12·50	14·50
S7	S 5	50s. on 17½c. orange (431)		55·00	55·00
S8	S 6	50s. on 17½c. orange (431)		12·00	12·00
S9	S 2	60s. on 2½c. olive-bistre (398)		7·50	5·25
S10		80s. on 3c. yellow-green (399)		7·50	7·50
		a. Surch inverted		55·00	55·00
S11	S 5	1r. on 10c. vermilion (429)		6·00	6·00
		a. Surch double		55·00	55·00
		b. Perf 13 (429a)		2·40	3·75
S12	S 6	1r. on 10c. vermilion (429)		2·30	3·75
S1/12 *Set of 12*				75·00	80·00

The overprints on Nos. S7, S11/b and S12 are on stamps previously overprinted with Type **8** of the Japanese Occupation issues.

The overprints on Nos. S1/4 and S9 are found on previously unoverprinted stamps or on stamps with various local Japanese handstamps.

Repoebelik	**Repoebelik**
Indonesia	**Indonesia**

(S 7)	(S 8)

1946. *Nos. 429 (Wilhelmina) of Netherlands Indies and 58B (No. 429 optd) of Japanese Occupation optd at Padang.*

(a) Optd "Repoebelik Indonesia" without bars.

S13	–	10c. vermilion (I) (429)		4·75	8·00
S14	–	10c. vermilion (II) (58B)		3·75	6·50

(b) Optd with Types S 7/8.

S15	S 7	10c. vermilion (I) (429)		£140	£170
S16	S 8	10c. vermilion (I) (429)		£1600	

The overprints on Nos. S13/16 may be found on stamps previously overprinted with various local Japanese handstamps.

S 9 Ploughing	S 10 Pres. Sukarno	(S 11)

(Typo at Palembang)

1946 (17 May–17 Aug). *Freedom Fund. Type S 9 and similar designs inscr "FONDS KEMERDEKAAN". No gum.* P 11½.

S17		5s.(+25s.) pale green		75	2·30
		a. Imperf		25·00	25·00
S18		5s.(+25s.) turquoise-blue (17.8)		20	1·50
S19		15s.(+35s.) carmine		1·90	3·75
		a. Imperf		25·00	25·00

S20		15s.(+35s.) violet-blue (17.8)		20	1·50
S21		40s.(+60s.) orange		90	2·30
		a. Imperf		25·00	25·00
S22		40s.(+60s.) red (17.8)		75	4·50
S23		40s.(+60s.) purple-brown (17.8)		7·50	24·00
S24		40s.(+60s.) dark brown (17.8)		12·50	42·00
S17/24 *Set of 8*				20·00	80·00

Designs:—15s. Soldier and flag; 40s. Oil well and factories, Palembang.

1946. *Typo. No gum.* P 11½.

S25	S 10	40s.(+60s.) scarlet (thin white paper)		75	5·75
		a. Imperf		34·00	34·00
S26		40s.(+60s.) dark red (thick grey paper)		12·50	24·00

In the sheets of 50 (10 × 5) of No. S26 the rays behind the head differ in each stamp in the sheet. In the sheets of 100 (10 × 10) of No. S25 the layout of the top 50 stamps, which is the same as that for No. S26, is repeated in the bottom 50 stamps.

1946. *Nos. S18 and S22 with "FONDS KEMERDEKAAN" obliterated with double bars.*

S27	5s. turquoise-blue		45·00	£110
S28	40s. red		45·00	45·00
	b. Obliterated with a single bar		30·00	45·00

The basic stamps may also be found with "FONDS KEMERDEKAAN" crossed out by pen with ink lines.

1946–47. *Type S 9 and similar designs, but with blank panel instead of "FONDS KEMERDEKAAN" at top. Typo. No gum.* P 11½.

S29	2s. rose-red (1947)		45	4·50
	b. Imperf		26·00	—
S30	2s. dark brown (1947)		2·75	11·50
S31	3s. olive-green (1947)		75	4·50
	b. Imperf		26·00	—
S32	3s. rose-red (1947)		3·00	11·50
S33	3s. blue (1947) (imperf)		†	
S34	5s. turquoise-blue		25	2·75
	b. Imperf		26·00	
S35	15s. indigo		25	1·50
	b. Imperf		26·00	
S36	15s. dark green (1947)		3·00	11·50
	b. Imperf		26·00	
S37	40s. purple-brown		30	1·90
S38	40s. dark blue (1947)		15·00	27·00
	b. Imperf		26·00	
S29/32 and S34/8 *Set of 9* (perf 11½)			23·00	70·00

Designs:—2, 3, 5s. Type S **9**; 15s. Soldier and flag; 40s. Oil well and factories, Palembang.

1947 (Apr). *Fund for Palembang War Victims. Nos. S18, S20 and S23 handstamped with Type S 11, in violet.*

S39	5s. turquoise-blue		75·00	90·00
S40	15s. violet-blue		75·00	90·00
S41	40s. purple-brown		75·00	90·00

The stamps were sold at 15 rupiah per set of three.

"BPKPP" = Badan pernolong korban pristiwa Palembang (Help for the victims of the Palembang incident).

S 12	S 13

1947 (12 May). *Palembang provisional issue. Fiscal stamps of Japanese Occupation with blank panels optd in black with "prangko N.R.I." and value as in Type S 12. Litho.* P 11 × 11½.

S42	S 12	0f.50 salmon		13·50	30·00
S43		1f. salmon		11·50	23·00
S44		2f. salmon		17·00	30·00
S45		2f.50 salmon		12·00	15·00
		a. Imperf (pair)		80·00	

It is believed that "f" stands for florin, the equivalent of a gulden.

1947 (May). *Nos. S25/6 surch as Type* S **13**.

S46	S **10**	50s. on 40s. dark red	5·00	5·00
S47		1f. on 40s. dark red	6·75	6·75
S48		1f.50 on 40s. scarlet	4·25	4·25
S49		2f.50 on 40s. dark red	75	2·30
		a. "Rp." for "F."	60·00	
S50		3f.50 on 40s. dark red	75	2·30
S51		5f. on 40s. dark red	75	2·30
		a. No dash after "5."	6·75	6·50
S46/51	*Set of 6*		16·00	21·00

No. S49a is position 7 in the sheet of 50 in the first printing. The error was later corrected. There are many varieties of numerals and lettering in these surcharges.

2
Roepiah   **5 0**   **f 2,50**
(S **14**)   (S **15**)   (S **16**)

1947. *Type* S **9** *and similar designs surch as Type* S **14** *(small ornament, occurring upright, inverted or sideways either way).*

(a) On No. S22 *(single bar through inscr).*

S52	30s.on 40s. red	60	1·50
	a. Surch double	—	£120

(b) On Nos. S34A *and* S37A *(blank panels).*

S53	50s. on 5s. turquoise-blue	6·00	4·50
S54	1f. on 5s. turquoise-blue	4·50	4·50
S55	1f.50 on 5s. turquoise-blue	6·00	6·00
S56	1r. on 40s. purple-brown	40	3·00
S57	2r. on 5s. turquoise-blue	60	3·00
	a. Surch inverted	65·00	
	b. Surch double	65·00	

(c) No. S56 *further surch with Type* S **15**.

S58	50r. on 1r. on 40s. purple-brown	45·00	55·00

1947. *Type* S **9** *and similar designs surch as Type* S **16** *(large ornament).*

(a) On No. S22A *(double bars through inscr).*

S59	50s. on 40s. red	11·50	15·00
S60	1f. on 40s. red	40	1·50
S61	1f.50 on 40s. red	3·00	5·25
S62	2f.50 on 40s. red	40	1·50

(b) Nos. S32/3, S35 *and unissued colour (blank panels).*

S63	1s. on 15s. indigo (R.)	45	1·90
S64	5s. on 3s. blue (R.)	45	1·90
	a. Imperf (pair)	48·00	
S65	10s. on 15s. rose-red	50	1·90
S66	50s. on 3s. rose-red	15·00	38·00
S59/66	*Set of 8*	28·00	60·00

Pos Udara

10 Rp.   **R1,=**   *50 sen*
(S **17**)   (S **18**)   (S **19**)

F 2.50   **R 2,50**   **R100,—**
(S **20**)   (S **21**)   (S **22**)

1947. *AIR. Nos.* S22 *and* S34A *surch as Type* S **17**.

S67	10r. on 40s. red	1·90	2·30
S68	20r. on 5s. turquoise-blue	1·10	2·30

The Dutch offensive of 20 July 1947 cut off Atjeh, in the extreme north of Sumatra, from the rest of the island. The following surcharges therefore had to be made in Atjeh to meet inflation of the currency.

1947. *Atjeh provisional surcharges, made in Koetaradja.*

(i) Stamps of 1946–47 (Nos. S29/37). P 11½

(a) Surch in large figures as Type S **18**.

S69	10s. on 15s. indigo	11·50	11·50
	a. Surch inverted	70·00	
S70	20s. on 15s. indigo	11·50	11·50
	a. Surch inverted		
S71	30s. on 15s. indigo	11·50	6·00
S72	1r. on 2s. rose-red	47·00	47·00
S73	2f.50 on 15s. indigo	14·00	14·00
S74	5f. on 40s. purple-brown	£225	£170

(b) Surch in small figures as Types S **19/21**.

S75	50s. on 5s. turquoise-blue	£600	£550
S76	50s. on 15s. indigo	£600	£600
S77	0f.50 on 15s. indigo	£550	£550
S78	1f. on 5s. turquoise-blue	£140	£140
S79	1f. on 15s. indigo	£275	£375
S80	2f.50 on 5s. turquoise-blue	£750	£650
S81	2f.50 on 15s. indigo	£130	£130
S82	2f.50 on 40s. purple-brown	£550	£650
S83	5f. on 15s. indigo	£750	£750
S84	5f. on 40s. purple-brown	95·00	95·00
S85	2r.50 on 3s. olive-green (R.)	19·00	28·00
S86	5r. on 15s. indigo (R.)	6·50	9·75
S87	10r. on 3s. olive-green (R.)	70·00	70·00

(c) Surch as Type S **22**.

S88	2r. on 3s. olive-green	33·00	65·00
S89	5r. on 15s. indigo (R.)	7·00	11·50
S90	10r. on 3s. olive-green (R.)	22·00	32·00
S91	20r. on 2s. rose-red (R.)	£225	£475
S92	50r. on 15s. indigo (R.)	£325	£475
S93	100r. on 15s. indigo (R.)	£110	£110

(ii) No. S22 *lurch as Type* S **22** *and with penstroke through "FONDS KEMERDEKAAN". Obliterating rectangle (A)* 4½ *mm square; (B)* 4½ × 6½ *mm.*

S94	150r.on 40s. red (A)	£140	£140
S95	150r.on 40s. red (B)	85·00	85·00

Stamps of the Atjeh issues cancelled with a large circular violet handstamp "Perjetakan Negara. Koetaradja. N.R.I." are printers' waste. The fall in value of the Japanese occupation money current in the Republic led to the introduction, as from 28 October 1946, of Indonesian Republican money ("Oeang Repoeblik Indonesia"). The change-over was gradual and took place in Sumatra in 1947, except in Atjeh, which was cut off by Dutch forces, All available stamps were handstamped "O.R.I.". We list all those which do not also bear unlisted Japanese or Indonesian handstamps.

(S **23**)   (S **24**)   (S **25**)

("O R I" = Oeang Repoeblik Indonesia)

1947. *Change of Currency. Various stamps handstamped as Type* S **23**, *in red, violet, blue or black.*

(a) Netherlands Indies issue, 1938–40 (Rice cultivation).

S96	3c. yellow-green (399) (Bk.)	4·75	6·00

(b) Netherlands Indies Dancers issue, 1941/5.

S97	4c. brown-olive (464) (Bk.)	7·25	8·00
S98	5c. blue (465) (Bk.)	3·50	5·50

(c) Netherlands Indies Postage Due issue, 1941.

S99	1c. pale salmon (D445) (V.)	8·00	8·50
S100	15c. pale salmon (D448) (Bk.)	6·00	7·25

The stamps were used for ordinary postage.

(d) Japanese Occupation issue for Sumatra, 1943–44 (Nos. 15/25).

S101	1c. olive-green (V.)	1·10	1·50
S102	2c. yellow-green (V., Bk.)	1·10	1·25
S103	3c. greenish blue (V., Bk.)	1·10	1·25
S104	3½c. rose-red (V., Bk.)	1·50	1·90

S105	4c. ultramarine (V.)	2·50	3·75
S106	5c. red-orange (R., V., Bk.)	1·50	1·90
S107	10c. grey-blue (Bk.)	6·00	6·75
S108	20c. lake-brown (Bk.)	6·00	6·75
S109	30c. bright purple (Bk.)	1·10	1·10
S110	50c. bistre-brown (Bk.)	2·20	2·20

Designs:—1, 2, 3c. Batak house; 3½, 4, 5c. Minangkabau house; 10, 20c. Ploughing with oxen; 30c. Lake Toba; 50c. Carabao Canyon.

(e) Japanese Occupation issue for Sumatra, 1944 (Queen Wilhelmina issue overprinted).

S111	10c. vermilion (I) (57B) (Bk.)	85	1·10
S112	10c. vermilion (II) (58B) (Bk.)	1·40	1·90
S113	25c. green (62B) (V.)	10·00	12·00
S114	30c. yellow-brown (63B) (V.)	8·00	9·00
S115	50c. brown-lake (66B) (R.)	10·50	13·00
S116	60c. bright blue (67B) (R.)	5·50	6·00
S117	80c. vermilion (68B) (R.)	5·50	7·25
S118	1g. violet (69B) (R.)	11·00	12·50

(f) Stamps of Japan, 1937–40.

S119	1s. chestnut (317) (V)	1·00	1·50
S120	3s. green (319) (V.)	1·00	1·50
S121	4s. green (320) (V.)	5·00	5·50
S122	6s. orange (322) (Bk.)	1·50	2·00
S123	25s. brown and chocolate (329) (V.)	1·00	1·40
S124	30s. blue-green (330) (Bk.)	2·40	3·50
S125	50s. olive and bistre (331) (V., Bk.)	1·00	1·50
S126	1y. red-brown & chocolate (332) (V.)	2·40	3·50

Designs:—1s. Rice harvesting; 3s. Hydro-electric power station; 4s. Admiral Togo; 6s. Garambi lighthouse; 25s. Horyu Temple; 30s. Itsukushima Shrine; 50s. Kinkaku Temple; 1y. Great Buddha, Kamakura.

(g) Sumatra Pematang Siantar surcharges, 1946.

S127	20s. on 3½c. slate (S2) (Bk.)	6·50	7·50
S128	30s. on 1c. slate-violet (S3) (R.)	6·50	8·00
S129	40s. on 2c. purple (S4) (V., Bk.)	3·00	5·00
	a. Surch inverted		
S130	40s. on 2c. purple (S5) (V., Bk.)	3·00	4·75
	a. Surch inverted		
S131	40s. on 2c. purple (S5) (R.)	2·75	4·50

(h) Sumatra "FONDS KEMERDEKAAN" issue, 1946.

S132	5s. pale green (S17) (V., Bk.)	2·50	4·00
S133	5s. turquoise-blue (S18) (R., V., Bk.)	90	1·30
S134	15s. violet-blue (S20) (R., V., Bk.)	2·40	4·25
S135	40s. red (S22) (V., Bk.)	2·75	3·50

(i) Sumatra issue with blank panel, 1946–47.

S136	2s. rose-red (S29A) (V., Bk.)	2·50	3·00
S137	3s. olive-green (S31A) (V., B., Bk.)	6·50	6·50
S138	3s. rose-red (S32A) (V.)	1·00	1·70
S139	5s. turquoise-blue (S34A) (V. Bk.)	75	1·10
S140	15s. indigo (S35A) (V., Bk.)	75	1·10
S141	15s. dark green (S36A) (V.)	3·75	5·00
S142	40s. purple-brown (S37A) (V., Bk.)	70	1·00

(j) Sumatra surcharged Sukarno head issue, 1947.

S143	1f.50 on 40s. scarlet (S48) (V., Bk.)	6·50	6·50
S144	2f.50 on 40s. dark red (S49) (V.)	6·25	7·50
S145	3f.50 on 40s. dark red (S50) (V., Bk.)	6·25	7·50

(k) Sumatra surcharges on "FONDS KEMERDEKAAN" issue, 1947.

S146	30s. on 40s. red (S52) (Bk.)	80	1·30
S147	1f.50 on 40s. red (S61) (Bk.)	6·50	7·50
S148	2f.50 on 40s. red (S62) (V., Bk.)	6·25	7·50

(l) Sumatra surcharges on blank panel, 1947.

S149	1s. on 15s. indigo (S63) (V.)	70	1·40
S150	10s. on 15s. rose-red (S65) (V.)	2·40	3·75
S151	50s. on 5s. turquoise-bl (S53) (V., Bk.)	1·80	2·40
S152	1f.50 on 5s. turquoise-bl (S55) (V.)	5·50	7·25
S153	2r. on 5s. turquoise-blue (S57) (V.)	1·60	2·50

(m) Sumatra air stamp, 1947.

S154	10r. on 40s. red (S67) (V.)	7·50	10·00

1947–48. Change of Currency. Atjeh issue. Atjeh provisional surcharges handstamped as Type S 18, in violet, blue or black.

(a) Stamps surch as Type S 18.

S155	10s. on 15s. indigo (S69) (V., Bk.)	6·50	13·00
S156	20s. on 15s. indigo (S70) (V., Bk.)	6·50	13·00

S157	2f.50 on 15s. indigo (S73) (Bk.)	12·50	18·00
S158	5f. on 40s. purple-brn (S74) (V., Bk.)	15·00	31·00

(b) Stamps surch as Types S 19/21 (Nos. S75/80, S84).

S159	50s. on 5s. turquoise-blue (V.)	3·25	3·50
S160	50s. on 15s. indigo (V.)	3·25	3·50
S161	0f.50 on 15s. indigo (B.)	5·25	8·00
S162	1f. on 5s. turquoise-blue (Bk.)	5·25	8·00
S163	1f. on 15s. indigo (V.)	5·25	8·00
S164	2f.50 on 5s. turquoise-blue (V., Bk.)	5·25	8·00
S165	5f. on 40s. purple-brown (V., Bk.)	14·00	19·00

There are several types of handstamp on Nos. S96/165.

("PTT URIPS" = Uang Republik Indonesia Propinsie Sumatera (Indonesian Republican Money, Province of Sumatra))

1947. *Change of Currency. South Sumatra issue. Various stamps handstamped as Type S 24, in black.*

(a) Japanese Occupation issue for Sumatra, 1943–44.

S166	2c. yellow-green (16) (Batak house)	7·50	9·00
S167	3½c. rose-red (18) (Minangkabau house)	7·50	9·00

(b) Sumatra issue with blank panel, 1946–47.

S168	2s. rose-red (S29A)	3·25	3·75
S169	3s. olive-green (S31A)	7·25	8·00
S170	5s. turquoise-blue (S34A)	14·50	22·00
S171	15s. indigo (S35A)	5·25	7·75
S172	40s. purple-brown (S37A)	6·75	8·50

(c) Sumatra surcharged Sukarno head issue, 1947.

S173	50s. on 40s. dark red (S46)	5·25	6·50
S174	2f.50 on 40s. dark red (S49)	5·25	6·50
S175	3f.50 on 40s. dark red (S50)	5·25	6·50
S176	5f. on 40s. dark red (S51)	5·25	6·50

(d) Sumatra surcharge on "FONDS KEMERDEKAAN" issue, 1947.

S177	50s. on 40s. red (S59)	24·00	29·00

(e) Sumatra air stamp, 1947.

S178	10r. on 40s. red (S67)	7·25	9·75

1949. *No. J77B of Indonesian Republic (Java) surch with Type S 25 for use in Sumatra.*

S179	J 18	15r. on 100s. red	21·00	35·00

The war ended in Sumatra on 14 August 1949.

NETHERLANDS INDIES

Dutch merchants first landed in Bantam, in Western Java, in 1596 and in 1602 the Dutch East India Company was formed. In 1619 Jan Pieterszoon Coen founded Batavia, Having obtained supremacy over the Spaniards and Portuguese he entered into competition with the English, culminating in a massacre of English traders at Amboina in 1623. From then until the French Revolutionary and Napoleonic Wars, it was Dutch policy to obtain suzerainty rather than sovereignty over the Indies. The Dutch officials were merchants, who concentrated on making their own fortunes. The Dutch East India Company, crippled by this and by wars, came to an end in 1799, being taken over by the Batavian Republic in Holland. After the Netherlands became part of Napoleon's empire, a British expedition took Java, which from 1811 to 1816 was ruled by Sir Stamford Raffles, founder of Singapore. In 1816 Java was restored to the Dutch and in 1824 the British exchanged Benkoelen in Sumatra for Malacca, During the 19th century there were many revolts against Dutch rule, forcing the Dutch to extend their control over the interior of the islands. Atjeh, in north Sumatra, was not subdued until 1907, after 34 years of war, and the conquest of Bali was not completed until 1906. From 1908, Indonesian nationalist associations sprang up and leaders such as Sukarno, Hatta and Sjahrir were exiled by the Dutch, who remained opposed to the idea of home rule.

100 Cents = 1 Gulden

PRINTERS. The stamps of Netherlands Indies were printed by Messrs. J. Enschedé and Sons, Haarlem, *except where otherwise stated.*

King William III

17 March 1849–23 November 1890

1

(Des and eng J. W. Kaiser. Recess Mint, Utrecht)

1864 (1 Apr). *Yellowish paper.* Imperf.
1	**1**	10c. carmine	£325	£100

1868. *Yellowish paper.* P 12½ × 12.
2	**1**	10c. carmine	£1000	£180

2   **1 CENT.** (i)   **1 CENT.** (ii)

Two varieties of the 1 cent
(i) "CENT" 5½ *mm long.* (ii) 7½ *mm*

(Des Virey Bros. Eng E. Schilling. Typo)

1870–88. A. *Thick to medium paper.* P 14, small holes (1870).
3	**2**	5c. pale blue-green	80·00	9·00
4		10c. orange-brown	28·00	90
5		20c. ultramarine	£110	3·50
6		50c. carmine	28·00	3·50
7		2g.50 green and purple	90·00	18·00

B. *Thinner paper (1874–88)*

(a) P 14, larger holes.
8	**2**	25c. purple	£700	£170
9		50c. carmine	35·00	4·25
10		2g.50 green and purple	90·00	21·00

(b) P 13 × 14, small holes.
11	**2**	1c. bronze-green (i)	9·00	6·50
12		5c. blue-green	65·00	7·00
13		10c. pale orange-brown	42·00	3·00
14		15c. ochre	42·00	3·50
15		20c. ultramarine	£110	5·25
16		25c. purple	35·00	4·50
17		50c. carmine	27·00	3·25

(c) P 13–13½ × 14, large holes.
18	**2**	1c. bronze-green (i)	9·00	7·00
19		10c. pale orange-brown	20·00	1·75
20		15c. ochre	30·00	3·50
21		25c. purple	32·00	1·75

(d) P 13½, large holes (frequently gauging 13½ × 13).
22	**2**	1c. bronze-green (ii) (1876)	4·75	2·75
23		2c. cinnamon (1881)	10·00	4·50
24		10c. orange-brown	25·00	90
25		20c. ultramarine	£130	16·00
26		25c. purple	25·00	1·75

(e) P 12½ × 12.
27	**2**	1c. bronze-green (ii) (1876)	5·50	3·50
		a. Perf 11½ × 12	9·00	6·25
28		2c. brown-purple (1876)	£100	90·00
		a. Perf 11½ × 12	£200	£140
29		2c. cinnamon (1881)	8·00	4·50
		a. Perf 11½ × 12	13·50	6·25
		b. Pale brown	8·00	4·50
		ba. Perf 11½ × 12	13·50	6·25
30		2½c. buff (1876)	45·00	23·00
		a. Perf 11½ × 12	80·00	50·00
31		5c. green	65·00	5·25
		a. Perf 11½ × 12	95·00	7·00
32		10c. orange-brown	18·00	1·10
		a. Perf 11½ × 12	£300	14·00
		b. Pale orange-brown	18·00	1·10

33		12½c. drab (1887)	—	£1700
34		15c. ochre	23·00	2·50
		a. Perf 11½ × 12	£600	70·00
35		20c. ultramarine	£100	3·00
		a. Perf 11½ × 12	£170	10·50
		b. Dull blue	£110	4·50
36		25c. dull purple	24·00	1·40
		a. Perf 11½ × 12	55·00	7·00
		b. Purple	24·00	1·40
37		50c. carmine	25·00	1·75
		a. Perf 11½ × 12	42·00	4·50
38		2g.50 green and dull purple	90·00	16·00
		a. Perf 11½ × 12	£400	42·00
		b. Green and dull purple	90·00	16·00

(f) P 12½, small holes.
39	**2**	10c. orange-brown	£250	6·25
40		12½c. drab (1887)	5·25	2·50
41		25c. purple	45·00	7·00
42		50c. carmine	25·00	2·75

(g) P 12½, large holes.
43	**2**	10c. orange-brown	18·00	35
44		30c. green (1888)	40·00	4·50

D 3   **D 4**

(Des J. Schmidin. Typo)

1874–75. *POSTAGE DUE.*

(a) P 13 × 14, small holes.
D56	D **3**	5c. yellow-ochre	£300	£250
D57		10c. green/*yellow*	£110	90·00
D58		20c. green/*blue*	35·00	15·00

(b) P 12½ × 12.
D59	D **3**	15c. orange/*yellow* (1875)	22·00	18·00
		a. Perf 11½ × 12	45·00	45·00
D60		20c. green/*blue*	35·00	14·50
		a. Perf 11½ × 12	80·00	32·00

In Nos. D56/60 the frames are as follows: 5c. Type IV, 10c. Type III, 15c. Type I, 20c. Type II (*see* enlarged illustrations below).

Frame types for D **3**, D **4** and D **7**

(I)

(II)

(III)

(IV)

I. 34 loops. "T" of "BETALEN" over centre of loop; top branch of "E" of "TE" shorter than lower branch.

II. 33 loops. "T" of "BETALEN" over the space between two loops; all the horizontal strokes of the "E" of "TE" of equal length.
III. 32 loops. "T" of "BETALEN" slightly to the left of loop; top branch of first "E" of "BETALEN" shorter than lower branch.
IV. 37 loops. Letters of "PORT" and "TE" of "BETALEN" larger than in the other three types.

(Des J. Schmidlin. Typo)

1882–88. *POSTAGE DUE*. Type I.

(a) P 13½ (1882).

D63	**D 4**	2½c. black and rose-red	65	1·10
		a. Type II	6·25	1·50
		b. Type III	55	1·10
		c. Type IV	3·50	3·75
D64		5c. black and rose-red	75	1·10
		a. Type II	1·00	1·40
		b. Type III	55	1·40
		c. Type IV	2·75	3·75
D65		10c. black and rose-red	4·50	5·00
		a. Type II	4·50	5·00
		b. Type III	3·50	3·25
		c. Type IV	22·00	25·00
D66		20c. black and rose-red	£110	1·00
		a. Type II	£130	90
		b. Type III	£110	75
		c. Type IV	£250	9·00
D67		75c. black and rose-red	1·10	1·40
		a. Type II	1·25	1·90
		b. Type III	1·40	1·40
		c. Type IV	3·50	5·50

(b) P 12½ × 12 (1882–87).

D68	**D 4**	2½c. black and rose-red	65	1·40
		a. Perf 11½ × 12	8·00	10·50
		b. Type II	1·25	1·60
		ba. Perf 11½ × 12	3·25	5·25
		c. Type III	65	1·10
		ca. Perf 11½ × 12	7·25	10·50
		d. Type IV	3·50	4·25
		da. Perf 11½ × 12	12·50	22·00
D69		5c. black and rose-red	1·25	90
		a. Perf 11½ × 12	8·00	10·50
		b. Type II	75	90
		ba. Perf 11½ × 12	2·50	4·50
		c. Type III	55	75
		ca. Perf 11½ × 12	2·75	4·50
		d. Type IV	1·75	3·50
		da. Perf 11½ × 12	8·00	12·50
D70		15c. black and rose-red	4·50	4·50
		a. Perf 11½ × 12	22·00	27·00
		b. Type II	5·50	5·50
		ba. Perf 11½ × 12	14·50	16·00
		c. Type III	3·50	3·25
		ca. Perf 11½ × 12	16·00	17·00
		d. Type IV	22·00	22·00
D71		20c. black and rose-red	£110	3·50
		a. Perf 11½ × 12	£700	£120
		b. Type II	£110	2·75
		ba. Perf 11½ × 12	£350	65·00
		c. Type III	90·00	55
		ca. Perf 11½ × 12	£650	£110
		d. Type IV	£225	9·00
		da. Perf 11½ × 12	£700	£180
D72		40c. black and rose-red	2·10	2·75
		a. Perf 11½ × 12	7·25	9·00
		b. Type II	2·50	1·25
		ba. Perf 11½ × 12	3·50	6·25
		c. Type III	2·10	2·75
		ca. Perf 11½ × 12	6·25	3·50
		d. Type IV	3·50	4·50
		da. Perf 11½ × 12	22·00	27·00
D73		50c. black and pink (1887)	1·75	2·10
		a. Type II	2·00	2·40
		b. Type III	1·40	1·60
		c. Type IV	14·50	18·00

D74		75c. black and rose-red	1·10	2·00
		a. Perf 11½ × 12	5·50	7·25
		b. Type II	1·25	2·40
		ba. Perf 11½ × 12	2·75	3·50
		c. Type III	1·10	1·50
		ca. Perf 11½ × 12	5·50	5·50
		d. Type IV	2·10	3·50
		da. Perf 11½ × 12	17·00	22·00

(c) P 12½ (1888).

D75	**D 4**	20c. black and rose	£110	90
		a. Type II	£120	90
		b. Type III	90·00	55
D76		30c. black and dull red	5·25	7·25
		a. Type II	10·00	10·00
		b. Type III	3·50	4·50

5	6	D 7

1883–90. *Typo*.

(a) P 12½ × 12.

83	**5**	1c. olive-green (1888)	2·75	1·40
84		2c. yellow-brown (1884)	1·40	80
		a. Perf 11½ × 12	70·00	25·00
		b. Chestnut	1·00	50
85		2½c. buff	2·10	1·40
		a. Perf 11½ × 12	16·00	7·00
		b. Pale buff	2·10	1·40

(b) P 12½, small holes.

86	**5**	5c. yellow-green (1887)	45·00	26·00

(c) P 12½, large holes.

87	**5**	1c. olive-green	1·40	20
		a. yellow-olive	1·40	20
		b. Pale yellow-olive	1·40	20
88		2c. brown	1·40	20
		a. Red-brown	1·40	20
89		2½c. buff	1·40	70
		a. Pale buff	1·40	70
90		3c. purple (1890)	1·75	20
		a. Deep purple	1·75	20
		b. Reddish purple	1·75	20
91		5c. ultramarine (1890)	14·00	20
		a. Grey-blue	14·00	20
		b. Dull blue	14·00	20
87/91		*Set of 5*	18·00	1·40

Queen Wilhelmina

23 November 1890–6 September 1948

(Die eng E. Schilling. Typo)

1892–97. P 12½.

94	**6**	10c. orange-brown	7·00	40
95		12½c. grey	12·00	24·00
96		15c. ochre	17·00	1·60
97		20c. dull blue	38·00	1·60
		a. Ultramarine	38·00	1·60
98		25c. pale reddish purple	32·00	1·60
		a. Reddish purple	32·00	1·60
99		30c. green	48·00	2·00
100		50c. carmine	35·00	1·60
101		2g.50 pale blue and orange-brown	£130	38·00
		a. Ultramarine and chestnut	£130	38·00
94/101		*Set of 8 (cheapest)*	£300	65·00

1892–1909. *POSTAGE DUE*. Type D 7 (Type I). P 12½.

D102		2½c. carmine-rose and black (1908)	1·10	35
		a. Long fraction bar projecting above "½"	2·75	1·90
D103		5c. carmine-rose and black (1909)	3·50	30
D104		10c. rose and black (*shades*)	16·00	9·00
		a. Type II	15·00	14·50
		b. Type III	4·50	2·50

D105		15c. carmine-rose and black (1895)	15·00	2·50
D106		20c. rose and black (*shades*)	15·00	9·00
		a. Type II	9·00	8·00
		b. Type III	5·50	2·00
D107		30c. carmine-rose and black (1906)	23·00	8·00
D108		40c. rose and black	20·00	3·00
D109		50c. rose and black	12·50	1·25
D110		75c. rose and black	25·50	5·50
D102/110		*Set of* 9 (*cheapest*)	£100	23·00

10 Ct
2.50
2.50

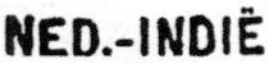
NED.-INDIË
(7)

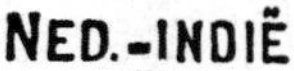
NED.-INDIË
(8)

1900. *T* **11** *(*2g.50*) and* **13** *(others) of Netherlands (Queen Wilhelmina) surch as T* **7** *(Nos.* 111/16*) or* **8** *(No.* 117*).*

111		10c. on 10c. grey-lilac	2·40	40
112		12½c. on 12½c. blue	3·00	80
113		15c. on 15c. brown	4·00	80
114		20c. on 20c. green	20·00	80
115		25c. on 25c. blue and rose	17·00	80
116		50c. on 50c. lake and bronze-green	32·00	1·10
117		2½g. on 2½g. dull lilac (*p* 11½ × 11)	50·00	19·00
		a. Perf 11	65·00	24·00
111/117		*Set of* 7	£110	21·00

The 10, 12½ and 15c. exist without dots over the "E" in "INDIE", and the 10c. also with only one dot.

1/2
(9)

2 1/2
(10)

1902. *Surch with T* **9** *or* **10**. P 12½.

118	**5**	½ on 2c. red-brown (15.5)	50	35
119		2½ on 3c. purple (20.5)	55	50
		a. Reddish purple	55	50

The ½ exists inverted and both values with surcharge double, but beware of forgeries of these.

NEDERLANDSCH-INDIE
7½
7½ CENT
11

POSTZEGEL
NEDERLANDSCH-INDIE
20 CENT
12

NEDERLANDSCH-INDIE
POSTZEGEL
1 GULDEN
13

(T **11** des Enschedé. T **12**/**13** des J. Veth. T **11**/**12** typo; T **13** recess)

1902 (25 June)–**09**.

(a) P 12½.

120	**11**	½c. bright lilac	60	30
121		1c. olive-green	60	30
122		2c. brown	4·00	35
123		2½c. green	2·40	20
124		3c. orange	2·75	1·25
125		4c. ultramarine (1909)	14·00	9·00
126		5c. rose-red	6·00	20
127		7½c. slate (5.08)	4·00	35
128	**12**	10c. slate	1·60	20
		a. Slate-blue	1·60	20
129		12½c. deep blue (4.06)	2·00	20
130		15c. brown	9·75	2·10
131		17½c. bistre (9.08)	4·00	30
132		20c. greenish slate	2·00	1·50
133		20c. olive (1.06)	27·00	25
134		22½c. olive and brown (1908)	4·75	30
135		25c. deep violet	11·50	30
136		30c. chestnut	32·00	30
137		50c. lake-brown (1.05)	25·00	30

(b) P 11 × 11½.

138	**13**	1g. dull lilac (5.06)	60·00	40
		a. Perf 11	75·00	4·75
		b. Perf 11½ × 11	60·00	40
139		2½g. slate (1905)	70·00	1·60
		a. Perf 11½	70·00	1·60
		b. Perf 11½ × 11	80·00	1·60
		c. Perf 11	£850	

(c) No. 130 *optd with two horiz black bars across head.*

140	**12**	15c. brown (1909)	2·00	70
120/140		*Set of* 21	£250	18·00

These bars were applied to distinguish this stamp from the 50c. See also Nos. 206/7.

WARNING. A late printing of some values on toned paper was in soluble ink (see note after No. 222).

10 cent.
(**14**)

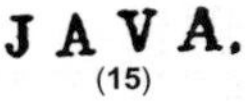
J A V A.
(**15**)

BUITEN
BEZIT.
(**16**) (= "Outer Possessions")

1905 (1 Aug). *No.* 132 *surch diagonally with T* **14**.

141	**12**	10c.on 20c. greenish slate	2·75	1·25

There are many varieties of the surcharge, in both the figures and the word.

1908 (1 July). *Issue for Java and Madura. Stamps of* 1902–9 *optd with T* **15**.

142	**11**	½c. bright lilac	35	20
		a. Opt inverted	1·10	2·50
		b. Opt double	£500	
143		1c. olive-green	60	30
		a. Opt inverted	75	2·75
144		2c. brown	2·50	2·50
		a. Opt inverted	2·50	6·25
145		2½c. green	1·50	20
		a. Opt inserted	2·75	3·50
146		3c. orange	1·10	1·00
		a. Opt inverted	21·00	21·00
147		5c. rose-red	2·50	20
		a. Opt inverted	2·50	3·50
		b. Final "A" of "JAVA" omitted	45·00	55·00
		c. "JA.VA"	19·00	22·00
148		7½c. slate	2·00	1·75
149	**12**	10c. slate-blue	1·00	20
		a. Opt inverted	1·25	1·75
		b. Final "A" of "JAVA" omitted	45·00	55·00
		c. "JA.VA"	19·00	22·00
150		12½c. deep blue	2·10	70
		a. Opt inverted	3·50	5·50
		b. Opt double, one inverted	£130	£120
		c. "JA.VA"	22·00	24·00
151		15c. brown (140)	3·25	3·00
		a. Opt inverted	3·50	10·00
		b. "JA.VA"	20·00	22·00
152		17½c. bistre	1·75	65
153		20c. olive	10·00	70
		a. Opt inverted	10·00	10·00
154		22½c. olive and brown	4·75	2·75
		a. "JA.VA"	22·00	24·00
155		25c. deep violet	4·75	30
		a. Opt inverted	5·50	10·00
		b. "JA.VA"	19·00	22·00
156		30c. chestnut	28·00	2·50
		a. Opt inverted	23·00	27·00
		b. "JA.VA"	21·00	24·00
157		50c. lake-brown	19·00	70
		a. Opt inverted	15·00	21·00
		b. "JA.VA"	22·00	24·00

158	**13**	1g. dull lilac (*p* 11½ × 11)		45·00	3·00
		a. Perf 11		50·00	3·50
		b. Opt inverted		£150	£160
		c. Perf 11 × 11½		65·00	42·00
159		2½g. slate (*p* 11½ × 11)		65·00	50·00
		a. Opt inverted		£2250	£2750
142/159 *Set of* 18				£175	65·00

The stop after "JAVA" is often found omitted.

1908 (1 July). *Issue for Netherlands Indies apart from Java and Madura, Stamps of 1902–9 optd as T* **16**, *reading up (various sizes).*

160	**11**	½c. bright lilac		45	35
		a. Opt inverted		70	3·50
		b. Pair, one without opt			
161		1c. olive-green		55	35
		a. Opt inverted		70	2·50
162		2c. brown		1·90	2·50
		a. Opt inverted		3·50	5·25
163		2½c. green		1·10	35
		a. Opt inverted		1·40	2·75
164		3c. orange		1·00	1·10
		a. Opt inverted		27·00	60·00
165		5c. rose-red		3·10	50
		a. Opt inverted		3·50	2·75
166		7½c. slate		3·00	2·50
167	**12**	10c. slate-blue		1·10	20
		a. Opt inverted		1·00	2·40
168		12½c. deep blue		9·75	2·25
		a. Opt inverted		5·25	8·00
169		15c. brown (140)		4·50	2·50
		a. Opt inverted		30·00	65·00
		b. Opt inverted and double		£170	£200
170		17½c. bistre		2·10	1·75
171		20c. olive		8·75	2·10
		a. Opt inverted		9·00	8·00
172		22½c. olive and brown		6·25	4·50
		a. Opt inverted		£1400	£1700
173		25c. deep violet		7·00	35
		a. Opt inverted		7·00	8·00
174		30c. chestnut		15·00	2·10
		a. Opt inverted		13·50	16·00
175		50c. lake-brown		7·00	80
		a. Opt inverted		9·00	9·00
176	**13**	1g. dull lilac (*p* 11½ × 11)		55·00	4·50
		a. Opt inverted		£200	£225
		b. Perf 11		60·00	5·50
		c. Perf 11 × 11½		60·00	5·00
177		2½g. slate (*p* 11½ × 11)		85·00	55·00
		a. Opt inverted		£2500	£2750
160/177 *Set of* 18				£190	75·00

The stop after "BEZIT" is often found omitted.

(O **17**)

(O **18**)

1911 (1 Oct). *OFFICIAL. Stamps of 1892–97 optd with Type* O **17**.

O178	**6**	10c. orange-brown		2·40	1·40
		a. Opt inverted		10·50	29·00
O179		12½c. grey		4·00	5·25
		a. Opt inverted		£275	£250
O180		15c. ochre		4·00	3·50
		a. Opt inverted		£250	£250
O181		20c. dull blue		3·50	2·10
		a. Opt inverted		80·00	65·00
		b. Ultramarine		3·75	2·25
O182		25c. pale reddish purple		13·00	9·75
		a. Opt inverted		£350	£350
O183		50c. carmine		3·00	2·00
		a. Opt inverted		10·50	60·00
O184		2g.50 pale blue & orange- brown		55·00	55·00
		a. Opt inverted		£500	£900
O178/184 *Set of* 7				75·00	70·00

The 10c., 50c. and 2g.50 exist with a similar handstruck overprint. The 30c. value with handstamp is a proof.

1911. *OFFICIAL. Optd with Type* O **18**.

(a) No. 91.

O185	**5**	2½c. buff		90	1·90

(b) Stamps of 1902–9.

O186	**11**	½c. bright lilac		35	70
		a. Opt inverted		50·00	£120
O187		1c. olive-green		35	35
		a. Opt inverted		3·25	16·00
O188		2c. brown		35	35
		a. Opt inverted		3·25	16·00
O189		2½c. green		1·75	1·75
		a. Opt inverted		10·00	24·00
O190		3c. orange		55	50
		a. Opt inverted		£100	35·00
O191		4c. ultramarine		35	35
O192		5c. rose		1·10	90
		a. Opt inverted		3·25	16·00
O193		7½c. slate		2·75	2·75
O194	**12**	10c. slate-blue		35	35
		a. Opt inverted		3·25	5·50
O195		12½c. deep blue		2·50	2·50
		a. Opt inverted		32·00	48·00
O196		15c. brown (130)		90	90
O197		15c. brown (140)		35·00	
		a. Opt inverted		45·00	
O198		17½c. bistre		3·50	2·75
O199		20c. olive		90	55
		a. Opt inverted		£160	55·00
O200		22½c. olive and brown		3·50	3·50
O201		25c. deep violet		2·10	1·90
		a. Opt inverted		£1300	£1100
O202		30c. chestnut		1·10	65
		a. Opt inverted		£200	£110
O203		50c. lake-brown		14·00	9·00
		a. Opt inverted		30·00	29·00
O204	**13**	1g. dull lilac (*p* 11 × 11½)		3·50	1·60
		a. No stop after "DIENST"		5·50	3·50
		b. Perf 11½ × 11		4·50	1·60
		ba. Opt inverted		£500	£900
		bb. No stop after "DIENST"		5·50	3·50
O205		2½g. slate (*p* 11½)		32·00	35·00
		a. No stop after "DIENST"		40·00	40·00
		b. Perf 11½ × 11		45·00	48·00
		ba. Opt inverted		£225	£650
		bb. No stop after "DIENST"		48·00	48·00
O186/205 *Set of* 20				95·00	
O186/205 *Set of* 19 (*excl.* O197)					60·00

On Type **11** the overprint reads diagonally downwards and on the remainder diagonally upwards.

1912. P 11 × 11½. *Coloured paper.*

206	**13**	1g. dull lilac/*blue*		42·00	4·75
		a. Perf 11		50·00	48·00
207		2½g. slate/*blue*		60·00	26·00
		a. Perf 11		75·00	80·00

19

20

(Des Enschedé. Typo)

1912 (Nov)–**15**. P 12½.

208	**19**	½c. lilac (9.13)		30	20
209		1c. olive-green		30	20
210		2c. yellow-brown		55	20
211		2½c. green (9.13)		1·40	20
212		3c. ochre		55	20
213		4c. ultramarine		1·10	20
214		5c. carmine-pink		1·25	20
215		7½c. grey-brown (4.14)		70	20
216	**20**	10c. carmine (1.14)		1·10	20
217		12½c. blue (4.14)		1·25	20
218		17½c. red-brown (3.15)		1·25	20
219		20c. green (3.15)		2·10	20
220		22½c. orange (3.15)		2·10	75

221	**20**	25c. mauve (3.15)	. . . . . .	2·10	20
222		30c. slate (3.15)	. . . . . .	2·10	20
208/222 *Set of 15*				16·00	3·00

See also Nos. 264/79 and 427.

> **WARNING.** Some printings and values of Types **19**, **20** and D **7** and late printings of Types **11** and **12** were in soluble inks. Do not put in water.

21

(23)

(Eng D. Harting. Recess.)

1913–14. P 11½.

223	**21**	50c. green (1.14)	. . . . . .	4·75	20
		a. Perf 11 × 11½		5·00	20
224		1g. sepia (5.14)	. . . . . .	4·00	20
		a. Perf 11 × 11½		4·00	20
225		2½g. carmine-rose	. . . .	16·00	1·25
		a. Perf 11 × 11½		16·00	20

See also Nos. 280/4.

1913–40. *POSTAGE DUE. Type D* **7** *and similar type* (1g.). *Frame Type I. Typo in one colour by Enschedé.* P 12½.

D226	1c. salmon (9.39)	. . . .	10	1·75
D227	2½c. salmon	. . . .	10	10
D228	3½c. salmon (1.1.39)	. . . .	10	1·75
D229	5c. salmon	. . . .	10	10
D230	7½c. salmon (1921)	. . . .	10	10
D231	10c. salmon	. . . .	10	10
D232	12½c. salmon (1921)	. . . .	2·75	10
D233	15c. salmon (1921)	. . . .	2·75	10
D234	20c. salmon	. . . .	20	10
D235	25c. salmon (1921)	. . . .	20	10
D236	30c. salmon	. . . .	20	20
D237	37½c. salmon (1930)	. . . .	18·00	14·50
D238	40c. salmon	. . . .	20	20
D239	50c. salmon	. . . .	2·10	10
D240	75c. salmon	. . . .	2·75	20
D241	1g. salmon (1.1.39)	. . . .	5·00	7·25
D242	1g. light blue (1940)	. . . .	35	3·50
D226/242 *Set of 17*		. . . .	32·00	27·00

For litho issue, see Nos. D445/52 and for stamps in other colours, see Nos. D489/501 and D527.

1915 (10 June). *Red Cross. Fund Surch as T* **23**, *in red.*

243	**19**	1c.+5c. olive-green	. . . .	5·50	5·50
		a. Narrow spacing		£225	£275
244		5c.+5c. rose-pink	. . . .	5·50	5·50
		a. Narrow spacing		£325	£450
245	**20**	10c.+5c. carmine	. . . .	7·00	7·00

In Nos. 243a and 244a the cross at left is only 1 mm from figure "5" instead of 2 mm. The spacing is 1 mm on No. 245.

$$\frac{1}{2}$$ **1** $17\frac{1}{2}$ **30 CENT**

(24)   **(25)**   **(26)**   **(27)**

1917–18. *Surch locally with T* **24/7.**

246	**19**	½c. on 2½c. green	. . .	35	35
247		1c. on 4c. ultramarine (1918)	. .	35	55
248	**12**	17½c. on 22½c. olive and brown (1918)	. .	1·75	70
		a. Surch inverted		£350	£600
249	**13**	30c. on 1g. dull lilac (*p* 11 × 11½) (1918)	.	6·25	1·75
		a. Perf 11½ × 11		£100	50·00
246/249 *Set of 4*		. . . . . .	7·75	3·00

$12\frac{1}{2}$ **CENT**   **40 CENT**

(28)   **(29)**   M **30**

1921. *Surch as T* **28** *or* **29.**

250	**20**	12½c. on 17½c. brown (R.)	. .	30	20
251		12½c. on 22½c. orange (R.)	. .	35	20
252		20c. on 22½c. orange (B.)	. .	35	20
		a. Surch double		—	£1800
253	**21**	32½c. on 50c. green (B.) (I) (*p* 11½)	.	1·00	20
		a. Surch Type II (perf 11½)	. .	9·00	20
		b. Surch Type I (perf 11 × 11½)		£1100	5·25
		c. Surch Type II (perf 11 × 11½)		21·00	1·40
254		40c. on 50c. green (R.)	. .	3·50	50
255		60c. on 1g. sepia (B.)	. .	5·75	35
256		80c. on 1g. sepia (R.)	. .	6·25	80
250/256 *Set of 7*			32·00	3·00

Type I of the 32½c. on 50c. has the bars of the surch widely spaced as in T **29**. In Type II the spacing is closer.

(Des C. A. Lion Cachet (15c. to 75c.), Leo Geste (others). Recess)

1921. *MARINE INSURANCE. Type* M **30** *and similar types inscr* "DRIJVENDE BRANDKAST". P 11½.

M257	15c. myrtle-green	. . . .	9·00	28·00
M258	60c. rose-carmine	. . . .	9·00	45·00
M259	75c. drab	. . . .	9·00	48·00
M260	1.50g. indigo	. . . .	27·00	£225
M261	2.25g. chestnut	. . . .	32·00	£275
M262	4½g. black	. . . .	60·00	£550
M263	7½g. rose-red	. . . .	75·00	£600
M257/263 *Set of 7*			£200	£1600

These stamps were used to prepay the fee for the inclusion of mails in a patent safe, unsinkable in case of shipwreck.

1922–32. *Typo.* P 12½.

264	**19**	2c. grey (5.30)	. . . .	55	20
265		2½c. rose	. . . .	70	20
266		3c. green (1929)	. . . .	1·10	20
267		4c. green (1928)	. . . .	1·10	20
268		4c. yellow-bistre (7.30)	. .	9·00	4·00
269		5c. green	. . . .	1·10	20
270		5c. pale ultramarine (1928)	.	70	20
271		7½c. yellow-bistre	. . . .	70	20
272		10c. lilac	. . . .	1·75	20
273	**20**	12½c. scarlet (1925)	. .	1·25	35
274		15c. blue (1929)	. . . .	7·00	30
275		20c. blue	. . . .	2·10	20
276		20c. orange (1932)	. .	12·50	20
277		32½c. violet and orange	. .	2·10	30
278		35c. chestnut (1929)	. .	7·25	55
279		40c. green	. . . .	2·75	20

Recess. (a) P 11½.

280	**21**	60c. blue	. . . .	6·00	20
281		80c. orange	. . . .	4·75	35

(b) P 12½.

282	**21**	50c. green (1932)	. . . .	4·75	35
283		1g.75 lilac (1931)	. . . .	20·00	1·75
284		2½g. carmine-rose (1932)	. .	16·00	55
264/284 *Set of 21*			80·00	9·75

For 5c. litho, see No. 427.

3de N. I.
JAARBEURS

(31)

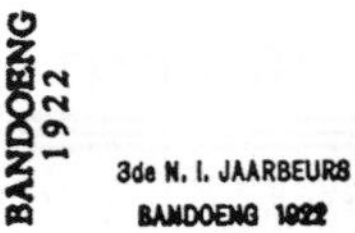

BANDOENG
1922
3de N. I. JAARBEURS
BANDOENG 1922

(32)

1898-1923
5
Ct
NED-INDIE

33

1922 (Sept). *Bandoeng Industrial Fair. T* **19** *optd with T* **31** *and T* **20** *optd with T* **32** *(vert up on No. 293).*

285	**19**	1c. olive-green (R.)	7·00	7·00
286		2c. brown (B.)	7·00	7·00
287		2½c. rose (G.)	55·00	60·00
288		3c. yellow (R.)	7·00	8·00
289		4c. ultramarine (R.)	35·00	35·00
290		5c. green (R.)	12·50	10·00
291		7½c. grey-brown (B.)	9·50	8·00
292		10c. lilac	65·00	80·00
293	**20**	12½c. on 22½c. orange (B.)	8·00	9·00
294		17½c. red-brown	5·50	7·00
295		20c. blue	7·00	7·00
285/295		*Set of* 11	£200	£225

Nos. 285/95 were sold at a premium for 3, 4, 5, 6, 8, 9, 10, 12½, 15, 20 and 22c. respectively.

(Des H. Cheffer (head) and H. Seegers (frame). Recess)

1923 (31 Aug). *Queen's Silver Jubilee.* P 11½.

296	**33**	5c. blue-green	35	35
		a. Perf 11 × 11½	4·50	60
		b. Perf 11½ × 11	£900	£110
297		12½c. carmine	35	35
		a. Perf 11 × 11½	1·25	35
		b. Perf 11½ × 11	1·60	55
298		20c. indigo	70	35
		a. Perf 11½ × 11	3·50	55
299		50c. orange	2·50	90
		a. Perf 11 × 11½	6·25	1·10
		b. Perf 11½ × 11	2·50	90
		c. Perf 11	4·50	90
300		1g. brown-purple	4·25	60
		a. Perf 11½ × 11	7·00	90
301		2½g. olive-grey	38·00	32·00
302		5g. brown	£120	£110
296/302		*Set of* 7	£150	£130

LUCHTPOST
10

(34)

LUCHTPOST
1½
1½

(35)

1928 (20 Sept). *AIR. T* **20/21** *variously surch with aeroplane and new value as T* **34** *or* **35**, *by Topographical Service, Batavia.*

303	**20**	10c. on 12½c. scarlet	1·25	1·25
304		20c. on 25c. mauve	2·75	2·75
305	**21**	40c. on 80c. orange	2·10	2·10
306		75c. on 1g. sepia (B.)	1·10	1·10
307		1½g. on 2½g. carmine-rose	7·25	7·25
303/307		*Set of* 5	13·00	13·00

LUCHTPOST
20
20
NEDERLANDSCH-INDIE

36

30

(37)

(Des Fokko Mees. Litho)

1928 (1 Dec). *AIR.* P 12½ × 11½.

308	**36**	10c. purple	35	35
309		20c. brown	90	75
310		40c. carmine	1·10	75
311		75c. green	2·40	35
312		1g.50 orange	4·25	75
308/312		*Set of* 5	8·00	2·75

1930 (13 Oct)–**32**. *AIR. Surch with T* **37**, *by Topographical Service, Batavia.*

313	**36**	30c. on 40c. carmine	1·10	40
314		30c. on 40c. carmine (G.) (12.7.32)	2·00	40

JEUGDZORG 1930
NEDERL-INDIE
5
Ct

38 Watch-tower

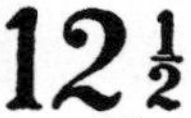

12½

(39)

1STE POST-VLUCHT
NEDERL
INDIE
JAVA-AUSTRALIE

40 M. P. Pattist in Flight

1930 (1 Dec). *Child Welfare. T* **38** *and similar types inscr* "JEUGDZORG 1930". *Photo.*

(a) P 11½ × 11.

315	2c.(+1c.) brown and violet	1·10	1·00
316	5c.(+2½c.) brown and green	4·50	3·50

(b) P 11 × 11½.

317	12½c.(+2½c.) brown and scarlet	3·50	70
318	15c.(+5c.) brown and blue	5·00	5·25
315/318	*Set of* 4	12·50	9·25

Designs: *Vert*—2c. Bali Temple. *Horiz*—12½c. Minangkabau compound; 15c. Buddhist Temple, Borobudur.

1930 (22 Dec). *Surch with T* **39**, *in vermilion.*

319	**20**	12½c. on 20c. blue	80	20
		a. Surch inverted	£350	£700

(Des M. Pirngadi. Photo)

1931 (1 Apr). *AIR. First Java–Australia Mail.* P 12½.

320	**40**	1g. brown and blue	15·00	12·50

30
Cent
LUCHTPOST
30
Cent
NEDERLANDSCH-INDIE

41

WITTE KRUIS KOLONIE 1931
NEDERLANDSCH-INDIE

42 Ploughing

(Des M. Pirngadi. Photo)

1931 (12 May). *AIR.* P 12½.

321	**41**	30c. magenta	2·75	35
322		4½g. blue	9·00	2·75
323		7½g. green	11·50	3·50

(Des A. Kreisler. Recess)

1931 (1 Dec). *Lepers Colony. T* **42** *and similar horiz designs.* P 12½.

324	2c.(+1c.) bistre-brown	2·50	2·00
325	5c.(+2½c.) blue-green (Fishing)	4·00	4·00
326	12½c.(+2½c.) scarlet (Actors)	3·25	65
327	15c.(+5c.) blue (Musicians)	7·75	6·75
324/327	*Set of* 4	16·00	12·00

(43)   **44** Plaiting Rattan

1932 (21 July). *AIR. Surch with T **43**, by Topographical Service, Batavia.*
328	**36**	50c. on 1g.50 orange (B.)		3·25	55
		a. Surch inverted		£1900	£2500

(Des M. Pirngadi. Photo)

1932 (1 Dec). *Salvation Army. T **44** and similar types. P 12½.*
329	2c.(+1c.) bistre and purple		55	55
330	5c.(+2c.) bistre and green		3·00	2·25
331	12½c.(+2½c.) bistre and carmine		90	35
332	15c.(+5c.) bistre and blue		4·25	3·50
329/332 *Set of 4*			7·75	6·00

Designs:—2c. Weaving; 12½c. Textile worker; 15c. Metal worker.

45 William of Orange   **46** Rice Cultivation   **47** Queen Wilhelmina

(Des H. Seegers. Photo)

1933 (18 Apr). *400th Birth Anniv of William I of Orange. P 12½.*
333	**45**	12½c. vermilion	1·60	40

See boxed note below No. 359.

(Des A. Kreisler. Photo)

1933–37. No wmk.

(a) P 12½ (1933).
334	**47**	12½c. orange-brown	8·00	30

(b) P 11½ × 12½ (1934–37).
335	**46**	1c. slate-violet	30	20
336		2c. purple	30	20
337		2½c. olive-bistre	30	20
338		3c. yellow-green	30	20
339		3½c. slate (1937)	30	20
340		4c. bronze-green	90	20
341		5c. ultramarine	30	20
342		7½c. violet	1·10	20
343		10c. scarlet	2·00	20
344	**47**	10c. scarlet (12.37)	55	20
345		12½c. vermilion	55	20
346		15c. ultramarine	55	20
347		20c. purple	70	20
348		25c. blue-green	2·10	20
349		30c. indigo	3·50	20
350		32½c. olive-bistre	9·00	8·25
351		35c. violet	5·25	1·10
352		40c. yellow-green	2·75	20
353		42½c. yellow	2·75	30

(c) Larger (30 × 30 mm). P 12½ (1934).
354	**47**	50c. indigo	5·00	35
355		60c. ultramarine	5·50	70
356		80c. scarlet	7·00	1·10
357		1g. violet	8·75	30
358		1g.75 yellow-green	18·00	10·00
359		2g.50 purple	21·00	1·70
334/359 *Set of 26*			95·00	22·00

For watermarked issue, see Nos. 396/415.

48   **49** Woman and Lotus Blossom

(Des Aart van Dobbenburgh. Photo)

1933 (1 Dec). *AIR. Special Flights. P 12½.*
360	**48**	30c. blue	1·50	1·50

(Des F. A. Wagner. Photo)

1933 (1 Dec). *Relief Fund. T **49** and similar designs, inscr "CRISISWERK A.M.V.J." (Y.M.C.A.). P 12½.*
361	2c.(+1c.) olive-brown and purple		70	45
362	5c.(+2½c.) olive-brown and green		2·40	2·00
363	12½c.(+2½c.) olive-brown and orange		2·75	30
364	15c.(+5c.) olive-brown and blue		3·25	2·75
361/364 *Set of 4*			8·25	5·00

Designs:—5c. Symbolizing the sea of life; 12½c. Y.M.C.A. Emblem; 15c. Unemployed man.

(50)   (51)

1934. *T **36** and **41** (No. 367) surch with new values, by Topographical Service, Batavia. for use as postage stamps.*
365	**50**	2c. on 10c. purple	35	50
366		2c. on 20c. brown	35	30
367	**51**	2c. on 30c. magenta	35	65
368	**50**	42½c. on 75c. green	4·75	35
369		42½c. on 1g.50 orange	4·75	50
365/369 *Set of 5*			9·50	2·10

52 Dowager Queen Emma   **53** Cavalryman and Wounded Soldier   **54** Dinner-time

(Des H. Seegers from photo by F. Ziegler. Photo)

1934 (15 Sept). *Anti-tuberculosis Fund. P 13 × 14.*
370	**52**	12½c.(+2½c.) black-brown	1·75	55

(Des F. A. Wagner. Photo)

1935 (1 Apr). *Christian Military Home. T **53** and similar types inscr "CHR. MILITAIRE TEHUIZEN". P 12½.*
371	2c.(+1c.) olive-brown and purple		1·75	1·25
372	5c.(+2½c.) olive-brown and green		3·50	3·50
373	12½c.(+2½c.) olive-brown and orange		3·50	30
374	15c.(+5c.) olive-brown and blue		5·25	9·25
371/374 *Set of 4*			12·50	9·25

Designs:—2c. Engineer; 12½c. Artilleryman and volcano victim; 15c. Infantry bugler.

(Des J. Sjollema. Photo)

1936 (1 Dec). *Salvation Army. As T* **54** *(2c. 23 × 20 mm; others 30 × 27 mm).* P 12½.

375	2c.(+1c.) purple		1·25	70
376	5c.(+2½c.) slate-blue		1·50	1·25
377	7½c.(+2½c.) violet		1·50	1·60
378	12½c.(+2½c.) orange		1·50	40
379	15c.(+5c.) bright blue		2·50	2·40
375/379	*Set of 5*		7·50	5·75

55 Boy Scouts	**(56)** **(57)**	**(D 58)**

(Des A. Kreisler. Photo)

1937 (1 May). *Scouts' Jamboree.* P 12½.

380	**55**	7½c. (+2½c.) bronze-green	1·00	95
381		12½c. (+2½c.) carmine	1·00	55

1937. *T* **20** *surch.*

382	**56**	10 on 30c. slate (R.)	2·50	30
		a. Surch double	£2100	
383	**57**	10 on 32½c. violet and orange	2·75	35

1937 (10 Oct). *POSTAGE DUE. No. D237 surch with Type* D **58**.

D384	D **7**	20 on 37½c. salmon	90	50

59 Sifting Rice	**60** Queen Wilhelmina	**61** Wmk horiz

1937 (1 Dec). *Relief Fund As T* **59** *(local scenes inscr "A. S. I. B").* Photo. P 12½.

385	2c.(+1c.) sepia and orange		1·40	80
386	3½c.(+1½c.) grey		1·40	90
387	7½c.(+2½c.) blue-green and orange		1·50	1·10
388	10c.(+2½c.) scarlet and orange		1·50	30
389	20c.(+5c.) blue		1·40	1·40
385/389	*Set of 5*		6·50	4·00

Designs:—3½c. Mother and children, 7½c. Ox-team ploughing a rice-field; 10c. Ox-team and cart; 20c. Man and woman.

(Des P. Koch and J. van Krimpen. Photo)

1938 (30 Aug). *40th Anniv of Coronation.* W **61**. P 12½ × 12.

390	**60**	2c. violet	10	10
391		10c. lake	10	10
392		15c. blue	1·40	70
393		20c. vermilion	70	35
390/393	*Set of 4*		2·10	1·10

62 Douglas "DC-2" Airliner	**63** Nurse and Child

1938 (15 Oct). *Air Service Fund. 10th Anniv of Royal Netherlands Indies Air Lines. T* **62** *and similar type.* Photo. W **61**. P 12½.

394	17½c. (+5c.) sepia		90	90
395	20c. (+5c.) slate		90	55

Design:—20c. as T **62**, but showing reverse side of airliner.

1938–40. W **61**.

(a) P 12½ × 11½.

396	**46**	1c. slate-violet (9.39)	35	80
397		2c. purple (9.39)	10	40
398		2½c. olive-bistre (9.39)	55	55
399		3c. yellow-green (9.39)	1·40	1·60
400		4c. bronze-green (9.39)	1·40	1·60
401		5c. ultramarine (9.39)	10	10
		a. Perf 11½ × 12½ (early 1939)	1·25	55
402		7½c. violet (9.39)	2·40	1·40
403	**47**	10c. scarlet (9.39)	10	10
404		15c. ultramarine (9.39)	10	10
405		20c. purple (9.39)	35	10
		a. Perf 11½ × 12½ (early 1939)	1·25	55
406		25c. blue-green (9.39)	24·00	22·00
407		30c. indigo (9.39)	9·00	1·50
408		35c. violet (9.39)	5·00	1·50
409		40c. yellow-green (1940)	5·25	35

(b) Larger (30 × 30 mm). P 12½.

410	**47**	50c. indigo (10.40)	£275	†
411		60c. ultramarine (12.39)	13·00	3·50
		a. Wmk vert	£475	£275
412		80c. scarlet (12.39)	70·00	40·00
413		1g. violet (12.39)	30·00	3·50
414		2g. blue-green (16.11.38)	25·00	12·50
415		5g. olive-bistre (16.11.38)	24·00	6·25
396/415	*Set of 20*		£450	
396/409, 411/415	*Set of 19*		£190	85·00

The 50c. was not sent to the Netherlands Indies but was on sale at the philatelic counters in the Netherlands.

1938 (1 Dec). *Child Welfare. As T* **63** *(inscr "CENTRAAL MISSIE-BUREAU").* Photo. W **61**.

(a) Size 20 × 20 mm. P 12½.

416	2c. (+1c.) violet		80	55

(b) Size 23 × 23 mm. P 11½ × 12½ (3½c.) or 12½ × 11½ (others).

417	3½c.(+1c.) green		1·25	1·10
418	7½c.(+2½c.) brown-red		90	90
419	10c.(+2½c.) scarlet		1·00	30
420	20c.(+5c.) ultramarine		1·25	1·10
416/420	*Set of 5*		4·75	3·50

Designs:—Nurse with a child suffering from injuries to eye (3½c.), arm (7½c.), head (20c.),and a nurse bathing a baby (10c.).

63a Group of Natives

64 European Nurse and Patient	**65** Native Nurse and Patient

(Des W. Hartman. Photo)

1939 (1 Dec). *Netherlands Indies Social Bureau and Protestant Church Funds. Designs as T* **63a/5**. W **61**. P 11½ × 13 (2c., 7½c.) or 13 × 11½ (others).

421	–	2c.(+1c.) reddish violet	30	30
422	**65**	3½c.(+1½c.) blue-green	35	30
423	**63a**	7½c.(+2½c.) brown-red	30	30

424	**65**	10c.(+2½c.) vermilion		1·60	1·00
		a. Pair. Nos. 424/5		4·50	5·50
425	**64**	10c.(+2½c.) vermilion		1·60	90
426		20c.(+5c.) blue		55	50
421/426	Set of 6			4·25	3·00

Designs:—2c. as T **63a**, but group in European clothes.
Nos. 424/5 were issued together in *se-tenant* pairs within the sheet.

No. 270   No. 427

(Litho Topographical Service, Batavia)

1940 (15 Nov). *Local printing. As No. 270, but redrawn with five (instead of four) lines of shading in scroll, at right of "E" of "INDIE". P 12½.*

427	**19**	5c. blue		1·60	20

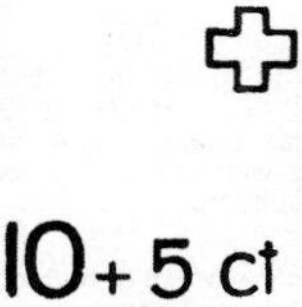

IO+5 ct
(66)

67 Queen Wilhelmina

68 Queen Wilhelmina

1940 (2 Dec). *Red Cross Fund. No. 345 surch locally with T* **66**.

428	**47**	10c.+5c. on 12½c. vermilion (V.)		3·50	55

(Des W. A. van Konijnenburg. Lettering J. van Krimpen. Photo G. Kolff & Co, Batavia)

Two Types of 10c.

I. Space between "10" and "CENT" 1¼ mm
II. Space 2 mm

1941. No wmk.

(a) 18 × 23 mm. P 12½.

429	**67**	10c. vermilion (I)		55	35
		a. Perf 13		75	35
		b. Type II		55	35
430		15c. bright blue		2·50	1·75
431		17½c. orange		1·00	70
432		20c. magenta		30·00	32·00
433		25c. green		40·00	42·00
434		30c. yellow-brown		4·50	1·40
435		35c. purple		£160	£350
436		40c. yellow-green		12·00	3·50

(b) 20½ × 26 mm. P 13 or 12½ (5g.).

437	**67**	50c. brown-lake		3·50	75
438		60c. bright blue		3·00	75
439		80c. vermilion		3·00	75
440		1g. violet		3·00	75
441		2g. blue-green		16·00	1·75
442		5g. yellow-brown		£300	£600
443		10g. green		42·00	18·00

(c) Type **68**. *P 13.*

444	**68**	25g. orange		£250	£140
429/444	Set of 16			£800	£1100

(Litho G. Kolff & Co, Batavia)

1941. *POSTAGE DUE. As Nos. D226, etc but litho on thicker, yellowish paper, in fainter colours and with smaller perforation holes.*

D445	D **7**	1c. pale salmon		1·40	2·50
D446		5c. pale salmon		1·60	1·40
D447		10c. pale salmon		15·00	11·50
D448		15c. pale salmon		1·90	1·25

D449	20c. pale salmon		1·40	1·25
D450	30c. pale salmon		2·25	1·25
D451	40c. pale salmon		1·90	1·25
D452	1g. light blue		1·40	90
D445/452	Set of 8		24·00	19·00

For stamps in other colours, see Nos. D489/501 and D527.

69 Netherlands Coat of Arms

70 Doctor and Child

71 Wayangwong Dancer

(Des D. Ruhl. Litho Kolff & Co, Batavia)

1941 (10 May). *Prince Bernhard Fund to Equip Dutch Forces. P 12½.*

453	**69**	5c.+5c. ultramarine and orange		75	15
454		10c.+10c. ultramarine and scarlet		75	15
455		1g.+1g. ultramarine and grey		16·00	10·75

(Des J. F. Dickhoff. Photo Kolff & Co)

1941 (22 Sept). *Indigent Mohammedans' Relief Fund. T* **70** *and similar designs. P 12½.*

456		2c.(+1c.) yellow-green		1·10	55
457		3½c.(+1½c.) violet-brown		5·25	2·75
458		7½c.(+2½c.) violet		4·50	3·50
459		10c.(+2½c.) red		1·75	35
460		15c.(+5c.) blue		13·00	7·00
456/460	Set of 5			23·00	12·50

Designs:—3½c. Native eating rice; 7½c. Nurse and patient; 10c. Nurse and children, 15c. Basket-weaver.

(Des J. F. Dickhoff. Photo Kolff & Co)

1941–45. *As T* **71** *(various dancers). P 12½.*

461		2c. scarlet (1945)		30	15
462		2½c. claret		55	15
463		3c. green		55	35
464		4c. brown-olive		50	35
465		5c. blue		10	10
466		7½c. violet		55	10
461/466	Set of 6			2·25	1·00

Designs:—Menari (2c.), Nias (2½c.), Legon (3c.), Padjoge (5c.) and Dyak (7½c.) dancers.
Stocks of No. 461 were first issued by the Indonesian Republicans. They were mostly overprinted (see under Indonesia in Part 21 (*South-East Asia*) of this catalogue).
See also Nos. 514/16.

JAPANESE OCCUPATION

In the Second World War, the Japanese landed in Borneo and Celebes on 11 January 1942. After winning the naval battle of the Java Sea, they landed on 1 March in Java, which surrendered on 8 March. The defenceless remainder of the Netherlands Indies was soon occupied. Three Japanese administrative areas were established: (i) Java; (ii) Malaya and Sumatra; (iii) the Japanese Naval Control Area, covering the other islands of the Netherlands Indies.

I. JAVA

100 Sen or Cents = 1 Rupee

PRINTERS. Nos. 1 to 26 were lithographed by G. Kolff & Co, Batavia.

1 Eastern Asia

(Litho Kolff & Co, Batavia)

1943 (9 Mar). *First Anniv of Japanese Occupation of Java. Designs with vert panel of characters as in T* **1**. P 12½.

1	2s. red-brown		4·00	3·25
2	3½s. carmine		4·00	3·25
3	5s. green		5·50	3·25
4	10s. light blue		15·00	4·00
1/4	*Set of* 4		25·00	12·50

Designs:—3½s. Farmer ploughing ricefield; 5s. Mt. Soemer; 10s. Bantam Bay.

2 Native Soldier

(Litho Kolff & Co, Batavia)

1943 (20 Mar). *Savings Campaign.* P 12½.

5	**2**	3½c. rose		22·00	8·00
6		10c. blue		50·00	5·50

3 Wajang Doll    **4** Map of Java    **5** Bird of Vishu and Mt. Soemer

(Des D. Ruhl (Nos. 8/10), Basoeki-Abdoellah (others). Litho Kolff & Co, Batavia)

1943 (29 Apr)–**45**. *Designs with horiz panel of characters as at foot of T* **3/5**. P 12½.

7	3½c. carmine (29.4.43)		2·75	1·75
8	5s. green (20.1.45)		2·75	1·75
9	10c. blue (29.4.43)		2·75	1·75
	a. Perf 12		4·50	4·50
10	20c. grey-olive (3.6.43)		2·75	1·75
11	40c. purple (3.6.43)		3·00	1·75
12	60c. red-orange (3.6.43)		4·00	3·00
13	80s. lake-brown (20.1.45)		7·25	4·00
14	1r. violet (20.1.45)		19·00	4·75
7/14	*Set of* 8		40·00	18·00

Designs: *As T* **3** (18 × 22½ *mm*)—3½c. Native head; 10c. Borobudur Temple; 40c. Seated dancer and Borobudur Temple. *As T* **5** (20 × 28 *mm*)—80s. Ploughing with oxen; 1r. Terraced ricefields.

II. SUMATRA

100 Cents = 1 Rupee

During 1942 and 1943 various local overprints were applied to stamps of the Netherlands Indies in the following residencies of Sumatra and the adjacent islands:—Atjeh, Bangka, Benkoelen, Billiton, Djambi, Lampong, Palembang, Sumatra's E. Coast, Sumatra's W. Coast and Tapanoeli. These overprints are of great interest to specialists, but as they are of a local character, we do not list them.

During the Japanese Occupation various small islands near Singapore were administered as part of Malaya. Stamps of the Japanese Occupation of Malaya (listed in Part 1 (*British Commonwealth*) under Malaysia) were issued to the post offices of Dabo Singkep, Puloe Samboe, Tanjong Balei, Tanjong Batu, Tanjong Pinang and Terempa between 1942 and 1945. The overprinted issues were also used by a number of districts in Northern Sumatra whose postal services were administered from Singapore until the end of March 1943.

6 Lake Toba    (7)    (8)

(Litho Kolff & Co, Batavia)

1943 (29 Apr)–**44**. *Various designs with horizontal panel of characters as at foot of T* **6**. P 12½.

15	1c. olive-green (1.8.44)		1·90	1·50
16	2c. yellow-green (1.8.44)		1·90	1·50
17	3c. greenish blue (1.8.44)		1·90	1·50
18	3½c. rose-red (29.4.43)		3·50	1·50
19	4c. ultramarine (1.8.44)		2·50	1·50
20	5c. red-orange (1.8.44)		1·90	1·10
21	10c. grey-blue (29.4.43)		5·00	1·10
22	20c. lake-brown (1.8.44)		2·50	1·10
23	30c. bright purple (1.8.44)		2·75	1·90
24	40c. chocolate (1.8.44)		3·25	2·10
25	50c. bistre-brown (1.8.44)		7·75	3·25
26	1r. violet-blue (1.8.44)		40·00	5·25
15/26	*Set of* 12		65·00	21·00

Designs: (18 × 22½ *mm*)—1, 2, 3c. Batak house; 3½, 4, 5c. Minangkabau house; 10, 20c. Ploughing with oxen; 40c. As Type **6**. (20 × 28 *mm*)—50c., 1r. Carabao Canyon.

1944 (1 Jan). *Various stamps optd for use in the whole of Sumatra as T* **7** (*handstamps, five types*) *or* **8** (*machine-printed*).

(a) 1933–37 *unwatermarked stamps of Netherlands Indies* (*T* **46/7**)

A. *Handstamped as T* **7**.

27A	**46**	3½c. slate		80	1·90
28A	**47**	10c. scarlet		10·00	13·50
29A		12½c. vermilion		13·00	22·00
30A		15c. ultramarine		7·00	13·00
31A		25c. blue-green		4·00	6·50
32A		30c. indigo		21·00	28·00
33A		35c. violet		60·00	80·00
34A		42½c. yellow		45·00	50·00
35A		50c. indigo		20·00	27·00
36A		2g.50 purple		£250	£325

B. *Optd with T* **8**.

31B	**47**	25c. blue-green		4·75	5·50

(b) 1938–40 *stamps of Netherlands Indies* (*T* **46/7**). W **61**.

A. *Handstamped as T* **7**.

37A	**46**	1c. slate-violet		60	1·60
38A		2c. purple		60	1·60
39A		2½c. olive-bistre		60	1·60
40A		3c. yellow-green		27·00	38·00
41A	**47**	10c. scarlet		95·00	£130
42A		15c. ultramarine		4·00	6·50
43A		20c. purple		15·00	27·00
44A		25c. blue-green		3·75	6·50
45A		30c. indigo		20·00	27·00
46A		35c. violet		4·50	6·50
47A		40c. yellow-green		4·50	6·50
48A		2g. blue-green		£400	£550
49A		5g. olive-bistre		45·00	65·00

B. *Optd with T* **8**.

42B	**47**	15c. ultramarine		1·75	5·25
43B		20c. purple		1·90	1·60
44B		25c. blue-green		1·75	2·75
46B		35c. violet		1·75	2·75
47B		40c. yellow-green		2·75	2·75
49B		5g. olive-bistre		18·00	27·00

(c) 1941 *stamps of Netherlands Indies* (*T* **67/8**).

A. *Handstamped as T* **7**.

50A	**67**	10c. vermilion (I)		7·00	8·00
51A		10c. vermilion (II)		7·25	8·00
52A		15c. bright blue		3·00	5·00
53A		17½c. orange		2·75	5·00
54A		20c. magenta		25·00	32·00
55A		25c. green		25·00	32·00

56A	**67**	30c. yellow-brown		6·50	10·50
57A		35c. purple		18·00	9·00
58A		40c. yellow-green		50·00	80·00
59A		50c. brown-lake		13·00	20·00
60A		60c. bright blue		11·50	17·00
61A		80c. vermilion		14·50	24·00
62A		1g. violet		4·75	6·50
63A		2g. blue-green		20·00	28·00
64A		5g. yellow-brown		£170	£225
65A		10g. green		35·00	55·00
66A	**68**	25g. orange		£325	£450

B. Optd with T 8.

50B	**67**	10c. vermilion (I)		1·00	1·60
		a. Perf 13		29·00	42·00
		b. Opt inverted			
51B		10c. vermilion (II)		4·75	6·50
52B		15c. bright blue		1·90	2·75
53B		17½c. orange		1·75	2·75
54B		20c. magenta		35·00	40·00
55B		25c. green		2·50	32·00
56B		30c. yellow-brown		1·25	2·75
58B		40c. yellow-green		1·90	4·00
59B		50c. brown-lake		2·75	3·25
60B		60c. bright blue		2·50	3·25
61B		80c. vermilion		3·25	4·25
62B		1g. violet		4·00	5·50
		a. Opt inverted			
63B		2g. blue-green		3·50	5·50
64B		5g. yellow-brown		£200	£275
65B		10g. green		38·00	50·00

(d) 1941 stamps (dancers) of Netherlands Indies. Handstamped as T 7.

66	–	3c. green		80	2·00
67	**71**	4c. brown-olive		80	2·00
68	–	5c. blue		80	2·00
69	–	7½c. violet		80	2·00

(e) 1940 stamps of Netherlands (T 94). Handstamped as T 7.

70	**94**	5c. blue-green		9·75	12·25
71		12½c. ultramarine		4·75	10·50

III. JAPANESE NAVAL CONTROL AREA

(BORNEO, CELEBES, MOLUCCAS AND LESSER SUNDA IS.)

100 Cents = 1 Gulden

On 15 July 1942, the Japanese naval authorities ordered all Netherlands Indies stamps in the area under their control to be overprinted with an anchor and the Japanese characters "Dat Nippon". This was done at the capital of each district. The following different types exist:—
1. BORNEO: Bandjermasin, Pontianak (4 types), Samarinda (5 types)
2. CELEBES. Macassar, Menado.
3. MOLUCCAS. Amboina. (A circular opt containing 8 Japanese characters was also applied here.)
4. LESSER SUNDA IS: Bali and Lombok, Lombok, Timor.
We confine ourselves to listing the Macassar overprint, which is the one most commonly found.

(9)

1942. Various stamps handstamped with T 9, in black, violet, blue or red.

(a) Stamps of Netherlands Indies, 1933–37, no wmk.

80	**46**	1c. slate-violet		90	4·25
81		3c. yellow-green		1·10	4·25
82		3½c. slate		5·50	10·50
83		4c. bronze-green		25·00	40·00
84		5c. ultramarine		10·00	15·00
85	**47**	25c. blue-green		5·50	7·50
86		30c. indigo		40·00	40·00
87		35c. violet		6·50	11·50

88		50c. indigo		55·00	75·00

(b) Stamps of Netherlands Indies, 1938–40, W 61.

89	**46**	1c. slate-violet		4·00	16·00
90		2c. purple		90	3·50
91		2½c. olive-bistre		75	3·50
92		3c. yellow-green		70	3·50
93		4c. bronze-green		12·00	18·00
94		5c. ultramarine		30·00	40·00
95	**47**	10c. scarlet		50·00	65·00
96		15c. ultramarine		9·00	14·00
97		20c. purple		95	3·50
98		25c. blue-green		4·25	8·00
99		30c. indigo		22·00	30·00
100		35c. violet		95	3·50
101		40c. yellow-green		95	3·50
102		80c. scarlet		£200	£300
103		1g. violet			
104		2g. blue-green			
105		5g. olive-bistre			

(c) Netherlands Indies, 1933, Special Flights Air Stamp.

106	**48**	30c. blue		£225	£325

(d) Netherlands Indies, 1940, numeral type.

107	**19**	5c. blue (427)		1·00	3·25

(e) Stamps of Netherlands Indies, 1941 (Queen).

108	**67**	10c. vermilion (I)		3·00	4·00
109		10c. vermilion (II)		3·00	4·00
110		15c. bright blue		3·75	15·00
111		17½c. orange		1·10	4·00
112		20c. magenta		22·00	32·00
113		25c. green		27·00	42·00
114		30c. yellow-brown		4·00	10·00
115		35c. purple		45·00	55·00
116		40c. yellow-green		18·00	26·00
117		50c. brown-lake		9·50	11·00
118		60c. bright blue		4·50	8·50
119		80c. vermilion		8·00	14·00
120		1g. violet		6·00	11·00
121		2g. blue-green		40·00	65·00
122		5g. yellow-brown			
123	**68**	25g. orange			

(f) Stamps of Netherlands Indies, 1941 (dancers).

124	–	2½c. claret		4·50	7·50
125	–	3c. green		2·00	3·75
126	**71**	4c. brown-olive		2·75	3·50
127	–	5c. blue		6·00	14·00
128	–	7½c. violet		90	4·00

(g) Stamps of Netherlands, 1940 (Queen).

129	**94**	5c. blue-green			
130		12½c. ultramarine			

1942. POSTAGE DUE. Postage Due stamps of Netherlands Indies, 1913–41, handstamped with T 9, in various colours.

(a) Enschedé print, 1913–40 (Nos. D226, etc.).

D131	D **7**	1c. salmon		11·00	18·00
D132		2½c. salmon		1·50	3·50
D133		3½c. salmon		3·25	6·75
D134		5c. salmon		1·75	3·50
D135		7½c. salmon		1·75	3·50
D136		10c. salmon		1·25	3·50
D137		20c. salmon		1·75	3·50
D138		20 on 37½c. salmon (D384)		50·00	80·00
D139		25c. salmon		1·50	3·50
D140		30c. salmon		3·75	8·25
D141		40c. salmon		2·00	4·00

(b) Kolff print, 1941 (Nos. D445, etc.).

D142	D **7**	1c. pale salmon		6·75	13·50
D143		5c. pale salmon		2·00	4·00
D144		15c. pale salmon		1·75	3·50
D145		20c. pale salmon		1·75	4·00
D146		40c. pale salmon		2·00	4·00
D147		1g. light blue		5·75	10·00

1943. Air. Stamps of Netherlands Indies handstamped with T 9 and further surch. in red.

(a) Stamp of 1933–37, no wmk.

148	**46**	"f.2" on 1c. slate-violet		12·50	20·00

(b) Stamp of 1938–40, W 61.

151	**46**	"f. 8.50" on 2½c. olive-bistre		40·00	65·00

Examples of the 2f. on 1c. (no wmk), 2f. on 5c. (Numeral), 7f. on 2½c. (wmk), 8f.50 on 2½c. (wmk) and 8f.50 on 3c. (with or without wmk) overprinted in red with an additional line of text were for use on telegraph money orders.

10 Japanese Flag
and Palms

11 Mt. Fuji, Flag
and Bird

(Typo, 2c, to 20c.; recess, others. Govt Ptg Wks, Japan)

1943 (2 July–8 Aug). *Wmk vert wavy lines.* P 13.

152	**10**	2c. brown (8.8)	80	16·00
153		3c. yellow-green (8.8)	80	16·00
154		3½c. brown-orange (8.8)	1·40	15·00
155		5c. blue (8.8)	80	12·00
156		10c. carmine	80	12·00
157		15c. ultramarine (8.8)	90	12·00
158		20c. dull violet (8.8)	90	12·00
159	**11**	25c. orange (8.8)	3·00	14·00
160		30c. blue (8.8)	3·00	15·00
161		50c. slate-green (8.8)	6·00	23·00
162		1g. brown-purple (8.8)	27·00	30·00
152/162 *Set of 11*			40·00	£160

DUTCH RULE RESTORED

1945. 100 Cents 1 Gulden
1949. 100 Sen - 1 Rupiah

On 14 August 1945 Japan surrendered. In the islands already captured from the Japanese by U.S. and Australian troops, Dutch administration was restored without difficulty. In Java, Madura and Sumatra an Indonesian Republic was declared and the Dutch never obtained complete control again. The following stamps were used in those parts of the Indies over which Dutch rule was restored, including fluctuating areas in Java and Sumatra. Stamps issued by the Republicans are listed under Indonesia in Part 21 (*South-East Asia*) of this catalogue.

"NICA" (Nederlandsch-Indie Civiel Administratie). Stamps of Japan and the Netherlands Indies may be found handstamped "NICA TIMOR" in two lines in violet, and Netherlands Indies stamps handstamped with an anchor and Japanese characters may be found with a further black handstamp of "NICA SOEMBA" and a horse's head within a frame. These were issued when Dutch rule was restored in Timor and Soemba.

72 Paddyfield

73 Queen
Wilhelmina

TE BETALEN

P O R T

2½

74 Queen Wilhelmina

(D **75**)

(Recess American Bank Note Co)

1945–46. *T* **72** *and similar designs and T* **73/4**. P 12.

467	**72**	1c. yellow-green	55	15
468	–	2c. bright magenta	55	30
469	–	2½c. purple	55	15
470	–	5c. blue	35	15
471	–	7½c. olive-grey	75	15
472	**73**	10c. red-brown	35	15
473		15c. blue	35	15
474		17½c. carmine	35	15
475		20c. brown-purple	35	15
476		30c. slate-grey	35	15
477	**74**	60c. slate-grey	35	15
478		1g. turquoise-green	75	15
479		2½g. red-orange	3·50	70
467/479 *Set of 13*			8·75	2·25

Designs:—2c. Lake in W. Java; 2½c. Medical School, Batavia; 5c. Seashore; 7½c. Aeroplane over Bromo Volcano.

Stamps of this issue were handstamped "PORT" (for postage due) by the postmaster at Medan, Sumatra, in May–June 1946, but they are considered to be of local status.

1946 (11 Mar). *POSTAGE DUE. Queen Wilhelmina stamps of 1941 surch with Type D* **75** *or optd only, at Macassar.*

D480	2½c. on 10c. vermilion (No. 429)		90	90
D481	10c. vermilion (No. 429)		2·00	2·00
D482	20c. magenta (No. 432)		5·50	5·50
D483	40c. yellow-green (No. 436)		45·00	45·00
D480/483 *Set of 4*			48·00	48·00

 3 **45**

1947

76 Railway
Viaduct near
Soekaboemi

(**77**)

(**78**)

(**79**)

(Typo Netherlands Indies Govt Ptg Wks, Melbourne, Australia)

1946. *As T* **76** *(various views). Wmk T* **15** *of Australia (Mult Crown over "C of A").* P 15 × 14.

484	1c. green (18.11)		30	20
485	2c. sepia (18.11)		30	20
486	2½c. scarlet (18.11)		30	20
487	5c. indigo (22.7)		30	20
488	7½c. ultramarine (18.11)		30	20
484/488 *Set of 5*			1·25	90

Designs:—2c. Power station; 2½c. Minangkabau house; 5c. Tondano scene (Celebes); 7½c. Buddhist Stupas, Java.

(Typo Netherlands Indies Govt Ptg Wks, Melbourne, Australia)

1946. *POSTAGE DUE. Wmk T* **15** *of Australia (Mutt Crown over "C of A").* P 15 × 14.

D489	D **7**	1c. violet	75	90
D490		2½c. orange-brown	2·00	1·60
D491		3½c. ultramarine	70	90
D492		5c. red-orange	90	90
D493		7½c. blue-green	90	90
D494		10c. magenta	90	90
D495		20c. pale-blue	90	1·10
D496		25c. yellow-olive	90	1·10
D497		30c. purple-brown	1·10	1·10
D498		40c. green	1·10	1·25
D499		50c. yellow	1·50	1·50
D500		75c. greenish blue	1·50	1·50
D501		100c. yellow-green	1·50	1·50
D489/501 *Set of 13*			13·00	13·50

See also No. D527.

1947 (25 Sept).

(a) Nos. 486, 488 and 484 surch with new values, as T **77**.

502	3 on 2½c. scarlet		30	20
503	3 on 7½c. ultramarine		30	20
	a. Surch double		£160	£200
504	4 on 1c. green		30	20

(b) No. 411 surch with T **78**, *in red*.

505	45 on 60c. ultramarine		1·40	95
	a. Wmk vert		£200	
502/505	*Set of 4*		2·10	1·40

1947 (25 Sept). *Queen Wilhelmina stamps variously optd as T* **79**.

(a) Without wmk.

506	**47**	12½c. vermilion	35	20

(b) W **61**.

507	**47**	25c. blue-green (R.)	35	20
		a. Error. On stamp without wmk	—	£250
508	**67**	40c. yellow-green	55	20
509	**47**	50c. indigo (R.)	75	30
510		80c. scarlet	1·10	65
		a. Wmk vert	2·10	2·40
		b. Error. On stamp without wmk	£500	£225
511	**67**	2g. blue-green	4·00	55
512		5g. yellow-brown	10·75	6·75
506/512	*Set of 7*		16·00	9·75

Horiz opt—12½c. and 25c. are as illustrated; 50c. and 80c. are larger and the latter has a bar above "1947". Vert opt—40c. and 5g. at left and 2g. at right.

(80)

81 Queen Wilhelmina

1948 (2 Feb). *Relief for Victims of the Terror. No. 344 surch with T* **80**.

513	**47**	15c.+10c. on 10c. scarlet	30	30
		a. Surch inverted	£180	£250

(Des J. F. Dickhoff. Litho Kolff & Co)

1948 (15 May–Sept). *Dancers. Vert designs as T* **71**. P 12½.

514	3c. scarlet (Menari)	35	20
515	4c. grey-olive (Legon)	35	20
516	7½c. brown (Dyak) (Sept)	70	65

(Des S. L. Hartz and J. van Krimpen. Photo G. Kolff & Co)

1948 (15 May–Sept).

(a) Size 18 × 22½ mm. P 12½.

517	**81**	15c. orange (Sept)	90	70
518		20c. light blue	35	35
519		25c. blue-green	35	35
520		40c. green	35	35
521		45c. magenta	55	70
522		50c. claret	50	35
523		80c. scarlet	55	35

(b) Size 21 × 26 mm. P 13.

524	**81**	1g. violet	50	35
		a. Perf 12½ × 12	1·10	55
525		10g. green	30·00	12·50
526		25g. orange	60·00	50·00
517/526	*Set of 10*			

(Litho G. Kolff & Co)

1948. *POSTAGE DUE. No wmk.* P 12.

D527	D **7**	2½c. red-brown	1·10	1·25

82 Queen Wilhelmina   **83** Queen Juliana

(Des S. L. Hartz and J. van Krimpen. Photo G. Kolff & Co)

1948 (31 Aug). *Golden Jubilee.* P 12½ × 12.

528	**82**	15c. orange	40	30
529		20c. bright blue	40	30

Queen Juliana

6 September 1948

(Des S. L. Hartz and J. van Krimpen. Photo Enschedé)

1948 (25 Sept). W **61**. P 14 × 13.

530	**83**	15c. scarlet	50	35
531		20c. blue	50	35

INDONESIA

In September 1948 the Netherlands Indies were officially renamed Indonesia.

INDONESIA
(84)

INDONESIA
(85)

1948–49. *Optd with T* **84** *or* **85** *(gulden values).*

(a) Optd typo in glossy black ink by G. C. T van Dorp & Co, Batavia. Top bar of T **84** 1.8 mm (1948).

532	**81**	15c. orange (31.12)	90	30
533		20c. light blue (31.12)	35	30
534		25c. blue-green (8.12)	30	30
535		40c. green (8.12)	35	30
536		80c. scarlet (8.12)	90	30
537		1g. violet (Dec)	1·10	30
		a. Perf 12½ × 12	1·25	30
538	**74**	2½g. red-orange (Dec)	45·00	9·50
539	**81**	10g. green (Dec)	90·00	30·00
540		25g. orange	£125	55·00
532/540	*Set of 9*		£250	85·00

(b) Optd photo in dull black ink by G. Kolff & Co, Batavia. Top bar of T **84** 2.2 mm (1949).

541	**81**	15c. orange (Mar)	90	30
542		20c. light blue (Mar)	55	30
543		25c. blue-green (Mar)	30	30
544		45c. magenta (Mar)	1·10	90
545		50c. claret (17.1)	35	30
546		80c. scarlet (Mar)	1·10	30
541/546	*Set of 6*		3·75	2·10

(c) Optd typo as T **85** *but with three bars, by G. Kolff & Co* (1949).

547	**81**	1g. violet (p 12½ × 12) (Mar)	8·00	35
		a. Opt double	£650	£350

86 **87** Portal to Tjandi Poentadewa Temple **88** Toradja House

(Des H. G. Smelt. Photo G. Kolff & Co, Batavia)

1949 (Feb)–**50**. *New Currency. Various designs.* A. P 12½.

548A	**86**	1s. grey	35	20
549A		2s. purple	55	20
550A		2½s. olive-brown	35	20
551A		3s. crimson	55	20
552A		4s. green	55	55
553A		5s. blue	55	20
554A		7½s. deep green	55	20
555A		10s. mauve	35	20
556A		12½s. orange-red	1·75	20
557A	**87**	15s. carmine	1·60	55
558A		20s. grey-black	90	20
559A		25s. ultramarine	90	20
560A	—	30s. orange-red	1·10	20
561A	—	40s. green	1·10	20
562A	—	45s. purple	2·50	4·50
563A	—	50s. red-brown	1·40	20
564A	—	60s. chocolate	1·40	1·75
565A	—	80s. scarlet	3·50	35
566A	**88**	1r. violet	75	20
567A		2r. grey-green	4·50	20
568A		3r. purple	90·00	20
569A	—	5r. chocolate	65·00	35
570A	—	10r. grey-black	80·00	1·75
571A	—	25r. red-brown	75	1·75
548A/571A		*Set of 24*	£225	13·50

B. P 11½.

548B	**86**	1s. grey	55	75
549B		2s. purple	29·00	29·00
550B		2½s. olive-brown	35	20
551B		3s. crimson	1·40	1·40
553B		5s. blue	1·10	20
554B		7½s. deep green	1·10	55
555B		10s. mauve	—	£450
556B		12½s. orange-red	2·10	1·75
557B	**87**	15s. carmine	35	20
558B		20s. grey-black	35	20
559B		25s. ultramarine	35	20
560B	—	30s. orange-red	35	20
561B	—	40s. green	35	20
562B	—	45s. purple	55	3·50
563B	—	50s. red-brown	55	20
564B	—	60s. chocolate	75	1·75
565B	—	80s. scarlet	1·10	20

Designs. As T **87**—30s. to 45s. Sculpture from Temple at Bedjoening, Bali; 50s. to 80s. Minangkabau house, Sumatra. As T **88**—5r. to 25r. Detail of Temple of Panahan.

Unoverprinted stamps of this issue were on sale in post offices of the Indonesian Republic until 23 May 1958 and they were valid for use until 30 June 1958. In 1952 new printings of the 1r. in a brighter violet and of the 2r. in a greyer green were made.

(Des H. G. Smelt. Photo G. Kolff & Co, Batavia)

1949 (1 Oct). *75th Anniv of Universal Postal Union.* P 12½.

572	**89**	15s. scarlet	1·10	35
573		25s. blue	1·10	35

STAMP BOOKLETS

The following checklist covers, in simplified form, booklets issued by Netherlands Indies.

Prices are for complete booklets

Booklet No.	Date	Contents and Face Value	Price
SB1	1904	*Numeral* (T **11**) 4 panes, No. 121 × 6 (24c.)	£1100
SB2	1904	*Wilhelmina* (T **12**) 4 panes, No. 128 × 6 (2g.40)	£800
SB3	1911	*Numeral* (T **11**) *and Wilhelmina* (T **12**) 1 pane, No. 121 × 6; 1 pane, No. 123 × 6; 1 pane, No. 126 × 6; 1 pane, No. 129 × 6; 2 panes, No. 128 × 6 (2g.46)	£800
SB4	1913	*Numeral* (T **19**) 4 panes, No. 209 × 6 (24c.)	—
SB5	1913	*Wilhelmina* (T **20**) 4 panes, No. 216 × 6 (2g.40)	£800
SB6	1914	*Numeral* (T **19**) *and Wilhelmina* (T **20**) 1 pane, No. 209 × 6; 1 pane, No. 211 × 6; 1 pane, No. 214 × 6; 1 pane, No. 217 × 6; 2 panes, No. 216 × 6 (2g.46)	—
SB7	1922	*Numeral* (T **19**) 4 panes, No. 265 × 6 (60c.)	£800
SB8	1922	*Wilhelmina* (T **20**) *surch* 4 panes, No. 250 × 6 (3g.)	—
SB9	1922	*Numeral* (T **19**) *and Wilhelmina* (T **20**) *surch* 1 pane, No. 265 × 6; 1 pane, No. 271 × 6; 1 pane, No. 250 × 6; 1 pane, No. 252 × 6 (2g.55)	£800

UNITED STATES OF INDONESIA

On 27 December 1949, Indonesia, comprising all the former Netherlands Indies except New Guinea, became independent as an equal partner in the Netherlands-Indonesian Union under the title of the Republic of the United States of Indonesia, or "Republik Indonesia Serikat". The Indonesian Republic in Java and Sumatra was the leading state in this federation.

89 Globe and Arms of Berne

90 Indonesian Flag

BAJAR

2½ sen

PORTO   RIS

(D **91**)   (**92**)

R I S (**93**)

(Photo G. Kolff & Co, Djakarta)

1950. *Inauguration of United States of Indonesia.*

(a) Size 20½ × 26 mm. P 12½.

574	**90**	15s. scarlet (17.1.50)	1·10	25

(b) Size 18 × 23 mm. P 11½.

575	**90**	15s. scarlet (22.6.50)	6·50	1·10

1950 (Apr). *POSTAGE DUE. Nos. D499/501 of Netherlands Indies surch as Type D* **91.**

D576	**D 7**	2½s. on 50c. yellow	1·00	65
D577		5s. on 100c. yellow-green	2·75	1·00
		a. Error, "5" inverted	£375	
D578		10s. on 75c. greenish blue	5·75	1·40

("RIS" = Republik Indonesia Serikat)

1950 (15 Aug). *Nos. 548/71 of Netherlands Indies (inscr "INDONESIA") optd.*

(a) With T **92** *(horiz opt). P 11½.*

579	**86**	1s. grey	80	65
580		2s. purple	1·40	1·80
		b. Perf 12½	1·10	2·75
581		2½s. olive-brown	80	65
		b. Perf 12½	1·10	55
582		3s. crimson	80	40
		b. Perf 12½	80	40
583		4s. green	80	65
		b. Perf 12½	1·40	80
584		5s. blue	80	65
585		7½s. deep green	80	65
		b. Perf 12½	80	65
586		10s. mauve	80	60
		b. Perf 12½	1·40	1·40
587		12½s. orange-red (perf 12½)	1·00	65

(b) With T **93** *(vert opt). P 11½.*

588	**87**	20s. grey-black	24·00	28·00
		b. Perf 12½	—	—
589		25s. ultramarine	80	60
		b. Perf 12½	1·40	65
590	—	30s. orange-red	8·25	18·00
		b. Perf 12½	41·00	55·00
591		40s. green	80	40
		b. Perf 12½	80	40
592		45s. purple	1·60	1·00
593		50s. red-brown	1·40	85
594		60s. chocolate	7·00	10·50
		b. Perf 12½	—	29·00
595	—	80s. scarlet	2·75	1·00
		b. Perf 12½	2·75	80

(c) As T **93** *(vert opt), but 2½ × 12 mm. P 12½.*

596	**88**	1r. violet	2·10	45
597		2r. grey-green	£350	90·00
598		3r. purple	£120	55·00
599	—	5r. chocolate	49·00	16·00
600	—	10r. grey-black	90·00	35·00
601	—	25r. red-brown	20·00	13·50

Designs:—1s. to 12½s. Numeral; 20, 25s. Portal to Tjandi Poentadawa Temple; 30 to 45s. Sculpture from Bali temple; 50 to 80s. Minangkabau house; 1 to 3r. Toradja house; 5 to 25r. Temple of Panahan.

INDONESIAN REPUBLIC

During the early months of 1950 the states of the United States of Indonesia were successively amalgamated with the original Indonesian Republic (Java and Sumatra) until on 15 August 1950 a unitary state was proclaimed under the title of the Indonesian Republic ("Republik Indonesia"). This remained within the Netherlands-Indonesian Union until that Union was dissolved on 10 August 1954.

94 Indonesian Arms **95** Map and Torch

(Des D. Hendronoto. Photo G. Kolff & Co, Djakarta)

1950 (17 Aug). *Fifth Anniv of Proclamation of Independence.* P 12½.

602	**94**	15s. scarlet	2·00	25
603		25s. grey-green	2·75	1·10
604		1r. sepia	9·75	1·70

(Des Sutopo. Photo G. Kolff & Co, Djakarta)

1951 (2 Jan). *Asiatic Olympic Games, New Delhi.* P 12½ × 12.

605	**95**	5s.+3s. green	10	10
606		10s.+5s. deep blue	10	10
607		20s.+5s. scarlet	10	10
608		30s.+10s. brown	25	15
609		35s.+10s. ultramarine	2·75	2·10
605/609	*Set of 5*		3·00	2·30

96 I II

I. Stamp 18 mm wide
II. Stamp 17½ mm wide

97 General Post-Office Bandung **98** "Spirit of Indonesia" **99** President Sukarno

(Des M. Irot (T **96/7**), S. Ratnojo (T **98**). Photo G. Kolff & Co, Djakarta)

1951–55. P 12½.

610	**96**	1s. grey (9.51)	40	75
611		2s. magenta (9.51)	40	60
612		2½s. sepia (7.51)	5·00	15
613		5s. carmine (2.51)	40	15
614		7½s. light green (7.51)	40	15
615		10s. blue (I) (2.51)	40	15
		a. Perf 11½	6·75	6·75
		b. Type II (2.51)	40	20
616		15s. violet (4.51)	40	15
617		15s. purple (1955)	40	20
618		20s. red (I) (4.51)	40	15
		a. Type II (12.51)	45	20
619		25s. olive-green (4.51)	40	15
620	**97**	30s. orange-red (3.53)	10	10
621		35s. violet (3.53)	65·	10
622		40s. blue-green (7.53)	10·	10
623		45s. reddish purple (7.53)	10·	25
624		50s. brown (6.53)	3·00	10
625	**98**	60s. sepia (7.53)	10	10
626		70s. grey (3.53)	10	10
627		75s. bright blue (6.53)	10	10
628		80s. reddish purple (7.53)	10	10
629		90s. deep bluish green (7.53)	10	10
610/629	*Set of 20*		11·25	3·00

(Photo J. Enschedé and Sons, Haarlem until 1957, then Pertjetakan Kebajoran, Djakarta)

1951–53. P 12½ × 12.

630	**99**	1r. reddish violet (2.51)	25	10
631		1r.25 orange (1.6.53)	1·60	10
632		1r.50 bistre-brown (1.6.53)	25	10
633		2r. green (3.51)	25	10
634		2r.50 lake-brown (1.6.53)	25	10
635		3r. blue (3.51)	25	10
636		4r. bright olive (1.6.53)	25	10
637		5r. sepia (3.51)	25	10
638		6r. dull mauve (1.6.53)	25	10
639		10r. blue-grey (3.51)	25	10
640		15r. yellow-ochre (1.6.53)	25	10
641		20r. slate-purple (1.6.53)	25	10
642		25r. red (3.51)	65	10
643		40r. yellow-green (1.6.53)	80	2·10
644		50r. blue-violet (1.6.53)	1·10	10
630/644 *Set of 15*			6·25	3·25

The figures of value are slightly thicker in the Djakarta printings than in the Enschede printings, especially on Nos. 640/4. From 1963 the Djakarta printings were on fluorescent paper.

D 100

101 Sports Emblem

102 Doves

(Des Snoek. Litho G. Kolff & Co, Djakarta)

1951 (June)**–53**. *POSTAGE DUE.* P 12½.

D645	**D 100**	2½s. orange	15	55
D646		5s. orange	15	10
D647		10s. orange	15	10
D648		15s. claret (1953)	15	15
D649		20s. pale blue (6.52)	15	15
D650		25s. brown-olive (6.52)	25	15
D651		30s. red-brown (6.52)	25	25
D652		40s. green (6.52)	25	25
D653		50s. orange	14·00	1·00
D654		1r. pale yellow-green (12.51)	1·60	1·50
D645/654 *Set of 10*			15·00	3·75

See also No. D772/84 and D1058/9.

(Des D. Hendronoto. Photo G. Kolff & Co, Djakarta)

1951 (15 Oct). *National Sports Festival.* P 12½ × 12.

655	**101**	5s.+3s. grey-green	35	40
656		10s.+5s. deep blue	35	40
657		20s.+5s. vermilion	35	40
658		30s.+10s. sepia	35	40
659		35s.+10s. bright blue	35	1·00
655/659 *Set of 5*			1·60	2·30

(Des A. Sadeli. Recess American Bank Note Co)

1951 (24 Oct). *United Nations Day.* P 12.

660	**102**	7½s. blue-green	2·75	80
661		10s. violet	80	40
662		20s. vermilion	2·00	80
663		30s. carmine	2·75	1·00
664		35s. ultramarine	2·75	1·00
665		1r. sepia	21·00	3·25
660/665 *Set of 6*			28·00	6·50

(103)

104 Melati Flowers

105 Merapi Volcano in Eruption

1953 (8 May). *Natural Disasters Relief Fund.* No. 621 *surch with T* **103**.

666	**97**	35s.+10s. violet	25	15

(Des D. Djazh. Photo G. Kolff & Co, Djakarta)

1953 (22 Dec). *Mothers' Day and 25th Anniv of Indonesian Women's Congress.* P 12½.

667	**104**	50s. dull blue-green	20·00	55

(Des Amat bin Djupri. Litho G. Kolff & Co, Djakarta)

1954 (15 Apr–July). *Natural Disasters Relief Fund.* P 12½ (3, 5r.) or 12½ × 12 (others).

668	**105**	15s.+10s. blue-green	1·10	1·40
669		35s.+15s. violet	1·10	1·10
670		50s.+25s. vermilion	1·10	1·10
671		75s.+25s. ultramarine	1·10	1·10
672		1r.+25s. bright carmine	1·10	1·10
673		2r.+50s. sepia	2·75	1·10
674		3r.+1r. bronze green	14·00	7·00
		a. Perf 12½ × 12 (7.54)	14·00	7·00
675		5r.+2r.50 chestnut	16·00	9·75
		a. Perf 12½ × 12 (7.54)	16·00	9·75
668/675 *Set of 8* (*cheapest*)			34·00	21·00

106 Girls with Musical Instruments

107 Globe and Doves

108 Semaphore Signaller

(Des Amat bin Djupri. Photo G. Kolff & Co, Djakarta)

1954 (22 Dec). *Child Welfare.* T **106** *and similar vert designs inscr* "untuk anak". P 12.

676	**106**	10s.+10s. purple	10	55
677		15s.+10s. deep dull green	10	65
678		35s.+15s. cerise	15	65
679		50s.+25s. brown-purple	50	65
680		75s.+25s. bright blue	25	2·50
681		1r.+25s. orange-red	35	4·50
676/681 *Set of 6*			1·30	8·55

Designs:—15s. Menangkabau boy and girl performing Umbrella Dance; 35s. Girls playing "Tjongkak"; 50s. Boy on bamboo stilts; 75s. Ambonese boys playing flutes; 1r. Srimpi dancing girl.

(Des Koernia and Kok from suggestions by Prime Minister Dr. Ali Sastroamidjojo. Photo G. Kolff & Co, Djakarta)

1955 (18 Apr). *Asian-African Conference, Bandung.* P 12½.

682	**107**	15s. grey-black	1·00	65
683		35s. reddish brown	1·00	65
684		50s. bright crimson	3·00	65
685		75s. blue-green	1·60	65
682/685 *Set of 4*			6·00	2·50

(Des Koernia (15s.), Amat bin Djupri (others). Photo G. Kolff & Co, Djakarta)

1955 (27 June). *National Scout Jamboree. T 108 and similar vert designs inscr "DJAMBORE NASIONAL KEI". P 12½.*
686	15s.+10s. blue-green		15	15
687	35s.+15s. bright blue		15	15
688	50s.+25s. scarlet		15	15
689	75s.+25s. brown		15	15
690	1r.+50s. reddish violet		15	15
686/690 *Set of 5*			70	70

Designs:—15s. Indonesian scout badge; 50s. Scouts round campfire; 75s. Scout feeding baby sika deer; 1r. Scout saluting.

109 Proclamation of Independence

110 Postmaster Sukarto

(T **109/10**. Des Amat bin Djupri. Photo G. Kolff & Co, Djakarta)

1955 (17 Aug). *Tenth Anniv of Independence. P 12½.*
691	**109**	15s. blue-green	80	65
692		35s. bright blue	80	65
693		50s. brown	5·25	40
694		75s. deep claret	1·10	55
691/694 *Set of 4*			7·25	2·00

1955 (27 Sept). *Tenth Anniv of Indonesian Post Office. P 12½.*
695	**110**	15s. brown	80	65
696		35s. brown-red	80	65
697		50s. dull ultramarine	6·00	1·50
698		75s. deep grey-green	2·40	65
695/698 *Set of 4*			9·00	3·00

111 Electors

112 Memorial Column, Wreath and Helmet

(Des Koernia and Kok. Photo Pertjetakan Kebajoran, Djakarta)

1955 (29 Sept). *First General Indonesian Elections. No gum. P 12 × 12½.*
699	**111**	15s. deep reddish purple	40	35
700		35s. green	55	65
701		50s. carmine-red	2·00	80
702		75s. dull blue	75	35
699/702 *Set of 4*			3·25	2·00

(Des Amat bin Djupri. Photo G. Kolff & Co, Djakarta)

1955 (10 Nov). *Heroes' Day. P 12½.*
703	**112**	25s. deep bluish green	65	25
704		50s. bright blue	1·60	55
705		1r. claret	12·00	25

113 Weaving

114 Torch and Book

(Des Amat bin Djupri. Photo G. Kolff & Co, Djakarta)

1956 (4 Jan). *Blind Relief Fund. T 113 and similar vert designs. P 12½.*
706	15s.+10s. deep blue-green		55	55
707	35s.+15s. yellow-brown		55	55
708	50s.+25s. carmine		1·20	1·10
709	75s.+50s. bright blue		55	55
706/709 *Set of 4*			2·50	2·50

Designs:—35s. Basketwork; 50s. Map reading; 75s. Reading.

(Des A. Sadeli. Photo G. Kolff & Co, Djakarta)

1956 (26 May). *Asian and African Students Conference, Bandung. P 12½.*
710	**114**	25s. blue	1·00	25
711		50s. carmine	5·00	1·00
712		1r. blue-green	2·10	1·00

PRINTERS. All the following issues, unless otherwise stated, were printed in photogravure by the State Security Printing Works, Djakarta, which in 1972 became the Government Banknote Printing Company and Mint.

115 Lesser Malay Chevrotain

116 Red Cross

117

(Des Sumarno Atmodipuro)

1956 (26 June)–**58**. *T 115 and similar horiz animal designs. P 12½ × 13½.*
713	5s. grey-blue (7.56)		10	10
714	10s. light brown (7.56)		10	10
715	15s. purple		10	10
716	20s. deep dull green (7.56)		10	10
717	25s. purple-brown		10	10
718	30s. red-orange (4.58)		10	10
719	35s. deep violet-blue		10	10
720	40s. apple-green (4.58)		10	10
721	45s. reddish purple (4.58)		1·10	15
722	50s. bistre-brown		10	10
723	60s. indigo (4.58)		15	10
724	70s. orange-red (4.58)		1·60	25
725	75s. blackish brown		15	10
726	80s. scarlet (4.58)		15	15
727	90s. yellow-green (4.58)		15	15
713/727 *Set of 15*			3·75	2·50

Designs:—5, 10, 15s. Type **115**; 20, 25, 30s. Hairy-nosed otter; 35, 40, 45s. Malayan pangolin; 50, 60, 70s. Banteng; 75, 80, 90s. Sumatran rhinoceros.

(Des Amat bin Djupri. Litho G. Kolff & Co, Djakarta)

1956 (26 July). *Red Cross Fund. T 116 and similar vert designs inscr "PALANG MERAH INDONESIA". P 12½.*
728	10s.+10s. red and green		10	10
729	15s.+10s. red and carmine-red		10	10
730	35s.+15s. red and brown		15	15
731	50s.+15s. red and blue-green		25	15
732	75s.+25s. red and orange		35	25
733	1r.+25s. red and reddish violet		50	40
728/733 *Set of 6*			1·30	1·00

Designs:—10s., 15s. T **116**; 35s., 50s. Blood transfusion bottle; 75s., 1r. Hands and drop of blood.

(Des Sadjirun)

1956 (7 Oct). *Bicentenary of Djokjakarta. P 12½ × 12.*
734	**117**	15s. bronze green	1·60	50
735		35s. purple-brown	1·60	50
736		50s. slate-blue	3·00	80
737		75s. claret	3·00	80
734/737 *Set of 4*			8·25	2·40

118 Crippled Child   **119** Telegraph Key and Tape   **120** Two Men with Savings-box

(Des Amat bin Djupri. Photo G. Kolff & Co, Djakarta)

1957 (26 Mar). *Cripples' Rehabilitation Fund. T* **118** *and similar vert designs inscr "UNTUK PENDERITA TJATJAT".* P 12½.

738	10s.+10s. ultramarine	10	10
739	15s.+10s. brown	10	10
740	35s.+15s. scarlet	10	10
741	50s.+15s. violet	25	25
742	75s.+25s. blue-green	35	35
743	1r.+25s. crimson	50	50
738/743 *Set of 6*		1·25	1·25

Designs:—10s. One-legged woman painting cloth; 15s. One-handed artist; 35s. One-handed machinist; 50s. T **119**; 75s. Doctor tending cripple; 1r. Man writing with artificial arm.

(Des Junalies)

1957 (10 May). *Centenary of Telegraphs in Indonesia.* P 12½ × 12.

744	**119**	10s. rose-red	2·40	50
745		15s. blue	50	25
746		25s. grey-black	40	15
747		50s. deep Venetian red	50	25
748		75s. emerald	50	15
744/748 *Set of 5*			3·75	1·10

(Des Amat bin Djupri. Photo G. Kolff & Co, Djakarta)

1957 (12 July). *Co-operation Day. T* **120** *and similar vert design.* P 12½.

749	**120**	10s. blue	55	40
750	–	15s. carmine	55	40
751	**120**	50s. myrtle green	1·00	65
752	–	1r. violet	1·40	15
749/752 *Set of 4*			3·00	1·40

Design:—15s. 1r. "Co-operative Prosperity" (hands holding ear of rice and cotton).

121 Kembodja (*Plumeria acuminata*)   **122** Convair CV 340 Airliner

(Des Abedey and K. Risman Suplanto)

1957 (23 Dec). *Various Charity Funds. T* **121** *and similar horiz floral designs.* Multicoloured. P 13½ × 12½.

753	10s.+10s. Type **121**	2·10	1·00
754	15s.+10s. Tjempaka-kuning (michelia)	1·50	1·00
755	35s.+15s. Matahari (sunflower)	1·00	80
756	50s.+15s. Melati (jasmine)	65	65
757	75s.+15s. Larat (orchid)	65	65
753/757 *Set of 5*		5·25	3·50

(Des K. Risman Suplanto)

1958 (9 Apr). *National Aviation Day. Vert designs as T* **122** *inscr "HARI PENERBANGAN NASIONAL 9–4–1958".* P 12½.

758	**122**	10s. brown	15	10
759	–	15s. blue	15	15
760	–	35s. orange	35	25
761	**122**	50s. pale blue-green	65	40
762	–	75s. grey	1·10	55
758/762 *Set of 5*			2·10	1·30

Designs:—15s. Hiller "Skeeter" 12C helicopter; 35s. Nurtiano Nu-2 Sikumbang; 75s. De Havilland D.H.100 Vampire jet fighter.

123 "Helping Hands"   **124** Thomas Cup

(Des Prasodo and K. Risman Suplanto)

1958 (1 July). *Indonesian Orphans Welfare Fund. T* **123** *and similar vert design inscr "ANAK PIATU".* P 12½ × 12.

763	**123**	10s.+10s. blue	15	15
764	–	15s.+10s. brown-red	15	15
765	**123**	35s.+15s. grey-green	15	15
766	–	50s.+25s. dull olive	15	15
767	**123**	75s.+50s. red-brown	15	15
768	–	1r.+50s. bistre-brown	15	15
763/768 *Set of 6*			80	80

Design:—15s., 50s., 1r. Girl and boy orphans.

(Des K. Risman Suplanto)

1958 (15 Aug). *Indonesian Victory in Thomas Cup World Badminton Championships, Singapore.* P 13½ × 12½.

769	**124**	25s. carmine	15	15
770		50s. brown-orange	15	15
771		1r. brown	25	15

(Litho State Security Ptg Wks, Djakarta)

1958 (Aug)–**63**. *POSTAGE DUE.* P 13½ × 12½.

D772	**100**	10s. orange	25	55
D773		15s. orange (1959)	25	55
D774		20s. orange (1961)	25	55
D775		25s. orange	25	55
D776		30s. orange (1960)	25	50
D777		50s. orange	1·50	55
D778		50s. blue-green (1962)	10	10
D779		100s. orange (1960)	80	55
D780		100s. yellow-brown (1962)	10	10
D781		250s. blue (18.1.63)	25	10
D782		500s. yellow (18.1.63)	10	10
D783		750s. lilac (18.1.63)	25	10
D784		1000s. salmon (18.1.63)	15	15
D772/784 *Set of 13*			4·00	4·00

125 Satellite encircling Globe   **126** Racing Cyclist

(Des K. Risman Suplanto)

1958 (15 Oct). *International Geophysical Year.* P 12½ × 12.

785	**125**	10s. rose, deep green and pale blue	90	55
786		15s. drab, violet and grey	25	15
787		35s. blue, sepia and pink	25	15
788		50s. chocolate, blue and pale drab	25	15
789		75s. lilac, black and pale yellow	25	15
785/789 *Set of 5*			1·70	1·00

(Des K. Risman Suplanto)

1958 (15 Nov). *Tour of Java Cycle Race.* P 13½ × 12½.
790 **126** 25s. blue 50 25
791 50s. brown-red 80 25
792 1r. deep grey 50 25

127 "Human   128 Babirusa   129 Indonesian
Rights"   Scout Badge

(Des Junalies)

1958 (10 Dec). *Tenth Anniv of Declaration of Human Rights. Vert designs as T* **127** *inscr "10–XII 1948–58". P* 12½ × 12.
793 10s. deep sepia 15 15
794 15s. red-brown 15 15
795 35s. blue 25 15
796 50s. bistre-brown 25 15
797 75s. blue-green 25 15
793/797 *Set of 5* 95 70
Designs:—15s. Hands grasping "Flame of Freedom"; 35s. Native holding candle; 50s. Family acclaiming "Flame of Freedom"; 75s. "Flame" superimposed on figure "10".

(Des Junalies)

1959 (1 June). *Animal Protection Campaign. Vert designs as T* **128**. P 12½ × 12.
798 10s. sepia and olive-bistre 15 15
799 15s. sepia and orange-brown . . . 25 25
800 20s. sepia and dull yellow-green . . 35 35
801 50s. sepia and yellow-brown . . . 50 50
802 75s. sepia and brown-red . . . 50 50
803 1r. black and bluish green . . . 55 55
798/803 *Set of 6* . . . . . . 2·10 2·10
Animals:—15s. Anoa (buffalo); 20s. Orang-utan; 50s. Javan rhinoceros; 75s. Komodo lizard; 1r. Malayan tapir.

(Des K. Risman Suplanto)

1959 (17 July). *Tenth World Scout Jamboree, Manila. T* **129** *and similar vert design inscr "DJAMBORE SEDUNIA KE–10".* P 12½ × 12.
804 **129** 10s.+5s. brown-red & yellow-
         bistre 15 15
805 – 15s.+10s. brn-red & dp bluish
         grn 25 15
806 **129** 20s.+10s. brown-red & slate-
         violet 25 25
807 – 50s.+25s. brown-red & olive-
         brown 25 40
808 **129** 75s.+35s. brown-red and brown . 25 40
809 – 1r.+50s. brown-red and slate . 35 40
804/809 *Set of 6* . . . . . 1·30 1·60
Design:—15s., 50s., 1r. Scout Badge within compass.

130   131 Factory and   132
         Girder

(Des Pres. Sukarno)

1959 (17 Aug). *Re-adoption of 1945 Constitution.* P 12 × 12½.
810 **130** 20s. red and steel blue . . . 15 15
811 50s. black and carmine-red . . . 15 15

812 75s. scarlet and sepia 15 15
813 1r.50 black and green . . . 25 15
810/813 *Set of 4* 65 55

(Des K. Risman Suplanto)

1959 (26 Oct). *11th Colombo Plan Conference, Djakarta. Vert designs as T* **131**. P 12½ × 12.
814 **131** 15s. black and blue-green . . . 15 10
815 – 20s. black and yellow-orange . . 15 10
816 **131** 50s. black and red 15 10
817 – 75s. black and blue 15 10
818 – 1r.15 black and deep magenta . . 15 10
814/818 *Set of 5* 70 45
Designs:—20s., 75s. Cogwheel and diesel train; 1r.15 Various forms of transport and communications.

(Des M. A. Asjik)

1960 (14 Feb). *Indonesian Youth Conference, Bandung. T***132** *and similar vert designs inscr "1960". P* 12½ × 12.
819 **132** 15s.+5s. sepia and yellow-bistre . 10 25
820 – 20s.+10s. sepia and grey-green . 15 25
821 **132** 50s.+25s. purple and blue . . 15 25
822 – 75s.+35s. deep green and bistre . 15 25
823 – 1r.15+50s. black and carmine-
         red 35 25
819/823 *Set of 5* . . . . . 80 1·10
Designs:—2s., 75s. Test-tubes in frame; 1r. Youth wielding manifesto.

133 Refugee Camp   134 Tea plants

(Des M. A. Asjik)

1960 (7 Apr). *World Refugee Year. T* **133** *and similar vert designs inscr "WORLD REFUGEE YEAR". P* 12½ × 12.
824 10s. black and maroon 10 15
825 15s. black and yellow-ochre . . . 10 15
826 20s. black and chestnut 10 15
827 50s. black and green 15 15
828 75s. black and deep blue . . . 35 15
829 1r.15 black and red 35 90
824/829 *Set of 6* . . . . . 1·00 1·50
Design:—10s. T **133**; 15s., 75s. Outcast family; 20s., 1r.15 "Care of Refugees".

(Des Junalies)

1960 (17 Aug). *Agricultural Products. T* **134** *and similar horiz designs.* P 12 × 12½.
830 5s. grey (17.10) 15 10
831 10s. brown (17.10) 15 10
832 15s. maroon (17.10) 15 10
833 20s. yellow-brown (17.10) . . . 15 10
834 25s. blue-green 15 10
835 50s. deep blue 15 10
836 75s. vermilion 15 10
837 1r.15 crimson 15 15
830/837 *Set of 8* . . . . . 1·10 75
Designs:—5s. Oil palm; 10s. Sugar cane; 15s. Coffee plant; 20s. Tobacco plant; 50s. Coconut palm; 75s. Rubber trees; 1r.15 Rice plants.

135 Mosquito

136 Socialist Emblem

(Des I. Cusjairi and Junalies)

1960 (12 Nov). *World Health Day.* P 12 × 12½.

838	**135**	25s. carmine	10	10
839		50s. dull vermilion	15	10
840		75s. emerald	15	10
841		3r. bright orange	40	15
838/841 *Set of 4*			75	40

(Des Karnedi)

1960 (20 Dec). *Third Socialist Day.* T **136** *and similar vert designs inscr* "HARI SOSIAL KE III". P 12½ × 12.

842	10s.+10s.	yellow-brown and black	10	15
843	15s.+15s.	maroon and black	10	15
844	20s.+20s.	blue and black	15	15
845	50s.+25s.	black and brown	15	25
846	75s.+25s.	black and green	15	25
847	3r.+50s.	black and red	15	40
842/847 *Set of 6*			75	1·20

Designs:—15s. Emblem similar to T **136** within plants; 20s. Lotus flower; 50s. Boy and girl; 75s. Ceremonial watering of plant; 3r. Mother and children.

137 Pres. Sukarno and Workers Hoeing

1961 (15 Feb). *National Development Plan.* P 12½ × 12.

848	**137**	75s. black	25	15

BENTJANA ALAM 1961

+10 s

(138)

1961 (17 Feb). *Flood Relief Fund. Nos. 832/3, 836 surch as T* **138** *(in one line on Nos. 850/1).*

849	15s.+10s. maroon		10	10
850	20s.+15s. yellow-brown		10	10
851	75s.+25s. vermilion		10	10

139 Bull Race

140 Stadium

(Des Mahriajub (10s.), R. Asmara (20s., 1r.50), Junalies (1r., 2r.), K. Risman Suplanto (others))

1961 (15 Mar–1 June). *Tourist Publicity. Horiz designs as T* **139**. P 13½ × 13.

852	10s. reddish purple (15.5)		50	40
853	15s. olive-grey (15.5)		50	40
854	20s. orange (15.4)		50	40
855	25s. red		50	40

856	50s. cerise (15.4)	50	40
857	75s. brown	50	40
858	1r. emerald	90	40
859	1r.50 yellow-brown (15.5)	90	40
860	2r. turquoise-blue (15.4)	1·30	40
861	3r. grey	1·30	40
852/861 *Set of 10*		6·50	3·50

MS862 Three sheets each 140 × 105mm containing (a) Nos. 852/3, 859; (b) Nos. 854, 856, 860; (c) Nos. 857/8 and a fourth sheet 105 × 140 mm containing Nos. 855, 861.
Imperf (1.6) . . . . . . 24·00 24·00

Designs:—10s. Ambonese boat; 15s. Tangkuban Perahu crater; 25s. Daja dancer; 50s. Toradja houses; 75c. Balinese temple; 1r. Lake Toba; 1r.50, Bali dancer; 2r. "Buffalo Hole" (gorge); 3r. Borobudur temple.

(Des K. Risman Suplanto)

1961 (1 June). *Thomas Cup World Badminton Championships.* P 13½ × 12½.

863	**140**	75s. lilac and blue	10	10
864		1r. yellow-olive and deep green	15	10
865		3r. salmon and deep blue	25	15

141 "United Efforts"

142 Sultan Hasanuddin

(Des Junalies)

1961 (6 July). *16th Anniv of Independence.* P 13½ × 12½.

866	**141**	75s. violet and light blue	10	10
867		1r.50 green and cream	10	10
868		3r. carmine-red and salmon	35	15

(Des M. Gozjali)

1961 (17 Aug)–**62**. *National Independence Heroes. Horiz designs as T* **142**. *Portraits in sepia.* P 13½ × 12½.

869	20s. brown-olive (10.11.61)		10	35
870	25s. grey-olive		15	35
871	30s. reddish violet (10.11.61)		15	35
872	40s. orange-brown (5.10.61)		15	35
873	50s. pale slate-green (5.10.61)		15	35
874	60s. deep bluish green (5.10.62)		15	35
875	75s. pale brown		90	35
876	1r. light blue (10.11.61)		90	35
877	1r.25 sage-green (10.11 62)		75	35
878	1r.50 emerald		90	35
879	2r. red (5.10.62)		75	35
880	2r.50 claret (10.11.61)		90	35
881	3r. slate (10.11.61)		75	35
882	4r. olive-green (5.10.61)		75	35
883	4r.50 bright purple (10.11.62)		35	35
884	5r. vermilion		80	35
885	6r. ochre (10.11.62)		90	35
886	7r.50 violet-blue (5.10.62)		1·10	35
887	10r. bluish green (10.11.62)		75	35
888	15r. orange (5.10.62)		75	35
869/888 *Set of 20*			10·50	6·25

Portraits:—20s. Abdul Muis; 25s. T **142**; 30s. Surjopranoto; 40s. Tengku Tjhik Di Tiro; 50s. Teuku Umar; 60s. K. H. Samanhudi; 75s. Capt. Pattimura; 1r. Raden Adjeng Kartini; 1r.25, K. H. Achmad Dahlan; 1r.50, Tuanku Imam Bondjol; 2r. Si Singamangaradja XII; 2r.50, Mohammad Husni Thamrin; 3r. Ki Hadjar Dewantoro; 4r. Gen. Sudirman; 4r.50, Dr. G. S. S. J. Ratulangie; 5r. Pangeran Diponegoro; 6r. Dr. Setyabudi; 7r.50, H. O. S. Tjokroaminoto; 10r. K. H. Agus Salim; 15r. Dr. Soetomo.

143 Census Emblems

144 Nenas
(pineapple)

147 Games Emblem

148 Campaign
Emblem

(Des S. Soemarsono)

1961 (15 Sept). *First Indonesian Census.* P 13½ × 12½.
889 **143** 75s. reddish purple 25 15

(Des Soeroso (20s.), K. Risman Suplanto (75s.), J. Kartono (3r.))

1961 (20 Dec). *Charity. Various Fruits as T* **144**. P 12½ × 13½.
890 20s.+10s. yellow, red and greenish
blue 50 40
891 75s.+25s. brown-purple, bl-grn & slate . . 75 40
892 3r.+1r. red, yellow and emerald . . . . 1·20 1·20
Fruits:—75s. Manggis; 3r. Rambutan.

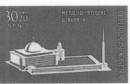

145 Djataju   **146** Aerial view of Mosque

(Des Mardio and Junalies)

1962 (15 Jan). *Ramayana Dancers. T* **145** *and similar vert designs.* P 12 × 12½.
893 30s. red-brown and ochre 35 40
894 40s. violet and dull purple 35 40
895 1r. maroon and dull green 50 40
896 1r.50 deep bluish green and salmon . . 50 40
897 3r. deep blue and light green . . . . . 1·60 40
898 5r. chocolate and buff . . . . 1·40 40
893/898 *Set of 6* . . . . 4·25 2·10
Dancers:—40s. Hanoman; 1r. Dasamuka; 1r.50, Kidang Kentjana; 3r. Dewi Sinta; 5r. Rama.

(Des K. Risman Suplanto)

1962 (22 Feb). *Construction of Istiqlal Mosque. T* **146** *and similar horiz design.* P 12½ × 12.
899 **146** 30s.+20s. turq-bl & greenish yell . . 35 25
900 — 40s.+20s. carm-verm & greenish
yell 35 25
901 **146** 1r.50+50s. brown & greenish
yell 35 25
902 — 3r.+1r. green and greenish
yellow 35 25
899/902 *Set of 4* . . . . 1·25 90
Design:—40s., 3r. Ground-level view of Mosque.

(Des Soeroso (10s., 20s., 1r.50, 2r.50, 7r.50, 15r, 20r.); Junalies (15s.); K. Risman Suplanto (25s., 30s., 70s.), J. Kartono (40s.); Soemarsono (50s., 75s., 1r., 1r.75, 10r.); Sadjirun (4r.50, 6r.); Karnedi (others))

1962 (24 Mar–24 Aug). *Fourth Asian Games, Djakarta. Designs as T* **147** *inscr "ASIAN GAMES IV".* P 12½.
903 10s. emerald and yellow (24.6) 15 15
904 15s. deep olive-brown and ochre
(24.8) 15 15
905 20s. brt reddish lilac & turq-grn (24.7) . . 35 25
906 25s. brown-red & turquoise-green
(24.8) 35 25
907 30s. bluish green and buff (24.8) 35 15
908 40s. ultramarine and slate-blue (20.5) . . 35 15
909 50s. chocolate and drab (20.5) 35 35
910 60s. deep mauve and violet-grey
(20.5) 35 35
911 70s. purple-brown & Venetian red
(24.8) 35 35
912 75s. deep brown and orange (24.7) . . . 35 15
913 1r. brt reddish violet & pale blue
(24.6) 35 35
914 1r.25 deep blue and pale magenta . . . 40 40
915 1r.50 vermilion and mauve (24.6) . . . 1·20 40
916 1r.75 carmine and rose (24.7) 80 40
917 2r. sepia and green 75 40
918 2r.50 bright blue & pale green (24.7) . . 80 40
919 3r. black and deep orange-red 75 40
920 4r.50 deep green and red (20.5) 75 40
921 5r. bronze-green and bistre 55 40
922 6r. deep brown-red and ochre (20.5) . . 55 40
923 7r.50 red-brown and pink (24.6) 55 25
924 10r. deep ultramarine & pale blue
(24.6) . . . . 1·10 55
925 15r. violet and slate-violet (24.7) . . . 1·20 1·10
926 20r. myrtle-green and bistre (24.8) . . . 3·00 1·40
903/926 *Set of 24* . . . . 14·00 8·50
Designs: *Vert*—10s. Basketball; 20s. Weight-lifting; 40s. Throwing the discus; 50s. Diving; 60s. Football; 70s. Press building; 75s. Boxing; 1r. Volleyball; 1r.25, 2r, 3r., 5r., T **147**; 1r.50, Badminton; 1r.75, Wrestling; 2r.50, Shooting; 4r.50, Hockey; 6r. Water polo; 7r.50, Tennis; 10r. Table-tennis; 15r. Cycling; 20r. "Welcome" monument. *Horiz*—15s. Main stadium; 25s. Hotel Indonesia; 30s. Road improvement.

(Des H. Hartman)

1962 (7 Apr). *Malaria Eradication.* P 12½.
927 **148** 40s. light blue and violet 10 10
928 1r.50 yellow-orange &
chocolate 10 10
929 3r. light green and deep blue 10 10
930 6r. light reddish violet and
black 25 15
927/930 *Set of 4* 50 40
The 1r.50 and 6r. have "DUNIA", etc., at top.

149 National Monument   **150** Atomic Symbol

(Des K. Risman Suplanto)

1962 (20 May). *National Monument. T* **149** *and similar vert design.*
P 12 × 12½.

931	**149**	1r.+50s. chestnut and black	15	15
932	–	1r.50+50s. olive-green and blue	15	15
933	**149**	3r.+1r. magenta and green	25	15
934	–	6r.+1r.50 violet-blue and red	25	15
931/934 *Set of 4*			75	55

Design:—1r.50, 6r. Aerial view of Monument.

(Des Junalies)

1962 (24 Sept). *"Science for Development".* P 12 × 12½.

935	**150**	1r.50 deep blue and yellow	15	15
936		4r.50 red and yellow	25	25
937		6r. green and yellow	40	25

151
*Phalaenopsis
amabilis*

152 West Irian
Monument,
Djakarta

153 Conference
Emblem

(Des Soeroso)

1962 (20 Dec). *Charity. Orchids. T* **151** *and similar multicoloured
designs.* P 13½ × 12½ (*horiz*) or 12½ × 13½ (*vert*).

938	1r.+50s. *Vanda tricolor* (*horiz*)	30	15
939	1r.50+50s. Type **151**	35	15
940	3r.+1r. *Dendrobium phalaenopsis*	35	10
941	6r.+1r.50 *Paphiopedilum praestans* (*horiz*)	25	10
938/941 *Set of 4*		1·10	45

(Des Soeroso)

1963 (15 Feb). *Construction of West Irian Monument.* P 12½ × 13½.

942	**152**	1r.+50s. deep green and red	25	10
943		1r.50+50s. sepia, black & magenta	15	10
944		3r.+1r. brown and blue	25	10
945		6r.+1r.50 bistre and green	25	15
942/945 *Set of 4*			80	40

(Des Hasto Mahriajub (1r., 3r.), S. Soemarsono (others))

1963 (14 Mar). *12th Pacific Area Travel Association Conference,
Djakarta. T* **153** *and similar vert designs.* P 12 × 12½.

946	**153**	1r. blue and light green	15	15
947	–	1r.50 deep blue and yellow-olive	15	15

948	**153**	3r. blue and yellow-brown	40	15
949	–	6r. deep blue and brown-orange	40	15
946/949 *Set of 4*			1·00	55

Designs:—1r.50, Prambanan Temple and Mt. Merapi; 6r.
Balinese Meru in Pura Taman Ajun.

154 Rice
Sheaves

155 Lobster

(Des R. Bintarti)

1963 (21 Mar). *Freedom from Hunger. T* **154** *and similar design.*
P 12½ × 12 (*vert*) or 12 × 12½ (*horiz*).

950	**154**	1r. yellow and blue	10	10
951	–	1r.50 blue and light emerald	15	10
952	**154**	3r. yellow and rose-carmine	15	10
953	–	6r. black and yellow-orange	25	15
950/953 *Set of 4*			60	40

Designs:—*Horiz*—1r.50, 6r. Tractor. Nos. 950/1 are inscribed
"CONTRE LA FAIM" and Nos. 952/3 "FREEDOM FROM
HUNGER".

(Des J. Kartono)

1963 (6 Apr). *Marine Life. T* **155** *and similar horiz designs.
Multicoloured.* P 12½ × 12.

954	1r. Type **155**	35	15
955	1r.50 Kawakawa	35	15
956	3r. River snapper	80	35
957	6r. Chinese pomfret	80	50
954/957 *Set of 4*		2·10	1·00

156 Conference Emblem

(Des Mahriajub and D. Sjamsumar)

1963 (24 Apr). *Asian–African Journalists' Conference. T* **156** *and
similar designs.* P 12½ × 12.

958	1r. new blue and dull vermilion	15	10
959	1r.50 reddish-brown and lavender	15	10
960	3r. blue, black and olive-bistre	40	15
961	6r. dull scarlet and black	55	25
958/961 *Set of 4*		1·10	35

Designs: *Horiz*—1r.50, Pen, emblem and map. *Vert*—3r. Pen,
globe and broken chain; 6r. Pen severing chain around globe.

157 Indonesia, from Atjeh to
Merauke

158 Centenary
Emblem

(Des Soeroso)

1963 (1 May). *Acquisition of West Irian (West New Guinea). T* **157** *and similar horiz designs.* P 12.
962   1r.50 light orange-red, red and black . . . 15   10
963   4r.50 light blue, green and grey-purple . . 15   15
964   6r. brown, yellow and green 80   50
   Designs:—4r.50, Parachutist; 6r. Greater bird of paradise.

(Des K. Risman Suplanto)

1963 (8 May). *Centenary of Red Cross. T* **158** *and similar vert designs.* P 12½ × 12.
965   **158**   1r. emerald and red 25   15
966   —   1r.50 red and dull blue 25   15
967   **158**   3r. deep grey and red 25   15
968   —   6r. red and bistre 25   15
965/968 *Set of 4* 90   30
   Designs:—1r.50, 6r. Red Cross (inscribed in English).

159 Volcano

160 Bank of Indonesia, Djakarta

(Des K. Risman Suplanto)

1963 (29 June). *Bali Volcano Disaster Fund.* P 13½ × 12½.
969   **159**   4r.(+2r.) carmine-red 15   10
970   —   6r.(+3r.) deep bluish green 15   15

(Des S. Soemarsono)

1963 (5 July). *National Banking Day. T* **160** *and similar design.* P 12 × 12½ (*horiz*) or 12½ × 12 (*vert*).
971   **160**   1r.75 purple and light blue . . . 15   15
972   —   4r. deep green and olive-yellow . . 15   15
973   **160**   6r. olive-brown and light green . . . 15   10
974   —   12r. brown-purple and orange . . . 40   15
971/974 *Set of 4* 75   50
   Designs: *Vert*—4, 12r. Daneswara, God of Prosperity.

161 Athletes with Banners

162 *Papilio blumei*

(Des Junalies (1r.25, 1r.75, 6r.), J. Kartono (10r.), S. Soemarsono (4r., 12r., 25r.), Soeroso (50r.))

1963 (10 Nov). *Games of the New Emerging Forces, Djakarta. Horiz designs as T* **161**. P 12½.
975   1r.25 sepia and pale bluish violet . . . 10   10
976   1r.75 olive and yellow-orange 10   10
977   4r. sepia and light emerald 10   10
978   6r. sepia and brown-red 25   15
979   10r. sepia and yellow-green 25   15
980   12r. olive and crimson 35   15
981   25r. ultramarine and light blue . . . 50   35
982   50r. sepia and red 65   40
975/982 *Set of 8* . . . . 2·10   1·30
   Designs:—1r.75, "Pendet" dance; 4r. Conference Hall, Djakarta; 6r. Archery; 10r. Badminton; 12r. Throwing the javelin; 25r. Sailing; 50r. "Ganefo" Torch.

(Des J. Kartono)

1963 (20 Dec). *Social Day. Butterflies. T* **162** *and similar horiz designs.* Multicoloured. P 12 × 12½.
983   1r.75+50s. Type **162** 40   15
984   4r.+1r. *Polyura dehaani* (*Charaxes dehaani*) 40   15

985   6r.+1r.50 *Graphium weiskei* 40   15
986   12r.+3r. *Troides amphrysus* 80   40
983/986 *Set of 4* . . . . 1·80   75

163 Pres. Sukarno

164 Lorry and Trailer

165 Rameses II, Abu Simbel

(Des Junalies)

1964 (6 Jan–6 June). P 12½ × 12.
987   **163**   6r. ultramarine and brown . . . 15   15
988   —   12r. bright purple and bistre (6.4) 15   15
989   —   20r. orange and blue (6.6) . . . 15   15
990   —   30r. blue and orange (6.6) . . . 15   15
991   —   40r. brown and green (6.6) . . . 15   15
992   —   50r. green and red (6.4) . . . 15   15
993   —   75r. orange-red and violet (6.4) . . 15   15
994   —   100r. red-brown and silver-grey . . 15   15
995   —   250r. silver-grey and deep blue . . 35   15
996   —   500r. gold and red 50   35
987/996 *Set of 10* . . . . 1·80   1·50

(Des Soeroso)

1964 (6 Feb–15 July). *T* **164** *and similar designs.* P 12½ × 12 (2r.50) or 12 × 12½ (others).
997   1r. reddish purple (15.7) 15   15
998   1r.25 brown 15   15
999   1r.75 greenish blue 15   15
1000   2r. orange-red 15   15
1001   2r.50 blue (15.7) 15   15
1002   4r. blue-green 15   15
1003   7r. olive-brown (15.7) 15   15
1004   7r.50 emerald-green (15.7) 15   15
1005   10r. orange (20.5) 15   15
1006   15r. deep blue (20.5) 15   15
1007   25r. violet-blue (20.5) 35   15
1008   35r. chestnut (20.5) 35   15
997/1008 *Set of 12* . . . . . . 2·00   1·60
   Designs: *Horiz*—1r. Ox-cart; 1r.75, *Hadji Agus Salim* (freighter); 2r. Lockheed L.188 Electra airliner; 4r. Cycle-postman; 5r. Douglas DC-3 airliner; 7r.50, Tele-typist; 10r. Diesel train; 15r. *Sam Ratulangi* (freighter); 25r. Convair 990A Coronado airliner; 35r. Telephone operator. *Vert*—2r.50, Buginese sailing ship.

(Des Junalies)

1964 (8 Mar). *Nubian Monuments Preservation. T* **165** *and similar vert design.* P 12½ × 12.
1009   **165**   4r. olive-brown and drab . . . 35   15
1010   —   6r. olive-brown and light blue . . 35   15
1011   **165**   12r. olive-brown and salmon-pink 35   15
1012   —   18r. olive-brown and light green . . 35   15
1009/1012 *Set of 4* . . . . . . 1·20   55
   Design:—6r., 18r., Trajan's Kiosk, Philae.

166 Various Stamps of Netherlands Indies and Indonesia

(Des J. Kartono)

1964 (1 Apr). *Stamp Centenary.* P 12½.
1013 **166** 10c. multicoloured . . . . 1·10 15

167 Indonesian Pavilion at Fair

168 Thomas Cup

(Des Junalies)

1964 (16 May). *New York World's Fair.* P 12½ × 12.
1014 **167** 25r. red, grey-blue and silver . . . 55 40
1015 50r. red, turquoise-blue and
gold . . . . 1·40 40

(Des K. Risman Suplanto)

1964 (15 Aug). *Thomas Cup World Badminton Championships.*
P 12½ × 13½
1016 **168** 25r. gold, red and blue-green . . . 25 25
1017 50r. gold, red and blue 25 25
1018 75r. gold, red and reddish violet . . 80 80

169 *Sandjaja* and *Siliwanghi*
(destroyers)

170 Pied Fantail

(Des S. Soemarsono)

1964 (5 Oct). *Indonesian Navy.* T **169** and similar horiz designs.
P 12½ × 12.
1019 20r. brown and yellow 40 10
1020 30r. black and light rose-red 40 10
1021 40r. blue and light green 80 80
Designs:—30r. *Nanggala* (submarine); 40r. *Matjan Tutul*
(torpedo-boat).

(Des K. Risman Suplanto)

1965 (25 Jan). *Social Day.* T **170** and similar vert bird designs.
P 12½ × 13½.
1022 4r.+1r. black, pale lilac and yellow . . 35 25
1023 6r.+1r.50 black, buff and green . . . 35 25
1024 12r.+3r. black, pale blue & yellow-
olive 55 35
1025 20r.+5r. greenish yellow, red and deep
slate-purple 55 40
1026 30r.+7r.50 black, grey-green & mag . . 1·00 40
1022/1026 *Set of 5* . . . . 2·50 1·50
Birds:—6r. Zebra dove; 12r. Black drongo; 20r. Black-naped
oriole; 30r. Java sparrow.

171 Map and Mosque

172 Scroll in Hand

(Des Mahriajub)

1965 (6 Mar). *Afro-Asian Islamic Conference, Bandung.* T **171** and
similar vert design. P 12½.
1027 **171** 10r. light blue and violet 35 10
1028 — 15r. brown-red and yellow-
orange 35 10
1029 **171** 25r. light blue-green and brown . . 50 15
1030 — 50r. deep slate-purple & brown-
red 50 50
1027/1030 *Set of 4* . . . . 1·50 75
Designs.—15, 50r. Mosque and handclasp.

(Des A. L. Roring (15r., 50r.), Conference Committee (others))

1965 (18 Apr). *10th Anniv of First Afro-Asian Conference,
Bandung.* T **172** and similar vert design. P 12½.
1031 **172** 15r. carmine and silver-grey . . . 25 10
1032 — 25r. gold, vermilion & turquoise-
grn 25 10
1033 **172** 50r. ultramarine and gold 40 15
1034 — 75r. gold, vermilion and lilac . . . 65 65
1031/1034 *Set of 4* . . . . 1·40 90
Design:—25, 75r. Conference 10th-anniversary emblem.

173 Pres. Sukarno

174 Makara Mask and
Rays

1965 (2 May–12 Aug). *Conference of New Emerging Forces,
Djakarta. Value, "Conefo" and frame in red; portrait colour
given.* P 12½ × 12.
1035 **173** 1r.+1r. chestnut (3.7) 15 10
1036 1r.25+1r.25 brown-red 15 10
1037 1r.75+1r.75 dp slate-purple
(7.6) 15 10
1038 2r.+2r. bronze-green (3.7) . . . 15 10
1039 2r.50+2r.50 red-brown (7.6) . . . 15 10
1040 4r.+3r.50 blue 15 10
1041 6r.+4r. emerald 15 10
1042 10r.+5r. yellow-brown (5.8) . . . 15 10
1043 12r.+5r.50 yellow-orange (3.7) . . 15 10
1044 15r.+7r.50 turquoise (5.8) . . . 15 10
1045 20r.+10r. sepia (5.8) 15 10
1046 25r.+10r. reddish violet (7.6) . . 15 10
1047 40r.+15r. dp reddish purple
(1965) 15 10
1048 50r.+15r. violet (12.8) 15 10
1049 100r.+25r. olive-brown (12.8) . . 25 15
1035/1049 *Set of 15* . . . . 2·10 1·40

(Des Soeroso)

1965 (17 July). *Campaign against Cancer.* P 12 × 12½.
1050 **174** 20r.+10r. brown-red and blue . . . 25 15
1051 30r.+15r. greenish blue & brn-
red 25 15

175 "Happy Family"

(Des Soeroso)

1965 (17 Aug). *The State's Five Principles and 20th Anniv of Republic. T* **175** *and similar vert designs.* P 12½.

1052	10r.+5r. yellow, black & orange-		
	brown	40	25
1053	20r.+10r. red, black and yellow	25	25
1054	25r.+10r. green, black and rose-red	25	25
1055	40r.+15r. black, red and cobalt	50	25
1056	50r.+15r. yellow, black & deep		
	mauve	50	25
1052/1056 *Set of 5*		1·70	1·10

Designs: "State's Principles"—20r. "Humanitarianism" (globe and clasped hands); 25r. "Nationalism" (map and garland); 40r. "Democracy" (council meeting); 50r. "Belief in God" (churches and mosques).

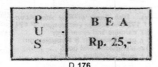

D **176**

1965 (1 Nov). *POSTAGE DUE. Provisional issue for use on parcels. Letters "PUS" 3 mm high.* P 11.

D1057	D **176** 25r. black/yellow	15	
a. "PUS" 2½ mm high		25	

Printed in sheets of 48 with the outer edges imperf.
No. D1057a occurs on Nos. 38 to 42 and 44 to 48 in the sheet.

1965 (Nov). *POSTAGE DUE. Values in rupiahs. Photo.* P 13½ × 12½.

D1058	D **100** 50r. red	10	10
D1059	100r. brown-lake	15	15

177 Samudra Beach Hotel

178 *Gloriosa superba*

(Des M. Kawamura and S. Soemarsono)

1965 (1 Dec). *Tourist Hotels. T* **177** *and similar horiz design.* P 12½ × 12.

1060	10r.+5r. blue and turquoise	25	25
1061	25r.+10r. slate-violet, black & yell-grn	35	35

1062	40r.+15r. chocolate, black &		
	ultramarine	40	35
1063	80r.+20r. reddish purple & yellow-		
	orge	65	35
1060/1063 *Set of 4*		1·50	1·20

Designs:—10, 40r. Type **177**; 25, 80r. Ambarrukmo Palace Hotel.

(Des K. Risman Suplanto)

1965 (20 Dec). *Flowers. T* **178** *and similar vert designs inscr "1965" and with commas and dashes after figures of value. Multicoloured.* P 12 × 12½.

1064	**178** 30r.+10r. Type **178**	1·00	1·00
1065	40r.+15r. *Hibiscus tiliaceus*	1·00	1·00
1066	80r.+20r. *Impatiens balsamina*	1·00	1·00
1067	100r.+25r. *Lagerstroemia indica*	1·00	1·00
1064/1067 *Set of 4*		3·50	3·50

See also Nos. 1108/16.

Currency Revaluation

100 (old) Rupiahs = 1 (new) Rupiah

(179)

180 Pres. Sukarno

D **180a**

1965 (13 Dec). *Various stamps optd in revalued currency as T* **179**.

(a) On Nos. 989/94, in red.

1068	**163**	20s. on 20r. orange and blue	15	10
1069		30s. on 30r. blue and orange	15	15
1070		40s. on 40r. brown and green	15	15
1071		50s. on 50r. green and red	15	15
1072		75s. on 75r. orange-red &		
		violet	15	2·10
1073		100s. on 100r. red-brn & sil-		
		grey	50	15

(b) On Nos. 1005/7.

1074	– 10s. on 10r. orange	25	10
1075	– 15s. on 15r. deep blue (R.)	25	10
1076	– 25s. on 25r. violet-blue	25	10
1068/1076 *Set of 9*		1·80	2·75

1966 (Jan)–67. *Revalued Currency. Inscr "1967" (12r.) or "1966" (others). Values and frames in turquoise-green (12r., 25r.) or chocolate (others); portrait and country name in colour given.* P 12½ × 12.

1077	**180**	1s. turquoise-blue	15	10
1078		3s. yellow-olive	15	10
1079		5s. scarlet	15	10
1080		8s. turquoise	15	10
1081		10s. royal blue	15	10
1082		15s. black	15	10
1083		20s. olive-green	15	10
1084		25s. red-brown	15	10
1085		30s. greenish blue	15	10
1086		40s. chestnut	15	10
1087		50s. violet	15	10
1088		80s. orange	15	10
1089		1r. emerald	15	10
1090		1r.25 olive-brown	15	10
1091		1r.50 green	15	10
1092		2r. purple	25	10
1093		2r.50 slate	25	15
1094		5r. yellow-orange	35	35
1095		10r. olive-green	35	15
1096		12r. red-orange (3.67)	35	15
1097		25r. bright reddish violet (1967)	35	35
1077/1097 *Set of 21*		3·75	2·50

1966 (Jan). *POSTAGE DUE. Dated "1966". Photo.* P 13½ × 12½.

D1098	D **180a**	5s. dp bluish green & yell	25	25
D1099		10s. red and light blue	25	25
D1100		20s. deep blue and pink	25	25
D1101		30s. sepia and light red	25	25
D1102		40s. reddish vio & yell-bistre	25	25
D1103		50s. blackish ol & pale mve	25	10
D1104		100s. brown-lake & lt yell-grn	25	10
D1105		200s. emerald and light pink	25	10
D1106		500s. yellow and light blue	25	10
D1107		1000s. claret & greenish yellow	25	15
D1098/1107 *Set of 10*			2·20	1·60

See also Nos. D1168/74, D1320a, D1346/7 and D1401.

1966 (10 Feb). *Flowers. Vert designs as T 178 but inscr "1966" and additionally inscr "sen" instead of commas and dashes. Multicoloured.* P 12 × 12½.

1108	10s.+5s. *Cassia alata*	1·00	1·00
1109	20s.+5s. *Barleria cristata*	1·00	1·00
1110	30s.+10s. *Ixora coccinea*	1·00	1·00
1111	40s.+10s. *Hibiscus rosa sinensis*	1·00	1·00
1108/1111 *Set of 4*		3·50	3·50
MS1112 58 × 78 mm. No. 1111. Imperf		9·75	2·75

1966 (2 May). *National Disaster Fund. Vert floral designs as T 178 additionally inscr "BENTJANA ALAM NASIONAL 1966". Multicoloured.* P 12 × 12½.

1113	15s.+5s. *Gloriosa superba*	65	65
1114	25s.+5s. *Hibiscus tiliaceus*	65	65
1115	30s.+10s. *Impatiens balsamina*	65	65
1116	80s.+20s. *Lagerstroemia indica*	65	65
1113/1116 *Set of 4*		2·30	2·30

181 Cleaning Ship's Rudder

182 Gen. A. Yani

(Des Soeroso)

1966 (23 Sept–23 Oct). *Maritime Day. T 181 and similar vert designs.* P 12 × 12½.

1117	20s. yellow-green and light blue	25	10
1118	40s. deep blue and pink	25	10
1119	50s. brown and light green	25	10
1120	1r. gold, green, light blue & salmon-red	25	10
1121	1r.50 bronze-grn & pale lilac (23.10)	25	10
1122	2r. orange-red and light grey (23.10)	25	15
1123	2r.50 brown-red & pale mve (23.10)	25	20
1124	3r. black and light emerald (23.10)	35	15
1117/1124 *Set of 8*		1·90	90
MS1125 60 × 78mm. No. 1124. Imperf (23.10)		12·00	12·00

Designs:—40s. Anyer Kidul lighthouse; 50s. Fisherman; 1r. Maritime emblem; 1r.50, Madurese sailing boat; 2r. Quayside; 2r.50, Pearl-diving; 3r. Liner in dry dock.

(Des Soedirno)

1966 (10 Nov). *Victims of Attempted Communist Coup, 1965. T 182 and similar vert portrait designs. Frames and date in ultramarine; portrait colours given.* P 12½ × 12.

1126	**182**	5r. chestnut	35	15
1127	A	5r. blue-green	35	15
1128	B	5r. dull purple	35	15
1129	C	5r. yellow-olive	35	15
1130	D	5r. brownish grey	35	15
1131	E	5r. reddish violet	35	15
1132	F	5r. bright purple	35	15
1133	G	5r. slate-green	35	15
1134	H	5r. reddish purple	35	15
1135	I	15r. red-orange	35	15
1126/1135 *Set of 10*			3·25	1·30

Portraits:—A, Lt.-Gen. R. Soeprapto; B, Lt.-Gen. M. Harjono; C, Lt.-Gen. S. Parman; D, Maj-Gen. D. Pandjaitan; E, Maj-Gen. S. Siswomihardjo; F, Brig.-Gen. Katamso; G, Col. Soegijono; H, Capt. P. Tendean; I, Insp. K. S. Tubun.

183 Python

184 Tjlempung

(Des Soewarsono)

1966 (20 Dec). *Reptiles. T 183 and similar horiz designs.* P 12½ × 12.

1136	2r.+25s. chocolate, green and flesh	15	15
1137	3r.+50s. green, yellow-brown and lilac	15	15
1138	4r.+75s. dp pur-brn, yell-buff & emer	40	15
1139	6r.+1r. black, orange-brown & lt blue	55	15
1136/1139 *Set of 4*		1·10	55

Reptiles:—3r. Chameleon; 4r. Crocodile; 6r. Green turtle.

(Des K. Risman Suplanto)

1967 (1 Feb–1 Mar). *Musical Instruments. T 184 and similar vert designs.* P 12½ × 12.

1140	50s. red and black	35	35
1141	1r. sepia and orange-red	35	35
1142	1r.25 lake and bright blue (1.3)	35	35
1143	1r.50 myrtle-green and bluish violet	35	35
1144	2r. ultramarine and ochre	35	35
1145	2r.50 bronze-green and Venetian red	35	35
1146	3r. blue-green and brown-purple	35	35
1147	4r. ultramarine and orange	55	35
1148	5r. brown-red and blue	55	35
1149	6r. deep blue and magenta	40	40
1150	8r. brown-lake and turquoise-green	40	40
1151	10r. reddish violet and scarlet (1.3)	40	35
1152	12r. olive-green & lt reddish violet (1.3)	65	55
1153	15r. violet and yellow-olive (1.3)	50	35
1154	20r. black and sepia (1.3)	50	35
1155	25r. black and green (1.3)	60	35
1140/1155 *Set of 16*		6·25	5·25

Instruments:—1r. Sasando; 1r.25, Foi doa; 1r.50, Kultjapi; 2r. Arababu; 2r.50, Genderang; 3r. Katjapi; 4r. Hape; 5r. Gangsa; 6r. Serunai; 8r. Rebab; 10r. Trompet; 12r. Totobuang; 15r. Tamburu; 20r. Kulintang; 25r. Keledi.

185 Pilot and Mikoyan Gurevich MiG-21 Fighter

186 Thomas Cup and Silhouettes

(Des 2nd Lieut. Noordono (Indonesian Air Force), Sugijono and Soeroso)

1967 (9 Apr). *Aviation Day. T* **185** *and similar vert designs. Multicoloured. P* 12½.

1156	2r.50 Type **185**	35	25
1157	4r. Convair 990A Coronado airliner and control tower	35	20
1158	5r. Lockheed C-130 Hercules transport airplane on tarmac	55	25

(Des Mahriajub)

1967 (31 May). *Thomas Cup World Badminton Championships. T* **186** *and similar vert design. Multicoloured.* P 12 × 12½.

1159	5r. Type **186**	25	15
1160	12r. Thomas Cup on Globe	50	15

187 Balinese Girl

188 Heroes Monument

(Des Soeroso and Soeripto)

1967 (1 July–Sept). *International Tourist Year. P* 12½.

1161	**187** 12r. multicoloured	1·10	90
MS1162 85 × 80 mm. No. 1161. Imperf (sold at 15r.) (Sept)		5·00	5·00

(Des "Lembinmentra" team)

1967 (17 Aug). *"Heroes of the Revolution" Monument. T* **188** *and similar designs. P* 12½ × 12 (5r.) *or* 12 × 12½ (others).

1163	2r.50 chocolate and pale green	15	10
1164	5r. bright purple and light drab	40	25
1165	7r.50 bluish green and pink	40	25
Designs: *Horiz*—5r. Monument and shrine. *Vert*—7r.50, Shrine			

E **189** "Garuda" Bird

1967 (Aug). *EXPRESS LETTER. Inscr "1967". P* 13½ × 12½.

E1166	E **189** 10r. dull purple and cobalt	55	15
E1167	15r. dull purple and red-orange	1·00	40

For stamps inscribed "1968", see Nos, E1202/6 and "1969", Nos. E1250/2.

1967 (Aug). *POSTAGE DUE. As Type* D **180a** *but dated "1967".*

D1168	50s. blackish green and lilac	15	15
D1169	100s. claret and light green	15	15
D1170	200s. green and pink	15	15
D1171	500s. brown-ochre and azure	50	35
D1172	1000s. mauve and yellow	50	35
D1173	15r. orange and light grey	1·00	50
D1174	25r. violet and light olive-grey	3·50	2·40
D1168/1174 *Set of* 7		3·50	2·40

190 "Forest Fire"

191 Flood Victims

(Des Junalies)

1967 (30 Oct). *Paintings by Raden Saleh. T* **190** *and similar horiz design. P* 12½.

1175	25r. orange-red and bronze-green	40	40
1176	50r. dull purple and orange-red	55	40
MS1177 95 × 63 mm. No. 1175 (sold at 30r.)		6·25	6·25
Painting:—50r. "A Fight to the Death".			

(Des Soeroso and Soeripto)

1967 (20 Dec). *National Disaster Fund. T* **191** *and similar vert designs. P* 12½.

1178	1r.25+10s. chalky blue and yellow	35	35
1179	2r.50+25s. chalky blue and yellow	35	35
1180	4r.+40s. black and red-orange	35	35
1181	5r.+50s. black and red-orange	35	35
1178/1181 *Set of* 4		1·25	1·25
MS1182 95 × 89 mm. Nos. 1180/1 (sold at 12r.50)		37·00	37·00

Designs:—2r.50, Landslide; 4r. Burning house; 5r. Erupting volcano.

Bajar Sumbangan Ongkos Tjetak. This inscription does not relate to postage due but signifies "printing cost contribution paid". Such printing-cost stamps of 1968 onwards had to be affixed to non-postal forms sold at post offices. They were then given normal postal cancellations.

192 Human Rights Emblem

193 Academy Badge

(Des Junalies)

1968 (1 Jan). *Human Rights Year*. P 12½.
1183 **192** 5r. orge-red, myrtle-grn & lt vio-
bl 20 10
1184 12r. orge-red, myrtle-grn & lt
drab 20 10

(Des Soeroso)

1968 (29 Jan). *Indonesian Military Academy*. P 12½.
1185 **193** 10r. yellow, green, red-brn & lt
bl 50 25

194   **195**   **196**

"Sudhana and Manohara at Court of Druma" (relief on wall of Borobudur)

(Des K. Risman Suplanto)

1968 (1 Mar). *"Save Borobudur Monument"*. T **194/6** *and similar design.* P 12½.
1186 **194** 2r.50+25s. bronze green & bl-
grn 35 35
    a. Horiz strip of 3. Nos. 1186/8 1·20
1187 **195** 2r.50+25s. bronze green & bl-
grn 35 35
1188 **196** 2r.50+25s. bronze green & bl-
grn 35 35
1189 — 7r.50+75s. bronze grn & red-
orge 65 35
1186/1189 *Set of 4* . . . . 1·25 1·25
MS1190 105 × 64 mm. Nos. 1186/8 (sold at
12r.50) . . . . 37·00 37·00
Designs:—7r.50, Buddhist and statue of Buddha.
Nos. 1186/8 were issued together in horizontal *se-tenant* strips of three stamps within the sheet, each strip forming the composite design illustrated.

197 W.H.O. Emblem and "20"

198 Steam Train (1867) and Diesel Train (1967)

(Des Mahriajub)

1968 (7 Apr). *20th Anniv of World Health Organization.* T **197** *and similar vert design.* P 12½.
1191 2r. deep slate-purple and bistre-
yellow 35 25
1192 20r. black and light green 35 25
Designs:—20r. W.H.O. emblem.

(Des Junalies)

1968 (15 May). *Centenary of Indonesian Railways (in 1967).* P 12½ × 12.
1193 **198** 20r. multicoloured 75 25
1194 30r. multicoloured . . . . . . 1·10 90

199 Scout with Pick   **200** Butterfly Dancer

(Des Junalies)

1968 (1 June). *"Wirakarya" Scout Camp.* T **199** *and similar designs.* P 12½.
1195 5r.+50s. brown and red-orange 25 15
1196 10r.+1r. olive-grey and chestnut 55 35
1197 30r.+3r. deep olive-brown and
emerald 90 55
Designs: *Vert*—10r. Bugler on hillside. *Horiz*—(69 × 29 mm) 30r. Scouts in camp.

(Des Soeroso)

1968 (1 July). *Tourism.* P 12½.
1198 **200** 30r. multicoloured . . . . . . 1·40 1·40
MS1199 84 × 88 mm. No. 1198 (sold at 35r.) 6·50 6·50

1968 (Sept). *EXPRESS LETTER. As Nos.* E1166/7, *but inscr* "1968".
E1202 E **189** 10r. dull purple and cobalt . . . 55 15
E1203 15r. dull purple and red-
orange 80 25
E1204 20r. dull purple and olive-
yellow 80 25
E1205 30r. dull purple and light
emerald . . . . 1·20 50
E1206 40r. dull purple and light
purple 80 25
E1202/6 *Set of 5* . . . . 3·75 1·25

202 Observatory and Stars

(Des K. Risman Suplanto)

1968 (20 Sept). *40th Anniv of Bosscha Observatory. T* 202 *and similar design.* P 12½ × 12 (15r.) or 12 × 12½ (30r.).
1207   15r. ultramarine, yellow and black   40   25
1208   30r. violet and orange   65   25
Design: Vert—30r. Observatory on Globe.

203   Sailing   **204**

(Des Junalies)

1968 (12 Oct). *Olympic Games, Mexico. T* 203/4 *and similar designs.* P 12½.
1209   5r. dp blue-green, orange-brown & black   10   10
1210   7r.50 blue, greenish yellow & rose-red   25   15
        a. Horiz pair. Nos. 1210/11   50
1211   7r.50 blue, greenish yellow & rose-red   25   15
1212   12r. scarlet-vermilion, blue & olive-yellow   25   10
1213   30r. blackish-brown, turq-grn & red-orge   50   25
1209/1213 *Set of* 5   1·20   70
MS1214 95 × 65 mm. Nos. 1210/11 (sold at 20r.)   7·00   7·00
Designs: 28½ × 44½ mm—5r. Weightlifting; 12r. Basketball. 44½ × 28½ mm—30r. Dove and Olympic flame.
Nos. 1210/11 were issued together in horizontal *se-tenant* pairs within the sheet, each pair forming the composite design illustrated.

205 *Eugenia aquea*

206 I.L.O. Emblem and part of Globe

(Des Soeroso)

1968 (20 Dec). *Fruits. T* 205 *and similar multicoloured designs.* P 12 × 12½ (30r.) or 12½ × 12 (others).
1215   7r.50 Type **205**   35   15
1216   15r. *Carica papaya* (*horiz*)   50   25
1217   30r. *Durio zibethinus* (*vert*)   80   40
MS1218 Two sheets (a) 96 × 62 mm. No. 1216; (b) 62 × 96 mm. No. 1217 (sold at 55r. the pair)   10·50   10·50

(Des Junalies and Soeripto)

1969 (1 Feb). *50th Anniv of International Labour Organisation. T* 206 *and similar square design.* P 12½.
1219 **206**   5r. carmine-red and olive-green   10   10
1220   –   7r.50 deep bluish green & orange   15   10
1221 **206**   15r. orange-red and reddish violet   25   15
1222   –   25r. brown-red and turquoise   50   25
1219/1222 *Set of* 4   90   55
Design:—7r.50, 25r. I.L.O. emblem.

207 R. Dewi Sartika

208 Woman with Flower

(Des Soeroso and Soedirno)

1969 (1 Mar). *National Independence Heroes. T* 207 *and similar vert portraits.* P 12½ × 12.
1223 **207**   15r. emerald-green & reddish violet   35   15
1224   A   15r. bright purple and olive-green   35   15
1225   B   15r. ultramarine and vermilion   35   15
1226   C   15r. yellow-ochre and red   35   15
1227   D   15r. sepia and blue   35   15
1228   E   15r. reddish lilac and deep blue   35   15
1223/1228 *Set of* 6   1·90   80
Portraits:—A, Tjut Nja Din, B, Tjut Nja Meuthia, C, Sutan Sjahrir; D, Dr. F. L. Tobing; E, General G. Subroto.

(Des Soeripto)

1969 (21 Apr). *Women's Emancipation Campaign.* P 13½ × 12½.
1229 **208**   20r.+2r. red, yellow and emerald   65   35

209 Red Cross "Mosaic"

210 "Planned" Family and Factory

(Des Junalies and Mahriajub)

1969 (5 May). *50th Anniv of League of Red Cross Societies. T* 209 *and similar vert design.* P 12½ × 12.
1230   15r. carmine-red and blue-green   40   15
1231   20r. carmine-red and yellow   40   35
Design:—20r. Hands encircling Red Cross.

(Des Soeroso and Soeripto)

1969 (2 June). *South East Asia and Oceania Family Planning Conference. T* 210 *and similar horiz design.* P 12½.
1232   10r. yellow-orange and bluish green   35   15
1233   20r. magenta and pale grey-green   50   25
Design:—20r. "Planned" family and "National Prosperity".

211 Balinese Mask

(Des K. Risman Suplanto)

1969 (1 July). *Tourism in Bali. T* 211 *and similar horiz designs. Multicoloured.* P 12½ × 12.
1234   12r. Type **211**   35   25
1235   15r. Girl with offerings   65   35

1236	30r. Cremation rites	65	35

MS1237 96 × 64mm. No. 1236. P 12 (sold at
35r.)   5·00 5·00

BOOKLET PANES AND STAMPS. From May 1978 booklets, each containing one pane, were issued. Each pane is listed under the lowest value contained in it. As the panes have their outer edges imperforate, all booklet stamps have one side imperf. These are listed as such but most of them also differ from the sheet stamps in shade and some in minor details of design.

212 "Agriculture" **213** Dish Aerial

(Des K. Risman Suplanto, Soeroso, Soedirno and Soeripto)

1969 (17 Aug)–**78**. *Five-year Development Plan. T **212** and similar horiz designs.* P 12 × 12½.

1238	5r. blue and yellow-green (27.9.69)	25	10
1239	7r.50 lemon and brown-purple	25	10
1240	10r. red and slate-blue (27.9.69)	25	10
1241	12r. orange-red and blue	1·40	65
1242	15r. orge-yell & bronze-grn (27.9.69)	25	10
1243	20r. yellow and violet (27.9.69)	25	10
1244	25r. orange-red and black (27.9.69)	25	15
1245	30r. black and carmine	50	15
1246	40r. yellow-orange and light blue-green	55	15
1247	50r. dull purp-brn & orange (27.9.69)	1·10	15
	a. Perf 3 sides. Booklets (31.8.78)	80	30
	ab. Booklet pane. Nos. 1247a × 4 (in bottom row), 1434a × 4 plus two labels (31.8.78)	6·50	
	ac. As ab. but No. 1247a in top row	6·50	
1238/1247 Set of 10		4·50	1·60

Designs:—5r. Religious emblems ("Co-existence"); 10r. Modern family ("Social Welfare"); 12r. Crane and crate ("Overseas Trade"); 15r. Bobbins ("Clothing Industry"); 20r. Children in class ("Education"); 25r. Research worker ("Scientific Research"); 30r. Family and hypodermic syringe ("Health Care"); 40r. Fish and net ("Fisheries"); 50r. Graph ("Statistics").

In the 1980s the 50r. in orange-red (background and bottom panel) and dull purple-brown (i.e. colouring reversed) appeared on the market. Its status is uncertain.

(Des Junalies and Soeroso)

1969 (29 Sept). *Satellite Communications and Inauguration of Djatiluhur Earth Station. T **213** and similar vert design. Multicoloured.* P 12½.

1248	15r. Type **213**	40	15
1249	30r. Communications satellite	55	50

1969. *EXPRESS LETTER. As Nos. E1166/7, but inscr "1969".*

E1250	E **189**	20r. dull purple and olive-yellow	40	15
E1251		30r. dull purple and light emerald	40	15
E1252		40r. dull purple and light purple	55	15

214 Vickers Vimy G-EAOU **215** *Cymbiola nobilis* over Borobudur Temple (Noble Volute Shell)

(Des Soewarsono)

1969 (1 Nov). *50th Anniv of First England–Australia Flight, by Ross and Keith Smith. T **214** and similar horiz design.* P 13½ × 12½.

1253	75r. slate-purple and orange-red	55	50
1254	100r. deep blue-green and yellow	55	55

Design:—100r. Vickers Vimy G-EAOU and map of Indonesia.

(Des Soeroso and Soedirno)

1969 (20 Dec). *Sea-shells. T **215** and similar square designs. Multicoloured.* P 12½.

1255	5r.+50c. Type **215**	55	55
1256	7r.50+50c. *Cymatium pileare* (Common hairy triton)	55	55
1257	10r.+1r. *Lambis lambis* (Common spider conch)	80	80
1258	15r.+1r.50. *Murex tribulus* (Bramble murex)	80	80
1255/1258 Set of 4		2·40	2·40

216 Indonesian Pavilion **217** Prisoner's Hands and Scales of Justice

(Des Bandung Institute of Technology, Soeroso and Soeripto)

1970 (15 Feb). *"EXPO 70" World Fair, Osaka, Japan. T **216** and similar horiz design.* P 12 × 12½.

1259	**216** 5r. greenish yell, bl-grn & bis-brn	55	25
1260	– 15r. scarlet, ultramarine & apple-grn	75	35
1261	**216** 30r. yellow, blue and scarlet	1·40	55

Design:—15r. Indonesian "Garuda" symbol

(Des Muchamed Markus and Soewarsono)

1970 (15 Mar). *"Purification of Justice".* P 12½.

1262	**217** 10r. purple and orange-red	55	35
1263	15r. purple and bright green	90	35

218 U.P.U. Monument, **219** Timor Dancers
Berne

(Des Soedirno)

1970 (20 May). *Inauguration of New Universal Postal Union Headquarters Building, Berne. T **218** and similar horiz design.* P 12 × 12½.

1264	15r. brown-red and bright green	65	35
1265	30r. bright blue and ochre	1·40	80

Design:—30r. New Headquarters building.

(Des Soeroso and Soeripto)

1970 (1 July). *"Visit Indonesia Year". Traditional Dancers. T **219** and similar vert design. Multicoloured.* P 12 × 12½.

1266	20r. Type **219**	1·10	50
1267	45r. Bali dancers	1·60	80
MS1268 63 × 97mm. No. 1267 (sold at 60r.)		8·25	8·25

220 "Productivity" Symbol

221 Independence Monument

(Des Soeripto)

1970 (1 Aug). *Asian Productivity Year.* P 12½ × 12.
1269 **220**   5r. vermilion, yellow and
                 emerald 65   15
1270   30r. vermilion, yellow & slate-
                 violet . . . . 1·40   65

(Des Soewarsono)

1970 (17 Aug). *25th Anniv of Independence.* P 12 × 12½.
1271 **221** 40r. reddish violet, brt pur & lt
                 bl . . . . 16·00   5·00

222 Emblems of Post and Giro, and of Telecommunications

223 U. N. Emblem and Doves

(Des Junalies and Soeripto)

1970 (27 Sept). *25th Anniv of Indonesian Post and Telecommunications Services.* T **222** and similar design. P 12 × 12½ (10r.) or 12½ × 12 (25r.).
1272   10r. yellow-brn, greenish yell & bl-grn . . 5·00   25
1273   25r. black, greenish yellow and pink . . 10·50   65
Design:—25r. Telephone dial and P.T.T. worker.

(Des Soeripto)

1970 (10 Oct). *25th Anniv of United Nations.* P 12½.
1274 **223** 40r. multicoloured . . . . 16·00   5·00

224 I.E.Y. Emblem on Globe

225 *Chrysocoris javanus* (shieldbug)

(Des Junalies)

1970 (16 Nov). *International Education Year.* T **224** and similar vert design. P 12½.
1275   25r. sepia, carmine & lt greenish
              yellow . . . . 9·75   3·25
1276   50r. carmine, black and pale blue . . . 20·00   5·00
Design:—50r. I.E.Y. emblem.

1970 (21 Dec). *Insects. T* **225** *and similar vert designs. Multicoloured.* P 12½.
1277   7r.50+50c. Type **225** . . . . 7·00   1·60
1278   15r.+1r.50 *Orthetrum testaceum*
              (darter) . . . . 12·00   8·25
1279   20r.+2r. *Xylocopa flavonigrescens*
              (carpenter bee) . . . . 24·00   5·75

226 Batik Handicrafts

(Des Junalies, K. Risman Suplanto and Soewarsono)

1971 (26 May). *"Visit ASEAN (Association of South East Asian Nations) Year".* T **226** and similar multicoloured designs. P 12½.
1280   20r. Type **226** . . . . 3·00   1·40
1281   50r. Javanese girl playing angklung
              (vert) . . . . 4·50   3·75
1282   75r. Wedding group, Minangkabau . . . 11·50   5·25
MS1283 64 × 97 mm. No. 1281 (sold at 70r.) 55·00   55·00

227 Restoration of Fatahillah Park

228 Sita and Rama

1971 (19 June). *444th Anniv of Djakarta. T* **227** *and similar horiz designs. Multicoloured.* P 12½.
1284   15r. Type **227** . . . . 2·50   1·10
1285   65r. Performance at Lenong Theatre . . 4·50   4·00
1286   80r. Ismail Marzuki Cultural Centre . . 10·50   3·50
MS1287 121 × 103 mm. 30r. Djakarta City Hall
        (sold at 60r.) . . . . 26·00   26·00

(Des Art Academy, Djokjakarta)

1971 (31 Aug). *International Ramayana Festival. T* **228** *and similar horiz design.* P 12½.
1288   30r. multicoloured . . . . 2·75   80
1289   100r. black, new blue and vermilion . . 4·00   1·80
Design:—100r. Rama.

229 Pigeon with Letter, and Workers

230 U.P.U. Monument, Berne, and Hemispheres

(Des E. Kartasubarna)

1971 (20 Sept). *Fifth Asian Region Telecommunications Conference.* P 12 × 12½.
1290 **229** 50r. chocolate, yell-brn & pale
                 buff . . . . 2·10   1·00

(Des Kosdyana and Soeripto)

1971 (4 Oct). *Universal Postal Union Day.* P 13½ × 12½.
1291　**230**　40r. dull purple, black and blue ... 2·00　1·00

231 Schoolgirl　　**232** Clown Surgeonfish (*Acanthurus lineatus*)

(Des Soeripto)

1971 (11 Dec). *25th Anniv of U.N.I.C.E.F.* T **231** *and similar vert design. Multicoloured.* P 12½.
1292　20r. Type **231** ... 2·75　55
1293　40r. Boy with rice-stalks ... 4·00　1·10

(Des Soewarsono)

1971 (27 Dec). *Fishes (1st series).* T **232** *and similar horiz designs. Multicoloured.* P 12½.
1294　15r. Type **232** ... 5·25　1·40
1295　30r. Moorish idol (*Zanclus cornutus*) ... 10·50　3·75
1296　40r. Emperor angelfish (*Pomacanthus imperator*) ... 16·00　5·25
See also Nos. 1318/20, 1343/5, 1390/2 and 1423/5.

233 Microwave Tower　　**234** Human Heart

(Des Mahriajub, Junalies and Soeripto)

1972 (28 Mar). *25th Anniv of U.N. Economic Commission for Asia and the Far East.* T **233** *and similar designs.* P 12½.
1297　40r. blue and light greenish blue ... 3·50　1·00
1298　75r. multicoloured ... 3·50　1·00
1299　100r. multicoloured ... 5·25　2·10
Designs: *Vert*—40r. E.C.A.F.E. emblem. *Horiz*—100r. Irrigation and highways.

(Des Soeripto and National Heart Institute)

1972 (7 Apr). *World Heart Month.* P 12½.
1300　**234**　50r. multicoloured ... 2·10　80

235 Ancient and Modern Textile Production
236 Children reading Books

(Des P. Hadiwardojo and Soeripto)

1972 (22 Apr). *50th Anniv of Textile Technology Institute.* P 12½.
1301　**235**　35r. purple, greenish yell & red-orge ... 2·10　80

(Des Koentjono and Sadjiroen)

1972 (15 May). *International Book Year.* P 13½ × 12½.
1302　**236**　75r. multicoloured ... 2·75　1·20

237 "Essa 8" Weather Satellite
238 Hotel Indonesia

(Des Soewarsono)

1972 (20 July). *Space Exploration.* T **237** *and similar vert designs.* P 12½.
1303　35r. ochre, bluish violet and light blue ... 2·00　65
1304　50r. light greenish blue, black and pink ... 3·75　3·50
1305　60r. black, turquoise-green & chestnut ... 6·50　1·10
Designs:—50r. Astronaut on Moon; 60r. Indonesian "Kartika 1" rocket.

(Des Siswandi and Soewarsono)

1972 (5 Aug). *10th Anniv of Hotel Indonesia.* P 12½.
1306　**238**　50r. green, pale green and carmine ... 2·50　1·10

239 "Silat" (unarmed combat)
240 Family and Religious Buildings
241 Moluccas Dancer

(Des Soeripto and Prijono)

1972 (26 Aug). *Olympic Games, Munich.* T **239** *and similar vert designs.* P 12½.
1307　20r. plum, deep cobalt and light blue ... 1·40　15
1308　35r. bluish violet, lake-brown & mauve ... 1·40　40
1309　50r. emerald, bronze-grn & apple-grn ... 2·75　75
1310　75r. bright rose, brown-purple & pink ... 5·75　1·80
1311　100r. brown, blue and pale green ... 5·75　3·00
1307/1311 *Set of 5* ... 12·50　5·50
Designs:—35r. Running; 50r. Diving; 75r. Badminton; 100r. Olympic stadium.

(Des Mahriajub and Family Planning Committee)

1972 (27 Sept). *Family Planning Campaign.* T **240** *and similar vert designs. Multicoloured.* P 12½ × 13½.
1312　30r. Type **240** ... 2·00　65
1313　75r. "Healthy family" ... 3·75　2·40
1314　80r. "Family of workers" ... 6·00　3·00

(Des Soeripto and Junalies)

1972 (28 Oct). *"Art and Culture" (1st series).* T **241** *and similar designs.* P 13½ × 12½ (100r.) or 12½ × 13½ (others).
1315　30r. deep brown, pink and green ... 2·00　65
1316　60r. multicoloured ... 5·00　2·75
1317　100r. greenish bl, red-brn & cinnamon ... 7·00　2·75
Designs: *Vert*—60r. Couple and Toraja traditional house. *Horiz*—100r. West Irian traditional house.
See also Nos. 1336/8, 1373/5 and 1401/3.

(Des Soewarsono)

1972 (4 Dec). *Fishes (2nd series). Horiz designs as T* **232**. *Multicoloured.* P 12½.
1318   30r. Triangle butterflyfish (*Chaetodon triangulum*) . . . . 7·00   2·00
1319   50r. Regal angelfish (*Pygoplites diacanthus*) . . . . 12·00   3·00
1320   100r. Clown triggerfish (*Balistoides conspicillum*) . . . . 16·00   5·25

1973. *POSTAGE DUE. As Type* D **180a** *but inscribed* "BAYAR PORTO" *and dated* "1973".
D1320a   25r. violet and light olive-grey . . . . 1·10   15

242 Thomas Cup and Shuttlecock

243 Emblem, Anemometer and "Gatotkaca"

(Des Umar Sanusi, Soewarsono and Soeripto)

1973 (2 Jan). *Thomas Cup Badminton Championships, Djakarta. T* **242** *and similar vert designs.* P 12½.
1321   30r. new blue and bright green 80   25
1322   75r. carmine and dull green . . . . 1·80   50
1323   80r. olive-brown and vermilion . . . . 3·50   1·00
Designs:—75r. Thomas Cup and Sports Centre; 80r. Thomas Cup and player.

(Des Soehardi and Soeripto)

1973 (15 Feb). *I.M.O. and W.M.O. Weather Organization Centenary.* P 13½ × 12½.
1324 **243** 80r. multicoloured . . . . 2·00   80

244 "Health begins at Home"

245 Java Mask

(Des Masino and Soeripto)

1973 (7 Apr). *25th Anniv of World Health Organization.* P 12½.
1325 **244** 80r. blue, salmon & dp blue-green . . . . 1·60   80

(Des Soedirno)

1973 (1 June). *Tourism. Indonesian Folk Masks. T* **245** *and similar vert designs. Multicoloured.* P 12½.
1326   30r. Type **245** . . . . 5·25   90
1327   60r. Kalimantan mask . . . . 8·25   3·50
1328   100r. Bali mask . . . . 13·00   1·80

246 Savings Bank and Thrift Plant

247 Chess

(Des Martosuhardjo (25r.), Soeripto (30r.))

1973 (2 July). *Two-Year National Savings Drive. T* **246** *and similar design.* P 12½.
1329   25r. black, greenish yellow and bistre . . 90   50
1330   30r. dp bluish grn, gold & greenish yell . . . . 1·60   50
Design: *Horiz*—30r. Hand and "City" savings bank.

(Des Soeripto)

1973 (4 Aug). *National Sports Week. T* **247** *and similar multicoloured designs.* P 12½.
1331   30r. Type **247** . . . . 1·60   1·10
1332   60r. Karate . . . . 2·75   1·10
1333   75r. Hurdling (*horiz*) . . . . 5·00   90

248 International Policemen

249 "Food Cultivation"

(Des W. Djatmika, Soetrisno and J. Prijono)

1973 (3 Sept). *50th Anniv of International Criminal Police Organization (Interpol). T* **248** *and similar multicoloured design.* P 12½.
1334   30r. Type **248** 90   35
1335   50r. Giant temple guard (*vert*) . . . . 1·60   65

(Des Soewarsono)

1973 (9 Oct). *"Art and Culture" (2nd series). Weaving and Fabrics. Horiz designs as T* **241**. *Multicoloured.* P 12½.
1336   60r. Parang Rusak pattern . . . . . 2·50   2·00
1337   80r. Pagi Sore pattern . . . . 5·00   2·10
1338   100r. Merak Ngigel pattern . . . . . . 9·00   3·75

(Des Dwidjotanojo and Mahriayub)

1973 (24 Oct). *10th Anniv of World Food Programme.* P 12½.
1339 **249** 30r. multicoloured . . . . 2·10   65

250 "Religion"

251 Admiral Sudarso and Naval Battle of Arafuru

(Des Soeripto)

1973 (10 Nov). *Family Planning. T* **250** *and similar horiz designs. Multicoloured.* P 12½.
1340   20r. Type **250** 80   40
1341   30r. "Population Education" . . . . . 1·60   65
1342   60r. "Health" . . . . 3·25   55

(Des Soewarsano)

1973 (10 Dec). *Fishes (3rd series). Horiz designs as T* **232**. *Multicoloured.* P 12½.

1343	40r. Powder-blue surgeonfish (*Acanthurus leucosternon*)	1·60	1·10
1344	65r. Melon butterflyfish (*Chaetodon trifasciatus*)	6·50	2·00
1345	100r. Blue-ringed angelfish (*Pomacanthus annularis*)	8·25	3·25

1974. *POSTAGE DUE. As Type* D **180a** *but inscr* "BAYAR PORTO" *and dated* "1974". P 13½ × 12½.

D1346	65r. blackish olive & yellow-ochre	1·80	40
D1347	125r. purple and pale rose	3·50	1·20

(Des Junalies)

1974 (15 Jan). *Naval Day.* P 12½.

1346	**251**	40r. multicoloured	1·80	80

252 Bengkulu Costume

254 Pres. Suharto

1974 (28 Mar). *Pacific Area Travel Association Conference, Djakarta. T* **252** *and similar vert designs showing Provincial Costumes. Multicoloured.* P 12½.

1347	5r. Type **252**	16·00	1·10
1348	7r.50 Kalimantan, Timor	8·25	1·10
1349	10r. Kalimantan, Tengah	1·60	80
1350	15r. Jambi	1·60	80
1351	20r. Sulawesi, Tenggara	1·60	80
1352	25r. Nusatenggara, Timor	1·60	80
1353	27r.50 Maluku	1·60	1·60
1354	30r. Lampung	1·60	1·60
1355	35r. Sumatera, Barat	1·60	80
1356	40r. Aceh	1·60	80
1357	45r. Nusatenggara, Barat	4·00	80
1358	50r. Riau	2·40	2·40
1359	55r. Kalimantan, Barat	3·25	80
1360	60r. Sulawesi, Utara	3·25	80
1361	65r. Sulawesi, Tengah	3·25	80
1362	70r. Sumatera, Selatan	3·50	80
1363	75r. Java, Barat	3·50	80
1364	80r. Sumatera, Utara	3·50	80
1365	90r. Yogyakarta	3·75	3·75
1366	95r. Kalimantan, Selatan	3·50	80
1367	100r. Java, Timor	3·50	1·60
1368	120r. Irian Jaya	6·50	1·10
1369	130r. Java, Tengah	6·50	80
1370	135r. Sulawesi, Selatan	7·25	80
1371	150r. Bali	7·25	80
1372	160r. Djakarta	7·25	1·60
1347/1372 *Set of 26*		95·00	26·00

(Des Soedino, Suwarsono and Soeripto)

1974 (1 June). "*Art and Culture*" (*3rd series*). *Shadow Plays. Vert designs as T* **241**. *Multicoloured.* P 12½.

1373	40r. Baladewa	3·00	1·30
1374	80r. Kresna	5·25	2·50
1375	100r. Bima	6·50	2·50

(Des Soerdino)

1974 (17 Aug). P 12½.

1376	**254**	40r. sepia, black and light green	80	10
1377		50r. sepia, black and light blue	2·00	15

1378	65r. sepia, black and light magenta	1·10	65
1379	75r. sepia, black & lt greenish yell	2·00	15
1380	100r. sepia, black & lt orange-yellow	2·00	15
1381	150r. sepia, black and light olive	2·00	15
1376/1381 *Set of 6*		8·75	1·20

See also Nos. 1444/7.

255 "Improvement of Living Standards"

256 "Welfare"

(Des Soeripto)

1974 (19 Aug). *World Population Year.* P 12½.

1382	**255**	65r. multicoloured	1·50	50

(Des Suplanto and Soeripto)

1974 (9 Sept). *Family Planning. T* **256** *and similar horiz designs. Multicoloured.* P 12½.

1383	25r. Type **256**	1·00	40
1384	40r. "Development"	1·00	40
1385	65r. "Religion"	3·00	40

257 Bicycle Postmen

(Des S. Martosuhardjo)

1974 (9 Oct). *Centenary of Universal Postal Union. T* **257** *and similar horiz designs. Multicoloured.* P 12½.

1386	20r. Type **257**	2·50	50
1387	40r. Mail cart	2·50	75
1388	65r. Mounted postman	2·50	75
1389	100r. East Indies galley	2·50	2·00
1386/1389 *Set of 4*		9·00	3·50

(Des Soewarsono)

1974 (30 Oct). *Fishes (4th series). Horiz designs as T* **232**. *Multicoloured.* P 12½.

1390	40r. Sail-finned tang (*Zebrasoma veliferum*)	2·50	50
1391	80r. Blue-girdled angelfish (*Euxiphipops navarchus*)	4·00	2·00
1392	100r. Mandarin fish (*Synchiropus splendidus*)	6·50	2·40

258 Drilling for Oil

(Des S. Martosuhardjo)

1974 (10 Dec). *17th Anniv of Pertamina Oil Complex. T* **258** *and similar multicoloured designs.* P 13½.

1393	40r. Type **258**		55	35
1394	75r. Oil refinery		55	35
1395	95r. Control centre (*vert*)		55	35
1396	100r. Road tanker (*vert*)		55	35
1397	120r. Fokker F.28 Fellowship airliner over storage tank farm (*vert*)		90	35
1398	130r. Pipeline and tanker (*vert*)		90	35
1399	150r. Petrochemical storage tanks		90	35
1400	200r. Offshore drilling rig		90	35
1393/1400 *Set of 8*			5·25	2·50

1975. *POSTAGE DUE. As Type* D **180a** *but inscr "BAYAR PORTO" and dated "1975".* P 13½ × 12½.

D1401	25r. reddish violet and pale drab		1·40	90

(Des K. Suplanto)

1975 (24 Feb). *"Art and Culture" (4th series). Vert designs as T* **241**. P 12½.

1401	50r. silver, red and black		1·50	1·30
1402	75r. silver, green and black		2·40	1·30
1403	100r. yellow, new blue and black		4·50	1·30

Designs:—50r. Sumatra spitoon; 75r. Sumatran "sirh" dish, 100r. Kalimantan "sirh" dish

260 "Donorship"

261 Measures and Globe

(Des Soerdino)

1975 (7 Apr). *Blood Donors Campaign.* P 12½.

1404	**260**	40r. carmine-red, lt yellow & green	1·10	65

(Des Mustalien Sudalie and Mahriajub)

1975 (20 May). *Centenary of Metre Convention.* P 12½.

1405	**261**	65r. new blue, red and yellow	2·00	65

262 Women in Public Service

(Des Suplanto and Soeripto)

1975 (25 June). *International Women's Year. T* **262** *and similar multicoloured design.* P 12½.

1406	40r. Type **262**		1·60	65
1407	100r. I.W.Y. Emblem (21 × 29 *mm*)		2·10	65

263 *Dendrobium pakarena*

264 Stupas and Damaged Temple

(Des Junalies)

1975 (21 July). *Tourism. Indonesian Orchids. T* **263** *and similar vert designs dated "1975". Multicoloured.* P 12½.

1408	40r. Type **263**		5·00	1·10
1409	70r. *Aeridachnis bogor*		5·00	2·10
1410	85r. *Vanda genta*		9·00	3·25

(Des R. Spencer)

1975 (10 Aug). *UNESCO "Save Borobudur Temple" Campaign. T* **264** *and similar multicoloured designs.* P 12½.

1411	25r. Type **264**		3·25	80
1412	40r. Buddhist shrines and broken wall		3·75	1·10
1413	65r. Stupas and damaged building (*horiz*)		7·25	4·50
1414	100r. Buddhas and stupas (*horiz*)		10·50	4·50
1411/1414 *Set or 4*			22·00	9·75

265 Battle of Banjarmasin

266 "Education"

(Des S. Martosuhardjo)

1975 (17 Aug). *30th Anniv of Independence. T* **265** *and similar horiz designs.* P 12½.

1415	25r. black and yellow		80	50
1416	40r. black and orange-red		1·10	50
1417	75r. black and pale red		1·60	1·30
1418	100r. black and yellow-orange		1·60	1·00
1415/1418 *Set of 4*			4·50	3·00

Designs: 40r. Battle of Batua; 75r. Battle of Margarana; 100r. Battle of Palembang.

(Des K. R. Suplanto)

1975 (20 Oct). *Family Planning. T* **266** *and similar vert designs. Multicoloured.* P 12½.

1419	20r. Type **266**		65	15
1420	25r. "Religion"		1·00	25
1421	40r. "Prosperity"		1·60	50

267 Heroes' Monument, Surabaya

D **268**

(Des Junalies)

1975 (10 Nov). *30th Anniv of Independence.* P 12½.
1422 **267** 100r. brown-lake and bronze-
green . . . . 2·40 50

(Des Soewarsano)

1975 (15 Dec). *Fishes (5th series). Multicoloured designs
as T **232**.* P 12½.
1423 40r. Twin-spotted wrasse (*Coris
angulata*) . . . . . . 1·60 50
1424 75r. Saddle butterflyfish (*Chaetodon
ephippium*) . . . . . 5·00 1·50
1425 150r. Dusky batfish (*Platax pinnatus*)
(*vert*) . . . . . 6·50 3·00

1976. *POSTAGE DUE. Dated "1976".* P 13½ × 12½.
D1426 **D 268** 25r. reddish violet & pale
drab 50 50
D1427 65r. blackish olive & yell-
ochre . . . . . 1·00 1·00

269 Thomas Cup   **270** Refugees and New Village

(Des Mahriajub and Soedirno)

1976 (31 Jan). *Indonesian Victory in World Badminton
Championships.* T **269** *and similar vert designs. Multicoloured.*
P 12½.
1428 20r. Type **269** . . . . . 1·00 25
1429 40r. Uber cup . . . . . 1·00 55
1430 100r. Thomas and Uber cups . . . 2·10 55

(Des Soeripto)

1976 (28 Feb). *World Human Settlements Day.* T **270** *and similar
horiz designs. Multicoloured.* P 12½.
1431 30r. Type **270** 80 15
1432 60r. Old and restored villages . . . 1·50 40
1433 100r. Derelict and rebuilt houses . . . 1·60 40

271 Early and Modern   **272** Human Eye
Telephones

(Des S. Martosuhardjo)

1976 (10 Mar)–**78**. *Telephone Centenary.* P 12½.
1434 **271** 100r. sepia, red and pale
yellow . . . . . 1·30 50
a. Perf 3 sides. Booklets
(31.8.78) . . . . . 1·10 50

(Des Masino)

1976 (7 Apr). *World Health Day.* T **272** *and similar horiz design.
Multicoloured.* P 12½.
1435 20r. Type **272** 40 25
1436 40r. Blind man with stick 90 40

273 Main Stadium, Montreal   **274** Lake Tondano,
Sulawesi

(Des R. Suplanto)

1976 (17 May). *Olympic Games, Montreal.* P 12½.
1437 **273** 100r. ultramarine . . . . . 1·30 55

(Des Junalies. Photo)

1976 (1 June)–**78**. *Tourism.* T **274** *and similar horiz designs.
Multicoloured.* P 12½.
1438 35r. Type **274** 80 40
1439 40r. Lake Kelimutu, Flores . . . 80 40
1440 75r. Lake Maninjau, Sumatra . . . 1·60 50
a. Perf 3 sides. Booklets (3.5.78) . . 1·20 45
ab. Booklet pane. Nos. 1440a × 7,
1470a (in top row) plus two labels
(3.5.78) . . . . . 8·75
ac. As ab. but No. 1470a in bottom row
(3.5.78) . . . . . 8·75

275 "Light Traffic"   **276** Vanda "Putri Serang"
Station

(Des S. Martosuhardjo)

1976 (8 July)–**78**. *Inauguration of Domestic Satellite
System.* T **275** *and similar horiz designs.* P 12½.
1441 20r. multicoloured 80 35
1442 50r. black and bright green . . . 80 35
1443 100r. greenish blue, royal blue and
reddish violet . . . . 1·40 65
a. Perf 3 sides. Booklets (3.5.78) . . 1·30 50
Designs:—50r. "Master control" station; 100r. "Palapa" satellite.

(Des Soedirno)

1976 (17 Aug). *Vert design as T **254** but with background of vert
wavy lines.* P 12½.
1444 200r. blackish brown, new blue & bl-
grn . . . . . 8·25 15
1445 300r. blackish brown, lake and flesh . 2·10 15
1446 400r. blackish brn, emer & greenish
yell . . . . . 4·00 35
1447 500r. blackish brown, carm-lake &
lilac . . . . . 5·75 1·00
1444/1447 *Set of 4* . . . . . 18·00 1·50

(Des K. R. Suplanto)

1976 (7 Sept). *Orchids.* T **276** *and similar horiz designs.
Multicoloured.* P 12½.
1448 25r. *Arachnis flos-aeris* . . . . 2·40 1·00
1449 40r. Type **276** . . . . . 2·40 1·00
1450 100r. *Coelogyne pandurata* . . . 3·50 2·10
MS1451 67 × 90 mm. No. 1448 (sold at 60r.) 65·00 65·00

277 Stylized Tree **278** Kelewang Dagger and Sheath
(Timor)

(Des H. Irawady)

1976 (4 Oct). *Reafforestation Week.* P 12½.
1452 **277** 20r. emerald, new blue & orange-
    brn   80 35

(Des Soeripto, Mahriajub and Soerdino)

1976 (1 Nov). *Daggers and Sheaths.* T **278** *and similar horiz designs.* P 12½.
1453 25r. grey-green, black & yellow-
   brown   1·10 40
1454 40r. dp brn, greenish yell & reddish
   orge   1·80 75
1455 100r. deep brown, greenish yellow and
   yellowish green   2·50 2·10
MS1456 94 × 64 mm. 40r. No. 1454 (sold at
70r.)   16·00 16·00
Designs:—40r. Mandau dagger and sheath (Borneo); 100r. Rencong dagger and sheath (Aceh).

279 Open Book **280** U.N.I.C.E.F. **281** Ballot Box
      Emblem

(Des Y. Musbar)

1976 (8 Dec). *Books for Children.* T **279** *and similar vert design.* P 12½.
1457 20r. blue-grn, reddish orge & Prussian
   bl   65 25
1458 40r. dull violet, carmine and lemon 1·30 40
Design:—40r. Children reading book.

(Des Soeripto)

1976 (11 Dec)–**78**. *30th Anniv of United Nations Children's Fund.* P 12½.
1459 **280** 40r. royal blue, greenish blue &
    violet   1·10 50
    a. Perf 3 sides. Deep violet,
    greenish blue and reddish
    violet. Booklets (3.5.78) 85
    ab. Booklet pane. Nos. 1459a × 5,
    1443a × 4 plus label (top edge
    imperf) (3.5.78)   7·75
    ac. As ab. but label imperf at foot
    (3.5.78)   7·75

(Des Junalies)

1977 (5 Jan). *Elections.* T **281** *and similar vert designs.* P 12½.
1460 40r. new blue, yellow & greenish
   grey   2·10 25
1461 75r. new blue, yellow and flesh 2·40 40
1462 100r. olive-bistre, rosine and black 3·75 1·30
Designs:—75r. Ballot box, factory and produce; 100r. Indonesian arms.

282 Scout Emblems and **283** Letter and A.O.P.U.
   Camp   Emblem

(Des Karnedi and S. Martosuhardjo)

1977 (28 Feb). 11*th National Scout Jamboree.* T **282** *and similar horiz designs. Multicoloured.* P 12½.
1463 25r. Type **282**   60 35
1464 30r. Emblems, tent and trees 60 35
1465 40r. Emblems, tent and flags 1·40 75

(Des Soeripto)

1977 (1 Apr). 15*th Anniv of Asian–Oceanic Postal Union.* T **283** *and similar horiz design. Multicoloured.* P 12½.
1466 65r. Type **283**   80 35
1467 100r. Stylized carrier pigeon 1·40 50

284 Anniversary   **285** Rose
  Emblem

(Des Joedien, Iskandor and Indra)

1977 (23 May)–**78**. 450*th Anniv of Djakarta.* T **284** *and similar vert designs.* P 12½.
1468 20r. greenish blue and orange-red 80 40
1469 40r. light green and greenish blue 80 40
1470 100r. slate blue and greenish blue 1·60 80
   a. Perf 3 sides. Booklets (3.5.78) 2·10 1·40
MS1471 72 × 96 mm. No. 1470 (sold at
125r.)   9·00 9·00
Designs: 40, 100r. Similar to Type **284** but with emblem and arms differently arranged.

(Des Elisabeth)

1977 (26 May)–**78**. *"Amphilex 77" International Stamp Exhibition, Amsterdam.* T **285** *and similar vert design.* P 12½.
1472 **285** 100r. scarlet, light green and
    black   1·40 50
    a. Perf 3 sides. Booklets
    (27.9.78)   1·20 50
    b. Pair. Nos. 1472 and 1473 2·75
1473 — 100r. scarlet, light green and
    black   1·40 50
MS1474 Two sheets (sold at 550r.). (a)
71 × 95 mm. Nos. 1472/3, each × 2; (b)
72 × 63 mm. **285** 100r. scarlet, light blue and
black   20·00 20·00
Design:—No. 1473, Envelope.
Nos. 1472/3 were issued together in *se-tenant* pairs within the sheet.

286 Sports Pictograms

287 Trophy

(Des S. Martosuhardjo)

1977 (22 June). *National Sports Week. T* **286** *and similar vert designs.* P 12½.
1475   40r. silver, myrtle green & deep
    claret   2·50   1·60
1476   50r. silver, dull ultramarine & dp
    claret   3·50   1·60
1477   100r. gold, black and carmine-red   5·75   3·50
Designs:—50, 100r. Similar to Type **286** but with different pictograms.

(Des A. Nasibu and A. Syoukani)

1977 (20 July). *Tenth National Koran Reading Contest. T* **287** *and similar vent design.* P 12½.
1478   40r. red-brown, yellowish green &
    yell   2·40   50
1479   100r. black, greenish yellow & blue-
    grn   3·00   90
Design—100r. Emblem.

288 Carrier Pigeon and Map

289 Government Officer, Djakarta Region

(Des Y. Musbar)

1977 (8 Aug). *Tenth Anniv of Association of South-East Asian Nations. T* **288** *and similar horiz designs. Multicoloured.* P 12½.
1480   25r. Type **288**   50   15
1481   35r. Map of A.S.E.A.N. members   2·10   65
1482   50r. Flags of members and various
    forms of transport   2·10   80

(Des Soeripto)

1977 (19 Aug). *Indonesia–Pakistan Economic and Cultural Co–operation Organization.* P 12½.
1483   **289** 25r. red-brown, gold and green   65   25

290 *Taeniophyllum* sp.

291 Child and Mosquito

(Des Mahriajub)

1977 (28 Oct). *Orchids. T* **290** *and similar vert designs. Multicoloured.* P 12½.
1484   25r. Type **290**   2·40   80
1485   40r. *Phalaenopsis violacea*   2·40   1·60
1486   100r. *Dendrobium spectabile*   5·00   2·40
MS1487 86 × 71 mm. As No. 1486 but with new blue background (sold at 125r.)   11·50   11·50

(Des Masino and Y. Musbar)

1977 (7 Nov)–**78**. *National Health Campaign.* P 12½.
1488   **291** 40r. carmine-red, green and
    black   65   25
    a. Perf 3 sides. Booklets
      (27.9.78)   50   35
    ab. Booklet pane. Nos. 1488a × 5,
      1472a × 4 plus label (imperf at
      top) (27.9.78)   7·50
    ac. As ab. but label imperf at foot
      (27.9.78)   7·50

292 Proboscis Monkey (*Narsalis larvatus*)

293 Hands holding U.N. Emblem

(Des Soeripto)

1977 (22 Dec). *Wildlife (1st series). T* **292** *and similar horiz designs. Multicoloured.* P 12½.
1489   20r. Type **292**   80   40
1490   40r. Indian elephant (*Elephas
    indicus*)   2·00   80
1491   100r. Tiger (*Panthera tigris*)   5·25   1·60
MS1492 94 × 64 mm. As No 1491 but colours of country name and value reversed (sold at 125r.)   9·75   9·75
See also Nos. 1515/**MS**1518 and 1558/**MS**1561.

(Des Y. Musbar)

1978 (27 Mar). *United Nations Conference on Technical Co-operation among Developing Countries.* P 12½.
1493   **293** 100r. pale blue and ultramarine   1·40   55
    No. 1493 was first issued in normal sheets of 100. Later it was reissued in sheets with the bottom five horizontal rows printed upside down, giving *tête-bêche* pairs in the middle of the sheet. These pairs could only be purchased as part of a vertical strip of ten stamps.

294 Mother feeding Baby   **295** Dome of the Rock

(Des D. Hendronoto and D. Ismail)

1978 (7 Apr). *Campaign for Promotion of Breast Feeding. T* **294** *and similar vert design.* P 12½.
1494	40r. pale blue-green and greenish blue	50	25
1495	75r. deep brown and dull vermilion	90	40

Design:—75r. Stylized mother and child.
Téte-bêche pairs come from specially printed sheets issued later. These pairs could only be purchased as part of a vertical strip of ten stamps.

1978 (15 May). *Palestinian Welfare.* P 12½.
1496	**295** 100r. multicoloured	1·30	50

296 World Cup Emblem   **297** Head and Blood Circulation Diagram

1978 (1 June). *World Cup Football Championship, Argentina.* P 12½.
1497	**296** 40r. dull yellow-green, black & blue	65	25
1498	100r. light magenta, black and blue	1·20	65

(Des Masino)

1978 (17 June). *World Health Day.* P 12½.
1499	**297** 100r. new blue, black and red	1·20	50

298 Leather Puppets   (D **299**)

1978 (22 July). *Puppets from Wayang Museum, Djakarta. T* **298** *and similar horiz designs. Multicoloured.* P 12½.
1500	40r. Type **298**	2·40	65
1501	75r. Wooden puppets	2·50	1·30
1502	100r. Actors wearing puppet masks	5·00	2·10

1978 (July). *POSTAGE DUE. Nos.* 1141, 1144, 1147/8, 1151 *and* 1153 *surch as Type* D **299** *in red.*
D1503	25r.on 1r. sep & orge-red	40	40
	b. Surch in black (1 Sept)	40	40
D1504	50r.on 2r. ultram & ochre	40	40
	b. Surch in black (1 Sept)	40	40
D1505	100r.on 4r. ultram & orge	80	80
	b. Surch in black (1 Sept)	80	80

D1506	200r.on 5r. brown-red & blk	1·60	1·60
	b. Surch in black (1 Sept)	1·60	1·60
D1507	300r.on 10r. reddish violet and scarlet	2·30	2·30
	b. Surch in black (1 Sept)	2·30	2·30
D1508	400r.on 15r. vio & yell-ol	2·40	2·40
	b. Surch in black (1 Sept)	2·40	2·40
D1503/1508 *Set of 6*		7·00	7·00
D1503b/1508b *Set of 6*		7·00	7·00

300 Congress Emblem   **301** I.A.Y. Emblem   **302** Couple and Tree

1978 (1 Aug). *27th Congress of World Confederation of Organizations of the Teaching Profession, Djakarta.* P 12½.
1509	**300** 100r. greenish slate	1·00	40

1978 (16 Aug). *International Anti-apartheid Year.* P 12½.
1510	**301** 100r. Prussian blue and orange-red	1·10	40

(Des H. Engeler and R. Bellincamp)

1978 (16 Oct). *Eighth World Forestry Congress, Djakarta. T* **302** *and similar vert design.* P 12½.
1511	40r. dull blue and bright green	25	15
1512	100r. blackish green and bright green	1·00	50

Design:—100r. People and trees.

303 Anniversary Emblem   **304** *Phalaenopsis sri rejeki*

(Des S. Martosuhardjo)

1978 (28 Oct)–**79**. *50th Anniv of Youth Pledge. T* **303** *and similar vert design.* P 12½.
1513	40r. reddish brown and rosine	65	25
1514	100r. Indian red, rosine and flesh	1·00	40
	a. Perf 3 sides. Booklets (8.8.79)	1·00	40
	ab. Booklet pane. Nos. 1514a × 3, 1535a × 3, 1536a × 3 plus label (imperf at top) (8.8.79)	9·25	
	ac. As ab. but label imperf at foot (8.8.79)	9·25	

Design:—100r. Similar to Type **303** but with value and country name arranged differently.

(Des Soeripto)

1978 (1 Nov). *Wildlife (2nd series). Horiz designs as T* **292**. *Multicoloured.* P 12½.
1515	40r. Long-nosed echidna (*Zaglosus bruijni*)	1·60	40
1516	75r. Sambar (*Cervus unicolor*)	2·40	80

1517   100r. Clouded leopard (*Neofelis
           nebulosa*) . . . .   4·00   1·20
MS1518 Two sheets (sold at 700r.). (a)
94 × 63 mm. No. 1517; (b) 115 × 157 mm.
Nos. 1516 and 1517 × 4 but with colours of
inscriptions and value reversed . . . . .   6·00   6·00
The miniature sheets have inscriptions commemorating the
Essen International Stamp Fair.

(Des Sugiyanto)

1978 (22 Dec). *Orchids. T* **304** *and similar vert designs.
Multicoloured.* P 12½.
1519   40r. Type **304** . . . .   1·20   40
1520   75r. *Dendrobium macrophillum* . . . .   1·60   65
1521   100r. *Cymbidium fynlaysonianum* . . .   3·25   90
MS1522 63 × 96 mm. As No. 1521 but with
some colours changed (sold at 150r.) . . .   6·00   6·00

BAYAR PORTO
(D **305**)   306 Douglas DC-3 RI-ODI over
                      Volcano

1978. *POSTAGE DUE. Stamps surch as Type* D **305**.

(a) No. 1145.

D1523   40r.on 2r.50 bronze green and
            Venetian red . . . .   1·10   1·10
        a. Pair. Nos. D1523 and D1525 . .   3·50
D1524   65r.on 2r.50 bronze green and
            Venetian red . . . .   1·10   1·10
        a. Pair. Nos. D1524 and D1526 . .   4·50
D1525   125r.on 2r.50 bronze green and
            Venetian red . . . .   1·30   1·30
D1526   150r.on 2r.50 bronze green and
            Venetian red . . . .   2·30   2·30

(b) No. 1152.

D1527   40r.on 12r. olive-grn & lt reddish
            vio   75   75
        a. Pair. Nos. D1527 and D1529 . .   3·50
D1528   65r.on 12r. olive-grn & lt reddish
            vio . . . .   1·80   1·80
        a. Pair. Nos. D1528 and D1530 . .   4·50
D1529   125r.on 12r. olive-grn & lt reddish
            vio . . . .   3·00   3·00
D1530   150r.on 12r. olive-grn & lt reddish
            vio   75   75
D1523/1530 *Set of 8* . . . .   11·00   11·00
Each sheet of stamps was surcharged with two different values
giving the listed *se-tenant* pairs

(Des Hardiyono)

1979 (26 Jan). *30th Anniv of Garuda Indonesian Airways. T* **306**
and similar horiz designs. Multicoloured. P 12½.
1531   40r. Type **306**   80   35
1532   75r. Douglas DC-9-30 over village . .   1·00   35
1533   100r. Douglas DC-10 over temple . . .   1·80   1·00

307 Thomas Cup   **308** *Paphiopedilum lowii*
and Badminton
Player

(Des Sanusi and Soeripto)

1979 (24 Feb). *Thomas Cup Badminton Championships,
Djakarta. T* **307** *and similar vert designs.* P 12½.
1534   40r. rosine and dull greenish blue . . .   50   50
1535   100r. orange-brown and rosine . . . .   1·00   80
        a. Perf 3 sides. Booklets (8.8.79) . .   1·00   80
1536   100r. orange-brown and rosine . . . .   1·00   80
        a. Perf 3 sides. Booklets (8.8.79) . .   1·00   80
Designs: No. 1535, Player on left side of net hitting shuttlecock;
1536, Player on right side of net.
Nos. 1535/6 were printed together in *se-tenant* pairs within the
sheet, each pair forming a composite design.
For booklet panes containing Nos. 1535/6 see Nos. 1514ab/ac.

(Des Y. Musbar)

1979 (22 Mar). *Orchids. T* **308** *and similar vert designs.
Multicoloured.* P 12½.
1537   60r. Type **308** . . . .   1·10   35
1538   100r. *Vanda limbata* . . . .   1·60   50
1539   125r. *Phalaenopsis gigantea* . . . .   2·40   80
MS1540 63 × 96 mm. As No. 1539 (sold at
175r.) . . . .   5·00   5·00
See also No. **MS**1548.

309 Family and   **310** Mrs R. A. Kartini **311**
Horses

(Des Sugiyanto)

1979 (1 Apr–Sept). *Third Five Year Development Plan. T* **309** *and
similar horiz designs.* P 12½.
1541   35r. drab and green   15   10
1542   60r. brown-olive and greenish blue . .   25   15
1543   100r. agate and greenish blue   50   15
1544   125r. red-brown and brown-olive . . .   65   25
1545   150r. bistre-yell, pale orge & rose-
            carm   80   25
        a. Perf 3 sides. Booklets (27.9.79) . .   80   25
        ab. Booklet pane. Nos. 1545a,
            1552a × 5 plus four labels (imperf
            at top) (27.9.79)) . . . . .   7·50
        ac. As ab. but labels imperf at foot . .   7·50
1541/1545 *Set of 5* . . . .   2·10   80
Designs:—60r. Pylon, dam and fields; 100r. School and clinic;
125r. Loading produce at factory; 150r. Delivering mail.

(Des Soeripto)

1979 (21 Apr). *Birth Centenary of Mrs. R. A Kartini (pioneer of women's rights).* P 12½.

1546	**310**	100r. olive-sepia and olive-green	80	40
		a. Horiz pair. Nos. 1546/7	1·60	
1547	**311**	100r. olive-green and olive-sepia	80	40

Nos. 1546/7 were issued together in horizontal *se-tenant* pairs within the sheet, each pair forming a composite design.

(Des Y. Musbar)

1979 (24 May). *"Asien-Philatelie '79" International Stamp Exhibition, Dortmund. Sheet* 96 × 119 *mm. Multicoloured.* P 12½.

MS1548	250r. Type **308**; 300r. As No. 1538 (sold at 650r.)	8·25	8·25

312 Bureau Emblem

313 Self-defence

(Des Soeripto)

1979 (25 May). *50th Anniv of International Bureau of Education.* P 12½.

1549	**312**	150r. new blue, blue & reddish lilac	1·10	40

(Des Wagiono and D. Mulyadi)

1979 (21 June–Sept). *Tenth South-East Asian Games, Djakarta.* T **313** *and similar horiz designs.* P 12½.

1550	60r. greenish yell, blk & yellowish grn		55	25
1551	125r. orange, bluish grey & dp ultram		90	40
1552	150r. lemon, black and deep carmine		1·30	65
	a. Perf 3 sides. Booklets (27.9.79)		1·40	75

Designs:—125r. Games emblem; 150r. Main stadium, Senayan. For booklet panes containing No. 1552a see Nos. 1545ab/ac.

314 Co-operation Emblem

315 National I.Y.C. Emblem

(Des Mahriajub)

1979 (12 July). *Co-operation Day.* P 12½.

1553	**314**	150r. multicoloured	1·00	35

(Des Soeripto and S. Sugiyanto)

1979 (4 Aug). *International Year of the Child.* T **315** *and similar vert design.* P 12½.

1554		60r. black and pale green	40	15
1555		150r. bright greenish blue and black	1·00	40

Design:—150r. International I.Y.C. emblem.

316 Exhibition Emblem

317 Drug Addict

1979 (20 Sept). *Third World Telecommunication Exhibition, Geneva.* P 12½.

1556	**316**	150r. grey, deep blue & red-orange	1·00	50

1979 (17 Oct). *"End Drug Abuse" Campaign.* P 12½.

1557	**317**	150r. black and rose	1·00	50

(Des Soeripto)

1979 (24 Nov). *Wildlife (3rd series). Horiz designs as* T **292**. *Multicoloured.* P 12½.

1558	60r.	Bottle-nosed dolphin (*Tursiops aduncus*)	1·10	65
1559	125r.	Irrawaddy dolphin (*Orcaella brevirostris*)	2·75	90
1560	150r.	Leatherback turtle (*Dermochelys coriacea*)	4·50	1·20
MS1561	96 × 64 mm. 200r. As No. 1560 (sold at 250r.)		8·25	8·25

318 Pinisi Sailing Ship

319 Riding the Rapids

(Des S. Sugiyanto)

1980 (12 Mar). *Djakarta–Amsterdam Spice Race.* T **318** *and similar designs.* P 12½.

1562	60r. blue	40	15
1563	125r. reddish brown	65	40
1564	150r. purple	1·50	40
MS1565	64 × 120 mm. 300r. reddish brown	4·50	4·50

Designs: *Horiz*—125, 300r. Schooner made of cloves. *Vert*—150r. Madurese sailing boat.
See also No. **MS**1578.

(Des Soeripto)

1980 (21 Mar). *Adventure Sports.* T **319** *and similar vert designs. Multicoloured.* P 13½ × 12 (60, 300r.) or 12½ × 13½ (others).

1566	60r.	Type **319**	50	15
1567	125r.	Mountaineering	90	50
1568	150r.	Hang-gliding	1·30	75
MS1569	62 × 76 mm. 300r. Type **319** (sold at 350r.)		4·50	4·50

320 Cigarettes and Heart

321 Artificial Flowers in Vase

(Des Y. Musbar)

1980 (15 Apr). *Anti-smoking Campaign.* P 12½.
1570 **320** 150r. flesh, black and salmon-
pink . . . . 1·00 40

(Des Y. Musbar)

1980 (21 Apr). *Second Flower Festival, Djakarta. T* **321** *and similar vert design. Multicoloured.* P 12½.
1571 125r. Type **321** . . . . . . 1·50 40
1572 150r. Artificial bouquet . . . 1·80 65
See also No. **MS**1579.

| **322** Conference Building and Globe | **323** Danau Poso Statue | **324** Discus Thrower |

(Des Subagiyanto)

1980 (24 Apr). *25th Anniv of First Asian–African Conference, Bandung.* P 12½ × 13½.
1573 **322** 150r. pale magenta and gold . . 1·00 40
MS1574 76 × 104 mm. **322** 300r. magenta and
gold (sold at 350r.) . . . . 4·50 4·50

(Des S. Sugiyanto)

1980 (2 May). *Prehistoric Monuments. T* **323** *and similar vert designs. Multicoloured.* P 12½.
1575 60r. Type **323** 65 25
1576 125r. Elephant stone, Pasemah Village,
South Sumatra 80 50
1577 150r. Taman Bali sarcophagus . . . . 1·30 65
See also No. **MS**1579.

(Des S. Sugiyanto (**MS**1578), Soeripto (**MS**1579))

1980 (6 May). *"London 1980" International Stamp Exhibition. Two sheets.* P 12½.
MS1578 120 × 63 mm. **318** 500r. bright blue
(sold at 550r.) . . . . . . 16·00 16·00
MS1579 120 × 150 mm. 100r. Type **321**; 100r.
As No. 1572; 200r. Type **323**; 200r. As
No. 1577; each × 2 (sold at 1300r.) . . . 6·50 6·50

(Des I. Maaruf)

1980 (18 May). *Olympics for the Disabled.* P 12½.
1580 **324** 75r. chocolate and orange-red . . 90 35

| **325** Draughtsman in Wheelchair | **326** President Suharto |

(Des Y. Musbar)

1980 (18 May). *30th Anniv of Disabled Veterans' Corps.* P 12½.
1581 **325** 100r. multicoloured 90 35

(Des H. Soeroso)

1980 (8 June)–**83.** P 13½ × 12½.
1581a **326** 10r. dp brn-ol & dull grn
(26.2.83) . . . . . 1·60 10
1582 12r.50 green & pale grn
(26.7.80) 35 10
1582a 25r. deep chestnut and salmon
(26.2.83) 50 10
1583 50r. greenish blue & pale turq-
grn 35 35
1583a 55r. dp carmine & vermilion
(7.83) 50 10
1584 75r. chestnut & pale olive-
yellow 75 15
1585 100r. blue, violet and pale
magenta (dated "1980") . 1·40 35
a. Dated "1981". Booklets
(15.11.81) . . . . . 1·30 35
ab. Booklet pane.
Nos. 1585a × 6, 1586a × 2
plus two labels
(15.11.81) . . . . . 7·75
1586 200r. chestnut and dull orange
(dated "1980") . . . 2·00 75
a. Dated "1981". Booklets
(15.11.81) . . . . . 2·20 95
1586b 300r. reddish violet, lilac and gold
(8.6.81) . . . . . 2·00 25
1586c 400r. greenish slate, salmon-pink
and gold (8.6.81) . . . 2·00 25
1581a/1586c Set of 10 (cheapest) . . . 10·00 2·25
See also Nos. 1830/4.

| **327** People and Map of Indonesia | **328** Ship laying Cable |

(Des A. Soelarso)

1980 (17 July). *Population Census.* P 12½.
1587 **327** 75r. new blue and carmine-
rose 40 15
1588 200r. blue and orange-yellow . . 1·00 40

(Des A. Soelarso)

1980 (8 Aug). *Inauguration of Singapore–Indonesia Submarine Cable.* P 12½.
1589 **328** 75r. yellowish grn, slate grn &
orge 55 15
1590 200r. new blue, dp blue &
vermilion . . . . . 1·00 50

| **329** Immigrants | **330** 50s. 1946 Stamp |

1980 (11 Aug). *Indonesian Immigration.* P 12½.
1591 **329** 12r.50 claret and yellow-olive . . 35 10

(Des Mahriajub)

1980 (17 Aug). *35th Anniv of Independence. T* **330** *and similar designs.* P 12½.
1592 75r. cream, black and orange-brown . . 50 35
1593 100r. cream, dp reddish purple &
gold . . . . . . 1·10 40
1594 200r. cream, bright rose and silver . . 1·50 65

Designs: *Horiz*—100r. 1946 15s. stamp. *Vert*—200r. 1946 15s. Freedom Fund stamp.

331 Map of A.O.P.U. Members

332 O.P.E.C. Emblem on Globe

(Des A. Soelarso)

1980 (10 Sept). *Tenth Anniv of Asian—Oceanic Postal Union Training School, Bangkok.* P 12½.
1595 **331** 200r. blue, pale blue & greenish
　　　bl . . . . 1·30　25

1980 (14 Sept). *20th Anniv of Organization of Petroleum Exporting Countries.* P 12½.
1596 **332** 200r. turq-grn, new bl &
　　　crimson . . . . 1·30　35

333 Service Members with Linked Arms

D **333a**

1980 (5 Oct). *35th Anniv of Armed Forces. T 333 and similar horiz design. Multicoloured.* P 13½ × 12½.
1597 75r. Indonesians hailing flag . . . . 75　25
1598 200r. Type **333** . . . . . 1·10　40

1980 (Oct). *POSTAGE DUE. Dated "1980".* P 13½ × 12½.
D1599 D **268** 25r. deep mauve & pale
　　　　drab . . . . . . 15　15
D1600 D **333a** 50r. slate-green & bright
　　　　lilac . . . . . 40　40
D1601 75r. maroon and carmine-
　　　　rose . . . . . 65　65
D1602 D **268** 125r. deep mauve & rose-
　　　　pink . . . . 1·00　75
D1599/1602 *Set of 4* . . . . 2·00　1·75
　See also Nos. D1641/5, D1728/31, D1772/4 and D1912/15.

334 Pesquet's Parrot (*Psittrichas fulgidus*)

335 *Dendrobium insigne*

(Des Soeripto)

1980 (25 Nov). *Parrots. T 334 and similar horiz designs. Multicoloured.* P 12½.
1599 75r. Type **334** . . . . . 2·40　75
1600 100r. Chattering lory (*Lorius garrula*) . . 2·40　1·50
1601 200r. Rainbow lory (*Trichoglossus haematodus rubritorquis*) . . 4·00　2·10
MS1602 95 × 120 mm. 250r. As No. 1601; 350r.
　Type **334**; 400r. As No. 1600 . . . . . 24·00　24·00

(Des S. Sugiyanto)

1980 (10 Dec). *Orchids. T 335 and similar vert designs. Multicoloured.* P 12½ × 13½.
1603 75r. Type **335** . . . . . 1·10　15
1604 100r. *Dendrobium discolor* . . . . . 1·80　90
1605 200r. *Dendrobium lasianthera* . . . 3·50　65
MS1606 74 × 104 mm. 250r. As No. 1604; 350r.
　As No. 1605 . . . . 16·00　16·00

336 Von Stephan and U.P.U. Emblem

1981 (7 Jan). *150th Birth Anniv of Heinrich von Stephan (founder of Universal Postal Union).* P 13½ × 12½.
1607 **336** 200r. bright new blue and deep
　　　blue . . . . 1·30　65

337 Jamboree and Scouting Emblems

338 Ship (relief carving)

(Des C. H. Joeda (100r.), T. Gany (others))

1981 (22 Feb–Aug). *Sixth Asia–Pacific Scout Jamboree, Cibubur. T 337 and similar multicoloured designs.* P 13 × 13½ (100r.) or 13½ × 13 (others).
1608 75r. Type **337** . . . . . 40　35
1609 100r. Scout and guide map-reading
　　　(*vert*) . . . . . 1·10　35
1610 200r. Jamboree emblem and tents . . . 1·30　75
MS1611 77 × 63 mm. 150r. As No. 1609
　(14.8) . . . . 1·60　1·60

(Des Wagiono)

1981 (18 Mar). *Fifth Asian–Oceanic Postal Union Congress, Yogyakarta.* P 12½.
1612 **338** 200r. turquoise-blue, black & new
　　　bl . . . . 1·50　35

339 Child holding Blood Drop

340 Monuments

(Des S. Tjendana, D. Arianto and E. Bastian)

1981 (22 Apr). *Blood Donors. T 339 and similar vert designs.* P 12½.
1613 75r. new blue, black and bright
　　　scarlet . . . . . 50　15
1614 100r. bright scarlet and deep grey . . 75　35
1615 200r. bright scarlet, grey-blue and
　　　cobalt . . . . . 1·10　65
　Designs:—100r. Hands holding blood drop; 200r. Hands and blood drop.

(Des Subagiyanto)

1981 (26 Apr). *International Family Planning Conference.* P 12½.
1616 **340** 200r. light blue, brown and new
blue . . . . 1·00 40

341 "Song of Sritanjung"

342 Secretariat Building and Emblem

(Des Wagiono)

1981 (2 May). *Traditional Balinese Paintings.* T **341** and similar horiz design. Multicoloured. P 12½.
1617 100r. Type **341** . . . . 1·10 35
a. Vert pair. Nos. 1617/18 . . 2·20
1618 200r. "Song of Sritanjung" (*different*) . 1·60 75
MS1619 96 × 96 mm. 400r. and 600r. "Birth of
the Eagle" . . . . 10·50 10·50
Nos. 1617/18 were issued together in vertical *se-tenant* pairs within the sheet, each pair forming a composite design.
No. **MS**1619 bears the "Wipa 1981" International Stamp Exhibition logo, it also exists with an additional marginal inscription "Indonesian grüsst WIPA".

(Des C. Abdi and A. Soelarso)

1981 (9 May). *Inauguration of Association of South-East Asian Nations Secretariat, Djakarta.* P 12½.
1620 **342** 200r. yellow, yellow-orange &
maroon . . . . 1·50 50

343 Uber Cup

344 "Tree of Life" (relief from Candi Mendut)

(Des Soeripto)

1981 (22 May). *International Ladies' Badminton Championship, Tokyo.* P 12½.
1621 **343** 200r. sepia, greenish yell & orge-
verm . . . . 2·40 50

(Des M. Djajadiningrat)

1981 (5 June). *World Environment Day.* T **344** and similar horiz design. P 12½.
1622 75r. olive-bistre, slate and black . . . 75 15
1623 200r. olive-bistre, slate and black . . . 1·20 35
Design:—200r. "Yaksha Apacaka".

345 Students reading Koran, Mosque and Emblem

346 Blind Man

(Des Subagiyanto)

1981 (7 June). *12th National Koran Reading Contest, Banda Aceh.* P 13½ × 12½.
1624 **345** 200r. black, dull scarlet & bistre-
yell . . . . 1·00 50

(Des Y. Musbar)

1981 (31 July). *International Year of Disabled Persons.* T **346** and similar horiz design. P 12½.
1625 75r. purple-brn, greenish yell &
bistre 40 15
1626 200r. new blue, purple-brown & lt
green . . . . 1·00 50
Design:—200r. Deaf and dumb person.

347 Soekarno-Hatta Monument, Djakarta

348 Parachute Jumping

(Des Y. Musbar)

1981 (17 Aug). *Independence Monument.* P 12½.
1627 **347** 200r. slate-blue, greenish yell &
gold . . . . 1·50 40

(Des. A. Soelarso)

1981 (19 Sept). *National Sports Week, Djakarta.* T **348** and similar designs. P 12½.
1628 75r. scarlet, black and blue 40 15
1629 100r. black, blue and scarlet 65 65
1630 200r. dp reddish brown, dull grn &
scar . . . . 1·30 50
See also No. **MS**1907.
Designs. *Horiz*—100r. Scuba diving. *Vert*—200r. Horse riding.

349 Food Produce

350 Arms of Aceh Special Territory

(Des Soegiarto and S. Sugiyanto)

1981 (16 Oct). *World Food Day.* P 12½.
1631 **349** 200r. multicoloured . . . . 2·40 75

(Des Subagiyanto (Nos. 1632, 1634, 1636), Mahriajub (1633, 1635))

1981 (28 Oct–Dec). *Provincial Arms.* T **350** and similar horiz designs. P 12½.
1632 100r. yellow, emerald and gold . . . 2·40 75
1633 100r. multicoloured (28.11) . . . . 2·40 75
1634 100r. multicoloured (28.11) . . . . 2·40 75
1635 100r. multicoloured (28.12) . . . . 3·25 1·80
1636 100r. multicoloured (28.12) . . . . 10·50 90
1632/1636 *Set of 5* . . . . 19·00 4·25
Designs:—No. 1633, Bali; 1634, Bengkulu; 1635, Irian Jaya; 1636, Djakarta.
See also Nos. 1641/62 and No. 1710.

351 Salmon-crested Cockatoo (*Cacatua molyccensis*)

352 Hands enclosing Family

(Des Soeripto)

1981 (10 Dec). *Cockatoos. T* **351** *and similar vert designs. Multicoloured.* P 12½.

1637	75r. Type **351**	3·75	80
1638	100r. Sulphur-crested cockatoo (*Cacatua galerita galerita*)	4·00	80
1639	200r. Palm cockatoo (*Probosciger aterrimus stenolophus*)	6·50	3·00
MS1640	73 × 64 mm. 150r. As No. 1638; 350r. As No. 1639	18·00	18·00

1981. *POSTAGE DUE. Dated "1981".* P 13½ × 12½.

D1641	D **333a**	25r. purple and stone	15	15
D1642		50r. slate-green and bright lilac	35	35
D1643		75r. maroon and carmine-rose	50	50
D1644		125r. dp reddish our & yell-grn	1·00	1·00
D1641/1644 *Set of 4*			4·00	1·80

1982. *POSTAGE DUE. Dated "1982".* P 13½ × 12½.

D1645	D **333a**	125r. purple and rose-pink	25	15

(Des S. Sugiyanto (Nos. 1641, 1643/4, 1654), Subagiyanto (others))

1982 (28 Jan)–**83**. *Provincial Arms. Horiz designs as T* **350**. *Multicoloured.* P 12½.

1641	100r. Jambi	1·10	50
1642	100r. Java Barat (West)	1·10	50
1643	100r. Java Tengah (Central) (28.2)	1·10	50
1644	100r. Java Timur (East) (28.2)	1·10	50
1645	100r. Kalimantan Barat (West) (28.3)	1·10	50
1646	100r. Kalimantan Selatan (South) (28.3)	1·10	50
1647	100r. Kalimantan Timur (East) (28.3)	1·10	50
1648	100r. Kalimantan Tengah (Central) (28.4)	1·10	50
1649	100r. Lampung (28.4)	1·10	50
1650	100r. Moluccas (28.4)	75	50
1651	100r. Nusa Tenggara Barat (West) (28.5)	75	15
1652	100r. Nusa Tenggara Timur (East) (28.5)	75	15
1653	100r. Riau (28.9)	75	25
1654	100r. Sulawesi Tengah (Central Celebes) (28.6)	75	15
1655	100r. Sulawesi Tenggara (South-east Celebes) (28.6)	75	15
1656	100r. Sulawesi Selatan (South Celebes) (28.9)	75	25
1657	100r. Sulawesi Utara (North Celebes) (28.7)	90	15
1658	100r. Sumatera Barat (West) (28.7)	90	15
1659	100r. Sumatera Selatan (South) (28.8)	75	15
1660	100r. Sumatera Utara (North) (28.8)	75	15
1661	100r. Yogyakarta (28.10)	1·80	15
1662	250r. Republic of Indonesia (45 × 29 mm) (17.8)	1·00	35
1641/1662 *Set of 22*		18·00	6·50

(Des Soeprapto)

1982 (12 Feb). *70th Anniv of Bumiputera Mutual Life Insurance Company. T* **352** *and similar horiz designs.* P 12½.

1663	75r. yellow, plum and bright purple	40	15
1664	100r. yellow, bright green & grey-green	80	35
1665	200r. multicoloured	1·10	55

Designs:—100r. Family in countryside; 200r. Hands supporting industrial activities.

353 Helicopter Rescue

354 Houses and Ballot Boxes

(Des Subagiyanto)

1982 (28 Feb). *Tenth Anniv of Search and Rescue Institute.* P 13 × 13½.

1666	**353**	250r. multicoloured	1·50	35

(Des Soeripto and Bambang Tri Djaja)

1982 (1 Mar). *General Election. T* **354** *and similar horiz designs. Multicoloured.* P 12½.

1667	75r. Type **354**	40	15
1668	100r. Rural houses and ballot boxes	65	25
1669	200r. Houses and national arms	1·50	65

355 Human Figures, Satellite and Dove

356 Thomas Cup

(Des Soeripto)

1982 (19 Apr). *Second United Nations Conference on Exploration and Peaceful Uses of Outer Space, Vienna. T* **355** *and similar vert design.* P 12½ × 13½.

1670	150r. blue, bright reddish violet & black	75	40
1671	250r. myrtle green, yellowish green and deep blue-green	1·30	65

Design:—250r. Peace dove and text.

(Des Subagiyanto)

1982 (19 May–June). *Thomas Cup Badminton Championship, London.* P 12½.

1672	**356** 250r. multicoloured	1·80	50
MS1673	72 × 95 mm. No. 1672 × 2 (11.6)	45·00	45·00

No. **MS**1673 bears the "Philexfrance 82" International Stamp Exhibition emblem in the margin. This sheet also exists with the stamps overprinted "INDONESIE SALUE PHILEXFRANCE" in black or red.

357 Footballers

358 Taman Siswa Emblem

(Des Trisna)

1982 (14 June). *World Cup Football Championship, Spain.* P 12½.
1674	**357**	250r. multicoloured		1·80	50
MS1675 96 × 72 mm. No. 1674 × 2				70·00	70·00

(Des A. Soelarso)

1982 (3 July). *60th Anniv of Taman Siswa (educational organization).* P 12½.
1676	**358**	250r. pale yellow, emerald & carmine	1·00	35

359 Flags forming "15"

360 President Suharto

(Des I. Tirtawidjaja)

1982 (8 Aug). *15th Anniv of Association of South-East Asian Nations.* P 12½.
1677	**359**	150r. salmon, vermilion and blue	1·60	50

(Des H. Soeroso)

1982 (17 Sept)–83. P 12½.
1678	**360**	110r. lake and salmon (27.9.83)	40	15
1679		250r. reddish brown and pale orange	80	15
1680		275r. myrtle green & ol-yell (27.9.83)	1·30	15

ITALIA WORLD CHAMPION
(361)

362 Rothschild's Mynah (*Leucopsar rotschildi*)

1982 (24 Sept). *World Cup Football Championship Result. No.* **MS**1675 optd with T **361** in red or black.
MS1681 96 × 72 mm. 250r. × 2, multicoloured		70·00	70·00

(Des Soeripto)

1982 (11 Oct). *Third World National Parks Congress, Bali.* T **362** and similar vert designs. Multicoloured. P 12½ × 13½.
1682		100r. Type **362**	3·25	40
1683		250r. King bird of paradise (*Cincinnurus regius*)	5·00	1·20
MS1684 76 × 104 mm. 500r. Type **362**			14·00	14·00

363 River Bridge

364 Arfak Parotia (*Parotia sefilata*)

(Des S. Sugiyanto)

1982 (29 Nov). *Five Year Plan.* P 12½.
1685	**363**	17r.50 chocolate & yellowish green	50	10

(Des Soeripto)

1982 (20 Dec). *Birds of Paradise.* T **364** and similar vert designs. Multicoloured. P 12½ × 13½.
1686		100r. Type **364**	2·00	40
1687		150r. Twelve-wired bird of paradise (*Seleucides melanoleuca*)	3·25	80
1688		250r. Red bird of paradise (*Paradisea rubra*)	5·00	1·20
MS1689 76 × 105 mm. 200r. Type **364**; 300r. As No. 1688			20·00	20·00

365 Scouts and Anniversary Emblem

366 Temple Restoration and Relief

(Des A. Soelarso)

1983 (22 Feb). *75th Anniv of Boy Scout Movement.* P 13½ × 12½.
1690	**365**	250r. new blue, emerald & bluish violet	1·60	35

(Des N. Tjahaja (100r.), B. Trisyanto (150r.), Z. Abidin (250, 500r.))

1983 (23 Feb). *Borobudur Temple.* T **366** and similar designs. P 12½.
1691		100r. blackish green, bright blue & lt bl	1·60	50
1692		150r. apple green, deep green & red-brn	1·60	50
1693		250r. brownish black, ol-brn & orge-brn	5·25	2·75
MS1694 96 × 64 mm. 500r. multicoloured			16·00	16·00

Designs: *Vert*—150r. Temple and statue. *Horiz*—250, 500r. Silhouette of Temple and seated Buddha.

367 President Suharto   **368** Gas Storage Tanks

(Des Soenardi. Recess)

1983 (11 Mar). P 12½ × 13.
1695 **367** 500r. purple-brown . . . . 1·40   35

(Des Pramono)

1983 (16 May). *Seventh International Liquified Natural Gas Conference, Djakarta.* P 12½.
1696 **368** 275r. multicoloured . . . . . . 1·40   35

369 Ships and Bird   **370** Man and Woman reading Koran

(Des I. Tittaatmadja, E. Bastian and G. Wismatya)

1983 (17 May). *World Communications Year. T* **369** *and similar vert designs.* P 13 × 13½.
1697   75r. multicoloured   25   15
1698   110r. multicoloured   50   25
1699   175r. bright rose-red and new blue . . .   80   40
1700   275r. turquoise-blue, dp turq-blue &
         scar . . . . 1·20   65
1697/1700 *Set of 4* . . . . 2·50 1·30
Designs:—110r. Satellite and receiving station; 175r. Airplane and dish aerial; 275r. Globe and letter.
See also Nos. **MS**1716 and **MS**1720.

(Des Subagiyanto)

1983 (23 May). *13th National Koran Reading Competition, Padang.* P 13½ × 12½.
1701 **370** 275r. bistre-yellow, green and
         black . . . . 1·20   55

371 Eclipse and Map of Indonesia   **372** Satellite transmitting to Indonesia

(Des A. Soelarso)

1983 (11 June). *Total Solar Eclipse. T* **321** *and similar horiz design.* P 12½.
1702   110r. brown-ochre, deep brown &
         black   65   25
1703   275r. greenish blue, slate-vio & brn-
         pur . . . . 2·00   40
MS1704 96 × 64 mm. 500r. greenish blue, slate-
         violet and brown-purple . . . . . 14·00 14·00
Design:—275, 500r. Map of Indonesia showing path of eclipse.

(Des A. Soelarso)

1983 (18 June). *Launching of "Palapa B" Communications Satellite.* P 12½ × 13½.
1705 **372** 275r. turquoise-green, dp bl &
         silver . . . . 1·20   55

373 Patient receiving Radiation Treatment   **374** Agricultural Produce

(Des Soeripto)

1983 (1 July). *Anti-cancer Campaign.* P 12½.
1706 **373** 55r.+20r. multicoloured   65   40
1707   75r.+25r. multicoloured . . . . . 1·10   40

(Des S. Sugiyanto)

1983 (17 July). *Agricutural Census. T* **374** *and similar horiz design.* P 12½.
1708   110r. grey, bright green and black . . .   65   15
1709   275r. red, black and bright green . . . 1·10   25
Design:—275r. Farmer with produce.

1983 (28 July). *Provincial Arms. Horiz design as T* **350**. *Multicoloured.* P 12½.
1710   100r. Timor Timur . . . . 1·80   15

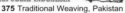

375 Traditional Weaving, Pakistan   **376** Eruption of Krakatoa

(Des Subagiyanto)

1983 (19 Aug). *Indonesia–Pakistan Economic and Cultural Co-operation. T* **375** *and similar horiz design. Multicoloured.* P 12½.
1711   275r. Type **375** . . . . 1·60   75
1712   275r. Traditional weaving, Indonesia . . 1·60   75

(Des Subagiyanto)

1983 (26 Aug). *Centenary of Krakatoa Volcanic Eruption. T* **376** *and similar horiz design. Multicoloured.* P 12½.
1713   110r. Type **376**   50   25
1714   275r. Map showing position of
         Krakatoa . . . . 1·60   40

377 Casa-Nurtanio CN-235 PK-NZG
Airliner

(Des A. Soelarso)

1983 (10 Sept). *Indonesian Aircraft.* P 12½.
1715 **377** 275r. multicoloured . . . . . . 1·20 55

1983 (29 Sept). *World Communications Year. Opening of Philatelic Museum, Djakarta.* Sheet 51 × 84 *mm.* P 12½ × 13½.
MS1716 500r. As No. 1700 . . . . 7·00 7·00

378 Tiger Barb (*Puntius tetrazona*)

379 Wilson's Bird of
Paradise (*Diphyllodes
respublica*)

(Des Y. Musbar)

1983 (17 Oct). *Tropical Fishes. T* **378** *and similar horiz designs. Multicoloured.* P 12½.
1717 110r. Type **378** . . . . 2·00 65
1718 175r. Brilliant rasbora (*Rasbora
einthoveni*) . . . . 2·00 65
1719 275r. Archerfish (*Toxotes jaculator*) . . . 6·00 2·00

1983 (26 Oct). *"Telecom 83" Exhibition, Geneva.* Sheet 75 × 83 *mm. Multicoloured.* P 13 × 13½.
MS1720 400r. As No. 1698 . . . . 8·25 8·25

(Des Soeripto)

1983 (25 Nov). *Birds of Paradise. T* **379** *and similar vert designs. Multicoloured.* P 12½.
1721 110r. Type **379** . . . . 1·60 40
1722 175r. Black sicklebill (*Epimachus
fastuosus*) . . . . 2·40 50
1723 275r. Black-billed sicklebill (*Drepanornis
albertisi*) . . . . 3·75 1·10
1724 500r. As No. 1723 . . . . 5·75 3·00
1721/1724 *Set of 4* . . . . 12·00 4·50
MS1725 64 × 95 mm. No. 1724 . . . . . 20·00 20·00

380 Emblems of Peace and Co-
operation

381 "Stop"
Emblem

(Des I. Soeroto)

1983 (20 Dec). *Palestinian Solidarity.* P 13½ × 13.
1726 **380** 275r. blue, ochre and silver . . . 1·40 35

1983. *POSTAGE DUE. Dated "1983".* P 13½ × 12½.
D1728 D **333a** 200r. deep lilac and light
blue 50 15
D1729 300r. slate-grn & greenish
yell 50 15
D1730 400r. deep olive and buff . . . 75 35
D1731 500r. sepia and flesh . . . . 1·00 50
D1728/1731 *Set of 4* . . . . 2·50 1·00

(Des A. Soelarso)

1984 (17 Feb). *Anti-poliomyelitis Campaign. T* **381** *and similar vert design.* P 12½.
1732 110r. brown-lake, purple and bright
blue 40 15
1733 275r. purple, reddish orange & brt
scar . . . . 1·40 35
Design:—275r. Save the Children Fund emblem.

382 Agriculture

383 Manufacturing
Plywood

(Des A. Soelarso and M. Nurasyid)

1984 (1 Apr). *Fourth Five Year Plan. T* **382** *and similar horiz designs.* P 12½.
1734 55r. olive-yellow and turquoise-blue . . 15 10
1735 75r. dp turquoise-green & yellow-
brown 25 15
1736 110r. new blue and pale orange . . . 40 25
1737 275r. multicoloured . . . . . . 1·10 65
1734/1737 *Set of 4* . . . . 1·70 1·00
Designs:—75r. Casa-Nurtiano CN-235 airliner (aircraft industry);
110r. Shipbuilding; 275r. Telephone (telecommunications).

(Des Subagiyanto and S. Talahatu)

1984 (17 May). *Forestry. T* **383** *and similar vert designs. Multicoloured.* P 12½.
1738 75r. Type **383** . . . . 1·10 15
1739 110r. Seedling . . . . 1·10 15
1740 175r. Measuring tree trunk . . . . 1·10 40
1741 275r. Transporting trees . . . . . 1·10 55
1738/1741 *Set of 4* . . . . 4·00 1·10
MS1742 96 × 80 mm. Nos. 1740/1 . . . . 12·00 12·00

384 Children playing with Toys

1984 (17 June). *Children's Day. T* **384** *and similar horiz designs. Multicoloured.* P 13½ × 13.
1743 75r.+25r. Type **384** . . . . . . 1·10 15
1744 110r.+25r. Scout camp 65 25

1745	175r.+25r. Children on farm	1·60	40
1746	275r.+25r. Scouts and guides in camp	1·60	50
1743/1746	*Set of 4*	4·50	1·10

See also No. **MS**1760.

385 Flags of Member Nations   **386** Pole Vaulting

(Des S. Talahatu)

1984 (9 July). *Association of South-East Asian Nations Meeting, Djakarta.* P 12½.

1747	**385**	275r. multicoloured	1·80	55

1984 (28 July). *Olympic Games, Los Angeles.* T **386** *and similar horiz designs. Multicoloured.* P 12½.

1748	75r. Type **386**		50	15
1749	110r. Archery		50	15
1750	175r. Boxing		50	15
1751	250r. Shooting		1·60	50
1752	275r. Weightlifting		2·00	50
1753	325r. Swimming		3·50	25
1748/1753	*Set of 6*		7·75	1·50

387 Horse Dance   **388** Thomas Cup (badminton)

1984 (17 Aug). *Art and Culture.* T **387** *and similar vert designs. Multicoloured.* P 13 × 13½.

1754	75r. Type **387**		80	15
1755	110r. "Reyog" mask		1·20	25
1756	275r. Lion dance		1·20	65
1757	325r. "Barong" mask		2·75	65
1754/1757	*Set of 4*		5·25	1·50

See also No. **MS**1761.

1984 (9 Sept). *National Sports Day.* T **388** *and similar horiz design. Multicoloured.* P 13½ × 13.

1758	110r. Type **388**		80	25
1759	275r. Keep-fit exercise		1·60	40

1984 (9 Sept). *"Filacento" International Stamp Exhibition, The Hague. Two sheets.*
MS1760 101 × 101 mm. No. 1746 × 4 plus two labels. P 14½ × 12½   18·00   18·00
MS1761 73 × 64 mm. No. 1757 plus label.
    P12½ × 13½   45·00   45·00

1984 (21 Sept). *"Ausipex 84" International Stamp Exhibition, Melbourne, Sheet* 101 × 76 mm. P 13½ × 13.
MS1762 Nos. 1745/6   29·00   29·00

389 Map and Post Code Zones   **390** Lauterbach's Bowerbird (*Chlamydera lauterbachi*)

(Des A. Soelarso)

1984 (27 Sept). *Introduction of New Post Code Zones.* P 12½.

1763	**389**	110r. pale blue, lt brown & brt orge	50	25
1764		275r. brt orange, greenish bl & lt brn	1·10	65

(Des Soeroso)

1984 (15 Oct). *Birds.* T **390** *and similar vert designs. Multicoloured.* P 12½ × 13½.

1765	75r. Type **390**	2·75	35
1766	110r. Flamed bowerbird (*Sericulus aureus*)	4·00	65
1767	275r. Arfak bird of paradise (*Astrapia nigra*)	5·25	2·40
1768	325r. Superb bird of paradise (*Lophorhina superba*)	5·25	1·60
1765/1768	*Set of 4*	15·00	4·50
MS1769	76 × 105 mm. Nos. 1765 and 1768	26·00	26·00

No. **MS**1769 is inscribed for "Philakorea 1984" International Stamp Exhibition.

391 Flag and Fists   **392** Boeing 747-200

(Des Subagiyanto)

1984 (28 Oct). *Youth Pledge.* P 12½.

1770	**391**	275r. black and rosine	1·10	75

(Des M. Nurasyid)

1984 (7 Dec). *40th Anniv of International Civil Aviation Organization.* P 13½ × 12½.

1771	**392**	275r. red, black and blue	1·20	75

1984. *POSTAGE DUE. Dated "1984".* P 14½ × 13 (25r.) or 13½ × 12½ (others).

D1772	D **333a**	25r. purple and stone	75	25
D1773		50r. slate-green and reddish lilac	75	35
D1774		500r. sepia and cinnamon	7·75	1·00

FLUORESCENT SECURITY MARKINGS. These consist of the Indonesian Postal Service emblem (bird on globe within pentagon) repeated several times.

393 *Tyro*
(oceanographic
survey ship) and
Geological Structure
of Seabed

394 Stylized Birds

397 Conference Building

398 Globe and
Teenagers waving
Palm Leaves

(Des Soeripto, S. Talahatu and M. Nurasyid)

1985 (27 Feb). *Indonesia–Belanda Expedition. T* **393** *and similar vert designs. Fluorescent security markings.* P 12½ × 13½.
1772	50r. blue and chestnut		65	15
1773	100r. blue and purple		1·10	15
1774	275r. blue and deep turquoise-green		1·20	35

Designs:—100r. *Tyro* and map; 275r. *Tyro* and coral reef.

(Des M. Nurasyid and I. Soeroto)

1985 (8 Mar). *International Women's Day. T* **394** *and similar vert design. Fluorescent security markings.* P 12½ × 13½.
1775	100r. deep mauve and carmine-vermilion		2·00	65
1776	275r. rosine and yellow-brown		3·00	3·00

Design:—275r. Profile silhouettes.

(Des. A. Soelarso)

1985 (24 Apr). *30th Anniv of First Asian–African Conference, Bandung. Fluorescent security markings.* P 12½.
1786	**397**	350r. multicoloured	1·60	50

(Des S. Sugiyanto (75r.), S. Talahatu (140r.))

1985 (12 July). *International Youth Year. T* **398** *and similar vert design. Fluorescent security markings.* P 12½ × 13½.
1787	75r. orange-yellow, red-brown & bl-grn		55	15
1788	140r. cobalt, light green and deep mauve		1·40	15

Design:—140r. Flower on globe supported by teenagers.

395 Jet Airliner and Workers

396 President
Suharto

(Des Soeripto, S. Talahatu and M. Nurasyid)

1985 (1 Apr). *Fourth Five Year Plan. T* **395** *and similar horiz designs. Fluorescent security markings.* P 13½ × 12½.
1777	75r. red and bistre-brown		35	15
1778	140r. greenish grey and reddish brown		55	40
1779	350r. turquoise-green and bistre-brown		1·50	1·00

Designs:—140r. Children in classroom; 350r. Industrial equipment and buildings.

399 Profiles

400 Housing and
Hydro-electricity

(Des T. Margono and M. Nurasyid)

1985 (26 July). *United Nations Women's Decade. T* **399** *and similar vert design. Fluorescent security markings.* P 12½ × 13½.
1789	55r. yellow-brown & dull yellowish grn		50	25
1790	140r. black, emerald and chestnut		80	25

Design:—140r. Globe and decade emblems.

(Des I. Soeroto and T. Margono)

1985 (1 Aug). *40th Anniv of Indonesian Republic. T* **400** *and similar vert design. Fluorescent security markings.* P 12½ × 13½ (140r.) or 12½ × 14½ (350r.).
1791	140r. deep turquoise-green and vermilion		55	15
1792	350r. blue, magenta and greenish yellow		1·50	35

Design:—350r. Tractor and industrial complex.

1985 (10 Apr). *Fluorescent security markings.* P 12½.
1780	**396**	140r. deep brown and red	65	15
1781		350r. deep bright mauve & vermilion	1·50	15

Nos. 1782/5 *are vacant.*

401 Sky Diving

402 O.P.E.C.
Emblem and
Globe

(Des M. Soeroso (55r.), S. Talahatu (100r.), A. Soelarso (140r.), M. Faisol (350r.))

1985 (9 Sept). *National Sports Week, Djakarta. T* **401** *and similar multicoloured designs. Fluorescent security markings.* P 12½ × 13½ (350r.) or 13½ × 12½ (others).

1793	55r. Type **401**		35	10
1794	100r. Unarmed combat		80	15
1795	140r. High jumping		80	25
1796	350r. Windsurfing (*vert*)		1·30	50
1793/1796 *Set of* 4			3·00	90

(Des S. Sugiyanto)

1985 (14 Sept). *25th Anniv of Organization of Petroleum Exporting Countries. Fluorescent security markings.* P 12½.

1797	**402**	140r. blue, dp mauve & yellow-orange	1·00	25

403 Tanker

404 Doves, "40" and U.N. Emblem

(Des S. Talahatu (140r.), T. Margono (250r.), I. Soeroto (350r.))

1985 (8 Oct). *Centenary of Indonesian Oil Industry. T* **403** *and similar horiz designs. Multicoloured. Fluorescent security markings.* P 13½ × 12½.

1798	140r. Type **403**		50	25
1799	250r. Refinery		90	40
1800	350r. Derrick and rigs		1·30	80

(Des F. Mustofa (140r.), M. Nurasyid (300r.))

1985 (24 Oct). *40th Anniv of United Nations Organization. T* **404** *and similar vert design. Multicoloured. Fluorescent security markings.* P 12½.

1801	140r. Type **404**		50	15
1802	300r. Bombs and green leaves		1·10	40

405 Javan Rhinoceros (*Rhinoceros sondaicus*)

406 Emblem

(Des F. Mustofa and H. Purnomo)

1985 (27 Dec). *Wildlife. T* **405** *and similar horiz designs. Fluorescent security markings.* P 13½ × 12½ (300r.) or 14½ × 13 (others).

1803	75r. bistre-brown, yellow-green & blue		1·00	25
1804	150r. yellow-brown, salmon & olive-grn		1·30	40
1805	300r. cinnamon, light blue & brt crimson		2·50	65

Designs:—150r. Anoa (*Anoa depressicornis*); 300r. Komodo dragon (*Varanus komodoensis*).

(Des A. Soelarso and S. Talahatu)

1986 (8 Feb). *Economic Census. T* **406** *and similar vert design, each yellow-orange and reddish violet. Fluorescent security markings.* P 12½.

1806	175r. Type **406**		65	25
	a. Horiz pair. Nos. 1806/7		1·30	
1807	175r. Symbols of economy		65	25

Nos. 1806/7 were issued together in horizontal *se-tenant* pairs within the sheet.

407 Baby feeding, Powdered Milk, Syringe and Graph

408 Industry

(Des S. Talahatu)

1986 (15 Mar). *40th Anniv of United Nations Children's Fund. T* **407** *and similar horiz design. Fluorescent security markings.* P 12½.

1808	75r. multicoloured		55	15
1809	140r. flesh, deep brown and rose-pink		90	25

Design:—140r. Vaccinating baby.

(Des H. Soeroso and A. Soelarso)

1986 (1 Apr). *Fourth Five Year Plan. T* **408** *and similar horiz design, Fluorescent security markings.* P 12½.

1810	140r. multicoloured		50	15
1811	500r. lemon, chestnut and new blue		50	15

Design:—500r. Agriculture.

409 Thomas Cup and Racket

410 Pinisi Sailing Ship

(Des I. Soeroto)

1986 (22 Apr). *Thomas (men's) and Uber (women's) Cup Badminton Championships, Djakarta. T* **409** *and similar design. Fluorescent security markings.* P 12½.

1812	55r. black, chrome-yellow & greenish bl		65	25
1813	150r. vermilion, agate and gold		1·10	25

Design: *Horiz*—150r. Thomas and Uber Cups and shuttlecock.

(Des Priyanto)

1986 (2 May). *"Expo 86" World's Fair, Vancouver. T* **410** *and similar vert designs. Fluorescent security markings.* P 12½ × 13½ (150r.) or 12½ × 14½ (others).

1814	75r. black, vermilion & greenish yellow		50	15
1815	150r. multicoloured		1·00	25
1816	300r. silver, orange-vermilion & brt purple		1·50	35

Designs:—150r. Kentongan village drum and "Palapa" satellite; 300r. Indonesian pavilion emblem.

411 Guides on Parade

(Des H. Purnomo, S. Talahatu and M. Desmal)

1986 (21 June). *National Jamboree. T **411** and similar multicoloured designs. Fluorescent security markings.* P 12½ × 13½ (210r.) or 13½ × 12½ (others).

1817	100r. Type **411**	35	15
1818	140r. Guides cooking over fire	1·30	35
1819	210r. Scouts consulting map (*vert*)	1·60	55

412 "86"

(Des S. Sugiyanto)

1986 (23 June). *Indonesia Air Show. Fluorescent security markings.* P 13½ × 12½.

1820	**412** 350r. multicoloured	1·30	65

413 Tari Legong Kraton

414 Woman planting

(Des I. Soeroto, H. Purnomo and M. Nurasyid)

1986 (30 July). *Traditional Dances. T **413** and similar horiz designs. Fluorescent security markings.* P 12½.

1821	140r. Type **413**	1·30	15
1822	350r. Tari Barong	2·10	50
1823	500r. Tari Kecak	3·00	55

(Des S. Sugiyanto)

1986 (25 Aug). *19th International Society of Sugar Cane Technologists Congress, Djakarta. T **414** and similar vert design. Multicoloured. Fluorescent security markings.* P 12½ × 13½.

1824	150r. Type **414**	55	15
1825	300r. Cane and sugar spilled from sack	1·40	25

415 Route Map of Cable

416 Doves, Wheat and Globe

(Des H. Purnomo and T. Margono)

1986 (8 Sept). *Opening of Sea-Me-We Communications Cable. T **415** and similar horiz design. Fluorescent security markings.* P 12½.

1826	140r. dp bluish green, brt orange & violet	55	25
1827	350r. blue-green, orge-yell & dull ultram	1·40	55

Design:—350r. Route map of cable (*different*).

(Des M. Faisol and Triyadi)

1986 (17 Dec). *International Peace Year. T **416** and similar vert design, each brown-ochre, blue-green and brownish black. Fluorescent security markings.* P 12½.

1828	350r. Type **416**	1·10	40
1829	500r. Dove with olive twig flying around globe	1·50	15

1986 (29 Dec)–**87**. *Fluorescent security markings.* P 13½ × 12½.

1830	**326**	50r. deep brown and light brown	15	10
1831		55r. carmine and rose-pink (21.6.87)	35	10
1832		100r. dull ultramarine and light blue	25	10
1833		300r. dp turq-grn, pale grey-grn & gold	15	10
1834		400r. deep bluish green, blue-green and gold (21.6.87)	1·00	10
1830/1834 Set of 5			1·50	35

Nos. 1835/39 *are vacant.*

417 Party Emblems and Buildings

418 Satellite and Globe

(Des I. Soeroto, A. Soelarso and Subagiyanto)

1987 (19 Jan). *General Election. T **417** and similar horiz designs. Fluorescent security markings.* P 12½.

1840	75r. blue, lemon and chestnut	50	10
1841	140r. brown-olive, bright orange & yellow	50	15
1842	350r. turquoise-blue, orange-yellow & blk	1·30	35

Designs:—140r. Party emblems and arms; 350r. Party emblems, map, wheat and ballot box.

(Des I. Soeroto and S. Talahatu)

1987 (21 Mar). *Launch of "Palapa B2" Satellite. T **418** and similar design. Fluorescent security markings.* P 12½.

1843	350r. brt lemon, grey-green & lake-brown	1·00	40
1844	500r. multicoloured	1·50	25

Design: *Vert*—500r. Rocket and satellite.

419 Boy carving Figures

420 Crab and Scanner Unit

(Des A. Soelarso and M. Nurasyid)

1987 (1 Apr). *Fourth Five Year Plan. T* **419** *and similar vert design. Fluorescent security markings.* P 12½.
1845	140r.	reddish brown, orange-yell & turq-bl	25	15
1846	350r.	brt reddish vio, lt grn & reddish orge	65	35

Design:—350r. Graph and cattle.

(Des I. Soeroto)

1987 (12 May). *Tenth Anniv of Indonesian Cancer Foundation. Fluorescent security markings.* P 12½.
1847	**420**	350r.+25r. lemon and violet-blue	1·10	50

421 East Kalimantan Couple

422 Weightlifting

(Des I. Soeroto, M. Nurasyid and M. Desmal)

1987 (25 May). *Wedding Costumes (1st series). T* **421** *and similar vert designs. Multicoloured. Fluorescent security markings.* P 12½ × 13½.
1848	140r.	Type **421**	1·60	35
1849	350r.	Aceh couple	9·75	4·50
1850	400r.	East Timor couple	11·50	1·00

See also Nos. 1891/6, 1955/**MS**1961, 1992/7 and 2010/15.

(Des M. Nurasyid, M. Desmal and H. Purnomo)

1987 (10 June). *14th South-East Asia Games, Djakarta. T* **422** *and similar horiz designs showing pictograms. Fluorescent security markings.* P 12½.
1851	140r.	greenish yellow, red & dull ultram	40	15
1852	250r.	dull ultram, orge-yell & brt carm	75	25
1853	350r.	brt carm, dull ultram & reddish brn	1·10	40

Designs:—250r. Swimming; 350r. Running.

423 Emblems

424 Children reading

(Des S. Talahatu and I. Soeroto)

1987 (20 June). *460th Anniv of Djakarta and 20th Anniv of Djakarta Fair. T* **423** *and similar vert design. Fluorescent security markings.* P 12½.
1854	75r.	dull ultramarine, blk & chrome yell	75	15
1855	100r.	blue, brownish black & brt lemon	1·40	15

Design: *Vert*—100r. Emblems (*different*).

(Des F. Mustofa)

1987 (23 July). *Children's Day and National Family Planning Co-ordination Board. T* **424** *and similar vert design. Fluorescent security markings.* P 12½.
1856	100r.	bright purple and dull orange	40	15
1857	250r.	orange-yellow and dull ultramarine	75	15

Design: *Vert*—250r. Globe, baby in cupped hands and dropper.

425 Headquarters, Djakarta

426 Emblem

(Des I. Soeroto)

1987 (8 Aug). *20th Anniv of Association of South-East Asian Nations. Fluorescent security markings.* P 12½.
1858	**425**	350r. multicoloured	1·30	50

(Des H. Purnomo)

1987 (23 Aug). *30th Anniv and Seventh National Congress of Association of Specialists in Internal Diseases. Fluorescent security markings.* P 12½.
1859	**426**	300r. orange-vermilion & dp turq-bl	1·00	15

427 Mt. Bromo and Sand Craters

428 Woman with Broken Chains, Helmet and Pennant flying from Pen

(Des F. Mustofa, M. Desmal and H. Purnomo)

1987 (20 Oct). *Tourism. T* **427** *and similar horiz designs. Multicoloured. Fluorescent security markings.* P 13½ × 12½.
1860	140r.	Type **427**	50	15
1861	350r.	Bedugul Lake, Bali	1·60	55
1862	500r.	Sea gardens, Bunaken Island	2·10	25

(Des I. Soeroto)

1987 (10 Nov). *"Women's Physical Revolution". T* **428** *and similar horiz design. Fluorescent security markings.* P 12½.
1863	75r.	bronze green, rosine and lemon	35	15
1864	100r.	green, yellow and scarlet	65	15

Design: 100r. Women with rifles and barbed wire.

429 Giant Gourami (*Osphronemus goramy*)

430 Soldiers

(Des F. Mustofa, M. Nurasyid and E. Sugianto)

1987 (30 Dec). *Fishes. T* **429** *and similar horiz designs. Fluorescent security markings.* P 12½.
1865	150r.	mag, greenish yell & dull ultram	1·60	65
1866	200r.	magenta, greenish yell & new bl	1·60	35
1867	500r.	black, chrome yellow & greenish bl	5·00	35

Designs: 200r. Goldfish (*Cyprinus carpio*); 300r. Walking catfish (*Clarias batrachus*).

(Des H. Purnomo)

1988 (2 Jan). *31st Anniv of Veterans Legion. Fluorescent security markings.* P 12½.
1868	**430**	250r. blue-green and dull orange	80	15

431 Welder

432 Carved Snake and Frog

(Des A. Soelarso)

1988 (12 Jan). *National Safety and Occupational Health Day. Fluorescent security markings.* P $13\frac{1}{2} \times 12\frac{1}{2}$.

1869	**431**	350r. dull ultramarine & dp blue-green	1·10	50

(Des R. Widjoseno, H. Purnomo, Suyatno and I. Nami)

1988 (3 Mar). *Eighth Anniv of National Crafts Council. T 432 and similar horiz designs. Fluorescent security markings.* P $12\frac{1}{2}$.

1870	120r. blue and reddish brown	65	10
1871	350r. light blue and brown	1·00	50
1872	500r. red-brown and yellow-green	1·60	15

Designs:—350r. Cane rocking-chair; 500r. Bamboo goods.

433 Industrial Symbols

434 Indonesian Girls

(Des M. Nurasyid and A. Soelarso)

1988 (1 Apr). *Fourth Five Year Plan. T 433 and similar horiz design. Fluorescent security markings.* P $12\frac{1}{2}$.

1873	140r. new blue and yellowish green	25	15
1874	400r. bright purple and red	65	35

Design:—400r. Fishing industry.

(Des Wagiono and H. Purnomo)

1988 (30 Apr). *"Expo 88" World's Fair, Brisbane. T 434 and similar vert designs. Each blue, bright magenta and greenish yellow. Fluorescent security markings.* P $12\frac{1}{2}$.

1875	200r. Type **434**	90	15
1876	300r. Indonesian girl	90	15
1877	350r. Indonesian girl and boy	1·50	65
MS1878	96 × 96 mm. Nos. 1875/7. Perf or imperf	9·75	9·75

435 Anniversary Emblem

436 Dendrobium none betawi

437 Running

(Des H. Purnomo)

1988 (8 May). *125th Anniv of Red Cross. Fluorescent security markings.* P $12\frac{1}{2}$.

1879	**435**	350r. brownish grey, brownish black and bright scarlet	1·00	25

(Des F. Mustofa and H. Purnomo)

1988 (17 May). *Flowers. T 436 and similar vert design. Fluorescent security markings.* P $12\frac{1}{2} \times 13\frac{1}{2}$ (400r.) or $12\frac{1}{2} \times 14\frac{1}{2}$ (500r.).

1880	400r. Type **436**	1·60	50
1881	500r. Dendrobium abang betawi	1·60	35

(Des M. Nurasyid, M. Desmal, S. Talahatu, A. Soelarso and T. Margono)

1988 (15 June). *Olympic Games, Seoul. T 437 and similar vert designs. Fluorescent security markings.* P $12\frac{1}{2}$.

1882	75r. black, orange-brown and gold	50	15
1883	100r. black, orange-red and gold	1·10	15
1884	200r. black, bright magenta and gold	1·10	50
1885	300r. black, yellowish green and gold	50	50
1886	400r. black, turquoise-blue and gold	65	40
1887	500r. black, violet-blue and gold	3·00	40
1882/1887	Set of 6	6·25	1·90

MS1888 Two sheets, each 72 × 96 mm. Perf or imperf. (a) Nos. 1882, 1885 and 1887; (b)
Nos. 1883/4 and 1886 .... 36·00 36·00
Designs:—100r. Weightlifting; 200r. Archery; 300r. Table tennis; 400r. Swimming; 500r. Tennis.

438 Figures around Emblem

439 Family, Water and Ear of Wheat

(Des Y. Trenggono and M. Nurasyid)

1988 (26 June). *Centenary of International Women's Council. Fluorescent security markings.* P $12\frac{1}{2}$.

1889	**438**	140r. black and blue	65	15

(Des S. Dwidjotanojo and S. Talahatu)

1988 (9 July). *National Farmers' and Fishermen's Week. Fluorescent security markings.* P $12\frac{1}{2}$.

1890	**439**	350r. yellow-ochre and crimson	1·10	50

(Des H. Purnomo, M. Desmal, I. Soeroto, S. Talahatu and T. Margono)

1988 (5 July). *Wedding Costumes (2nd series). Vert designs as T 421. Multicoloured. Fluorescent security markings.* P $12\frac{1}{2} \times 14\frac{1}{2}$ (55, 200, 250r.) or $12\frac{1}{2} \times 13\frac{1}{2}$ (others).

1891	55r. Sumatera Barat (West)	25	15
1892	75r. Jambi	15	10
1893	100r. Bengkulu	65	10
1894	120r. Lampung	90	10
1895	200r. Moluccas	1·60	15
1896	250r. Nusa Tenggara Timur (East)	2·10	1·10
1891/1896	Set of 6	5·00	1·50

440 President Suharto

441 Emblem

442 Doves and Envelopes

(Des H. Purnomo)

1988 (17 Aug)–**90**. *Fluorescent security markings.* P 12½.

1897	**440**	200r. dull ultram, pk & red (20.12.89)	35	15
1898		700r. deep mauve, pale green and yellowish green (17.2.90)	1·10	15
1899		1000r. multicoloured	1·10	15

On Nos. 1897/8 the inscriptions are in a sans-serif font.

No. 1900 *is vacant.*

(Des Indonesian National News Agency and I. Soeroto)

1988 (29 Sept). 13*th Non-aligned News Agencies Co-ordinating Committee Meeting, Djakarta. Fluorescent security markings.* P 12½.

1901	**441**	500r. new blue and bright carmine	1·20	35

(Des T. Margono)

1988 (9 Oct). *International Correspondence Week. Fluorescent security markings.* P 12½.

1902	**442**	140r. new blue and vermilion	90	15

1988 (18 Oct). *"Filacept 88" International Stamp Exhibition, The Hague. Two sheets, each* 72 × 96 *mm, each containing design as No.* 1630 *but colours changed. Fluorescent security markings.* P 12½ or imperf.

MS1903 Two sheets. (a) 200r. × 4, black, emerald and rosine; (b) 200r. dull ultramarine, orange and rosine plus label   29·00   29·00

443 Transport and Communications

444 Al Mashun Mosque, Medan

(Des H. Purnomo)

1988 (24 Oct). *Asian–Pacific Transport and Communications Decade. Fluorescent security markings.* P 12½.

1904	**443**	350r. greenish blue and black	1·10	50

(Des I. Soeroto, Soeripto and Subagiyanto)

1988 (25 Nov). *Tourism.* T **444** *and similar horiz designs. Multicoloured. Fluorescent security markings.* P 13½ × 12½.

1905	**444**	250r. Type **444**	55	40
1906		300r. Pagaruyung Palace, Batusangkar	90	35
1907		500r. Keong Emas Theatre, Djakarta	2·10	35

MS1908 96 × 57 mm. 1000r. As No. 1906.
P 14½ × 12½ or imperf   18·00   18·00
See also No. **MS**1954.

445 *Papilio gigon*

446 *Rafflesia* sp.

(Des E. Sugianto and I. Soeroto)

1988 (20 Dec). *Butterflies.* T **445** *and similar vert design. Multicoloured. Fluorescent security markings.* P 12½ × 13½.

1909		400r. Type **445**	1·50	40
1910		500r. *Graphium androcles*	2·50	55

MS1911 49 × 93 mm. 1000r. As No. 1910.
P 12½ × 14½ or imperf   29·00   29·00

1988. *POSTAGE DUE. Dated "1988".* P 13½ × 12½.

D1912	D **333a**	1000r. plum and brownish grey	75	55
D1913		2000r. bright scarlet and mauve	1·50	1·10
D1914		3000r. brown-lake & orange-yell	2·50	1·60
D1915		5000r. emerald and pale blue	4·50	2·10
D1912/1915 *Set of* 4			8·25	4·75

(Des T. Margono and M. Nurasyid)

1989 (7 Jan). *Flowers.* T **446** *and similar vert design. Multicoloured. Fluorescent security markings.* P 12½ × 13½.

1916		200r. Type **446**	90	40
1917		1000r. *Amorphophallus titanum*	2·75	40

MS1918 50 × 103 mm. 1000r. As No. 1917.
P 12½ × 14½   49·00   49·00

447 "40" and Boeing 747

448 Mother and Baby

(Des H. Purnomo)

1989 (26 Jan). 40*th Anniv of Garuda Airline. Fluorescent security markings.* P 12½.

1919	**447**	350r. new blue and blue-green	2·00	55

(Des S. Talahatu (**MS**1924), M. Faisal, I. Soeroto, H. Purnomo and E. Sugianto)

1989 (6 Mar). *Endangered Animals. The Orang-Utan (*Pongo pygmaeus*).* T **448** *and similar vert designs. Multicoloured. Fluorescent security markings.* P 12½.

1920		75r. Type **448**	3·75	1·60
1921		100r. Orang-utan in tree	3·75	75
1922		140r. Mother and baby in trees	3·75	75
1923		500r. Orang-utan	11·50	6·50
1920/1923 *Set of* 4			20·00	8·50

MS1924 Two sheets, each 95 × 125 mm. (a)
Nos. 1920/1; (b) Nos. 1922/3   £200   £200

449 Industrial Site

450 Stamp and Map

(Des Soeripto and A. Soelarso)

1989 (1 Apr). *Fifth Five Year Plan. T* **449** *and similar horiz designs. Fluorescent security markings.* P 12½.
1925	55r. bright reddish violet and blue-green		10	10
1926	150r. dull ultramarine and olive-sepia		25	15
1927	350r. dp turquoise-green & yellow-orge		55	15

Designs:—150r. Cement works; 350r. Gas plant.

(Des S. Sugiyanto)

1989 (1 Apr). *125th Anniv of First Netherlands Indies Stamp. Fluorescent security markings.* P 12½.
1928	**450**	1000r. green, brt purple & royal blue	2·00	15

451 Ki Hadjar Dewantara and Graduate

452 Emblem on Map

(Des E. Sugianto and A. Soelarso)

1989 (2 May). *National Education Day. T* **451** *and similar horiz design. Fluorescent security markings.* P 12½.
1929	140r. red and bright purple		55	15
1930	300r. deep reddish violet & light emerald		1·00	35

Design:—300r. Dewantara (founder of Taman Siswa School), pencil and books.

(Des S. Sugiyanto)

1989 (1 July). *Tenth Anniv of Asia–Pacific Telecommunity. Fluorescent security markings.* P 12½.
1931	**452**	350r. deep reddish purple and dull yellowish green	1·00	75

453 Flag and Cup

454 Students

455 Headquarters

(Des H. Purnomo)

1989 (3 July). *Sudirman Cup.* P 12½.
1932	**453**	100r. ochre and rosine	1·60	15

(Des A. Soelarso)

1989 (23 July). *Children's Day. T* **454** *and similar vert design. Fluorescent security markings.* P 12½.
1933	100r. olive-sepia and yellow-orange		50	10
1934	250r. royal blue and bright green		90	25

Design:—250r. Youths exercising.

(Des I. Soeroto)

1989 (29 July). *Tenth Anniv of Asia–Pacific Integrated Rural Development Centre. Fluorescent security markings.* P 12½.
1935	**455**	140r. chestnut and new blue	75	15

456 Skull of "Sangiran 17" and Hunters

457 Globe and People

(Des I. Soeroto, T. Margono, M. Nurasyid, S. Talahatu, Soeripto and M. Desmal)

1989 (31 Aug). *Centenary of Palaeoanthropology in Indonesia. T* **456** *and similar designs. Fluorescent security markings.* P 12½.
1936	100r. black and orange-brown		65	10
1937	150r. yellow-olive and Venetian red		90	15
1938	200r. greenish blue and orange-brown		1·40	35
1939	250r. reddish violet and chestnut		1·60	25
1940	300r. deep green and Indian red		2·00	40
1941	350r. greenish blue and orange-brown		2·40	25
1936/1941	*Set of 6*		8·00	1·30

Designs: *Horiz*—150r. Skull of "Perning 1" and cavemen, 200r. Skull of "Sangiran 10" and hunter. *Vert*—250r. Skull of "Wajak 1"; 300r. Skull of "Sambungmacan 1"; 350r. Skull of "Ngandong 7".

(Des T. Margono)

1989 (4 Sept). *Centenary of Interparliamentary Union. Fluorescent security markings.* P 12½.
1942	**457**	350r. yellowish grn & dp ultramarine	1·00	75

458 Kung Fu

459 Taman Burung

(Des H. Purnomo)

1989 (16 Sept). *12th National Games, Djakarta. T* **458** *and similar horiz designs. Multicoloured. Fluorescent security markings.* P 12½.
1943	75r. Type **458**		55	15
1944	100r. Tennis		55	15
1945	140r. Judo		55	15
1946	350r. Volleyball		1·60	75
1947	500r. Boxing		2·75	25
1948	1000r. Archery		3·50	65
1943/1948	*Set of 6*		8·50	1·90

(Des M. Desmal and S. Talahatu)

1989 (9 Oct). *Tourism. T* **459** *and similar multicoloured designs. Fluorescent security markings.* P 12½ × 13½ (500r.) or 13½ × 12½ (others).
1949	120r. Type **459**		75	10
1950	350r. Prangko Museum		1·10	55
1951	500r. Istana Anak-Anak (*vert*)		2·00	35
MS1952	100 × 51 mm. 1500r. As No. 1950		11·50	11·50

460 Trophy

461 Worker wearing Safety Belt and Flag

(Des Subagiyanto)

1989 (11 Nov). *Film Industry. Fluorescent security markings.*
P 12½.
1953 **460** 150r. ochre and agate . . . . . . 1·00 15

1989 (17 Nov). *"World Stamp Expo '89" International Stamp Exhibition, Washington D.C. Sheet 102 × 50 mm containing designs as Nos. 1905/6. Multicoloured. Fluorescent security markings.* P 14½ × 12½.
MS1954 1500r. Type **444**, 2500r. As
No. 1906 . . . . 11·50 11·50

(Des Soeripto (**MS**1961), I. Soeroto, M. Nurasyid and M. Desmal)

1989 (11 Dec). *Wedding Costumes (3rd series). Vert designs as T* **421**. *Multicoloured. Fluorescent security markings.* P 12½ × 13½.
1955 50r. Sumatera Utara (North) 35 10
1956 75r. Sumatera Selatan (South) 35 10
1957 100r. Djakarta 35 10
1958 140r. Sulawesi Utara (North Celebes) . . 75 15
1959 350r. Sulawesi Tengah (Central
    Celebes) . . . . 1·10 1·10
1960 500r. Sulawesi Selatan (South
    Celebes) . . . . 1·60 55
1955/1960 *Set of 6* . . . . 4·00 1·00
MS1961 50 × 102 mm. 1500r. As No. 1958. Perf
or imperf . . . . 7·00 7·00

(Des M. Nurasyid)

1990 (12 Jan). *Occupational Safety. Fluorescent security markings.* P 12½.
1962 **461** 200r. orange-brown and blue-
    green 80 15

REPUBLIK INDONESIA **200**r
462 Benteng Marlborough, Bengkulu

(Des M. Desmal, S. Sugiyanto and Subagiyanto)

1990 (1 Feb). *Tourism. T* **462** *and similar horiz designs. Multicoloured. Fluorescent security markings.* P 14½ × 12½ (200r.) or 13½ × 12½ (others).
1963 200r. Type **462** . . . . 1·00 15
1964 400r. National Museum, Djakarta . . . 1·50 35
1965 500r. Baiturrahman Mosque, Banda
    Aceh . . . . 1·50 50
MS1966 102 × 51 mm. 1000r. As No. 1964;
1500r. As No. 1965 . . . . . . 9·75 9·75

463 *Mammilaria fragilis*   **464** Tree-felling
                                         Equipment

(Des H. Purnomo and F. Mustofa)

1990 (1 Mar). *Plants. T* **463** *and similar horiz design. Multicoloured. Fluorescent security markings.* P 13½ × 12½.
1967 75r. Type **463** 40 10
1968 1000r. Bonsai of *Gmelina elliptica* . . . 2·00 50
MS1969 105 × 50 mm. 1500r. As No. 1968 . . 12·00 12·00

(Des S. Talahatu and Soeripto)

1990 (1 Apr). *Fifth Five Year Plan. T* **464** *and similar horiz design. Fluorescent security markings.* P 12½.
1970 200r. reddish brown and turquoise-
    blue 35 15
1971 1000r. black and new blue . . . . . . 1·60 1·00
Design:—1000r. Lighthouse and freighter.

465 Arrow pointing to Indonesia   **466** Battle and
                                          Disabled Man
                                          using Soldering-
                                          iron

(Des I. Soeroto and F. Mustofa)

1990 (1 May). *Visit Indonesia Year (1991) (1st issue). T* **465** *and similar vert design. Multicoloured. Fluorescent security markings.* P 13½ × 12½ (100r.) or 12½ × 13½ (500r.).
1972 100r. Type **465** 35 10
1973 500r. Temple . . . . 1·30 35
See also Nos. **MS**1974 and 1998/**MS**2001.

1990 (3 May). *"Stamp World London 90" International Stamp Exhibition. Sheet 88 × 52 mm. Fluorescent security markings.* P 14½ × 12½.
MS1974 **465** 5000r. multicoloured . . . . . 18·00 18·00

(Des T. Margono)

1990 (18 May). *40th Anniv of Disabled Veterans Corps. Fluorescent security markings.* P 12½.
1975 **466** 1000r. orange and grey-green . . 1·50 1·00

467 Player and   **468** Lampung Bridal
Goalkeeper   Pair

(Des H. Purnomo)

1990 (8 June). *World Cup Football Championship, Italy. T* **467** *and similar vert designs. Multicoloured. Fluorescent security markings.* P 12½.
1976 75r. Type **467** . . . . 1·60 1·00
1977 150r. Player tackling 55 10
1978 400r. Players competing for high ball . . 80 15
MS1979 98 × 65 mm. 1500r. As No. 1978 . . . 9·00 9·00

1990 (10 June). *National Stamp Exhibition. Sheet 68 × 95 mm.* P 12½ × 14½.
MS1980 **468** 2000r. multicoloured . . . . . 7·00 7·00
No. **MS**1980 also bears inscriptions commemorating various stamp exhibitions and a label for "Stamp World London 90".

469 U.N. Population Award

470 Figure with Pencil and Open Book

(Des A. Soelarso)

1990 (29 June). *20th Anniv of Family Planning Movement. Fluorescent security markings.* P 12½.
1981 **469** 60r. brown and rosine 40 10

(Des S. Sugiyanto)

1990 (1 July). *Population Census. Fluorescent security markings.* P 12½.
1982 **470** 90r. bright green and blue-green 55 10

471 Children

472 Soldier planting Flag

(Des S. Talahatu)

1990 (23 July). *Children's Day. Fluorescent security markings.* P 12½.
1983 **471** 500r. deep reddish purple and scarlet . . . . 1·10 40

(Des M. Desmal and F. Mustofa)

1990 (17 Aug). *45th Anniv of Independence.* T **472** *and similar vert design. Multicoloured. Fluorescent security markings.* P 12½ × 13½.
1984 200r. Type **472** 65 15
1985 500r. Modern building and roads . . . . 1·10 50
MS1986 50 × 105 mm. 1000r. As No. 1985 . . . 8·25 8·25

473 Buildings and Cultural Identities

474 Emblem

(Des M. Nurasyid)

1990 (19 Aug). *Indonesia–Pakistan Economic and Cultural Co-operation Organization.* T **473** *and similar multicoloured design. Fluorescent security markings.* P 13½ × 12½ (75r.) or 12½ × 13½ (400r.).
1987 75r. Type **473** 50 15
1988 400r. Dancer (*vert*) . . . . 1·10 40

(Des S. Sugiyanto)

1990 (10 Sept). *20th Anniv of Asian–Pacific Postal Training Centre. Fluorescent security markings.* P 12½.
1989 **474** 500r. new blue and deep ultramarine . . . . . . 1·00 40

475 Anniversary Emblem

476 Houses

477 Dancer and House

(Des M. Nurasyid)

1990 (14 Sept). *30th Anniv of Organization of Petroleum Exporting Countries. Fluorescent security markings.* P 12½.
1990 **475** 200r. black, deep grey & bright orange 80 15

(Des A. Soelarso)

1990 (24 Oct). *Environmental Health. Fluorescent security markings.* P 12½.
1991 **476** 1000r. multicoloured . . . . . . 2·00 35

(Des I. Soeroto, M. Nurasyid and M. Desmal)

1990 (1 Nov). *Wedding Costumes (4th series). Vert designs as* T **421**. *Multicoloured. Fluorescent security markings.* P 12½ × 13½.
1992 75r. Java Barat (West) 35 10
1993 100r. Java Tengah (Central) 40 10
1994 150r. Yogyakarta 40 10
1995 200r. Java Timur (East) 55 15
1996 400r. Bali 80 40
1997 500r. Nusa Tenggara Barat (West) . . . 90 50
1992/1997 *Set of 6* . . . . 3·00 1·25

(Des S. Talahatu and Soeripto)

1991 (1–12 Jan). *Visit Indonesia Year (2nd issue). Dancers and Traditional Houses.* T **477** *and similar vert designs. Fluorescent security markings.* P 13 × 13½.
1998 200r. Type **477** . . . . 1·00 15
1999 500r. House and dancer with saucers . . . . 1·40 55
2000 1000r. Dancer and house (*different*) . . 2·50 40
MS2001 50 × 100 mm. 1500r. Type **477** (12 Jan) . . . . 14·00 14·00

478 Emblem

479 Palace of Sultan Ternate, Moluccas

(Des Subagiyanto)

1991 (4 Feb). *16th National Koran Reading Competition, Yogyakarta. Fluorescent security markings.* P 12½.
2002 **478** 200r. dp bluish green & greenish yell 80 15

(Des A. Soelarso (**MS**2005). M. Desmal and I. Soeroto (others))

1991 (1 Mar). *Tourism.* T **479** *and similar horiz design. Multicoloured. Fluorescent security markings.* P 13½ × 12½.
2003 500r. Type **479** . . . . 1·00 25
2004 1000r. Bari House, Palembang . . . . 1·60 35
MS2005 100 × 50 mm. 2500r. As No. 2004 . . 6·50 6·50
No. **MS**2005 also commemorates Fiap Exco Meeting, Yogyakarta.

480 Steel Mill   **481** Damaged Lungs and Cigarette Smoke forming Skull   **482** Hands

(Des Soeripto and M. Nurasyid)

1991 (1 Apr). *Fifth Five Year Plan. T* **480** *and similar design. Fluorescent security markings.* P 12½.
2006   75r. orange-red and bright blue   10   10
2007   200r. new blue and black   25   15
Design: *Horiz*—200r. Computer technology.

(Des H. Purnomo)

1991 (31 May). *Anti-smoking Campaign. Fluorescent security markings.* P 12½.
2008   **481**   90r. carmine-red and black   55   10

(Des A. Soelarso)

1991 (1 June). *24th Anniv of National Federation for the Welfare of the Mentally Handicapped. Fluorescent security markings.* P 12½.
2009   **482**   200r.+25r. black and scarlet . . .   80   25

(Des M. Desmal, Soeripto, M. Nurasyid and S. Talahatu)

1991 (15 June). *Wedding Costumes (5th series). Vert designs as T* **421**. *Multicoloured. Fluorescent security markings.* P 12½ × 13½.
2010   100r. Kalimantan Barat (West)   25   10
2011   200r. Kalimantan Tengah (Central) . .   80   15
2012   300r. Kalimantan Selatan (South) . .   50   15
2013   400r. Sulawesi Tenggara (South-east Celebes)   55   25
2014   500r. Riau   80   35
2015   1000r. Irian Jaya . . . .   1·00   55
2010/2015 *Set of 6* . . . .   3·50   1·40

483 Tents   **484** Monument

(Des A. Soelarso)

1991 (15 June). *National Boy Scout Jamboree, Cibubur. Fluorescent security markings.* P 12½.
2016   **483**   200r. new blue, black and orange-red . . . .   1·10   15

(Des H. Purnomo)

1991 (6 July). *42nd Anniv of Return of Republican Government to Djokjakarta. Fluorescent security markings.* P 12½.
2017   **484**   200r. brown-olive and red-brown   80   15

485 Temples and Family   **486** Cells

(Des M. Desmal)

1991 (15 July). *Farmers' Week. Fluorescent security markings.* P 12½.
2018   **485**   500r. bright lemon and new blue . . . .   1·40   15

(Des A. Soelarso)

1991 (28 July). *"chemindo'91" Chemistry Congress, Surabaya. Fluorescent security markings.* P 12½.
2019   **486**   400r. orange-red and emerald . .   1·00   15

487 Weightlifters   **488** Parachutists   **489** Red Cross and Hands

(Des M. Desmal)

1991 (24 Aug). *Fifth Junior Men's and Fourth Women's Asian Weightlifting Championships, Manado. Fluorescent security markings.* P 12½.
2020   **487**   300r. rosine and black . . . . . .   1·00   15

(Des M. Desmal)

1991 (30 Aug). *World Parachuting Championships. Fluorescent security markings.* P 12½.
2021   **488**   500r. bright mauve and new blue . . . .   1·00   15

(Des A. Soelarso)

1991 (17 Sept). *46th Anniv of Indonesian Red Cross. Fluorescent security markings.* P 12½.
2022   **489**   200r. rosine & bright turquoise-green   80   15

490 Radio Mast   **491** Script and Mosque

(Des Subagiyanto)

1991 (6 Oct). *Eighth International Amateur Radio Union Region III Conference, Bandung. Fluorescent security markings.* P 12½.
2023   **490**   300r. blue and lemon . . . . . .   1·00   15

(Des T. Margono)

1991 (15 Oct). *Istiqlal Festival, Djakarta. Fluorescent security markings.* P 12½.
2024   **491**   200r. black and vermilion . . . .   1·00   15

REPUBLIK INDONESIA *500r*
492 Dancer and Inspectors

Pongo pygmaeus 200r
REPUBLIK INDONESIA
493 Orang-utan

(Des H. Purnomo)

1991 (22 Oct). *International Convention on Quality Control Circles, Bali. Fluorescent security markings.* P 12½.
2025 **492** 500r. multicoloured . . . . 1·20 50

(Des F. Mustofa, I. Soeroto and T. Margono)

1991 (18 Dec). *International Conference on Great Apes of the World. The Orang-utan (Pongo pygmaeus). T **493** and similar vert designs. Multicoloured. Fluorescent security markings.* P 12½ × 13½.
2026 200r. Type **493** . . . . . . 1·00 15
2027 500r. Orang-utan on forest path . . . . 1·20 25
2028 1000r. Orang-utan sitting on ground . . 2·50 55
MS2029 50 × 100 mm. 2500r. As No. 2028 . . 8·25 8·25

REPUBLIK INDONESIA *200r*
494 Model of Djakarta Post Office

(Des H. Pornomo and M. Desmal)

1992 (9 Jan). *Automation of Postal Service. T **494** and similar horiz design. Multicoloured. Fluorescent security markings.* P 13½ × 12½.
2030 200r. Type **494** 40 15
2031 500r. Sorting machine 80 35

REPUBLIK INDONESIA *200r*
495 *Phalaenopsis ambilis*

REPUBLIK INDONESIA *75r*
496 Buildings, Ballot Boxes and State Arms

(Des T. Margono (**MS**2035), M. Nurasyid (others))

1992 (20 Jan). *Flowers. T **495** and similar horiz designs. Multicoloured. Fluorescent security markings.* P 13½ × 12½.
2032 200r. Type **495** 40 15
2033 500r. *Rafflesia arnoldii* 80 35
2034 1000r. *Jasminum sambac* . . . . . 1·80 40
MS2035 106 × 50 mm. 2000r. As No. 2034 . . 8·25 8·25

(Des F. Mustofa, Subagiyanto and S. Sugiyanto)

1992 (10 Feb). *Parliamentary Elections. T **496** and similar horiz designs. Multicoloured. Fluorescent security markings.* P 12½.
2036 75r. Type **496** 15 10
2037 100r. Ballot boxes and globe 40 10
2038 500r. Ballot boxes and hands holding voting slips . . . . 1·00 25

REPUBLIK INDONESIA *300r*
497 Lembah Baliem, Irian Jaya

REPUBLIK INDONESIA *150r*
498 Road-building

(Des M. Nurasyid, I. Soeroto and Soeripto)

1992 (1 Mar). *Visit ASEAN Year. T **497** and similar horiz designs. Multicoloured. Fluorescent security markings.* P 13½ × 12½.
2039 300r. Type **497** 65 15
2040 500r. Tanah Lot, Bali . . . . . . 1·00 35
2041 1000r. Lembah Anai, Sumatra Barat . . 2·10 35
MS2042 100 × 50 mm. 3000r. As No. 2040 . . 8·25 8·25

(Des Soeripto and I. Soeroto)

1992 (1 Apr). *Fifth Five Year Plan. T **498** and similar horiz design. Fluorescent security markings.* P 12½.
2043 150r. deep dull purple and blue-green 15 15
2044 300r. new blue and magenta 55 15
Designs:—300r. Aircraft.

REPUBLIK INDONESIA *500r*
499 Emblem and Crab

500 Weightlifting

(Des S. Sugiyanto and I. Soeroto)

1992 (12 May). *15th Anniv of Indonesian Cancer Foundation. Fluorescent security markings.* P 12½.
2045 **499** 200r.+25r. carm-red & reddish brn 40 15
2046 500r.+50r. but crimson & ultram 80 25

(Des H. Purnomo and T. Margono)

1992 (1 June). *Olympic Games, Barcelona. T **500** and similar vert designs. Multicoloured. Fluorescent security markings.* P 12½ × 13½.
2047 75r. Type **500** 25 10
2048 200r. Badminton 35 15
2049 300r. Sports pictograms 65 15
2050 500r. Tennis 80 40
2051 1000r. Archery . . . . 2·00 40
2047/2051 *Set of 5* . . . . 3·75 1·10
MS2052 75 × 100 mm. 2000r. As No. 2048; 3000r. As No. 2051 . . 9·75 9·75

REPUBLIK INDONESIA *100,-*
501 White-crested Laughing Thrush (*Garrulax leucolophus*)

REPUBLIK INDONESIA *75r*
502 Busy Street (Tammy Filia)

(Des A. Soelarso (**MS**2057), Suprayitno and M. Desmal (others))

1992 (1 July). *Birds.* T **501** *and similar vert designs. Multicoloured. Fluorescent security markings.* P 12½ × 13½.

2053	100r. Type **501**	25	10
2054	200r. Common Gold-backed woodpecker (*Dinopium javanense*)	50	15
2055	400r. Rhinoceros hornbill (*Buceros rhinoceros*)	1·00	50
2056	500r. Amboina king parrot (*Alisterus amboinensis*)	1·50	55
2053/2056 *Set of 4*		3·00	1·20
MS2057 50 × 100 mm. 3000r. Type **501**		8·25	8·25

(Des T. Margono)

1992 (23 July). *National Children's Day.* T **502** *and similar horiz designs showing children's paintings. Multicoloured. Fluorescent security markings.* P 12½.

2058	75r. Type **502**	10	10
2059	100r. Children with balloons (Cynthia Widiyana Halim)	25	10
2060	200r. Native boats (Dandy Rahmad Adi Kurniawan)	55	15
2061	500r. Girl and bird (Intan Sari Dewi Saputro)	1·40	80
2058/2061 *Set of 4*		2·10	1·00

503 Anniversary Emblem

504 Earth and "Palapa B-4" (satellite)

(Des M. Desmal, H. Purnomo and I. Soeroto)

1992 (8 Aug). *25th Anniv of Association of South-East Asian Nations.* T **503** *and similar horiz designs. Multicoloured. Fluorescent security markings.* P 13½ × 12½.

2062	200r. Type **503**	40	15
2063	500r. Map and flags of member nations	1·20	40
2064	1000r. "25" and flags	2·40	50

(Des H. Purnomo and Subagiyanto)

1992 (16 Aug). *Communications.* T **504** *and similar vert designs. Multicoloured. Fluorescent security markings.* P 12½ × 13½.

2065	200r. Type **504**	40	15
2066	500r. "Palapa" satellite (16th anniv of launch)	80	40
2067	1000r. Old and modern telephones (modernization of telephone system)	2·00	50

505 Emblem

506 Ngremo Dance, East Java

1992 (1 Sept). *Tenth Non-Aligned Countries' Summit, Djakarta.* T **505** *and similar vert design. Multicoloured. Fluorescent security markings.* P 12½ × 13½.

2068	200r. Type **505**	35	10
2069	500r. Members' flags and emblem	55	10

(Des I. Soeroto and Suprayitno)

1992 (1 Oct). *Traditional Dances (1st series).* T **506** *and similar vert design. Multicoloured. Fluorescent security markings.* P 12½ × 13½.

2070	200r. Type **506**	25	15
2071	500r. Gending Sriwijaya dance, South Sumatra	1·20	1·20
MS2072 50 × 100 mm. 3000r. Type **506**		7·25	7·25

See also Nos. 2122/5, 2168/73, 2211/15, 2292/6, 2366/71 and 2476/81.

507 Anniversary Emblem

508 Antara Building, Djakarta

(Des S. Sugiyanto)

1992 (29 Nov). *40th Anniv of International Planned Parenthood Federation. Fluorescent security markings.* P 12½.

2073	**507** 200r. dull ultramarine & yellowish grn	80	15

(Des I. Soeroto)

1992 (13 Dec). *55th Anniv of Antara News Agency. Fluorescent security markings.* P 12½.

2074	**508** 500r. black and new blue	1·00	15

509 Planting Saplings

(**510**)

(Des T. Margono)

1992 (24 Dec). *National Afforestation. Fluorescent security markings.* P 13½ × 12½.

2075	**509** 500r. multicoloured	1·00	25

1993 (1 Feb). *No. 1831 surch with* T **510**.

2076	**326** 50r.on 55r. carmine and rose-pink	40	10

511 State Arms and Assembly Building

512 Soldiers and Buildings

(Des H. Purnomo)

1993 (1 Mar). *Tenth People's Consultative Assembly.* T **511** *and similar horiz design. Multicoloured. Fluorescent security markings.* P 13½ × 12½.

2077	300r. Type **511**	40	15
2078	700r. Assembly hall	1·00	25

(Des H. Purnomo, M. Nurasyid and M. Desmal)

1993 (1 Apr). *Fifth Five Year Plan. T* **512** *and similar horiz designs. Multicoloured. Fluorescent security markings.* P 12½.
2079	300r. Type **512**		35	35
2080	700r. Workers and arrow		75	75
2081	1000r. Runners		1·10	1·10

513 Swarm of *Ornithoptera goliath*

(Des I. Soeripto)

1993 (20 Apr). *Fluorescent security markings.* P 12½.
2082	**513**	1000r. multicoloured	1·60	25

514 Peristiwa Hotel, Yamato, and Adipura Kencana Medal

1993 (29 May). *700th Anniv of Surabaya (300, 700r.) and "indo tourism 93" (1000r.). T* **514** *and similar horiz designs. Multicoloured. Fluorescent security markings.* P 13½ × 12½.
2083	300r. Type **514**		35	35
2084	700r. Modern city and World Habitat Award, 1992		75	75
2085	1000r. Candi Bajang Ratu (temple)		1·10	1·10

(515) | **516** Mascot

1993 (29 May). *"indopex'93" Asian Stamp Exhibition, Surabaya.*

(a) Nos. 2082/5 optd as T **515** in red.
2086	300r. multicoloured		35	15
2087	700r. multicoloured		75	35
2088	1000r. multicoloured (No. 2082)		2·00	80
2089	1000r. multicoloured (No. 2085)		1·30	50
2086/2089 *Set of* 4			4·00	1·60

The overprint on No. 2088 is larger.

(b) *Sheet* 101 × 50 *mm. Fluorescent security markings.* P 13½ × 12½.
MS2090	**516** 3500r. multicoloured		5·25	5·25

517 *Jasminum sambac* | **518** Scouts making Road

1993 (5 June). *Environmental Protection. T* **517** *and similar vert designs. Multicoloured. Fluorescent security markings.* P 12½ × 13½.
2091	300r. Type **517**		35	15
	a. Horiz strip of 3. Nos. 2091/3		2·00	
2092	300r. Moth orchid (*Phalaenopsis amabilis*)		35	15
2093	300r. *Rafflesia arnoldi* (flower)		1·30	40
2094	700r. Komodo dragon (*Varanus komodoensis*)		1·30	40
	a. Horiz strip of 3. Nos. 2094/6		4·00	
2095	700r. Asian bonytongue (*Scleropages formosus*) (wrongly inscr "formasus")		1·30	40
2096	700r. Java hawk eagle (*Spizaetus bartelsi*)		1·30	40
2091/2096 *Set of* 6			5·25	1·75
MS2097 75 × 105 mm. 1500r. Type **517**; 1500r. As No. 2094			6·00	6·00

Stamps of the same value were issued together in horizontal se-tenant strips of three stamps, each strip forming a composite design.

(Des E. Yunalies and M. Nurasyid)

1993 (27 July). *First World Community Development Camp, Lebakharjo. T* **518** *and similar horiz design. Fluorescent security markings. Photo.* P 13½ × 12½.
2098	300r. Type **518**		35	15
2099	700r. Pres. Suharto greeting girl scout		1·00	15

519 Pres. Suharto | **520** *Papilio blumei* | **521** Swimming

1993 (17 Aug). *Fluorescent security markings.* P 12½.
2100	**519**	150r. multicoloured	15	15
2101		300r. multicoloured	35	15
2102		700r. multicoloured	75	50

On No. 2102 part of the background is a draped flag.

1993 (24 Aug). *International Butterfly Conference, Ujungpandang. Fluorescent security markings.* P 12½ × 13½.
2103	**520**	700r. multicoloured	1·00	15
MS2104 50 × 100 mm. **520** 3000r. multicoloured			5·75	5·75

See also No. MS2110.

1993 (9 Sept). *"Pon XIII" Sports Week, Djakarta. T* **521** *and similar vert designs. Multicoloured. Fluorescent security markings. Photo.* P 12½ × 13½.
2105	150r. Type **521**		15	15
2106	300r. Cycling		35	35
2107	700r. Mascot		75	75
2108	1000r. High jumping		1·10	1·10
2105/2108 *Set of* 4			2·10	2·10
MS2109 51 × 101 mm. 3500r. As No. 2108			5·25	5·25

1993 (1 Oct). *"Bangkok 1993" International Stamp Exhibition. Sheet* 67 × 75 *mm containing design as T* **520** *but without top inscription. Fluorescent security markings.* P 12½ × 13½.
MS2110 3000r. multicoloured			6·00	6·00

522 Sigura-Gura
Waterfall, North
Sumatra

523 General
Soedirman

524 *Michelia champaca*

527 Emblems

528 Working
Women

1993 (4 Oct). *World Tourism Organization Meeting, Bali. T* **522** *and similar multicoloured designs. Fluorescent security markings. Photo.* P 13½ × 12½ (1000r.) or 12½ × 13½ (others).

2111	300r. Type **522**	35	35
2112	700r. Goa Petruk (cave), Central Java	75	75
2113	1000r. Danau Segara Anak (cove), West Nusa Tenggara (*horiz*)	1·10	1·10
MS2114	71 × 75 mm. 3000r. Similar design to Type **522**	4·50	4·50

1993 (5 Oct). *Armed Forces. T* **523** *and similar vert design, each light brown, black and rose-red. Fluorescent security markings. Photo.* P 12½.

2115	300r. Type **523**	35	15
	a. Horiz pair. Nos. 2115/16	70	
2116	300r. Lt.-Gen. Oerip Soemohardjo	35	15

Nos. 2115/16 were issued together in horizontal *se-tenant* pairs within the sheet, each pair forming a composite design.

1993 (5 Nov). *Flora and Fauna. T* **524** *and similar vert designs. Multicoloured. Fluorescent security markings.* P 12½ × 13½.

2117	300r. Type **524**	75	15
	a. Block of 4. Nos. 2117/20	3·00	
2118	300r. *Cananga odorata*	75	15
2119	300r. Orange-tailed shama (*Capsychus pyrropygus*)	75	15
2120	300r. Southern grackle (*Gracula religiosa robusta*)	75	15
2117/2120	*Set of 4*	2·75	65

Nos. 2117/20 were issued together in *se-tenant* blocks of four stamps within the sheet.

525 Plantation

526 South
Sumatran Dancer

1993 (4 Dec). *Resettlement Programme. Fluorescent security markings.* P 12½.

2121	**525** 700r. multicoloured	75	75

1993 (22 Dec). *Traditional Dances (2nd series). T* **526** *and similar vert design. Multicoloured. Fluorescent security markings.* P 12½ × 13½.

2122	300r. Type **526**	55	15
2123	700r. West Kalimantan	1·00	15
2124	1000r. Irian Jaya	1·30	25
MS2125	50 × 101 mm. 3500r. As No. 2124	5·25	5·25

1994 (1 Mar). *International Year of the Family. Fluorescent security markings.* P 13½ × 12½.

2126	**527** 300r. multicoloured	40	15

1994 (1 Apr). *Sixth Five Year Plan. T* **528** *and similar vert designs. Multicoloured. Fluorescent security markings.* P 12½.

2127	100r. Type **528**	10	10
2128	700r. Graduate and school pupils	75	75
2129	2000r. Doctor, nurse and children	2·10	2·10

529 Netherlands Indies, Japanese
Occupation and Indonesia Stamps

1994 (1 Apr). *130th Anniv of First Netherlands Indies Stamps. Fluorescent security markings.* P 12½.

2130	**529** 700r. multicoloured	80	40

530 Ladiges' Rainbowfish
(*Telmatherina ladigesi*)

1994 (20 Apr). *Fishes. T* **530** *and similar horiz design. Multicoloured. Fluorescent security markings.* P 13½ × 12½.

2131	300r. Type **530**	35	15
2132	700r. Boeseman's rainbowfish (*Melanotaenia boesemani*)	90	35
MS2133	103 × 50 mm. 3500r. As No. 2132	5·00	5·00

531 Emblem

532 Figure, Globe
and Anniversary
Emblem

1994 (30 Apr). *National Kidney Foundation. Fluorescent security markings.* P 13½ × 12½.

2134	**531** 300r.+30r. multicoloured	50	25

1994 (5 May). *75th Anniv of International Red Cross Red Crescent Organization. Fluorescent security markings.* P 12½ × 13½.
2135 **532** 300r. black, red and new blue . . 40 15

533 Map and Emblem

REPUBLIK INDONESIA
534 Player

1994 (13 June). *Asia–Pacific Ministerial Conference on Women, Djakarta. Fluorescent security markings.* P 13½ × 12½.
2136 **533** 700r. multicoloured 80 35

1994 (17 June). *World Cup Football Championship, U S.A. T* **534** *and similar designs. Fluorescent security markings.* P 12½ × 13½ (vert) or 13½ × 12½ (horiz).
2137 150r. multicoloured 15 10
2138 300r. multicoloured 35 15
2139 700r. ultramarine, rosine and black . 75 40
2140 1000r. multicoloured . . . . 1·20 50
2137/2140 *Set of 4* . . . . 2·20 1·00
MS2141 109 × 50 mm. 3500r. multicoloured . 5·00 5·00
Designs: *Vert*—300r. Striker (mascot). *Horiz*—700r. Emblem; 1000, 3500r. Ball in net.

REPUBLIK INDONESIA
535 Player and Uber Cup
(Women's)

1994 (22 June). *Indonesian Victories in World Team Badminton Championships. T* **535** *and similar vert design. Multicoloured. Fluorescent security markings.* P 12½.
2142 300r. Type **535** 40 15
 a. Horiz pair. Nos. 2142/3 80
2143 300r. Thomas Cup (Men's) 40 15
MS2144 86 × 92 mm. 1750r. Type **535**; 1750r.
 As No. 2143 . . . . 5·00 5·00
Nos. 2142/3 were issued together in horizontal *se-tenant* pairs within the sheet, each pair forming a composite design.

536 Hand holding
Scales

537 Vase with Bead
Cover

1994 (27 July). *National Commission on Human Rights. Fluorescent security markings.* P 12½ × 13½.
2145 **536** 700r. multicoloured 80 15

1994 (16 Aug). *"Philakorea 1994" International Stamp Exhibition, Seoul. Sheet* 85 × 91 *mm. Fluorescent security markings.* Imperf.
MS2146 **529** 3500r. multicoloured . . . . . 5·00 5·00

1994 (19 Aug). *Indonesia–Pakistan Economic and Cultural Co-operation Organization. T* **537** *and similar vert design. Multicoloured. Fluorescent security markings.* P 12½ × 13½.
2147 300r. Type **537** 25 25
2148 700r. Blue and white vase 65 65

REPUBLIK INDONESIA
538 Skeleton of Quadruped

539 Mascots

1994 (22 Aug). *Centenary of Bogoriense Zoological Museum. T* **538** *and similar horiz design. Multicoloured. Fluorescent security markings.* P 13½ × 12½.
2149 700r. Type **538** 80 50
2150 1000r. Outline and skeleton of whale
 (80 × 22 *mm*) . . . . 1·10 55
MS2151 123 × 48 mm. 3500r. As No. 2150 . 5·00 5·00

1994 (2 Oct). *12th Asian Games, Hiroshima, Japan. T* **539** *and similar horiz design. Multicoloured. Fluorescent security markings.* P 13½ × 12½.
2152 300r. Type **539** 25 25
2153 700r. Hurdling 65 65

REPUBLIK INDONESIA
540 Communications and Map

541 *Morus macroura*

1994 (17 Oct). *25th Anniv of Bakosurtanal. Fluorescent security markings.* P 13½ × 12½.
2154 **540** 700r. multicoloured 80 35

1994 (5 Nov). *Flora and Fauna. T* **541** *and similar vert designs. Multicoloured. Fluorescent security markings.* P 12½ × 13½.
2155 150r. Type **541** 40 15
 a. Strip of 10. Nos. 2155/64 . . . . 4·00
2156 150r. *Oncosperma tiqillaria* 40 15
2157 150r. *Eucalyptus urophylla* 40 15
2158 150r. Moth orchid (*Phalaenopsis amabilis*) 40 15
2159 150r. *Pometia pinnata* 40 15
2160 150r. Great argus pheasant (*Argusianus argus*) 40 15
2161 150r. Blue-crowned hanging parrot (*Loriculus pusillus*) 40 15
2162 150r. Timor helmeted friarbird (*Philemon buceroides*) 40 15
2163 150r. Amboina king parrot (*Alisterus amboinensis*) 40 15
2164 150r. Twelve-wired bird of paradise (*Seleucidis melanoleuca*) 40 15
2155/2164 *Set of 10* . . . . 3·75 1·40
MS2165 48 × 81 mm. 3500r. As No. 2162 . 5·00 5·00
Nos. 2155/64 were issued together in *se-tenant* strips of ten stamps within the sheet.

542 Venue

1994 (15 Nov). *Asia–Pacific Economic Co-operation Summit, Bogor. Fluorescent security markings.* P 13½ × 12½.
2166 **542** 700r. multicoloured 80 25

543 Airplane

1994 (7 Dec). *50th Anniv of International Civil Aviation Organization. Fluorescent security markings.* P 13½ × 12½.
2167 **543** 700r. multicoloured 80 25

1994 (27 Dec). *Traditional Dances (3rd series). Vert designs as T 506. Multicoloured. Fluorescent security markings.* P 12½ × 13½.
2168 150r. Mengaup, Jambi 15 10
    a. Booklet pane. Nos. 2168/72, each
      × 2 (1995) . . . . . . 7·50
2169 300r. Topeng, West Java 25 15
2170 700r. Anging Mamiri, South
    Sulawesi 65 35
2171 1000r. Pisok, North Sulawesi 90 25
2172 2000r. Bidu, East Nusa Tenggara . . . 1·80 1·00
2168/2172 *Set of 5* . . . . 3·50 1·70
MS2173 47 × 87 mm. 3500r. As No. 2169 . . . 3·25 3·25

544 Yogyakarta Palace

(Des T. Margono (300r.), S. Talahatu (700r.), E. Yurnalis (1000r.))

1995 (2 Jan). *20th Anniv of World Tourism Organization. T 544 and similar horiz designs. Multicoloured. Fluorescent security markings.* P 13½ × 12½.
2174 300r. Type **544** 25 25
2175 700r. Floating market, Banjarmasin . . . 65 65
2176 1000r. Pasola (equestrian tradition),
    Sumba 90 90

545 Children, President Suharto and First Lady

(Des Y. Arwadinata)

1995 (11 Mar). *"Dedication to the Nation". Fluorescent security markings.* P 13½ × 12½.
2177 **545** 700r. multicoloured 65 65

546 Letter from King of Klungkung, Bali

547 *Schizostachyum brachycladum*

(Des T. Margono (300r.), Soebagyanto (700r.))

1995 (1 Apr). *Sixth Five Year Plan. National Letter Writing Campaign. T 546 and similar horiz design. Multicoloured. Fluorescent security markings.* P 12½.
2178 300r. Type **546** 25 25
2179 700r. Carrier pigeon (campaign mascot)
    and letters 65 65

(Des E. Jatmiko (300r.), K. Wiarsana (700r.). Photo and litho)

1995 (19 June). *Fourth International Bamboo Congress, Ubud, Bali. T 547 and similar vert design. Multicoloured. Fluorescent security markings.* P 12½ × 13½.
2180 300r. Type **547** 25 25
2181 700r. *Dendrocalamus asper* 65 65

548 N250 and National Flag

(Des Y. Arwadinata. Photo and litho)

1995 (10 Aug). *Inaugural Flight of I.P.T.N. N250 Airliner. Fluorescent security markings.* P 13½ × 12½.
2182 **548** 700r. multicoloured 65 65

549 Anniversary Emblem

550 Kota Intan Drawbridge

(Des Y. Arwadinata (700, 2500r.) Photo and litho)

1995 (17 Aug). *50th Anniv of Indonesian Republic. T 549 and similar horiz design. Multicoloured. Fluorescent security markings.* P 13½ × 12½.
2183 300r. Type **549** 25 25
2184 700r. Boy with national flag 65 65
MS2185 102 × 48 mm. 2500r. As No. 2184 . . . 4·50 4·50

(Des I. Wiarsana (2186), Suprayitno (2187). Litho and photo)

1995 (19 Aug). *"Jakarta '95" Asian Stamp Exhibition. T 550 and similar horiz design. Multicoloured. Fluorescent security markings.* P 13½ × 12½.
2186 300r. Type **550** 25 25
2187 700r. Fatahillah Jakarta History
    Museum 65 65

551 *Dewarutji* (cadet barquentine) and Flag

(Des E. Jatmiko. Litho and photo)

1995 (19 Aug). *"Sail Indonesia '95" Tall Ships Race and Fleet Review.* P 13½ × 13.
2188 **551** 700r. multicoloured 65 65
MS2189 91 × 48 mm. **551** 2500r.
multicoloured . . . . 4·50 4·50

552 "Mother Love" (Patricia Saerang)

553 Mushaf Istiqlal (illuminated Islamic text)

1995 (12 Sept). *Tenth Asia and Pacific Regional Conference of Rehabilitation International, Indonesia. Fluorescent security markings. Litho and photo.* P 13½ × 12½.
2190 **552** 700r.+100r. multicoloured 75 75

(Des S. Priyanto. Litho and photo)

1995 (23 Sept). *Istiqlal Festival. Fluorescent security markings.* P 12½ × 13½.
2191 **553** 700r. multicoloured 65 65

554 PTT Monument

555 Rice

(Des Y. Arwadinata)

1995 (27 Sept). *50th Anniv of Take-over of PTT Headquarters by Republicans. Fluorescent security markings.* P 13½ × 12½.
2192 **554** 700r. multicoloured 65 65

(Des I. Soeroto. Litho and photo)

1995 (16 Oct). *50th Anniv of Food and Agriculture Organization. Fluorescent security markings.* P 12½ × 13½.
2193 **555** 700r. multicoloured 65 65

556 Flags and Emblem

557 *Cyrtostachys renda*

(Des S. Talahatu (2194), Y. Arwadinata (2195). Litho and photo)

1995 (24 Oct). *50th Anniv of United Nations Organization. T 556 and similar vert design. Multicoloured. Fluorescent security markings.* P 12½ × 12½.
2194 300r. Type **556** 25 25
2195 700r. Emblem, Earth and rainbow . . . 65 65

(Des H. Purnomo (2197, **MS**2206), E. Junalies (2199), Rudiyana (2200), E. Jatmiko (2201), A. Kurniawan (2202), T. Margono (2204), K. Wiarsana (2205), Suprayitno (others). Litho and photo)

1995 (5 Nov). *Flora and Fauna. T 557 and similar vert designs. Multicoloured. Fluorescent security markings.* P 12½ × 13½.
2196 150r. Type **557** 15 10
    a. Block of 10. Nos. 2196/2205 . 1·50
2197 150r. Tiger (*Panthera tigris*) . . . 15 10
2198 150r. *Bouea macrophylla* . . . 15 10
2199 150r. Javan rhinoceros (*Rhinoceros sondaicus*) 15 10
2200 150r. *Santalum album* . . . 15 10
2201 150r. Komodo dragon (*Varanus komodoensis*) . . . 15 10
2202 150r. *Diospyros celebica* . . . 15 10
2203 150r. Maleo fowl (*Macrocephalon maleo*) . . . 15 10
2204 150r. *Nephelium ramboutan-ake* . . . 15 10
2205 150r. Malay peacock-pheasant (*Polyplectron schleiermacheri*) . . 15 10
2196/2205 *Set of 10* . . . . 1·40 90
MS2206 48 × 95 mm. 2500r. As No. 2197 . . . 7·75 7·75

558 Yogyakarta Palace

(Des Soebagyanto. Litho and photo)

1995 (23 Nov). *Award of Aga Khan Prize for Architecture to Indonesia. T 558 and similar horiz design. Multicoloured. Fluorescent security markings.* P 13½ × 12½.
2207 300r. Type **558** 25 25
2208 700r. Surakarta Palace 65 65

559 Hill and Postal Carriers

(Des Y. Arwadinata. Litho and photo)

1995 (3 Dec). *Birth Bicentenary of Sir Rowland Hill (instigator of postal stamps). T 559 and similar horiz design. Multicoloured. Fluorescent security markings.* P 13½ × 12½.
2209 300r. Type **559** 25 25
2210 700r. Hill and Indonesian Postal Service emblem 65 65

(Des M. Nurasyid (150r.), I. Soeroto (300r.), A. Soelarso (700r.), S. Talahatu (1000r.). Litho and photo)

1995 (27 Dec). *Traditional Dances (4th series). Vert design as T **506**. Multicoloured. Fluorescent security markings.* P 12½ × 13½.

2211	150r. Nguri dance, West Nusa Tenggara	15	15
2212	300r. Muli Betanggai dance, Lampung	25	25
2213	700r. Mutiara dance, Moluccas	65	65
2214	1000r. Gantar dance, East Kalimantan	90	90
2211/2214 *Set of 4*		1·75	1·75
MS2215 48 × 81 mm. 2500r. As No. 2211		3·75	3·75

560 Economic Sectors

561 Satellite orbiting Earth

(Des S. Talahatu)

1996 (2 Jan). *Economic Census. T **560** and similar design. Fluorescent security markings.* P 12½.

2216	300r. yellow-orange and indigo	25	25
2217	700r. deep turquoise and yellow-orange (horiz)	65	65

Design: Horiz—700r. Graph of economic activity.

(Des J. Menggambarkan)

1996 (31 Jan). *Launch of "Palapa-C" Satellite. T **561** and similar design. Multicoloured. Fluorescent security markings.* P 13½ × 12½ (300r.) or 12½ (700r.).

2218	300r. Type **561**	25	25
2219	700r. Satellite orbiting Earth (triangular)	55	55

562 Mixed Flowers

563 Soemanang Soeriowinoto (Association head, 1946–7 and 1949–50)

(Des Rudiyana (150r.), D. Soeripto (300r.), A. Soelarso (700r.))

1996 (1 Feb). *Greetings Stamps. "Happy Holiday". T **562** and similar horiz designs inscr "Selamat Hari Raya". Multicoloured. Fluorescent security markings.* P 12½.

2220	150r. Type **562**	10	10
2221	300r. Mixed flowers (*different*)	25	25
2222	700r. Mixed flowers (*different*)	55	55

(Des E. Junalies (300r.), S. Talahatu (700r.). Litho and photo)

1996 (9 Feb). *50th Anniv of Indonesian Journalists' Association. T **563** and similar horiz design. Multicoloured. Fluorescent security markings.* P 12½.

2223	300r. Type **563**	25	25
2224	700r. Djamaluddin Adinegoro (head of Indonesian Press Bureau Foundation and founder of Academy of Publicity and Publicity Faculty, Padjadjaran University)	55	55

564 Tank firing and Map

(Des H. Purnomo. Litho and photo)

1996 (1 Mar). *47th Anniv of Return of Republican Government to Djokjakarta. T **564** and similar horiz design. Multicoloured. Fluorescent security markings.* P 13½ × 12½.

2225	700r.+100r. Type **564**	65	65
	a. Horiz pair. Nos. 2225/6	1·30	
2226	700r.+100r. Attack on Palace	65	65

Nos. 2225/6 were issued together in horizontal *se-tenant* pairs within the sheet, each pair forming a composite design.

565 State House, Bandung

566 Indonesian Bear Cuscus

(Des Suprayitno (300r.), K. Wiarsana (700r.). Litho and photo)

1996 (21 Mar). *"indonesia '96" International Youth Stamp Exhibition, Bandung. T **565** and similar horiz design. Multicoloured. Fluorescent security markings.* P 13½ × 12½.

2227	300r. Type **565**	25	25
2228	700r. Painted parasols	55	55
MS2229 99 × 73 mm. 1250r. Type **565**; 1250r. As No. 2228		4·00	4·00

(Des Rosemary Ganf and Josephine Mure)

1996 (22 Mar). *Cuscuses. T **566** and similar vert design. Multicoloured. Fluorescent security markings.* P 12½ × 13½.

2230	300r. Australian spotted cuscus	25	25
	a. Horiz pair. Nos. 2230/1	50	
	b. Booklet pane. No. 2230a × 5	2·50	
2231	300r. Type **566**	25	25
MS2232 98 × 81 mm. 1250r. As No. 2230; 1250r. Type **566**		2·10	2·10

Nos. 2230/1 were issued together in horizontal *se-tenant* pairs within the sheet, each pair forming a composite design.
The booklet pane has a perforated margin around the block.

567 Roses

568 Students

(Des T. Margono (150r.), M. Nurasyid (300r.), E. Junalies (700r.))

1996 (15 Apr). *Greetings Stamps. "Congratulations and Best Wishes". T **567** and similar horiz designs inscr "Selamat dan Sukses". Multicoloured. Fluorescent security markings.* P 12½.

2233	150r. Type **567**	10	10
2234	300r. Orchids	25	25
2235	700r. Chrysanthemums	55	55

(Y. Edwin Purwanto)

1996 (2 May). *Compulsory Nine Year Education Programme. Winning Entries in Children's Stamp Design Competition. T* **568** *and similar horiz designs. Multicoloured. Fluorescent security markings. Litho and photo.* P $13\frac{1}{2} \times 12\frac{1}{2}$.

2236	150r. Type **568**	10	10
2237	300r. Children in playground (Andi Pradhana)	25	25
2238	700r. Teacher and pupils (Intan Sari Dewi)	55	55

569 Archery

(Des H. Purnomo. Litho and photo)

1996 (15 May). *Olympic Games, Atlanta. T* **569** *and similar horiz designs. Multicoloured. Fluorescent security markings.* P $13\frac{1}{2} \times 12\frac{1}{2}$.

2239	300r. Type **569**	25	25
2240	700r. Weightlifting	55	55
2241	1000r. Badminton	90	90
MS2242	81×48 mm. 2500r. Type **569**	2·10	2·10

中国'96 — 第9届亚洲国际集邮展览
CHINA'96 — 9th Asian International Philatelic Exhibition
(570) ($\frac{3}{4}$-size illustration)

1996 (18 May). *"China '96" International Stamp Exhibition, Peking. No.* **MS**2232 *optd with T* **570** *in gold in the margin.*
MS2243 98×81 mm. 1250r. × 2, multicoloured   5·75   5·75

571 Pres. Suharto and Procession

572 Nusantara N-2130 Prototype over Soekarno-Hatta Airport

1996 (8 June). *National Youth Kirab. T* **571** *and similar horiz design. Multicoloured. Fluorescent security markings. Litho and photo.* P $13\frac{1}{2} \times 12\frac{1}{2}$.

2244	300r. Type **571**	25	25
2245	700r. Pres. Suharto presenting national flag	55	55

(Des T. Margono (300r.), Suprayitno (700r.). Litho and photo)

1996 (22 June). *Aviation and Maritime Year. T* **572** *and similar horiz design. Multicoloured. Fluorescent security markings.* P $12\frac{1}{2}$.

2246	300r. Type **572**	25	25
2247	700r. *Palindo Jaya* (inter-island ferry)	55	55

573 Scouts climbing Rope Ladders

574 Prows and Wave

(Des T. Margono and Desmal. Litho and photo)

1996 (26 June). *National Scout Jamboree, Djakarta. T* **573** *and similar horiz designs. Multicoloured. Fluorescent security markings.* P $12\frac{1}{2}$.

2248	150r. Type **573**	10	10
	a. Block of 8. Nos. 2248/55	80	
2249	150r. Scouts on ladder and death slide	10	10
2250	150r. Scouts at base of rope ladders	10	10
2251	150r. Girl scouts constructing wooden apparatus	10	10
2252	150r. Scouts on unicycle and climbing frame	10	10
2253	150r. Girl scouts building frame on campsite	10	10
2254	150r. Soldering metal	10	10
2255	150r. Girl at radio taking notes	10	10
2248/2255	*Set of 8*	75	75

Nos. 2248/55 were issued together in *se-tenant* blocks of eight stamps within the sheet, Nos. 2248/51 and 2252/5 respectively forming composite designs.

(Des M. Hadi. Litho and photo)

1996 (5 July). *50th Anniv of Bank BNI. T* **574** *and similar horiz design. Multicoloured. Fluorescent security markings.* P $12\frac{1}{2}$.

2256	300r. Type **574**	25	25
2257	700r. *Pinisi* sailing ship	55	55

575 Mother and Child reading (Salt Iodization Programme)

576 Ibu Tien Suharto

(Des H. Purnomo)

1996 (23 July). *50th Anniv of United Nations Children's Fund. T* **575** *and similar horiz designs. Each yellow-brown, blue-green and deep mauve. Fluorescent security markings.* P $13\frac{1}{2} \times 12\frac{1}{2}$.

2258	300r. Type **575**	25	25
2259	700r. Giving oral vaccine to children (elimination of polio)	55	55
2260	1000r. Children (Children's Rights Convention)	90	90

(Des Y. Arwadinata. Litho and photo)

1996 (5 Aug). *Ibo Tien Suharto (First Lady) Commemoration. Fluorescent security markings.* P $12\frac{1}{2} \times 13\frac{1}{2}$.

2261	**576**	700r. multicoloured	55	55
MS2262		47×96 mm. **576** 2500r. multicoloured	2·10	2·10

No. 2261 was issued both in sheets of 50 stamps and in sheetlets of ten.

577 Softball

(Des Rudiyana (300r.), I. Wiarsana (700r.), E. Junalies (1000r.))

1996 (2 Sept). *National Sports Week. T 577 and similar horiz designs. Multicoloured. Fluorescent security markings.* P 13½ × 12½.

2263	300r. Type **577**	25	25
2264	700r. Hockey	55	55
2265	1000r. Basketball	90	90

1996 (7 Sept). *"Istanbul '96" Stamp Exhibition, Turkey. Two sheets, each 94 × 80 mm, each containing one stamp (62 × 46 mm) featuring composite designs formerly issued in blocks of four. Fluorescent security markings.* P 12½.
MS2266 Two sheets. (a) 1250r. As
Nos. 2248/51; (b) 1250r. As No. 2252/5 . . . 1·60   1·60

578 Head of Sumatran Rhinoceros
579 Flower Arrangement

(Des D. Bason. Photo)

1996 (2 Oct). *The Sumatran Rhinoceros (Dicerorhinus sumatrensis) and the Javan Rhinoceros (Rhinoceros sondaicus). T 578 and similar horiz designs. Multicoloured. Fluorescent security markings.* P 13½ × 12½.

2267	300r. Type **578**b	40	25
	a. Block or strip of 4.		
	Nos. 2267/70	1·60	
2268	300r. Sumatran rhinoceros	40	25
2269	300r. Javan rhinoceros	40	25
2270	300r. Adult and baby Javan		
	rhinoceros	40	25
2267/2270 *Set of 4*		1·40	90

MS2271 100 × 47 mm. 1500r. Javan rhinoceros;
1500r. Sumatran rhinoceros . . . 3·75   3·75
Nos. 2267/70 were issued together in *se-tenant* blocks and strips both in sheets of 16 stamps and in sheetlets of eight sold at 3000r.
The sheetlet of eight (Nos. 2267/70, each × 2) was re-issued on 11 October 1997 overprinted "Bursa Filateli SEA Games XIX Jakarta, 11–19 Oktober 1997" in gold on the sheet margin.

(Des Suprayitno (150r.), A. Kurniawan (300r.), Desmal (700r.))

1996 (15 Oct). *Greetings Stamps. "Happy New Year". T 579 and similar horiz designs inscr "Selamat Tahun Baru". Multicoloured. Fluorescent security markings.* P 12½.

2272	150r. Type **579**	10	10
2273	300r. Arrangement including red and		
	yellow roses	25	25
2274	700r. Arrangement including white rose		
	and yellow chrysanthemums	55	55

580 Coins and Banknotes
581 Sulawesi Hornbill (*Aceros cassidix*)

(Des S. Sugiyanto. Litho and photo)

1996 (30 Oct). *50th Anniv of Financial Day. Fluorescent security markings.* P 13½ × 12½.
2275   **580**   700r. multicoloured . . . 55   55

(Des S. Talahatu (2276), Soebagyanto (2277), Suprayitno (2278, 2283), Rudiyana (2279), K. Wiarsana (2280), Desmal (2281), I. Suroto (2282), I. Kurniawan (2284), T. Margono (2285). Litho and photo)

1996 (5 Nov). *National Flora and Fauna Day. T 581 and similar vert designs. Multicoloured. Fluorescent security markings.* P 12½ × 13½.

2276	300r. Type **581**	25	25
	a. Block of 10. Nos. 2276/85	2·50	
2277	300r. Irrawaddy dolphin (*Orcaella brevirostris*)	25	25
2278	300r. Black-naped oriole (*Oriolus chinensis*)	25	25
2279	300r. Sun bear (*Helarctos malayanus*)	25	25
2280	300r. Rothschild's mynah (*Leucopsar rothschildi*)	25	25
2281	300r. Lontar palms (*Borassus flabellifer*)	25	25
2282	300r. Black orchid (*Coelogyne pandurata*)	25	25
2283	300r. Michelia (*Michelia alba*)	25	25
2284	300r. Giant aroid lily (*Amorphophallus titanum*)	25	25
2285	300r. Majegau (*Dysoxylum densiflorum*)	25	25
2276/2285 *Set of 10*		2·25	2·25

MS2286 Two sheets, each 47 × 80 mm. (a)
1250r. As No. 2280; (b) 1250r. As No. 2282
See also No. **MS**2287. . . . 1·20   1·20

1996 (14 Dec). *"Aseanpex '96" International Stamp Exhibition, Manila, Philippines. Sheet 47 × 94 mm. Fluorescent security markings.* P 12½ × 13½.
MS2287 **581** 2000r. multicoloured . . . 5·00   5·00

582 Somba Opu Fortress
583 Schoolchildren at Play

(Des E. Junalies (300r.), Soebagyanto (700r.). Litho and photo)

1996 (18 Dec). *Eastern Region. T 582 and similar horiz design. Multicoloured. Fluorescent security markings.* P 13½ × 12½.

2288	300r. Divers and sea-bed	25	25
2289	700r. Type **582**	55	55
See also No. **MS**2304.			

(Des Y. Arwadinata)

1996 (20 Dec). *National Movement of Foster Parents. T 583 and similar multicoloured design. Fluorescent security markings.* P 12½ × 13½ (150r.) or 13½ × 12½ (300r.).

2290	150r. Type **583**	15	15
2291	300r. Poor children and photograph of		
	schoolchild (*horiz*)	25	25

(Des Desman (150r.), E. Junalies (300r.), S. Talahatu (700r.), Suprayitno (1000r.). Litho and photo)

1996 (27 Dec). *Traditional Dances (5th series). Vert designs as T 506. Multicoloured. Fluorescent security markings.* P 12½ × 13½.

2292	150r. Baksa Kembang dance, South Kalimantan	10	10
2293	300r. Ngarojeng dance, Djakarta	25	25
2294	700r. Rampai dance, Aceh	55	55
2295	1000r. Boituka dance, East Timor	90	90
2292/2295 *Set of 4*		1·60	1·60

MS2296 46 × 75 mm. 2000r. As No. 2293 . . . 2·00   2·00

584 Dish Aerial and Control Room

585 Children shaking Hands "Happy Birthday"

(Des Y. Arwadinata. Litho and photo)

1997 (1 Jan). *Telecommunications Year. T* **584** *and similar horiz design. Multicoloured. Fluorescent security markings.* P 13½ × 12½.
2297   300r. Type **584**   25   25
2298   700r. Key pad, communications satellite orbiting Earth and woman using telephone   55   55

(Des I. Suroto (2299), K. Wiarsana (2300). Photo)

1997 (15 Jan). *Greetings Stamps. T* **585** *and similar horiz design. Fluorescent security markings.* P 12½.
2299   600r. multicoloured   50   50
2300   600r. black, light brown and magenta .   50   50
Design:—No. 2300, Heart and ribbons "Best Wishes".

586 Transport, Ballot Boxes and National Flag

(Des I. Suroto (300r.), Sukirman (700r.), Desmal (1000r.). Litho and photo)

1997 (3 Feb). *General Election. T* **586** *and similar horiz designs. Multicoloured. Fluorescent security markings.* P 13½ × 12½.
2301   300r. Type **586**   25   25
2302   700r. State arms, map, ballot boxes and buildings   55   55
2303   1000r. State arms, ballot boxes, map and city skyline   90   90

1997 (12 Feb). *"Hong Kong '97" Stamp Exhibition. Sheet* 81 × 47 *mm. Fluorescent security markings.* P 13½ × 12½.
MS2304 2000r. As Type **582** but with addition of postmark . . . .   2·00   2·00

587 Pres. Suharto and Wahyu Nusantaraaji

588 Children with Stamp Collection

(Des National Family Planning Programme Co-ordinating Board Information Bureau. Litho and photo)

1997 (24 Mar). *Indonesia's 200 Millionth Citizen. Fluorescent security markings.* P 13½ × 12½.
2305   **587**   700r. multicoloured   55   55

(Des M. Nurasyid (300r.), Suprayitno (700r.). Litho and photo)

1997 (29 Mar). *75th Anniv of Indonesian Philatelic Association. T* **588** *and similar vert design. Multicoloured. Fluorescent security markings.* P 12½ × 13½.
2306   300r. Type **588**   25   25
2307   700r. Magnifying glass on 1994 150r. Flora and Fauna stamp   55   55

589 Wage Rudolf Soepratman

590 Picture Jasper

(Des S. Sugiyanto (1000r.), Hardjanto (others). Litho and photo)

1997 (30 Apr). *Cultural Anniversaries. T* **589** *and similar vert designs. Multicoloured. Fluorescent security markings.* P 12½ × 13½.
2308   300r. Type **589** (composer of *Indonesia Raya* (national anthem), 60th death anniv (1998))   25   25
2309   700r. Usmar Ismail (film director, 25th death anniv (1996))   55   55
2310   1000r. Self-portrait of Affandi (painter, 90th birth anniv)   90   90
MS2311 47 × 79 mm. 2000r. As No. 2310 . . . .   2·00   2·00

(Des Jonas Digital Imaging Communication, Bandung. Litho and photo)

1997 (20 May). *"Indonesia 2000" International Stamp Exhibition, Bandung (1st issue). Minerals. T* **590** *and similar horiz designs. Multicoloured. Fluorescent security markings.* P 13½ × 12½.
2312   300r. Type **590**   25   25
2313   700r. Chrysocolla   55   55
2314   1000r. Geode   90   90
MS2315 80 × 47 mm. 2000r. Banded agate . .   2·00   2·00
Nos. 2312/14 were issued both separately in sheets of 20 and together in *se-tenant* sheetlets of nine stamps and one label.
Nos. 2312/14 and No. **MS**2315 were issued on 3 November 1997 overprinted "3 TAHUN LAGI 3 YEARS TO GO" in gold in the margin.
Nos. 2312/14 and **MS**2315 were also issued in presentation folders, they were sold above face value with the difference going to the organisers of "Indonesia 2000" philatelic exhibition.
See also Nos. 2403/**MS**2407, 2529/**MS**2533 and 2593/**MS**2597.

591 Black-naped Oriole (*Oriolus chinensis*)

592 Crowd giving Thumbs Up to "No Smoking" Sign

1997 (29 May). *"Pacific 97" International Stamp Exhibition, San Francisco. Sheet* 49 × 91 *mm. Fluorescent security markings. Litho and photo.* P 12½ × 13½.
MS2316 **591** 2000r. multicoloured . . . . . .   2·00   2·00

(Des Riawati)

1997 (31 May). *World (No Smoking) Day. Winning Entry in Students' Design Competition. Fluorescent security markings. Photo.* P 12½.

2317	**592**	1000r. multicoloured	90	90

593 Fishes and Coral Reef

594 Paksi Naga Liman Carriage (built by Pangeran Losari)

(Des S. Talahatu (2000r.), M. Nurasyid and I. Soeroto (others). Litho and photo)

1997 (5 June). *World Environment Day. T 593 and similar vert designs. Multicoloured. Fluorescent security markings.* P 12½ × 13½.

2318	150r. Type **593**		15	15
2319	300r. Rays and other fishes by brain and other corals		25	25
2320	700r. Two coralfishes amongst corals		55	55
MS2321	47 × 79 mm. 2000r. Coral reef		2·00	2·00

(Des Rudiyana (300r.), E. Jatmiko (700r.). Litho and photo)

1997 (1 July). *Second Indonesian Royal Palace Festival, Cirebon. T 594 and similar horiz design. Multicoloured. Fluorescent security markings.* P 13½ × 12½.

2322	300r. Type **594**		25	25
2323	700r. Singa Barong carriage (built by Ki Nataguna), 1549		55	55

595 Venue's Main Gateway

(Des T. Margono (300r.), A. Kurniawan (700r.). Photo)

1997 (9 July). *18th National Koran Reading Contest, Jambi. T 595 and similar horiz design. Multicoloured. Fluorescent security markings.* P 12½.

2324	300r. Type **595**		25	25
2325	700r. Al Ikhsaniah Mosque, Olak Kemang, Jambi		55	55

596 Co-operatives Monument, Tasikmalaya

597 Pres. Suharto and Dr. Mohammad Hatta (first vice-president)

(Des I. and Rita Widagdo. Litho and photo)

1997 (12 July). *50th Anniv of Co-operatives Movement. T 596 and similar vert designs and T 597. Multicoloured. Fluorescent security markings.* P 12½ (700r.) or 12½ × 13½ (others).

2326	150r. Type **596**		10	10
	a. Pair. Nos. 2326/7		20	
2327	150r. Co-operatives Monument, Djakarta		10	10
2328	300r. Child's hand clasping adult's hand		25	25
	a. Pair. Nos. 2328/9		50	
2329	300r. Figure before globe		25	25
2330	700r. Type **597**		55	55
2326/2330	*Set of* 5		1·10	1·10

Stamps of the same value were issued together in *se-tenant* pairs within their sheets.

598 Hands on Globe

599 Games Emblem and Mascot

(Des A. Es-Be. Litho and photo)

1997 (8 Aug). *30th Anniv of Association of South-East Asian Nations. T 598 and similar horiz designs. Multicoloured. Fluorescent security markings.* P 13½ × 12½.

2331	300r. Type **598**		25	25
2332	700r. Ears of cereals forming "30th" and globe		55	55

(Des Sylvia Yudhira. Litho and photo)

1997 (9 Sept). *19th South-East Asian Games, Djakarta. T 599 and similar horiz designs. Multicoloured. Fluorescent security markings.* P 12½.

2333	300r. Type **599**		25	25
	a. Pair. Nos. 2333/4		50	
	b. Perf 3 sides. Booklets		25	
	ba. Booklet pane. Nos. 2333b, 2334a, 2335b and 2336a, each × 2		3·25	
2334	300r. Torch carrier, flags and emblem		25	25
	a. Perf 2 or 3 sides. Booklets		25	
2335	700r. Running and throwing the discus		55	55
	a. Pair. Nos. 2335/6		1·10	
	b. Perf 3 sides. Booklets		55	
2336	700r. Hurdling and sprinting		55	55
	a. Perf 2 or 3 sides.		55	
2333/2336	*Set of* 4		1·40	1·40

Booklets Stamps of the same value were issued together in *se-tenant* pairs within their sheets.

The booklet pane has its outer edges imperforate giving stamps with one or two adjacent sides imperf.

600 Coach, Bus, Java "International Harvester" Bus and Bullock Cart

1997 (17 Sept). *National Communications Day. Transport Development. T 600 and similar horiz designs. Multicoloured. Fluorescent security markings. Litho and photo.* P 12½.

2337	300r. Type **600**		25	25
	a. Pair. Nos. 2337/8		50	
2338	300r. Electric, express, diesel and steam railway locomotives		25	25

2339 700r. Container ship, passenger ship,
cargo vessel and lette (Madurese
sailing boat) 55 55
    a. Pair. Nos. 2339/40 . . . . . . 1·10
2340 700r. Seulawah and IPTN CN-235,
CN-250 and N-2130 airliners . . . 55 55
2337/2340 Set of 4 . . . . 1·40 1·40
Stamps of the same value were issued together in *se-tenant*
pairs within the sheet.

601 U.P.U. Monument and Mas
Soeharto (first head of Indonesian
P.T.T.)

(Des Y. Arwadinata. Litho and photo)

1997 (27 Sept). *50th Anniv of Indonesian Membership of Universal
Postal Union. T* **601** *and similar horiz design. Multicoloured.
Fluorescent security markings.* P 13½ × 12½.
2341 300r. Type **601** 25 25
2342 700r. Heinrich von Stephan (founder of
U.P.U.) and monument 55 55

602 Assembly Emblem and Building

(Des A. Es-Be. Litho and photo)

1997 (1 Oct). *People's Consultative Assembly General Session.
Fluorescent security markings.* P 12½.
2343 **602** 700r. multicoloured 55 55

603 Village Programme (Army)

(Des E. Jatmiko, H. Desmal, M. Nurasyid and I. Soeroto. Litho
and photo)

1997 (5 Oct). *Armed Forces Day. T* **603** *and similar horiz designs.
Multicoloured. Fluorescent security markings.* P 13½ × 12½.
2344 300r. Type **603** 25 25
    a. Block of 4. Nos. 2344/7 . . . . 1·00
2345 300r. Frigates and Jalesveva Jayamahe
Monument, Surabaya (Navy) . . . 25 25
2346 300r. "Blue Falcon" acrobatic team (Air
Force) 25 25
2347 300r. Rapid Reaction Unit (Police
Force) 25 25
2344/2347 Set of 4 . . . . 90 90
Nos. 2344/7 were issued together in *se-tenant* blocks of four
within the sheet.

604 White Buffalo   **605** Duku Fruit
(*Lansium
domesticum*)

(Des H. Mintareja. Litho and photo Perum Percetakan Uang,
Djakarta)

1997 (11 Oct). *"MAKASSAR '97" National Stamp Exhibition,
Ujung Pandeng. Sheet 106 × 49 mm.* P 13½ × 12½.
MS2348 **604** 2000r. multicoloured . . . . . . 1·30 1·30

(Des E. Junalies, E. Jatmiko,
Suprayitno, M. Desmal, I. Soeroto, A. Kurniawan
and S. Talahatu. Litho and photo)

1997 (5 Nov). *National Flora and Fauna Day. T* **605** *and similar
vert designs. Multicoloured. Fluorescent security markings.*
P 12½ × 13½.
2349 300r. Type **605** 25 25
    a. Block or horiz strip of 10.
     Nos. 2349/58 . . . . 2·50
2350 300r. Salacca of Condet (*Salacca
zalacca*) 25 25
2351 300r. Tengawang tungkul (*Shorea
stenoptera*) 25 25
2352 300r. Ebony (*Diospyros macrophylla*) . . 25 25
2353 300r. Fibre orchid (*Diplocaulobium
utile*) 25 25
2354 300r. Belida fish (*Chitala lopis*) 25 25
2355 300r. Brahminy kite (*Haliastur indus*) . . 25 25
2356 300r. Helmeted hornbill (*Rhinoplax
vigil*) 25 25
2357 300r. Timor deer (*Cervus timorensis*) . . 25 25
2358 300r. Anoa (*Bubalus depressicornis*) . . 25 25
2349/2358 Set of 10 . . . . 2·25 2·25
MS2359 98 × 80 mm. 1250r. As No. 2351;
1250r. As No. 2355 . . . . . . 1·80 1·80
Nos. 2349/58 were issued together in *se-tenant* blocks and
horizontal strips of ten stamps within the sheet.

606 Oil Field

(Des Y. Arwadinata. Litho and photo)

1997 (24 Nov). *Association of South-East Asian Nations Council
on Petroleum Conference, Djakarta. T* **606** *and similar horiz
designs. Multicoloured. Fluorescent security markings.*
P 13½ × 12½.
2360 300r. Type **606** 25 25
    a. Block of 4. Nos. 2360/3 . . . . 1·00
2361 300r. Oil refinery 25 25
2362 300r. Eka Putra (oil tanker) 25 25
2363 300r. Petrol tankers 25 25
2360/2363 Set of 4 . . . . 90 90
Nos. 2360/3 were issued together in *se-tenant* blocks of four
stamps within the sheet.

607 AIDS Ribbon

(Des M. Desmal)

1997 (1 Dec). *World AIDS Awareness Day. Fluorescent security markings.* P 13½ × 12½.

2364	**607**	700r.+100r. multicoloured	50	50

608 Letter from Foster Son

(Des Y. Arwadinata)

1997 (20 20). *National Foster Parents Movement. Fluorescent security markings.* P 13½ × 12½.

2365	**608**	700r. multicoloured	50	50

(Des M. Desmal, A. Soelarso, I. Wiarsana and S. Talahatu)

1997 (27 Dec). *Traditional Dances (6th series). Vert designs as T 506. Multicoloured. Fluorescent security markings.* P 12½ × 13½.

2366	150r.	Mopuputi Cengke dance, Central Sulawesi	10	10
2367	300r.	Mandau Talawang Nyai Balau dance, Central Kalimantan	25	25
2368	600r.	Gambyong dance, Central Java	40	40
2369	700r.	Cawan dance, North Sumatra	50	50
2370	1000r.	Legong Keraton dance, Bali	65	65
2366/2370		*Set of 5*	1·70	1·70
MS2371		48 × 79 mm. 2000r. As No. 2368	1·30	1·30

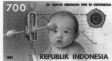

609 Baby and Scales

1997 (27 Dec). *25th Anniv of Family Welfare Movement. Fluorescent security markings. Litho and photo.* P 13½ × 12½.

2372	**609**	700r. multicoloured	50	50

610 Erau Festival, East Kalimantan

(Des H. Mintareja. Litho and photo)

1998 (1 Jan). *Year of Art and Culture. Festivals. T 610 and similar horiz design. Multicoloured. Fluorescent security markings.* P 12½.

2373	300r.	Type **610**	10	10
2374	700r.	Tabot Festival, Bengkulu	25	25

611 Malin Kundang and his Mother

(Des A. Thoriq and Omik Nasional Studio. Litho and photo)

1998 (2 Feb). *Folk Tales (1st series). T 611 and similar horiz designs. Multicoloured. Fluorescent security markings.* P 13½ × 12½.

(a) "Malin Kundang".

2375	300r.	Type **611**	10	10
	a.	Sheetlet of 20. Nos. 2375/94	2·00	
2376	300r.	Malin returning home and rejecting Mother	10	10
2377	300r.	Malin's mother praying to God to curse him	10	10
2378	300r.	Malin's ship in storm	10	10
2379	300r.	Malin turned to stone	10	10

(b) "Sangkuriang".

2380	300r.	Dayang Sumbi weaving	10	10
2381	300r.	Dayang Sumbi expelling her son Sanguriang after he killed their dog	10	10
2382	300r.	Sanguriang discovering his lover is her son	10	10
2383	300r.	Dayang Sumbi creating fake dawn and Sanguriang hurling wooden boat	10	10
2384	300r.	Tangkuban Parahu (upturned boat) Mountain	10	10

(c) "Roro Jonggrang".

2385	300r.	Pengging people attacking Prambanan people	10	10
2386	300r.	Bandung Bondowoso proposing to Roro Jonggrang	10	10
2387	300r.	Bandung Bondowoso building temples	10	10
2388	300r.	Women banging rice-mothers to prematurely announce dawn	10	10
2389	300r.	Prambanan Temple and petrified Roro Jonggrang	10	10

(d) "Tengger".

2390	300r.	Roro Anteng and Joko Seger marrying	10	10
2391	300r.	Roro and Joko praying to gods for a child	10	10
2392	300r.	Volcano erupting	10	10
2393	300r.	Raden Kusuma (youngest son) sacrificing himself	10	10
2394	300r.	Tengger people giving offerings to volcano	10	10
2375/2394		*Set of 20*	1·80	1·80
MS2395		62 × 64 mm. 2500r. As No. 2394	65	65

Nos. 2375/94 were issued together in *se-tenant* sheetlets of 20 stamps, each horizontal strip forming a composite design.

See also Nos. 2489/**MS**2509, 2572/**MS**2592 and 2679/**MS**2699.

612 Djakarta Palace

613 Man and Pregnant Woman

(Des Y. Madya. Litho and photo)

1998 (1 Apr). *Presidential Palaces.* T **612** *and similar horiz designs. Multicoloured. Fluorescent security markings.* P $13\frac{1}{2} \times 12\frac{1}{2}$.

2396	300r. Type **612**	10	10
	a. Horiz strip of 5. Nos. 2396/2400	50	
2397	300r. Bogor Palace	10	10
2398	300r. Cipanas Palace	10	10
2399	300r. Yogyakarta Palace	10	10
2400	300r. Tampak Siring Palace, Bali	10	10
2396/2400 *Set of 5*		45	45

Nos. 2396/2400 were issued together in horizontal *se-tenant* strips of five stamps within the sheet.

1998 (7 Apr). *50th Anniv of World Health Organization.* T **613** *and similar multicoloured design. Fluorescent security markings. Litho and photo.* P $12\frac{1}{2}$.

2401	300r. Type **613**	10	10
2402	700r. Mother and child (*horiz*)	10	10

(Des A. Kalake. Litho and photo)

1998 (20 May). *"Indonesia 2000" International Stamp Exhibition, Bandung (2nd issue). Minerals. Horiz designs as* T **590**. *Fluorescent security markings.* P $13\frac{1}{2} \times 12\frac{1}{2}$.

2403	300r. Chrysopal	10	10
2404	700r. Tektite	15	15
2405	1000r. Amethyst	25	25
MS2406	80 × 48 mm. 2500r. Petrified wood	40	40
MS2407	Two sheets. (a) 81 × 48 mm. 2500r.		

Opal; (b) 118 × 133 mm. Nos. 2403/5, each × 2, plus stamps as in No. **MS**2406 and
MS2407a (pair of sheets sold at 35000r.)

(3 Aug)	80	80

Nos. 2403/5 were issued both separately in sheets of 20 and together in *se-tenant* sheetlets of nine stamps and one label.

Nos. 2403/5 and **MS**2406 were also issued in presentation folders, they were sold above face value at 25000r. (Nos. 2403/5) and 10000r. (**MS**2406) with the difference going to the organisers of "Indonesia 2000" philatelic exhibition.

614 Boys playing Football

(Des P. Baiq and Cimot. Litho and photo)

1998 (1 June). *World Cup Football Championship, France.* T **614** *and similar horiz designs. Multicoloured. Fluorescent security markings.* P $13\frac{1}{2} \times 12\frac{1}{2}$.

2408	300r. Type **614**	10	10
2409	700r. Boys and goal-posts	15	15
2410	1000r. Boys challenging for ball	25	25
MS2411	87 × 57 mm. 2500r. As No. 2411	40	40

615 Tropical Rainforest

616 Fishing Cat

(Des Y. Arwadinata. Litho and photo)

1998 (5 June). *Environmental Protection. Ecophila Stamp Day.* T **615** *and similar horiz design. Multicoloured. Fluorescent security markings.* P $13\frac{1}{2} \times 12\frac{1}{2}$.

2412	700r. Type **615**	15	15
	a. Horiz pair. Nos. 2412/13	30	
	b. Tête-bêche (block of 4)	75	
2413	700r. Tropical rainforest (*different*)	15	15

Nos. 2412/13 were issued together in *se-tenant* horizontal pairs within the sheet, each pair forming a composite design. The sheet consisted of two blocks of eight stamps (2 × 4) separated by an illustrated gutter, with alternate horizontal rows inverted.

(Des T. Sugiarta. Litho and photo)

1998 (18 June). *"Juvalux '98" Youth Stamp Exhibition, Luxembourg. Sheet* 48 × 83 *mm. Fluorescent security markings.* P $12\frac{1}{2} \times 13\frac{1}{2}$.

MS2414	**616** 5000r. multicoloured	65	65

HARI ANTI MADAT SEDUNIA
REPUBLIK INDONESIA
617 Schoolchildren and Drug Addict

(Des I. Soeroto. Litho and photo)

1998 (26 June). *International Day Against Drug Abuse and Illicit Trafficking.* T **617** *and similar vert design. Multicoloured. Fluorescent security markings.* P $12\frac{1}{2} \times 13\frac{1}{2}$.

2415	700r. Type **617**	15	15
	a. Horiz pair or tête-bêche (vert pair). Nos. 2415/16	30	
2416	700r. Students campaigning against drugs	15	15

Nos. 2415/16 were issued together in *se-tenant* pairs within sheets of 16 stamps, consisting of two horizontal rows of eight stamps and two labels with the lower row inverted.

618 Besakih Temple ($\frac{1}{4}$-*size illustration*)

(Des Miko and Ketut. Litho and photo)

1998 (1 July). *Tourism.* T **618** *and similar horiz design. Multicoloured. Fluorescent security markings.* P $12\frac{1}{2}$.

2417	700r. Type **618**	15	15
	a. Horiz pair. Nos. 2417/18	30	
2418	700r. Taman Ayun Temple (31 × 23 mm)	15	15
MS2419	77 × 45 mm. 2500r. Central part of design in Type **618** (41 × 24 mm)	40	40

Nos. 2417/18 were issued together in horizontal *se-tenant* pairs within the sheet.

619 Tiger (*Panthera tigris*)

(Des A. Es-Be and L. Madjunwati. Litho and photo)

1998 (23 July). *"Singpex '98" Asian Stamp Exhibition, Singapore. Sheet* 102 × 48 *mm. Fluorescent security markings.* P 13½ × 12½.

MS2420 **619** 5000r. multicoloured . . . . . . 2·75 2·75

620 Cattle Wagon and Truck

(Des T. Sugiarta and A. Es-Be. Litho and photo)

1998 (10 Aug). *Railway Rolling Stock.* T **620** *and similar horiz design. Multicoloured. Fluorescent security markings.* P 13½ × 12½.

2421	300r. Type **620**		10	10
	a. Block of 10. Nos. 2421/30 (normal			
	or tête- bêche)		1·00	
2422	300r. Truck and goods wagon		10	10
2423	300r. Green and yellow passenger			
	carriages		10	10
2424	300r. Passenger carriage and tender		10	10
2425	300r. Class B50 steam locomotive		10	10
2426	300r. Front half of Class D52 steam			
	locomotive		10	10
2427	300r. Back half of Class D52 steam			
	locomotive with tender		10	10
2428	300r. Passenger carriage with two			
	doors		10	10
2429	300r. Observation car		10	10
2430	300r. Goods wagon		10	10
2421/2430 *Set of 10*			90	90
MS2431 76 × 48 mm. 2500r. Steam				
locomotive			50	50

Nos. 2421/30 were issued together in *se-tenant* blocks of ten within sheets of 20 stamps (5 × 4), each horizontal strip forming a composite design of a train. The bottom two rows were inverted.

621 Pres. Bacharuddin Habibie

622 Fencing

(Des K. Warsana, H. Purnomo and E. Jatmiko. Litho and photo)

1998 (17 Aug). T **621** *and similar vert designs. Fluorescent security markings.* P 12½ × 13½.

2432	**621**	300r. multicoloured	10	10
2433		700r. multicoloured	15	15
2434		4500r. multicoloured	90	90
2435		5000r. multicoloured	1·00	1·00
2432/2435 *Set of 4*			1·90	1·90

(Des A. Es-Be. Litho and photo)

1998 (9 Sept). *13th Asian Games, Bangkok, Thailand.* T **622** *and similar horiz designs. Multicoloured. Fluorescent security markings.* P 13½ × 12½.

2436	300r. Type **622**		10	10
2437	700r. Taekwondo		15	15
2438	4000r. Kung fu		80	80
MS2439 79 × 100 mm. Nos. 2436/8			1·00	1·00

623 *Baruna Jaya IV* (research ship)

(Des H. Purnomo. Litho and photo)

1998 (26 Sept). *International Year of the Ocean. Fluorescent security markings.* P 13½ × 12½.

2440	**623**	700r. multicoloured	15	15

624 Javan Kingfisher (*Halcyon cyannoventris*)

625 U.P.U. Stamp

1998 (8 Oct). *Fifth Dutch Stamp Dealers' Association Stamp Exhibition, The Hague, Netherlands. Two sheets containing* T **624** *or similar multicoloured design. Fluorescent security markings. Litho and photo.* P 13½ × 12½ (5000r.) or 12½ × 13½ (35000r.).

MS2441 Two sheets. (a) 71 × 46 mm. 5000r. Type **624**; (b) 71 × 60 mm. 35000r. Javanese wattled lapwing (*Vannelus macropterus*) (*vert*) . . . . 9·50 9·50

1998 (9 Oct). *World Stamp Day.* T **625** *and similar vert design. Multicoloured. Fluorescent security markings.* P 12½ × 13½.

2442	700r. Type **625**		15	15
	a. Horiz pair or tête-bêche vert pair.			
	Nos. 2443/4		30	
2443	700r. 1955 15s. Post Office Anniversary			
	stamp		15	15

Nos. 2442/3 were issued together in sheets with each alternate row inverted, giving horizontal normal *se-tenant* pairs and vertical tête-bêche pairs.

626 Magpie Goose (*Anseranas semipalmata*)

627 Djakarta Cathedral

(Des Pradhika Studio. Litho, photo and holography)

1998 (19 Oct). *Water Fowl (1st series).* T **626** *and similar horiz designs. Multicoloured. Fluorescent security markings.* P 13½ × 13.

2444	4000r. Type **626**		1·00	1·00
2445	5000r. Spotted whistling duck			
	(*Dendrocygna guttata*)		1·20	1·20
2446	10000r. Salvadori's duck (*Anas waigiuensis*)		2·40	2·40

2447	15000r. Radjah shelduck (*Tadorna radjah*)	3·50	3·50
2448	20000r. White-winged wood duck (*Cairina scutulata*)	5·00	5·00
2444/2448 *Set of 5*		11·50	11·50
MS2449 206 × 115 mm. Nos. 2444/8		13·00	13·00

The hologram shows the postal emblem.
See also Nos. 2468/**MS**2475 and 2628/9.

1998 (23 Oct). *"Italia '98" International Stamp Exhibition, Milan.* Fluorescent security markings. P $12\frac{1}{2} \times 13\frac{1}{2}$.
MS2450 55 × 79 mm. **627** 5000r.

multicoloured	1·20	1·20

628 State Flag and Jayawijaya Peak

629 State Flag

(Des M. Ainy)

1998 (28 Oct). *"The Red and White Flag".* T **628** and similar vert design. Multicoloured. Fluorescent security markings. P $12\frac{1}{2} \times 13\frac{1}{2}$.

2451	700r. Type **628**	15	15
	a. Pair. Nos. 2451/2	30	
2452	700r. State flag and Himalayan peak	15	15

Nos. 2451/2 were issued in *se-tenant* pairs within the sheet.

(Des C. Akbar (2454), A. Es-Be (2455), T. Margono and S. Sugiyanto (2456). Litho and photo)

1998 (28 Oct). *Political Reforms.* T **629** and similar horiz designs. Multicoloured. Fluorescent security markings. P $13\frac{1}{2} \times 13$.

2453	700r. Type **629**	15	15
	a. Pair. Nos. 2453/4	30	
2454	700r. Dove and State flag	15	15
2455	1000r. Students in front of Parliament building (82 × 25 *mm*)	25	25

Nos. 2453/5 were issued together in *se-tenant* pairs within the sheet.

630 *Stelechocarpus burahol*

631 Monument at Blitar and Museum, Bogor

1998 (5 Nov). *Flora and Fauna.* T **630** and similar vert designs. Multicoloured. Fluorescent security markings. Litho and photo. P $13 \times 13\frac{1}{2}$.

2456	500r. Type **630**	15	15
	a. Strip of 10. Nos. 2456/65	1·50	
2457	500r. Tuberose (*Polianthes tuberosa*)	15	15
2458	500r. Four o'clock (*Mirabilis jalapa*)	15	15
2459	500r. Mangifera casturi	15	15
2460	500r. Ficus minahassae	15	15
2461	500r. Zebra dove (*Geopelia striata*)	15	15
2462	500r. Red and green junglefowl hybrid (*Gallus varius × G. gallus*)	15	15

2463	500r. Indian elephant (*Elephas maximus*)	15	15
2464	500r. Proboscis monkey (*Nasalis larvatus*)	15	15
2465	500r. Eastern tarsier (*Tarsius spectrum*)	15	15
2456/2465 *Set of 10*		1·40	1·40
MS2466 Two sheets (a) 48 × 80 mm. 2500r. As No. 2457; (b) 48 × 92 mm. 2500r. As No. 2464		50	50

Nos. 2456/65 were issued together in horizontal *se-tenant* strips of ten stamps within sheets of 20.

(Des H. Purnomo. Litho and photo)

1998 (10 Nov). *55th Anniv of Formation of Volunteer National Armed Forces (independence fighters).* Fluorescent security markings. P $12\frac{1}{2} \times 13\frac{1}{2}$.

2467	**631** 700r.+100r. multicoloured	15	15

632 Australian White-eyed Duck (*Aythya australis*)

633 Water Wheel and Power Lines

(Des Pradhika Studio)

1998 (1 Dec). *Water Fowl (2nd series).* T **632** and similar vert designs. Multicoloured. Fluorescent security markings. P $12\frac{1}{2}$.

2468	250r. Type **632**	10	10
2469	500r. Pacific black duck (*Anas superciliosa*)	10	10
2470	700r. Grey teal (*Anas gibberifrons*)	15	15
2471	1000r. Cotton teal (*Nettapus coromandelianus*)	25	25
2472	1500r. Green pygmy goose (*Nettapus pulchelus*)	35	35
2473	2500r. Indian whistling duck (*Dendrocygna javanica*)	50	50
2474	3500r. Wandering whistling duck (*Dendrocygna arcuata*)	75	75
2468/2474 *Set of 7*		2·00	2·00
MS2475 45 × 83 mm. 5000r. Type **632**		1·00	1·00

1998 (27 Dec). *Traditional Dances (7th series).* Vert designs as T **506**. Multicoloured. Fluorescent security markings. Litho and photo. P $12\frac{1}{2} \times 13\frac{1}{2}$.

2476	300r. Oreng oreng gae dance, Sulawesi Tenggara (South-east Celebes)	10	10
2477	500r. Persembahan dance, Bengkulu	10	10
2478	700r. Kipas (fan) dance, Riau	15	15
2479	1000r. Srimpi dance, Yogyakarta	25	25
2480	2000r. Pasambahan, Sumatera Barat (West)	40	40
2476/2480 *Set of 5*		90	90
MS2481 48 × 80 mm. 5000r. As No. 2480		1·00	1·00

(Des S. Talahatu, Ketut and Rudiyana. Litho and photo)

1999 (1 Jan). *Year of Creation and Engineering.* T **633** and similar horiz design. Multicoloured. Fluorescent security markings. P $12\frac{1}{2}$.

2482	500r. Type **633**	10	10
2483	700r. Water pipe and pipe network in valley	15	15

634 Putting the Shot   **635** Emblem

(Des E. Jatmiko. Litho and photo)

1999 (10 Jan). *Seventh Far East and South Pacific Games for Disabled Persons, Bangkok. T* **634** *and similar vert design. Multicoloured. Fluorescent security markings.* P 12½.
2484	500r. Type **634**	10	10
	a. Horiz pair. Nos. 2484/5	20	
2485	500r. Medal and wheelchair	10	10

Nos. 2484/5 were issued together in *se-tenant* pairs within the sheet.

(Des Megindo. Litho and photo)

1999 (26 Jan). *50th Anniv of Garuda Indonesia (state airline). T* **635** *and similar vert design. Multicoloured. Fluorescent security markings.* P 12½ × 13½.
2486	500r. Type **635**	10	10
2487	700r. Jet engine	15	15
2488	2000r. Pilot, stewardess and airplane	40	40

Nos. 2486/8 were each issued in sheets of 16 stamps and four labels showing a composite design of an airplane.

(Des A. Thoriq. Litho and photo)

1999 (15 Feb). *Folk Tales (2nd series). Horiz designs as T* **611**. *Multicoloured. Fluorescent security markings.* P 13½ × 12½.

(a) "Lake Toba".
2489	500r. Man and yellow fish	15	15
	a. Sheetlet of 20. Nos. 2489/508	3·00	
2490	500r. Man proposing to woman	15	15
2491	500r. Woman giving food for father to son Sam and Sam eating it	15	15
2492	500r. Wife turning back into a fish	15	15
2493	500r. Samosir Island and Lake Toba	15	15

(b) "Banjarmasin".
2494	500r. Rebels and contenders to throne	15	15
2495	500r. Local governors crown Prince Samudera	15	15
2496	500r. Tumenggung sends fleet to Samudera's capital, Bandar Masih	15	15
2497	500r. Samudera and Tumenggung meet on board ship	15	15
2498	500r. Ships in Banjarmasin Harbour	15	15

(c) "Buleleng".
2499	500r. I Gusti Gede Paseken leaving with guards for Den Bukit	15	15
2500	500r. Forest giant appearing to I Gusti Gede Paseken	15	15
2501	500r. I Gusti Gede Paseken lifting stranded ship	15	15
2502	500r. I Gusti Gede Paseken arriving before King of Den Bukit	15	15
2503	500r. Procession in kingdom of Buleleng	15	15

(d) "Woiram".
2504	500r. Woiram teaching archery to Woiwallytmang and with wife Donadebu	15	15
2505	500r. Mesan and Mecy looking for shrimps	15	15
2506	500r. Woiram cursing Demontin village	15	15
2507	500r. Woiwallytmang and Mecy clinging to tree trunk	15	15
2508	500r. Woiram's footprints in rock	15	15
2489/2508	*Set of* 20	2·75	2·75
MS2509	75 × 66 mm. 5000r.	1·00	1·00

As No. 2493 Nos. 2489/2508 were issued together in *se-tenant* sheetlets of 20 stamps, each horizontal strip forming a composite design.

636 Malang Apple   **637** Eastern Tarsier
(*Tarsius spectrum*)

1999 (4 Mar). *"Surabaya '99" National Stamp Exhibition. Sheet* 78 × 58 *mm. Fluorescent security markings. Litho and photo.* P 13½ × 12½.
MS2510	**636** 5000r. multicoloured	1·00	1·00

No. **MS**2510 was issued overprinted in gold in the margin with "APPI SHOW '99 SURABAYA, 10–18 JULI 1999" on 10 July 2000.

1999 (19 Mar). *"Australia '99" International Stamp Exhibition, Melbourne. Sheet* 60 × 92 *mm. Fluorescent security markings.* P 12½ × 13½.
MS2511	**637** 5000r. multicoloured	1·00	1·00

No. **MS**2511 was issued overprinted in gold in the margin with "The 13th Thaipex China Stamp Exhibition Bangkok '99 4–15.8.99" on 4 August 2000.

638 *Ascosparassis heinricherii*

1999 (1 Apr). *Fungi. Multicoloured. Fluorescent security markings. Litho and photo.*

(a) Sheet stamps. T **638** *and similar diamond-shaped designs.* P 12½.
2512	500r. Type **638**	10	10
	a. Strip or block of 3. Nos. 2512/14	30	
2513	500r. *Mutinus bambusinus*	10	10
2514	500r. *Mycena* sp.	10	10
2515	700r. *Gloephyllum imponens*	15	15
	a. Strip or block of 3. Nos. 2515/17	45	
2516	700r. *Microporus xanthopus*	15	15
2517	700r. *Termitomyces eurrhizus*	15	15
2518	1000r. *Boedijnopeziza insititia*	25	25
	a. Strip or block of 3. Nos. 2518/20	75	

2519	1000r. *Aseroe rubra*	25	25
2520	1000r. *Calostoma orirubra*	25	25
2512/2520	Set of 9	1·40	1·40

(b) *Booklet stamps. As Nos. 2512/14 but rectangular designs, size 31 × 23 mm. P 12½.*

2521	500r. As No. 2513	15	15
	a. Booklet pane. Nos. 2521/3, each × 3, plus one label	1·40	
2522	500r. As No. 2512	15	15
2523	500r. As No. 2514	15	15

(c) *Sheet 62 × 92 mm. P 12½ × 13½.*

MS2524	5000r. *Termitomyces eurrhizus* (different) (24½ × 41 mm)	1·00	1·00

Sheet stamps of the same value were issued together in horizontal and diagonal *se-tenant* strips and blocks of three stamps within the sheet.

Nos. 2512/20 were also issued together in *se-tenant* sheetlets of nine stamps.

639 Doctor and Patients outside Surgery

640 *Dendrobium abang betawi*

1999 (7 Apr). *Public Health Care Insurance. Fluorescent security markings.* P 13½ × 13.

2525	**639**	700r. multicoloured	15	15
		a. Tête-bêche (vert pair)	40	

No. 2525 was issued in sheets of 20 (5 × 4) with each alternate row inverted, giving vertical *tête-bêche* pairs

1999 (27 Apr). *"iBRA '99" International Stamp Exhibition, Nuremberg, Germany. Sheet 63 × 98 mm. Fluorescent security markings. Litho and photo.* P 12½ × 13½.

MS2526	640 5000r. multicoloured	1·40	1·40

641 Y2K "Bug"

1999 (2 May). *Millennium Bug (computer programming fault). T **641** and similar horiz design. Multicoloured. Fluorescent security markings.* P 13½ × 13.

2527	500r. Type **641**	15	15
	a. Horiz pair. Nos. 2527/8	30	
2528	500r. Robot exploding	15	15

Nos. 2527/8 were issued together in horizontal *se-tenant* pairs, each pair forming a composite design, within sheets of 16 stamps and four different labels.

642 Chrysoprase

1999 (20 May). *"Indonesia 2000" International Stamp Exhibition, Bandung (3rd issue). Gemstones. T **642** and similar horiz designs. Multicoloured. Fluorescent security markings. Litho and photo.* P 13½ × 12½.

2529	500r. Type **642**	15	15
2530	1000r. Smoky quartz	25	25
2531	2000r. Blue opal	55	55
MS2532	80 × 48 mm. 4000r. Silicified coral	1·00	1·00
MS2533	Two sheets (a) 80 × 48 mm. 4000r. Javan jade; (b) 122 × 160 mm. 2529 × 4, 2530 × 2, 2531 × 2 plus stamps as in Nos.		
	MS2532 and MS2533a	3·75	3·75

Nos. **MS**2533 are inscribed "1 Year to Go" in the margins.

Nos. 2529/31 were issued both separately in sheets of 20 and together in *se-tenant* sheetlets of nine stamps and one label.

643 People carrying Banner

1999 (4 June). *General Election. T **643** and similar horiz design. Multicoloured. Fluorescent security markings. Litho and photo.* P 13½ × 12½.

2534	1000r. Type **643**	15	10
	a. Horiz pair. Nos. 2534/5	30	
2535	1000r. Ballot box and map of Indonesia	15	10

Nos. 2533/4 were issued together in horizontal *se-tenant* pairs within the sheet, each pair forming a composite design.

644 Girl in Blanket and People walking through Water

645 Prambanan Temple

1999 (5 June). *Environmental Protection. Ecophila Stamp Day. T **644** and similar horiz designs. Multicoloured. Fluorescent security markings. Litho and photo.* P 13½ × 12½.

2536	500r. Type **644**	15	15
2537	1000r. Boy swimming with duck, plant and berry	40	40
2538	2000r. Elderly woman drinking from jug	80	80
MS2539	79 × 46 mm. 3000r. As No. 2537	1·20	1·20

1999 (2 July). *"Philexfrance '99" International Stamp Exhibition, Paris. Sheet 59 × 94 mm. Fluorescent security markings. Litho and photo.* P 12½ × 13½.

MS2540	**645** 5000r. multicoloured	2·00	2·00

646 Nurses helping Children

1999 (12 Aug). *Red Cross. Fluorescent security markings. Litho.* P 12½.

2541	**646**	1000r. multicoloured	35	35

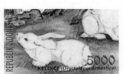

647 Frans Kaisiepo (Governor of Irian Jaya, 1964)

648 Rabbit

(Des H. Purnomo. Recess and litho)

1999 (17 Aug). *National Heroes and Heroines.* T **647** *and similar square designs. Fluorescent security markings.* P 12½.

2542	500r. blackish brown and cinnamon		15	15
	a. Booklet pane. No. 2542 × 4		90	
2543	500r. blackish brown and cinnamon		15	15
	a. Booklet pane. No. 2543 × 4		90	
2544	500r. blackish brown and cinnamon		15	15
	a. Booklet pane. No. 2544 × 4		90	
2545	500r. blackish brown and cinnamon		15	15
	a. Booklet pane. No. 2545 × 4		90	
2542/2545 *Set of 4*			55	55

Designs:—No. 2543, María Walanda Maramis (founder of "PIKAT" (women's education organization, 1917)); 2544, Dr. W. Z. Johannes (founder of Indonesian Christian Party, 1942); 2545, Martha Christina Tijahahu (revolutionary).

1999 (21 Aug). *"CHINA '99" International Stamp Exhibition, Beijing. Sheet* 81 × 60 *mm. Fluorescent security markings. Litho and photo.* P 13½ × 12½.

MS2546	**648**	5000r. multicoloured	1·60	1·60

649 University Building, 1949

1999 (19 Sept). *50th Anniv of Gadjah Mada University, Yogyakarkta.* T **649** *and similar horiz design. Multicoloured. Fluorescent security markings. Litho.* P 12½.

2547	500r. Type **649**		15	15
2548	1000r. University faade, 1999		40	40

650 Woman painting Parasol

651 Batik Design, Cirebon

1999 (1 Oct). *International Year of the Elderly Person. Fluorescent security markings.* P 13½ × 12½.

2549	**650**	500r. multicoloured	15	15

(Des S. Talahatu)

1999 (1 Oct). *Batik Designs.* T **651** *and similar square designs showing different Batik designs. Fluorescent security markings. Multicoloured.* P 12½.

2550	500r. Type **651**		15	15
	a. Sheetlet of 16. Nos. 2550/3, each × 4		2·40	
2551	500r. Madura		15	15
2552	500r. Yogyakarta		15	15
2553	500r. Jambi		15	15
2550/2553 *Set of 4*			55	55

Nos. 2550/3 were issued together in sheetlets of 16 stamps, each design in a block of four with the stamp rotated through 90 degrees to form the block.

652 Pillar Box, Postman and Kantoon Post Office (½-size illustration)

(Des Studio RedPoint. Photo (2554/5) or litho (2556/7))

1999 (9 Oct). *125th Anniv of Universal Postal Union.* T **652** *and similar multicoloured designs. Fluorescent security markings.* P 12½.

2554	500r. Type **652**		15	15
	a. Horiz pair. Nos. 2554/5, plus label		30	
2555	500r. Modern postal building, motorcycle postman and pillar box		15	15
2556	1000r. Pillar box, left-hand side of Kantoon Post Office and postman on horseback (30 × 31 *mm*)		80	80
	a. Horiz pair. Nos. 2556/7, plus two labels		1·60	
2557	1000r. Motorcycle postman, modern postal building and pillar box (30 × 31 *mm*)		80	80
2554/2557 *Set of 4*			1·75	1·75

Nos. 2556/7 show elements similar to those in Nos. 2554/5, but differently arranged.

Nos. 2554/5 and 2556/7 were issued together in *se-tenant* horizontal pairs with interleaving half stamp-size label, showing postal emblems within sheetlets of eight stamps and four labels.

Nos. 2556/7 were issued in horizontal pairs together with *se-tenant* half stamp-size labels within sheets of ten stamps and ten labels. Sheets could also be "Personalized" by the addition of a portrait photograph in place of the logo on the labels for the cost of 2000r. per sheetlet.

653 Dog and Puppy

1999 (5 Nov). *Domestic Animals.* T **653** *and similar multicoloured designs. Fluorescent security markings. Litho and photo.* P 13½ × 12½.

2558	500r. Type **653**		15	15
	a. Pair. Nos. 2558/9		30	
2559	500r. Cockerel, hen and chick		15	15
2560	500r. Cat		15	15
	a. Pair. Nos. 2560/1		30	
2561	500r. Rabbits		15	15
2562	1000r. Feral rock pigeon (20 × 50 *mm*)		40	40
	a. Pair. Nos. 2562/3		80	
2563	1000r. Geese and gosling (20 × 50 *mm*)		40	40
2558/2563 *Set of 6*			1·25	1·25
MS2564	79 × 47 mm. 4000r. As No. 2561		1·50	1·50

Nos. 2558/9, 2560/1 and 2562/3 respectively were issued together in *se-tenant* pairs within large sheets, and also together in *se-tenant* sheetlets of six showing the composite design of a garden.

654 Globe, Diary and Clock Face	**655** Satellite and Fishes

(Des E. Jatmiko. Litho and photo)

1999 (31 Dec)–**2000**. *New Millennium. T* **654** *and similar horiz design. Multicoloured. Fluorescent security markings.* P 13½ × 13.

2565	1000r. Type **654**	40	40
2566	1000r. "2000" and child's face (1.1.00)	40	40
MS2567	Two sheets each 86 × 57 mm. (a) 20000r. As Type **654**; (b) 20000r. As No. 2566 (1.1.00)	7·75	7·75

No. 2566 was issued in *se-tenant* sheetlets of 20 stamps and 20 plain labels. These sheets could be personalized by the addition of a portrait photograph on the labels for the cost of 38000r. per sheet.

NOTE. From 1 January 2000 stamps are inscribed "Indonesia".

(Des I. Warsana. Litho and photo)

2000 (1 Jan). *Year of Technology. T* **655** *and similar vert design. Multicoloured. Fluorescent security markings.* P 12½ × 13½.

2568	500r. Type **655**	15	15
2569	1000r. Greenhouse and plant	40	40

656 University Campus, Salemba

(Des A. Mujirun and M. Nurasyid. Litho and photo)

2000 (2 Feb). *50th Anniv of University of Indonesia. T* **656** *and similar horiz design. Multicoloured. Fluorescent security markings.* P 12½.

2570	500r. Type **656**	15	15
2571	1000r. University building, Depok	40	40

(Des A. Thoriq. Litho and photo)

2000 (5 Feb). *Folk Tales (3rd series). Horiz designs as T* **611**. *Multicoloured. Fluorescent security markings.* P 13½ × 12½.

(a) "Tapak Tuan".

2572	500r. Dragon finding baby on shore	25	25
	a. Sheetlet of 20. Nos. 2572/91	5·00	
2573	500r. Girl meeting other people	25	25
2574	500r. Dragon attacking boat and man	25	25
2575	500r. Man and dragon fighting	25	25
2576	500r. Dead dragon	25	25

(b) "Batu Ballah".

2577	500r. Mak Risah and children	25	25
2578	500r. Children playing	25	25
2579	500r. Mak Risah saddened by her children	25	25

2580	500r. Mak Risah being swallowed by stone	25	25
2581	500r. Mak Risah Rock	25	25

(c) "Sawerigading".

2582	500r. Sawerigading proposing marriage to twin sister	25	25
2583	500r. We Tanriabeng refusing marriage	25	25
2584	500r. Sawerigading in stern of boat	25	25
2585	500r. Bow of boat and wedding	25	25
2586	500r. Bulupoloe Mountain	25	25

(d) "Putri Kahyangan".

2587	500r. Prince hiding wings and angel weeping	25	25
2588	500r. Prince and angel with their children and angel flying away from Earth	25	25
2589	500r. Prince flying on eagle's back to reclaim wife	25	25
2590	500r. Angel refusing to return to Earth	25	25
2591	500r. Prince wearing magical crown	25	25
2572/2591	*Set of* 20	4·50	4·50
MS2592	84 × 61 mm. 5000r. As No. 2576	2·00	2·00

Nos. 2572/91 were issued together in *se-tenant* sheetlets of 20 stamps, each horizontal strip forming a composite design.

657 Prehnite	**658** I Brewok (Gun-Gun)

2000 (1 Mar–20 May). *"Indonesia 2000" International Stamp Exhibition, Bandung (4th issue). Gemstones. T* **657** *and similar horiz designs. Multicoloured. Fluorescent security markings. Litho and photo.* P 13½ × 12½.

2593	500r. Type **657**	25	25
2594	1000r. Chalcedony	40	40
2595	2000r. Volcanic obsidian	75	75
MS2596	80 × 48 mm. 5000r. Jasperized limestone (sold at 10r.)	2·00	2·00
MS2597	Two sheets (a) 80 × 48 mm. 5000r. Copper jasper. (b) 121 × 156 mm.		

No. 2593 × 4, 2594 × 2, 2595 × 2 plus stamps as in **MS**2596a and **MS**2597a (pair of sheets sold at 50r.) (20.5) .... 3·75 3·75

No. **MS**2597 are inscribed "4 months to go" in the margins.

Nos. 2593/5 were issued both separately in sheets of 20 and together in *se-tenant* sheetlets of nine stamps and one label.

Nos. 2593/5 plus one example of the jasperized limestone stamp were issued in *se-tenant* sheetlets of 20 stamps and 20 plain labels. These sheets could be personalized by the addition of a portrait photograph on the labels for the cost of 41000r. per sheet.

(Des T. Sugiarta)

2000 (13 Mar). *Cartoon Characters. T* **658** *and similar vert designs. Each black and rosine. Fluorescent security markings.* P 12½ × 13½.

2598	500r. Type **658**	25	25
2599	500r. "Pak Tuntung" (Basuki)	25	25
2600	500r. "Pak Bei" (Masdi Sunardi)	25	25
2601	500r. "Mang Ohle" (Didin D. Basuni)	25	25
2602	500r. "Panji Koming" (Dwi Koendoro)	25	25
2598/2602	*Set of* 5	1·10	1·10

Nos. 2598/602 were issued together in *se-tenant* sheetlets of 15 stamps and one label.

659 Emblem and Weather Chart

(Des Red Point Studio)

2000 (23 Mar). *50th Anniv of World Meteorological Organization. Fluorescent security markings.* P 12½.
2603 **659** 500r. multicoloured 25 25
    a. Tête-bêche pair . . . . . .

660 King Dragon

(Des C. Akbar)

2000 (25 Mar). *World Youth Stamp Exhibition and 13th Asian Stamp Exhibition, Bangkok. Sheet 79 × 49 mm. Fluorescent security markings.* P 13½ × 12½.
MS2604 **660** 5000r. multicoloured . . . . . . 1·60 1·60

661 Cycling

2000 (1 Apr). *15th National Sports Week. T 661 and similar horiz designs. Multicoloured. Fluorescent security markings.* P 13½ × 13.
2605 500r. Type **661** 50 25
2606 1000r. Canoeing . . . . 1·10 40
2607 2000r. High-jumping . . . . 2·10 55

662 Coelacanth (*Latimeria menadoensis*)

2000 (22 May). *"Stamp Show 2000" International Stamp Exhibition, London. Sheet 78 × 54 mm. Fluorescent security markings.* P 13½ × 12½.
MS2608 **662** 5000r. multicoloured . . . . . . 1·60 1·60

663 Red-footed Boobys in Nest

2000 (5 June). *Environmental Protection. Ecophila Stamp Day. T 663 and similar horiz designs. Multicoloured. Fluorescent security markings. Litho and photo.* P 13½ × 12½.
2609 500r. Type **663** 50 25
2610 1000r. Monkey . . . . 1·10 40
2611 2000r. Fishes . . . . 2·10 55
MS2612 68 × 62 mm. 4000r. As No. 2610 . . . 1·50 1·50

664 Boxing

2000 (1 July). *Olympic Games, Sydney. T 664 and similar horiz designs. Multicoloured. Fluorescent security markings. Litho and photo.* P 13½ × 12½.
2613 500r. Type **664** 15 15
    a. Horiz pair. Nos. 2613/14 30
2614 500r. Judo 15 15
2615 1000r. Badminton 35 35
    a. Horiz pair. Nos. 2615/16 70
2616 1000r. Weightlifting 35 35
2617 2000r. Swimming 65 65
    a. Horiz pair. Nos. 2617/18 . . . . 1·30
2618 2000r. Running 65 65
2613/2618 *Set of 6* . . . . . . 2·10 2·10
MS2619 84 × 51 mm. 5000r. As No. 2616 . . 1·60 1·60
Stamps of the same value were issued together in horizontal *se-tenant* pairs within the sheets.

665 Komodo Dragon

2000 (13 Aug). *Endangered Species. The Komodo Dragon (Varanus komodoensis). T 665 and similar horiz designs. Multicoloured. Fluorescent security markings. Litho and photo.* P 13½ × 12½.
2620 500r. Type **665** 40 40
2621 500r. Two dragons fighting 40 40
2622 500r. On branch 40 40
2623 500r. Two dragons walking 40 40
2620/2623 *Set of 4* . . . . . . 1·40 1·40
MS2624 101 × 56 mm. 2500r. As Type **665**;
2500r. As No. 2621 . . . . 2·75 2·75

666 President Abdurrahman Wahid

667 Rhythmic Gymnastics

(Des E. Jatmiko. Recess and photo)

2000 (17 Aug). *President and Vice-President. T* **666** *and similar diamond-shaped design. Multicoloured. Fluorescent security markings.* P 12½.

2625	1000r. Type **666**	40	40
	a. Horiz pair. Nos. 2625/6	80	
2626	1000r. Vice-President Megawati Soekarnoputri	40	40

Nos. 2625/6 were issued together in horizontal *se-tenant* pairs within the sheet.

2000 (15 Sept). *"Olymphilex 2000" Stamp Exhibition, Sydney. Sheet* 52 × 79 *mm. Fluorescent security markings. Litho and photo.* P 12½ × 13½.

MS2627 **667** 5000r. multicoloured	2·50	2·50

2000 (27 Sept). *Waterfowl (3rd series). Vert designs as T* **632**. *Multicoloured. Fluorescent security markings.* P 12½.

2628	800r. Indian whistling duck (*Dendrocygna javanica*)	80	80
2629	900r. Australian white-eyed duck (*Aythya australis*)	1·00	1·00

668 Couple from D. I. Aceh

669 Chairil Anwar (poet)

2000 (28 Oct). *Regional Costumes. T* **668** *and similar vert designs showing couples wearing traditional costumes from different regions. Multicoloured. Fluorescent security markings. Litho and photo.* P 12½.

2630	900r. Type **668**	35	35
	a. Sheetlet of 28. Nos. 2630/57 plus 7 labels	10·00	
2631	900r. Jambi	35	35
2632	900r. Banten	35	35
2633	900r. D. I. Yogyakarta	35	35
2634	900r. Kalimantan Tengah	35	35
2635	900r. Sulawesi Tenggara	35	35
2636	900r. Nusa Tenggara Timur	35	35
2637	900r. Sumatera Utara	35	35
2638	900r. Bengkulu	35	35
2639	900r. D. K. I. Jakarta	35	35
2640	900r. Jawa Timur	35	35
2641	900r. Kalimantan Timur	35	35
2642	900r. Sulawesi Selatan	35	35
2643	900r. Maluku	35	35
2644	900r. Sumatera Barat	35	35
2645	900r. Sumatera Selatan	35	35
2646	900r. Jawa Barat	35	35
2647	900r. Kalimantan Barat	35	35
2648	900r. Sulawesi Utara	35	35
2649	900r. Bali	35	35
2650	900r. Maluku Utara	35	35
2651	900r. Riau	35	35
2652	900r. Lampung	35	35
2653	900r. Jawa Tengah	35	35
2654	900r. Kalimantan Selatan	35	35
2655	900r. Sulawesi Tengah	35	35
2656	900r. Nusa Tenggara Barat	35	35
2657	900r. Irian Jaya	35	35
2630/2657 *Set of 28*		9·00	9·00

Nos. 2630/57 were issued together in *se-tenant* sheetlets of 28 stamps, comprising of two blocks of 14 stamps (7 × 2) separated by a row of seven labels showing traditional weapons.

2000 (1 Nov). *Personalities. T* **669** *and similar multicoloured designs. Fluorescent security markings.* P 13½ × 12½.

2658	900r. Type **669**	35	35
	a. Horiz or vert strip of 5. Nos. 2658/62	1·75	
2659	900r. Ibu Sud (children's song writer)	35	35
2660	900r. Bing Slamet (entertainer)	35	35
2661	900r. S. Sudjojono (artist)	35	35
2662	900r. I. Ketut Maria (actor)	35	35
2658/2662 *Set of 5*		1·60	1·60
MS2663 62 × 92 mm. 4000r. Chairil Anwar (*different*) (*vert*). P 12½ × 13½.		1·50	1·50

Nos. 2658/62 were issued together in *se-tenant* horizontal and vertical strips of five stamps within the sheet.

670 Hand holding 1989 500r. Endangered Species Stamp

2000 (20 Dec). *Communications. T* **670** *and similar multicoloured designs. Fluorescent security markings.* P 12½.

2664	800r. Type **670**	25	25
2665	900r. Satellite, map, television and letter (*horiz*)	35	35
2666	1000r. Globe and computer monitor	40	40
2667	4000r. Airplane, globe and computer	1·50	1·50
2664/2667 *Set of 4*		2·25	2·25

In addition to the usual post office emblem the hand (800r.), computer monitor (1000r.) and sunrise (900, 4000r.) are also fluorescent.

671 Pluto

672 Arsa Wijaya, Bali

2001 (1 Jan). *The Solar System. T* **671** *and similar horiz designs. Multicoloured. Fluorescent security markings. Photo.* P 13½ × 12½.

2668	900r. Type **671**	25	25
	a. Horiz block of 10. Nos. 2668/77	2·50	
2669	900r. Neptune	25	25
2670	900r. Uranus	25	25
2671	900r. Saturn	25	25
2672	900r. Jupiter	25	25
2673	900r. Mars	25	25
2674	900r. Earth	25	25
2675	900r. Venus	25	25
2676	900r. Mercury	25	25
2677	900r. Sun	25	25
2668/2677 *Set of 10*		2·25	2·25
MS2678 120 × 71 mm. 5000r. Sun (*different*)		1·40	1·40

Nos. 2668/77 were issued together in *se-tenant* sheetlets of either ten or 20 stamps, or in sheets of 20 stamps and 20 plain labels. These sheets could be personalized by the addition of a photograph on the labels at the cost of 36000r.

(Des A. Thoriq. Litho and photo)

2001 (2 Feb). *Folk Tales (4th series). Horiz designs as T* **611**.
Multicoloured. Fluorescent security markings. P 13½ × 12½.

(a) "Batang Tuaka".

2679	900r.	Two snakes fighting and Tuaka with stone	25	25
	a.	Sheetlet of 20. Nos. 2679/98	5·00	
2680	900r.	Tuaka selling stone to merchant in Tumasik Port	25	25
2681	900r.	Tuaka as a successful merchant with wife	25	25
2682	900r.	Mother cursing Tuaka and his wife	25	25
2683	900r.	Tuaka and wife become birds	25	25

(b) "Si Pitung".

2684	900r.	Si Pitung and gang stealing money from Dutch sympathizers	25	25
2685	900r.	Si Pitung's gang leaving money for villagers	25	25
2686	900r.	Dutch ruler fighting Si Pitung	25	25
2687	900r.	Villagers mourning dead Si Pitung	25	25
2688	900r.	Si Pitung Mosque	25	25

(c) "Terusan Nusa".

2689	900r.	Tambing finding and eating dragon's egg	25	25
2690	900r.	Tambing turning into dragon	25	25
2691	900r.	Dragon (Tambing) eating all the fish in the river	25	25
2692	900r.	Tambing dying after eating his own tail	25	25
2693	900r.	Empty river	25	25

(d) "Ile Mauraja".

2694	900r.	Raja dreaming	25	25
2695	900r.	Raja receiving cotton seeds from bearded man	25	25
2696	900r.	Raja and wife	25	25
2697	900r.	Snake on bed, burning village and snakes causing upheaval of village	25	25
2698	900r.	Mountain formed by village	25	25
2679/2698 *Set of 20*			4·50	4·50
MS2699 84 × 61 mm. 5000r. No. 2686			1·40	1·40

Nos. 2679/98 were issued together in *se-tenant* sheetlets of 20 stamps, each horizontal strip forming a composite design.

(Des M. Triadi. Litho and photo)

2001 (2 Mar). *Traditional Masks. T* **672** *and similar vert designs showing left (a) or right (b) sides of masks. Multicoloured. Fluorescent security markings.* P 12½ × 13½.

2700	500r.	Type **672**	15	15
	a.	Horiz pair. Nos. 2700/1	30	
2701	500r.	Arsa Wijaya (b)	15	15
2702	800r.	Asmat, Irian Jaya (a)	25	25
	a.	Horiz pair. Nos. 2702/3	50	
2703	800r.	Asmat (b)	25	25
2704	800r.	Cirebon, Jawa Barat (a)	25	25
	a.	Horiz pair. Nos. 2704/5	50	
2705	800r.	Cirebon (b)	25	25
2706	900r.	Hudoq, Kalimantan Timur (a)	35	35
	a.	Horiz pair. Nos. 2706/7	70	
2707	900r.	Hudoq (b)	35	35
2708	900r.	Wayang Wong, Yogyakarta (a)	35	35
	a.	Horiz pair. Nos. 2708/9	70	
2709	900r.	Wayang Wong (b)	35	35
2700/2709 *Set of 10*			30	
MS2710 61 × 96 mm. 5000r. No. 2706			1·60	1·60

Nos. 2700/1, 2702/3, 2704/5, 2706/7 and 2708/9 were issued together in *se-tenant* horizontal pairs within sheetlets of ten stamps and two labels, each pair forming a composite design.

The fluorescent security markings consist of the usual Postal Service emblem, but with the addition of fluorescence to various parts of the masks. No. **MS**2710 was re-issued for Hafnia '01 International Stamp Exhibition, Copenhagen with additional inscription and exhibition emblem on the margin in silver.

673 Beduk

(Des H. Mintareja)

2001 (10 Mar). *Traditional Instruments. T* **673** *and similar horiz designs. Multicoloured. Fluorescent security markings.* P 12½.

2711	900r.	Type **673**	15	15
	a.	Vert and horiz strip of 4. Nos. 2711/14	60	
	b.	Sheetlet of 8. Nos. 2711/14, each × 2 plus 2 labels	1·30	
2712	900r.	Bende (bronze drum)	15	15
2713	900r.	Kentongan (percussion)	15	15
2714	900r.	Nafiri (horn)	15	15
2711/2714 *Set of 4*			55	55

Nos. 2711/14 were issued together in vertical *se-tenant* strips of four stamps within sheets of 40 stamps and, each × 2, in sheetlets of eight stamps plus two labels.

674 Bouquet   **675** Children and Fish (Surayadi)

(Des PosKreatif)

2001 (21 Apr). *Greetings Stamps. T* **674** *and similar horiz designs. Multicoloured. Fluorescent security markings. Paper with fluorescent fibres.* P 12½.

2715	800r.	Type **674**	15	15
2716	900r.	Rose	25	25
2717	1000r.	Bouquet of orange roses and leaves	35	35
2718	1500r.	Large white flower and dark green leaf	40	40
2719	2000r.	Bouquet of yellow flowers with pink bow	55	55
2720	4000r.	Amaryllis flower and ribbon	1·20	1·20
2721	5000r.	Table decoration and candles	1·50	1·50
2722	10000r.	White flower with yellow centre	3·00	3·00
2715/2722 *Set of 8*			6·75	6·75

The fluorescent markings consist of part of each design in addition to the Indonesian Postal Service emblem.

(Des DaTaSign (900r.))

2001 (5 June). *World Environment Day. Winning entries in Stamp Design Competition (Nos. 2723, 2425). T* **675** *and similar horiz designs. Multicoloured. Fluorescent security markings. Paper with fluorescent fibres.* P 13½.

2723	800r.	Type **675**	25	25
2724	900r.	Boys feeding deer	25	25
2725	1000r.	Boy swimming with turtle (Lambok Hutabarat)	35	35
MS2726 82 × 50 mm. 3000r. As No. 2724			90	90

No. **MS**2726 also exists imperforate.

676 Youthful Sukarno wearing Turban

(Des H. Purnomo)

2001 (6 June). *Birth Centenary of Dr. Ahmed Sukarno (Bung Karno) (nationalist leader and first president). T **676** and similar horiz designs. Multicoloured. Fluorescent security markings. Paper with fluorescent fibres.* P 13½ × 12½ (**MS**2731) or 12½ (others).

2727	500r. Type **676**	15	15
	a. Sheetlet of 8. Nos. 2727/30, each ×2	1·00	
2728	800r. As young man wearing collar and tie	25	25
2729	900r. Wearing high-necked jacket	25	25
2730	1000r. Wearing uniform with lapel badges	35	35
2727/2730 *Set of 4*		90	90
MS2731 138 × 59 mm. 5000r. Giving speech		1·50	1·50

Nos. 2727/30 were issued individually in sheets of 40 stamps and together (each ×2) in *se-tenant* sheetlets of eight stamps.

The fluorescent markings consist of Sukarno's signature in addition to the Indonesian Postal Service emblem.

677 Policeman guiding Children across
the Road

(Des DaTaSign)

2001 (1 July). *Indonesian Police Force. T **677** and similar horiz design. Multicoloured. Fluorescent security markings. Paper with fluorescent fibres.* P 13½ × 12½.

2732	1000r. Type **677**	35	35
	a. Pair. Nos. 2732/3	70	
2733	1000r. Helicopter and women police officers giving directions	35	35

Nos. 2732/3 were issued together in horizontal *se-tenant* pairs within the sheet.

678 Scouts raising Flag

(Des A. Kurniawan)

2001 (3 July). *National Scout Jamboree, Banyumas, Java. T **678** and similar horiz design. Multicoloured. Fluorescent security markings. Paper with fluorescent fibres.* P 13½ × 12½.

2734	1000r. Type **678**	35	35
	a. Pair. Nos. 2734/5	70	
2735	1000r. Erecting tent	35	35

Nos. 2734/5 were issued together in horizontal *se-tenant* pairs forming a composite design within the sheet.

679 Kaki Siapa (blind man's buff)

(Des Sumber Bagus Studio)

2001 (23 July). *National Children's Day. Children's Games. T **679** and similar horiz designs. Multicoloured. Fluorescent security markings. Paper with fluorescent fibres.* P 13½ × 12½.

2736	800r. Type **679**	15	15
2738	900r. Erang Bambu (stilt walking)	25	25
2739	1000r. Dakon (counting game)	25	25
2740	2000r. Kuda Pelepah Pisang (hobby horses)	40	40
2736, 2738/40 *Set of 4*		95	95

680 Sunflower

(Des DaTaSign. Litho)

2001 (1 Aug). *Philanippon '01 International Stamp Exhibition. Sheet 93 × 46 mm. Fluorescent security markings.* P 13½ × 12½.

MS2741 **680** 10000r. multicoloured . . . . 3·25 3·25

681 Dr. R. Soeharso (founder) and
Operating Theatre

(Des DaTaSign. Litho and photo)

2001 (28 Aug). *50th Anniv of Dr. R. Soeharso Orthopaedic Hospital. Fluorescent security markings.* P 13½ × 12½.

2742 **681** 1000r. multicoloured 15 15

682 Makasaar Post Office

(Des PosKreatif. Litho and photo)

2001 (27 Sept). *Post Office Architecture. T **682** and similar horiz designs showing Post Office building. Multicoloured. Fluorescent security markings.* P 13½ × 12½.

2743	800r. Type **682**	10	10
2744	900r. Bandung	15	15
2745	1000r. Balikpapan	15	15
2746	2000r. Padang	25	25
2743/2746 *Set of 4*		60	60

The fluorescent markings consist of the outline of the buildings in addition to the Indonesian Postal Service emblem.

683 Perahu (boat)

(Des Team Peruri. Litho and photo)

2001 (27 Sept). *Traditional Transport. T* **683** *and similar horiz designs. Multicoloured. Fluorescent security markings.* P 13½ × 12½.

2747	1000r. Type **683**		15	15
	a. Sheetlet. Nos. 2747/9, each ×3 plus label	1·40		
2748	1000r. Becak Dayung (tricycle rickshaw)		15	15
2749	1000r. Andong (horse-drawn taxi)		15	15

Nos. 2747/9, each ×3, were issued in *se-tenant* sheetlets of nine stamps and one label.

684 Rose Quartz

(Des Adi Es-Be. Litho and photo)

2001 (1 Oct). *Gemstones. T* **684** *and similar horiz designs. Multicoloured. Fluorescent security markings.* P 13½ × 12½.

2750	800r. Type **684**		10	10
	a. Sheetlet. Nos. 2750/2, each ×3 plus label	1·30		
2751	900r. Brecciated Jasper		15	15
2752	1000r. Malachite		15	15
MS2753	80 × 47 mm. 5000r. Diamond	1·60	1·60	

Nos. 2750/52, each ×3, were issued in *se-tenant* sheetlets of nine stamps and one label.

685 Children encircling Globe   **686** Agestrata dehaan

(Des Urska Golob. Litho and photo)

2001 (9 Oct). *United Nations Year of Dialogue among Civilizations. Fluorescent security markings.* P 12½ × 13½.

2754	**685**	1000r. multicoloured	15	15

The fluorescent markings consist of stars.

(Des PostKreatif. Litho and photo)

2001 (5 Nov). *Insects. T* **686** *and similar vert designs. Multicoloured. Fluorescent security markings.* P 12½ × 13½.

2755	800r. Type **686**		10	10
	a. Booklet pane. Nos. 2756/60 plus label	75		
2756	900r. *Mormolyce phyllodes*		15	15
2757	1000r. *Batocera rosenbergi*		15	15

2758	1000r. *Chrysochroa buqueti*		15	15
2759	1000r. *Chalcosoma caucasus*		15	15
2755/2759	Set of 5		65	65
MS2760	61 × 90 mm. No. 2760		2·10	2·10

STAMP BOOKLETS

The following checklist covers, in simplified form, booklets issued by Indonesia. It is intended that it should be used in conjunction with the main listings and details of stamps and panes listed are not repeated.

Prices are for complete booklets

Booklet No.	Date	Contents and Face Value	Price
SB10	3.5.78	*U.N.I.C.E.F. (T* **280***) and "Palapa" Satellite*	
		1 pane (600r.)	
		(a) No. 1459ab	8·75
		(b) No. 1459ac	8·75
SB11	3.5.78	*Lake Maninjau and 450th Anniv of Djakarta*	
		1 pane (625r.)	
		(a) No. 1440ab	7·75
		(b) No. 1440ac	7·75
SB12	31.8.78	*Graph and Telephone Centenary (T* **271***)*	
		1 pane (600r.)	
		(a) No. 1247ab	6·50
		(b) No. 1247ac	6·50
SB13	27.9.78	*National Health Campaign (T* **291***) and "Amphilex 77" Stamp Exhibition (T* **285***)*	
		1 pane (600r.)	
		(a) No. 1488ab	7·50
		(b) No. 1488ac	7·50
SB14	8.8.79	*Youth Pledge and Thomas Cup*	
		1 pane (900r.)	
		(a) No. 1514ab	9·25
		(b) No. 1514ac	9·25
SB15	27.9.79	*Mail Delivery and South-East Asian Games*	
		1 pane (900r.)	
		(a) No. 1545ab	7·50
		(b) No. 1545ac	7·50
SB16	15.11.81	*President Suharto (T* **326***)*	
		1 pane, No. 1585ab (1000r.)	7·75
SB17	1995	*Traditional Dances*	
		1 pane, No. 2168a (8300r.)	7.50
SB18	22.3.96	*Cuscuses*	
		1 pane, No. 230b (3000r.)	2.50
SB19	9.9.97	*South-East Asian Games*	
		1 pane, No. 2333ba (4000r.)	3.25
SB20	1.4.99	*Fungi*	
		1 pane, No. 2521a (4500r.)	1.40
SB21	17.8.99	*National Heroes and Heroines*	
		4 panes, No. 2542a/45a (sold at 10000r.)	3.75
SB22	5.11.01	*Insects (T* **687***)*	
		1 pane, Nos. 2755/60 plus label	70

RIAU-LINGGA ARCHIPELAGO

The Indonesian islands comprising the Riau-Lingga Archipelago lie just south of Singapore, and to ease trade the Indonesian rupiah current in these islands was tied to the Singapore dollar at par. To prevent speculators taking advantage of the fall in the value of the rupiah in other parts of Indonesia, the stamps used in the archipelago were overprinted "Riau".

	RIAU	RIAU
(1)	(2)	(3)

1954 (1 Jan).

(i) Stamps of Indonesia overprinted.

(a) Nos. 613/19 optd with T **1**.

1	96	5s. carmine	28·00	19·00
2		7½s. light green	20	35
3		10s. blue (II)	32·00	40·00
4		15s. violet	80	80
5		20s. red (II)	95	1·10
6		25s. olive-green	65·00	22·00

(b) Nos. 620/9 optd with T **2**.

7	97	30s. orange-red	2·40	1·60
8		35s. violet	20	35
9		40s. blue-green	20	35
10		45s. reddish purple	25	35
11		50s. brown	£190	32·00
12	98	60s. sepia	20	35
13		70s. grey	60	65
14		75s. bright blue	3·25	1·60
15		80s. reddish purple	50	1·90
16		90s. deep bluish green	50	1·10

(ii)		*Stamps of Netherlands Indies, Nos.* 566/71 (inscr "INDONESIA") optd with T **1**.		
17	88	1r. violet	6·25	1·60
18		2r. grey-green	65	1·90
19		3r. purple	95	1·90
20	–	5r. chocolate	95	1·90
21	–	10r. grey-black	1·25	2·40
22	–	25r. red-brown	1·25	2·40
1/22	Set of 22		£300	£120

1957 (12 Jan). *Indonesian stamps of 1956–58 optd with T* **3**.

23	10s. light brown (714)	3·25	2·40
24	25s. purple-brown (717)	9·25	9·25
25	50s. bistre-brown (722)	3·25	2·40

1958–64. *Indonesian stamps of 1956–58 optd with T* **2**.

26	5s. grey-blue (713)	20	35
27	10s. light brown (714)	40	35
28	15s. purple (715) (1964)	40	1·50
29	20s. deep dull green (716) (1960)	40	35
30	25s. purple-brown (717)	40	35
31	30s. red-orange (718)	40	35
32	50s. bistre-brown (722)	40	35
26/32	Set of 7	2·25	3·25

1960 (21 May). *Indonesian stamps of 1951–55 optd with T* **1**.

33	99	1r.25 orange	95	3·25
34		1r.50 bistre-brown	95	3·25
35		2r.50 lake-brown	1·25	4·75
36		4r. bright olive	25	4·75
37		6r. dull mauve	25	4·75
38		15r. yellow-ochre	25	4·75
39		20r. slate-purple	25	6·25
40		40r. yellow-green	25	7·00
41		50r. blue-violet	35	7·50
33/41	Set of 9		4·25	42·00

These stamps were withdrawn when the rupiah was revalued in December 1965.

WEST IRIAN

In 1828 north-west New Guinea was declared a Dutch possession. Until the end of 1949 stamps of the Netherlands Indies were used there. From 1950–62 Netherlands New Guinea had its own stamps and these are listed in Part 4 (*Benelux*) of this catalogue.

From 1950 Indonesia made repeated claims to the territory and by an agreement of 15 August 1962 administration was transferred to the United Nations on 1 October 1962. Overprinted stamps issued by this administration are also listed in Part 4.

West New Guinea, as it was known while under U.N. administration, was transferred to Indonesian rule on 1 May 1963 and renamed Irian Barat (West Irian).

IRIAN BARAT

(1)

1963 (1 May). *Various stamps of Indonesia surch as T* **1** *or optd only.*

1	1s.on 70s. orange-red (724)	10	15
2	2s.on 90s. yellow-green (727)	10	15
3	5s. grey (830)	10	15
4	6s.on 20s. yellow-brown (833)	10	15
5	7s.on 50s. deep blue (835)	10	15
6	10s. brown (831)	10	15
7	15s. maroon (832)	10	15
8	25s. blue-green (834)	10	20
9	30s. on 75s. vermilion (836)	10	20
10	40s.on 1r.15 crimson (837)	10	20
11	1r. reddish violet (630)	20	35
12	2r. green (633)	25	45
13	3r. blue (635)	50	65
14	5r. sepia (637)	80	1·10
1/14	Set of 14	2·25	3·75

1963 (1 May). *POSTAGE DUE. Design similar to Type D* **100** *of Indonesia, optd "IRIAN BARAT" as T* **1**. *Litho. P* $13\frac{1}{2} \times 12\frac{1}{2}$.

D15	1s. slate-purple	10	25
D16	5s. brown-olive	10	25
D17	10s. turquoise-blue	10	25
D18	25s. slate	10	25
D19	40s. red-orange	10	50
D20	100s. yellow-brown	15	95
D15/20	Set of 6	50	2·25

PRINTERS. All the following issues were photogravure-printed by the State Security Printing Works, Djakarta.

1963 (1 May). *Acquisition of West Irian. Designs as Nos. 962/4 of Indonesia, additionally inscr "IRIAN BARAT".*

21	12s. light orange-red, red and black	10	15
22	17s. light orange-red, red and black	10	15
23	20s. light blue, green and grey-purple	10	15
24	50s. light blue, green and grey-purple	10	20
25	60s. brown, yellow and green	75	35
26	75s. brown, yellow and green	95	40
21/26	Set of 6	1·75	1·25

Designs:—12s., 17s. Map of Indonesia, from Atjeh to Merauke; 20s., 50s. Parachutist; 60s., 75s. Greater bird of paradise.

2 *Maniltoa gemmipara*

(Des K. Risman Suplanto, Soedirno, Soeroso and Soewarsono)

1968 (17 Aug)–**70**. *Flora and Fauna. T* **2** *and similar vert designs. P* $12\frac{1}{2} \times 12$.

27	5s. maroon and bluish green	25	25
28	15s. reddish violet and bright green	25	25
29	30s. blue-green and orange	35	35
30	40s. bright reddish violet and olive-yellow	35	35
31	50s. black and cerise	85	50
32	75s. black and light blue	1·40	75
33	1r. black and orange-brown	1·10	80
34	3r. black and light yellow-green	2·40	1·60
35	5r. multicoloured (26.10.70)	1·10	1·25
36	10r. multicoloured (26.10.70)	2·25	1·90
27/36	Set of 10	6·25	6·75

Designs:—15s. *Dendrobium lancifolium*; 30s. *Gardenia gjellerupii*; 40s. *Maniltoa gemmipara* (blossom); 50s. Phalanger; 75s. One-wattled cassowary; 1r. Kangaroo; 3r. Blue crowned pigeons; 5r. Black-capped lory; 10r. Greater bird of paradise.

In the 1980s the 30s. in brown and greenish slate appeared on the market. Its status is uncertain.

1968 (17 Aug). *POSTAGE DUE. As Type D* **180a** *of Indonesia, with background incorporating "1968", optd "*IRIAN BARAT*" as in T* **1**. P $13\frac{1}{2} \times 12\frac{1}{2}$.

D37	1s. blue and pale green	. . . . .	10	25
D38	5s. emerald-green and pale pink	. . .	10	25
D39	10s. red and pale grey	. . . . .	10	25
D40	25s. emerald and pale yellow	. . . .	10	25
D41	40s. maroon and pale bluish green	. .	20	50
D42	100s. orange-red and pale yellow-olive		35	95
D37/42 *Set of 6*	. . . .		85	2·50

REPUBLIK INDONESIA

3 Map of Indonesia

(Des Soeripto)

1968 (17 Aug). *West Irian People's Pledge of 9 May* 1964.

43	**3**	10s. gold and ultramarine	. . . . .	65	25
44		25s. gold and red	. . . .	95	40

4 Mother and Child Figurine

(Des K. Risman Suplanto, Mahriajub and Soewarsono)

1970 (15–30 Apr). *West Irian Woodcarvings. T* **4** *and similar vert designs. Multicoloured.* P $12\frac{1}{2} \times 12$.

45	5s. Type **4** (30.4)	. . . . . .	10	15
46	6s. Carved shield (30.4)	. . . . .	10	15
47	7s. Man and serpents (30.4)	. . . .	10	15
48	10s. Drum (30.4)	. . . .	10	15
49	25s. Seated warrior (30.4)	. . . . .	15	20
50	30s. "Female" drum	. . . . . .	20	20
51	50s. Bamboo vessel	. . . . . .	20	20
52	75s. Seated man and tree	. . . . .	20	20
53	1r. Decorated shield	. . . . . .	25	35
54	2r. Seated figure	. . . .	25	35
45/54 *Set of 10*	. . . .	1·50	1·90

West Irian stamps were withdrawn from sale on 31 May 1971 and Indonesian stamps are now used. In March 1973 Irian Barat was renamed Irian Jaya.

SOUTH MOLUCCAS

Early in 1950 the South Moluccas, part of the state of East Indonesia, revolted against attempts to force them to join a unitary state. On 25 April 1950 they declared their independence as the Republic of the South Moluccas (Republik Maluku Selatan) and issued the following stamps. These have been recorded postally used at Amboina and Saparoea.

Republik Maluku Selatan

(1)

1950. *Various stamps optd as T* **1**, *with bars at top or bottom obliterating the old inscription.*

*(a) Stamps of Netherlands Indies, 1949–50, inscr "*INDONESIA*".*

1	86	1s. grey (p $12\frac{1}{2}$)	. . . .	20·00
2		2s. purple (p $12\frac{1}{2}$)	. . . .	20·00
3		$2\frac{1}{2}$s. olive-brown (p $12\frac{1}{2}$)	. . . .	25·00
4		3s. crimson (p $12\frac{1}{2}$)	. . . . . .	25·00
5		4s. green (p $12\frac{1}{2}$)	. . . . . .	30·00
6		5s. blue (p $11\frac{1}{2}$)	. . . .	20·00
		a. Perf $12\frac{1}{2}$	. . . . . .	
7		$7\frac{1}{2}$s. deep green (p $11\frac{1}{2}$)	. . . .	20·00
		a. Perf $12\frac{1}{2}$	. . . . .	
8		10s. mauve (p $12\frac{1}{2}$)	. . . . . .	15·00
9	87	20s. grey-black (p $11\frac{1}{2}$) (R.)	. .	30·00
10		25s. ultramarine (p $11\frac{1}{2}$) (R.)	. .	40·00
11	—	30s. orange-red (p $11\frac{1}{2}$)	. . .	35·00
12	—	40s. green (p $11\frac{1}{2}$) (R.)	. . .	35·00
13	—	50s. red-brown (p $11\frac{1}{2}$) (R.)	. .	25·00
14	—	60s. chocolate (p $11\frac{1}{2}$) (R.)	. .	30·00
15	—	80s. scarlet (p $11\frac{1}{2}$)	. . . .	30·00
16	88	1r. violet (p $12\frac{1}{2}$)	. . . . . .	£100

(b) Inauguration stamp of United States of Indonesia, 1950.

17	**90**	15s. scarlet (574)	. . . . . .	45·00
1/17 *Set of 17*	. . . . .		£500

Amboina was taken by Indonesian troops on 3 November 1950, but resistance continued on other islands, especially on Ceram, until 1955.

PICTORIAL STAMPS. Several issues of pictorial stamps, inscribed "Republik Maluku Selatan", appeared on the market in the United States in 1951–54. There is no evidence that they were on sale in the South Moluccas and therefore we do not list them.

International Commission in Indo-China

The International Control Commisions for Indo-China were established in August 1954 as part of the Geneva Declaration which partitioned Vietnam and sought to achieve stable settlements in Cambodia and Laos. The three supervisory commissions were chaired by India with Canada and Poland as the other members. Joint inspection teams of servicemen from the three countries were also provided.

The Indian contingent included a postal unit which handled mail for the three commssions and the inspection teams. The unit arrived in Indo-China on 3 September 1954 and opened field post offices at Saigon (F.P.O. 742), Hanoi (F.P.O. 743), Vientiane (F.P.O. 744) and Phnom Penh (F.P.O. 745).

Types of India

307 Ajanta Panel

316 Kandarya Mahadeva Temple

361 Map of India

449 Jawaharlal Nehru (from 1r. coin)

461 Bidri Vase

474 Medieval Sculpture

(N 1)

(N 2)

(N 3)

1954 (1 Dec). *Stamps of India.* W N **69** *(Stars).*

*(a) Optd as Type N **1**, for use in Cambodia.*

N1	307	3p. slate-violet	80	5·00
N2	328	1a. turquoise	1·10	90
N3	311	2a. carmine	1·10	90
N4	316	8a. turquoise-green	2·50	4·00
N5	317	12a. dull blue	2·75	4·25

*(b) Optd as Type N **2**, for use in Laos.*

N6	307	3p. slate-violet	85	4·50
N7	328	1a. turquoise	1·10	80
N8	311	2a. carmine	1·10	90
N9	316	8a. turquoise-green	2·30	4·00
N10	317	12a. dull blue	2·50	4·50

*(c) Optd as Type N **3**, for use in Vietnam.*

N11	307	3p. slate-violet	85	4·75
N12	328	1a. turquoise	1·00	85
N13	311	2a. carmine	1·00	85
N14	316	8a. turquoise-green	2·20	3·75
N15	317	12a. dull blue	2·40	4·25
N1/15	*Set of 15*		21·00	40·00

Designs: *As T* **307**—**311**, Nataraja; **328**, Bodhisattva. *As T* **316**—**317**, Golden Temple, Amritsar.

1957 (1 Apr). *Stamps of India.* W **69** *(sideways).*

*(a) Optd as Type N **1**, for use in Cambodia.*

N16	361	2n.p. light brown	70	35
N17		6n.p. grey	60	35
N18		13n.p. bright carmine-red	80	40
N19		50n.p. orange	2·50	1·40
N20		75n.p. reddish purple	2·50	1·40

*(b) Optd as Type N **2**, for use in Laos.*

N21	361	2n.p. light brown	85	35
N22		6n.p. grey	70	35
N23		13n.p. bright carmine-red	80	50
N24		50n.p. orange	2·50	1·60
N25		75n.p. reddish purple	2·50	1·60

*(c) Optd as Type N **3**, for use in Vietnam.*

N26	361	2n.p. light brown	95	35
N27		6n.p. grey	60	35
N28		13n.p. bright carmine-red	80	50
N29		50n.p. orange	2·40	1·30
N30		75n.p. reddish purple	2·30	1·30
N16/30	*Set of 15*		19·00	11·00

F.P.O. 744 (Vientiane) was closed on 25 July 1958 and F.P.O. 745 (Phnom Penh) on 26 June 1958.

1960 (Sept)–65. *Stamps of India.* W **374** *(Asokan Capital).*

*(a) Optd as Type N **2**, for use in Laos.*

N38	361	2n.p. light brown (1962)	20	2·40
N39		3n.p. deep brown (1.8.63)	20	25
N40		5n.p. bright green (1.8.63)	20	25
N41		50n.p. orange (1965)	3·25	2·75
N42		75n.p. reddish purple (1965)	3·25	3·00

*(b) Optd as Type N **3**, for use in Vietnam.*

N43	361	1n.p. blue-green	20	20
N44		2n.p. light brown (1962)	20	2·75
N45		3n.p. deep brown (1963)	20	25
N46		5n.p. bright green (1963)	20	20
N47		50n.p. orange (1965)	3·50	2·75
N48		75n.p. reddish purple (1965)	3·50	3·00
N38/48	*Set of 11*		7·00	10·50

F.P.O. 744 (Vientiane) re-opened on 22 May 1961.

Examples of the 2n.p. value overprinted as Type N **1** for use in Cambodia exist, but were never placed on sale there as the Phnom Penh F.P.O. 745 was closed on 26 June 1958. Used examples appear to originate from unauthorized use of the F.P.O. 745 postmark which was in store at Saigon.

ICC
(N **4**)

ICC
(N **5**)

1965 (15 Jan). *No. 492 of India optd with Type N **4**, for use in Laos and Vietnam.*

N49	449	15p. slate (C.)	35	3·25

F.P.O. 743 (Hanoi) was closed in 1966.

1968 (2 Oct). *Nos. 504/505, 506, 509/10, 515 and 517/18 etc of India optd as Type N **5**, in red, for use in Laos and Vietnam.*

N50	2p. red-brown	20	1·70
N51	3p. brown-olive	20	1·70
N52	5p. cerise	20	55
N53	10p. new blue	1·70	1·40
N54	15p. bronze green	70	1·40
N55	60p. deep grey	50	1·40
N56	1r. red-brown and plum	55	1·90
N57	2r. new blue and deep slate-violet	1·10	1·70
N50/57	*Set of 8*	4·75	17·00

Designs: *As T* **461**. *Vert*—3p. Brass lamp; 5p. "Family Planning"; 60p. Somnath Temple. *Horiz*—10p. Electric railway locomotive; 15p. Plucking tea. *As T* **474** *but horiz*—2r. Dal Lake, Kashmir.

The final two field post offices, No. 742 (Saigon) and No. 744 (Vintiane) closed at the end of 1968 when the inspection teams withdrew.

Laos

1951. 100 Cents = 1 Piastre
1955. 100 Cents = 1 Kip

In 1353 Fa Ngum (born in Muang Sua, 1316–1393), the son of Crown Prince Phi Fa of Xieng Dong-Xieng Thong (Luang Prabang), united territories that now include Laos under a geopolitical mandala of power known as The Kingdom of Lan Xang Hom Khao ("The Land of a Million Elephants and the White Parasol"). In 1707 this mandala disintegrated into three states—Luang Prabang, Vieng Chan, and Champassak—ruled by a grandson and two nephews of the last great ruler of Lan Xang, Souligna Vongsa, who ruled from 1637 to 1690. In the years 1778 to 1827 these three kingdoms were all conquered by Siam and made to acknowledge Siamese suzerainty.

In the Second World War, French Indo-China was occupied by Japanese troops from 1941 to 1945. The French returned in 1946, and on 10 May 1947 a constitution proclaimed the unity of the Laotian provinces as the kingdom of Laos, an independent state, with King Sisavang Vong (king of Luang Prabang since 1904) as ruler. On 19 July 1949, Laos became an Associated State within the French Union, and on 22 October 1953 it became fully independent within that Union. Laos left the French Union on 7 December 1956.

INTERNATIONAL COMMISSION. Overprinted Indian stamps were used from field post offices in Laos from 1954 to 1968. For details see under INTERNATIONAL COMMISSION IN INDO-CHINA

KINGDOM

King Sisavang Vong
10 May 1947–29 October 1959

PRINTERS AND IMPERFORATE STAMPS. All stamps of the Kingdom of Laos were printed at the Government Printing Works, Paris, *unless otherwise stated.* Imperforate examples come from limited printings.

1 River Mekong

2 King Sisavang Vong

1951 (13 Nov). *T* **1** *and similar horiz designs and T* **2.** *Recess.*
P 13.

1	**1**	10c. bright green and blue-green		35	35
2		20c. carmine and claret		35	35
3		30c. bright blue and indigo		1·50	1·10
4	–	50c. purple-brown and deep brown		35	35
5	–	60c. orange and vermilion		35	35
6	–	70c. greenish blue and bright blue		35	35
7	–	1p. reddish violet and violet		75	75
8	**2**	1p.50 brown-purple and deep brown		1·10	1·10
9	–	2p. grey-green and blue-green		15·00	5·50
10	–	3p. red and claret		1·10	90
11	–	5p. bright blue and indigo		1·50	1·10
12	–	10p. brown-purple and deep brown		2·20	1·50
1/12		*Set of* 12		22·00	12·50

Designs: *Horiz*—50c. to 70c. Luang Prabang; 1p., 2p. to 10p. Vientiane.

3 Laotian Woman

D **5** Vat
Sisaket
Shrine

D **6** Sampans

4 Laotian Woman Weaving

(Des M. Leguay. Eng R. Serres (T **3**), Pheulpin (T **4**). Recess)

1952 (13 Apr–19 July). P 13.

(a) POSTAGE.

13	**3**	30c. reddish violet and indigo		75	35
14		80c. deep blue-green and emerald		75	35
15		1p.10 carmine-red and crimson		75	75
16		1p.90 blue and indigo		1·10	1·10
17		3p. black-brown and purple-brown		1·10	1·10

(b) AIR. T **4** *and similar horiz design inscr* "POSTE AERIENNE".

18	–	3p.30 violet and deep violet (19.7)		1·10	75
19	**4**	10p. deep blue-green and ultramarine		1·80	1·10
20		20p. orange-red and crimson		3·75	2·50
21		30p. purple-brown and brown-black		5·50	5·50
13/21		*Set of* 9		15·00	12·00

Design:—3p.30, Vat Pra Keo shrine.

(Des M. Leguay. Eng Dufresne (10c. to 5p.). Pheulpin (10p.). Recess)

1952 (13 Apr)–**53.** *POSTAGE DUE.* P 13.

D22	D **5**	10c. chocolate		15	15
D23		20c. deep violet		15	15
D24		50c. carmine-red		15	15
D25		1p. deep green		20	20
D26		2p. blue		20	20
D27		5p. bright purple		75	75
D28	D **6**	10p. Indigo (14.7.53)		1·10	1·10
D22/28		*Set of* 7		2·40	2·40

1952 (13 Apr). *Anniversary of First Issue of Laos Stamps. Souvenir booklet containing 26 sheets inscr* "ROYAUME DU LAOS" *in French and Laotian. Nos.* 1/12, 13/17, 19/21 *and* D22/7.
MS21b 26 sheets each 130 × 90 mm £325

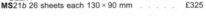

5 King Sisavang Vong and U.P.U. Monument

(Des and eng. Pheulpin. Recess)

1952 (7 Dec). *First Anniv of Admission of Laos into Universal Postal Union.* P 13.

(a) POSTAGE.

22	**5**	80c. deep reddish violet, blue and indigo	1·10	1·10
23		1p. chestnut, carmine-red and lake	1·10	1·10
24		1p.20 blue and deep reddish violet	1·10	1·10
25		1p.50 purple-brown, emerald & dp grn	1·10	1·10
26		1p.90 deep blue-green & blackish brn	1·10	1·10

(b) AIR. Inscr "POSTE AVION".

27	**5**	25p. indigo and ultramarine	4·50	4·50
28		50p. blackish brown, maroon & purbrn	4·50	4·50
22/28 *Set of 7*			13·00	13·00

6 Girl carrying her Brother **7** Court of Love

(Des M. Leguay. Eng Pheulpin. Recess)

1953 (14 July). *Red Cross Fund.* P 13.

29	**6**	1p.50+1p. red, brown-purple & indigo	2·50	2·50
30		3p.+1p.50 red and deep blue-green	2·50	2·50
31		3p.90+2p.50 red, brown-pur & dp brn	3·00	3·00

(Des Leliepvre. Eng Pheulpin. Recess)

1953 (14 July). P 13.

32	**7**	4p.50 turquoise-blue and indigo	95	75
33		6p. chocolate and violet-grey	95	75

8 Buddha

(Des M. Leguay. Eng Dufresne (4p.), Pheulpin (others) Recess)

1953 (18 Nov). *AIR. Various statues of Buddha as T 8 and similar designs.* P 13.

34		4p. green	95	75
35		6p.50 deep bluish green	1·30	95
36		9p. blue-green	1·90	1·30
37		11p.50 yellow-orange, chocolate & scar	3·00	2·50
38		40p. deep purple	7·00	2·50
39		100p. yellow-olive	13·50	9·50
34/39 *Set of 6*			25·00	16·00

Designs: *Horiz*—4p. Reclining. *Vert*—6p.90, Seated; 9p. Standing (full-face); 40p. Standing (facing right); 100p. Buddha and temple dancer.

9 Vientiane

(Des M. Leguay. Eng Pheulpin. Recess)

1954 (4 Mar). *Golden Jubilee of King Sisavang Vong.* P 13.

(a) POSTAGE.

40	**9**	2p. reddish violet and indigo	48·00	31·00
41		3p. brown-red and deep brown	48·00	34·00

(b) AIR. Inscr "POSTE AERIENNE".

42	**9**	50p. turquoise-blue and indigo	£150	£150

10 Ravana

(Des M. Leguay. Eng Pheulpin. Recess)

1955 (28 Oct). *AIR. New Currency. "Ramayana" (dramatic poem). Various designs as T 10.* P 13.

43		2k. indigo, emerald and bluish green	95	75
44		4k. red and lake-brown	1·30	1·10
45		5k. yellow-olive, blackish brn & rosered	2·50	1·50
46		10k. black, orange and sepia	4·50	3·00
47		20k. yellow-olive, deep green & brt violet	5·50	3·75
48		30k. black, brown and ultramarine	7·50	5·25
43/48 *Set of 6*			20·00	14·00

Designs: *Horiz*—4k. Hanuman, the white monkey; 5k. Ninh Laphath, the black monkey. *Vert*—10k. Sita and Rama, 20k. Luci and Ravana's friend; 30k. Rama.

11 Buddha and Worshippers

(Des M. Leguay. Eng Pheulpin. Recess)

1956 (24 May). *2500th Anniv of Buddhist Era.* P 13.

(a) POSTAGE.

49	**11**	2k. red-brown	3·00	2·50
50		3k. black	3·75	2·50
51		5k. blackish brown	5·50	3·00

(b) AIR. Inscr "POSTE AERIENNE".

52	**11**	20k. carmine and carmine-red	34·00	27·00
53		30k. yellow-olive and bistre	35·00	32·00
49/53 *Set of 5*			75·00	60·00

Nos. 49/53 are wrongly inscribed as commemorating the birth anniversary of Buddha.

12 U.N. Emblem

13 U.N. Emblem

(Des M. Leguay. Eng Pheulpin. Recess)

1956 (14 Dec). *First Anniv of Admission of Laos into United Nations Organization.*

(a) POSTAGE. P 14 × 13.

54	12	1k. black	75	60
55		2k. deep blue	95	90
56		4k. scarlet	1·30	95
57		6k. deep reddish violet	1·60	1·30

(b) AIR. Inscr "POSTE AERIENNE". P 13.

58	13	15k. blue	6·25	6·25
59		30k. lake	8·75	8·75
54/59		*Set of 6*	17·00	17·00

14 Khouy

(Des M. Leguay. Eng Pheulpin. Recess)

1957 (25 Mar). *Native Musicians. Various designs as T* **14**. P 13.

(a) POSTAGE.

60	2k. red, brown, blue and green	1·80	1·30
61	4k. red, brown, green and blue	1·80	1·30
62	8k. blue, red-brown and orange	3·25	1·50

(b) AIR. Inscr "POSTE AERIENNE".

63	12k. red, brown, bistre and bright violet	2·50	2·50
64	14k. red, orange, black and brown	3·00	3·00
65	20k. dp reddish violet, ol, grn & yell-grn	3·75	3·75
60/65	*Set of 6*	14·50	12·00

Designs: *Vert*—4k. Khene; 14k. So; 20k. Kong. *Horiz*—8k. Ranat; 12k. Khong Vong.

15 Harvesting Rice

(Des M. Leguay. Eng Pheulpin. Recess)

1957 (22 July). *Rice Cultivation. Various designs as T* **15**. P 13.

66	3k. multicoloured	1·10	60
67	5k. chocolate, red and dull green	1·10	75
68	16k. dp lilac, yellow-olive & greenish blue	2·20	1·30
69	26k. chocolate, brown and green	3·00	2·20
66/69	*Set of 4*	6·50	4·25

Designs: *Vert*—5k. Drying rice; 16k. Winnowing rice. *Horiz*—26k. Polishing rice.

16 "The Offertory" **17** Carrier Elephants

(Des M. Leguay-Eng Pheulpin. Recess)

1957 (5 Nov). *AIR. Buddhism. T* **16** *and similar designs.* P 13.

70	10k. multicoloured	90	90
71	15k. chestnut, yellow and chocolate	1·30	1·30
72	18k. olive-yellow and blackish green	1·60	1·60
73	24k. brown-lake, black and yellow	3·75	3·75
70/73	*Set of 4*	6·75	6·75

Designs: *As T* **16**. *Horiz*—15k. "Meditation" (children on river craft). *Vert*—18k. "Serenity" (head of Buddhist). 48 × 36½ *mm*—24k. "The Great Renunciation" (dancers with horse).

(Des C. Prisayane. Eng Pheulpin. Recess)

1958 (17 Mar). *Laotian Elephants. Various designs as T* **17**. *Multicoloured.* P 13.

74	10c. Type **17**	50	35
75	20c. Elephant's head with head-dress	50	35
76	30c. Elephant with howdah (*vert*)	50	35
77	2k. Elephant hauling log	1·00	35
78	5k. Elephant walking with calf (*vert*)	2·40	1·10
79	10k. Caparisoned elephant (*vert*)	3·00	1·10
80	13k. Elephant bearing throne (*vert*)	4·00	2·20
74/80	*Set of 7*	10·50	5·25

18 Mother and Child **19**

(Des M. Lequay Eng Pheulpin. Recess)

1958 (2 May). *AIR. Third Anniv of Laotian Red Cross.* P 13.

81	18	8k. black, violet-grey and vermilion	1·10	1·10
82		12k. olive-brown, brown and vermilion	1·10	1·10
83		15k. dp bluish grn, blackish grn & verm	1·30	1·30
84		20k. violet, bistre and vermilion	1·50	1·50
81/84		*Set of 4*	4·50	4·50

(Des C. Prisayane. Eng Pheulpin. Recess)

1958 (3 Nov). *Inauguration of United Nations UNESCO Headquarters Building, Paris. T* **19** *and similar designs.* P 13.

85	50c. deep blue, yellow-orange and rosine	35	20
86	60c. deep violet, purple-brown and emerald	35	20

87 70c. ultramarine, chocolate and
    vermilion 35 20
88 1k. brown-lake, turquoise-blue and
    bistre 75 45
85/88 Set of 4 . . . . . 1·60 95
Designs: Vert—60c. Woman, children and part of exterior of
U.N.E.S.C.O. building; 70c. Woman and children hailing
U.N.E.S.C.O. building superimposed on globe. Horiz—1k. General
view of U.N.E.S.C.O. building and Eiffel Tower.

20 King Sisavang Vong

(Des C. Prisayane. Eng Pheulpin. Recess)

1959 (16 Sept). P 13.
89 **20** 4k. lake 50 50
90 6k.50 Indian red 50 50
91 9k. magenta 50 50
92 13k. deep green 75 75
89/92 Set of 4 . . . . . 2·00 2·00

21 Stage Performance   **22** Portal of Vat Phou
                            Temple, Paksé

(Des C. Prisayane. Eng Pheulpin (1k., 5k.). R. Fenneteaux
(2k.), J. Miermont (3k.). Recess)

1959 (1 Oct). Education and Fine Arts. Various designs as T **21**.
P 12½ × 13.
93 1k. bistre, violet, blue and black 35 20
94 2k. lake, violet and black 35 20
95 3k. black, green and purple 75 20
96 5k. blue-green, orange-yell & reddish
    vio 75 45
93/96 Set of 4 . . . . . 2·00 95
Designs: Vert—2k. Student and "Lamp of Learning"; 5k. Stage
performers and Buddhist temple. Horiz—3k. Teacher and children
with "Key to Education".

(Des C. Prisayane. Eng Serres (50c.), Pheulpin (1k.50, 12k.50),
Gandon (2k.50), Mazelin (7k.), Munier (11k.) Recess)

1959 (2 Nov). Laotian Monuments. Various designs as T **22**. P 13.
97 50c. multicoloured 20 15
98 1k.50 multicoloured 35 20
99 2k.50 multicoloured 45 35
100 7k. multicoloured 75 45
101 11k. multicoloured 80 65
102 12k.50 multicoloured . . . . . 1·10 80
97/102 Set of 6 . . . . . 3·25 2·30
Designs: Horiz—1k.50, Thật Ing Hang, Savannakher; 2k.50, Vat
Phou Temple, Pakse; 11k. Thật Luang, Vientiane. Vert—7k. Thật
Luang, Vientiane (different view); 12k.50, Phou-Si Temple, Luang
Prabang.

King Savang Vatthana
4 November 1959–3 December 1975

ANNEE
MONDIALE
DU
REFUGIE
+1ᴷ 1959-1960
(23)
24 Plain of Jars,
Xieng Khouang

1960 (7 Apr). World Refugee Year. Nos. 79 and 89 surch as T **23**.
103 4k.+1k. lake . . . . . 3·75 3·75
104 10k.+1k. multicoloured . . . . . 5·50 5·50

(Des C. Prisayane; eng Pheulpin (9k.50, 12k.). Des M. Leguay,
eng Miermont (15k.), Fenneteaux (19k.). Recess)

1960 (1 July). AIR. Tourism. T **24** and similar designs. P 13.
105 9k.50 brown-lake, bistre and blue 75 75
106 12k. lake brown, bluish violet & yellow-
    ol 95 95
107 15k. brown-lake apple green & olive-
    brn . . . . . 1·20 1·20
108 19k. orange-brown, orange and olive-
    green . . . . . 1·40 1·40
105/108 Set of 4 . . . . . 3·75 3·75
Designs: Horiz—12k. Phapheng Falls, Champassak; 15k. Pair
of bullocks with cart. Vert—19k. Buddhist monk and village.

25 Funeral Urn   **26** Temples and
                     Statues ("Pou Gneu
                     Nha Gneu")

(Des C. Prisayane. Eng Pheulpin (4k., 6k.50), Frères (9k.), Piel
(25k.). Recess)

1961 (29 Apr). Funeral of King Sisavang Vong. T **25** and similar
vert designs. P 13.
109 4k. bistre, black and orange-red . . . . . 1·10 1·10
110 6k.50 brown-ochre and black . . . . . 1·10 1·10
111 9k. brown-ochre and black . . . . . 1·10 1·10
112 25k. black . . . . . 3·00 3·00
109/112 Set of 4 . . . . . 5·50 5·50
Designs:—6k.50, Urn under canopy; 9k. Catafalque on dragon
carriage; 25k. King Sisavang Vong.

(Des M. Lequay. Eng R. Fenneteaux (11k.), A. Frères
(14k.), J. Pheulpin (others). Recess)

1962 (19 Feb). AIR. Festival of Makha Bousa. T **26** and similar
vert designs. P 13.
113 11k. brown-ochre, rosine & dp blue-
    green 75 75
114 14k. dull ultramarine and orange 90 90

115   20k. dp green, orange-yellow &
    magenta . . . . 1·30   1·30
116   25k. Indian red, blue and deep olive . . . 1·60   1·60
113/116 *Set of 4* . . . . 4·00   4·00
Designs: *As T* **26**—14k. Bird ("Garuda"); 20k. Flying deities
("Hanuman"). 36 × 48 *mm*—25k. Warriors ("Nang Teng One").

27 King   **28** Laotian Boy
Savang Vatthana

(Des C. Prisayane. Eng J. Pheulpin. Recess)

1962 (16 Apr). P 13.
117 **27**   1k. purple-brown, scarlet &
            ultram 20   20
118   2k. purple-brown, scarlet & brt
            pur 45   20
119   5k. purple-brown, scarlet & turq-
            bl 45   35
120   10k. purple-brown, scarlet and
            bistre 80   45
117/120 *Set of 4* . . . . 1·70   1·10

(Des M. Leguay (4k., 9k.), C. Prisayane (10k.). Eng Munier
(4k.), Pheulpin (9k.). Fenneteaux (10k.). Recess)

1962 (19 July). *Malaria Eradication. T* **28** *and similar vert designs.*
P 13.
121   4k. olive, black and blue-green 35   15
122   9k. brown, black and turquoise-blue . . 45   35
123   10k. carmine-red, yellow and olive . . . 80   45
MS123*a* 130 × 100 mm. Nos. 121/3. Imperf . . £225
Designs:—9k. Laotian girl; 10k. Campaign emblem.

29 Royal Courier   **30** Fishermen

(Des C. Prisayane. Eng J. Combet (50c.). J. Pheulpin
(70c.). P. Bequet (1k.). A. Frères (1k.50). Recess)

1962 (15 Nov)–**63**. *Philatelic Exhibition, Vientiane, and Stamp
Day. T* **29** *and similar designs.* P 13.
124   50c. multicoloured 50   50
125   70c. multicoloured 50   50
126   1k. brownish black, green and lake . . 1·10   1·10
127   1k.50 multicoloured 90   90
124/127 *Set of 4* . . . . 2·75   2·75
MS127*a* Two sheets (each 129 × 100 mm)
   containing Nos. 124/5 and 126/7 (6.2.63) . . 75·00
MS127*b* As above but imperf . . . . 75·00

Designs: *Horiz*—50c. Modern mail transport; 70c. Dancer and
globe. *Vert*—1k. Royal courtier on elephant.
Nos. **MS**127*a/b* were also issued together in souvenir booklets.

(Des C. Prisayane. Eng Fenneteaux (1k.), Pheulpin (4k.),
Miermont (5k.), Mazelin (9k.). Recess)

1963 (21 Mar). *Freedom from Hunger. T* **30** *and similar designs.*
P 13.
128   1k. bistre, reddish violet & yellowish
       green 35   20
129   4k. deep blue, light brown and green . . 50   35
130   5k. indigo, bistre and green 50   45
131   9k. deep violet-blue, green & brown-
       ochre 90   50
128/131 *Set of 4* . . . . 2·00   1·30
MS131*a* 220 × 100 mm. Nos. 128/31. Imperf
   (sold at 25k.) . . . . 3·75   3·75
Designs: *Vert*—4k. Threshing rice; 9k. Harvesting rice. *Horiz*—
5k. Ploughing paddy field.
No. **MS**131*a* was issued with white or yellow gum.

31 Queen of Laos   **32** Laotian supporting U.N.
                            Emblem

(Des C. Prisayane. Eng C Mazelin. Recess)

1963 (10 Oct). *Centenary of Red Cross.* P 13.
132 **31**   4k. scarlet, deep blue and deep
            brown 50   50
133   6k. multicoloured 60   60
134   10k. scarlet, deep blue and
            chocolate 95   95
MS134*a* 140 × 100 mm. Nos. 132/4 . . . . . 4·50   4·50

(Des and eng A. Frères. Recess)

1963 (10 Dec). *15th Anniv of Declaration of Human Rights.* P 13.
135 **32**   4k. purple, blue and orange red . . . 1·30   90
         a. Imperf . . . . 1·30   90

33 Temple, Map and Rameses II

1964 (8 Mar). *Nubian Monuments Preservation. Recess.* P 13.
136 **33**   4k. multicoloured 35   35
137   6k. multicoloured 50   50
138   10k. multicoloured 75   75
MS138*a* 185 × 100 mm. Nos. 136/8 (sold at
   25k.) . . . . 2·75   2·75

34 Offertory Vase and Horn   **35** Phra Vet and Wife

(Des Thao Tuan. Eng R. Cottet (10k.), P. Forget (15k.), C. Mazelin (others). Recess)

1964 (30 July–Aug). *"Constitutional Monarchy". T* **34** *and similar square designs. Multicoloured.* P 13.

139	10k. Type **34**	45	20
140	15k. Seated Buddha of Vat Pra Keo	50	30
141	20k. Laotians walking across map	60	45
142	40k. Royal Palace, Luang Prabang	1·10	60
139/142	Set of 4	2·40	1·40
MS142a	140 × 140 mm. Nos. 139/42 (Aug)	3·75	3·75

A presentation booklet containing No. **MS**142a imperforate exists (*Price* £5 *un*).

(Photo Delrieu)

1964 (17 Nov). *Folklore. Phra Vet Legend. T* **35** *and similar vert designs. Multicoloured.* P 12½.

143	10k. Type **35**	45	45
144	32k. "Benediction"	65	65
145	45k. Phame and wife	95	95
146	55k. Arrest of Phame	1·30	1·30
143/146	Set of 4	3·00	3·00
MS146a	140 × 180 mm. Nos. 143/6. Imperf	6·25	6·25

No. **MS**146a has a control number. Presentation booklets containing the sheet without control number exist (*Price* £10 *un*).

36 Meo Warrior   **37** Red Lacewing (*Cethosia biblis*)

(Des Thao Tuan (25k.), M. Leguay (others). Eng R. Fenneteaux (5k.), J. Pheulpin (10k.), C. Mazelin (25k.), A. Frères (50k.). Recess)

1964 (15 Dec). *"Peoples of Laos". T* **36** *and similar vert designs.* P 13.

(a) POSTAGE.

147	25k. black, orange-brown & pale yell-grn	75	75

(b) AIR. Inscr "POSTE AERIENNE".

148	5k. slate, brown, orge-red & apple-grn	30	15
149	10k. flesh, slate and bright purple	45	20
150	50k. orange-brown, drab and lilac	1·60	90
147/150	Set of 4	2·75	1·80
MS150a	150 × 115 mm. Nos. 147/50	4·50	4·50

Designs:—10k. Kha hunter; 25k. Girls of three races, 50k. Thai woman.

Presentation booklets containing No. **MS**150a imperforate exist (*Price* £20 *un*).

(Des M. Leguay (20k.), S. Rodboon (others). Eng J. Pheulpin (10k., 25k.), R. Cami (20k., 40k.). Recess)

1965 (13 Mar). *Butterflies and Moths. T* **37** *and similar designs.* P 13.

(a) POSTAGE.

151	10k. chestnut, blackish brown and green	95	50
152	25k. violet-blue, black and orange-yellow	1·90	75
153	40k. yellow, chocolate and bright green	4·00	1·50

(b) AIR. Inscr. "POSTE AERIENNE".

154	20k. Venetian red and yellow	2·20	1·10
151/154	Set of 4	8·00	3·50

Butterflies: *As T* **37**—25k. *Precis cebrene.* 48 × 27 *mm*—20k. *Attacus atlas*; 40k. *Dysphania militaris* (moth).

38 Wattay Airport ("French Aid'")

(Des Ng. Cam. Eng Monvoisin (25k.), Miermont (45k.), Bétemps (55k.), Combet (75k.). Recess)

1965 (30 Mar). *Foreign Aid. T* **38** *and similar designs.* P 13.

155	25k. magenta, lt brown & turquoise-green	35	20
156	45k. light brown and bronze green	50	45
157	55k. yellow-brown and new blue	75	60
158	75k. multicoloured	1·10	80
155/158	Set of 4	2·40	1·80

Designs: *Vert*—45k. Mother bathing child (water resources: "Japanese Aid"); 75k. School and plants (education and cultivation: "American Aid"). *Horiz*—55k. Studio of radio station ("British Aid").

39 Hophabang   **40** Teleprinter-operator, Globe and Map

(Des Ng Cam. Eng R. Fenneteaux. Recess)

1965 (23 Apr). P 13 × 12½.

159	**39** 10k. multicoloured	30	20

(Des Manoutham. Eng Monvoisin (5k., 30k.). Des Soutavong. Eng Pheulpin (50k.). Recess)

1965 (15 June). *Centenary of International Telecommunications Union. T* **40** *and similar horiz designs.* P 13 × 12½.

160	5k. brown, bluish violet & bright purple	35	20
161	30k. orange-brown, blue & dp bluish grn	50	45
162	50k. multicoloured	95	80
MS162a	150 × 100 mm. Nos. 160/2	2·75	2·75

Designs: 30k. Globe, map, telephonist and radio operator; 50k. Globe, radio receiver and mast.

No. **MS**162a also exists in a presentation booklet (*Price* £4 *un*).

━
ຄ[ຶ]

1^K
━

(41)

1965 (5 July). *Nos. 89/90 surch as T* **41**.
163   **20**   1k.on 4k. lake (B.)   15   10
164   5k.on 6k.50 chestnut (B.)   20   15

42 Mother and Baby   **43** Leopard Cat

(Des Fazzi. Eng Pheulpin. Recess)

1965 (15 Sept). *Sixth Anniv of U.N. "Protection of Mother and Child"*. P 12½ × 13.
165   **42**   35k. ultramarine and red   90   75
MS165*a* 130 × 100 mm. No. 165   3·75   3·75

(Des S. Rodboon. Eng Fenneteaux (25k., 75k.), Aufschneider (others). Recess)

1965 (7 Oct). *AIR. Laotian Fauna. T* **43** *and similar vert designs.* P 12½ × 13.
166   25k. orange-yellow, brown and green   45   35
167   55k. brown, sepia and light blue   75   65
168   75k. brown and blue-green   90   80
169   100k. brown, black and yellow   1·60   1·10
170   200k. black and red   3·75   2·50
166/170 *Set of 5*   6·50   4·75
Fauna:—55k. Phayre's flying squirrel; 76k. Javan mongoose; 100k. Chinese porcupine; 200k. Binturong.

44 U.N. Emblem on   **45** Bulls in Combat
Map

(Des S. Rodboon. Eng A. Frères. Recess)

1965 (24 Oct). *20th Anniv of United Nations Organization.* P 12½ × 13.
171   **44**   5k. royal blue, brownish grey & lt green   20   20
172   25k. royal blue, brownish grey & brt mag   45   35
173   40k. royal bl, brownish grey & brt turq-bl   65   65

(Des S. Rodboon. Eng G. Bétemps (10, 50k.), J. Miermont (20k.), A. Frères (25k.). Recess)

1965 (23 Dec). *Laotian Pastimes. T* **45** *and similar horiz designs.* P 13 × 12½.
174   10k. reddish brn, brownish blk & brt orge   35   20
175   20k. Prussian blue, vermilion & deep green   35   30
176   25k. vermilion, new blue and blue-green   50   35
177   50k. multicoloured   75   60
174/177 *Set of 4*   1·75   1·30
Designs:—20k. Tikhy (form of hockey); 25k. Pirogue race; 50k. Rocket festival.

46 Slaty-headed Parakeet   **47** W.H.O. Building
(*Psittacula himalayana*)

(Des S. Rodboon. Eng J. Combet (5k., 15k.), Pheulpin (20k., 45k.). Recess)

1966 (10 Feb). *Birds. Horiz designs as T* **46**. P 13 × 12½.
178   5k. yellow-green, bistre-brown & car   50   45
179   15k. brown, black and turquoise-green   75   50
180   20k. sepia, ochre and greenish blue   1·30   90
181   45k. greenish blue, sepia & bluish violet   3·00   2·20
178/181 *Set of 4*   5·00   3·50
Birds:—15k. White-crested laughing thrush (*Garrulay leucolophus*); 20k. Osprey (*Pandion haliaetus*); 45k. Indian roller (*Coracias benghalensis*).

(Des S. Rodboon. Recess)

1966 (3 May). *Inauguration of World Health Organization Headquarters, Geneva.* P 13 × 12½.
182   **47**   10k. indigo and turquoise-green   35   20
183   25k. deep bluish green & carmine-red   35   30
184   50k. black and ultramarine   75   60
MS185 150 × 100 mm. Nos. 182/4 (sold at 150k.)   16·00   16·00

48 Ordination of Priests

(Des S. Rodboon. Eng R. Cami (10k.), G. Bétemps (25k.), C. Mazelin (30k.), J. Pheulpin (50k.). Recess)

1966 (20 May). *Laotian Ceremonies. T* **48** *and similar designs.* Multicoloured. P 13.
186   10k. Type **48**   35   20
187   25k. Sand-hills ceremony   45   35
188   30k. "Wax pagoda" procession (*vert*)   65   45
189   40k. "Sou-Khouan" ceremony (*vert*)   80   50
186/189 *Set of 4*   2·00   1·30

49 U.N.E.S.C.O. Emblem

(Des S. Rodboon)

1966 (7 July). *20th Anniv of United Nations Educational, Scientific and Cultural Organization.* P 13.
190   **49**   20k. yellow-orange and black   20   20
191   30k. new blue and black   45   35
192   40k. emerald and black   50   45
193   60k. scarlet and black   75   65
190/193 *Set of 4* . . . .   1·70   1·50
MS194 140 × 140 mm. Nos. 190/3 (sold at
250k.) . . . .   2·75   2·75

50 Letter, Carrier Pigeon and Emblem

(Des S. Rodboon. Eng Miermont. Recess)

1966 (7 Sept). *International Correspondence Week.* P 13.
195   **50**   5k. blue, brown and carmine-red . .   20   15
196   20k. brt purple, black & turquoise-
                green   45   30
197   40k. brown, carmine-red and blue . .   50   35
198   45k. black, turquoise-green & brt
                pur   75   60
195/198 *Set of 4* . . . .   1·70   1·30
MS199 130 × 100 mm. Nos. 195/8 (sold at
240k.) . . . .   3·00   3·00

51 Flooded Village

52 Carving, Siprapouthbat Pagoda

(Des S. Rodboon. Eng Fenneteaux (20k.), Haley (40k.), Pheulpin (60k.). Recess)

1967 (18 Jan). *Mekong Delta Flood Relief.* T **51** *and similar horiz designs.* Multicoloured. P 13 × 12½.
200   20k.+5k. Type **51**   50   50
201   40k.+10k. Flooded market-place . . .   80   80
202   60k.+15k. Flooded airport . . . .   1·30   1·30
MS203 150 × 100 mm. Nos. 200/2 (sold at
250k.) . . . .   4·50   4·50

(Des S. Rodboon. Eng Bétemps (5k., 20k.), Cami (50k.). Pheulpin (70k.). Recess)

1967 (21 Feb). *Buddhist Art.* T **52** *and similar vert designs.* P 12½ × 13.
204   **52**   5k. green and bistre-brown   20   20
205   20k. grey-blue and sepia   45   20
206   50k. maroon and sepia   95   60
207   70k. brownish drab and purple-brown . .   1·30   90
204/207 *Set of 4* . . . .   2·50   1·70
Designs (carvings in temple pagodas, Luang Prabang):—20k. Visoun; 50k. Xiengthong; 70k. Visoun (*different*).

53 General Post Office

54 Giant Snakehead(*Ophicephalus micropeltes*)

(Des Khamleuang. Eng Miermont. Recess)

1967 (6 Apr). *Opening of New G.P.O. Building, Vientiane.* P 13 × 12½.
208   **53**   25k. yellow-brown, green & brn-
                pur   30   15
209   50k. new blue, green and slate-
                blue   45   35
210   70k. brown-red, green & yellow-
                brown   75   60

(Des S. Rodboon. Eng Bétemps (20k.), Fenneteaux (35k.), Cottet (45k.), Miermont (60k.). Recess)

1967 (8 June). *Fishes.* T **54** *and similar horiz designs.* P 13 × 12½.
211   20k. black, bistre and greenish blue . .   50   35
212   35k. slate, bistre and turquoise-blue . .   60   45
213   45k. sepia, ochre and light blue-green . .   1·10   65
214   60k. black, bistre and myrtle-green . .   1·50   75
211/214 *Set of 4* . . . .   3·25   2·00
Designs:—35k. Giant catfish (*Pangasianodon gigas*); 45k. Tire-track spiny eel (*Mastocembelus armatus*); 60k. Bronze knifefish (*Notopterus*).

55 Cassia fistula

56 Harvesting

(Des S. Rodboon. Eng Forget (30k., 75k.), Cottet (55k., 80k.). Recess)

1967 (10 Auq). *Flowers.* T **55** *and similar vert designs.* P 12½ × 13.
215   30k. chrome-yellow, green & dp
           magenta   50   35
216   55k. carmine-lake, brt green & brt
           orange   75   45
217   75k. vermilion, green and greenish
           blue . . . .   1·10   80
218   80k. yellow magenta and emerald . .   1·50   90
215/218 *Set of 4* . . . .   3·50   2·25
Designs:—55k. *Curcuma singularis*; 75k. *Poinciana regia*; 80k. *Plumeria acutifolia*.

(Des S. Rodboon. Eng C. Prisayane. Recess)

1967 (5 Oct). *Tenth Anniv of Laotian Red Cross.* P 13.
219	**56**	20k.+5k. multicoloured		35	35
220		50k.+10k. multicoloured		75	75
221		60k.+15k. multicoloured		1·20	1·20

MS222 185 × 99 mm. Nos. 219/21 (sold at
250k.+30k.) . . . . 2·50 2·50

57 Banded Krait (*Bungarus multicinctus*)

(Des S. Rodboon. Eng Fenneteaux (5k.), Bétemps (40k.),
Gauthier (100k.), Jumelet (200k.). Recess)

1967 (7 Dec). *Reptiles. T 57 and similar horiz designs.* P 13.
223	5k. indigo, yellow and green		35	35
224	40k. deep brown, bistre and green		75	60
225	100k. chocolate, orge-brn & yellowish			
	grn		2·75	1·60
226	200k. black, light brown and deep			
	green		5·25	3·00

223/226 *Set of 4* . . . . 8·00 5·00
Designs:—40k. Marsh crocodile (*Crocodilus palustre*); 100k. Pit
viper (*Agkistrodon rhodostoma*); 200k. Water monitor (*Varanus
salvator*).

58 Human Rights Emblem

(Des S. Rodboon. Recess)

1968 (8 Feb). *Human Rights Year. Emblem in red and myrtle-
green.* P 13.
227	**58**	20k. light emerald		35	20
228		30k. light bistre-brown		35	20
229		50k. light greenish blue		75	50

MS230 190 × 100 mm. Nos 227/9 (sold at
250k.) . . . . 2·75 2·75

59 Military Parade

60 W.H.O. Emblem

(Des C. Prisayane. Eng Miermont (15k., 20k.), Frères (60k.),
Fenneteaux (200k., 300k.). Recess)

1968 (15 May). *Army Day. T 59 and similar multicoloured designs.*
P 13.

(a) POSTAGE.
231	15k. Type **59**		35	20
232	20k. Soldiers and tank in battle		35	30
233	60k. Soldiers and Laotian flag		65	50

(b) AIR. Inscr "AERIENNE".
234	200k. Parade of colours before National			
	Assembly building		1·30	90
235	300k. As 200k.		2·10	1·30

231/235 *Set of 5* . . . . 4·25 2·75
MS236 80 × 110 mm. Nos. 231/5 (sold at
600k.) . . . . 5·25 5·25

1968 (5 July). *20th Anniv of World Health Organisation. Recess.*
P 13.
237	**60**	15k. yellow-brown, orange-red &		
		pur	20	20
238		30k. yellow-brown, bl-grn & new		
		bl	35	30
239		70k. yellow-brown, pur & orge-		
		red	60	35
240		110k. yellow-brown, brt purple &		
		brn	95	75
241		250k. yellow-brown, new bl & bl		
		grn	2·20	1·60

237/241 *Set of 5* . . . . 3·75 2·75
MS242 130 × 115 mm. Nos. 237/41 (sold at
500k.) . . . . 5·25 5·25

61 *Chrysochroa
mniszechi*

62 Mango (*Mangifera
indica*)

(Des S. Rodboon. Eng Haley (30k.), Hanniquet (50k.), Jumelet
(90k.), Guillame (120k.), Lacaque (160k.). Recess)

1968 (28 Aug). *Beetles. T 61 and similar designs.* P 13.

(a) POSTAGE.
243	30k. ultramarine, yellow and blue-			
	green		60	35
244	50k. black, yellow-orange & brt purple		95	45
245	90k. indigo, orange and ochre		1·60	80

(b) AIR. Inscr "POSTE AERIENNE".
246	120k. black and orange		1·30	50
247	160k. multicoloured		1·90	80

243/247 *Set of 5* . . . . 5·50 2·50
Insects: *Vert*—50k. *Aristobia approximator*; 90k. *Eutaenia
carbetti. Horiz*—120k. *Dorysthenes walkeri*; 160k. *Megaloxantha
bicolor*.

(Des S. Rodboon. Eng Jumelet (20k.), Monvoisin (50k.),
Miermont (180k., 250k.). Recess)

1968 (3 Oct). *Laotian Fruits. T 62 and similar designs.* P 13.
248	20k. yellow-green, greenish blue &			
	blk		35	20
249	50k. bright green, crimson & light			
	blue		50	30
250	180k. apple-green, bistre-brown & orge		1·80	1·10
251	250k. light green, brown and yellow		2·50	1·60

248/251 *Set of 5* . . . . 4·50 2·75
Designs: *Vert*—50k. Tamarind (*Tamarindus indica*). *Horiz*—
180k. Jackfruit (*Artocarpus intregrifolia*); 250k. African watermelon
(*Citrullus vulgaris*).

63 Hurdling

(Des S. Rodboon. Eng Hanniquet (15k.), Guillame (80k.),
Lacaque (100k., 110k.). Recess)

1968 (15 Nov). *Olympic Games, Mexico. T* **63** *and similar designs.*
P 13.
252	15k. emerald, indigo & orange-brown		20	20
253	80k. olive-brown, turquoise-green & ind		60	45
254	100k. indigo, light brown & bright green		75	50
255	110k. light brown, light red and indigo		80	60
252/255 *Set of* 4			2·10	1·60

Designs:—80k. Tennis; 100k. Football; 110k. High jumping.

64 Panel, East Gate, Vat
Ongtu (detail)

65 "Pharak praying to the
Gods"

(Des Phanhprasith and Thong Ching, Photo)

1969 (7 Mar). *Vat Ongtu Temple. T* **64** *and similar vert design.*
P 12 × 13.
256	150k. gold, black and red		1·80	1·10
257	200k. gold, black and red		2·40	1·60

Design:—200k. Panels of central gate, Vat Ongtu.

(Des Tiao Mani. Photo De La Rue)

1969 (26 Mar–24 July). *Laotian "Ballet Royal". T* **65** *and similar
square designs, showing dance characters. Multicoloured.* P 14.

(a) POSTAGE.
258	10k. Type **65**	35	20
259	15k. "Soukhib ordered to attack"	50	35
260	20k. "Thotsakan reviewing troops"	60	50
261	30k. "Nang Sida awaiting punishment" (24.7)	95	60
262	40k. "Pharam inspecting his troops" (24.7)	1·30	75

263	60k. "Hanuman about to rescue Nang Sida" (24.7)		1·90	1·30

(b) AIR. Inscr "POSTE AERIENNE".
264	110k. "Soudagnou battling with Thotsakan" (24.7)		2·75	2·20
265	300k. "Pharam dancing with Thotsakan"		6·25	4·00
258/265 *Set of* 8			13·00	9·00

MS266 Two sheets each 106 × 106 mm. (a)
Nos. 258/60, 265 (sold at 650k.) (26.3); (b)
Nos. 261/4 (sold at 480k.) (24.7). Imperf . . 8·75 8·75
No. **MS**266(a) is known with the inscription "Ballet Royal" etc
omitted.

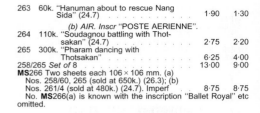

66 Handicrafts Workshop, Vientiane

(Des Ky Phungchaleun (30, 60k.), A. Souvandoane
(300k.).Eng J. Miermont. Recess)

1969 (7 May). *50th Anniv of International Labour
Organization. T* **66** *and similar horiz design.* P 13 × 12½.

(a) POSTAGE.
267	**66**	30k. reddish violet and claret	35	35
268		60k. purple-brown and slate-green	75	65

(b) AIR. Inscr "POSTE AERIENNE".
269	–	300k. black and bistre-brown	4·00	2·75

Design:—300k. Elephants moving logs.

67 Chinese Pangolin

(Des Ky Phungchaleun. Photo)

1969 (6 Nov). *Wild Animals (1st series). T* **67** *and similar
multicoloured designs.* P 11½ × 13 (120k.) or 13 × 11½ (others).

(a) POSTAGE.
270	15k. Type **67**	35	15
271	30k. Type **67**	75	35

(b) AIR. Inscr "POSTE AERIENNE".
272	70k. Sun bear	95	60
273	120k. Common gibbon (*vert*)	1·80	1·10
274	150k. Tiger	2·40	1·30
270/274 *Set of* 5		5·50	3·25

See also Nos. 300/3 and 331/5.

 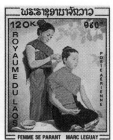

68 Royal Mausoleum,
Luang Prabang

69 "Lao Woman being
Groomed" (Leguay)

(Des and eng M. Monvoisin. Recess)

1969 (19 Nov). *10th Death Anniv of King Sisavang Vong. T* **68**
and similar vert design. P 13.
275   50k. ochre, blue and deep green   75   50
276   70k. ochre and brown-lake   75   50
Design:—70k. King Sisavang Vong (medallion).
Nos. 275/6 were issued together within the sheet, separated
vertically by a half stamp-size label bearing an inscription.

1969 (25 Dec). *AIR. Paintings by Marc Leguay (1st series). T* **69**
and similar multicoloured design. Photo. P 11½ × 13 (120k.) or
13 × 11½ (150k.).
277   120k. Type **69** . . . .   1·50   75
278   150k. "Village Market" (*horiz*) . . . .   2·20   1·10
See also Nos. 285, 307/9 and 357/61.

70 Carved Capital, Wat
Xiengthong

72 Franklin D. Roosevelt

71 "Noon" Drum

(Des Ky Phungchaleun. Photo)

1970 (10 Jan). *Laotian Pagodas. T* **70** *and similar multicoloured
designs.* P 13 × 11½ (120k.) or 11½ × 13 (others).
(a) POSTAGE.
279   70k. Type **70** . . . .   1·10   75
(b) AIR. Inscr "POSTE AERIENNE".
280   100k. Library, War Sisaket   90   35
281   120k. War Xiengthong (*horiz*) . . . . .   1·30   75

(Des Ky Phungchaleun. Eng J. Miermont (30k.), R. Fenneteaux
(55k.), C. Jumelet (125k.). Recess)

1970 (30 Mar). *Laotian Drums. T* **71** *and similar designs.* P 13.
(a) POSTAGE.
282   30k. multicoloured   75   60
283   55k. black, yellow-green & orange-brn .   1·10   90
(b) AIR. Inscr "POSTE AERIENNE".
284   125k. bistre-brown, orange-yell & flesh .   2·20   1·50
Designs: *Horiz*—55k. Kangphong (bronze) drum. *Vert*—125k.
Pag (wooden) drum.

1970 (8 Apr). *AIR. Paintings by Marc Leguay (2nd series). Horiz
design, similar to T* **69**. *Multicoloured. Photo.* P 13 × 11½.
285   150k. "Banks of the Mekong" . . . . .   1·80   1·30

(Des and eng M. Monvoisin. Recess)

1970 (12 Apr). *AIR. 25th Death Anniv of Franklin D. Roosevelt
(American statesman).* P 13.
286   **72**   120k. slate and olive-green . . . .   1·80   1·10

73 "Lenin explaining Electrification Plan"
(L. Shmatko)

(Litho State Security Printing Wks, Moscow)

1970 (22 Apr). *Birth Centenary of Lenin.* P 12½ × 12.
287   **73**   30k. multicoloured . . . .   1·30   45
288   70k. multicoloured   80   60

**Soutien aux Victimes
de la Guerre
+ 5 K**
(74)

75 Weaving Silk

1970 (1 May). *"Support for War Victims". Nos. 258/65 surch
with T* **74**.
(a) POSTAGE.
289   10k.+5k. multicoloured   45   45
290   15k.+5k. multicoloured   45   45
291   20k.+5k. multicoloured   45   45
292   30k.+5k. multicoloured   45   45
293   40k.+5k. multicoloured   90   90
294   60k.+5k. multicoloured . . . .   1·00   1·00
(b) AIR. Inscr "POSTE AERIENNE".
295   110k.+5k. multicoloured . . . .   2·20   2·20
296   300k.+5k. multicoloured . . . .   3·25   3·25
289/296 *Set of 8* . . . .   8·00   8·00

(Des Ky Phungchaleun (125k.), Thong Ching (others).
Eng C. Jumelet (30k.), J. Miermont (70k.), R. Fenneteaux
(125k.). Recess)

1970 (7 July). *"EXPO 70" World Fair, Osaka, Japan. Laotian Silk Industry. T* **75** *and similar square designs.* P 13.

(a) POSTAGE.

297	30k. indigo, chocolate and scarlet		45	30
298	70k. multicoloured		90	60

(b) AIR. Inscr "POSTE AERIENNE".

299	125k. multicoloured		1·30	90

Designs:—70k. Silk-spinning; 125k. Winding skeins.

76 Wild Boar

77 Buddha, U.N. Emblem and New York Headquarters

(Des Ky Phungchaleun. Eng R. Fenneteaux (20, 60k.), C. Jumelet (210k.), J. Miermont (500k.). Recess)

1970 (7 Sept). *Wild Animals (2nd series). T* **76** *and similar horiz designs.* P 13 × 12½.

(a) POSTAGE.

300	**76**	20k. brown and green	45	20
301		60k. brown and olive-brown	90	45

(b) AIR. Inscr "POSTE AERIENNE".

302	210k. blackish brown, carmine and yellow		2·20	1·60
303	500k. slate-green, brown and light orange		4·50	3·00
300/303	*Set of 4*		7·25	4·75

Designs:—210k. Leopard; 500k. Gaur.

(Des Ky Phungchaleun. Eng J. Miermont. Recess)

1970 (24 Oct). *25th Anniv of United Nations. T* **77** *and similar vert designs.*

(a) POSTAGE. P 13.

304	**77**	30k. brown, cerise and ultramarine	60	35
305		70k. brown, reddish lilac and emerald	90	50

(b) AIR. Inscr "POSTE AERIENNE". P 12½ × 13.

306	125k. multicoloured		1·90	1·10

Design: (26 × 36 *mm*)—125k. Nang Thorani ("Goddess of the Earth") and New York Headquarters.

1970 (21 Dec). *AIR. Paintings by Marc Leguay (3rd series). Multicoloured designs similar to T* **69**. *Photo.* P 13 × 11½ (120k.) or 11½ × 13 (others).

307	100k. "Village Track"		1·10	50
308	120k. "Paddy-field in the Rainy Season" (*horiz*)		1·50	60
309	150k. "Village Elder"		1·60	80

78 "Nakhanet"

(Des Ky Phungchaleun. Eng J. Miermont (70k.), C. Jumelet (85k.), R. Fenneteaux (125k.). Recess)

1971 (5 Feb). *Laotian Mythology (1st series). Frescoes from Triumphal Arch, Vientiane. T* **78** *and similar designs.* P 13.

(a) POSTAGE.

310	70k. red-orange, brown and brown-red		60	45
311	85k. light emerald, lemon and new blue		75	50

(b) AIR. Inscr "POSTE AERIENNE".

312	125k. multicoloured		1·50	80

Designs: *As T* **78**.—85k. "Rahu". *Horiz* (49 × 36 *mm*).—125k. "Underwater duel between Nang Matsa and Hanuman".
See also Nos. 352/4 and 385/7.

79 Silversmiths

(Des C. Prisayane. Eng J. Miermont (30k.), R. Fenneteaux (50k.), C. Jumelet (70k.). Recess)

1971 (12 Apr). *Laotian Traditional Crafts. T* **79** *and similar multicoloured designs.* P 13.

313	30k. Type **79**		20	20
314	50k. Potters		35	20
315	70k. Pirogue building (*horiz*, 49 × 36 *mm*)		65	35

80 Laotian and African Children

(Des Ky Phungchaleun. Eng J. Miermont. Recess)

1971 (1 May). *Racial Equality Year. T* **80** *and similar horiz design.* P 13.

316	30k. Indigo brown-red and emerald		30	20
317	60k. reddish vio, brn red & greenish yell		50	30

Design:—60k. Laotian dancers and musicians.

81 Buddhist Monk at That Luang

82 *Dendrobium aggregatum*

(Des Ky Phungchaleun. Eng C. Jumelet (30k.), J Miermont (70k.). Recess)

1971 (28 June). *50th Anniv of Vientiane Rotary Club. T **81** and similar design.* P 13 × 12½ (30k.) or 12½ × 13 (70k.).
318 30k. reddish violet, orange-brn & dp bl . . . 35 20
319 70k. olive-grey, rosine and deep blue . . 1·10 50
Design: *Vert*—70k. Laotian girl on "Dragon" staircase.

1971 (7 July)–*72. Laotian Orchids. T **82** and similar multicoloured designs.* Photo. P 12½ × 13 (30k.), 13 × 12½ (50, 70k.) or 13 (others).

(a) POSTAGE.
320 30k. Type **82** 75 35
321 40k. *Rynchostylis giganterum* (1.5.72) . . 75 50
322 50k. *Ascocentrum miniatur* (*horiz*) . . 1·10 45
323 60k. *Paphiopedilum exul* (1.5.72) . . 1·30 75
324 70k. *Trichoglottis fasciata* (*horiz*) . . 1·50 80
325 80k. *Cattleya* (*horiz*) (1.5.72) . . 1·60 80

(b) AIR. Inscr "POSTE AERIENNE".
326 125k. Brasilian cattleya (*horiz*) . . 3·25 1·10
327 150k. *Vanda teres* (*horiz*) (1.5.72) . . 3·75 1·30
320/327 *Set of 8* . . . . 12·50 5·50
Nos. 321, 323 and 325 are smaller, 22 × 36 or 36 × 22 mm. Nos. 326/7 are larger, 48 × 27 mm.

83 Dancers from France and Laos

84 Common Palm Civet

(Des M. Leguay. Eng J. Miermont. Recess)

1971 (6 Aug). *AIR. "Twin Cities" of Saint Astier (France) and Keng-Kok (Laos).* P 13.
328 **83** 30k. lake-brown and light brown . . 20 15
329 70k. reddish purple and plum . . . 35 15
330 100k. green and blackish green . . 50 20

(Des Ky Phungchaleun. Eng P. Gandon (50k.), R. Fenneteaux (85k.), J. Miermont (others). Recess)

1971 (16 Sept). *Wild Animals (3rd series). T **84** and similar square designs.* P 13.

(a) POSTAGE.
331 25k. black, reddish violet & ultramarine . . 50 30
332 40k. black, emerald and olive . . . 75 45
333 50k. yellow-orange and light blue-green . . 1·10 60
334 85k. light brown, blackish green & emer . . . . 1·80 95

(b) AIR. Inscr "POSTE AERIENNE".
335 300k. bistre-brown and bright green . . . 4·00 2·40
331/335 *Set of 5* . . . . 7·25 4·25
Designs:—25, 40k. T **84**; 50k. Lesser Malay Chevrotain; 85k. Sambar; 300k. Javan rhinoceros.

85 Laotian Woman (design from 1952 issue)

(Des M. Leguay. Eng R. Serres (30k.), J. Pheulpin (others). Recess)

1971 (2 Nov). *20th Anniv of Laotian Stamps. T **85** and similar designs, adapted from previous issues.* P 13.

(a) POSTAGE.
336 30k. chocolate, brown and reddish violet . . 20 15
337 40k. multicoloured 45 20
338 50k. black, flesh and bright blue . . . 60 35

(b) AIR. Inscr "POSTE AERIENNE".
339 125k. reddish violet, ochre & bluish grn . . 1·40 90
336/339 *Set of 4* . . . . 2·40 1·40
MS340 180 × 110 mm. **85** 30k. chocolate, brown and reddish violet; 60k. deep red and brown, 85k. deep bluish green, green and blue . . 3·00 3·00
Designs: 36 × 48 *mm*—40k. Violinist (1957 issue); 50k. Rama (1965 issue); 125k. "The Offertory" (1957 issue).

86 "Sunset on the Mekong" (C. Prisayane)

1971 (20 Dec). *AIR. Paintings by Chamnane Prisayane. T **86** and similar horiz design.* Multicoloured. Photo. P 13 × 11½.
341 125k. Type **85** . . . . 1·20 90
342 150k. "Quiet Morning at Ban Tane Pieo" . . . . . 1·60 1·10

87 Children reading Book

(Des S. Anoulom. Eng J. Miermont (30k.), R. Fenneteaux (70k.), C. Jumelet (125k.). Recess)

1972 (30 Jan). *International Book Year. T **87** and similar horiz designs.* P 12.

(a) POSTAGE.
343 30k. turquoise-green 20 15
344 70k. yellow-brown 50 35

(b) AIR. Inscr "POSTE AERIENNE".
345 125k. reddish violet . . . . 1·10 80
Designs: (36 × 22 *mm*)—70k. Laotian illustrating manuscript. (48 × 27 *mm*)—125k. Father showing manuscripts to children.

88 Nam Ngum Dam and Obelisk

(Des S. Anoulom. Eng C. Jumelet (40, 80k.), J. Miermont (145k.). Recess)

1972 (28 Mar). *25th Anniv of U.N. Economic Commission for Asia and the Far East (E.C.A.F.E.). T* **88** *and similar horiz design. Multicoloured.* P 13.

(a) POSTAGE.
346 40k. Type **88** 30 20
347 80k. Type **88** 60 35

(b) AIR. Inscr "POSTE AERIENNE".
348 145k. Lake and spill-way, Nam Ngum
Dam . . . . 1·10 75

89 "The Water-carrier"

1972 (20 July). *25th Anniv of United Nations Children's Fund. Drawings by Laotian Schoolchildren. T* **89** *and similar horiz designs. Multicoloured. Recess.* P 13.

(a) POSTAGE.
349 50k. Type **89** 60 35
350 80k. "Teaching Bamboo-weaving" 75 45

(b) AIR. Inscr "POSTE AERIENNE".
351 120k. "Riding a Water-buffalo" . . . . . . 1·10 80

91 Festival Offerings

(Des Ky Phungchaleun. Eng J. Larrivière (100k.), C. Jumelet (120k.), J. Miermont (150k.). Recess)

1972 (15 Sept). *AIR. Laotian Mythology (2nd series). T* **90** *and similar vert designs.* P 13.
352 100k. turquoise 75 60
353 120k. slate-lilac ("Nang Kinnali") 95 75
354 150k. orange-brown ("Norasing") . . . . 1·30 90
Nos. 352/54 show scenes from Bas-reliefs from windows of Vat Sikhounvieng Dongmient, Vientiane by the sculptor Maha Oune Kham.

(Des Ky Phungchaleun. Eng C. Jumelet (110k.). Des Thong Ching. Eng J. Miermont (125k.). Recess)

1972 (18 Nov). *AIR. That Luang Religious Festival. T* **91** *and similar horiz design.* P 13.
355 110k. chestnut 75 50
356 125k. bright reddish purple . . . . . . 1·10 75
Design:—125k. Festival procession.

1972 (23 Dec). *AIR. Paintings by Marc Leguay (4th series). Vert designs, similar to T* **69**. *Multicoloured. Photo.* P 13.
357 50k. "In the Paddy Field" (detail) 45 35
358 50k. "In the Paddy Field" (different
detail) 45 35
359 70k. "Village in the Rainy Season"
(detail) 65 45
360 70k. "Village in the Rainy Season" (diff
detail) 65 45
361 120k. "Laotian Mother" . . . . 1·50 90
357/361 *Set of 5* . . . . 3·25 2·25
Nos. 357/8 and 359/60 when placed together form the complete painting in each case.

(Des Thon Ching (40, 150k.), Ky Phungchaleun (others). Eng C. Jumelet (150k.), J. Larrivière (others). Recess)

1973 (16 Feb). *Regional Religious Ceremonial Dress. T* **92** *and similar vert designs.* P 12½ × 13.

(a) POSTAGE.
362 40k. orange-yellow, magenta & pur-brn . 45 20
363 90k. black, brown-lake & orange-brown . 95 45

(b) AIR. Inscr "POSTE AERIENNE".
364 120k. orange-brown, sepia & brt
magenta 90 60
365 150k. ochre, brown-lake and brown . . . 1·10 80
362/365 *Set of 4* . . . . 3·00 1·90
Designs:—90k. Phongsaly festival dress; 120k. Luang Prabang wedding dress; 150k. Vientiane evening dress.

90 "Nakharath"

92 Attopeu Religious Dress

93 "Lion" Guardian, That Luang

94 Satellite passing Rahu

(Des Ky Phungchaleun. Eng C. Jumelet (40, 80k.), J. Larriviere (150k.). Recess)

1973 (30 Mar). *55th Anniv of Lions International* (1972). *T* **93** *and similar design.*

(a) POSTAGE. P 12½ × 13.

| 366 | **93** | 40k. carmine, reddish purple & ultram | 45 | 20 |
| 367 | | 80k. brown-red, yellow & ultramarine | 75 | 45 |

(b) AIR. Inscr "POSTE AERIENNE". *Horiz design,* 48 × 27 *mm. Multicoloured.* P 13.

| 368 | | 150k. Lions emblems and statue of King Saysetthathirath, Vientiane | 1·20 | 90 |

(Des M. Leguay. Eng J. Larriviere (80k.), C. Jumelet (150k.). Recess)

1973 (11 May). *AIR. Traditional and Modern Aspects of Space. T* **94** *and similar horiz design. Multicoloured.* P 13.

| 369 | | 80k. Type **94** | 50 | 35 |
| 370 | | 150k. Landing module and Laotian festival rocket | 95 | 50 |

95 Dr. Gerhard Hansen and Map of Laos

(Des S. Anoulom. Eng J. Larrivière. Recess)

1973 (28 June). *Centenary of Identification of Leprosy Bacillus by Hansen.* P 13.

| 371 | **95** | 40k. brt purple, dull purple & red-orge | 50 | 35 |
| 372 | | 80k. claret, brown and yellow | 95 | 45 |

96 "Benediction"

97 "Nang Mekhala" (Goddess of the Sea)

Des Ky Phungchaleun. Eng C. Jumelet (125k.), J. Larrivière (others). Recess)

1973 (1 Sept). *25th Anniv of Laotian Boy Scouts Association. T* **96** *and similar designs.*

(a) POSTAGE. P 12½ × 13.

| 373 | **96** | 70k. orange-yellow and brown | 65 | 35 |

(b) AIR. Inscr "POSTE AERIENNE". *Horiz designs,* 48 × 27 *mm.* P 13.

| 374 | | 110k. violet and yellow-orange | 65 | 35 |
| 375 | | 125k. turquoise-blue, drab and orge-brn | 90 | 50 |

Designs: *Horiz*—110k. Campfire entertainment; 125k. Scouts helping flood victims, Vientiane, 1966.

(Des Ky Phungchaleun. Eng C. Jumelet (90k.), Guedron (150k.). Recess)

1973 (24 Oct). *AIR. Centenary of World Meteorological Organization. T* **97** *and similar design.* P 13.

| 376 | | 90k. slate-lilac, scarlet and brown | 65 | 35 |
| 377 | | 150k. carmine-red, brown & orange-brn | 1·20 | 50 |

Design: *Horiz*—150k. "Chariot of the Sun".

D 98 Serpent

99 Interpol Headquarters, Paris

1973 (31 Oct). *POSTAGE DUE. Photo.* P 13.

D378	**D 98**	10k. black, yellow-brown & lemon	15	15
D379		15k. black, yellow and emerald	15	15
D380		20k. black, bright green & new bl	15	15
D381		50k. black, violet-blue and scarlet	35	35
D378/381	*Set of 4*		75	75

(Des Thong Ching. Eng J. Larrivière (40, 80k.). Des Ky Phungchaleun. Eng Guedron (150k.). Recess)

1973 (22 Dec). *50th Anniv of International Criminal Police Organization (Interpol). T* **99** *and similar horiz design.*

(a) POSTAGE. P 13 × 12½.

| 382 | **99** | 40k. turquoise-blue | 30 | 20 |
| 383 | | 80k. brown and yellow-brown | 45 | 30 |

(b) AIR. Inscr "POSTE AERIENNE". *Size* 48 × 27 *mm.* P 13.

| 384 | | 150k. violet, red and bronze-green | 90 | 50 |

Design:—150k. Woman in opium-poppy field.

100 "Phra Sratsvady"

101 Boy and Postbox

(Des Ky Phungchaleun. Eng J. Larrivière. Recess)

1974 (23 Mar). *AIR. Laotian Mythology (3rd series). T* **100** *and similar vert designs.* P 13.

385		100k. vermilion, blackish brn & slate-lilac	75	45
386		110k. sepia, reddish lilac and scarlet	95	50
387		150k. reddish violet, brown & orange-brn	1·50	80

Designs:—110k. "Phra Indra"; 150k. "Phra Phrom".

(Des Ky Phungchaleun. Eng J. Larrivière (200k.). Des Silon Phanorath. Eng C. Jumelet (others). Recess)

1974 (30 Apr). *Centenary of Universal Postal Union.* T **101** *and similar design.*

(a) POSTAGE. P 12½ × 13.

| 388 | **101** | 70k. orange-brown, green and blue | 50 | 35 |
| 389 | | 80k. orange-brn, new bl & bronze-grn | 60 | 50 |

(b) AIR. Inscr "POSTE AERIENNE". P 13.

| 390 | | 200k. yellow-brown and red | 2·20 | 1·50 |

Design: *Horiz* (48 × 36 *mm*)—200k. Laotian girls with letters, and U.P.U. Monument, Berne (Type **105**).

(Des Ky Phungchaleun. Eng P. Guedron (200k.), C. Jumelet (others). Recess)

1974 (28 Aug). *Birth Centenary of Guglielmo Marconi (radio pioneer).* T **104** *and similar horiz design.* P 13.

(a) POSTAGE.

| 398 | **104** | 60k. slate-green, slate & yellow-brn | 35 | 20 |
| 399 | | 90k. olive-brn, slate & bronze-grn | 1·80 | 90 |

(b) AIR. Inscr "POSTE AERIENNE".

| 400 | – | 200k. red-brown and ultramarine | 1·90 | 1·10 |

Design:—200k. "Communications".

102 *Eranthemum nervosum*   **103** Car Ferry, Mekong River

(Des Silon Phanorath (50k.), Ky Phungchaleun (others). Eng J. Larrivière (30k.), C. Jumelet (50k.), Guedron (others). Recess)

1974 (31 May). *Laotian Flora.* T **102** *and similar designs.*

(a) POSTAGE. P 12½ × 13 (30k.) or 13 × 12½ (others).

391	30k. bluish violet and green	50	35
392	50k. multicoloured	75	45
393	80k. vermilion, green and orange-brown	1·10	75

(b) AIR. Inscr "POSTE AERIENNE". P 13.

| 394 | 500k. bronze-green and orange-brown | 4·00 | 2·50 |
| 391/394 *Set of 4* | | 5·75 | 3·50 |

Designs. *As* T **102** *but horiz*—50k. Water lily (*Nymphea lotus*); 80k. Red silk-cotton (*Schefflera*). 36 × 36 *mm*—500k. Pitcher plant (*Nepenthes phillamphora*).

Although Nos. 391/4 were not issued until 31st May, First Day Covers are dated 17 May.

(Des Thavisouk (250k.), Panh (others). Eng Guedron (25k.), Panh (90k.), C. Jumelet (250k.). Recess)

1974 (31 July). *Laotian Transport.* T **103** *and similar designs.* P 13.

(a) POSTAGE.

| 395 | 25k. purple-brown and red-brown | 35 | 20 |
| 396 | 90k. bistre-brown and bistre | 1·80 | 90 |

(b) AIR. Inscr "POSTE AERIENNE".

| 397 | 250k. sepia and blue-green | 1·90 | 1·10 |

Designs: *Vert*—90k. Bicycle rickshaw. *Horiz*—250k. Mekong house boat.

105 U.P.U. Monument and Laotian Girls

(Des Ky Phungchaleun. Eng J. Larrivière. Recess)

1974 (9 Oct). *AIR. Centenary of Universal Postal Union.* P 13.

| 401 | **105** | 500k. reddish lilac and red | 4·50 | 2·75 |
| **MS**402 | 135 × 105 mm. No. 401 | | 4·50 | 4·50 |

For 200k. as T **105** see No. 390.

106 *Diastocera wallichi*   **107** Pagoda and Sapphire

(Des Ky Phungchaleun. Eng J. Larrivière (50k., 90k.), P. Guedron (100k.), C. Jumelet (110k.). Recess)

1974 (23 Oct). *Beetles.* T **106** *and similar horiz designs.* P 13 × 12½.

(a) POSTAGE.

403	50k. black, chestnut & turquoise-green	75	45
404	90k. black, bluish green & bright green	1·10	60
405	100k. black, orange and orange-brown	1·50	90

(b) AIR. Inscr "POSTE AERIENNE".

| 406 | 110k. bluish violet, brown-red & yell-grn | 1·30 | 50 |
| 403/406 *Set of 4* | | 4·25 | 2·20 |

Designs:—90k. *Macrochenus isabellunus*; 100k. *Purpuricenus malaccensis*; 110k. *Sternocera multipunctata*.

104 Marconi, and Laotians with Transistor Radio

(Des M. Chandavong. Eng J. Larrivière (100k.), P. Guedron (110k.). Recess)

1975 (12 Feb). *"Mineral Riches".* T **107** *and similar horiz design.* P 13 × 12½.

| 407 | 100k. new blue, bistre-brown & yell-brn | 75 | 50 |
| 408 | 110k. brown, greenish blue and yellow | 90 | 50 |

Design:—110k. Gold-panning and necklace.

Although Nos. 407/8 were not issued until 1975, First Day Covers are dated 31 Dec 1974.

108 King Savang Vatthana, Prince Souvanna
Phouma and Prince Souvanouvong

(Des C. Prisayane. Eng E. Lacaque. Recess)

1975 (21 Feb). *First Anniv* (1974) *of Laotian Peace Treaty (1st
issue).* P 13.
409	**108**	80k. brown, ochre and green	. . .	75	35
410		300k. brown, ochre and purple	. .	1·30	1·10
411		420k. brown, ochre and			
		turquoise	. . . .	1·50	1·10

See also No. **MS**419.
No. 412 is vacant.

109 Fortune-teller's Chart

(Des C. Prisayane. Eng J. Larrivière (40k.), P. Guedron
(200k.),C. Jumelet (350k.). Recess)

1975 (14 Apr). *Chinese New Year ("Year of the Rabbit"). T* **109**
and similar designs. P 13.
413	40k. orange-brown & pale olive-green		50	20
414	200k. grey-black, orge-brn & pale ol-			
	grn	. . . .	1·30	50
415	350k. bis-brn, yell-grn & pale greenish			
	bl	. . . .	2·40	1·30

Designs: *Horiz*—200k. Fortune-teller. *Vert*—350k. Woman
riding hare.
Nos. 413/14 were issued together *se-tenant* in horizontal pairs
within the sheet, forming a composite design.

110 UN Emblem and Frieze

(Des Thao Tuan. Eng P. Guédron (100k.), J. Larrivière (200k.).
Recess)

1975 (19 June). *International Women's Year. T* **110** *and similar
vert design.* P 13.
416	100k. ultramarine and greenish blue	. . .	35	30
417	200k. yellow-orange and emerald	. . . .	75	35
MS418	130 × 100 mm. Nos. 416/17	. . . . . .	4·75	4·75

Design:—200k. IWY emblem.

111 King Savang Vatthana, Prince Souvanna
Phouma and Prince Souvanouvong

(Des C. Prisayane. Die-stamped Martimor, Paris)

1975 (June). *First Anniv of Laotian Peace Treaty (2nd issue).
Sheet 90 × 70 mm.* Imperf.
MS419 **111** 2000k. gold, red and green . . . . 8·75 8·75

APPENDIX. Further commemorative issues which appeared in 1975 are recorded in the Appendix to this country.

112 **113** Buddha and Stupas

(Des C. Prisayane. Photo)

1975 (22 July). *"Pravet Sandone" Religious Festival. T* **112** *and
similar vert designs showing Laotian legends.* P 13.
420	80k. multicoloured	. . . .	50	30
421	110k. multicoloured	. . . .	50	35
422	120k. multicoloured	. . . .	65	45
423	130k. multicoloured	. . . .	1·10	60
420/423	*Set of 4*	. . . .	2·50	1·50

(Des Thao Touan. Eng J. Peulpin. Recess)

1975 (20 Aug). *UNESCO Campaign for Preservation of Borobudur
Temple (in Indonesia). T* **113** *and similar horiz design.* P 13.
424	100k. deep bluish green, blue & bis-			
	brn	. . . .	65	35
425	200k. ochre, green and bistre-brown	. . .	1·30	80
MS426	130 × 100 mm. Nos. 424/5	. . . . .	1·50	1·50

Design:—200k. Temple sculptures.

PEOPLE'S DEMOCRATIC REPUBLIC

On 2 December 1975 a congress convened by Pathet Lao
accepted the abdication of King Savang Vatthana and the
resignation of the government, and proclaimed the People's
Democratic Republic of Laos. The next day Prince Souvanouvong
(chairman of Pathet Lao) was named as president. During 1976
Kingdom of Laos stamps were used with "ROYAUME DU"
obliterated in crayon or ink.

IMPERFORATE STAMPS. Most of the stamps and perforated minature sheets from No. 427 to 496 also exist imperforate.

Currency Revaluation
1 (new) Kip = 20 (old) Kips

114 Laotian Arms   **115** Thathiang, Vien-
Tran

1976 (2 Dec). *Multicoloured, background colour given. Litho.* P 14.
427	**114**	1k. new blue	15	15
428		2k. magenta	15	15
429		5k. pale blue-green	20	15
430		10k. reddish violet	45	35
431		200k. salmon	3·00	2·20
427/431 *Set of 5*			3·50	2·75
MS432 165 × 70 mm. Nos. 427/31			11·00	11·00

(Des Chamnane. Litho)

1976 (18 Dec). *Pagodas. T* **115** *and similar vert design. Multicoloured.* P 13½.
433	1k. Type **115**		15	15
434	2k. Phonsi, Luang Prabang		20	15
435	30k. Type **115**		75	50
436	80k. As No. 434		1·50	1·10
437	100k. As No. 434		2·20	1·50
438	300k. Type **115**		3·75	2·75
433/438 *Set of 6*			7·50	5·50
MS439 Two sheets, each 113 × 75 mm. (a)				
Nos. 433, 435 and 438; (b) Nos. 434 and				
436/7			8·00	8·00

116 Silversmith   **117** Gubarev, Grechko
and "Salyut" Space
Station

(Litho German Bank Note Ptg Co, Leipzig)

1977 (1 Apr). *Crafts. T* **116** *and similar multicoloured designs.* P 12½ × 13 (50k.) or 13 × 12½ (others).
440	1k. Type **116**		10	10
441	2k. Weaver		15	10
442	20k. Potter		75	20
443	50k. Basket-weaver (*vert*)		1·30	45
440/443 *Set of 4*			2·10	75
MS444 Four sheets, 90 × 81 mm (d) or				
81 × 90 mm (others). (a) No. 440 × 2; (b)				
No. 441 × 2, (c) No. 442 × 2, (d)				
No 443 × 2			11·00	11·00

1977 (25 Oct). *60th Anniv of Russian Revolution. T* **117** *and similar multicoloured designs. Litho.* P 12.
445	5k. Type **117**		10	10
446	20k. Lenin		20	15
447	50k. As No. 446		50	30
448	60k. Type **117**		60	45
449	100k. Government Palace, Vientiane, and			
	Kremlin, Moscow (*horiz*)		1·00	75
450	250k. As No. 449		2·40	1·90
445/450 *Set of 6*			4·25	3·25
MS451 Two sheets, each 141 × 81 mm. (a)				
Nos. 445, 447 and 450; (b) Nos. 446 and				
448/9			8·75	8·75

118 Laotian Arms   **119** Soldiers with Flag

1978 (26 May). *Litho.* P 12½.
452	**118**	5k. orange-yellow and black	15	15
453		10k. olive-sepia and black	15	15
454		50k. bright purple and black	50	15
455		100k. bright green and black	95	50
456		250k. bright violet and black	1·90	1·10
452/456 *Set of 5*			3·50	1·80

1978 (15 Sept). *Army Day. T* **119** *and similar multicoloured designs. Litho.* P 12½.
457	20k. Type **119**		15	15
458	40k. Soldiers attacking village (*horiz*)		20	15
459	300k. Anti-aircraft guns		1·80	1·10

120 Marchers with Banner   **121** Printed Circuit
and Map of Laos

1978 (2 Dec). *National Day. T* **120** *and similar vert designs. Multicoloured. Litho.* P 11½ (20, 400k.) or rough perf 11 (50k.).
460	20k. Type **120**		35	15
461	50k. Women and flag		35	15
462	400k. Dancer		2·20	1·50
	a. Rough perf 11		2·20	1·50
MS463 Two sheets, each 160 × 105 mm, each				
containing Nos. 460/2, arranged from left (a)				
20, 50, 400k.; (b) 400, 50, 20k. Imperf			8·75	8·75

1979 (18 Jan). *World Telecommunications Day. T* **121** *and similar vert design. Litho.* P 12½.
464	30k. dull orange, olive-sepia and			
	silver		15	10
465	250k. multicoloured		1·50	80
Design:—250k. Printed circuit, map of Laos and transmitter				
tower.				

122 Woman posting Letter   **123** Children playing Ball

1979 (18 Jan). *15th Anniv of Asian-Oceanic Postal Union. T* **122** *and similar horiz design. Multicoloured. Litho.* P 12½.
466	5k. Type **122**	10	10
467	10k. Post office counter	10	10
468	80k. As No. 467	80	35
469	100k. Type **122**	95	50
466/469 *Set of 4*		1·75	95

1979 (1 Aug). *International Year of the Child (1st issue). T* **123** *and similar multicoloured designs. Litho. Without gum.* Rough perf 11.
470	20k. Type **123**	20	15
471	50k. Children in school (*horiz*)	45	15
472	200k. Mother feeding baby	2·20	80
473	500k. Doctor immunising child	6·25	1·80
470/473 *Set of 4*		8·00	2·50
MS474 215 × 110 mm. Nos. 470/3. Imperf		15·00	15·00

See also Nos. 479/**MS**482.

124 Elephant, Buffalo and   **125** Dancing Child
Pirogues

1979 (9 Oct). *Transport. T* **124** *and similar horiz design. Multicoloured. Litho.* P 12½.
475	5k. Type **124**	15	15
476	10k. Buffalo carts	15	15
477	70k. As No. 476	75	20
478	500k. Type **124**	2·75	1·50
475/478 *Set of 4*		3·45	1·80

1979 (25 Dec). *International Year of the Child (2nd issue). T* **125** *and similar multicoloured designs. Litho. Without gum.* P 11½. (100k.) or rough perf 11 (others).
479	100k. Children playing musical instruments (*horiz*)	50	35
480	200k. Child and dove within globe, and map of Laos	95	75
481	600k. Type **125**	3·25	1·80
MS482 189 × 109 mm. Nos. 479/81. Imperf		12·50	12·50

Because of the roughness of the perf 11, examples can be found which apparently have a different gauge. This particularly applies to the 200k.

Currency Revaluation
1 (new) Kip = 100 (old) Kips

126 Forest and Paddy   **127** Lenin reading
Field

1980 (30 May). *Fifth Anniv of Republic (1st issue) and 25th Anniv of People's Front. T* **126** *and similar multicoloured designs. Litho. Without gum.* Rough perf 11.
483	30c. Type **126**	15	15
484	50c. Classroom and doctor examining baby (*horiz*)	35	15
485	1k. Three women	50	35
486	2k. Dam and electricity pylons (*horiz*)	1·30	1·10
483/486 *Set of 4*		2·10	1·60
MS487 170 × 99 mm. Nos 483/6. Imperf		8·75	7·50
a. Without accent*		12·50	11·50

*On No. **MS**487 the second to last letter of the first word in red at the top of the sheet has an accent (a curved line) added by hand. This accent is missing on No. **MS**487*a*.

1980 (5 July). *110th Birth Anniv of Lenin. T* **127** *and similar multicoloured designs. Litho.* P 12.
488	1k. Type **127**	20	15
489	2k. Lenin writing	45	20
490	3k. Lenin and Red Flag (*vert*)	60	35
491	4k. Lenin making speech (*vert*)	1·10	50
488/491 *Set of 4*		2·10	1·10
MS492 136 × 95 mm. Nos. 488/91. Imperf		4·50	4·50

128 Workers in Field

1980 (2 Dec). *Fifth Anniv of Republic (2nd issue). T* **128** *and similar horiz designs. Multicoloured. Litho. Without gum.* P 11.
493	50c. Type **128**	15	10
494	1k.60 Loading logs on lorry and elephant hauling logs	35	15
495	4k.60 Veterinary workers tending animals	75	30
496	5k.40 Workers in paddy field	1·10	45
493/496 *Set of 4*		2·10	90
MS497 207 × 165 mm. Nos 193/6. Imperf		8·75	7·50

PRINTERS. From No. 498 all stamps of Laos were printed by the National Printing Works, Havana, Cuba, *unless otherwise stated.*

129 Emblems of Industry,
Technology, Sport and Art

130 Giant Pandas

1981 (26 June). *26th P.C.U.S. (Communist Party) Congress. T* **129** *and similar vert designs. Multicoloured. Litho.* P 12 × 12½.

498	60c. Type **129**	15	10
499	4k.60 Communist star breaking		
	manacles, and globe	1·50	45
500	5k.40 Laurel branch and broken		
	bomb	2·10	50
MS501	140 × 106 mm. Nos. 498/500. Imperf		
	(sold at 15k.)	6·25	4·00

1981 (Oct). *"Philatokyo '81" International Stamp Exhibition, Tokyo, Sheet 90 × 60 mm. Litho.* P 13.

MS502	**130** 10k. multicoloured	5·50	2·20

131 Player heading
Ball

132 Disabled person on
Telephone

1981 (15 Oct). *World Cup Football Championship, Spain (1982) (1st issue). T* **131** *and similar multicoloured designs.* P 12.

503	1k. Type **131**	15	10
504	2k. Receiving ball	35	15
505	3k. Passing ball	50	15
506	4k. Goalkeeper diving for ball (*horiz*)	80	15
507	5k. Dribbling	1·10	35
508	6k. Kicking ball	1·60	45
503/508	*Set of 6*	4·00	1·20

1981 (16 Nov). *International Year of Disabled Persons. T* **132** *and similar vert designs. Multicoloured. Litho.* P 12½.

509	3k. Type **132**	1·10	35
510	5k. Disabled teacher	1·30	75
511	12k. Person in wheelchair mending net	3·25	1·10

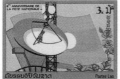

133 Dish Aerial and Flag

1981 (2 Dec). *Sixth National Day Festival. T* **133** *and similar horiz designs. Multicoloured. Litho.* P 12½.

512	3k. Type **133**	45	30
513	4k. Soldier and flag	65	35
514	5k. Girls presenting flowers to soldier, flag		
	and map of Laos	95	45

134 Wild Cat (*Felis silvestris ornata*)

1981 (30 Dec). *Wild Cats. T* **134** *and similar square designs. Multicoloured. Litho.* P 12½.

515	10c. Type **134**	15	15
516	20c. Fishing cat (*Felis viverrinus*)	15	15
517	30c. Caracal (*Felis caracal*)	15	15
518	40c. Clouded leopard (*Nefelis*		
	nebulosa)	15	15
519	50c. Flat-headed cat (*Felis planiceps*)	15	15
520	9k. Jungle cat (*Felis chaus*)	3·25	65
515/20	*Set of 6*	3·50	1·25

135 Indian Elephant

136 Laotian Wrestling

1982 (23 Jan). *Indian Elephant. T* **135** *and similar vert designs. Multicoloured. Litho.* P 12½ × 13.

521	1k. Type **135**	20	15
522	2k. Elephant carrying log	50	15
523	3k. Elephants with passengers	65	20
524	4k. Elephant in trap	90	30
525	5k. Elephant and young	1·20	35
526	5k.50 Herd of elephants	1·50	50
521/526	*Set of 6*	4·50	1·50

1982 (30 Jan). *Wrestling. T* **136** *and similar vert designs showing wrestling scenes. Litho.* P 12½.

527	50c. multicoloured	15	15
528	1k.20 multicoloured	15	15
529	2k. multicoloured	35	15
530	2k.50 multicoloured	60	20
531	4k. multicoloured	95	35
532	5k. multicoloured	1·50	50
527/532	*Set of 6*	3·25	1·40

137 *Nymphaea zanzibariensis*

138 Barn Swallow
(*Hirundo rustica*)

1982 (10 Feb). *Water Lilies. T* **137** *and similar vert designs. Multicoloured. Litho.* P 12½ × 13.

533	30c. Type **137**		15	15
534	40c. *Nelumbo nucifera* "Gaertn Rose"		15	15
535	60c. *Nymphaea rosea*		15	15
536	3k. *Nymphaea nouchali*		65	35
537	4k. *Nymphaea* White		95	35
538	7k. *Nelumbo nucifera* "Gaertn White"		1·90	45
533/538 *Set of 6*			3·50	1·40

1982 (9 Mar). *Birds. T* **138** *and similar multicoloured designs. Litho.* P 12½.

539	50c. Type **138**		15	15
540	1k. Hoopoe (*Upupa epops*)		15	15
541	2k. River kingfisher (*Alcedo atthis*)		50	15
542	3k. Black-naped blue monarch (*Hypothymis azurea*) (*horiz*)		75	20
543	4k. Grey wagtail (*Motacilla cinerea*) (*horiz*)		1·00	20
544	10k. Long-tailed tailor bird (*Orthotomus sutorius*) (*horiz*)		2·50	75
539/544 *Set of 6*			4·50	1·40

139 Football

1982 (7 Apr). *World Cup Football Championship, Spain (2nd issue). T* **139** *and similar horiz designs showing football scenes. Litho.* P 12½.

545	1k. multicoloured		20	15
546	2k. multicoloured		35	15
547	3k. multicoloured		50	15
548	4k. multicoloured		75	20
549	5k. multicoloured		95	30
550	6k. multicoloured		1·30	45
545/550 *Set of 6*			3·75	1·25
MS551 81 × 63 mm. 15k. multicoloured (footballers and flag) (36 × 28 *mm*). P 13			3·50	1·30

140 *Herona marathus*

141 Buddhist Temple, Vientiane

1982 (5 May). *Butterflies. T* **140** *and similar horiz designs. Multicoloured. Litho.* P 12½.

552	1k. Type **140**		20	15
553	2k. *Neptis paraka*		45	15
554	3k. *Euripus halitherses*		65	20
555	4k. *Lebadea martha*		95	20
556	5k. *Iton semamora* (42 × 26 *mm*)		1·50	35
557	6k. *Elymnias hypermnestra* (59 × 41 *mm*)		1·80	45
552/557 *Set of 6*			5·00	1·40

1982 (9 June). *"Philexfrance '82" International Stamp Exhibition, Paris. Sheet* 86 × 64 *mm. Litho.* P 13.

MS558 **141** 10k. multicoloured			2·75	1·30

142 Raft

1982 (24 June). *River Craft. T* **142** *and similar horiz designs. Multicoloured. Litho.* P 13.

559	50c. Type **142**		15	15
560	60c. Sampan		15	15
561	1k. House boat		20	15
562	2k. Passenger steamer		50	15
563	3k. Ferry		65	20
564	8k. Self-propelled barge		1·60	50
559/564 *Set of 6*			3·00	1·20

143 Vat Chanh

1982
(144)

1982 (2 Aug). *Pagodas. T* **143** *and similar horiz designs. Multicoloured. Litho.* P 12½.

565	50c. Type **143**		15	15
566	60c. Vat Inpeng		15	15
567	1k. Vat Dong Mieng		20	15
568	2k. Ho Tay		50	15
569	3k. Vat Ho Pha Keo		65	20
570	8k. Vat Sisaket		1·60	50
565/570 *Set of 6*			3·00	1·20

1982. *Various stamps optd with T* **144**.

571	**114**	1k. multicoloured (R.)		
572	**116**	1k. multicoloured (R.)		
		a. Black opt		
573	–	2k. multicoloured (441) (R.)		
		a. Black opt		
574	**117**	5k. multicoloured (R.)		
575	**118**	5k. orange-yellow and black (R.)		
576	**122**	5k. multicoloured (R.)		
577	**124**	5k. multicoloured (R.)		
578	–	10k. multicoloured (467) (R.)		
		a. Black opt		
579	–	10k. multicoloured (476) (R.)		
		a. Black opt		
580	–	20k. multicoloured (446) (R.)		
581	**119**	20k. multicoloured (457) (R.)		
582	**121**	30k. dull orange, olive sep & silver (R.)		
583	–	40k. multicoloured (458) (R.)		
584	–	50k. multicoloured (443) (R.)		
585	–	70k. multicoloured (477) (R.)		
586	–	80k. multicoloured (468)		

587 **122** 100k. multicoloured (R.) . . . . .
588 **114** 200k. multicoloured . . . .
589 **121** 250k. multicoloured . . . . .
For stamps similarly overprinted "1983" see Nos. 685a/b.

No. 590 is vacant.

145 Poodle

146 Woman watering Crops

1982 (13 Oct). *Dogs T **145** and similar horiz designs. Multicoloured. Litho.* P 12½.
591 50c. Type **145** 15 15
592 60c. Samoyed 15 15
593 1k. Boston terrier 20 15
594 2k. Cairn terrier 65 15
595 3k. Chihuahua 90 35
596 8k. Bulldog . . . . 2·40 60
591/596 *Set of 6* . . . . 4·00 1·40

1982 (16 Oct). *World Food Day. T **146** and similar vert design. Multicoloured. Litho.* P 12½.
597 7k. Type **146** . . . . . . 1·30 45
598 8k. Woman transplanting rice . . . . . . 1·50 50

147 Fiat, 1925

148 Pres. Souphanouvong

1982 (7 Nov). *Cars. T **147** and similar horiz designs. Multicoloured. Litho.* P 12½.
599 50c. Type **147** 15 15
600 60c. Peugeot, 1925 . . . . 15 15
601 1k. Berliet, 1925 . . . . 30 15
602 2k. Ballot, 1925 . . . . 60 15
603 3k. Renault, 1926 . . . . 90 35
604 8k. Ford, 1925 . . . . 1·80 60
599/604 *Set of 6* . . . . 3·50 1·40

1982 (2 Dec). *Seventh Anniv of Republic. T **148** and similar multicoloured designs. Litho.* P 12½.
605 50c. Type **148** 15 15
606 1k. Tractors (*horiz*) 20 15
607 2k. Cows (*horiz*) 30 15
608 3k. Lorry passing dish aerial (*horiz*) . . 50 20
609 4k. Nurse examining child 75 35
610 5k. Classroom (*horiz*) . . . . . 1·00 35
611 6k. Dancer . . . . 1·50 45
605/611 *Set of 7* . . . . 4·00 1·60

149 Dimitrov, Flag and Bulgarian Arms

150 Kremlin and Arms of U.S.S.R.

1982 (15 Dec). *Birth Centenary of Georgi Dimitrov (Bulgarian statesman). Litho.* P 12½.
612 **149** 10k. multicoloured . . . . 1·60 90

1982 (30 Dec). *60th Anniv of U.S.S.R. T **150** and similar vert design. Multicoloured. Litho.* P 12½.
613 3k. Type **150** 50 35
614 4k. Doves and map of U.S.S.R. and Laos 95 50
MS615 96 × 92 mm. Nos. 613/14. P 13 . . . 3·25 1·30

151 Hurdling

152 Bucking Horse

1983 (25 Jan). *Olympic Games, Los Angeles (1984) (1st issue). T **151** and similar vert designs. Multicoloured. Litho.* P 13.
616 50c. Type **151** 15 15
617 1k. Javelin throwing 20 15
618 2k. Basketball 30 15
619 3k. Diving 50 15
620 4k. Gymnastics 75 35
621 10k. Weightlifting . . . . 2·20 75
616/621 *Set of 6* . . . . 3·75 1·50
MS622 91 × 62 mm. 15k. Football (31 × 39 mm) . . . . 3·25 1·30
See also Nos. 708/**MS**715.

1983 (1 Feb). *Horses. T **152** and similar horiz designs. Multicoloured. Litho.* P 13.
623 50c. Type **152** 15 15
624 1k. Rearing black horse 20 15
625 2k. Trotting brown horse 35 15
626 3k. Dappled grey horse 65 20
627 4k. Wild horse crossing snow . . . 80 30
628 10k. Horse in paddock . . . . . 2·50 75
623/628 *Set of 6* . . . . 4·25 1·50

153 "St. Catherine of Alexandria"

154 A. Gubarev (Soviet) and V. Remek (Czechoslovak)

1983 (9 Mar). *500th Birth Anniv of Raphael (artist). T* **153** *and similar multicoloured designs. Litho.* P 12½ × 13.

629	50c. Type **153**	15	15
630	1k. "Adoration of the Kings"	20	15
631	2k. "Madonna of the Grand Duke"	35	15
632	3k. "St. George and the Dragon"	65	20
633	4k. "The Vision of Ezekiel"	80	30
634	10k. "Adoration of the Kings" (*different*)	2·50	75
629/634 *Set of 6*		4·25	1·50

MS635 74 × 123 mm. 10k. "Coronation of the Virgin" (39 × 31 *mm*). P 13 .... 3·00   90

1983 (12 Apr–24 July). *Cosmonauts. T* **154** *and similar vert designs. Multicoloured. Litho.* P 12½.

636	50c. Type **154**	15	15
637	50c. P. Klimuk (Soviet) and Miroslaw Hermaszewskl (Polish)	15	15
638	1k. V. Bykovsky (Soviet) and Sigmund Jahn (East German)	20	15
639	1k. Nikolai Rukavishnikov (Soviet) and Georgi Ivanov (Bulgarian)	20	15
640	2k. V. Kubasov (Soviet) and Bertalan Farkas (Hungarian)	35	15
641	3k. V. Dzhanibekov (Soviet) and Gurragchaa (Mongolian)	60	20
642	4k. L. Popov (Soviet) and D. Prunariu (Rumanian)	75	20
643	6k. Soviet cosmonaut and Arnaldo Tamayo (Cuban)	1·10	35
644	10k. Soviet and French cosmonauts	2·20	75
636/644 *Set of 9*		5·25	2·00

MS645 92 × 90 mm. 10k. V. Gorbatko (Soviet) and Pham Tuan (Vietnamese) (28 × 35 *mm*). P 13 (24.7) .... 2·50   90

155 Jacques Charles's Hydrogen Balloon, 1783

156 German Maybach Car

1983 (4 May). *Bicentenary of Manned Flight. T* **155** *and similar vert designs. Multicoloured. Litho.* P 12½ × 13.

646	50c. Type **155**	15	15
647	1k. Blanchard and Jeffries' balloon, 1785	20	15
648	2k. Vincenzo Lunardi's balloon (London–Ware flight), 1784	35	15
649	3k. Modern hot-air balloon over city	75	20
650	4k. Massed balloon ascent, 1890	90	35
651	10k. Auguste Piccard's stratosphere balloon *F.N.R.S.*, 1931	2·50	75
646/651 *Set of 6*		4·25	1·60

MS652 100 × 83 mm. 10k. Balloon *Double Eagle II* (31 × 39 *mm*). P 13 .... 2·50   95

1983 (21 May). *"Tembal '83" Stamp Exhibition, Basle. Sheet* 95 × 63 *mm. Litho.* P 13.

MS653 **156** 10k. multicoloured .... 3·00   95

157 *Dendrobium* sp.

1983 (10 June). *Flowers. T* **157** *and similar horiz designs. Multicoloured. Litho.* P 13.

654	1k. Type **157**	20	15
655	2k. *Aerides odoratum*	35	15
656	3k. *Dendrobium aggregatum*	60	20
657	4k. *Dendrobium*	75	20
658	5k. *Moschatum*	1·00	30
659	6k. *Dendrobium* sp. (*different*)	1·50	45
654/659 *Set of 6*		4·00	2·20

158 Downhill Skiing

159 Boatmen on Tachin River

1983 (2 July). *Winter Olympic Games, Sarajevo* (1984) *(1st issue). T* **158** *and similar horiz designs. Multicoloured. Litho.* P 13.

660	50c. Type **158**	15	15
661	1k. Slalom	20	15
662	2k. Ice hockey	35	15
663	3k. Speed skating	65	20
664	4k. Ski jumping	80	30
665	10k. Luge	2·20	75
660/665 *Set of 6*		4·00	1·50

MS666 91 × 57 mm. 15k. Bobsleigh (39 × 31 *mm*) .... 3·25   1·10

See also Nos. 696/**MS**703.

1983 (4 Aug). *"Bangkok 1983" International Stamp Exhibition. Sheet* 93 × 72 *mm. Litho.* P 13.

MS667 **159** 10k. multicoloured .... 2·50   90

160 Clown Knifefish (*Notopterus chitala*)

1983 (5 Sept). *Fish of Mekong River T* **160** *and similar horiz designs. Multicoloured. Litho. P* 12½.

668	1k. Type **160**	20	15
669	2k. Common carp (*Cyprinus carpio*)	35	15
670	3k. Lesser Mekong catfish (*Pangasius*) sp.	65	20
671	4k. Giant barb (*Catlocarpio siamensis*)	75	20
672	5k. Black sharkminnow (*Morulius*) sp.	1·20	30
673	6k. Nile mouthbrooder(*Tilapia nilotica*)	1·60	45
668/673	*Set of 6*	4·25	1·30

161 Magellan and *Vitoria*

1983 (8 Oct). *Explorers and their Ships. T* **161** *and similar horiz designs. Litho. P* 13 × 12½.

674	1k. Type **161**	20	15
675	2k. Jacques Cartier and *Grande Hermine*	35	15
676	3k. Columbus and *Santa Maria*	75	20
677	4k. Pedro Alvares Cabral and *El Ray*	90	20
678	5k. Cook and H.M.S. *Resolution*	1·10	30
679	6k. Charcot and *Pourquois-pas?*	1·60	45
674/679	*Set of 6*	4·50	1·30

No. 679 is wrongly inscribed "Cabot".

162 Tabby Cat

163 Marx, Book, Sun and Signature

1983 (9 Nov). *Domestic Cats. T* **162** *and similar vert designs. Multicoloured. Litho. P* 12½ × 13.

680	1k. Type **162**	20	15
681	2k. Long-haired Persian	75	15
682	3k. Siamese	65	20
683	4k. Burmese	80	20
684	5k. Persian	1·20	30
685	6k. Tortoiseshell	1·60	45
680/685	*Set of 6*	4·50	1·30

1983 (22 Nov). *Nos. 430 and 466 optd* "1983" *as T* **144** *in red.*

685a	**122**	5k. multicoloured		
685b	**114**	10k. multicoloured		

1983 (30 Nov). *Death Centenary of Karl Marx. T* **163** *and similar horiz designs. Multicoloured. Litho. P* 13.

686	1k. Marx, dove, globe and flags	30	15
687	4k. Type **163**	1·00	15
688	6k. Marx and flags	1·80	50

164 Elephant dragging Log

1983 (2 Dec). *Eighth Anniv of Republic. T* **164** *and similar multicoloured designs. Litho. P* 13 × 12½ (4k.) *or* 12½ × 13 (others).

689	1k. Type **164**	30	15
690	4k. Cattle and pig (*horiz*)	1·00	15
691	6k. Crops	1·80	50

165 Carrier Pigeon and Telex Machine

166 Ice Skating

1983 (15 Dec). *World Communications Year. T* **165** *and similar horiz designs. Multicoloured. Litho. P* 13.

692	50c. Type **165**	15	15
693	1k. Early telephone, handset and receiver	20	15
694	4k. Television tube and aerial	90	30
695	6k. Satellite and dish aerial	1·50	50
692/695	*Set of 4*	2·50	1·00

1984 (16 Jan). *Winter Olympic Games, Sarajevo (2nd issue). T* **166** *and similar multicoloured designs. Litho. P* 13.

696	50c. Type **166**	15	15
697	1k. Speed skating	20	15
698	2k. Biathlon	35	15
699	4k. Luge (*horiz*)	90	30
700	5k. Downhill skiing (*horiz*)	95	30
701	6k. Ski jumping	1·30	45
702	7k. Slalom	1·60	50
696/702	*Set of 7*	5·00	1·80
MS703	89 × 55 mm. 10k. Ice hockey (31 × 39 mm)	2·50	90

167 Tiger (*Panthera tigris*)

168 Diving

1984 (1 Feb). *Endangered Animals. The Tiger. T* **167** *and similar multicoloured designs. Litho.* P 13.

704	25c. Type **167**		35	15
705	25c. Tigers (*horiz*)		35	15
706	3k. Tiger and cubs (*horiz*)		4·00	50
707	4k. Tiger cubs		6·25	1·00
704/707 *Set of 4*			9·75	1·60

1984 (26 Mar). *Olympic Games. Los Angeles (2nd issue). T* **168** *and similar vert designs. Multicoloured.* P 13.

708	50c. Type **168**		15	15
709	1k. Volleyball		30	15
710	2k. Running		60	15
711	4k. Basketball		1·20	15
712	5k. Judo		1·30	30
713	6k. Football		1·80	35
714	7k. Gymnastics		2·10	45
708/714 *Set of 7*			6·50	1·50
MS715 98 × 81 mm. 10k. Wrestling (31 × 39 *mm*). P 12½			2·50	90

169 Tuned Drums

170 National Flag

1984 (27 Mar). *Musical Instruments. T* **169** *and similar horiz designs. Multicoloured.* P 13.

716	1k. Type **169**		20	15
717	2k. Xylophone		45	15
718	3k. Pair of drums		80	20
719	4k. Hand drum		1·00	30
720	5k. Barrel drum		1·30	30
721	6k. Pipes and string instrument		2·10	45
716/721 *Set of 6*			5·25	1·40

1984 (30 Mar). *National Day T* **170** *and similar vert design. Multicoloured.* P 12½.

722	60c. Type **170**		20	15
723	1k. National arms		45	15
724	2k. As No. 723		60	20

171 Chess Game

172 "Cardinal Nino de Guevara" (El Greco)

1984 (13 Apr). *60th Anniv of World Chess Federation. T* **171** *and similar vert designs. Multicoloured.* P 12½ × 13.

725	50c. Type **171**		15	15
726	1k. Renaissance game from "The Three Ages of Man" (miniature attr. to Estienne Porchier)		20	15
727	2k. Woman teaching girls		50	15
728	2k. Margrave Otto IV of Brandenburg playing chess with his wife		50	15
729	3k. Four men at chessboard		90	30

730	4k. Two women playing		1·30	30
731	8k. Two men playing		2·75	45
725/731 *Set of 7*			5·50	1·50
MS732 87 × 70 mm. 10k. Human chess game (31 × 39 *mm*). P 13			2·50	90

Nos. 725, 727 and 729/31 show illustrations from King Alfonso X's *Book of Chess, Dice and Tablings.*

1984 (27 Apr). *"España 84" International Stamp Exhibition, Madrid. T* **172** *and similar vert designs. Multicoloured.* P 12½.

733	50c. Type **172**		15	15
734	1k. "Gaspar de Guzman, Duke of Olivares, on Horseback" (Velázquez)		30	15
735	2k. "The Annunciation" (Murillo)		45	15
736	2k. "Portrait of a Lady" (Zurbarán)		45	15
737	3k. "The Family of Charles IV" (Goya)		65	30
738	4k. "Two Harlequins" (Picasso)		95	30
739	8k. "Abstract" (Miro)		1·90	45
733/739 *Set of 7*			4·25	1·50
MS740 63 × 80 mm 10k. "Burial of the Count of Orgaz" (El Greco) P 13			2·50	90

173 *Adonis aestivalis*　　**174** Nazzaro

1984 (11 May). *Woodland Flowers. T* **173** *and similar vert designs. Multicoloured.* P 13.

741	50c. Type **173**		15	15
742	1k. *Alpinia speciosa*		20	15
743	2k. *Cassia lechenaultiana*		45	15
744	2k. *Aeschynanthus speciosus*		45	15
745	3k. *Datura meteloides*		75	30
746	4k. *Quamoclit pennata*		95	30
747	8k. *Commelina benghalensis*		1·90	45
741/747 *Set of 7*			4·25	1·50

1984 (19 June). *19th Universal Postal Union Congress Philatelic Salon, Hamburg. Cars. T* **174** *and similar horiz designs. Multicoloured. Litho.* P 13.

748	50c. Type **174**		15	15
749	1k. Daimler		20	15
750	2k. Delage		45	15
751	2k. Fiat "S 57/14B"		45	15
752	3k. Bugatti		90	30
753	4k. Itala		1·30	30
754	8k. Blitzen Benz		2·40	45
748/754 *Set of 7*			5·25	1·50
MS755 79 × 52 mm. 10k. Winton "Bullet". P 12½			2·50	95

175 "Madonna and Child"　　**176** "Luna 1"

1984 (26 June). *450th Death Anniv of Correggio (artist).* T **175** *and similar vert designs. Multicoloured. Litho.* P 13.

756	50c. Type **175**	15	15
757	1k. Detail showing riders resting	30	15
758	2k. "Madonna and Child" (*different*)	50	15
759	2k. "Mystical Marriage of St. Catherine"	50	15
760	3k. "Four Saints"	75	30
761	4k. "Noli me Tangere"	1·10	30
762	8k. "Christ bids Farewell to the Virgin Mary"	2·20	45
756/762 *Set of 7*		5·00	1·50

MS763 80 × 107 mm. 10k. "Madonna and Child" (*different*) (31 × 39 *mm*)   3·25   95

1984 (12 July). *Space Exploration.* T **176** *and similar horiz designs. Multicoloured. Litho.* P 13.

764	50c. Type **176**	15	15
765	1k. "Luna 2"	20	15
766	2k. "Luna 3"	45	15
767	2k. Kepler and "Sputnik 2"	45	15
768	3k. Newton and "Lunokhod 2"	95	20
769	4k. Jules Verne and "Luna 13"	1·30	35
770	8k. Copernicus and space station	2·40	60
764/770 *Set of 7*		5·25	1·60

177 Malaclemys Terrapin

1984 (20 Aug). *Reptiles.* T **177** *and similar multicoloured designs. Litho.* P 13.

771	50c. Type **177**	15	15
772	1k. Banded krait (*Bungarus fasciatus*)	20	15
773	2k. Indian python (*Python molurus*) (*vert*)	45	15
774	2k. Reticulated python (*Python reticulatus*)	45	15
775	3k. Tokay gecko (*Gekko gecko*)	95	20
776	4k. *Natrix subminiata* (snake)	1·30	35
777	8k. Dappled ground gecko (*Eublepharis macumillaris*)	2·50	60
771/777 *Set of 7*		5·25	1·60

178 Greater Glider (*Schoinobates volans*)

1984 (21 Sept). *"Ausipex 84" International Stamp Exhibition, Melbourne. Marsupials.* T **178** *and similar multicoloured designs. Litho.* P 13.

778	50c. Type **178**	15	15
779	1k. Platypus (*Ornithorhynchus anatinus*)	30	15
780	2k. Southern hairy-nosed wombat (*Lasiorhinus latifrons*)	45	15
781	2k. Tasmanian devil (*Sarcophilus harrisii*)	45	15
782	3k. Thylacine (*Thylacinus cynocephalus*)	95	20
783	4k. Tiger cat (*Dasyurops maculatus*)	1·20	35
784	8k. Walllaby (*Wallabia isabelinus*)	2·10	60
778/784 *Set of 7*		5·00	1·60

MS785 95 × 58 mm. 10k. Red kangaroo (*Macropus rufus*) 31 × 39 *mm*. P 12½   2·50   90

179 Nurse with Mother and Child

180 Dragon Stair-rail

1984 (29 Sept). *Anti-poliomyelitis Campaign.* T **179** *and similar horiz design. Multicoloured. Litho.* P 13.

786	5k. Type **179**	1·10	50
787	6k. Doctor inoculating child	1·30	50

1984 (26 Oct). *Laotian Art.* T **180** *and similar multicoloured designs. Litho.* P 13.

788	50c. Type **180**	15	15
789	1k. Capital of column	20	15
790	2k. Decorative panel depicting god	35	15
791	2k. Decorative panel depicting leaves	35	15
792	3k. Stylized leaves (*horiz*)	75	20
793	4k. Triangular flower decoration (*horiz*)	1·30	35
794	8k. Circular lotus flower decoration	2·40	60
788/794 *Set of 7*		5·00	1·60

181 River House Boats

1984 (17 Dec). *Ninth Anniv of Republic.* T **181** *and similar horiz designs. Multicoloured. Litho.* P 13.

795	1k. Type **181**	45	15
796	2k. Passengers boarding Fokker F.27 Friendship airliner	65	20
797	4k. Building a bridge	1·30	60
798	10k. Building a road	2·75	1·20
795/798 *Set of 4*		4·50	2·00

182 Players with Ball

1985 (18 Jan). *World Cup Football Championship, Mexico (1986) (1st issue).* T **182** *and similar multicoloured designs. Litho.* P 13.

799	50c. Type **182**	15	15
800	1k. Heading the ball	20	15
801	2k. Defending the ball	60	15
802	3k. Running with ball	90	15
803	4k. Taking possession of ball	1·30	30
804	5k. Heading the ball (*different*)	1·60	35
805	6k. Saving a goal	1·90	60
799/805 *Set of 7*		6·00	1·60

MS806 56 × 72 mm. 10k. Flag, player and ball (31 × 39 *mm*). P 12½   2·75   90

See also Nos. 868/**MS**875.

1985
(183a)

183 Motor Cycle

1985 (25 Feb). *Centenary of Motor Cycle. T* **183** *and similar horiz designs. Multicoloured. Litho.* P 12½.

807	50c. Type **183**	15	15
808	1k. Gnome Rhone, 1920	20	15
809	2k. F.N. "M67C", 1928	50	15
810	3k. Indian "Chief", 1930	75	15
811	4k. Rudge Multi, 1914	1·10	30
812	5k. Honda "Benly J" 1953	1·30	35
813	6k. CZ, 1938	1·60	60
807/813 *Set of 7*		5·00	1·60

1985. *Various stamps optd as T* **183a** *(smaller on some values) in red.*

813a	–	40k. multicoloured (458)
813b	–	50k. multicoloured (443)
813c	–	50k. multicoloured (447)
813d	–	70k. multicoloured (477)
813e	–	80k. multicoloured (468)
813f	–	100k. multicoloured (449)
813g	**122**	100k. multicoloured
813h	**114**	200k. multicoloured
813i	–	250k. multicoloured (450)
813j	**118**	250k. bright violet and black
813k	**121**	250k. multicoloured
813m	–	300k. multicoloured (459)

184 *Amanita muscaria*

184a Battle Plan, Kursk, and Tanks

1985 (8 Apr). *Fungi. T* **184** *and similar vert designs. Multicoloured. Litho.* P 13.

814	50c. Type **184**	15	15
815	1k. *Boletus edulis*	20	15
816	2k. *Coprinus comatus*	50	15
817	2k. *Amanita rubescens*	50	15
818	3k. *Xerocomus subtomentosus*	1·00	30
819	4k. *Macrolepiota procera (Lepiota procera)*	1·60	35
820	8k. *Paxillus involutus*	2·75	65
814/820 *Set of 7*		6·00	1·70

(Litho State Ptg Wks. Moscow)

1985 (May). *40th Anniv of End of Second World War. T* **184a** *and similar horiz designs. Multicoloured.* P 12½ × 12.

820a	1k. Type **184a**	35	15
820b	2k. Monument and military parade, Red Square, Moscow	65	15
820c	4k. Street battle and battle plan, Stalingrad	1·30	35
820d	5k. Battle plan and Reichstag, Berlin	1·60	45
820e	6k. Soviet Memorial, Berlin-Treptow, and military parade at Brandenburg Gate	1·90	50
820a/820e *Set of 5*		5·25	1·40

185 Lenin reading *Pravda*

186 *Cattleya percivaliana*

1985 (28 June). *115th Birth Anniv of Lenin. T* **185** *and similar multicoloured designs. Litho.* P 12½.

821	1k. Type **185**	35	15
822	2k. Lenin (*vert*)	60	15
823	10k. Lenin addressing meeting (*vert*)	2·50	75

1985 (5 July). *"Argentina '85" International Stamp Exhibition, Buenos Aires. Orchids. T* **186** *and similar vert designs. Multicoloured. Litho.* P 13.

824	50c. Type **186**	15	15
825	1k. *Odontoglossum luteo-purpureum*	20	15
826	2k. *Cattleya lueddemanniana*	45	15
827	2k. *Maxillaria sanderiana*	45	15
828	3k. *Miltonia vexillaria*	75	20
829	4k. *Oncidium varicosum*	1·00	30
830	8k. *Cattleya dowiana*	2·20	60
824/830 *Set of 7*		4·50	1·50
MS831 82 × 63 mm. 10k. *Catasetum fimbriatum* (31 × 39 *mm*).		3·00	95

187 Rhesus Macaque (*Macaca mulatta*)

188 "Saturn" Rocket on Launch pad

1985 (15 Aug). *Mammals. T* **187** *and similar multicoloured designs. Litho.* P 13.

832	2k. Type **187**	30	15
833	3k. Kouprey (*Bos sauveli*)	60	15
834	4k. Porcupine (*Hystrix leucura*) (*horiz*)	90	30
835	5k. Asiatic black bear (*Selenarctos thibetanus*) (*horiz*)	1·10	30
836	10k. Chinese pangolin (*Manis pentadactyla*)	2·40	60
832/836 *Set of 5*		4·75	1·40

1985 (6 Sept). *Tenth Anniv of "Soyuz"–"Apollo" Space Link. T* **188** *and similar multicoloured designs. Litho.* P 13.

837	50c. Type **188**	15	15
838	1k. Soviet rocket on launch pad	30	15
839	2k. "Apollo" approaching "Soyuz 19" (*horiz*)	45	15
840	2k. "Soyuz 19" approaching "Apollo" (*horiz*)	45	15
841	3k. "Apollo" and crew T. Stafford, V. Brand and D. Slayton (*horiz*)	75	20
842	4k. "Soyuz 19" and crew A. Leonov and V. Kubasov (*horiz*)	1·00	30
843	8k. "Apollo" and "Soyuz 19" docked (*horiz*)	2·10	60
837/843 *Set of 7*		4·75	1·50

189 Fiat Biplane

190 U.N. and National
Flags on Globe

1985 (25 Oct). *"Italia '85" International Stamp Exhibition, Rome. T* **189** *and similar horiz designs. Multicoloured. Litho.* P 13.

(a) Aircraft. As T **189**.

844	50c.	Type **189**	15	15
845	1k.	Cant Z.501 Gabbiano flying boat	20	15
846	2k.	Marina Fiat MF.5 flying boat	45	15
847	3k.	Macchi Castoldi MC-100 flying boat	65	20
848	4k.	Anzani biplane	90	30
849	5k.	Ambrosini biplane	95	30
850	6k.	Piaggio P-148	1·30	45
MS851	86 × 54 mm. 10k. Marina Fiat MF.4 flying boat (39 × 31 *mm*)		2·50	1·00

(b) Columbus and his Ships. Size 40 × 29 mm.

852	1k.	*Pinta*	20	15
	a.	Sheetlet. Nos. 852/6 plus 4 labels	4·50	
853	2k.	*Nina*	45	15
854	3k.	*Santa Maria*	65	20
855	4k.	*Christopher Columbus*	90	30
856	5k.	Map of Columbus's first voyage	1·10	35
844/850, 852/856 *Set of 12*			7·00	2·50

Nos. 852/6 were issued together in *se-tenant* sheetlets of five stamps and four labels showing exhibition emblem.

1985 (25 Oct). *40th Anniv of United Nations Organization. T* **190** *and similar vert designs. Multicoloured. Litho.* P 13.

857	2k.	Type **190**	65	20
858	3k.	Laotian arms and U.N. emblem on globe	95	30
859	10k.	Map of Laos on globe	2·75	95

191 Woman feeding
Child

192 Soldier, Workers and
Symbols of Industry and
Agriculture

1985 (15 Nov). *Lao Health Services. T* **191** *and similar multicoloured designs. Litho.* P 13.

860	1k.	Type **191**	20	15
861	3k.	Red Cross nurse injecting child (*horiz*)	80	15
862	4k.	Red Cross nurse tending patient (*horiz*)	1·00	30
863	10k.	Mother breast-feeding baby	2·20	75
860/863 *Set of 4*			3·75	1·25

1985 (2 Dec). *Tenth Anniv of Republic. T* **192** *and similar horiz design. Multicoloured. Litho.* P 13.

864	3k.	Type **192**	65	20
865	10k.	Soldier, workers and symbols of transport and communications	2·50	90

193 Soldier with Flag and Workers

1985 (30 Dec). *30th Anniv of Lao People's Revolutionary Party. T* **193** *and similar horiz design. Multicoloured.* P 13.

866	2k.	Type **193**	90	15
867	8k.	Soldier with flag and workers (*different*)	2·75	60

194 Footballers

194a Cosmonaut, "Mir"
Space Complex and Earth

1986 (20 Jan). *World Cup Football Championship, Mexico (2nd issue). T* **194** *and similar designs showing various footballing scenes. Litho.* P 13.

868	50c.	multicoloured	15	15
869	1k.	multicoloured	20	15
870	2k.	multicoloured	45	15
871	3k.	multicoloured	65	20
872	4k.	multicoloured	75	20
873	5k.	multicoloured	95	30
874	6k.	multicoloured	1·30	35
868/874 *Set of 7*			4·00	1·40
MS875	92 × 92 mm. 10k. multicoloured (39 × 31 *mm*)		3·75	90

(Litho State Ptg Wks. Moscow)

1986 (27 Jan). *17th Soviet Communist Party Congress. T* **194a** *and similar vert design. Multicoloured.* P 12 × 13½.

875a	4k.	Type **194a**	1·00	30
875b	20k.	Lenin and Red Flag	4·00	95

195 *Pelargonium
grandiflorum*

196 *Aporia hippia*

1986 (28 Feb). *Flowers. T* **195** *and similar vert designs.*
Multicoloured. Litho. P 13.

876	50c.	Type **195**	15	15
877	1k.	Columbine (*Aquilegia vulgaris*)	20	15
878	2k.	*Fuchsia globosa*	45	15
879	3k.	*Crocus aureus*	65	20
880	4k.	Hollyhock (*Althaea rosea*)	75	20
881	5k.	*Gladiolus purpureo*	95	30
882	6k.	*Hyacinthus orientalis*	1·30	35
876/882	*Set of 7*		4·00	1·40

1986 (30 Mar). *Butterflies. T* **196** *and similar vert designs.*
Multicoloured. Litho. P 13.

883	50c.	Type **196**	15	15
884	1k.	*Euthalia irrubescens*	20	15
885	2k.	*Japonica lutea*	45	15
886	3k.	*Pratapa ctesia*	65	20
887	4k.	*Kallina inachus*	75	20
888	5k.	*Ixias pyrene*	95	30
889	6k.	*Danaus sita* (*Parantica sita*)	1·30	35
883/889	*Set of 7*		4·00	1·40

197 Rocket launch at Baikanur Space Centre

198 Giraffe (*Giraffa camelopardalis*)

1986 (12 Apr). *25th Anniv of First Man in Space. T* **197** *and similar multicoloured designs. Litho.* P 13.

890	50c.	Type **197**	15	15
891	1k.	"Molniya" communications satellite	30	15
892	2k.	"Salyut" space station (*horiz*)	45	15
893	3k.	Yuri Gagarin, "Sputnik 1" and rocket debris (*horiz*)	80	15
894	4k.	"Luna 3" and moon	1·10	20
895	5k.	Vladimir Komarov on first space walk	1·60	35
896	6k.	"Luna 16" lifting off from moon	1·80	45
890/896	*Set of 7*		5·50	1·40
MS897	88 × 66 mm. 10k. "Soyuz" preparing to dock with "Salyut" (39 × 31 *mm*)		2·50	90

1986 (22 May). *Animals. T* **198** *and similar multicoloured designs. Litho.* P 13 × 12½ (6k.) or 12½ × 13 (others).

898	50c.	Type **198**	15	15
899	1k.	Lion (*Panthera leo*)	20	15
900	2k.	African elephant (*Loxodonta africana*)	45	15
901	3k.	Red kangaroo (*Macropus rufus*)	65	20
902	4k.	Koala (wrongly inscr "Gymnobelideus leadbeateri")	90	20
903	5k.	Greater flamingo (*Phoenicopterus ruber*)	1·00	30
904	6k.	Giant panda (*Ailuropoda melanoleucus*) (*horiz*)	1·80	50
898/904	*Set of 7*		4·50	1·50
MS905	80 × 60 mm. 10k. American bison (*Bison bison*) (31 × 39 *mm*). P 13		2·50	1·00

No. **MS**905 commemorates "Ameripex '86" International Stamp Exhibition, Chicago.

199 Boeing 747-100

1986 (2 June). *AIR. Aircraft. T* **199** *and similar horiz design. Multicoloured. Litho.* P 12½.

906	20k.	Type **199**	3·75	30
907	50k.	Ilyushin Il-86	8·75	80

200 Great Argus Pheasant (*Argusianus argus*)

1986 (29 June). *Pheasants. T* **200** *and similar horiz designs. Multicoloured. Litho.* P 12 × 13.

908	50c.	Type **200**	15	15
909	1k.	Silver pheasant (*Gennaeus nycthemerus*)	20	15
910	2k.	Common pheasant (*Phasianus colchicus*)	45	15
911	3k.	Lady Amherst's pheasant (*Chrysolophus amherstiae*)	65	20
912	4k.	Reeves's pheasant (*Syrmaticus reevesii*) (wrongly inscr "Symaticus")	75	20
913	5k.	Golden pheasant (*Chrysolophus pictus*)	95	30
914	6k.	Copper pheasant (*Syrmaticus soemmerringii*)	1·30	35
908/914	*Set of 7*		4·00	1·40

201 Scarlet King Snake (*Lampropeltis doliata*)

1986 (21 July). *Snakes. T* **201** *and similar multicoloured designs. Litho.* P 12½ × 13 (*vert*) or 13 × 12½ (*horiz*).

915	50c.	Corn snake (*Elaphe guttata*) (*vert*)	15	15
916	1k.	Type **201**	20	15
917	1k.	Richard's blind snake (*Thalerophis richardi*) (*vert*)	45	15
918	2k.	Western ring-necked snake (*Diadophis amabilis*)	65	20
919	4k.	Mangrove snake (*Boiga dendrophila*)	75	20
920	5k.	Indian python (*Python molurus*)	95	30
921	8k.	Common cobra (*Naja naja*) (*vert*)	1·30	35
915/921	*Set of 7*		4·00	1·40

202 Bayeux Tapestry (detail) and Comet Head

203 Keeshond

1986 (22 Aug). *Appearance of Halley's Comet. T **202** and similar multicoloured designs.* P 12 × 13.

922	50c. Comet over Athens (65 × 21 *mm*)	15	15
923	1k. Type **202**	20	15
	a. Horiz pair. Nos. 923/4	70	35
924	2k. Edmond Halley (astronomer) and comet tail (20 × 21 *mm*)	45	15
925	3k. "Vega" space probe and comet head	65	20
	a. Horiz pair. Nos. 925/6	1·50	45
926	4k. Galileo and comet tail (20 × 21 *mm*)	75	20
927	5k. Comet head (20 × 21 *mm*)	95	30
	a. Horiz pair. Nos. 927/8	2·30	70
928	6k. "Giotto" space probe and comet tail	1·30	35
922/928 *Set of 7*		4·00	1·40

MS929 100 × 45 mm. 10k. Surface of Earth and comet head (39 × 31 *mm*). P 13 . . 2·50 90

Nos. 923/4, 925/6 and 927/8 respectively were issued together in *se-tenant* pairs within their sheets, each pair forming a composite design.

1986 (28 Aug). *"Stockholmia 86" International Stamp Exhibition. Dogs. T **203** and similar multicoloured designs.* Litho. P 13.

930	50c. Type **203**	15	15
931	1k. Elkhound (*horiz*)	20	15
932	2k. Bernese (*horiz*)	50	15
933	3k. Pointing griffon (*horiz*)	80	20
934	4k. Collie (*horiz*)	80	20
935	5k. Irish water spaniel (*horiz*)	1·00	30
936	6k. Briard (*horiz*)	1·60	50
930/936 *Set of 7*		4·50	1·50

MS937 78 × 60 mm. 10k. Brittany spaniels chasing grey partridge (39 × 31 *mm*) . . 3·00 95

204 *Mammillaria matudae*

205 Arms and Dove on Globe

1986 (28 Sept). *Cacti. T **204** and similar vert designs. Multicoloured.* Litho. P 13.

938	50c. Type **204**	15	15
939	1k. *Mammillaria theresae*	20	15
940	2k. *Ariocarpus trigonus*	45	15
941	3k. *Notocactus crassigibbus*	65	20
942	4k. *Astrophytum asterias* hybrid	75	20
943	5k. *Melocactus manzanus*	95	30
944	6k. *Astrophytum ornatum* hybrid	1·30	35
938/944 *Set of 7*		4·00	1·50

1986 (24 Oct). *International Peace Year. T **205** and similar vert designs.* Litho. P 13.

945	3k. multicoloured	80	20
946	5k. black, new blue and bright scarlet	1·30	35
947	10k. multicoloured	2·50	90

Designs:—5k. Dove on smashed bomb; 10k. People supporting I.P.Y. emblem.

206 Vat Phu Champasak

207 Speed Skating

1986 (4 Nov). *40th Anniv of United Nations Educational, Scientific and Cultural Organization. T **206** and similar multicoloured designs.* Litho. P 13.

948	3k. Type **206**	65	20
949	4k. Dish aerial and map of Laos on globe	90	30
950	9k. People reading books (*horiz*)	1·80	60

1987 (14 Jan). *Winter Olympic Games, Calgary (1988) (1st issue). T **207** and similar multicoloured designs.* Litho. P 13.

951	50c. Type **207**	15	15
952	1k. Biathlon	20	15
953	2k. Figure skating (pairs)	45	15
954	3k. Luge (*horiz*)	65	20
955	4k. Four-man bobsleigh (*horiz*)	75	20
956	5k. Ice hockey (*horiz*)	95	30
957	6k. Ski jumpng (*horiz*)	1·30	35
951/957 *Set of 7*		4·00	1·40

MS958 78 × 58 mm. 10k. Skiing (31 × 39 *mm*) . . 2·50 1·00

See also Nos. 1046/**MS**1052.

208 Gymnastics and Urn

209 Great Dane

1987 (2 Feb). *Olympic Games, Seoul (1988) (1st issue). T **208** and similar multicoloured designs showing sports and Greek pottery.* Litho. P 12½ × 13 (vert) or 13 × 12½ (horiz).

959	50c. Type **208**	15	15
960	1k. Throwing the discus, and vase (*horiz*)	20	15
961	2k. Running and vase	45	15
962	3k. Show jumping and bowl (*horiz*)	65	20
963	4k. Throwing the javelin, and plate	75	20
964	5k. High jumping and bowl with handles (*horiz*)	95	30
965	6k. Wrestling and urn	1·30	35

959/965 *Set of 7* .... 4·00 1·40
MS966 82 × 55 mm. 10k. Runner leaving blocks
  (39 × 31 *mm*). P 12½ .... 2·20 90
  See also Nos. 1053/**MS**1060.

1987 (5 Mar). *Dogs. T* **209** *and similar vert designs. Multicoloured.*
  Litho. P 12½ × 13.
967 50c. Type **209** 15 15
968 1k. Black labrador 20 15
969 2k. St. Bernard 45 15
970 3k. Tervuren shepherd dog 75 20
971 4k. German shepherd 80 20
972 5k. Beagle .... 1·30 30
973 6k. Golden retriever .... 1·50 50
967/973 *Set of 7* .... 4·50 1·50

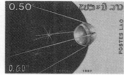

210 "Sputnik 1"

1987 (12 Apr). *30th Anniv of Launch of First Artificial*
  Satellite. T **210** *and similar multicoloured designs. Litho.* P 13.
974 50c. Type **210** 15 15
975 1k. "Sputnik 2" 20 15
976 2k. "Cosmos 97" 45 15
977 3k. "Cosmos" 65 20
978 4k. "Mars" 75 20
979 5k. "Luna 1" 95 30
980 9k. "Luna 3" (*vert*) .... 1·50 45
974/980 *Set of 7* .... 4·00 1·40

211 "MONTREAL" Handstamp on letter
to Quebec and *Tern* (schooner)

1987 (12 May). *"Capex 87" International Stamp Exhibition,*
  Toronto. Ships and Covers. T **211** *and similar horiz designs.*
  Multicoloured. Litho. P 13.
981 50c. Type **211** 15 15
982 1k. "PAID MONTREAL" on letter and
    Malahat (schooner) 20 15
983 2k. Letter from Montreal to London and
    William D. Lawrence (full-rigged
    ship) 45 15
984 3k. 1840 letter to Willamsburgh and
    Neptune (steamer) 65 20
985 4k. 1844 letter to London and *Athabasca*
    (steamer) 75 20
986 5k. 1848 letter and *Chicora* (paddle-
    steamer) 95 30
987 6k. 1961 letter and *Passport* (river
    paddle-steamer) .... 1·30 35
981/987 *Set of 7* .... 4·00 1·40
MS988 80 × 60 mm 10k. 1949 4c. Canadian
  stamp (39 × 31 *mm*). P 12½ .... 2·20 90

212 Horse

1987 (3 June). *Horses. T* **212** *and similar multicoloured designs.*
  Litho. P 13 × 12½ (50c.) or 12½ × 13 (others).
989 50c. Type **212** 15 15
990 1k. Chestnut (*vert*) 20 15
991 2k. Black horse with sheepskin
    noseband (*vert*) 45 15
992 3k. Dark chestnut (*vert*) 65 20
993 4k. Black horse (*vert*) 75 20
994 5k. Chestnut with plaited mane (*vert*) .. 95 30
995 6k. Grey (*vert*) .... 1·30 35
989/995 *Set of 7* .... 4·00 1·40

213 Volvo "480"   **214** *Vanda teres*

1987 (2 July). *Motor Cars. T* **213** *and similar horiz designs.*
  Multicoloured. Litho. P 12½.
996 50c. Type **213** 15 15
997 1k. Alfa Romeo "33" 20 15
998 2k. Ford "Fiesta" 45 15
999 3k. Ford "Fiesta" (*different*) 75 20
1000 4k. Ford "Granada" 80 20
1001 5k. Citroen "AX" .... 1·30 30
1002 6k. Renault "21" .... 1·50 50
996/1002 *Set of 7* .... 4·50 1·50
MS1003 65 × 52 mm. 10k. Skoda "Estelle"
  (39 × 31 *mm*). P 13 .... 2·75 95

1987 (10 Aug). *Orchids. T* **214** *and similar vert designs.*
  Multicoloured. Litho. P 13.
1004 3k. Type **214** 15 15
1005 7k. *Laeliocattleya* sp. 15 15
1006 10k. *Paphiopedilum* hybrid 20 15
1007 39k. *Sobralia* sp. 80 20
1008 44k. *Paphiopedilum* hybrid (*different*) .. 90 30
1009 47k. *Paphiopedilum* hybrid (*different*) .. 1·00 35
1010 50k. *Cattleya trianaei* .... 1·20 35
1004/1010 *Set of 7* .... 4·00 1·50
MS1011 52 × 75 mm. 95k. *Vanda tricolor*
  (31 × 39 *mm*). P 12½ .... 2·50 90

215 Elephants

1987 (2 Sept). *"Hafnia 87" International Stamp Exhibition, Copenhagen. Elephants.* T **215** *and similar multicoloured designs. Litho.* P 13.

1012	50c. Type **215**	15	15
1013	1k. Three elephants	20	15
1014	2k. Elephant feeding	45	15
1015	3k. Elephant grazing on grass	65	20
1016	4k. Adult with calf	75	20
1017	5k. Elephant walking	95	30
1018	6k. Elephant (*vert*)	1·30	35
1012/1018	*Set of 7*	4·00	1·50
MS1019	64 × 44 mm. 10k. Adults and calf (39 × 31 *mm*)	2·20	90

216 Building Bamboo House

1987 (5 Oct). *International Year of Shelter for the Homeless.* T **216** *and similar horiz designs. Multicoloured. Litho.* P 13.

1020	1k. Type **216**	15	15
1021	27k. Building wooden house	60	20
1022	46k. House on stilts	1·20	30
1023	70k. Street of houses on stilts	1·80	60
1020/1023	*Set of 4*	3·50	1·40

217 Clown Loach (*Botia macracantha*)

1987 (14 Oct). *Fishes.* T **217** *and similar horiz designs. Multicoloured. Litho.* P 13 × 12½.

1024	3k. Type **217**	15	15
1025	7k. Harlequin filefish (*Oxymocanthus longirostris*)	15	15
1026	10k. Silver-spotted squirrelfish (*Adioryx caudimaculatus*)	20	15
1027	39k. Mandarin fish (*Synchiropus splendidus*)	80	20
1028	44k. Coral hind (*Cephalopolis miniatus*)	90	30
1029	47k. Zebra lionfish (*Dendrochirus zebra*)	1·00	35
1030	50k. Semicircle angelfish (*Pomacantus semicirculatus*)	1·20	35
1024/1030	*Set of 7*	4·00	1·60

218 Watering Seedlings

219 Wounded Soldiers on Battlefield

1987 (16 Oct). *World Food Day.* T **218** *and similar multicoloured designs. Litho.* P 13.

1031	1k. Type **218**	15	15
1032	3k. Harvesting maize (*vert*)	15	15
1033	5k. Harvesting rice	15	15
1034	63k. Children with fish (*vert*)	1·30	45
1035	142k. Tending pigs and poultry	3·00	90
1031/1035	*Set of 5*	4·25	1·60

(Litho State Ptg Wks, Moscow)

1987 (7 Nov). *70th Anniv of Russian Revolution.* T **219** *and similar vert designs. Multicoloured.* P 12 × 12½.

1036	1k. Type **219**	20	15
1037	2k. Mother and baby	45	20
1038	4k. Storming the Winter Palace	80	20
1039	8k. Lenin amongst soldiers and sailors	1·60	45
1040	10k. Lenin labouring in Red Square	2·20	60
1036/1040	*Set of 5*	4·75	1·40

220 Hoeing

221 Laotheung Dress

1987 (9 Nov). *Rice Culture in Mountain Regions.* T **220** *and similar horiz design. Multicoloured. Litho.* P 13.

1041	64k. Type **220**	1·40	30
1042	100k. Working in paddy fields	2·40	75

1987 (2 Dec). *Ethinic Dress.* T **221** *and similar vert designs. Multicoloured. Litho.* P 13.

1043	7k. Type **221**	15	15
1044	38k. Laoloum dress	80	20
1045	144k. Laosoun dress	3·00	1·00

222 Two-man Bobsleigh

1988 (10 Jan). *Winter Olympic Games, Calgary (2nd issue).* T **222** *and similar horiz designs. Multicoloured. Litho.* P 13 × 12½.
1046	1k. Type **222**	15	15
1047	4k. Biathlon (shooting)	15	15
1048	20k. Cross-country skiing	45	15
1049	42k. Ice hockey	90	30
1050	63k. Speed skating	1·30	45
1051	70k. Slalom	1·50	50
1046/1051 *Set of 6*		4·00	1·50

MS1052 74 × 45 mm. 95k. Skiing (39 × 31 *mm*).
P 13 . . . . 2·20   90

223 Throwing the Javelin

1988 (7 Feb). *Olympic Games, Seoul (2nd issue).* T **223** *and similar horiz designs. Multicoloured. Litho.* P 12½.
1053	2k. Type **223**	15	15
1054	5k. Triple jumping	15	15
1055	10k. Men's gymnastics	20	15
1056	12k. Pirogue racing	35	15
1057	38k. Women's gymnastics	1·00	20
1058	46k. Fencing	1·30	30
1059	100k. Wrestling	2·75	65
1053/1059 *Set of 7*		5·25	1·60

MS1060 100 × 67 mm. 95k. Men's gymnastics
(*different*) (36 × 28 *mm*). P 13 . . . . 2·20   90

224 Tyrannosaurus

1988 (3 Mar). *"Juvalux 88" Youth Philately Exhibition, Luxembourg. Prehistoric Animals.* T **224** *and similar multicoloured designs. Litho.* P 13 × 12½ (horiz) or 12½ × 13 (vert).
1061	3k. Type **224** (wrongly inscr "Trachodon")	15	15
1062	7k. *Ceratosaurus nasicornis* (*vert*)	20	15
1063	39k. *Iguanodon bernissartensis* (*vert*)	1·10	20
1064	44k. *Scolosaurus* (*vert*)	1·10	35
1065	47k. *Phororhacus* sp. (*vert*)	1·10	35
1066	50k. Anatosaurus (wrongly inscr "Tyrannosaurus")	1·50	35
1061/1066 *Set of 6*		4·50	1·40

MS1067 73 × 94 mm. 95k. Pteranodon (39 × 31
mm). P 12½ . . . . 2·40   90

225 Adults in Hygiene Class

1988 (8 Apr). *40th Anniv of World Health Organization.* T **225** *and similar multicoloured designs. Litho.* P 12½.
1068	5k. Type **225**	15	15
1069	27k. Fumigating houses	50	15
1070	164k. Woman pumping fresh water (*vert*)	3·50	1·20

226 *Sans Pareil*, 1829   **227** Red Frangipani
(*Plumeria rubra*)

1988 (5 May). *"Essen 88" International Stamp Fair. Early Railway Locomotives.* T **226** *and similar multicoloured designs. Litho.* P 12½ × 13 (vert) or 13 × 12½ (horiz).
1071	6k. Type **226**	15	15
1072	15k. Stephenson's *Rocket*, 1829	35	15
1073	20k. *Royal George*, 1827 (*horiz*)	45	15
1074	25k. Trevithick's locomotive, 1804 (*horiz*)	60	20
1075	30k. *Novelty*, 1829 (*horiz*)	90	20
1076	100k. *Tom Thumb*, 1829 (*horiz*)	2·40	75
1071/1076 *Set of 6*		4·25	1·40

MS1077 82 × 70 mm. 95k. Stephenson's
Locomotion, 1825 (34 × 28 *mm*). P 13 . . 2·75   95

1988 (1 June). *"Finlandia 88" International Stamp Exhibition, Helsinki. Flowers.* T **227** *and similar vert designs. Multicoloured. Litho.* P 12½.
1078	8k. Type **227** (wrongly inscr "Plumieria")	15	15
1079	9k. Hollyhock (*Althaea rosea*)	20	15
1080	15k. Flame-of-the-forest (*Ixora coccinea*)	30	15
1081	33k. Golden shower (*Cassia fistula*)	65	20
1082	64k. *Dahlia coccinea* (red)	1·30	45
1083	69k. *Dahlia coccinea* (yellow)	1·50	50
1078/1083 *Set of 6*		3·75	1·40

MS1084 76 × 58 mm. 95k. Hollyhock, frangipani
and flame-of-the-forest (31 × 39 *mm*). P 13 . 2·75   1·00

228 Sash Pattern   **229** Dove and Figures

1988 (20 July). *Decorative Stencil Patterns.* T **228** *and similar designs. Litho.* P 13.
1085	1k. multicoloured	15	15
1086	2k. greenish yellow, rosine and black	15	15
1087	3k. multicoloured	20	15
1088	25k. multicoloured	65	20
1089	163k. multicoloured	3·25	1·40
1085/1089 *Set of 5*		4·00	1·80

Designs (stencils for): *Vert*—2k. Pagoda doors; 3k. Pagoda walls. *Horiz*—25k. Pagoda pillars; 163k. Skirts.

1988 (18 Aug). *125th Anniv of Red Cross Movement.* T **229** *and similar multicoloured designs. Litho.* P 13.

1090	4k. Type **229**		15	15
1091	52k. Red Cross workers with handicapped people		1·20	50
1092	144k. Red Cross worker vaccinating baby (*horiz*)		4·00	1·60

230 Stork-billed Kingfisher (*Pelargopsis capensis*)

231 Red Cross Workers loading Supplies into Pirogue

1988 (30 Sept). *Birds.* T **230** *and similar vert designs. Multicoloured. Litho.* P 13.

1093	6k. Type **230**		15	15
1094	10k. Japanese quail (*Coturnix japonica*)		20	15
1095	13k. Blossom-headed parakeet (*Psittacula roseata*)		30	15
1096	44k. Orange-breasted green pigeon (*Treron bicincta*)		65	20
1097	63k. Black-crested bulbul (*Pycnonotus melanicterus*)		1·30	45
1098	64k. Mountain imperial pigeon (*Ducula badia*)		1·50	50
1093/1098 *Set of 6*			3·75	1·40

1988 (30 Oct). *Completion of First Five Year Plan.* T **231** *and similar horiz designs. Multicoloured. Litho.* P 13.

1099	20k. Type **231**		50	20
1100	40k. Library		90	35
1101	50k. Irrigating fields		1·30	50
1102	100k. Improvement in communications		2·20	1·00
1099/1102 *Set of 4*			4·50	1·80

232 Ruy Lopez Segura

1988 (22 Nov). *Chess Masters.* T **232** *and similar horiz designs. Litho.* P 13.

1103	1k. Type **232**		15	15
1104	2k. Karl Andersson		15	15
1105	3k. Paul Morphy (wrongly inscr "Murphy")		15	15
1106	6k. Wilhelm Steinitz		20	15
1107	7k. Emanuel Lasker		30	15
1108	12k. José Raul Capablanca		45	20
1109	172k. Aleksandr Alekhine		4·00	1·00
1103/1109 *Set of 7*			4·75	1·75

233 Tortoiseshell and White

1989 (7 Jan). *"India 89" International Stamp Exhibition, New Delhi. Cats.* T **233** *and similar square designs. Multicoloured. Litho.* P 12½.

1110	5k. Type **233**		15	15
1111	6k. Brown tabby		15	15
1112	10k. Black and white		35	15
1113	20k. Red tabby		60	15
1114	50k. Black		1·20	35
1115	172k. Silver tabby and white		4·00	90
1110/1115 *Set of 6*			5·75	1·60
MS1116 70 × 94 mm. 95k. Brown tabby and white (31 × 39 *mm*). P 13			2·75	1·10

234 Gunboat, Tank, Soldiers and Flags

1989 (20 Jan). *40th Anniv of People's Army.* T **234** *and similar multicoloured designs. Litho.* P 13.

1117	1k. Type **234**		15	15
1118	2k. Soldier teaching mathematics (*vert*)		15	15
1119	3k. Army medics vaccinating civilians		15	15
1120	250k. Peasant, revolutionary, worker and soldiers		6·75	95
1117/1120 *Set of 4*			6·50	1·25

235 Footballers

1989 (4 Feb). *World Cup Football Championship, Italy* (1990) (*1st issue*). T **235** *and similar horiz designs. Litho.* P 13 × 12½.

1121	10k. Type **235**		20	15
1122	15k. Footballer looking to pass ball		30	15
1123	20k. Ball hitting player on chest		45	15
1124	25k. Tackle		60	20
1125	45k. Punching ball		90	30
1126	105k. Kicking ball		2·40	75
1121/1126 *Set of 6*			4·25	1·50
MS1127 52 × 65 mm. 95k. Players and goalkeeper (38 × 29 *mm*). P 13			2·20	1·10

See also Nos. 1168/**MS**1174.

236 Couple planting Sapling

1989 (30 Mar). *Preserve Forests campaign. T* **236** *and similar multicoloured designs. Litho.* P 13.
1128	4k. Type **236**	15	15
1129	10k. Burning and fallen trees	20	15
1130	12k. Man felling tree (*vert*)	20	20
1131	200k. Map of Laos showing distribution of forests (*vert*)	4·50	90
1128/1131 *Set of 4*		4·50	1·25

237 Camilo Cienfuegos, Fidel Castro and Flag

238 Skaters

1989 (20 Apr). *30th Anniv of Cuban Revolution. T* **237** *and similar vert design. Multicoloured. Litho.* P 13.
1132	45k. Type **237**	1·10	35
1133	50k. Cuban and Laotian flags	1·10	35

1989 (1 May). *Winter Olympic Games, Albertville (1992) (1st issue). Figure Skating. T* **238** *and similar multicoloured designs. Litho.* P 13.
1134	9k. Type **238**	20	15
1135	10k. Pair (*horiz*)	30	15
1136	15k. Ice dancing	45	15
1137	24k. Female skater	50	20
1138	29k. Pair	65	20
1139	114k. Male skater	2·75	90
1134/1139 *Set of 6*		4·25	1·60

MS1140 49 × 78 mm. 95k. Pair (*different*) (31 × 39 *mm*). P 12½ . . . 2·20 1·10
See also Nos. 1196/**MS**1202, 1237/**MS**1242 and 1276/**MS**1281.

239 High Jumping

240 "Poor on Seashore"

1989 (1 June). *Olympic Games, Barcelona (1992) (1st issue). T* **239** *and similar multicoloured designs. Litho.* P 12½.
1141	5k. Type **239**	15	15
1142	15k. Gymnastics	30	15
1143	20k. Cycling (*horiz*)	45	20
1144	25k. Boxing (*horiz*)	50	30

1145	70k. Archery	1·30	50
1146	120k. Swimming	2·75	60
1141/1146 *Set of 6*		5·00	1·70

MS1147 65 × 91 mm. 95k. Baseball (31 × 39 *mm*). P 13 . . . 2·20 1·10
See also Nos. 1179/**MS**1185, 1231/**MS**1236 and 1282/**MS**1287.

1989 (17 July). *Philexfrance '89" International Stamp Exhibition, Paris. Paintings by Picasso. T* **240** *and similar vert designs. Multicoloured. Litho.* P 12½ × 13.
1148	5k. Type **240**	15	15
1149	7k. "Motherhood"	20	15
1150	8k. "Portrait of Jaime S. le Bock"	20	15
1151	9k. "Harlequins"	45	20
1152	105k. "Boy with Dog"	2·75	60
1153	114k. "Girl on Ball"	2·75	75
1148/1153 *Set of 6*		5·75	1·80

MS1154 65 × 75 mm. 95k. "Woman in Hat" (31 × 39 *mm*). P 12½ . . . 2·75 1·10

241 Sapodillas (*Manilkara zapota*)

242 Sikhotabong Temple, Khammouane

1989 (18 Sept). *Fruits. T* **241** *and similar vert designs. Multicoloured. Litho.* P 13.
1155	5k. Type **241**	15	15
1156	20k. Sugar-apples (*Annona squamosa*)	50	20
1157	20k. Guavas (*Psidium guajava*)	50	20
1158	30k. Durians (*Durio zibethinus*)	75	30
1159	50k. Pomegranates (*Punica granatum*)	1·30	45
1160	172k. *Moridica charautia*	4·50	90
1155/1160 *Set of 6*		7·00	2·00

1989 (19 Oct). *Temples. T* **242** *and similar vert designs. Multicoloured. Litho.* P 12½.
1161	5k. Type **242**	15	15
1162	15k. Dam Temple, Vientiane	30	20
1163	61k. Ing Hang Temple, Savannakhet	1·20	50
1164	161k. Ho Vay Phra Luang Temple, Vientiane	3·75	1·00
1161/1164 *Set of 4*		5·00	1·70

243 Nehru and Woman

244 Footballer

1989 (9 Nov). *Birth Centenary of Jawaharlal Nehru (Indian statesman). T* **243** *and similar multicoloured designs. Litho.* P 12½.
1165	1k. Type **243**	15	15
1166	60k. Nehru and group of children (*horiz*)	1·30	45
1167	200k. Boy garlanding Nehru	4·50	1·00

1990 (10 Jan). *World Cup Football Championship, Italy (2nd issue). T* **244** *and similar vert designs showing players. Litho.* P 13.

1168	10k. multicoloured	20	15
1169	15k. multicoloured	30	15
1170	20k. multicoloured	45	15
1171	25k. multicoloured	50	20
1172	45k. multicoloured	95	30
1173	105k. multicoloured	2·40	75
1168/1173 *Set of 6*		4·25	1·60

MS1174 90 × 67 mm. 95k. multicoloured
(31 × 39 *mm*) . . . . 2·20   1·10

245 Teacher and Adult Class

246 Basketball

1990 (27 Feb). *International Literacy Year. T* **245** *and similar multicoloured designs. Litho.* P 12½.

1175	10k. Type **245**	20	15
1176	50k. Woman teaching child (*vert*)	1·20	65
1177	60k. Monk teaching adults	1·30	45
1178	150k. Group reading and writing under tree	3·25	1·00
1175/1178 *Set of 4*		5·25	2·00

1990 (5 Mar). *Olympic Games, Barcelona* (1992) *(2nd issue). T* **246** *and similar vert designs. Multicoloured. Litho.* P 12½ × 13.

1179	10k. Type **246**	20	15
1180	30k. Hurdling	60	15
1181	45k. High jumping	95	20
1182	50k. Cycling	1·20	30
1183	60k. Throwing the javelin	1·30	45
1184	90k. Tennis	2·20	75
1179/1184 *Set of 6*		5·75	1·80

MS1185 86 × 102 mm. 95k. Gymnastics
(31 × 39 *mm*). P 13 . . . . 2·20   1·10

247 Great Britain 1840 Penny Black and Mail Coach

1990 (26 Apr). *"Stamp World London 90" International Stamp Exhibition. T* **247** *and similar horiz designs. Multicoloured. Litho.* P 13 × 12½.

1186	15k. Type **247**	30	15
1187	20k. U.S. 1847 5c. stamp and early steam locomotive	45	20
1188	40k. France 1948 20c. stamp and mail balloons, Paris, 1870	90	20
1189	50k. Sardinia 1851 5c. stamp and post rider	1·00	30

1190	60k. Indo-China 1892 1c. stamp and elephant	1·30	45
1191	100k. Spain 1850 6c. stamp and galleon	1·90	65
1186/1191 *Set of 6*		5·25	1·75

MS1192 54 × 54 mm. 95k. Laos 1976 1k. stamp and Douglas DC-8 airliner (36 × 28 *mm*).
P 13 . . . . 2·20   1·10

248 Ho Chi Minh addressing Crowd

1990 (11 May). *Birth Centenary of Ho Chi Minh. T* **248** *and similar multicoloured designs. Litho.* P 13.

1193	40k. Type **248**	1·00	45
1194	60k. Ho Chi Minh and Laotian President	1·60	60
1195	160k. Ho Chi Minh and Vietnamese flag (*vert*)	4·50	1·60

249 Speed Skating

1990 (20 June). *Winter Olympic Games, Albertville* (1992) *(2nd issue). T* **249** *and similar multicoloured designs. Litho.* P 13.

1196	10k. Type **249**	20	15
1197	25k. Cross-country skiing (*vert*)	50	15
1198	60k. Downhill skiing	60	20
1199	35k. Tobogganing	90	20
1200	80k. Figure skating (pairs) (*vert*)	1·60	50
1201	90k. Biathlon	2·10	60
1196/1201 *Set of 6*		5·25	1·60

MS1202 97 × 83 mm. Ice hockey (31 × 39 *mm*).
P 12½ . . . . 2·40   1·21

250 That Luang, 1990

251 Parson Bird (*Prosthemadera novaeseelandie*)

1990 (25 July). *430th Anniv of That Luang. T* **250** *and similar multicoloured designs showing stages of restoration. Litho.* P 13.

1203	60k. That Luang, 1867 (*horiz*)	1·60	45
1204	70k. That Luang, 1930 (*horiz*)	2·20	60
1205	130k. Type **250**	3·75	1·00

1990 (24 Aug). *"New Zealand 1990" International Stamp Exhibition, Auckland. T* **251** *and similar vert designs. Multicoloured. Litho.* P 12½ × 13.

1206	10k. Type **251**	20	15
1207	15k. Eurasian sky lark (*Alauda arvensis*)	30	15
1208	20k. Variable oystercatcher (*Haematopus unicolor*)	45	20
1209	50k. Great cormorant (*Phalacro-corax carbo*)	1·30	30
1210	60k. Reef heron (*Demigretta sacra*)	1·50	45
1211	100k. Brown kiwi (*Apteryx australis*)	2·75	75
1206/1211 *Set of 6*		5·75	1·80
MS1212 56 × 82 mm. 95k. Rough-faced cormorant (*Phalacrocorax corunculatus*) (30 × 37 *mm*). P 12½		2·75	1·10

252 Brown-antlered Deer

1990 (15 Sept). *Mammals. T* **252** *and similar horiz designs. Multicoloured. Litho.* P 12½.

1213	10k. Type **252**	20	15
1214	20k. Gaur	45	15
1215	40k. Wild water buffalo	95	20
1216	45k. Kouprey	1·10	30
1217	120k. Javan rhinoceros	2·75	90
1213/1217 *Set of 5*		5·00	1·60

253 Surgeons Operating

1990 (24 Oct). *40th Anniv of United Nations Development Programme. T* **253** *and similar multicoloured designs. Litho.* P 13.

1218	30k. Type **253**	90	30
1219	45k. Fisherman inspecting catch	1·50	30
1220	80k. Air-traffic controller (*vert*)	2·20	90
1221	90k. Electricity plant workers	2·50	1·20
1218/1221 *Set of 4*		6·25	1·40

254 Rice Ceremony

1990 (20 Nov). *New Year. T* **254** *and similar horiz designs. Multicoloured. Litho.* P 13.

1222	5k. Type **254**	20	15
1223	10k. Elephant in carnival parade	30	15
1224	50k. Making offerings at temple	1·10	30
1225	150k. Family ceremony	3·25	1·10
1222/1225 *Set of 4*		4·25	1·50

255 Memorial, Wreath and Eternal Flame

1990 (2 Dec). *15th National Day Festival. T* **255** *and similar horiz designs. Multicoloured. Litho.* P 13.

1226	15k. Type **255**	45	20
1227	20k. Celebration parade	65	45
1228	80k. Hospital visit	2·20	90
1229	120k. Girls parading with banner	3·25	1·20
1226/1229 *Set of 4*		5·75	2·50

256 West German and Argentinian Players

1991 (10 Jan). *West Germany, World Cup Football Champion. Sheet* 86 × 58 *mm. Litho.* P 12½.

MS1230 **256** 95k. multicoloured .... 2·20 1·10

257 Two-man Kayak

258 Bobsleighing

1991 (25 Jan). *Olympic Games, Barcelona (1992) (3rd issue). T* **257** *and similar multicoloured designs. Litho.* P 12½.

1231	22k. Type **257**	15	15
1232	32k. Canoeing	15	15
1233	285k. Diving (*vert*)	90	20
1234	330k. Racing dinghies (*vert*)	1·10	30
1235	1000k. Swimming	2·75	90
1231/1235 *Set of 5*		4·50	1·50
MS1236 83 × 55 mm. 700k. Two-man canoeing (39 × 31 *mm*)		2·75	1·10

1991 (22 Feb). *Winter Olympic Games, Albertville (1992) (3rd issue). T* **258** *and similar multicoloured designs. Litho.* P 13.

1237	32k. Type **258**	15	15
1238	135k. Cross-country skiing (*horiz*)	45	15
1239	250k. Ski jumping (*horiz*)	75	20
1240	275k. Biathlon (*horiz*)	90	30
1241	900k. Speed skating (*horiz*)	2·75	90
1237/1241 *Set of 5*		4·50	1·60
MS1242 80 × 63 mm. 700k. Skiing (31 × 39 *mm*)		2·75	1·10

259 Pha Pheng Falls, Champassak

1991 (20 Mar). *Tourism. T* **259** *and similar multicoloured designs. Litho.* P 13 × 12½ (horiz) or 12½ × 13 (vert).

1243	155k. Type **259**	50	20
1244	220k. Pha Tang mountians, Vangvieng	75	30
1245	235k. Tat Set waterfall, Saravane (*vert*)	90	50
1246	1000k. Plain of Jars, Xieng Khouang (*vert*)	3·50	1·10
1243/1246 *Set of 4*		5·00	1·90

260 Match Scene

1991 (15 May). *World Cup Football Championship, U.S.A.* (1994) (*1st issue*). *T* **260** *and similar multicoloured designs. Litho.* P 13.

1247	32k. Type **260**	15	15
1248	330k. Goalkeeper catching ball	95	20
1249	340k. Player controlling ball (*vert*)	1·20	20
1250	400k. Player dribbling ball	1·50	30
1251	500k. Tackle	1·80	75
1247/1251 *Set of 5*		5·00	1·40
MS1252 75 × 57 mm. 700k. Player shooting at goal (31 × 39 *mm*). P 13		2·75	1·10

See also Nos. 1292/**MS**1297, 1370/**MS**1375 and 1386/**MS**1391.

261 Planting Saplings

1991 (1 June). *National Tree Planting Day. T* **261** *and similar horiz designs. Multicoloured. Litho.* P 12½.

1253	250k. Type **261**	75	30
1254	700k. Planting saplings (*different*)	2·20	75
1255	800k. Removing saplings from store	2·50	1·10

262 LNER Class A4 Steam Locomotive
No. 4468 *Mallard*, 1938, Great Britain

1991 (30 June). *"Espamer '91" Spain–Latin America Stamp Exhibition, Buenos Aires. Railway locomotives. T* **262** *and similar horiz designs. Multicoloured. Litho.* P 12½.

1256	25k. Type **262**	15	15
1257	32k. Paris - Orleans Class 4500 steam locomotive, France	20	15
1258	285k. American steam locomotive	95	30
1259	650k. Canadian Pacific Class T1b steam locomotive	1·90	65
1260	750k. East African Railways Class 59 steam locomotive (wrongly inscr "Garrant")	2·75	95
1256/1260 *Set of 5*		5·25	2·00
MS1261 80 × 64 mm. 700k. Class VT601 diesel-hydraulic Intercity express (39 × 31 *mm*)		2·75	1·10

263 Spindle Festival

1991 (10 July). *Traditional Music. T* **263** *and similar multi-coloured designs. Litho.* P 13.

1262	29k. Type **263**	15	15
1263	220k. Mong player (*vert*)	65	20
1264	275k. Siphandone singer (*vert*)	75	30
1265	545k. Khap ngum singer	1·80	65
1266	690k. Phouthaydam dance	2·20	90
1262/1266 *Set of 5*		5·00	2·00

264 Great Purple (*Sasakia charonda*) **265** Emblem and Pattern

1991 (15 Oct). *"Phila Nippon '91" International Stamp Exhibition, Tokyo. Butterflies. T* **264** *and similar horiz designs. Multicoloured. Litho.* P 12½.

1267	55k. Type **264**	20	15
1268	90k. *Luehdorfia puziloi* (wrongly inscr "Luendorfia")	30	15
1269	255k. *Papilio bianor*	90	20
1270	285k. Swallowtail (*Papilio machaon*)	1·00	30
1271	900k. Mikado swallowtail (*Graphium doson*)	3·00	90
1267/1271 *Set of 5*		4·75	1·60
MS1272 60 × 77 mm. 700k. Common map butterfly (*Cyrestis thyodamas*) (39 × 31 *mm*). P 13		2·75	1·10

1991 (1 Nov). *International Decade for Cultural Development* (1988–97). *T* **265** *and similar vert designs. Multicoloured. Litho.* P 13.

1273	285k. Type **265**	75	30
1274	330k. Emblem and drum	90	30
1275	1000k. Emblem and pipes	2·75	1·10

266 Bobsleighing   **267** Running

(Des J. Medina. Litho)

1992 (12 Jan). *Winter Olympic Games, Albertville (4th issue). T* **266** *and similar multicoloured designs.* P 12½.

1276	200k. Type **266**	50	15
1277	220k. Slalom skiing	65	20
1278	250k. Downhill skiing (*horiz*)	75	20
1279	500k. One-man luge	1·60	30
1280	600k. Figure skating	1·80	75
1276/1280 *Set of 5*		4·75	1·40

MS1281 77 × 61 mm. 700k. Speed skating (31 × 39 *mm*) . . . . 2·75   90

1992 (21 Feb). *Olympic Games, Barcelona (4th issue). T* **267** *and similar multicoloured designs. Litho.* P 13.

1282	32k. Type **267**	15	15
1283	245k. Baseball	65	20
1284	275k. Tennis	90	20
1285	285k. Basketball	90	30
1286	900k. Boxing (*horiz*)	3·00	75
1282/1286 *Set of 5*		5·00	1·40

MS1287 71 × 59 mm. 700k. Diving (39 × 31 *mm*) . . . . 2·75   90

268 Pest Control   **269** Argentinian and Italian Players and Flags

1992 (7 Apr). *World Health Day. T* **268** *and similar multicoloured designs. Litho.* P 13.

1288	200k. Type **268**	60	20
1289	255k. Anti-smoking campaign	65	30
1290	330k. Donating blood	95	60
1291	1000k. Vaccinating child (*vert*)	3·00	1·20
1288/1291 *Set of 4*		4·75	2·10

1992 (1 May). *World Cup Football Championship, U.S.A. (1994) (2nd issue). T* **269** *and similar vert designs. Multicoloured. Litho.* P 13.

1292	260k. Type **269**	60	15
1293	305k. German and English players and flags	80	20
1294	310k. United States flag, ball and trophy	90	30
1295	350k. Italian and English players and flags	1·30	45
1296	800k. German and Argentinian players and flags	2·75	90
1292/1296 *Set of 5*		5·75	1·80

MS1297 60 × 88 mm. 700k. Goalkeeper catching ball (31 × 39 *mm*). P 12½. . . . 3·00   90

270 Common Cobra (*Naja naja kaouthia*)   **271** Doorway and Ruins

(Des A. Franca. Litho)

1992 (10 July). *Snakes. T* **270** *and similar multicoloured designs.* P 13.

1298	280k. Type **270**	80	20
1299	295k. Common cobra (*Naja naja atra*)	80	20
1300	420k. Wagler's pit viper (*Trimeresurus wagleri*)	1·30	30
1301	700k. King cobra (*Ophiophagus hannah*) (*vert*)	2·75	90
1298/1301 *Set of 4*		5·00	1·40

1992 (22 Aug). *Restoration of Wat Phou. T* **271** *and similar multicoloured designs. Litho.* P 13.

1302	185k. Type **271**	60	35
1303	220k. Doorway (*different*)	65	35
1304	1200k. Doorway with collapsed porch (*horiz*)	4·00	1·60

272 *Pinta* and Juan Martinez's Map

(Des C. Echenagusia. Litho)

1992 (12 Sept). *"Genova '92" International Thematic Stamp Exhibition. T* **272** *and similar multicoloured designs.* P 12½ × 13 (300k.) or 13 × 12 (others).

1305	100k. Type **272**	20	15
1306	300k. Piri Reis's letter and caravelle (*vert*)	90	20
1307	350k. Magellan's *Vitoria* and Paolo del Pozo Toscanelli's world map	1·20	20
1308	400k. Gabriel de Vallseca's map and Vasco da Gama's flagship *Sao Gabriel*	1·30	45
1309	455k. Juan Martinez's map and Portuguese caravel	1·60	65
1305/1309 *Set of 5*		4·75	1·50

MS1310 94 × 63 mm. 700k. *Santa Maria* (39 × 31 *mm*). P 13 . . . . . . 3·00   90

273 Woman in Traditional Costume

274 Boy Drumming

1992 (2 Oct). *Traditional Costumes of Laotian Mountain Villages. T* **273** *and similar vert designs. Litho.* P 13.

1311	25k. multicoloured	15	15
1312	55k. multicoloured	20	15
1313	400k. multicoloured	1·30	45
1314	1200k. multicoloured	4·00	1·20
1311/1314 *Set of 4*		5·00	1·75

1992 (8 Nov). *International Children's Day. T* **274** *and similar multicoloured designs showing children at play. Litho.* P 13.

1315	220k. Type **274**	60	20
1316	285k. Girls skipping (*horiz*)	80	20
1317	330k. Boys racing on stilts	1·20	30
1318	400k. Girls playing "escape" game (*horiz*)	1·50	60
1315/1318 *Set of 4*		3·75	1·20

275 Praying before Buddha

276 Crested Gibbon (*Hylobates concolor*)

1992 (2 Dec). *National Customs. T* **275** *and similar multicoloured designs. Litho.* P 12½.

1319	100k. Type **275**	30	15
1320	140k. Wedding (*horiz*)	45	20
1321	160k. Religious procession (*horiz*)	75	20
1322	1500k. Monks receiving alms (*horiz*)	4·75	2·20
1319/1322 *Set of 4*		5·50	2·50

1992 (22 Dec). *Climbing Mammals. T* **276** *and similar vert designs. Multicoloured. Litho.* P 13.

1323	10k. Type **276**	20	15
1324	100k. Variegated langur (*Pygathrix nemaeus*)	30	20
1325	250k. Pileated gibbon (*Hylobates pileatus*)	30	30
1326	430k. Francois's monkey (*Trachypithecus francoisi*)	1·50	45
1327	800k. Lesser slow loris (*Nycticebus piomacus*)	3·00	80
1323/1327 *Set of 5*		5·00	1·70

277 New York

1993 (9 Jan). *130th Anniv of Underground Railway Systems. T* **277** *and similar horiz designs. Multicoloured. Litho.* P 13.

1328	15k. Type **277**	15	15
1329	50k. Berlin	20	15
1330	100k. Paris	30	20
1331	200k. London	80	30
1332	900k. Moscow	3·00	1·20
1328/1332 *Set of 5*		4·00	1·80
MS1333 85 × 55 mm. 700k. Royal Mail underground system, London (31 × 39 mm)		3·00	90

278 Malayan Bullfrog (*Kaloula pulchra*)

279 Common Tree-shrew (*Tupaia glis*)

1993 (1 Feb). *Amphibians. T* **278** *and similar multicoloured designs. Litho.* P 13.

1334	55k. Type **278**	20	15
1335	90k. Müller's clawed frog (*Xenopus muelleri*)	30	15
1336	100k. Glass frog (*Centrolenella vireovittata*) (*vert*)	45	20
1337	185k. Giant toad (*bufo marinus*)	65	30
1338	1200k. Common tree frog (*Hyla arborea*) (*vert*)	4·00	1·20
1334/1338 *Set of 5*		5·00	1·80

(Des J. Medina. Litho)

1993 (13 Mar). *Mammals. T* **279** *and similar vert designs. Multicoloured.* P 13.

1339	45k. Type **279**	20	15
1340	60k. Philippine flying lemur (*Cynocephalus volans*)	20	15
1341	120k. Loris (*Loris grasilis*)	45	20
1342	500k. Eastern tarsier (*Tarsius spectrum*) (wrongly inscr "Tarsium")	1·60	65
1343	600k. Giant gibbon (*Symphalangus syndactylus*)	1·90	1·20
1339/1343 *Set of 5*		4·00	2·10

280 Noble Scallop
(*Chlamys senatorius
nobilis*)

281 Drugs and Skull smoking

(Des J. Medina. Litho)

1993 (29 May). *Molluscs. T **280** and similar vert designs.
Multicoloured. P 12½.*
1344	20k. Type **280**		15	15
1345	30k. Precious wentletrap (*Epitonium pretiosum*)		15	15
1346	70k. Spider conch (*Lambis rugosa*)		30	20
1347	500k. Aulicus cone (*Conus aulicus*)		1·60	65
1348	1000k. Milleped spider conch (*Lambis millepeda*)		3·00	1·20
1344/1348 *Set of 5*			4·75	2·10

1993 (26 June). *Anti-drugs Campaign. T **281** and similar horiz
designs. Multicoloured. Litho. P 13.*
1349	200k. Type **281**		65	30
1350	430k. Burning seized drugs		1·40	60
1351	900k. Instructing on dangers of drugs		3·00	1·20

282 House

283 Greater Spotted
Eagle (*Aquila clanga*)

1993 (12 July). *Traditional Houses. T **282** and similar
multicoloured designs. Litho. P 13.*
1352	32k. Type **282**		15	15
1353	200k. Thatched house with gable end (*horiz*)		75	20
1354	650k. Thatched house (*horiz*)		1·90	60
1355	750k. House with tiled roof (*horiz*)		2·40	1·20
1352/1355 *Set of 4*			4·50	2·00

1993 (10 Aug). *Birds of Prey. T **283** and similar multicoloured
designs. Litho. P 13.*
1356	10k. Type **283**		15	15
1357	100k. Spotted little owl (*Athene brama*)		45	20
1358	330k. Pied harrier (*Circus melanoleucus*) (wrongly inscr "melanoleucus") (*horiz*)		1·60	45
1359	1000k. Short-toed eagle (*Circaetus gallicus*)		4·00	1·30
1356/1359 *Set of 4*			5·50	1·90

284 Fighting Forest Fire

1993 (25 Sept). *Environmental Protection. T **284** and similar horiz
designs. Multicoloured. Litho. P 13.*
1360	32k. Type **284**		15	15
1361	40k. Wildlife on banks of River Mekong		15	15
1362	260k. Paddy fields		90	30
1363	1100k. Oxen in river		4·00	1·20
1360/1363 *Set of 4*			4·50	1·60

285 *Narathura atosia*

286 Footballer

1993 (1 Oct). *"Bangkok 1993" International Stamp Exhibition.
Butterflies. T **285** and similar horiz designs. Multicoloured. Litho.
P 13.*
1364	35k. Type **285**		15	15
1365	80k. *Parides Philoxenus*		20	15
1366	150k. *Euploea harrisi*		45	20
1367	220k. Yellow orange-tip (*Ixias pyrene*)		65	30
1368	500k. Female common palm fly (*Elymnias hypermnestra*)		1·90	80
1364/1368 *Set of 5*			3·00	1·40
MS1369 85×69 mm. 700k. *Stichophthalma louisa* (39×31 *mm*)			3·00	90

(Des C. Echenagusia. Litho)

1993 (3 Nov). *World Cup Football Championship, U.S.A. (1994)
(3rd issue). T **286** and similar vert designs. Multicolored. P 13.*
1370	10k. Type **286**		15	15
1371	20k. Brazil player		15	15
1372	285k. Uruguay player		80	20
1373	400k. Germany player		1·40	45
1374	800k. Forward challenging goalkeeper		2·75	1·20
1370/1374 *Set of 5*			4·75	1·90
MS1375 99×72 mm. 700k. Ball on pitch (31×39 *mm*). P 12½			3·00	90

287 Hesperornis sp
(Hesperornis)

288 Olympic Flag and
flame

(Des A. Villamil Gil. Litho)

1994 (20 Jan). *Prehistoric Birds. T* **287** *and similar vert designs. Multicoloured.* P 13.
1376	10k. Type **287**	15	15
1377	20k. Mauritius dodo (Dronte)	15	15
1378	150k. Archaeopteryx (Archaeopterix)	60	20
1379	600k. Phororhacos sp (Phororhachos)	1·80	45
1380	700k. Giant moa (*Dinornis maximus*)	2·50	90
1376/1380 *Set of 5*		4·50	1·60
MS1381 80 × 55 mm. 700k. *Teratornis mirabilis* (Teratornis) (39 × 31 *mm*). P 12½		3·00	90

(Des Roman Company. Litho)

1994 (15 Mar). *Centenary of International Olympic Committee. T* **288** *and similar multicoloured designs.* P 12½.
1382	100k. Type **288**	30	15
1383	250k. Ancient Greek athletes (*horiz*)	80	20
1384	1000k. Pierre de Coubertin (founder) and modern athlete	3·50	1·40

289 Bridge and National Flags

290 World Map and Players

(Litho McPherson's Ptg Group, Mulgrave)

1994 (8 Apr). *Opening of Friendship Bridge between Laos and Thailand.* P 14 × 14½.
1385	**289**	500k. multicoloured	1·90	1·20

(Des Román Compañy. Litho)

1994 (15 June). *World Cup Football Championship, U.S.A. (4th issue). T* **290** *and similar horiz designs showing a world map and players.* P 13.
1386	40k. multicoloured	15	15
1387	50k. multicoloured	20	15
1388	60k. multicoloured	20	15
1389	320k. multicoloured	1·20	45
1390	900k. multicoloured	3·50	1·20
1386/1390 *Set of 5*		4·75	1·90
MS1391 82 × 59 mm. 700k. multicoloured (31 × 39 *mm*)		2·50	90

291 Pagoda

292 Bear eating

1994 (1 July). *Pagodas. T* **291** *and similar horiz designs showing gabled roofs. Litho.* P 12½.
1392	30k. multicoloured	15	15
1393	150k. multicoloured	45	20
1394	380k. multicoloured	1·20	30
1395	1100k. multicoloured	3·50	1·20
1392/1395 *Set of 4*		4·75	1·60

1994 (23 July). *The Malay Bear (Ursus malayanus). T* **292** *and similar horiz designs. Multicoloured. Litho.* P 13.
1396	50k. Type **292**	35	15
1397	90k. Bear's head	80	20
1398	200k. Adult and cub	1·80	30
1399	220k. Bear	1·90	45
1396/1399 *Set of 4*		4·25	1·00

293 Grass Snake (*Natrix natrix*)

294 Phra Xayavoraman 7

(Des A. Franca. Litho)

1994 (1 Aug). *Amphibians and Reptiles. T* **293** *and similar multicoloured designs.* P 12½.
1400	70k. Type **293**	20	15
1401	80k. Tessellated snake (*Natrix tessellata*)	20	15
1402	90k. Fire salamander (*Salamandra salamandra*)	30	15
1403	600k. Alpine newt (*Triturus alpestris*)	1·90	60
1404	800k. Green lizard (*Lacerta viridis*) (*vert*)	2·50	1·20
1400/1404 *Set of 5*		4·50	2·00
MS1405 79 × 50 mm. 700k. Great crested newt (*Triturus cristatus*) (39 × 31 *mm*)		2·50	90

(Litho Post Office Ptg Wks, Ho Chi Minh City)

1994 (25 Aug). *Buddhas. T* **294** *and similar vert designs. Multicoloured.* P 13.
1406	15k. Type **294**	15	15
1407	280k. Phra Thong Souk	90	30
1408	390k. Phra Manolom	1·30	45
1409	800k. Phra Ongtu	2·50	1·20
1406/1409 *Set of 4*		4·25	1·90

295 Family supporting
Healthy Globe

296 Kong Hang

(Des E. González. Litho)

1994 (24 Sept). *International Year of the Family. T* **295** *and similar multicoloured designs.* P 12½.
1410	200k. Type **295**		65	30
1411	500k. Mother taking child to school			
	(*horiz*)		1·60	80
1412	700k. Mother and children		2·40	1·20
MS1413	50 × 70 mm. 700k. Family and flag		2·50	90

1994 (20 Oct). *Traditional Laotian Drums. T* **296** *and similar horiz designs. Multicoloured. Litho.* P 12½.
1414	370k. Type **296**		1·30	35
1415	440k. Kong Léng (portable drum)		1·50	45
1416	450k. Kong Toum (drum on stand)		1·50	45
1417	600k. Kong Phéne (hanging drum)		2·10	65
1414/1417	*Set of 4*		5·75	1·75

297 Elephant in Procession

298 Theropodes

1994 (24 Nov). *Ceremonial Elephants. T* **297** *and similar multicoloured designs. Litho.* P 13.
1418	140k. Type **297**		45	20
1419	400k. Elephant in pavilion		1·30	80
1420	890k. Elephant in street procession			
	(*vert*)		2·75	1·30

(Litho Post Office Ptg Wks, Ho Chi Minh City)

1994 (8 Dec). *Prehistoric Animals. T* **298** *and similar vert designs. Multicoloured.* P 13.
1421	50k. Type **298**		20	15
1422	380k. Iguanodontides		1·80	60
1423	420k. Sauropodes		2·10	65

299 Playing Musical
Instruments

300 Trachodon

1995 (2 Jan). *20th Anniv of World Tourism Organization. T* **299** *and similar multicoloured designs. Litho.* P 13.
1424	60k. Type **299**		20	15
1425	250k. Women dancing		80	20
1426	400k. Giving alms to monks		1·30	45
1427	650k. Waterfall (*vert*)		1·80	80
1424/1427	*Set of 4*		3·75	1·40
MS1428	40 × 63 mm. 700k. Close-up view of			
	waterfall in No. 1427 (31 × 39 *mm*)		2·40	80

1995 (20 Feb). *Prehistoric Animals. T* **300** *and similar vert designs. Multicoloured. Litho.* P 12 × 13.
1429	50k. Type **300**		15	15
1430	70k. Protoceratops		15	15
1431	300k. Brontosaurus		80	30
1432	400k. Stegosaurus		1·10	45
1433	600k. Tyrannosaurus		1·80	65
1429/1433	*Set of 5*		3·50	1·50

301 Indian Jungle Mynah
(*Acridotheres javanicus*)

302 Children around
Emblem

1995 (10 Mar). *Birds. T* **301** *and similar horiz designs. Multicoloured. Litho.* P 13.
1434	50k. Type **301**		15	15
1435	150k. Jerdon's starling (*Sturnus*			
	burmannicus)		45	15
1436	300k. Common mynah (*Acridotheres*			
	tristis)		90	35
1437	700k. Southern grackle (*Gracula*			
	religiosa)		1·90	80
1434/1437	*Set of 4*		3·00	1·30

No. 1435 is erroneously inscribed "Starnus".

(Des Khamphet. Litho)

1995 (20 Mar). *25th Anniv of Francophonie. T* **302** *and similar vert designs. Multicoloured.* P 13.
1438	50k. Type **302**		15	15
1439	380k. Golden roof decorations		1·20	60
1440	420k. Map		1·30	65

303 Pole Vaulting

1995 (5 Apr). *Olympic Games, Atlanta (1st issue). T* **303** *and similar multicoloured designs. Litho.* P 13.
1441	60k. Type **303**		15	15
1442	80k. Throwing the javelin		20	15
1443	200k. Throwing the hammer		60	20
1444	350k. Long jumping		1·00	35
1445	700k. High jumping		2·10	80
1441/1445	*Set of 5*		3·75	1·50
MS1446	90 × 60 mm. 700k. Baseball (39 × 31			
	mm)		2·40	80

See also Nos. 1484/**MS**1489.

304 Chalice

305 Procession

1995 (1 May). *Antique Vessels. T* **304** *and similar multicoloured designs. Litho.* P 12½.

1447	70k. Type **304**	15	15
1448	200k. Resin and silver bowl (*horiz*)	50	20
1449	450k. Geometrically-decorated bowl (*horiz*)	1·30	50
1450	600k. Religious chalice (*horiz*)	1·80	65
1447/1450 *Set of 4*		3·50	1·40

1995 (1 June). *Rocket Festival. T* **305** *and similar multicoloured designs. Litho.* P 13.

1451	80k. Launching rocket (*vert*)	20	15
1452	160k. Type **305**	45	15
1453	500k. Musicians in procession	1·40	50
1454	700k. Crowds and rockets	2·10	80
1451/1454 *Set of 4*		3·75	1·40

306 Red Tabby Longhair

307 *Nepenthes villosa*

(Des J. Medina. Litho)

1995 (25 July). *Cats. T* **306** *and similar multicoloured designs.* P 13.

1455	40k. Type **306**	15	15
1456	50k. Siamese sealpoint	20	15
1457	250k. Red tabby longhair (*different*)	80	20
1458	400k. Tortoiseshell shorthair	1·30	30
1459	650k. Head of tortoiseshell shorthair (*vert*)	1·60	65
1455/1459 *Set of 5*		3·75	1·30
MS1460 49 × 70 mm. 700k. Tortoiseshell shorthair (*different*) (39 × 31 *mm*). P 12½		2·40	80

(Des R. Monnar. Litho)

1995 (24 Aug). *Insectivorous Plants. T* **307** *and similar vert designs. Multicoloured.* P 13.

1461	90k. Type **307**	20	15
1462	100k. *Dionaea muscipula*	30	15
1463	350k. *Sarracenia flava*	1·00	30
1464	450k. *Sarracenia purpurea*	1·30	30
1465	500k. *Nepenthes ampullaria*	1·50	60
1461/1465 *Set of 4*		4·00	1·30
MS1466 59 × 77 mm. 1000k. *Nepenthes gracillis* (31 × 39 *mm*). P 12½		3·00	90

308 Stag Beetle (*Lucanus cervus*)

1995 (20 Sept). *Insects. T* **308** *and similar horiz designs. Multicoloured. Litho.* P 13.

1467	40k. Type **308**	15	15
1468	50k. May beetle (*Melolontha melolontha*)	20	15
1469	500k. Blue carpenter beetle (*Xylocopa violacea*)	1·40	45
1470	800k. Great green grasshopper (*Tettigonia viridissima*)	2·40	80
1467/1470 *Set of 4*		3·75	1·40

309 Cattle grazing

1995 (16 Oct). *50th Anniv of Food and Agriculture Organization. T* **309** *and similar horiz designs. Multicoloured. Litho.* P 13.

1471	80k. Type **309**	20	15
1472	300k. Working paddy field	90	45
1473	1000k. Agriculture	3·00	1·20

310 At Meeting

(Des Khamphet. Litho Post Office Ptg Wks, Ho Chi Minh City)

1995 (24 Oct). *50th Anniv of United Nations Organization. T* **310** *and similar horiz designs showing peoples of different races. Multicoloured.* P 13.

1474	290k. Type **310**	80	35
1475	310k. Playing draughts	90	45
1476	440k. Children playing	1·40	65

311 Students and Nurse vaccinating Child

(Des Khamphet. Litho Post Office Ptg Wks, Ho Chi Minh City)

1995 (2 Dec). *20th Anniv of Republic. T* **311** *and similar horiz designs. Multicoloured.* P 13.

1477	50k. Type **311**	15	15
1478	280k. Agricultural land	80	45
1479	600k. Bridge	1·80	90

312 Mong

1996 (10 Jan). *Traditional New Year Customs. T* **312** *and similar horiz designs. Multicoloured. Litho.* P 13.

1480	50k. Type **312**		15	15
1481	280k. Phouthai		90	30
1482	380k. Ten Xe		1·20	45
1483	420k. Lao Loum		1·30	45
1480/1483 *Set of 4*			3·25	1·25

313 Cycling

314 Sun Bear
(*Helarctos malayanus*)

1996 (20 Feb). *Olympic Games, Atlanta, U.S.A. (2nd issue). T* **313** *and similar multicoloured designs. Litho.* P 13.

1484	30k. Type **313**		15	15
1485	150k. Football		30	15
1486	200k. Basketball (*vert*)		45	20
1487	300k. Running (*vert*)		65	30
1488	500k. Shooting		1·20	60
1484/1488 *Set of 5*			2·50	1·25
MS1489 80 × 60 mm. 1000k. High jumping (38 × 30 *mm*). P 12½			2·20	2·20

1996 (26 Feb). *Animals. T* **314** *and similar vert designs. Multicoloured. Litho.* P 13.

1490	40k. Type **314**		15	15
1491	60k. Grey pelican (*Pelecanus philippensis*)		15	15
1492	200k. Leopard (*Panthera pardus*)		45	20
1493	250k. Swallowtail (*Papilio machaon*)		60	30
1494	700k. Indian python (*Python molurus*)		1·50	80
1490/1494 *Set of 5*			2·50	1·40

315 Weaving

316 Rat

1996 (8 Mar). *International Women's Year. T* **315** *and similar multicoloured designs. Litho.* P 13.

1495	20k. Type **315**		15	15
1496	290k. Physical training instructress		65	30
1497	1000k. Woman feeding child (*vert*)		2·20	1·10

1996 (15 Apr). *New Year. Year of the Rat. T* **316** *and similar vert designs showing rats. Litho.* P 13½ × 13.

1498	50k. multicoloured		15	15
1499	340k. multicoloured		1·20	60

1500	350k. multicoloured		1·30	60
1501	370k. multicoloured		1·30	65
1498/1501 *Set of 4*			3·50	1·80

317 Players

318 Village Women grinding Rice

1996 (3 May). *World Cup Football Championship, France (1998) (1st issue). T* **317** *and similar vert designs showing different footballing scenes. Litho.* P 13.

1502	20k. multicoloured		15	15
1503	50k. multicoloured		15	15
1504	300k. multicoloured		65	30
1505	400k. multicoloured		90	45
1506	500k. multicoloured		1·10	50
1502/1506 *Set of 5*			2·75	1·40
MS1507 63 × 92mm. 1000k. multicoloured (30 × 37 *mm*)			2·20	2·20

See also Nos. 1589/**MS**1595.

1996 (1 June). *Children's Drawings. T* **318** *and similar horiz designs. Multicoloured. Litho.* P 13.

1508	180k. Type **318**		65	30
1509	230k. Women picking fruit		80	35
1510	310k. Village women preparing food		1·10	50
1511	370k. Women tending vegetable crops		1·30	65
1508/1511 *Set of 4*			3·50	1·60

319 Morane Monoplane

1996 (25 July). *"Capex'96" International Stamp Exhibition, Toronto, Canada. Aircraft. T* **319** *and similar horiz designs. Multicoloured. Litho.* P 13.

1512	25k. Type **319**		15	15
1513	60k. Sopwith Camel biplane		15	15
1514	150k. De Havilland D.H.4 biplane		30	15
1515	250k. Albatros biplane		50	30
1516	800k. Caudron biplane		1·80	90
1512/1516 *Set of 5*			2·50	1·50

320 Front View

321 *Dendrobium secundum*

1996 (21 Aug). *Ox-carts.* T **320** *and similar horiz designs. Multicoloured. Litho.* P 13.
1517	50k. Type **320**	15	10
1518	100k. Side view	20	15
1519	440k. Oxen pulling cart	1·00	50

1996 (25 Oct). *Orchids.* T **321** *and similar vert designs. Multicoloured. Litho.* P 13.
1520	50k. Type **321**	15	15
1521	200k. *Ascocentrum miniatum*	45	20
1522	500k. *Aerides multiflorum*	1·10	60
1523	520k. *Dendrobium aggregatum*	1·30	60
1520/1523 *Set of 4*		2·75	1·40

322 White Horse

323 Pupils displaying Slates to Teacher

1996 (5 Nov). *Saddle Horses.* T **322** *and similar vert designs. Multicoloured. Litho.* P 13.
1524	50k. Type **322**	15	15
1525	80k. Horse with red and black bridle	15	15
1526	200k. Bay horse with white bridle and reins	45	20
1527	400k. Horse with red and yellow cords braided into mane	90	45
1528	600k. Chestnut horse with white blaze	1·30	65
1524/1528 *Set of 5*		1·50	85
MS1529 89 × 69 mm. 1000k. Horse with ornate yellow and red bridle (28 × 36 *mm*)		2·20	2·20

1996 (11 Dec). *50th Anniv of United Nations Children's Fund.* T **323** *and similar multicoloured designs. Litho.* P 13.
1530	200k. Type **323**	65	30
1531	500k. Mother breastfeeding (*vert*)	1·80	80
1532	600k. Woman drawing water at public well	2·10	1·10

324 Leatherback Turtle (*Dermochelys coriacea*)

1996 (27 Dec). *25th Anniv of Greenpeace (environmental organization). Turtles.* T **324** *and similar horiz designs. Multicoloured. Litho.* P 13.
1533	150k. Type **324**	50	20
1534	250k. Leatherback turtle at water's edge	90	45
1535	400k. Hawksbill turtle (*Eretmochelys imbricata*) (wrongly inscr "Erethochelys")	1·50	75
1536	450k. *Chelonia agassizi*	1·60	80
1533/1536 *Set of 4*		4·00	2·00

Nos. 1533/6 were issued both in separate sheets and together in *se-tenant* sheetlets of four stamps.

325 Oral Vaccination

1997 (3 Jan). *National Vaccination Day.* T **325** *and similar horiz designs. Multicoloured. Litho.* P 13.
1537	50k. Type **325**	15	15
1538	340k. Nurse injecting child's leg	1·20	60
1539	370k. Nurse pushing child in wheelchair	1·30	65

326 George Stephenson and *Pioneer*, 1836

1997 (5 Jan). *Steam Railway Locomotives.* T **326** *and similar horiz designs. Multicoloured. Litho.* P 12½ (Nos. 1540 and **MS**1546) or 12 × 13 (others).
1540	100k. *Kinnaird*, 1846 (44 × 27 *mm*)	20	15
1541	200k. Type **326**	45	20
1542	300k. Robert Stephenson and long-boiler express locomotive, 1848	65	30
1543	400k. Stephenson locomotive *Adler*, 1835, Germany	90	45
1544	500k. *Lord of the Isles*, 1851–84	1·20	60
1545	600k. *The Columbine*, 1845	1·40	65
1540/1545 *Set of 6*		4·25	2·10
MS1546 69 × 93 mm. 2000k. South Carolina Railroad locomotive *Best Friend of Charleston*, 1830 (39 × 31 *mm*)		4·50	4·50

The 200 and 300k. are wrongly inscribed "Stepheson".

327 Pseudoryx lying down

328 Masked Lovebirds (*Agapornis personata*)

1997 (10 Feb). *Pseudoryx (Saola).* T **327** *and similar multicoloured designs. Litho.* P 13.
1547	350k. Type **327**	1·30	1·30
1548	380k. Grazing (*vert*)	1·40	1·40
1549	420k. Scratching with hind leg	1·50	1·50

1997 (4 Mar). *Lovebirds.* T **328** *and similar vert designs. Multicoloured. Litho.* P 13.
1550	50k. Type **328**	15	15
1551	150k. Grey-headed lovebird (*Agapornis cana*)	30	15
1552	200k. Nyasa lovebirds (*Agapornis lilianae*)	45	20
1553	400k. Fischer's lovebirds (*Agapornis fischeri*)	90	45

1554	500k. Black-cheeked lovebirds (*Agapornis nigregenis*)	1·10	60
1555	800k. Peach-faced lovebird (*Agapornis roseicollis*)	1·90	90
1550/1555	*Set of 6*	4·25	2·20

MS1556 91 × 74 mm. 2000k. Black-winged lovebirds (*Agapornis taranta*) (31 × 38 *mm*)

	4·50	4·50

1574	450k. African elephant in water (*horiz*)	1·00	50
1575	550k. African elephant with ears flapping	1·30	60
1570/1575	*Set of 6*	4·00	2·00

MS1576 117 × 74 mm. 2000k. Forequarter of African elephant (31 × 39 *mm*). P 12½

	4·50	4·50

329 Signs of the Chinese Zodiac   **330** Steaming Rice

1997 (12 Apr). *New Year. Year of the Ox.* T **329** *and similar multicoloured designs.* Litho. P 13½ × 13 (300k.) or 13 × 13½ (others).

1557	50k. Type **329**	15	15
1558	300k. Woman riding ox (*vert*)	1·20	1·20
1559	440k. Ox on float in procession	1·60	1·60

1997 (14 Apr). *Food Preparation.* T **330** *and similar multicoloured designs.* Litho. P 12½.

1560	50k. Type **330**	15	15
1561	340k. Water containers (*horiz*)	75	35
1562	370k. Table laid with meal (*horiz*)	80	35

331 *Vanda roeblingiana*   **332** Indian Elephant (*Elephas maximus*)

1997 (7 May). *Orchids.* T **331** *and similar vert designs. Multicoloured.* Litho. P 13.

1563	50k. Type **331**	15	15
1564	100k. *Dendrobium findleyanum*	20	15
1565	150k. *Dendrobium crepidatum*	30	15
1566	250k. *Sarcanthus birmanicus*	50	30
1567	400k. *Cymbidium lowianum*	90	45
1568	1000k. *Dendrobium gratiosissimum*	2·40	1·10
1563/1568	*Set of 6*	4·00	2·10

MS1569 95 × 70 mm. 2000k. *Paphiopedilum chamberlainianum* (31 × 37 *mm*). P 12½

	4·50	4·50

1997 (12 June). *Elephants.* T **332** *and similar multicoloured designs.* Litho. P 13.

1570	100k. Type **332**	20	15
1571	250k. Indian elephant carrying log (*horiz*)	50	30
1572	300k. Indian elephant with young (*horiz*)	65	30
1573	350k. African elephant (*Loxodonta africana*) (*horiz*)	80	35

333 Emblem and Brunei Flag

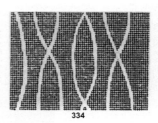

334

(Litho Thai British Security Ptg Co Ltd)

1997 (23 July). *Admission of Laos into Association of South East Asian Nations.* T **333** *and similar vert designs showing members' flags, centre flag given.* W **334** (sideways on No. **MS**1582). P 14 × 14½.

1577	550k. Type **333**	80	80
	a. Strip of 9. Nos. 1577/85	7·25	
1578	550k. Indonesia (red and white bands)	80	80
1579	550k. Laos (red, blue with white circle, red bands)	80	80
1580	550k. Malaysia (crescent and star on blue quarter, red and white stripes)	80	80
1581	550k. Myanmar (flower and stars on blue quarter, red)	80	80
1582	550k. Philippines (sun and stars on white triangle, blue and red bands)	80	80
1583	550k. Singapore (crescent and five stars on red band, white band)	80	80
1584	550k. Thailand (red, white, blue, red bands)	80	80
1585	550k. Vietnam (yellow star on red)	80	80
1577/1585	*Set of 9*	6·50	6·50

MS1586 Nine sheets, each 138 × 110 mm. P 13½. (a) No. 1577; (b) No. 1578; (c) No. 1579; (d) No. 1580; (e) No. 1581; (f) No. 1582; (g) No. 1583; (h) No. 1584; (i) No. 1585

	7·25	7·25

Nos. 1577/85 were issued together both in *se-tenant* strips of nine stamps within large sheets and in sheetlets of nine stamps and one label (perf 13½).

335 Headquarters, Djakarta, Indonesia

1997 (8 Aug). *30th Anniv of Association of South East Asian Nations. T* **335** *and similar horiz design. Multicoloured. Litho.* P 13.
1587	150k. Type **335**	60	60
1588	600k. Map of Laos and state flag	2·50	2·50

336 Players

1997 (10 Sept). *World Cup Football Championship, France (1998) (2nd issue). T* **336** *and similar vert designs showing different footballing scenes. Litho.* P 12½.
1589	100k. multicoloured	20	15
1590	200k. multicoloured	45	20
1591	250k. multicoloured	50	30
1592	300k. multicoloured	65	30
1593	350k. multicoloured	80	35
1594	700k. multicoloured	1·50	75
1589/1594 *Set of 6*		3·75	1·90
MS1595 111 × 84 mm. 2000k. multicoloured		4·50	4·50

337 Phoenician Nef

338 Headdress

1997 (25 Oct). *Sailing Ships. T* **337** *and similar horiz designs.* *Litho.* P 13.
1596	50k. Type **337**	15	15
1597	100k. 13th-century nef	20	15
1598	150k. 15th-century nef	30	15
1599	200k. 16th-century Portuguese caravel	45	20
1600	400k. 17th-century Dutch ship	90	45
1601	900k. H.M.S. *Victory* (Nelson's flagship)	2·10	1·00
1596/1601 *Set of 6*		3·75	1·90
MS1602 80 × 60 mm. 2000k. *Great Harry* (sail warship), 1514. P 12½		4·50	4·50

1997 (10 Nov). *Headdresses and Masks. T* **338** *and similar multicoloured designs. Litho.* P 13.
1603	50k. Type **338**	15	15
1604	100k. Headdress with flower at left	20	15
1605	150k. Mask with curved tusks (*horiz*)	30	15
1606	200k. Mask tipped with headdress decorated with two faces	50	20
1607	350k. Mask with green face	75	35
1603/1607 *Set of 5*		1·75	90

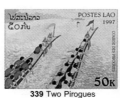

339 Two Pirogues

340 Sunken Net

1997 (26 Dec). *Pirogue Race. T* **339** *and similar horiz designs.* *Multicoloured. Litho.* P 13.
1608	50k. Type **339**	15	15
1609	100k. Crowd cheering competitors from land	20	15
1610	300k. Side view of two competing pirogues	65	30
1611	500k. People cheering from spectator boat	1·10	50
1608/1611 *Set of 4*		1·90	1·00

1998 (10 Feb). *Traditional Fishing Methods. T* **340** *and similar multicoloured designs. Litho.* P 13.
1612	50k. Type **340**	15	15
1613	100k. Fisherman throwing net (*horiz*)	30	30
1614	450k. Funnel net	1·40	1·40
1615	600k. Lobster pots (*horiz*)	1·90	1·90
1612/1615 *Set of 4*		3·25	3·25

341 Man riding Tiger

342 Wat Sisaket Shrine

1998 (15 Apr). *New Year. Year of the Tiger. Litho.* P 13.
1616	**341** 150k. multicoloured	60	60
1617	350k. multicoloured	1·40	1·40
1618	400k. multicoloured	1·80	1·80

(Litho Thai British Security Ptg Co Ltd)

1998 (1 Sept). *Temples. T* **342** *and similar multicoloured designs.* P 14 × 14½ (1000k.) or 14½ × 14 (others).
1619	10000k. Type **342**	7·50	7·50
1620	25000k. Wat Phou temple, Paksé (*horiz*)	15·00	15·00
1621	45000k. That Luang (royal mausoleum) (*horiz*)	22·00	22·00

343 Boat and Pole

(Litho Thai British Security Ptg Co Ltd)

1998 (30 Oct). *Water Transport. T **343** and similar horiz designs.*
P 14½ × 14.

1622	1100k. Type **343**	1·10	1·10
1623	1200k. Covered canoe	1·20	1·20
1624	2500k. Motorized canoe	2·50	2·50

344 Buddha, Luang Phabang
Temple

(Litho Thai British Security Ptg Co Ltd)

1998 (4 Nov). P 14 × 14½.

1625	**344** 3000k. multicoloured	2·10	2·10

345 *Paphiopedilum callosum*

(Litho Thai British Security Ptg Co Ltd)

1998 (16 Nov). *Orchids. T **345** and similar multicoloured designs.*
P 14½ × 14 (horiz) or 14 × 14½ (vert).

1626	900k. Type **345**	1·40	1·40
1627	950k. *Paphiopedilum concolor*	1·50	1·50
1628	1000k. *Dendrobium thyrsiflorum* (*vert*)	1·60	1·60
1629	1050k. *Dendrobium lindleyi* (*vert*)	1·60	1·60
1626/1629	*Set of 4*	5·50	5·50

346 Children in Classroom

347 Gaeng

(Litho Thai British Security Ptg Co Ltd)

1998 (10 Dec). *50th Anniv of Universal Declaration of Human
Rights. T **346** and similar horiz design.* P 14½ × 14.

1630	300k. Type **346**	35	35
1631	1700k. Woman posting vote into ballot box	2·20	2·20

(Litho Thai British Security Ptg Co Ltd)

1998 (25 Dec). *Wind Instruments. T **347** and similar vert designs.
Multicoloured.* P 14 × 14½.

1632	900k. Type **347**	1·30	1·30
1633	1200k. Khuoy (flute)	1·80	1·80
1634	1500k. Khaen (bamboo pipes of various lengths)	2·20	2·20

348 Military Personnel and Flag

(Litho Thai British Security Ptg Co Ltd, Thailand)

1999 (1 Jan). *50th Anniv of People's Army. T **348** and similar
multicoloured design.* P 13½.

1635	1300k. Type **348**	1·10	1·10
1636	1500k. Soldier with upraised arm and jungle fighters (*vert*)	1·30	1·30

349 Inscribed Monument (world
heritage)

(Litho Thai British Security Ptg Co Ltd, Thailand)

1999 (2 Feb). *U.N.E.S.C.O. World Heritage Site. Luang
Prabang. T **349** and similar multicoloured designs.* P 13½.

1637	400k. Type **349**	35	35
1638	1150k. House with veranda and dovecote (*horiz*)	95	95
1639	1250k. Wat Xiengthong (*horiz*)	1·00	1·00

350 Yao Children celebrating New Year, Muong Sing

351 Rabbit and Chinese Zodiac Animals

(Litho Thai British Security Ptg Co Ltd, Thailand)

1999 (2 Mar). *Tourism Year (1st issue).* T **350** *and similar multicoloured designs.* P 14 × 14½ (1300k.) or 14½ × 14 (others).

1640	200k. Type **350**	15	15
1641	500k. Phadeang, Vangvieng district	35	35
1642	1050k. Wat That Makmo, Luang Prabang	80	80
1643	1300k. Patuxay (victory monument), Vientiane (*vert*)	1·00	1·00
1640/1643 *Set of 4*		2·10	2·10

See also Nos. **MS**1653 and 1713/16.

(Litho Thai British Security Ptg Co Ltd, Thailand)

1999 (15 Apr). *New Year. Year of the Rabbit.* T **351** *and similar multicoloured design.* P 14 × 14½ (vert) or 14½ × 14 (horiz).

1644	1500k. Type **351**	75	75
1645	1600k. White rabbit (*horiz*)	1·60	1·60

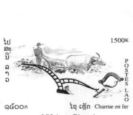

352 Iron Plough

353 Collared Owlet (*Glaucidium brodiei*)

(Litho Thai British Security Ptg Co Ltd, Thailand)

1999 (1 May). *Traditional Farming Implements.* T **352** *and similar horiz designs. Multicoloured.* P 14½ × 14.

1646	1500k. Type **352**	1·10	1·10
1647	2000k. Harrow	1·50	1·50
1648	3200k. Wooden plough	2·40	2·40

(Litho Thai British Security Ptg Co Ltd, Thailand)

1999 (2 July). *Owls and Bat.* T **353** *and similar vert designs. Multicoloured.* P 14 × 14½.

1649	900k. Type **353**	75	75
1650	1600k. Collared scops owl (*Otus lempiji*)	1·50	1·50
1651	2100k. Barn owl (*Tyto alba*)	2·20	2·20
1652	2800k. Black capped fruit bat (*Chironax melanocephalus*)	3·00	3·00
1649/1652 *Set of 4*		6·75	6·75

354 Patuxay (victory monument), Vientiane

(Die-stamped Thai British Security Ptg Co Ltd, Thailand)

1999 (4 Aug). *Tourism (2nd issue). Sheet* 135 × 100 *mm containing* T **354** *and similar horiz designs.* P 13½.

MS1653 2500k. Type **354**; 4000k. Ho Phra Keo, Vientiane; 5500k. Wat Xieng Thong, Luang Prabang; 8000k. Pha That Luang, Vientiane . . . . 10·50 10·50

No. **MS**1653, with a larger illustrated border showing a royal barge and temple, inscr "THAIPEX '99" and "CHINA STAMP EXHIBITION '99" was released on 4 August 1999 to coincide with the exhibition and again, with an illustrated border showing the great wall of China, inscr "CHINA 1999", on 22 August 1999.

355 Envelope and Globe

(Litho Thai British Security Ptg Co Ltd)

1999 (9 Oct). *125th Anniv of Universal Postal Union.* T **355** *and similar horiz design. Multicoloured.* P 14½ × 14.

1654	2600k. Type **355**	1·80	1·80
1655	3400k. Postman delivering letter	2·50	2·50

356 Carved Tree Stump

(Litho Thai British Security Ptg Co Ltd)

1999 (15 Oct). *International Horticultural Exposition, Kunming, China.* T **356** *and similar horiz designs showing exposition buildings. Multicoloured.* P 14½ × 14.

1656	300k. Type **356**	20	20
1657	900k. China Hall	45	45
1658	2300k. Science and Technology Hall	1·20	1·20
1659	2500k. Traditional Laotian house	1·40	1·40
1656/1659 *Set of 4*		3·00	3·00

357 Javan Rhino (*Rhinoceros sondaicus*)

(Litho Thai British Security Ptg Co Ltd)

1999 (10 Nov). *Animals.* T **357** *and similar horiz designs. Multicoloured.* P 14 × 14½ (1663, 1666) or 14½ × 14 (others).

1660	700k. Type **357**	50	50
1661	900k. Water buffalo (*Bubalus bubalis*) (*vert*)	65	65

1662	1700k. Spotted linsang (*Prionodon pardicolor*)	1·30	1·30
1663	1800k. Sambar deer (*Cervus unicolor*)	1·30	1·30
1664	1900k. Lion (*Panthera leo*) (*vert*) (August 2003)	1·40	1·40
1660/1664 *Set of 5*		4·50	4·50

358 Airport and Hospital

(Litho Thai British Security Ptg Co Ltd)

2000 (1 Jan). *Millennium (1st issue). T* **358** *and similar horiz designs. Multicoloured.* P 13½.

1665	2000k. Type **358**	75	75
	a. Block of 4. Nos. 1665/8	3·00	3·00
1666	2000k. Temple	75	75
1667	2000k. Building with portico	75	75
1668	2000k. River and traditional buildings	75	75
1665/1668 *Set of 4*		2·75	2·75
MS1669 124 × 181 mm. Nos. 1665/8		3·00	3·00

Nos. 1665/8 were issued in *se-tenant* blocks of four stamps, the four forming a composite design.

No. **MS**1669 was also available, imperforate, from a limited printing.

See also Nos. 1718/19.

359 Kor Loma

360 *Dendrobium draconis*

(Litho Thai British Security Ptg Co Ltd)

2000 (8 Mar). *Women's Regional Costumes. T* **359** *and similar vert designs. Multicoloured.* P 14 × 14½.

1670	100k. Type **359**	10	10
1671	200k. Kor Pchor	10	10
1672	500k. Nhuan Krom	15	15
1673	900k. Taidam	30	30
1674	2300k. Yao	65	65
1675	2500k. Meuy	75	75
1676	2600k. Sila	80	80
1677	2700k. Hmong	80	80
1678	2800k. Yao (*different*)	80	80
1679	3100k. Kor Nukkuy	90	90
1680	3200k. Kor Pouxang	95	95
1681	3300k. Yao Lanten	1·00	1·00
1682	3400k. Khir	1·10	1·10
1683	3500k. Kor	1·00	1·00
1684	3900k. Hmong (*different*)	1·20	1·20
1670/1684 *Set of 15*		9·50	9·50

(Litho Thai British Security Ptg Co Ltd)

2000 (25 Mar). *Orchids. T* **360** *and similar vert designs. Bangkok 2000 International Stamp Exhibition (***MS***1690). Multicoloured.* P 14 × 14½.

1685	500k. Type **360**	15	15
1686	900k. *Paphiopedilum hirsutissimum*	30	30
1687	3000k. *Dendrobium sulcatum*	95	95
1688	3400k. *Rhynchostylis gigantea*	1·10	1·10
1685/1688 *Set of 4*		2·20	2·20
MS1689 111 × 145 mm. Nos. 1685/88. P 13½		3·00	3·00

No. **MS**1689 was also available, imperforate, from a limited printing.

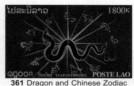

361 Dragon and Chinese Zodiac

(Litho Thai British Security Ptg Co Ltd)

2000 (1 Apr). *Year of the Dragon. T* **361** *and similar horiz design. Multicoloured.* P 14½ × 14.

1690	1800k. Type **361**	50	50
1691	2300k. Dragon swimming	75	75

362 River, Deer and Trees   **363** Peacock

(Litho Thai British Security Ptg Co Ltd)

2000 (1 June). *Children's Paintings. T* **362** *and similar multicoloured designs.* P 14 × 14½ (3200k.) or 14½ × 14 (others).

1692	300k. Type **362**	15	15
1693	400k. Animals running from fire	15	15
1694	2300k. Animals and birds	95	95
1695	3200k. Animals and birds (*vert*)	1·30	1·30
1692/1695 *Set of 4*		2·30	2·30

(Litho Thai British Security Ptg Co Ltd)

2000 (10 July). *The Peacock. T* **363** *and similar multicoloured designs.* P 14 × 14½ (vert) or 14½ × 14 (horiz).

1696	700k. Type **363**	20	20
1697	1000k. With tail displayed	35	35
1698	1800k. Peahen (*horiz*)	60	60
1699	3500k. Pair (*horiz*)	1·20	1·20
1696/1699 *Set of 4*		2·10	2·10
MS1700 146 × 110 mm. 10000k. Front showing tail displayed. P 13½		3·50	3·50

364 Bridge

(Litho and die-stamped gold foil (**MS**1704) or litho (others) Thai British Security Ptg Co Ltd)

2000 (2 Aug). *Pakse Bridge over Mekong River.* T **364** *and similar horiz designs. Multicoloured.* P 14½ × 14.
1701	900k. Type **364**	30	30
1702	2700k. Overview of bridge	95	95
1703	3200k. Bridge from right	1·10	1·10

MS1704 180 × 122 mm. 4000k. No. 1701;
7500k. No. 1702; 8500k. No. 1703. P 13½ . . 6·75 6·75
No. **MS**1704 was also available, imperforate, from a limited printing.

365 Cycling   366 Lao Theung

(Litho Thai British Security Ptg Co Ltd)

2000 (15 Sept). *Olympic Games, Sydney.* T **365** *and similar horiz designs. Multicoloured.* P 14½ × 14.
1705	500k. Type **365**	15	15
1706	900k. Boxing	30	30
1707	2600k. Kick boxing	90	90
1708	3600k. Canoeing	1·30	1·30

MS1709 124 × 180 mm. Nos. 1705/8. P 13½ . . 3·25 3·25
No. **MS**1709 was also available, imperforate, from a limited printing.

(Litho Thai British Security Ptg Co Ltd)

2000 (30 Oct). *Regional Wedding Costumes.* T **366** *and similar vert designs. Multicoloured.* P 14 × 14½.
1710	800k. Type **366**	30	30
1711	2300k. Lao Lum	75	75
1712	3400k. Lao Sung	1·20	1·20

367 Phousy Stupa,   368 Building Façade
Luang Prabang

(Litho Thai British Security Ptg Co Ltd)

2000 (20 Nov). *Tourism (3rd issue).* T **367** *and similar vert designs. Multicoloured.* P 14 × 14½.
1713	300k. Type **367**	15	15
1714	600k. Tham Chang cave	20	20
1715	2800k. Inhang Stupa	1·20	1·20
1716	3300k. Buddha, Phiawal temple, Xiengkhuang	1·40	1·40

1713/1716 *Set of 4* . . . . 2·75 2·75

(Litho Thai British Security Ptg Co Ltd)

2000 (2 Dec). *25th Anniv of Republic of Laos.* P 14½ × 14.
1717 **368** 4000k. multicoloured . . . . . 1·30 1·30

369 Satellites and   370 Roadway
Child writing

(Litho Thai British Security Ptg Co Ltd)

2001 (1 Jan). *Millennium (2nd issue).* T **369** *and similar vert design.* P 14 × 14½.
1718	3200k. Type **369**	1·00	1·00
1719	4000k. Electricity pylons and dam	1·30	1·30

(Litho Thai British Security Ptg Co Ltd)

2001 (14 Feb). *Route 13 Highway Improvement Project.* Sheet 120 × 190 mm *containing* T **370** *and similar horiz designs. Multicoloured.* P 13½.
MS1720 4000k. Type **370**; 4000k. Bridge and mountains; 4000k. Bridge (*different*) . . . . 4·00 4·00

371 Yao mane   372 Cocks
Huaphanh

(Litho Thai British Security Ptg Co Ltd)

2001 (20 Feb). *Men's Regional Costumes.* T **371** *and similar vert designs. Multicoloured.* P 14 × 14½.
1721	100k. Type **371**	10	10
1722	200k. Gnaheun Champasak	10	10
1723	500k. Katou Sarvane	15	15
1724	2300k. Hmong Dam Oudomxay	80	80
1725	2500k. Harlak Xekong	90	90
1726	2600k. Kui Luangnamtha	90	90
1727	2700k. Krieng Xekong	95	95
1728	3100k. Khmu Nhuan Luangnamtha	1·10	1·10
1729	3200k. Ta Oy Saravane	1·10	1·10
1730	3300k. TaiTheng Bolihamxay	1·20	1·20
1731	3400k. Hmong Khao Huaphanh	1·20	1·20
1732	3500k. Gnor Khammouane	1·30	1·30
1733	3600k. Phouthai Na Gnom ZVK	1·30	1·30
1734	4000k. Yao Ventiane	1·40	1·40
1735	5000k. Hmong LPQ	1·80	1·80
1721/1735 *Set of 15*		13·00	13·00

(Litho Thai British Security Ptg Co Ltd)

2001 (10 Mar). *Fighting Cocks.* T **372** *and similar multicoloured designs.* P 13½ (**MS**1740) or 14½ × 14 (others).
1736	500k. Type **372**	20	20
1737	900k. Pair with wings outstretched	35	35
1738	3200k. Pair, one in flight	1·30	1·30
1739	3500k. Pair resting	1·40	1·40
1736/1739 *Set of 4*		3·00	3·00

MS1740 140 × 111 mm. 10000k. Cock crowing
(36 × 51 *mm*). . . . . 4·00 4·00

373 Pou Nyer and Nya Nyer

374 Snake

(Litho Thai British Security Ptg Co Ltd)

2001 (13 Apr). *Luang Prabang New Year Celebrations. T* **373** *and similar multicoloured designs.* P 14½ × 14 (1000k.) or 14 × 14½ (others).

1741	300k. Type **373**	10	10
1742	600k. Hae Nang Sangkhan	20	20
1743	1000k. Sand Stupa (*horiz*)	35	35
1744	2300k. Hae Prabang	80	80
1745	4000k. Takbat	1·50	1·50
1741/1745 *Set of 5*		2·75	2·75

(Litho Thai British Security Ptg Co Ltd)

2001 (15 Apr). *Year of the Snake. T* **374** *and similar horiz design. Multicoloured.* P 14½ × 14.

1746	900k. Type **374**	30	30
1747	3500k. Snake and Chinese zodiac symbols	1·20	1·20

375 That Luang, Ventiane and Forbidden City, Beijing

(Litho Thai British Security Ptg Co Ltd)

2001 (25 Apr). *40th Anniv of Laos–China Diplomatic Relations.* P 14 × 14½.

1748	**375**	1000k. multicoloured	35	35

376 Nurse, Mother and Children

(Litho Thai British Security Ptg Co Ltd)

2001 (13 June). *Polio Eradication Campaign. Sheet* 135 × 101 *mm containing T* **376** *and similar horiz design.* P 13½.
MS1749 900k. Type **376**; 2500k. Family and
map . . . . 1·10 1·10

377 Mekong River

(Litho Thai British Security Ptg Co Ltd)

2001 (20 June). *Mekong River at Twilight. T* **377** *and similar horiz designs. Multicoloured.* P 14½ × 14.

1750	900k. Type **377**	30	30
1751	2700k. River with boats in foreground	90	90
1752	3400k. River (*different*)	1·10	1·10

378 Poppy Field

(Litho Thai British Security Ptg Co Ltd)

2001 (26 July). *Anti-Drug Campaign. T* **378** *and similar horiz design. Multicoloured.* P 14½ × 14.

1753	100k. Type **378**	35	35
1754	4000k. Burning seized drugs	1·10	1·10

379 Intermediate Egret (*Egretta intermedia*)

380 Temple Door

(Litho Thai British Security Ptg Co Ltd)

2001 (1 Aug). *Birds. Philanippon '01 International Stamp Exhibition. T* **379** *and similar multicoloured designs.* P 14½ × 14 (700, 3400k.) or 13½ (others).

1755	700k. Type **379**	20	20
1756	800k. Bulbucus ibis (33 × 49 *mm*)	20	20
1757	3100k. Grey Heron (*Ardea cinera*) (33 × 49 *mm*)	95	95
1758	3400k. Great Egret (*Egretta alba*)	1·00	1·00
1755/1758 *Set of 4*		2·10	2·10
MS1759 200 × 146 mm. Nos. 1755/8		3·00	3·00

No. **MS**1759 was also available, imperforate, from a limited printing.

(Litho Thai British Security Ptg Co Ltd)

2001 (17 Sept). *Buddhist Temple Doors. T* **380** *and similar vert designs showing different temple doors.* P 14 × 14½.

1760	600k. multicoloured	20	20
1761	2300k. multicoloured	80	80
1762	2500k. multicoloured	90	90
1763	2600k. multicoloured	90	90
1760/1763 *Set of 4*		2·50	2·50

381 White Frangipani

382 Women using Pestles and Mortar

(Litho Thai British Security Ptg Co Ltd)

2001 (2 Oct). *The Frangipani. T* **381** *and similar multicoloured designs.* P 14 × 14½ (2500k.) or 14½ × 14 (others).
1764	1000k. Type **381**		35	35
1765	2500k. Pink frangipani (vert)		90	90
1766	3500k. Red frangipani		1·20	1·20
MS1767	145 × 111 mm. Nos. 1764/6. P 13½		2·40	2·40

(Litho Thai British Security Ptg Co Ltd)

2001 (15 Nov). *Traditional Mortars. T* **382** *and similar multicoloured designs.* P 14½ × 14 (2600k.) or 14 × 14½ (others).
1768	900k. Type **382**		30	30
1769	2600k. Wheel driven pestle and mortar (horiz)		80	80
1770	3500k. Fulcrum and lever pestle and mortar		1·10	1·10

383 Himavanta

(Litho Thai British Security Ptg Co Ltd)

2001 (5 Dec). *Vessantara (Buddhist story illustrating charity). T* **383** *and similar vert designs. Multicoloured.* P 13½.
1771	200k. Type **383**		10	10
1772	900k. Vanapavesa		35	35
1773	3200k. Kumarakanda		1·30	1·30
1774	3600k. Sakkapabba		1·50	1·50
1771/1774	*Set of 4*		3·00	3·00
MS1775	120 × 151 mm. Nos. 1771/4		3·25	3·25

No. **MS**1775 was also available, imperforate, from a limited printing.

384 People and Emblem

(Litho Thai British Security Ptg Co Ltd)

2001 (29 Dec). *International Year of Volunteers.* P 13.
1776	**384**	1000k. multicoloured	35	35

APPENDIX

The following stamps have either been issued in excess of postal needs or have not been available to the public in reasonable quantities at face value. Such stamps may later be given full listing if there is evidence of regular postal use. Miniature sheets and imperforate stamps are excluded from this section.

1975

Centenary of Universal Postal Union. Postage 10, 15, 30, 40k.; *Air* 1000, 1500k. *Embossed on gold foil* 2500, 3000k.
"Apollo–Soyuz" Space Link. Postage 125, 150, 200, 300k.; *Air* 450, 700k.
Bicentenary of American Revolution. Postage 10, 15, 40, 50, 100, 125, 150, 200k.; *Air* 1000, 1500k.

NEUTRALIST GOVERNMENT

On 8 August 1960 Captain Kong Le carried out a bloodless coup during the absence of the Cabinet from Vientiane. With the consent of the King he installed Prince Souvanna Phouma as Prime Minister. On 16 December 1960 General Nosavan defeated Kong Le and installed Prince Boun Oum as head of the government. Kong Le's forces retreated to the Plain of Jars together with Souvanna Phouma's Cabinet which joined with leaders of the Pathet Lao (Lao country) to establish a neutralist government. This had control over a large part of the country and was recognised as the true government of Laos by a number of non-aligned countries.

Their influence and territory grew, and on 22 June 1962 the King installed a new coalition government in Vientiane under Souvanna Phouma with the approval of the Geneva Conference on Laos. However, sporadic fighting continued and on 1 June 1964 the Pathet Lao withdrew their government officials from Vientiane and a state of civil war developed as the fighting in the Plain of Jars became more involved with the Vietnam War.

N 1 Soldiers with Royal Laotian Flag

N 2 Young Girls, Luong Pagoda and Emblem

(Litho (N1/4) or recess and litho (N5/8) People's Ptg Wks, Peking)

1961 (18 July–Sept). *Anniversary of Coup of 8 August* 1960. *No gum (except 5k.).*

(a) Occupation of the Plain of Jars. P 11 × 11½.
N1	N **1**	0k.50 sepia, red and cobalt		
N2		2k. sepia, red and pale yellow		
N3		5k. sepia, red and grey-green		
N4		15k. sepia, red and pale slate-violet		

(b) Unity of the People. P 11½ × 11.
N5	N **2**	1k. grey-black and grey-green		
N6		5k. grey-black and orange (Sept)		
N7		10k. grey-black and slate-blue		
N8		20k. grey-black and rose-red		
N1/8	*Set of 8*		17·00	—

Despite their commemorative nature the above served as a definitive issue over a considerable period. They were first placed on sale at Xieng Khouang but were later on sale in other places. They had validity and were accepted throughout the country. It is understood that some foreign mail from northern areas was routed via China but the stamps were not recognised by Thailand and foreign mail routed that way had to be further franked with stamps of the Royal Laotian Government.

PATHET LAO

The following stamps were issued by the Pathet Lao authorities but were valid throughout the country.

P **1** Women and Pathet Lao Flag

(Litho State Ptg Wks, Hanoi)

1974 (2 Apr). *Type P* **1** *and similar vert designs. Multicoloured.*
P 11. *No gum.*

P1	10k. Type P **1**	
P2	10k. Nurse examining child	
P3	10k. Woman minding weaving machine	
P4	20k. Anti-aircraft attack	
P5	30k. Battle scene	
P6	40k. Women digging trench	
P7	60k. Soldiers in Plain of Jars	
P1/7	*Set of 7*	39·00 —

A further two unissued designs, 10k. Musicians and 30k. Militia women on wing of airplane, appeared on the market some years after the above stamps.

A peace treaty was signed in Vientiane on 19 February 1973 ending the civil war between the royal government (backed by Thailand and the United States) and the Pathet Lao (supported by North Vietnam). On 5 April 1974 a Provisional Government of National Unity was formed, headed by Prince Souvanna Phouma.

Myanmar

1937. 12 Pies = 1 anna; 16 Annas = 1 rupee
1953. 100 Pyas = 1 Kyat

BURMA

Stamps of India were used in Burma from 1854 and, after 1856, individual examples can be identified by the use of the concentric octagonal postmarks of the Bengal Postal Circle of which the following were supplied to Burmese post offices:

Type A No. B 156
(Rangoon)

Type B No. B5 (Akyab)

B5	Akyab	B146	Pegu
B12*	Bassein	B150	Prome
B22	Nga Thine Khyoung	B156*	Rangoon
B56	Amherst	B159	Sandoway
B108	Kyouk Phyoo	B165	Sarawah (to 1860)
B111	Meeaday	B165	Henzada (from 1861)
B112	Mengyee	B171	Shoay Gyeen
B127	Moulmein	B173	Sittang
B128	Mergui	B179	Thayetmyo
B129	Tavoy	B181	Toungoo
B133	Myanoung	B227	Port Blair
B136	Namayan		

*Exists in black or blue. Remainder in black only.

Akyab, Moulmein and Rangoon used postmarks as both Type A and Type B, Port Blair as Type B only and the remainder as Type A only.

From 1860 various types of duplex cancellations were introduced and Burmese examples can be identified when sufficient of the left-hand portion is visible on the stamp. Such marks were issued for the following offices:

Akyab	Rangoon
Bassein	Rangoon C.R.H. (Cantonment
Mandalay	Receiving House)
Moulmein	Thayetmyo
Port Blair	Toungoo
Prome	

1862 Duplex from Toungoo

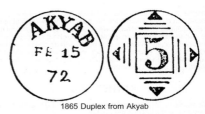

1865 Duplex from Akyab

During 1875, a further series of duplex marks was introduced in which the right-hand portion of the cancellation included the office code number, prefixed by the letter "R" for Rangoon:

R–1	Rangoon	R–9	Myanoung
R–1/1	Rangoon Cantonment	R–10	Port Blair
R–2	Akyab	1/R–10	Nancowry
R–3	Bassein	R–11	Prome
R–4	Henzada	R–12	Sandoway
R–5	Kyouk Phyoo	R–13	Shwegyeen
R–6	Mandalay	R–14	Tavoy
R–7	Mergui	R–15	Thayetmyo
R–8	Moulmein	R–16	Tounghoo
1/R–8	Amherst		

1875 type from Rangoon

1875 type from Rangoon Cantonment Receiving House

From 1886 the whole of Burma was united under the Crown and the post offices were supplied with circular date stamps giving the name of the town.

Most Indian stamps, both postage and official, issued during the period were supplied to post offices in Burma. None of the imperforates printed by De La Rue have been seen however, and from the later issues the following have not been recorded with Burma postmarks:

Nos. 39a, 66a, 68, 85a, 92a, 110a/b, 148a, 155a, 165, 192a/c, 195a/b, O15, O38, O40b, O50a/b, O76a, O101a, O102, O103a, O104/5 and O142.

The value of most India stamps used in Burma coincides proportionately with the used prices quoted for India, but some, especially the provisional surcharges, are extremely rare with Burmese postmarks. Stamps of the face value of 2r. and above from the reigns of Victoria and Edward VII are more common with telegraph cancellations than with those of the postal service.

PRICES FOR STAMPS ON COVER TO 1945		
Nos.	1/18	from × 6
Nos.	18a/33	from × 4
No.	34	from × 5
Nos.	35/50	from × 8
Nos.	O1/27	from × 15

BRITISH ADMINISTRATION

From 1 January 1886 Burma was a province of the Indian Empire but was separated from India and came under direct British administration on 1 April 1937.

BURMA
(1)

BURMA
(1a)

1937 (1 Apr). *Stamps of India. (King George V inscr "INDIA POSTAGE")* optd with *T* **1** or **1a** *(rupee values)*. W **69**. P 14.

1	3p. slate	60	10
	w. Wmk inverted	1·75	60
2	½a. green	1·00	10
	w. Wmk inverted	2·00	60
3	9p. deep green (*typo*)	1·00	10
	w. Wmk inverted	1·75	60
4	1a. chocolate	1·00	10
	w. Wmk inverted	1·75	60
5	2a. vermilion (*small die*)	75	10
6	2½a. orange	60	10
	w. Wmk inverted	1·75	60
7	3a. carmine	1·00	30
	w. Wmk inverted	3·50	1·25
8	3½a. deep blue	2·00	10
	aw. Wmk inverted	2·75	30
	b. Dull blue	8·50	6·00
	bw. Wmk inverted	6·00	4·00
9	4a. sage-green	1·00	10
	w. Wmk inverted	—	35·00
10	6a. bistre	75	35
	w. Wmk inverted	—	35·00
11	8a. reddish purple	1·50	10
12	12a. claret	4·25	1·25
	w. Wmk inverted	11·00	2·00
13	1r. chocolate and green	24·00	3·00
14	2r. carmine and orange	28·00	11·00
	w. Wmk inverted	40·00	14·00
15	5r. ultramarine and purple	38·00	18·00
16	10r. green and scarlet	90·00	60·00
	w. Wmk inverted	†	
17	15r. blue and olive (*wmk inverted*)	£325	£120
18	25r. orange and blue	£650	£300
	w. Wmk inverted	£650	£300
1/18	Set of 18	£1000	£450

The opt is at top on all values except the 3a.
The 1a. has been seen used from Yenangyaung on 22 Mar 1937.

2 King George VI and "Chinthes"

3 King George VI and "Nagas"

4 *Karaweik* (royal barge)

8 King George VI and Peacock

10 Elephants' Heads

Extra trees flaw (R. 11/8)

(Des Maung Kyi (2a.6p.), Maung Hline (3a.), Maung Ohn Pe (3a.6p.) and N. K. D. Naigamwalla (8a.). Litho Security Ptg Press, Nasik)

1938 (15 Nov)–**40**. *T* **2/4**, **8** *and similar designs.* W **10**. P 14 (vert) or 13½ × 13 (horiz).

18a	**2**	1p. red-orange (1.8.40)	3·00	1·00
19		3p. bright violet	20	1·00
20		6p. bright blue	20	10
21		9p. yellow-green	1·00	1·00
22	**3**	1a. purple-brown	20	10
23		1½a. turquoise-green	20	1·25
24		2a. carmine	45	10
25	**4**	2a.6p. claret	14·00	1·50
26	—	3a. dull violet	14·00	2·25
27	—	3a.6p. light blue and blue	1·25	4·50
		a. Extra trees flaw	55·00	
28	**3**	4a. greenish blue	60	10
29	—	8a. myrtle-green	5·00	30
30	**8**	1r. purple and blue	5·00	20
31	—	2r. brown and purple	16·00	1·75
32	—	5r. violet and scarlet	48·00	25·00
33	—	10r. brown and myrtle	55·00	50·00
18a/33	Set of 16		£150	80·00

Designs: *Horiz (as T* **4**)—3a. Burma teak; 3a.6p. Burma rice; 8a. River Irrawaddy. *Vert (as T* **8**)—5r., 10r. King George VI and "Nats".

The 1a. exists lithographed or typographed, the latter having a "Jubilee" line in the sheet margin.

COMMEMORATION POSTAGE STAMP 6th MAY 1840

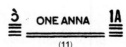

(11)

1940 (6 May). *Centenary of First Adhesive Postage Stamps. No. 25 surch with T* **11**.

34	**4**	1a. on 2a.6p. claret	4·00	2·00

For stamps issued in 1942–45 see under Japanese Occupation.

CHIN HILLS DISTRICT. This area, in the far north-west of the country, remained in British hands when the Japanese overran Burma in May 1942.

During the period July to December 1942 the local officials were authorised to produce provisional stamps and the letters "OHMS" are known overprinted by typewriter on Nos. 3, 20, 22/4, 28/9 and 31 of Burma or handstamped, in violet, on Nos. 25, 27 and 29. The two types can also occur together or in combination with a handstamped "SERVICE".

From early in 1943 ordinary postage stamps of India were used from the Chin Hills post offices of Falam, Haka, Fort White and Tiddim, this expedient continuing until the fall of Falam to the Japanese on 7 November 1943.

The provisional stamps should only be collected on Official cover where dates and the sender's handwriting can be authenticated.

BRITISH MILITARY ADMINISTRATION

Preparations for the liberation of Burma commenced in February 1943 when the Civil Affairs Service (Burma) (CAS(B)) was set up at Delhi as part of the proposed military administration structure. One of the specific tasks assigned to CAS(B) was the operation of a postal service for the civilian population.

Operations against the Japanese intensified during the second half of 1944. The port of Akyab in the Arakan was reoccupied in January 1945. The 14th Army took Mandalay on 29 March and Rangoon was liberated from the sea on 3 May.

Postal services for the civilian population started in Akyab on 13 April 1945 while post offices in the Magwe Division around Meiktila were operating from 4 March. Mandalay post offices opened on 8 June and those in Rangoon on 16 June, but the full network was only completed in December 1945, just before the military administration was wound up.

MILY ADMN				**MILY ADMN**	
(12)				(13)	

1945 (from 11 Apr). Nos. 18a to 33 optd with T **12** (small stamps) or **13** (others) by Security Printing Press, Nasik.

35	**2**	1p. red-orange		10	10
		a. Opt omitted (in pair with			
		normal)		£1600	
36		3p. bright violet		10	75
37		6p. bright blue		10	30
38		9p. yellow-green		30	75
39	**3**	1a. purple-brown (16.6)		10	10
40		1½a. turquoise-green (16.6)		10	15
41		2a. carmine		10	15
42	**4**	2a.6p. claret		2·00	1·00
43	—	3a. dull violet		1·50	20
44	—	3a.6p. light blue and blue		10	70
		a. Extra trees flaw		26·00	
45	**3**	4a. greenish blue		10	60
46	—	8a. myrtle-green		10	70
47	**8**	1r. purple and blue		40	50
48		2r. brown and purple		40	1·25
49	—	5r. violet and scarlet		40	1·25
50	—	10r. brown and myrtle		40	1·25
35/50	Set of 16			4·75	8·50

Only the typographed version of the 1a., No. 22, received this overprint.

The missing overprints on the 1p. occur on the stamps from the bottom row of one sheet. A further block with two examples of the variety caused by a paper fold also exists.

The exact dates of issue for Nos. 35/50 are difficult to establish.

The initial stock of overprints is known to have reached CAS(B) headquarters, Imphal, at the beginning of April 1945. Postal directives issued on 11 April refer to the use of the overprints in Akyab and in the Magwe Division where surcharged pre-war postal stationery envelopes had previously been in use. The 6p., 1a., 1½a. and 2a. values were placed on sale at Mandalay on 8 June and the 1a. and 2a. at Rangoon on 16 June. It has been suggested that only a limited service was initially available in Rangoon. All values were on sale by 9 August 1945.

BRITISH CIVIL ADMINISTRATION

1946 (1 Jan). As Nos. 19/33, but colours changed.

51	**2**	3p. brown		10	2·00
52		6p. deep violet		10	30
53		9p. green		15	2·50
54	**3**	1a. blue		15	20
55		1½a. orange		15	10
56		2a. claret		15	40
57	**4**	2a.6p. greenish blue		2·75	4·00
57a	—	3a. blue-violet		6·50	4·00

57b	—	3a.6p. black and ultramarine		50	2·00
		ba. Extra trees flaw		55·00	
58	**3**	4a. purple		50	30
59	—	8a. maroon		1·75	3·00
60	**8**	1r. violet and maroon		1·25	1·00
61		2r. brown and orange		6·00	3·75
62	—	5r. green and brown		6·00	17·00
63	—	10r. claret and violet		8·50	21·00
51/63	Set of 15			30·00	55·00

No. 54 was printed in typography only.

14 Burman

(Des A. G. I. McGeogh. Litho Nasik)

1946 (2 May). Victory. T **14** and similar vert designs. W **10** (sideways). P 13.

64		9p. turquoise-green		20	20
65		1½a. violet		20	10
66		2a. carmine		20	10
67		3a.6p. ultramarine		50	20
64/7	Set of 4			1·00	50

Designs:—1½a. Burmese woman; 2a. Chinthe; 3a.6p. Elephant.

INTERIM BURMESE GOVERNMENT

(18 Trans. "Interim Government")	18a	18b

Type **18a** shows the first character transposed to the end of the top line (R. 6/15).

Type **18b** shows the last two characters transposed to the front of the top line (R. 14/14).

Some sheets of the 3p. show both errors corrected by a handstamp as Type **18**.

1947 (1 Oct). Stamps of 1946 optd with T **18** (small stamps) or larger opt (others).

68	**2**	3p. brown		70	70
		a. Opt Type **18a**		42·00	
		ab. Corrected by handstamp as			
		Type **18**			
		b. Opt Type **18b**		42·00	
		ba. Corrected by handstamp as			
		Type **18**			
69		6p. deep violet		10	30
		a. Opt Type **18a**		23·00	
70		9p. green		10	30
		a. Opt inverted		21·00	25·00
71	**3**	1a. blue		10	30
		a. Vert pair, one with opt omitted			
72		1½a. orange		1·00	10
73		2a. claret		30	15
		a. Horiz pair, one with opt omitted			
		b. Opt Type **18a**		35·00	
74	**4**	2a.6p. greenish blue		1·75	1·00
75	—	3a. blue-violet		2·50	1·75
76	—	3a.6p. black and ultramarine		50	2·00
		a. Extra trees flaw		50·00	
77	**3**	4a. purple		1·75	30
78	—	8a. maroon		1·75	1·75
79	**8**	1r. violet and maroon		4·50	1·00
80		2r. brown and orange		4·50	4·00
81	—	5r. green and brown		4·50	4·50
82	—	10r. claret and violet		3·25	4·50
68/82	Set of 15			24·00	20·00

The 3p., 6p., 2a., 2a.6p., 3a.6p. and 1r. are also known with overprint inverted.

OFFICIAL STAMPS

BURMA

BURMA

SERVICE
(O 1)

SERVICE
(O 1a)

1937 (Apr–June). *Stamps of India (King George V inscr "INDIA POSTAGE") optd with Type O* **1** *or O* **1a** *(rupee values)*. W **69**. P 14.

O1	3p. slate		2·00	10
	w. Wmk inverted		—	17·00
O2	½a. green		9·00	10
	w. Wmk inverted		†	—
O3	9p. deep green		5·00	30
O4	1a. chocolate		5·00	10
O5	2a. vermilion (*small die*)		9·50	35
	w. Wmk inverted		—	17·00
O6	2½a. orange		5·00	2·00
O7	4a. sage-green		5·00	10
O8	6a. bistre		4·25	8·00
O9	8a. reddish purple (1.4.37)		4·00	1·00
O10	12a. claret (1.4.37)		4·00	6·00
O11	1r. chocolate and green (1.4.37)		15·00	4·25
O12	2r. carmine and orange		35·00	40·00
	w. Wmk inverted		40·00	45·00
O13	5r. ultramarine and purple		95·00	50·00
O14	10r. green and scarlet		£275	£130
O1/14 *Set of 14*			£425	£225

For the above issue the stamps were either overprinted "BURMA" and "SERVICE" at one operation or had the two words applied separately. Research has yet to establish if all values exist with both forms of overprinting.

SERVICE
(O 2)

SERVICE
(O 3)

1939. *Nos. 19/24 and 28 optd with Type O* **2** *(typo) and Nos. 25 and 29/33 optd with Type O* **3** *(litho)*.

O15	2	3p. bright violet	15	20
O16		6p. bright blue	15	20
O17		9p. yellow-green	4·00	3·75
O18	3	1a. purple-brown	15	15
O19		1½a. turquoise-green	3·50	1·75
O20		2a. carmine	1·25	20
O21	4	2a.6p. claret	16·00	14·00
O22	3	4a. greenish blue	4·50	50
O23	—	8a. myrtle-green	15·00	4·00
O24	8	1r. purple and blue	16·00	5·50
O25		2r. brown and purple	30·00	15·00
O26	—	5r. violet and scarlet	25·00	29·00
O27	—	10r. brown and myrtle	£130	38·00
O15/27 *Set of 13*			£225	£100

Both versions of the 1a. value exist with this overprint.

1946. *British Civil Administration. Nos. 51/6 and 58 optd with Type O* **2** *(typo) and Nos. 57 and 59/63 optd with Type O* **3** *(litho)*.

O28	2	3p. brown	2·00	3·50
O29		6p. deep violet	2·00	2·25
O30		9p. green	50	3·25
O31	3	1a. blue	20	2·00
O32		1½a. orange	20	20
O33		2a. claret	20	2·00
O34	4	2a.6p. greenish blue	1·75	6·50
O35	3	4a. purple	20	70
O36	—	8a. maroon	3·25	3·50
O37	8	1r. violet and maroon	60	4·25
O38		2r. brown and orange	7·50	45·00
O39	—	5r. green and brown	9·00	50·00
O40	—	10r. claret and violet	17·00	60·00
O28/40 *Set of 13*			40·00	£160

1947. *Interim Burmese Government. Nos. O28/40 optd with T* **18** *(small stamps) or larger opt (others)*.

O41	2	3p. brown	30	40
O42		6p. deep violet	2·00	10
O43		9p. green	3·00	90
O44	3	1a. blue	3·00	80
O45		1½a. orange	6·00	30
O46		2a. claret	3·25	15
O47	4	2a.6p. greenish blue	27·00	12·00
O48	3	4a. purple	13·00	40
O49	—	8a. maroon	12·00	4·00
O50	8	1r. violet and maroon	14·00	2·25
O51		2r. brown and orange	14·00	20·00
O52	—	5r. green and brown	14·00	20·00
O53	—	10r. claret and violet	14·00	30·00
O41/53 *Set of 13*			£110	80·00

Later stamp issues will be found listed in Part 21 (*South-East Asia*) of this catalogue.

BURMA

REPUBLIC OF THE UNION OF BURMA

By the Burma Independence Act, 1947, Burma became an independent state, outside the British Commonwealth and Empire, at 4.20 a.m., the time chosen by astrologers, on 4 January 1948.

10 Elephants' Heads

20 Aung San, Chinthe and Map of Burma

21 Martyrs' Memorial

(Des A. G. I. McGeogh. Litho De La Rue)

1948 (6 Jan). *Independence Day*. P 12½ × 12.

83	20	½a. yellow-green	10	10
84		1a. rose	10	10
85		2a. scarlet	20	15
86		3½a. blue	25	25
87		8a. brown	25	25
83/87 *Set of 5*			80	75

(Recess De La Rue)

1948 (19 July). *First Anniv of Murder of Aung San and his Ministers*. P 14½ × 13½.

88	21	3p. ultramarine	10	10
89		6p. yellow-green	10	10
90		9p. carmine	10	10
91		1a. violet	10	10
92		2a. magenta	10	10
93		3½a. grey-green	10	10
94		4a. brown	20	10
95		8a. red	20	15
96		12a. purple	25	15
97		1r. blue-green	45	25

98		2r. blue	90	50
99		5r. purple-brown	2·00	1·30
88/99		Set of 12	4·25	2·75

Nos. 88/93, 100/103 and 108 exist imperforate. Their status is uncertain but it is believed they were not issued.

22 Playing Cane-ball

25 Bell, Mingun Pagoda

26 Hintha (legendary bird)

27 Transplanting Rice

28 Lion Throne

(Recess De La Rue)

1949 (4 Jan). *First Anniv of Independence. T 22/28 and similar designs. P 12 × 12½ (105/7 and 109), 12½ (100/4 and 108), or 13 (T 28).*

100	**22**	3p. ultramarine	1·10	25
101	–	6p. green	20	10
102	–	9p. carmine	20	10
103	**25**	1a. vermilion	20	10
104	**26**	2a. yellow-orange	20	10
105	**27**	2a.6p. magenta	20	15
106	–	3a. violet	20	15
107	–	3a.6p. slate-green	25	15
108	–	4a. brown	25	15
109	–	8a. red	35	15
110	**28**	1r. blue-green	65	15
		a. Perf 14	4·50	3·00
111		2r. indigo	1·50	45
112		5r. brown	3·00	1·40
113		10r. red-orange	5·50	2·20
100/113		Set of 14	12·50	5·00

Designs: *As T 22*—6p. Dancer; 9p. Girl playing saunggaut (string instrument). *As T 25*—4a. Elephant hauling log. *As T 27*—3a. Girl weaving; 3a.6p. Royal Palace; 8a. Ploughing paddy field with oxen.

See note below No. 99.

See also Nos. 120/133 and 137/150.

(28a)

CONTROL OVERPRINTS. Following looting from Post Offices it was decided to overprint remaining stocks of Nos. 100/13 with the Burmese word "Pyidaungsu" as T **28a** (larger on Nos. 105/7 and 109/13), in black on the 2r. and gold on the other values. Only a small quantity was however completed and the overprints were not issued.

(O **29**) 13 mm

29 U.P.U. Monument, Berne

30 Independence Monument, Rangoon, and Map

1949 (4 Jan). *OFFICIAL. First Anniv of Independence. Nos. 100/104 and 107/113 optd as Type O 29 (3p. to 2a. and 4a.) or larger, 14½ mm long (others).*

O114	**22**	3p. ultramarine (R.)	55	15
O115	–	6p. green (R.)	10	10
O116	–	9p. carmine	10	10
O117	**25**	1a. vermilion	10	10
O118	**26**	2a. yellow-orange	20	15
O119	–	3a.6p. slate-green (R.)	20	15
O120	–	4a. brown	20	15
O121	–	8a. red	20	15
O122	**28**	1r. blue-green (R.)	55	25
O123		2r. indigo (R.)	90	45
O124		5r. brown	2·40	1·70
		a. Opt double		
O125		10r. red orange	6·00	4·25
O114/125		Set of 12	10·50	7·00

(Recess De La Rue)

1949 (9 Oct). *75th Anniv of Universal Postal Union. P 13.*

114	**29**	2a. orange	25	25
115		3½a. olive-green	25	15
116		6a. violet	35	25
117		8a. scarlet	45	45
118		12½a. ultramarine	90	60
119		1r. blue-green	1·10	85
114/119		Set of 6	3·00	2·30

(Litho Security Ptg Press, Nasik, India)

1952–53. *As Nos. 100/113, but colours and printing process changed. W 10. P 13½ × 13 (Nos. 125/7 and 129) or 14 (others).*

120	**22**	3p. red-orange	20	10
121	–	6p. purple	10	10
122	–	9p. light blue	10	10
123	**25**	1a. ultramarine	10	10
124	**26**	2a. green (1.7.52)	35	15
125	**27**	2a.6p. green	10	10
126	–	3a. vermilion (1.9.52)	20	15
127	–	3a.6p. red-orange	20	15
128	–	4a. vermilion	20	15
129	–	8a. light blue (1.9.52)	35	35
130	**28**	1r. reddish violet	55	50
131		2r. green	1·10	60
132		5r. ultramarine	3·25	1·70
133		10r. light blue	6·25	4·25
120/133		Set of 14	11·50	7·75

Overprints for Official mail (as Type O **29**) on Nos. 120/4 and 127/33 were prepared but not issued.

See also Nos. 137/150.

New Currency

(Litho Security Ptg Press, Nasik, India)

1953 (4 Jan). *Fifth Anniv of Independence. W 10 (sideways).*

(a) Size 22 × 18 mm. P 14.

134	**30**	14p. green	20	15

(b) Size 36½ × 26½ mm. P 13½ × 13.

135	**30**	20p. rose-red	25	15
136		25p. ultramarine	45	15
		a. Printed double		

The inscription across the centre of the design reads "Welfare State. Life free from Want and Fear".

(Litho Security Ptg Press, Nasik, India)

1954 (4 Jan). *New Currency. As Nos.* 120/133 *but values in pyas and kyats.* W **10**. P 13½ × 13 (10, 20, 25, 50p.) or 14 (others).

137	22	1p. red-orange		70	10
138	–	2p. purple		10	10
139	–	3p. light blue		10	10
140	25	5p. ultramarine		10	10
141	27	10p. green		10	10
142	26	15p. green		25	10
143	–	20p. vermilion		20	10
144	–	25p. red-orange		20	15
145	–	30p. vermilion		25	15
146	–	50p. light blue		25	15
147	28	1k. reddish violet		80	25
148	–	2k. green		1·50	45
149	–	5k. ultramarine		4·25	80
150	–	10k. light blue		7·75	1·40
137/150 *Set of 14*				15·00	3·75

1954–57. OFFICIAL. *Nos.* 137/40 *and* 142/50 *optd as Type* O **29** (1p. to 15p. and 30p.) or larger, 15½ mm long (25p., 50p.) or 14½ mm long (others).

O151	22	1p. red-orange		55	15
O152	–	2p. purple		20	15
O153	–	3p. light blue		20	15
O154	25	5p. ultramarine		20	15
O155	26	15p. green		20	15
O156	–	20p. vermilion (1957)		20	15
O157	–	25p. red-orange		20	15
O158	–	30p. vermilion		20	15
O159	–	50p. light blue		20	15
O160	28	1k. reddish violet		65	15
		a. Opt double			
O161	–	2k. green		1·50	35
O162	–	5k. ultramarine		3·00	95
O163	–	10k. light blue		6·50	3·00
O151/163 *Set of 13*				12·50	5·25

31 Sangiti Mahapasana Rock Cave in Grounds of Kaba-Aye Pagoda

32 Fifth Buddhist Council Monuments, Kuthodaw Pagoda

(Des Ba Kyi (10p., 2k.), Ba Moe (15p., 1k.), Ngwe Gaing (35, 50p.). Litho Security Ptg Press, Nasik, India)

1954 (17 May–15 Nov). *Sixth Buddhist Council, Rangoon. T* **31** *and similar horiz designs.* W **10**. P 13½ × 13.

151		10p. ultramarine (15.11)		10	10
152		15p. deep claret (15.11)		15	15
153		35p. bistre-brown		25	25
154		50p. green (15.11)		45	25
155		1k. bright rose-red (15.11)		95	50
156		2k. bright violet (15.11)		1·60	1·10
151/156 *Set of 6*				3·25	2·10

Designs:—10p. Rock cave and Sangha of Cambodia; 15p. Buddhist priests and Kuthodaw Pagoda, Mandalay; 50p. Rock cave and Sangha of Thailand; 1k. Rock cave and Sangha of Ceylon; 2k. Rock cave and Sangha of Laos.

(Photo Enschedé & Sons, Netherlands)

1956 (24 May). *Buddha Jayanti. T* **32** *and similar horiz designs inscr* "2500TH BUDDHIST ERA". No wmk. P 11 × 11½.

157		20p. bronze green and dull blue		15	10
158		40p. apple green and dull blue		35	25
159		60p. greenish yellow and deep green		45	35
160		1k.25 slate-blue and yellow		95	80
157/160 *Set of 4*				1·70	1·50

Designs:—40p. Thatbyinnyu Pagoda, Pagan; 60p. Shwedagon Pagoda, Rangoon; 1k.25, Sangiti Mahapasana Rock Cave and Kaba-Aye Pagoda, Rangoon (venue of Sixth Buddhist Council).

(33) "Mandalay Town—100 Years/ 1221–1321"

(34)

1959 (7 Nov). *Centenary of Mandalay. No.* 144 *surch with T* **33** *and Nos.* 147/8 *with two-line opt only.*

161	–	15p.on 25p. red-orange		25	15
162	28	1k. reddish violet		85	80
163		2k. green		1·70	1·20

1961 (June). *No.* 134 *surch with T* **34**.

164	30	15p.on 14p. green		60	25
		a. Surch inverted		17·00	

35 Torch-bearer in Rangoon   **36** Children at Play

(Des Mon San Tin (15p.), Ba Moe (others). Photo Enschedé)

1961 (11 Dec). *Second South-East Asian Peninsula Games, Rangoon. T* **35** *and similar designs.* P 14 × 13 (horiz) or 13 × 14 (vert).

165		15p. blue and scarlet		15	15
166		25p. myrtle green and orange-brown		25	15
167		50p. magenta and violet-blue		70	25
168		1k. greenish yellow and emerald		1·00	80
165/168 *Set of 4*				1·90	1·20

Designs: Vert—25p. Contestants; 50p. Women sprinting in Aung San Stadium, Rangoon. Horiz—1k. Contestants.

(Des U Mya. Litho De La Rue)

1961 (11 Dec). *15th Anniv of United Nations Children's Fund.* P 13.

169	36	15p. crimson and rose		35	10

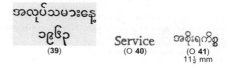

37 Flag and Map   FREEDOM FROM HUNGER **(38)**

(Recess Toppan Ptg Co, Tokyo)

1963 (2 Mar). *First Anniv of Military Coup by General Ne Win.* P 13 × 13½.

170	37	15p. scarlet		35	15

1963 (21 Mar). *Freedom from Hunger. Nos.* 141, 146 *optd with T* **38**.

171	27	10p. green (V.)		45	35
		a. Opt in red			
172	–	50p. light blue (R.)		85	70
		a. Opt inverted			

(39)   Service **(O 40)**   **(O 41)** 11½ mm

1963 (1 May). *Labour Day. No.* 143 *optd with T* **39**.
173　20p. vermilion . . . . 35　15

1964. *OFFICIAL. No.* 139 *optd locally with Type* O **40**.
O174　3p. light blue . . . . 10·50　7·00

1964. *OFFICIAL. Nos.* 137, 139, 140 *and* 142 *optd locally with Type* O **41**.
O175　**22**　1p. red-orange . . . . 3·00　60
O176　–　3p. light blue . . . . 3·00　60
O177　**25**　5p. ultramarine . . . . 3·00　60
O178　**26**　15p. green . . . . 3·00　60
O175/178 *Set of* 4 . . . . 20·00　8·50

40 White-browed Fantail　**41** I.T.U. Emblem and Symbols

(Photo Govt Ptg Wks, Tokyo)

1964 (16 Apr). *Burmese Birds* (1st Series). *T* **40** *and similar designs.* P 13½ (T **40**), 13 (20p.) or 13½ × 13 (others).
174　**40**　1p. brownish black . . . . . . 25　15
175　–　2p. carmine . . . . 25　15
176　–　3p. turquoise-green . . . . . 25　15
177　–　5p. royal blue . . . . 35　25
178　–　10p. orange-brown . . . . . . 45　25
179　–　15p. yellow-olive . . . . 45　25
180　–　20p. brown and rose-red . . . 70　35
181　–　25p. reddish brown and olive-
　　　　　　yellow . . . . 85　35
　　　　a. Deep brown and bright yellow-
　　　　　　olive . . . . 85　35
182　–　50p. grey-blue and red . . . . 1·30　45
183　–　1k. deep blue, yellow & brownish
　　　　　　grey . . . . 4·00　1·10
184　–　2k. deep blue, lt yellow-olive &
　　　　　　rosine . . . . 7·75　3·00
185　–　5k. multicoloured . . . . . . 16·00　7·50
174/185 *Set of* 12 . . . . 29·00　12·50
Birds: 22 × 26 *mm*—5p. to 15p. Indian roller. 27 × 36 *mm*—Crested serpent eagle; 50p. Sarus crane; 1k. Indian pied hornbill; 5k. Green peafowl. 35½ × 25 *mm*—20p. Red-whiskered bulbul. 37 × 27 *mm*—2k. Kalij pheasant.
See also Nos. 195/206.

1965. *OFFICIAL. Nos.* 175/7, 179 *and* 181 *optd locally with Type* O **41**.
O186　**40**　2p. carmine . . . . 2·50　60
O187　–　3p. turquoise-green . . . . . 3·00　60
　　　　a. Opt inverted . . . . —　13·00
O188　–　5p. royal blue . . . . 2·50　70
O189　–　15p. yellow-olive . . . . 3·00　70
O190　–　25p. reddish brown and olive-
　　　　　　yellow . . . . 2·50　70
O186/190 *Set of* 5 . . . . 12·00　3·00

(Litho De La Rue)

1965 (17 May). *Centenary of International Telecommunications Union.* P 15 (20p.) or 13 (50p.).
186　**41**　20p. magenta . . . . 15　15
187　–　50p. deep dull green (34 × 24½
　　　　　　mm) . . . . 45　45

42 I.C.Y. Emblem　**43** Harvesting

(Litho Govt Ptg Wks, Tokyo)

1965 (1 July). *International Co-operation Year.* P 13.
188　**42**　5p. ultramarine . . . . 15　10
189　–　10p. orange-brown . . . . . . 15　10
190　–　15p. yellow-olive . . . . 25　15

(Litho German Bank Note Ptg Co, Leipzig)

1966 (2 Mar). *Peasants' Day.* P 13½ × 13.
191　**43**　15p. multicoloured . . . . . . 25　15

(O **44**) 15 mm　(O **45**) 12 mm　(O **46**) 14½ mm

1966. *OFFICIAL. Nos.* 174/6 *optd locally with Type* O **44**, *and No.* 179 *optd with Type* O **45**.
O192　**40**　1p. brownish black . . . . . 3·50　85
O193　–　2p. carmine . . . . 3·50　85
O194　–　3p. turquoise-green . . . . . 3·50　85
O195　–　15p. yellow-olive . . . . 3·50　85
　　　　a. Opt inverted
　　　　b. Opt double
O192/195 *Set of* 4 . . . . 12·50　3·00

1966. *OFFICIAL. Nos.* 174/7 *and* 179/85 *optd with Type* O **46**, *by Govt Ptg Wks, Tokyo.*
O196　**40**　1p. brownish black . . . . . 15　15
O197　–　2p. carmine . . . . 25　25
O198　–　3p. turquoise-green . . . . . 25　25
O199　–　5p. royal blue . . . . 35　25
O200　–　15p. yellow-olive . . . . 35　25
O201　–　20p. brown and rose-red . . . 70　60
O202　–　25p. reddish brown & olive-yellow
　　　　　　(R.) . . . . 80　70
O203　–　50p. grey-blue and red . . . . 1·40　85
O204　–　1k. dp blue, yell & brownish grey
　　　　　　(R.) . . . . 4·00　1·10
O205　–　2k. dp blue, lt yellow-ol & rosine
　　　　　　(R.) . . . . 5·25　1·90
O206　–　5k. multicoloured (R.) . . . . 15·00　13·00
O196/206 *Set of* 11 . . . . 26·00　18·00
The 2k. was sold for normal postage use from 1990.

44 Cogwheel and Hammer　**45** Aung San and Agricultural Cultivation

(Litho German Bank Note Ptg Co, Leipzig)

1967 (1 May). *May Day.* P 13½ × 13.
192　**44**　15p. yellow, black and greenish
　　　　　　blue . . . . 25　15

(Litho German Bank Note Ptg Co, Leipzig)

1968 (4 Jan). *20th Anniv of independence.* P 13½.
193　**45**　15p. multicoloured . . . . 25　15

46 Burma Pearls   **47** Spike of Paddy

(Litho German Bank Note Ptg Co, Leipzig)

1968 (4 Mar). *Burmese Gems, Jades and Pearls Emporium, Rangoon.* P 13½.

194	**46**	15p. ultram, new blue & pale yellow	. . . .	45	15

(Photo German Bank Note Ptg Co, Leipzig)

1968 (1 July). *Burmese Birds (2nd series). Designs and colours as Nos. 174/85 but formats, sizes and printers changed.* P 14.

195	1p. brownish black	. . . .	25	25
196	2p. rose-red	. . . .	25	25
197	3p. turquoise-green	. . . .	35	35
198	5p. violet-blue	. . . .	35	35
199	10p. orange-brown	. . . .	45	45
200	15p. yellow-olive	. . . .	50	50
201	20p. brown and rose-red	. . . . .	50	50
202	25p. reddish brown and greenish yellow	. . . .	60	50
203	50p. slate-blue and red	. . . . .	1·30	1·00
	a. Slate-blue (shading on bird and inscriptions) omitted			
204	1k. deep blue, yellow and brownish grey	. . . .	11·50	1·00
205	2k. deep blue, light yellow-olive & rosine	. . . .	8·75	2·50
206	5k. multicoloured	. . . .	19·00	10·50
195/206 *Set of 12*		. . . . . .	40·00	16·00

New sizes: *Horiz* (21 × 17 *mm*)—1, 2, 3p.; (39 × 21 *mm*)—20p., 2k. *Vert* (23 × 28 *mm*)—5, 10, 15p.; (21 × 39 *mm*)—25, 50p., 1k., 5k.

1968 (1 July). OFFICIAL. *Nos. 195/8 and 200/6 optd as Type O* **46**, *but 13 mm long (1, 2, 3p.), 15 mm long (5, 15p.) or 14 mm long (others), by German Bank Note Ptg Co, Leipzig).*

O207	1p. brownish black	. . . .	15	15
O208	2p. rose-red	. . . .	15	15
O209	3p. turquoise-green	. . . . . .	15	15
O210	5p. violet-blue	. . . .	25	15
O211	15p. yellow-olive	. . . . . .	25	15
O212	20p. brown and rose-red	. . . .	25	15
O213	25p. reddish brown & greenish yell (R.)	. . . .	45	15
O214	50p. slate-blue and red	. . . .	85	45
O215	1k. deep blue, yellow and grey (R.)	. .	1·30	1·10
O216	2k. dp blue, lt yellow-olive & rosine (R.)	. . . . . .	2·75	2·30
O217	5k. multicoloured (R.)	. . . . .	6·50	5·75
O207/217 *Set of 11*		. . . . .	12·00	9·50

Nos. O213/14 and O216/17 were sold for normal postage use from 1990.

(Litho Pakistan Security Ptg Co Ltd)

1969 (2 Mar). *Peasants' Day.* P 13.

218	**47**	15p. greenish yellow, blue & lt emerald	. . . .	25	10

48 I.L.O. Emblem   **49** Football

(Photo Pakistan Security Ptg Corp Ltd)

1969 (29 Oct). *50th Anniv of International Labour Organization.* P 13.

219	**48**	15p. gold and bluish green	. . . .	15	15
220		50p. gold and carmine	. . . . .	45	25

(Litho German Bank Note Ptg Co, Leipzig)

1969 (1 Dec). *Fifth South East Asian Peninsular Games, Rangoon.* T **49** *and similar designs.* P 13 × 12½ (25p.) or 12½ × 13 (others).

221	15p. multicoloured	. . . . . .	15	15
222	25p. multicoloured	. . . . . .	25	15
223	50p. multicoloured	. . . . . .	50	15
224	1k. black, apple-green & greenish blue	. . . .	1·30	50
221/224 *Set of 4*		. . . . .	2·00	85

Designs: *Horiz*—25p. Running. *Vert*—50p. Weightlifting; 1k. Volleyball.

50 Marchers with Independence, Resistance and Union Flags

(Litho Pakistan Security Ptg Corp Ltd)

1970 (27 Mar). *25th Anniv of Burmese Armed Forces.* P 13.

225	**50**	15p. multicoloured	. . . . . .	25	15

51 "Peace and Progress"

(Des Ba Moe. Photo Govt Ptg Wks, Tokyo)

1970 (26 June). *25th Anniv of United Nations.* P 13.

226	**51**	15p. multicoloured	. . . . . .	25	10

52 Boycott Declaration and Marchers

(Des Myint Thein (50p.), Ba Lon Gale (others). Litho German Bank Note Ptg Co, Leipzig)

1970 (23 Nov). *National Day and 50th Anniv of University Boycott. T* **52** *and similar horiz designs. Multicoloured.* P 13.
227	15p. Type **52**		15	10
228	25p. Students on Boycott march		15	10
229	50p. Banner and demonstrators		45	25

53 Burmese Workers   **54** Child drinking Milk

(Des Ba Moe (5, 50p.), San Toe (15, 25p.). Litho Bradbury,Wilkinson)

1971 (28 June). *First Burmese Socialist Programme Party Congress. T* **53** *and similar horiz designs. Multicoloured.* P 13½.
230	5p. Type **53**		15	10
231	15p. Burmese races and flags		15	10
232	25p. Hands holding scroll		25	15
233	50p. Party flag		50	35
230/233	*Set of 4*		95	65
MS234	179 × 127 mm. Nos. 230/3. *Imperf*		11·50	11·50

(Des Thin Thin Aye. Litho Harrison)

1971 (11 Dec). *25th Anniv of United Nations Children's Fund. T* **54** *and similar square design. Multicoloured.* P 14½.
235	15p. Type **54**		25	10
236	50p. Marionettes		60	45

55 Aung San and Independence Monument, Panglong

(Litho Bradbury, Wilkinson)

1972 (12 Feb). *25th Anniv of Independence. T* **55** *and similar multicoloured designs.* P 14.
237	15p. Type **55**		15	10
238	50p. Aung San and Burmese in national costumes		25	15
239	1k. Flag and map (*vert*)		60	35

56 Burmese and Stars   **57** Human Heart

(Des Sai Yee Leik. Litho Harrison)

1972 (2 Mar). *10th Anniv of Revolutionary Council.* P 14.
240	**56**	15p. multicoloured	15	10

(Des U Ba Thit. Litho Harrison)

1972 (7 Apr). *World Health Day.* P 14 × 14½.
241	**57**	15p. carmine, black & greenish yellow	15	15

58 Ethnic Groups   **59** Casting Vote

(Des Min Naing. Litho Harrison)

1973 (12 Feb). *National Census.* P 14.
242	**58**	15p. multicoloured	25	15

(Litho Govt Security Ptg Wks, Wazi)

1973 (15 Dec). *National Constitutional Referendum. T* **59** *and similar multicoloured designs.* P 14½ × 14 (15p.) or 14 × 14½ (others).
243	5p. Type **59**		15	10
244	10p. Voters supporting map		15	10
245	15p. Burmese with ballot papers (*vert*)		15	15

SOCIALIST REPUBLIC OF THE UNION OF BURMA

Following a referendum in December 1973 and elections in January and February 1974, the military revolutionary council, which had been in power since 1962, was replaced and Burma became a one-party socialist republic on 2 March 1974.

PRINTER. From No 246 all stamps were printed at the Government Security Printing Works, Wazi, *unless otherwise stated.*

60 Open-air Meeting   **61** U.P.U. Emblem and Carrier Pigeon

1974 (2 Mar). *Opening of First Pyithu Hluttaw (People's Assembly). T* **60** *and similar horiz designs. Multicoloured. Photo.* P 13½.
246	15p. Burmese flags, 1752–1974 (80 × 26 mm)		15	15
247	50p. Type **60**		45	25
	a. Black (face value etc) omitted			
248	1k. Burmese badge		85	60

1974 (15 May). *Centenary of Universal Postal Union. T* **61** *and similar multicoloured designs. Photo.* P 13 × 13½ (horiz) or 13½ × 13 (vert).
249	15p. Type **61**		15	15
250	20p. Woman reading letter (*vert*)		25	15
251	50p. U.P.U. emblem on "stamps" (*vert*)		50	25
252	1k. Stylized doll (*vert*)		85	45
253	2k. Postman delivering letter to family		2·10	85
249/253	*Set of 5*		3·50	1·60

62 Kachin Couple   **63** Bamar Couple

1974 (1 Oct)–**78**. *T* **62**/**3** *and similar designs showing costumes.*
  Photo. P 13½.
254	1p. deep magenta	10	10
255	3p. agate and pale mauve	10	10
256	5p. bluish violet and mauve	10	10
257	10p. dp turquoise-blue (17 × 26 *mm*) (1978)	15	10
	a. Size 16½ × 25 mm	15	10
258	15p. deep olive and turquoise-green	10	10
	a. Yellow-green and pale green (1.11.74)	10	10
259	20p. black, brown-ochre & pale bl (1.11.74)	15	10
260	50p. violet, orge-brn & brn-ochre (1.11.74)	45	25
261	1k. reddish violet, mag & blk (1.11.74)	1·30	70
262	5k. multicoloured (1.11.74)	4·25	2·50
254/262 *Set of 9*		6·00	3·50

Designs: As *T* **62**—3p. Kayah girl; 5p. Kayin couple and bronze drum; 10p. Type **62**; 15p. Chin couple. As *T* **53**—50p. Mon woman; 1k. Rakhine woman; 5k. Musician.
  See also Nos. 309/11 and 313/16.

64 Woman on Globe and I.W.Y. Emblem   **65** Burmese and Flag

1975 (15 Dec). *International Women's Year. T* **64** *and similar design. Photo.* P 13.
263	50p. black and pale blue-green	35	25
264	2k. black and new blue	1·50	1·10

Design: *Vert*—2k. Globe on flower and I.W.Y. emblem.

1976 (3 Jan). *Constitution Day. T* **65** *and similar horiz designs. Photo.* P 14.
265	20p. black and new blue	15	15
266	50p. olive-sepia and pale blue	35	25
267	1k. multicoloured	1·00	60

Designs: As *T* **65**—50p. Burmese with banners and flag. 57 × 21 *mm*—1k. Map of Burma, Burmese and flag.

66 Emblem and Burmese learning Alphabet   **67** Early Train and Ox cart

1976 (8 Sept). *International Literacy Year. T* **66** *and similar designs Photo.* P 14.
268	10p. blackish brown and vermilion	10	10
269	15p. dp turquoise-grn, brt apple grn & blk	10	10
270	50p. blue, yellow-orange and black	45	25
271	1k. multicoloured	85	60
268/271 *Set of 4*		1·30	95

Designs: *Horiz*—15p. Abacus and open books; 50p. Emblem. *Vert*—1k. Emblem, open book and globe.

1977 (1 May). *Railway Centenary. T* **67** *and similar designs. Photo.* P 13½.
272	15p. emerald, black and cerise	4·00	1·00
273	20p. multicoloured	1·10	35
274	25p. multicoloured	1·70	45

275	50p. multicoloured	2·40	80
276	1k. multicoloured	5·25	1·60
272/276 *Set of 5*		13·00	3·75

Designs: 26 × 17 *mm*—15p. Early steam locomotive. As *T* **67**: *Horiz*—25p. Train approaching railway station; 50p. Railway bridge. *Vert*—1k. Diesel train emerging from tunnel.

68 Karaweik Hall   **69** Jade Naga and Gem

1978 (10 Aug). *T* **68** *and similar horiz design. Photo.* P 13½.
277	50p. light brown	50	35
278	1k. multicoloured	85	60

Design: 79½ × 25 *mm*—1k. Side view of Karaweik Hall.

1979 (1 Jan). *16th Gem Emporium. T* **69** *and similar designs. Photo.* P 14 (1k.) or 13½ (others).
279	15p. light green and deep turquoise-green	15	10
280	20p. new blue, yellow and magenta	35	15
281	50p. blue, ochre and blue-green	70	45
282	1k. multicoloured	1·40	80
279/282 *Set of 4*		2·30	1·75

Designs: As *T* **69**—20p. Hintha (legendary bird) holding pearl in beak; 50p. Hand holding pearl and amethyst pendant 55 × 20 *mm*—1k. Gold jewel-studded dragon.

70 "Intelsat IV" Satellite over Burma   **71** I.Y.C. Emblem on Map of Burma

1979 (12 Feb). *Introduction of Satellite Communications System. Photo.* P 13½.
283	**70**	25p. multicoloured	25	15

1979 (1 Dec). *International Year of the Child. Photo.* P 13½.
284	**71**	25p. yellow-orange and new blue	50	25
285		50p. vermilion and reddish violet	1·00	45

72 Weather Balloon   **73** Weightlifting

1980 (23 Mar). *World Meteorological Day. T* **72** *and similar vert design. Photo.* P 13½.

286	25p. new blue, bistre-yellow and black	35	15
287	50p. deep blue-green, black and rosine	50	45

Design:—50p. Meteorological satellite and W.M.O. emblem.

1980 (21 July). *Olympic Games, Moscow. T* **73** *and similar horiz designs. Litho.* P 14.

288	20p. bright blue-green, bright orge & blk	15	10
289	50p. black, bright orange and vermilion	50	25
290	1k. black, bright orange and bright blue	1·00	60

Designs:—50p. Boxing; 1k. Football.

74 I.T.U. and W.H.O. Emblems with Ribbons forming Caduceus

1981 (17 May). *World Telecommunications Day. Photo.* P 13½.

291	**74** 25p. bright orange and black	25	15

75 Livestock and Vegetables

1981 (16 Oct). *World Food Day. T* **75** *and similar horiz designs. Multicoloured. Photo.* P 13½.

292	25p. Type **75**	45	15
293	50p. Farm produce and farmer holding wheat	60	25
294	1k. Globe and stylized bird	85	50

76 Athletes and Person in Wheelchair

1981 (12 Dec). *International Year of Disabled Persons. Photo.* P 13½.

295	**76** 25p. multicoloured	25	25

77 Telephone, Satellite and Antenna   **78** Fish and Globe

1983 (15 Sept). *World Communications Year. Litho.* P 14½ × 14.

296	**77**	15p. new blue and black	15	10
297		25p. mauve and black	25	15
298		50p. emerald, black and crimson	50	35
299		1k. cinnamon, black and emerald	1·40	80
296/299 *Set of* 4			2·10	1·25

1983 (16 Oct). *World Food Day. Litho.* P 14 × 14½.

300	**78**	15p. yellow, new blue and black	15	10
301		25p. yellow-orange, bright green & black	25	15
302		50p. blue-green, orange-yellow & black	70	70
303		1k. brt blue, greenish yellow & black	2·10	1·60
300/303 *Set of* 4			3·00	2·30

79 Globe and Log   **80** Potted Plant

1984 (16 Oct). *World Food Day. Litho.* P 14½ × 14.

304	**79**	15p. brt new blue, orange-yellow & blk	10	10
305		25p. bright violet, lemon and black	15	15
306		50p. blue-green, carmine-rose and black	50	45
307		1k. mauve, green-yellow and black	1·30	1·00
304/307 *Set of* 4			1·80	1·50

1985 (15 Oct). *International Youth Year. Litho.* P 14 × 14½.

308	**80**	15p. multicoloured	25	15

REPUBLIC OF THE UNION OF BURMA

1989 (12 June)–**95**. *As Nos. 258 and 260/1 but inscr* "UNION OF BURMA". P 13½.

309	15p. deep yellow-green and dull yellowish green (26.6.89)	25	15
309a	20p. black, brown-ochre and pale blue (7.95)	£100	
310	50p. deep violet and brown-ochre	60	35
311	1k. reddish violet, magenta & blk (6.9.89)	95	70

Examples of No. 309a, which have been prepared several years earlier but not issued, were inadvertently supplied to Shan State post office in July 1995. Subsequently a limited quantity were sold to philatelists in Yangon.

MYANMAR

Myanmar is the Burmese name for their land. On 18 June 1989 this became the official name in "Western" script, with the spelling of the capital Rangoon changed to Yangon.

81 Fountain, National Assembly Park

1990 (27 May). *State Law and Order Restoration Council. Litho.*
P 14½ × 14.
312 **81** 1k. multicoloured . . . . 1·10 70

1990 (30 July).–**91**. *As Nos. 258/9 and 260/1 but inscr* "UNION
OF MYANMAR". P 13½.
313 15p. dp yellow-green & dull yellowish
grn 15 15
314 20p. black, brn-ochre & greenish bl
(1991) 20 15
315 50p. deep violet and brown-ochre
(13.8.90) 50 25
316 1k. reddish violet, magenta & blk
(11.90) . . . . 1·00 70

There is considerable variation in the background shade to
No. 315.
Nos. 317/21 are vacant.

82 Map and Emblem

83 Nawata Ruby

1990 (20 Dec). *40th Anniv of United Nations Development
Programme. Litho.* P 14 × 14½.
322 **82** 2k. new blue, chrome yellow and
black . . . . 2·20 1·40

(Des Kyaw Kyaw Win. Litho)
1991 (26 Jan). *Gene Emporium.* P 14 × 14½.
323 **83** 50p. multicoloured . . . . 1·00 70

84 "Grandfather giving
Sword to Grandson"
(statuette, Nan Win)

85 Emblem

1992 (4 Jan). *44th Anniv of Independence. T* **84** *and similar vert
design. Multicoloured. Litho.* P 14 × 14½.
324 50p. Warrior defending personification of
Myanmar and map (poster, Khin
Thein) 50 45
325 2k. Type **84** . . . . 2·30 1·70

1992 (10 Apr). *National Sports Festival. Litho.* P 14 × 14½.
326 **85** 50p. multicoloured 60 45

86 Campaign Emblem

87 Fish, Water Droplet
and Leaf

(Des National AIDS Committee. Litho)
1992 (1 Dec). *Anti-AIDS Campaign.* P 14 × 14½.
327 **86** 50p. rosine 50 45

(Des Maung Zaw Hein. Litho)
1992 (5 Dec). *International Nutrition Conference, Rome.*
P 14 × 14½.
328 **87** 50p. multicoloured 35 15
329 1k. multicoloured 60 45
330 3k. multicoloured . . . . 1·70 1·30
331 5k. multicoloured . . . . 3·00 2·20
328/331 *Set of 4* . . . . 5·00 3·50

88 Statue

89 Hintha (legendary
bird)

1993 (1 Jan). *National Convention for Drafting of New
Constitution. Litho.* P 14 × 14½.
332 **88** 50p. multicoloured 25 15
333 3k. multicoloured . . . . 1·70 1·30

1993 (1 Sept). *Statuettes. T* **89** *and similar vert design.
Multicoloured. Litho.* P 14½ × 14.
334 5k. Type **89** . . . . 2·75 2·30
a. Black double . . . .
335 10k. Lawkanat . . . . 5·75 4·75
There is considerable variation in the background shade to
No. 335.

90 Horseman aiming Spear at
target

91 Tree, Globe and
Figures

(Des Zaw Win. Litho)

1993 (23 Oct). *Festival of Traditional Equestrian Sports, Sittwe.*
P 14½ × 14.
336 **90** 3k. multicoloured . . . . 1·70 1·30

(Des Myint Than. Litho)

1994 (5 June). *World Environment Day.* P 14 × 14½.
337 **91** 4k. multicoloured . . . . 2·30 1·70

92 Association Emblem

1994 (15 Sept). *First Anniv of Union Solidarity and Development
Association. Litho.* P 14 × 14½.
338 **92** 3k. multicoloured . . . . 1·50 1·10

93 City and Emblem

1995 (27 Mar). *50th Anniv of Armed Forces Day. Litho.*
P 14½ × 14.
339 **93** 50p. multicoloured 45 45

94 Cross through   **95** Camera and Film
Poppy Head

1995 (26 June). *International Day against Drug Abuse. Litho.*
P 14 × 14½.
340 **94** 2k. multicoloured . . . . 1·60 1·20

1995 (17 Oct). *60th Anniv of Myanmar Film Industry. Litho.*
P 14 × 14½.
341 **95** 50p. multicoloured 45 45

96 Figures around   **97** Convocation Hall
Emblem

1995 (24 Oct). *50th Anniv of United Nations Organization. Litho.*
P 14 × 14½.
342 **96** 4k. multicoloured . . . . 3·00 3·00

1995 (1 Nov). *60th Anniv of Yangon University.* P 14 × 14½.
343 **97** 50p. multicoloured 45 45
344 2k. multicoloured . . . . 1·50 1·50

98 Punt   **99** Four-man Canoe

1996 (14 Mar). *Visit Myanmar Year.* T **98** *and similar horiz
designs. Multicoloured.* P 14½ × 14.
345 50p. Type **98** 35 35
346 4k. Karaweik Hall . . . . 2·75 2·75
347 5k. Mandalay Palace . . . . 3·50 3·50

1996 (7 Oct). *International Letter Writing Week. "Unity equals
Success".* T **99** *and similar multicoloured design. Litho.*
P 14½ × 14 (2k.) or 14 × 14½ (5k.).
348 2k. Type **99** . . . . 1·40 1·40
349 5k. Human pyramid holding flag aloft
(*vert*) . . . . 3·50 3·50

100 Breastfeeding   **101** Emblem and Map
of Myanmar

1996 (11 Dec). *50th Anniv of United Nations Children's Fund.*
T **100** *and similar vert designs. Multicoloured. Litho.* P 14 × 14½.
350 **100** 1k. Type **100** 70 70
351 2k. Nurse inoculating child . . . . 1·40 1·40
352 4k. Children outside school . . . . 2·75 2·75

1997 (24 July). *30th Anniv of Association of South East Asian
Nations. Litho.* P 14 × 14½.
353 **101** 1k. multicoloured 85 85
354 2k. multicoloured . . . . 1·70 1·70

102 Throne **103** Xylophone

1998 (4 Jan). *50th Anniv of Independence. Litho.* P 14 × 14½.
355 **102** 2k. multicoloured . . . . 1·60 1·60

1998 (28 Aug)–**2000**. *Musical Instruments.* T **103** *and similar vert designs. Multicoloured. Photo.* P 13½.
356 5k. Type **103** . . . . 4·00 4·00
357 10k. Mon brass gongs (9.10.98) . . . . 7·75 7·75
358 20k. Rakhine auspicious drum
       (12.2.99) . . . . 13·00 13·00
359 30k. Myanmar harp (17.5.99) . . . . . 19·00 19·00
360 50k. Shan pot drum (15.11.99) . . . . . 31·00 31·00
361 100k. Kachin Brass Gong (5.2000) . . . . 44·00 44·00
Numbers have been left for additions to this series.

104 Emblem **105** Dove and U.P.U. Emblem

1999 (10 Jan). *Asian and Pacific Decade of Disabled Persons. Seventh Far East and South Pacific Region Disabled Games. Litho.* P 14 × 14½.
365 **104** 2k. multicoloured . . . . 1·70 1·70
366 5k. multicoloured . . . . 3·50 3·50

1999 (20 Dec). *125th Anniv of Universal Postal Union. Photo.* P 14 × 14½.
367 **105** 2k. multicoloured . . . . 1·50 1·50
368 5k. multicoloured . . . . 3·25 3·25

106 People linking **107** Weathervane
Hands around Map of
Myanmar

2000 (4 Jan). *52nd Anniv of Independence. Litho.* P 14 × 14½.
369 **106** 2k. multicoloured . . . . 1·50 1·50

2000 (23 Mar). *World Meteorological Day. 50th Anniv of World Meteorological Organization.* T **107** *and similar designs. Litho.* P 14 × 14½ (2k.) or 14½ × 14 (others).
370 2k. black and bright greenish blue . . . 1·70 1·70
       a. Black double . . . .
371 5k. multicoloured . . . . 4·00 4·00
372 10k. multicoloured . . . . 7·50 7·50
Designs: *Horiz*—5k. Emblem and globe; 10k. Emblem and symbols for rain and sunshine.

108 Royal Palace Gate, Burma and Great Wall of China (⅝-*size illustration*)

2000 (8 June). *50th Anniv of Burma–China Relations. Litho.* P 14½ × 14.
373 **108** 5k. multicoloured . . . . 4·00 4·00

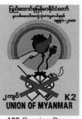

109 Burning Poppy **110** Television Set and
Heads and Needles Map of Myanmar

2000 (26 June). *Anti-Drugs Campaign. Litho.* P 14 × 14½.
374 **109** 2k. multicoloured . . . . 1·50 1·50

2001 (4 Jan). *53rd Anniv of Independence. Litho.* P 14 × 14½.
375 **110** 2k. multicoloured . . . . 1·50 1·50

111 National Flag and **112** Flag and Statue
Globe

2002 (4 Jan). *54th Anniv of Independence.* T **111** *and similar vert design. Multicoloured. Litho.* P 14 × 14½.
376 2k. Type **111** 50 50
377 30k. As No. 376 but inscriptions and face
       value in English . . . . 8·25 8·25

2003 (4 Jan). *55th Anniv of Independence.* T **112** *and similar vert design. Multicoloured. Litho.* P 14 × 14½.
378 2k. Type **112** 50 50
379 30k. As No. 378 but inscriptions and face
       value in English . . . . 8·25 8·25

113 Black Orchid

2004 (11 Feb). *Flora. T* **113** *and similar vert design. Multicoloured.*
Litho. P 14 × 14½.
380	30k. Type **113**	. . . .	5·25	5·25
381	30k. Mango	. . . .	5·25	5·25

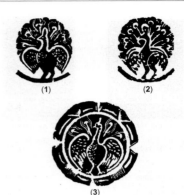

(1)   (2)

(3)

JAPANESE OCCUPATION OF BURMA

PRICES FOR STAMPS ON COVER

Nos.	J1/44	—
Nos.	J45/6	*from* × 6
Nos.	J47/56	*from* × 8
No.	J56*g*	—
Nos.	J57/72	*from* × 6
Nos.	J73/5	*from* × 25
No.	J76	*from* × 8
No.	J77	*from* × 20
Nos.	J78/81	*from* × 25
Nos.	J82/4	*from* × 10
Nos.	J85/7	*from* × 40
No.	J88	*from* × 12
Nos.	J89/97	*from* × 30
Nos.	J98/104	*from* × 50
Nos.	J105/111	*from* × 30

BURMA INDEPENDENCE ARMY ADMINISTRATION

The Burma Independence Army, formed by Aung San in 1941, took control of the Delta area of the Irrawaddy in May 1942. They reopened a postal service in the area and were authorised by the Japanese to overprint local stocks of stamps with the Burmese emblem of a peacock.

Postage and Official stamps with the peacock overprints or handstamps were used for ordinary postal purposes with the probable exception of No. J44.

DISTINGUISHING FEATURES. Type **1**. Body and head of Peacock always clearly outlined by broad uncoloured band. There are four slightly different sub-types of overprint Type **1**.

Type **2**. Peacock with slender neck and more delicately detailed tail. Clear spur on leg at right. Heavy fist-shaped blob of ink below and parallel to beak and neck.

Type **4**. No basic curve. Each feather separately outlined. Straight, short legs.

Type **5**. Much fine detail in wings and tail in clearly printed overprints. Thin, long legs ending in claws which, with the basic arc, enclose clear white spaces in well printed copies. Blob of colour below beak shows shaded detail and never has the heavy fist-like appearance of this portion in Type **2**.

Two sub-types may be distinguished in Type **5**, the basic arc of one having a chord of 14–15 mm and the other 12½–13 mm.

Type **6**. Similar to Type **5**, but with arc deeply curved and reaching nearly to the top of the wings. Single diagonal line parallel to neck below beak.

Collectors are warned against forgeries of these overprints, often in the wrong colours or on the wrong values.

1942 (May). *Stamps of Burma overprinted with the national device of a Peacock.*

I. Overprinted at Myaungmya.

A. With Type **1** *in black.*

On Postage Stamps of King George V.
J1		9p. deep green (No. 3)	. . . .	£110
J2		3½a. deep blue (No. 8)	. . . .	55·00

On Official Stamp of King George V.
J3		6a. bistre (No. O8)	. . . .	75·00

On Postage Stamps of King George VI.
J4	**2**	9p. yellow-green	. . . .	£150
J5	**3**	1a. purple-brown	. . . .	£550
J6		4a. greenish blue (opt black on red)	. .	£160
		a. Triple opt, black on double red	. .	£425

On Official Stamps of King George VI.
J7	**2**	3p. bright violet	. . . .	26·00	85·00
J8		6p. bright blue	. . . .	18·00	60·00
J9	**3**	1a. purple-brown	. . . .	18·00	50·00
J9*a*		1½a. turquoise-green	. . . . . .	£650	
J10		2a. carmine	. . . .	24·00	95·00
J11		4a. greenish blue	. . . .	24·00	75·00

The overprint on No. J6 was apparently first done in red in error, and then corrected in black. Some stamps have the black overprint so accurately superimposed that the red hardly shows. These are rare.

Nos. J5 and J9 exist with the Peacock overprint on both the typographed and the litho printings of the original stamps.

B. With Types **2** *or* **3** *(rupee values), in black.*

On Postage Stamps of King George VI.
J12	**2**	3p. bright violet	. . . .	18·00	70·00
J13		6p. bright blue	. . . .	50·00	£100
J14		9p. yellow-green	. . . .	21·00	65·00
J15	**3**	1a. purple-brown	. . . .	14·00	60·00
J16		2a. carmine	. . . .	21·00	80·00
J17		4a. greenish blue	. . . .	40·00	£100
		a. Opt double	. . . .	£650	
		b. Opt inverted	. . . .	£650	
		c. Opt double, one inverted	. . .	£425	
		d. Opt double, both inverted	. . .	£650	
J18		1r. purple and blue	. . . .	£275	
J19		2r. brown and purple	. . . . . .	£160	

The Myaungmya overprints (including No. J44) are usually clearly printed.

(4)   (5)   (6)

Type **5** generally shows the details of the peacock much less clearly and, due to heavy inking, or careless impression, sometimes appears as almost solid colour.

Type **6** was officially applied only to postal stationery. However, the handstamp remained in the possession of a postal official who used it on postage stamps after the war. These stamps are no longer listed.

II. Handstamped (at Pyapon?) with T **4**, in black (so-called experimental type).

On Postage Stamps of King George VI.

J19a	**2**	6p. bright blue		85·00	
J19b	**3**	1a. purple-brown		£100	£250
J20		2a. carmine		£130	£300
J21		4a. greenish blue		£700	£700

Unused specimens of Nos. J20/1 are usually in poor condition.

III. Overprinted at Henzada with T **5** in blue, or blue-black.

On Postage Stamps of King George V.

J22	3p. slate (No. 1)		3·50	20·00
	a. Opt double		10·00	50·00
J23	9p. deep green (No. 3)		24·00	65·00
	a. Opt double		80·00	
J24	2a. vermilion (No. 5)		£100	£180

On Postage Stamps of King George VI.

J25	**2**	1p. red-orange		£200	£300
J26		3p. bright violet		38·00	75·00
J27		6p. bright blue		25·00	50·00
		a. Opt double		£100	£150
		b. Clear opt, on back and front		£275	
J28		9p. yellow-green		£850	
J29	**3**	1a. purple-brown		9·00	40·00
		a. Opt inverted		£700	
J30		1½a. turquoise-green		21·00	65·00
		a. Opt omitted (in pair with normal)		£1900	
J31		2a. carmine		21·00	65·00
		a. Opt double		£700	
J32		4a. greenish blue		42·00	95·00
		a. Opt double		£250	
		b. Opt inverted		£1200	

On Official Stamps of King George VI.

J33	**2**	3p. bright violet		£130	£250
J34		6p. bright blue		£140	£250
J35	**3**	1½a. turquoise-green		£170	£300
J35a		2a. carmine		£350	£450
J36		4a. greenish blue		£1000	

(6a) ("Yon Thon" = "Office use")

V. Official Stamp of King George VI optd at Myaungmya with Type **6a** in black.

J44	**7**	8a. myrtle-green		90·00

No. J44 was probably for official use.

There are two types of T **6a**, one with base of peacock 8 mm long and the other with base about 5 mm long. The neck and other details also vary. The two types are found se-tenant in the sheet.

Stocks of the peacock types were withdrawn when the Japanese Directorate-General took control of the postal services in the Delta in August 1942.

7	8 Farmer

1942 (1 June). Impressed by hand. Thick yellowish paper. No gum. P 12 × 11.

J45	**7**	(1a.) red		38·00	65·00

This device was the personal seal of Yano Sitza, the Japanese official in charge of the Posts and Telegraphs department of the Japanese Army Administration. It was impressed on paper already perforated by a line machine. Some stamps show part of the papermaker's watermark, either "ABSORBO DUPLICATOR" or "ELEPHANT BRAND", each with an elephant.

Other impressions of this seal on different papers, and showing signs of wear, were not valid for postal purposes.

(Des T. Kato. Typo Rangoon Gazette Press)

1942 (15 June). Value in annas. Laid bâtonné paper. No gum. P 11 or 11 × 11½.

J46	**8**	1a. scarlet		17·00	17·00

Some stamps show part of the papermaker's watermark, either "ELEPHANT BRAND" or "TITAGHUR SUPERFINE", each with an elephant.

$\frac{1}{2}$**A.**   **1R.**

(9)   (10)

1942 (22 Sept). (a) Nos. 314/17, 320/2, 325, 327 and 396 of Japan surch as T **9/10**.

J47	**9**	½a.on 1s. chestnut (Rice harvesting)		28·00	35·00
		a. Surch inverted		£100	£100
		b. Surch double, one inverted		£150	
J48		½a.on 2s. bright scarlet (General Nogi)		35·00	38·00
		a. Surch inverted		90·00	95·00
		b. Surch double, one inverted		£150	
J49		¾a.on 3s. green (Power station)		60·00	65·00
		a. Surch inverted		£120	£120
		b. Surch double, one inverted		—	£160
J50		1a.on 5s. claret (Admiral Togo)		50·00	48·00
		a. Surch inverted		£170	£170
		b. Surch double, one inverted		£190	£190
		c. Surch omitted (in pair with normal)		—	£250
J51		3a.on 7s. green (Diamond Mts)		90·00	£100
		a. Surch inverted		£170	
J52		4a.on 4s. emerald (Togo)		48·00	50·00
		a. Surch inverted		£170	
J53		8a.on 8s. violet (Meiji Shrine)		£150	£150
		a. Surch inverted		£225	£225
		b. Surch double, one inverted		£350	
		c. Surch in red		£225	£250
		d. Red surch inverted		£350	
		e. Surch double (black and red)		£600	
J54	**10**	1r.on 10s. deep carmine (Yomei Gate)		19·00	25·00
		a. Surch inverted		80·00	90·00
		b. Surch double		80·00	£100
		c. Surch double (black and red)		£400	£400
		d. Surch omitted (in pair with normal)		£225	£225
		e. Surch omitted (in pair with inverted surch)		£325	

J55	2r.on 20s. ultramarine (Mt Fuji)	50·00	50·00
	a. Surch inverted	£110	£110
	b. Surch double, one inverted	£130	
	c. Surch omitted (in pair with normal black surch)	£160	£160
	d. Surch in red	50·00	50·00
	e. Red surch inverted	£110	£110
	f. Red surch double	£110	£110
	g. Surch omitted (in pair with normal red surch)	£200	£200
	ga. Surch omitted (in pair with double red surch)		
	h. Surch double (black and red)	£350	
J56 **9**	5r.on 30s. turquoise (Torii Shrine)	12·00	27·00
	a. Surch inverted	85·00	
	b. Surch double	£110	
	c. Surch double, one inverted	£150	
	d. Surch omitted (in pair with normal surch)	£190	£190
	e. Surch omitted (in pair with inverted black surch)	£275	
	f. Surch in red	26·00	32·00
	fa. Red surch inverted	90·00	90·00
	fb. J56a and J56fa se-tenant	£425	£425
	fc. Surch omitted (in pair with normal red surch)	£190	£190

(b) No. 386 of Japan commemorating the fall of Singapore similarly surch.

J56g **9**	4a.on 4+2s. green and red	£150	£160
	h. Surch omitted (in pair with normal)	£500	
	ha. Surch omitted (in pair with inverted surch)	£550	
	i. Surch inverted	£350	

(New Currency. 100 cents = 1 rupee)

15 C.   15 C.   15 C.
   (11)   (12)   (13)

1942 (15 Oct). *Previous issues, with "anna" surcharges obliterated, handstamped with new value in cents, as T* **11** *and* **12** *(No. J57 handstamped with new value only).*

(a) On No. J46.

J57	5c.on 1a. scarlet	14·00	18·00
	a. Surch omitted (in pair with normal)	£1200	

(b) On Nos. J47/53.

J58	1c.on ¼a. on 1s. chestnut	50·00	50·00
	a. "1c." omitted (in pair with normal)	£500	
	b. "¼a." inverted	£250	
J59	2c.on ½a. on 2s. bright scarlet	48·00	50·00
J60	3c.on ¾a. on 3s. green	50·00	50·00
	a. Surch in blue	£180	
J61	5c.on 1a. on 5s. claret	65·00	65·00
J62	10c.on 3a. on 7s. green	£110	£100
J63	15c.on 4a. on 4s. emerald	38·00	40·00
J64	20c.on 8a. on 8s. violet	£475	£425
	a. Surch on No. J53c (surch in red)	£275	£150

The "anna" surcharges were obliterated by any means available, in some cases by a bar or bars, and in others by the butt of a pencil dipped in ink. In the case of the fractional surcharges, the letter "A" and one figure of the fraction, were sometimes barred out, leaving the remainder of the fraction to represent the new value, e.g. the "1" of "½" deleted to create the 2c. surcharge or the "4" of "¾" to create the 3c. surcharge.

1942. *Nos. 314/17, 320/1 and 396 of Japan surcharged in cents only as T* **13**.

J65	1c.on 1s. chestnut (Rice harvesting)	24·00	20·00
	a. Surch inverted	£110	£110
J66	2c.on 2s. brt scarlet (General Nogi)	48·00	32·00

J67	3c.on 3s. green (Power station)	60·00	50·00
	a. Pair, with and without surch	—	£250
	b. Surch inverted	£120	
	c. Surch in blue	85·00	95·00
	d. Surch in blue inverted	£200	£225
J68	5c.on 5s. claret (Admiral Togo)	65·00	48·00
	a. Pair, with and without surch	£300	
	b. Surch in violet	£130	£150
	ba. Surch inverted	—	£225
J69	10c.on 7s. green (Diamond Mts)	80·00	60·00
J70	15c.on 4s. emerald (Togo)	18·00	21·00
	a. Surch inverted	£120	£130
	b. Pair, with and without surch	—	£225
J71	20c.on 8s. violet (Meiji Shrine)	£160	85·00
	a. Surch double	£300	

Nos. J67c and J68b were issued for use in the Shan States.

BURMESE GOVERNMENT

On 1 November 1942 the Japanese Army Administration handed over the control of the postal department to the Burmese Government. On 1 August 1943 Burma was declared by the Japanese to be independent.

    14 Burma State Crest   **15** Farmer

(Des U Tun Tin and Maung Tin from drawing by U Ba Than. Typo Rangoon)

1943 (15 Feb). *No gum.* P 11.

J72 **14**	5c. scarlet	19·00	23·00
	a. Imperf	20·00	23·00
	ab. Printed on both sides	85·00	

No. J72 was usually sold affixed to envelopes, particularly those with the embossed 1a. King George VI stamp, which it covered. Unused specimens off cover are not often seen and blocks are rare.

1943. *Typo. No gum.* P 11½.

J73 **15**	1c. orange (22 March)	3·00	4·50
	a. Brown-orange	2·25	4·75
J74	2c. yellow-green (24 March)	60	1·00
	a. "3" for "2" in face value (R. 2/10)	£170	
	b. Blue-green	9·50	
J75	3c. light blue (25 March)	3·00	1·00
	a. On laid paper	19·00	28·00
	b. Imperf between (horiz pair)	—	£275
J76	5c. carmine (small "c") (17 March)	18·00	12·00
J77	5c. carmine (large "C")	3·00	4·00
	a. Imperf (pair)	£110	
	b. "G" for "C" (R. 2/6)	£170	
J78	10c. grey-brown (25 March)	6·00	4·50
	a. Imperf (pair)	£110	
	b. Imperf between (horiz pair)	—	£275
J79	15c. magenta (26 March)	30	2·00
	a. Imperf between (vert strip of 3)	£110	
	b. On laid paper	6·00	18·00
	ba. Inverted "C" in value (R. 2/3)	£140	
J80	20c. grey-lilac (29 March)	30	1·00
J81	30c. deep blue-green (29 March)	30	1·25

The 1c., 2c. and 3c. have large "C" in value as illustrated. The 10c. and higher values have small "c". Nos. J73/81 had the face values inserted individually into the plate used for No. J46 with the original face value removed. There were a number of printings for each value, often showing differences such as missing stops, various founts of figures or "c", etc., in the value tablets.

The face value error, No. J74a, was later corrected.

Some sheets of No. J75a show a sheet watermark of Britannia seated within a crowned oval spread across fifteen stamps in each sheet. This paper was manufactured by T. Edmonds and the other half of the sheet carried the watermark inscription "FOOLSCAP LEDGER". No stamps have been reported showing letters from this inscription, but a block of 25 is known on laid paper showing a different sheet watermark "HERTFORDSHIRE LEDGER MADE IN ENGLAND". Examples showing parts of these sheet watermarks are rare.

No. J79a shows the horizontal perforations omitted between rows 3/4 and 4/5.

There are marked varieties of shade in this issue.

16 Soldier carving word "Independence"

17 Rejoicing Peasant

18 Boy with National Flag

Normal   Skyline flaw (R. 5/6)

(Des Maung Ba Thit (**16**), Naung Ohn Maung (**17**), and Maung Soi Yi (**18**). Typo State Press, Rangoon)

1943 (1 Aug). *Independence Day.*

(a) P 11.

J82	**16**	1c. orange		9·50	15·00
J83	**17**	3c. light blue		10·00	16·00
J84	**18**	5c. carmine		18·00	8·50
		a. Skyline flaw		80·00	
J82/4	*Set of 3*			35·00	35·00

(b) Rouletted.

J85	**16**	1c. orange		1·25	1·75
		b. Perf × roul		£100	£100
		c. Imperf (pair)		45·00	55·00
J86	**17**	3c. light blue		2·50	2·50
		b. Perf × roul		90·00	90·00
		c. Imperf (pair)		45·00	55·00
J87	**18**	5c. carmine		2·00	2·50
		a. Horiz roulette omitted (vert pair)			
		b. Perf × roul		60·00	60·00
		c. Imperf (pair)		45·00	55·00
		d. Skyline flaw		13·00	
J85/7	*Set of 3*			5·25	6·00

The stamps perf × rouletted may have one, two or three sides perforated.

The rouletted stamps often appear to be roughly perforated owing to failure to make clean cuts. These apparent perforations are very small and quite unlike the large, clean holes of the stamps perforated 11.

A few imperforate sets, mounted on a special card folder and cancelled with the commemorative postmark were presented to officials. These are rare.

19 Burmese Woman   **20** Elephant carrying Log   **21** Watch Tower, Mandalay

(Litho G. Kolff & Co, Batavia)

1943 (1 Oct). P 12½.

J88	**19**	1c. red-orange		20·00	15·00
J89		2c. yellow-green		50	2·00
J90		3c. deep violet		50	2·25
		a. Bright violet		1·75	3·75
J91	**20**	5c. carmine		65	60
J92		10c. blue		1·75	1·10
J93		15c. red-orange		1·00	3·00
J94		20c. yellow-green		1·00	1·75
J95		30c. olive-brown		1·00	2·00
J96	**21**	1r. red-orange		30	2·00
J97		2r. bright violet		30	2·25
J88/97	*Set of 10*			25·00	29·00

22 Bullock Cart   **23** Shan Woman   ၆မာနိုင်ငံတော်

၂၀ ဆင့်။

(**24** "Burma State" and value)

(Litho G. Kolff & Co, Batavia)

1943 (1 Oct). *Issue for Shan States.* P 12½.

J98	**22**	1c. olive-brown		28·00	35·00
J99		2c. yellow-green		28·00	35·00
J100		3c. bright violet		4·00	10·00
J101		5c. ultramarine		2·00	5·50
J102	**23**	10c. blue		14·00	17·00
J103		20c. carmine		30·00	17·00
J104		30c. olive-brown		19·00	48·00
J98/104	*Set of 7*			£110	£150

The Shan States, except for the frontier area around Keng Tung which was ceded to Thailand on 20 August 1943, were placed under the administration of the Burmese Government on 24 December 1943, and these stamps were later overprinted as T **24** for use throughout Burma.

1944 (1 Nov). *Optd as T* **24** *(the lower characters differ for each value).*

J105	**22**	1c. olive-brown		3·50	6·00
J106		2c. yellow-green		50	2·75
		a. Opt inverted		£400	£650
J107		3c. bright violet		2·25	7·00
J108		5c. ultramarine		1·00	1·50
J109	**23**	10c. blue		3·25	2·00
J110		20c. carmine		50	1·50
J111		30c. olive-brown		50	1·75
J105/11	*Set of 7*			10·00	20·00

Nepal

1881. 16 Annas = 1 Rupee
1907. 64 Pice = 1 Rupee
1954. 100 Paisa = 1 Rupee

In 1768 Prithvi Narayan Shah, King of the small kingdom of Gurkha in the Himalayas, conquered three other small neighbouring kingdoms and made Kathmandu his capital. He was the descendent of Rajput princes who had been driven from Udaipur by Moslem invaders, and he was the founder of the kingdom of Nepal, which was expanded by his successors. Gurkha raids into British India led to war in 1814–16, in which both sides showed a gallantry and chivalry which led to lasting respect between British and Gurkhas. The office of Prime Minister was made hereditary in the Rana family in 1846, with power greater than that of the king. During the Indian Mutiny, Jung Bahadur, then Prime Minister, sent troops to fight against the rebels, and Gurkha regiments have since formed part of the British army. In a treaty of friendship made in December 1923 the United Kingdom recognised the complete independence of Nepal. In 1951 King Tribhuvana took control as a constitutional monarch and the hereditary rule of the Rana family ended.

COLOURS. Owing to the primitive method of production, numerous shades exist of most values up to No. 63. Our colour descriptions have therefore been simplified, and where we have felt that we must list more than one colour for any value our descriptions are intended to cover groups of shades.

King Surendra
1847–17 May 1881

1 (1a.) Crown and Kukris   **2** (½a.) Bow and Arrow and Kukris

(T **1/2** typo Chhapakhana Press, Thapathali, Kathmandu)

1881 (Apr/May–June). *White wove paper.*

(a) White or brown gum. Pin-perf.

1	1	1a. blue		£225	£325
2		2a. purple		£250	£375
		a. Tête-bêche (pair)			
3		4a. yellow-green		£300	£550

(b) No gum. Imperf (from June).

4	1	1a. blue		£150	£140
5		2a. purple		£150	£150
		a. Tête-bêche			
6		4a. yellow-green		£225	£375

King Prithvi
17 May 1881–11 December 1911

1886–89. *Native paper of good quality. No gum. Imperf.*

(a) Early printings (during 1886 to 1889) on thin to medium paper. Very clear impressions.

7	1	1a. blue		90·00	£110
		a. Tête-bêche (pair)		£375	£450
8		2a. violet		75·00	90·00
		a. Tête-bêche (pair)		£375	£475
9		4a. green		90·00	£130
		a. Tête-bêche (pair)		£550	£650

The 2a. is also known in blue, including tête-bêche pairs.

(b) Later printings (during 1889 to 1898) on medium to thick paper. Slightly blurred impressions.

10	1	1a. blue		15·00	22·00
		a. Tête-bêche (pair)		37·00	44·00
11		2a. violet		26·00	22·00
		a. Tête-bêche (pair)		75·00	75·00
12		4a. green		30·00	37·00
		a. Tête-bêche (pair)		£180	£160

1898–99. *Thin, native paper of poor quality. Blurred impressions. Central design and outer frame of 1a. almost solid with colour. No gum.*

(a) Imperf (during 1898 to 1907)

13	1	1a. blue		37·00	37·00
		a. Tête-bêche (pair)		90·00	
14		1a. grey-green (*from* 1899)		48·00	48·00
		a. Tête-bêche (pair)		£180	
15		2a. violet		44·00	44·00
		a. Tête-bêche		£130	£130
16		2a. grey-lilac		37·00	37·00
		a. Tête-bêche (pair)		90·00	90·00
		b. Lavender		37·00	37·00
		ba. Tête-bêche (pair)		90·00	90·00
		c. Rose-lilac		37·00	37·00
		ca. Tête-bêche (pair)		37·00	37·00
17		4a. green		44·00	44·00
		a. Tête-bêche (pair)		90·00	£100

(b) Pin-perf (during 1898 to 1903).

18	1	1a. blue		44·00	44·00
		a. Tête-bêche (pair)		80·00	
19		1a. grey-green (*from* 1899)		60·00	60·00
		a. Tête-bêche (pair)		£190	
20		2a. violet		55·00	55·00
		a. Tête-bêche (pair)		£160	£160
		b. Lavender		60·00	
		ba. Tête-bêche (pair)		£100	
21		4a. green		33·00	44·00
		a. Tête-bêche (pair)		£190	£200

Due to very primitive printing methods, the number of inverted clichés in the plates increased and the quality of the printings and papers deteriorated constantly. However, isolated attempts were made to improve the plates: the 2a. plate was cleaned (resulting in some clear impressions in violet), its damaged clichés taken out and inverted clichés temporarily eliminated; two positions in the 1a. plate (24 and 64) were cleaned and completely recut.
See also Nos. 34/41.

1899–1900. *No gum.*

(a) Clear impression. Imperf (during 1899 to 1907).

22	2	½a. black		44·00	
		a. Tête-bêche (pair)		75·00	

(b) Pin-perf (during 1900 to 1903).

23	2	½a. black		18·00	11·00
		a. Tête-bêche (pair)		£110	41·00

See also Nos. 34/5.

I. Original frame

II. Recut frame with fewer lines (1a. only)

1901–17. T **1** recut with fewer lines in frame (II). No gum.

(a) White wove paper. (i) Imperf

24	**1**	1a. blue		£550	£600
		a. Tête-bêche (pair)			

(ii) Pin-perf (1902).

25	**1**	1a. blue		£375	£375
		a. Tête-bêche (pair)			

(b) Native paper. (i) Imperf.

26	**1**	1a. blue		11·00	8·00
		a. Tête-bêche (pair)		38·00	26·00
		b. Error. Blue-green (1917)		—	£200
		ba. Tête-bêche (pair)		—	£450
27		1a. ultramarine		18·00	18·00
		a. Tête-bêche (pair)		46·00	46·00

(ii) Pin-perf.

28	**1**	1a. blue		19·00
		a. Tête-bêche (pair)		49·00
29		1a. ultramarine		42·00
		a. Tête-bêche (pair)		95·00

New printings were made on native paper, imperf, from 1917 but these are difficult to distinguish separately. However, the later printings were mainly used on telegraph forms and copies with crescent-shaped telegraph cancellations are worth less than the used prices quoted for Nos. 26/a.

Nos. 26b/ba come from the later printings and prices quoted are for telegraphically cancelled stamps. For 1a. bright green, resulting from a wrong cliché in the 4a. plate, see No. 41b.

New Currency

3 Siva Mahadeva   A   B   C   **4**
(2 pice)

(Recess Perkins, Bacon & Co)

1907 (16 Oct). White wove paper. Date B.S. 1964 (= 1907/08) in lower corners. Right corner as Type A. P 13½–14.

30	**3**	2p. brown		5·50	1·50
31		4p. green		6·00	1·50
32		8p. carmine		7·50	1·50
33		16p. purple		15·00	3·75
30/33	*Set of 4*			30·00	7·50

Some stamps contain portions of the sheet watermark "SPECIAL POSTAGE / LONDON".

King Tribhuvana
11 December 1911–13 March 1955

1917–30. New printings on thin to medium native paper. Blurred impressions. No gum. Imperf.

34	**2**	2a. black		2·75	1·80
		a. Tête-bêche (pair)		7·25	4·00
35		½a. red-orange		£375	£190
		a. Tête-bêche (pair)			
36	**1**	2a. red			13·50
		a. Tête-bêche (pair)		—	32·00
37		2a. lilac			5·25
		a. Tête-bêche (pair)		—	19·00
38		2a. purple			12·50
		a. Tête-bêche (pair)		—	30·00
39		2a. maroon			8·75
		a. Tête-bêche (pair)		—	17·00
40		2a. brown (1929)		11·00	4·50
		a. Tête-bêche (pair)		16·00	10·50
41		4a. green		7·50	7·50
		a. Tête-bêche (pair)		£190	£190
		b. Error. **1** a. green (II) (1930)		£300	£300

There is a particularly wide range of shades in the 2a. We list the main colour groupings.

No. 41 can be distinguished from No. 17 by its very heavy, blurred, impression, with design details rarely visible.

No. 41b is the result of one inverted cliché of the **1** a. (recut frame) being included in the 4a. plate (position 8). For **1** a. printed in blue-green, from sheets printed in the wrong colour, see No. 26b.

Nos. 34/42 were issued imperforate only, trial pin-perforations were found among remainders and unissued stock. Pin-perforations on stamps with telegraphic cancellations are spurious.

These 1917–30 printings were used chiefly on telegraph forms with large cresent-shaped cancellations (at the rate of 1 anna = 1 pice). Our used prices are for such telegraphic cancellations.

1928. T **1** redrawn as T **4**. No gum. Imperf.

42	**4**	1a. deep blue		6·75	2·00
		a. Ultramarine		6·75	2·75

See last two paragraphs under No. 41.

(Recess Perkins, Bacon & Co.)

1930 (Aug–Dec). T **3** redrawn. Date B.S.1986 (= 1929/30) in lower corners. Right corner as Type B. White or cream wove paper. P 13½–14.

(a) Size 24¾ × 13¼ mm.

43	**3**	2p. brown		7·50	50
44		4p. green		7·50	75
45		8p. scarlet		27·00	1·80
46		16p. purple		18·00	1·80
47		24p. orange		15·00	2·20
48		32p. blue		18·00	2·20

(b) Size 26 × 19½ mm.

49	**3**	1r. vermilion		22·00	5·50

(c) Size 27¾ × 21¼ mm.

50	**3**	5r. black and red-brown		26·00	12·00
43/50	*Set of 8*			£130	24·00

1935 (Aug–Dec). T **3** again redrawn. Date B.S.1992 (= 1935/36) in lower corners. Right corner as Type C. White or cream wove paper. P 13½.

51	**3**	2p. brown		3·75	75
52		4p. green		3·75	1·10
53		8p. scarlet		48·00	5·50
54		16p. purple		8·75	1·80
55		24p. orange		8·75	2·75
56		32p. blue		8·75	2·75
51/56	*Set of 6*			70·00	13·00

(Typo Gurkha Patra Press, Kathmandu)

1941 (1 June)–**46.** Local printing. Plates reproduced from earlier issues. Right corner as Type C (2p. to 32p.) or Type B (1r.). P 11–12.

57	**3**	2p. brown (7.41)		35	35
		a. Imperf between (pair)			
		b. Error. Yellow-green (6.43)		7·50	
		ba. Imperf between (pair)			
58		4p. green (7.41)		1·10	75
		a. Imperf between (pair)		13·50	
59		8p. scarlet		75	50
		a. Imperf between (pair)		21·00	21·00
60		16p. purple-brown (4.46)		11·00	2·75
		a. Imperf between (pair)			
61		24p. orange (4.46)		11·00	1·80
		a. Imperf between (pair)			
62		32p. blue (4.46)		15·00	2·20
		a. Imperf between (pair)			
63		1r. red (1.46)		30·00	18·00
57/63	*Set of 7*			60·00	24·00

Some stamps contain portions of the sheet watermarks "HOWARD SMITH/ LUXOR BOND/MADE IN CANADA", "CLARENDON SCRIPT" or "STAR/BOND/SPM".

In the 1950s the lower denominations were re-issued, with or without gum, on wove papers and on laid papers (sheet wmk "STAR PAPER/FINE LAID/INDIA"). Imperforate examples of these final printings do not appear to have been regularly issued for sale to the public.

5
Swayambhunath
Temple,
Katmandu

6 Krishna Mandir
Temple, Patan

7 Guheswari Temple,
Patan

8 Sri Pashupati (Siva
Mahadeva)

(Litho Security Ptg Press, Nasik)

1949 (1 Oct). *Various designs as T* **7/10**. P 13½ × 14 (2p. to 8p.),
13½ (16p. to 32p.) or 13 (1r.).

64	**5**	2p. yellow-brown		90	75
65	–	4p. green		90	75
66	–	6p. carmine-pink		1·80	75
67	–	8p. vermilion		1·80	1·10
68	**6**	16p. purple		1·80	1·10
69	–	20p. blue		3·75	1·80
70	**7**	24p. crimson		3·00	1·10
71	–	32p. ultramarine		5·50	1·80
72	**8**	1r. orange		30·00	18·00
64/72		*Set of 9*		45·00	24·00

Designs: *As T* **5**—4p. Pashupatinath Temple, Katmandu; 6p.
Tri-Chundra College; 8p. Mahabuddha Temple. *As T* **7**—20p.
View of Kathmandu; 32p. The twenty-two fountains, Balaju.

New Currency

9 King
Tribhuvana

10 Map of Nepal

(T **9** and **10**. Litho Security Ptg Press, Nasik)

1954 (15 Apr). P 13½ × 14.

(a) Size 18 × 22 mm.

73	**9**	2p. chocolate		1·80	35
74		4p. green		6·00	1·10
75		6p. rose-red		1·50	35
76		8p. lilac		1·10	35
77		12p. orange-red		11·00	1·80

(b) Size 25½ × 29½ mm.

78	**9**	16p. red-brown		1·50	35
79		20p. carmine-red		3·00	1·10
80		24p. light maroon		2·50	1·10
81		32p. bright blue		3·75	1·10
82		50p. cerise		30·00	5·50
83		1r. scarlet		44·00	8·75
84		2r. brown-orange		37·00	7·50
73/84		*Set of 12*		£120	26·00

1954 (15 Apr). P 13½ × 14.

(a) Size 30 × 18 mm.

85	**10**	2p. chocolate		1·50	75
86		4p. green		6·00	1·10
87		6p. rose-red		15·00	1·80
88		8p. lilac		1·10	75

89		12p. orange-red		15·00	1·80
		(b) Size 38 × 21½ mm.			
90	**10**	16p. red-brown		1·80	75
91		20p. carmine-red		3·00	75
92		24p. light maroon		2·20	75
93		32p. bright blue		5·50	1·50
94		50p. cerise		30·00	5·50
95		1r. scarlet		48·00	7·50
96		2r. brown-orange		37·00	7·50
85/96		*Set of 12*		£150	27·00

**King Mahendra
13 March 1955–31 January 1972**

11 Mechanization
of Agriculture

12 Throne

13 Hanuman Dhoka,
Katmandu

14 King and Queen of
Nepal

(No. 98, photo Courvoisier. Others, litho Security Ptg
Press,Nasik)

1956 (2 May–3 July). *Coronation. T* **11** *and similar vert design
and T* **12/14**.

97	**11**	4p. green (p 13 × 14) (3.7)		6·00	6·00
98	**12**	6p. rosine and yellow (p 11½)		3·75	3·00
99	–	8p. bright violet (p 13 × 14) (3.7)		3·00	1·50
100	**13**	24p. bright carmine (p 13½) (3.7)		6·00	6·00
101	**14**	1r. Venetian red (p 14)		£110	95·00
97/101		*Set of 5*		£110	£100

Design: *As T* **11**—8p. Processional elephant.

A 1r. stamp as Type **14** but inscribed "KING'S CORONATION",
in red-orange, was prepared for use but not issued. Examples
exist both unused and with trial First Day cancellations (*price*
£300).

15 U.N. Emblem and Nepalese
Landscape

16 Nepalese
Crown

(T **15**, **16**. Litho Security Ptg Press, Nasik)

1956 (14 Dec). *First Anniv of Admission of Nepal into United
Nations Organization.* P 14.

102	**15**	12p. dull ultramarine and brown-ochre		7·50	6·00

1957 (22 June). P 13½ × 14.

(a) 18 × 22 mm.

103	**16**	2p. chocolate		75	75
104		4p. green		1·10	75

105		6p. rose-red		75	75
106		8p. violet		75	75
107		12p. orange-red		4·00	1·10

(b) Size 25½ × 29½ mm.

108	**16**	16p. red-brown		5·50	1·80
109		20p. carmine-rose		8·75	2·50
110		24p. cerise		5·50	2·20
111		32p. bright blue		7·50	2·50
112		50p. rose		15·00	5·50
113		1r. salmon		37·00	11·00
114		2r. yellow-orange		22·00	7·50
103/114 *Set of 12*				95·00	33·00

PERFORATION ERRORS. All locally printed stamps issued during 1958–60 (Nos. 115/16, 118/19, 134/37a) are known imperforate or imperf between. While some of these are believed to be genuine errors many are of spurious origin, including unauthorized printings. We only list those known to have been sold over post office counters.

17 Gaunthali carrying Letter   **18** Temple of Lumbini

(Des Amar. Typo Gurkha Patra Press, Kathmandu)

1958 (16 Oct). *AIR. Inauguration of Nepalese Internal Airmail Service. No gum.* P 11.

115	**17**	10p. deep blue (*shades*)		1·90	1·90

(Des Bed Prashad. Typo Gurkha Patra Press, Kathmandu)

1958 (10 Dec). *Human Rights Day. No gum.* P 11.

116	**18**	6p. yellow		1·50	1·50

Some stamps contain portions of the sheet watermarks "SWAN BOND/MADE IN SWEDEN" or "LOVELY BOND/MADE IN SWEDEN".

19 Nepalese Map and Flag   **20** Spinning Wheel

(Recess De La Rue)

1959 (18 Feb). *First Nepalese Elections.* P 15.

117	**19**	6p. carmine-red and green		50	45

(Typo Gurkha Patra Press, Kathmandu)

1959 (10 Apr). *Cottage Industries.* P 11.

118	**20**	2p. chocolate-brown		45	45

21 King Mahendra   **22** Vishnu   **23** Nyatopol Temple, Bhaktapur

(Typo Gurkha Patra Press, Kathmandu)

1959 (14 Apr). *Admission of Nepal to Universal Postal Union. With or without gum.* P 11.

119	**21**	12p. deep violet-blue		50	45

No. 119 was issued on three different papers: thick unwatermarked creamy paper, gummed; thick unwatermarked greyish-surfaced paper, ungummed; thin white paper with sheet watermark "LOVELY BOND/MADE IN SWEDEN", gummed.

(Litho Security Ptg Press, Nasik)

1959 (14 Apr)–**60**. *Various designs as T* **22/23**. P 14.

120	**22**	1p. chocolate		15	15
121	–	2p. slate-violet (16.4.59)		15	15
122	–	4p. ultramarine (17.4.59)		50	35
123	–	6p. salmon-pink (15.4.59)		50	15
124	–	8p. sepia (18.4.59)		35	15
125	–	12p. deep grey (20.4.59)		50	15
126	**23**	16p. violet and brown		50	15
127		20p. brown-red and blue		1·80	75
128		24p. rose-red and deep green		1·80	75
129		32p. ultramarine and deep lilac		1·10	75
130		50p. myrtle-green and carmine-red		1·80	75
131	–	1r. deep blue and red-brown (*shades*) (19.4.59)		16·00	6·00
132	–	2r. ultram & reddish pur (19.4.59)		15·00	6·25
133	–	5r. carmine-red and violet (13.4.60)		60·00	55·00
120/133 *Set of 14*				£110	75·00

Designs. As T **22**. *Horiz*—2p. Krishna; 8p. Siberian musk deer; 12p. Indian rhinoceros. *Vert*—4p. Himalayas; 6p. Gateway, Bhaktapur Palace. As T **23**. *Vert*—1r., 2r. Himalayan monal pheasant; 5r. Satyr tragopan.

24 King Mahendra opening Parliament

(Des Amar. Typo Gurkha Patra Press, Kathmandu)

1959 (1 July). *Opening of First Nepalese Parliament. With or without gum.* P 11.

134	**24**	6p. crimson		1·10	1·10

O **25** Nepalese Arms   **25** Sri Pashupatinath

(Litho Security Ptg Press, Nasik)

1959 (1 Nov). *OFFICIAL.* P 14.

(a) Size 30 × 18 mm.

O135	O **25**	2p. chocolate		10	10
O136		4p. yellow-green		15	10
O137		6p. scarlet		15	10
O138		8p. bright violet		15	15
O139		12p. orange-red		20	20

(b) Size 38 × 22 mm.

O140	O **25**	16p. red-brown		35	30
O141		24p. carmine-red		50	45
O142		32p. deep claret		60	60
O143		50p. ultramarine		1·10	1·00
O144		1r. scarlet		2·20	1·90
O145		2r. orange		4·50	4·00
O135/145 *Set of 11*				9·00	8·00

(Typo Gurkha Patra Press, Kathmandu)

1959 (19 Nov). *Renovation of Sri Pashupatinath Temple, Katmandu.* P 11.

135	**25**	4p. bronze-green (18 × 25 *mm*)	. . .	75	75
		a. Imperf between (horiz pair)	. . .	90·00	
136		8p. carmine-red (21 × 28 *mm*)	. . . .	1·50	75
137		1r. light blue (24½ × 33½ *mm*)	. . . .	8·75	6·00

26 Children, Pagoda and Mt. Everest   **27** King Mahendra   (O **28**)

(Des Hiranya Dhoy. Typo Gurkha Patra Press, Kathmandu)

1960 (1 Mar). *Children's Day.* P 11.

137*a*	**26**	6p. deep blue	. . . . . .	15·00	11·00

Issued in sheets of four.

(Photo Security Ptg Press, Nasik)

1960 (11 June). *King Mahendra's 41st Birthday.* P 14 × 13½.

138	**27**	1r. bright purple	. . . .	1·60	1·10

See also Nos. 163/4a.

1960 (11 June). *OFFICIAL. Optd as Type* O **28** (*"KAJ SARKARI" (On Government Service)), but slightly larger* (14½ *mm*).

O146	**27**	1r. bright purple	. . . .		90

See note below No. O150.

28 Mt. Everest   **29** King Tribhuvana

(Photo Security Ptg Press, Nasik)

1960 (30 June)–**61**. *Mountain Views. Vert designs as T* **28**. P 14 × 13½.

139		5p. sepia and purple (26.2.61)	. . . .	35	15
140		10p. purple and ultramarine	. . .	50	20
141		40p. red-brown and violet (26.2.61)	. .	1·30	80

Designs:—5p. Machha Puchhre; 40p. Manaslu (wrongly inscr "MANSALU").

(Photo Security Ptg Press, Nasik)

1961 (18 Feb). *Tenth Democracy Day.* P 13.

142	**29**	10p. red-orange, and chestnut	. . .	15	15

30 Prince Gyanendra cancelling Children's Day Stamps of 1960   **31** King Mahendra

(Typo Gurkha Patna Press, Kathmandu)

1961 (1 Mar). *Children's Day.* P 11.

143	**30**	12p. orange	. . . .	37·00	37·00

(Des Lain Singh Bangdel. Photo Security Ptg Press, Nasik)

1961 (11 June). *King Mahendra's 42nd Birthday.* P 14 × 15.

144	**31**	6p. bright emerald	. . . .	35	35
145		12p. ultramarine	. . . .	50	50
146		50p. carmine-red	. . . .	1·10	1·10
147		1r. brown	. . . .	1·80	1·80
144/147	*Set of 4*		. . . .	3·50	3·50

1961 (Oct)–**83**. *OFFICIAL. Optd with Type* O **28**.

O148	**35**	1p. rose-carmine (1.62)	. . . .	15	15
O149		2p. blue (1.62)	. . . .	15	15
O150		5p. yellow-brown	. . . .	20	20
O151	**36**	10p. reddish purple (1983)	. . . .	10	10
O152		40p. brown (1983)	. . . .	15	15
O153		75p. blue-green (1983)	. . . .	20	20
O154	**27**	2r. orange red (1983)	. . . .	60	60
O155		5r. grey-green (1983)	. . . .	1·60	1·60
O148/155	*Set of 8*		. . . .	2·75	2·75

In April 1983 remainders of Nos. O146 and O148 were placed on sale, together with Nos. O151/5 which were previously unissued. Unsold stock was subsequently made available for postage use, both on official and ordinary mail.

PRINTERS. From No. 148 to 403 all stamps were printed in photogravure at the Security Printing Press, Nasik, India, *unless otherwise stated.*

32 Campaign Emblem and House   **33** King Mahendra on horseback

1962 (7 Apr). *Malaria Eradication. T* **32** *and similar vert design.* P 13.

148		12p. light blue	. . . .	35	35
149		1r. yellow-orange and carmine	. . . .	1·10	1·10

Design:—1r. Emblem and Nepalese Flag.

(Des Uttam Prasad Nepali Karmacharya)

1962 (11 June). *King Mahendra's 43rd Birthday.* P 13.

150	**33**	10p. indigo	. . . .	20	20
151		15p. brown	. . . .	35	35
152		45p. purple-brown	. . . .	75	75
153		1r. deep olive-grey	. . . .	1·10	1·10
150/153	*Set of 4*		. . . .	2·10	2·10

34 Bhanu Bhakta Acharya

35 King Mahendra

36 King Mahendra

1962 (13 July–30 Aug). *Nepalese Poets. T **34** and similar vert portraits.* P 14 × 15.

154		5p. orange-brown	35	35
155		10p. turquoise (30.8)	35	35
156		40p. yellow-olive (30.8)	50	50

Portraits:—10p. Moti Ram Bhatta; 40p. Sambhu Prasad.

1962 (1 Dec)–**67**. P 14½ × 14 (T **35**), 14 × 14½ (T **36**) or 14 × 13½ (T **27**).

157	**35**	1p. rose-carmine	15	10
158		2p. blue	15	10
158a		3p. grey (18.2.66)	50	35
159		5p. yellow-brown	15	10
160	**36**	10p. reddish purple	15	15
161		40p. brown	35	35
162		75p. blue-green	11·00	11·00
162a	**35**	75p. blue-green (10.2.67)	1·50	75
163	**27**	2r. orange-red	1·50	1·50
164		5r. grey-green	3·00	3·00
164a		10r. bluish violet (18.2.66)	11·00	8·75
157/164a *Set of 11*			26·00	23·00

No. 162a is smaller, 17½ × 20 mm.

37 Emblems of Learning

38 Hands holding Lamps

1963 (6 Jan). *U.N.E.S.C.O. "Education for All" campaign.* P 14½ × 14.

165	**37**	10p. olive-black	35	15
166		15p. brown	50	35
167		50p. violet-blue	90	75

1963 (19 Feb). *National Day.* P 13.

168	**38**	5p. new blue	15	15
169		10p. red-brown	15	15
170		50p. bright purple	75	50
171		1r. blue-green	1·50	75
168/171 *Set of 4*			2·30	1·40

39 Campaign Symbols

40 Map of Nepal and Open Hand

1963 (21 Mar). *Freedom from Hunger.* P 14 × 14½.

172	**39**	10p. red-orange	35	15
173		15p. dull ultramarine	50	35
174		50p. deep grey-green	1·10	75
175		1r. brown	1·50	1·30
172/175 *Set of 4*			3·00	2·30

(Des Uttam Prasad Nepali Karmacharya)

1963 (14 Apr). *Rastruya Panchayat.* P 13½ × 13.

176	**40**	10p. dull green	15	15
177		15p. deep reddish purple	35	35
178		50p. slate	95	50
179		1r. deep violet-blue	1·50	90
176/179 *Set of 4*			2·75	1·70

41 King Mahendra

42 King Mahendra and Highway Map

(T **41/42** des Uttam Prasad Nepali Karmacharya)

1963 (11 June). *King Mahendra's 44th Birthday.* P 13.

180	**41**	5p. violet	15	15
181		10p. orange-brown	35	15
182		15p. deep green	50	35

1964 (19 Feb). *East-West Highway.* P 13½ × 13.

183	**42**	10p. orange and blue	15	15
184		15p. orange and deep violet-blue	35	20
185		50p. orange-brown and deep green	60	35

43 King Mahendra at Microphone

44 Crown Prince Birendra

(Des Shyam Das Ashanta)

1964 (11 June). *King Mahendra's 45th Birthday.* P 14 × 13½.

186	**43**	1p. light olive-brown	15	15
187		2p. greenish grey	20	20
188		2r. orange-brown	1·10	1·10

1964 (28 Dec). *Crown Prince's 19th Birthday.* P 14 × 14½.

189	**44**	10p. grey-green	90	75
190		15p. brown	90	75

45 Flag, Kukris, Rings and Torch

46 Nepalese Family

(Litho Pakistan Security Ptg Corp, Karachi)

1964 (31 Dec). *Olympic Games, Tokyo.* P 13½.
191 **45** 10p. ultramarine, rose-red and
pink 95   75

(Des Uttam Prasad Nepali Karmacharya)

1965 (18 Feb–16 Dec). *Land Reform.* T **46** *and similar vert designs.* P 14 × 13½.
192   2p. black and blue-green (16.12)   35   35
193   5p. bistre-brown & sage-green
(16.12)   35   35
194   10p. purple and pale grey (16.12)   35   35
195   15p. brown and greenish yellow   50   50
192/195 *Set of* 4   1·40 1·40
Designs:—2p. Farmer ploughing; 50p. Ears of wheat; 10p. Grain elevator.

47 Globe and Letters

48 King Mahendra

(Des Uttam Prasad Nepali Karmacharya)

1965 (13 Apr). *Introduction of International Insured and Parcel Service.* P 14½ × 14.
196 **47** 15p. reddish violet 35   35

(Des Shyam Das Ashanta)

1965 (11 June). *King Mahendra's 46th Birthday.* P 14 × 14½.
197 **48** 50p. purple 90   75

49 Four Martyrs

50 I.T.U. Emblem

1965 (11 June). *"Nepalese Martyrs".* P 13.
198 **49** 15p. blue-green 20   15

(Des Shyam Das Ashanta)

1965 (15 Sept). *Centenary of International Telecommunications Union.* P 13 × 13½.
199 **50** 15p. black and deep reddish
purple 50   35

51 I.C.Y. Emblem

52 Devkota (poet)

(Des Shyam Das Ashanta. Litho and recess Bradbury, Wilkinson)

1965 (24 Oct). *International Co-operation Year.* P 12 × 12½.
200 **51** 1r. multicoloured . . . . 1·10   90

(Des Shyam Das Ashanta)

1965 (24 Oct). *Devkota Commemoration.* P 14 × 14½.
201 **52** 15p. red-brown 35   30

54 Flag and King Mahendra

(Des Shyam Das Ashanta)

1966 (18 Feb). *Democracy Day.* P 14½ × 14.
202 **54** 15p. red and ultramarine 75   50

55 Siva Parvati and Pashuvati Temple

56 "Stamp" Emblem

(Des Shyam Das Ashanta)

1966 (18 Feb). *Maha Siva-Ratri Festival.* P 14 × 13½.
203 **55** 15p. bluish violet 45   35

(Des Uttam Prasad Nepali Karmacharya)

1966 (10 June). *Nepalese Philatelic Exhibition, Kathmandu.* P 14½ × 14.
204 **56** 15p. orange and myrtle-green . . . 50   35

57 King Mahendra

58 Queen Mother

59 Queen Ratna

(Des Uttam Prasad Nepali Karmacharya)

1966 (11 June). *King Mahendra's 47th Birthday.* P 13 × 13½.
205 **57** 15p. chocolate and light ochre-
yellow 45 30

1966 (5 July). *Queen Mother's 60th Birthday.* P 14 × 14½.
206 **58** 15p. orange-brown 35 35

(Des Uttam Prasad Nepali Karmacharya)

1966 (19 Aug). *Children's Day.* P 13 × 13½.
207 **59** 15p. deep chestnut and yellow . . . 45 35

60 Flute-player and
Dancer

61 "To render service . . ."

(Des Uttam Prasad Nepali Karmacharya)

1966 (7 Sept). *Krishna Anniversary.* P 13 × 13½.
208 **60** 15p. reddish violet and light
yellow 45 35

(Des Shyam Das Ashanta)

1966 (1 Oct). *First Anniv of Nepalese Red Cross.* P 14½ × 14.
209 **61** 50p. carmine and deep green . . . 4·50 1·50

62 W.H.O. Building on
Flag

63 L. Paudyal
(poet)

(T **62/3** des Shyam Das Ashanta)

1966 (11 Nov). *Inauguration of W.H.O. Headquarters, Geneva.*
P 13½ × 14.
210 **62** 1r. reddish violet . . . . 2·20 1·50

1966 (29 Dec). *Lekhnath Paudyal Commemoration.* P 14 × 13½.
211 **63** 15p. chalky blue 45 35

64 Rama and Sita

65 Buddha

(T **64/5** des Shyam Das Ashanta)

1967 (18 Apr). *Rama Navami, 2024, birthday of Rama.* P 14 × 13½.
212 **64** 15p. deep brown and yellow 45 35

1967 (23 May). *Buddha Jayanti, birthday of Buddha.* P 13½ × 13.
213 **65** 75p. purple and orange 35 35

66 King Mahendra addressing Nepalese

(Litho Pakistan Security Ptg Corp)

1967 (11 June). *King Mahendra's 48th Birthday.* P 13½ × 13.
214 **66** 15p. brown and light blue 45 35

67 Queen Ratna and
Children

68 Ama Dablam
(mountain)

(Litho Pakistan Security Ptg Corp)

1967 (20 Aug). *Children's Day.* P 13.
215 **67** 15p. brown and cream 45 35

(Des K. K. Karmacharya)

1967 (24 Oct). *International Tourist Year.* T **68** *and similar horiz
designs.*

(a) POSTAGE.
216 5p. bluish violet (p 14) 35 35
217 65p. red-brown (p 14½ × 14) 75 75
(b) AIR.
218 1r.80 brown-red & new bl (p 13½ × 13) . . 1·80 1·50
Designs: (38 × 20 mm)—65p. Bhaktapur Durbar Square
(35½ × 25½ mm)—1r.80, Plane over Kathmandu.

69 Open-air Class

70 Crown Prince Birendra,
Camp-fire and Scout Emblem

(Litho De La Rue)

1967 (16 Dec). *Constitution Day "Go to the Village" Educational
Campaign.* P 13.
219 **69** 15p. multicoloured 45 35

(Des K. K. Karmacharya)

1967 (29 Dec). *Diamond Jubilee of World Scouting.* P 14½ × 14.
220 **70** 15p. ultramarine 75 50

71 Prithvi Narayan Shah (founder of Kingdom)　**72** Arms of Nepal

(T **71/2** des K. K. Karmacharya)

1968 (11 Jan). *Bicentenary of the Kingdom*. P 14 × 14½.
221　**71**　15p. new blue and red . . . . 　75　50

(Des Uttam Nepali)

1968 (19 Feb). *National Day*. P 14 × 14½.
222　**72**　15p. ultramarine and carmine-red . . 　75　50

73 W.H.O Emblem and Nepalese Flag　**74** Sita and Janaki Temple

(Des K. K. Karmacharya)

1968 (7 Apr). *20th Anniv of World Health Organization*. P 13½ × 13.
223　**73**　1r.20 blue, red and orange-yellow . . 　3·00　2·20

(Des K. K. Karmacharya)

1968 (7 May). *Sita Jayanti*. P 14½ × 14.
224　**74**　15p. chestnut and bluish violet . . . 　50　35

75 King Mahendra and Himalayan Monal Pheasant　**76** Garuda and Airline Emblem

(Des K. K. Karmacharya. Photo Govt Ptg Wks, Tokyo)

1968 (11 June). *King Mahendra's 49th Birthday*. P 13½.
225　**75**　15p. multicoloured . . . . 　65　35

(Des K. K. Karmacharya)

1968 (1 July). *AIR. Tenth Anniv of Royal Nepalese Airlines*. T **76** *and similar designs*. P 13 (65p.) or 14½ × 14 (others).
226　15p. yellow-brown and new blue . . . 　35　35
227　65p. deep violet-blue . . . . 　75　75
228　2r.50 deep blue and red-orange . . . 　2·50　2·20
　Designs: 25½ × 25½ *mm*—65p. Route-map. *As T* **76**—2r.50, Convair CV 440 Metropolitan airliner over Mount Dhaulagiri.

77 Flag, Queen Ratna and Children　**78** Human Rights Emblem and Buddha

(Des K. K. Karmacharya)

1968 (19 Aug). *Children's Day and Queen Ratna's 41st Birthday*. P 13 × 13½.
229　**77**　5p. red, yellow and turquoise-
　　　　green . . . . 　35　30

(Des K. K. Karmacharya)

1968 (10 Dec). *Human Rights Year*. P 14½ × 14.
230　**78**　1r. red and deep green . . . . . . 　3·00　2·20

79 Crown Prince Birendra and Dancers　**80** King Mahendra, Flags and U.N. Building, New York

(Des K. K. Karmacharya)

1968 (28 Dec). *Crown Prince Birendra's 24th Birthday, and National Youth Festival*. P 14½ × 14.
231　**79**　25p. deep ultramarine . . . . 　75　50

(Des K. K. Karmacharya. Photo Govt Ptg Wks, Tokyo)

1969 (1 Jan). *Nepal's Election to United Nations Security Council*. P 13.
232　**80**　1r. multicoloured . . . . 　1·10　90

81 Amsu Varma (7th-century ruler)　**82** I.L.O. Emblem

(Des A. Chltrakar (15, 25p.), K. K. Karmacharya (others))

1969 (13 Apr)–**70**. *Famous Nepalese*. T **81** *and similar designs*. P 14½ × 14 (1r.) or 14 × 14½ (others).
233　15p. reddish violet and yellow-green . . . 　50　1·50
234　25p. turquoise . . . . 　75　75
235　50p. chestnut . . . . 　95　95
236　1r. purple and light ochre (14.4.70) . . . 　1·10　90
233/236 *Set of* 4 . . . . 　3·00　3·75
　Designs: *Vert*—25p. Ram Shah (17th-century King of Gurkha); 50p. Bhimsen Thapa (19th-century Prime Minister). *Horiz*—1r. Ral Bhadra Kunwar (19th-century warrior).

(Des K. K. Karmacharya)

1969 (1 May). *50th Anniv of International Labour Organization.*
P 14½ × 14.
237 **82** 1r. brown and cerise . . . . 5·50 3·75

83 King Mahendra

84 King Tribhuvana and Queens

(Des K. K. Karmacharya. Photo De La Rue)

1969 (20 June). *King Mahendra's 50th Birthday.* P 13½ × 13.
238 **83** 25p. multicoloured 45 45

(Des K. K. Karmacharya)

1969 (1 July). *64th Birth Anniv of King Tribhuvana.* P 14½ × 14.
239 **84** 25p. sepia and greenish yellow . . . 45 45

85 Queen Ratna, and Child with Toy

86 Rhododendron

87 Durga, Goddess of Victory

(Des K. K. Karmacharya)

1969 (20 Aug). *National Children's Day.* P 14 × 14½.
240 **85** 25p. cerise and blackish brown . . . 45 45

(Des K. K. Karmacharya. Photo Govt Ptg Wks, Tokyo)

1969 (17 Sept). *Flowers.* T **86** *and similar vert designs.*
Multicoloured. P 13.
241 25p. Type **86** 60 50
    a. Block of 4. Nos. 241/4 . . . . 2·40
242 25p. Narcissus 60 50
243 25p. Marigold 60 50
244 25p. Poinsettia 60 50
241/244 *Set of 4* . . . . 2·10 1·80
Nos. 241/4 were issued together in *se-tenant* blocks of four within the sheet of 16.

(Des K. K. Karmacharya)

1969 (17 Oct). *Durga Pooja Festival.* P 14 × 14½.
245 **87** 15p. black and orange 35 35
246 50p. violet and yellow-brown 80 80

88 Crown Prince Birendra and Princess Aishwarya

(Des K. K. Karmacharya. Photo Govt Ptg Wks, Tokyo)

1970 (27 Feb). *Royal Wedding.* P 13.
247 **88** 25p. multicoloured 45 20

89 Produce, Cow and Landscape

(Des K. K. Karmacharya. Litho State Ptg Wks, Warsaw)

1970 (21 Mar). *Agricultural Year.* P 12½.
248 **89** 25p. multicoloured 45 35

90 King Mahendra, Mt. Everest and Nepalese Crown

(Litho Bradbury, Wilkinson)

1970 (11 June). *King Mahendra's 51st Birthday.* P 11½.
249 **90** 50p. multicoloured 75 50

91 Lake Gosainkunda

(Des K. K. Karmacharya. Photo Govt Ptg Wks, Tokyo)

1970 (11 June). *Nepalese Lakes.* T **91** *and similar horiz designs.*
Multicoloured. P 13.
250 5p. Type **91** 35 35
251 25p. Lake Phewa Tal 50 50
252 1r. Lake Rara Daha 90 90

92 A.P.Y. Emblem

(Des K. K. Karmacharya)

1970 (1 July). *Asian Productivity Year.* P 14½ × 14.
253 **92** 1r. new blue 90 75

93 Queen Ratna and Children's
Palace, Taulihawa

(Des K. K. Karmacharya)

1970 (20 Aug). *National Children's Day.* P 14½ × 14.
254　**93**　25p. slate and chestnut .... 45　35

94 New Headquarters Building

(Des K. K. Karmacharya)

1970 (9 Oct). *New Universal Postal Union Headquarters, Berne.*
P 14½ × 14.
255　**94**　2r.50 drab and yellow-brown .... 1·80　1·50

95 U.N. Flag

(Des K. K. Karmacharya)

1970 (24 Oct). *25th Anniv of United Nations.* P 14½ × 14.
256　**95**　25p. light blue and brown-purple .. 45　35

96 Durbar Square, Patan　　**97** Statue of
　　　　　　　　　　　　　Harihar, Valmiki
　　　　　　　　　　　　　Ashram

(Des K. K. Karmacharya. Litho State Ptg Wks, Warsaw)

1970 (28 Dec). *Tourism. T* **96** *and similar multicoloured designs.*
P 11½ × 11 (25p.) or 11 × 11½ (others).
257　　15p. Type **96** .... 35　15
258　　25p. Boudhanath Stupa (temple) (*vert*) 50　35
259　　1r. Mt. Gauri Shankar .... 90　75

(Des K. K. Karmacharya)

1971 (26 Jan). *Nepalese Religious Art.* P 14 × 14½.
260　**97**　25p. black and yellow-brown .... 45　30

98 Torch within Spiral

(Des K. K. Karmacharya)

1971 (21 Mar). *Racial Equality Year.* P 13.
261　**98**　1r. orange-red and slate-blue .... 1·10　80

99 King Mahendra taking　**100** Sweta Bhairab
　　　Salute

(Des K. K. Karmacharya)

1971 (11 June). *King Mahendra's 52nd Birthday.* P 14½ × 14.
262　**99**　25p. plum and new blue ...... 45　30

(Des K. K. Karmacharya)

1971 (11 July). *Bhairab Statues of Shiva. T* **100** *and similar vert
designs.* P 13.
263　　15p. blackish brown and chestnut ... 35　35
264　　25p. blackish brown and dull green .. 35　35
265　　50p. blackish brown and greenish blue 75　75
　　Designs:—25p. Mahankal Bhairab; 50p. Kal Bhairab.

101 Child presenting Queen Ratna
with Garland

(Des K. K. Karmacharya. Photo Courvoisier)

1971 (20 Aug). *National Children's Day.* P 11½.
266　**101**　25p. multicoloured .... 45　30

102 Iranian and Nepalese Flags on
Map of Iran

(Des K. K. Karmacharya. Photo Courvoisier)

1971 (14 Oct). *2500th Anniv of Persian Empire.* P 11½.
267　**102**　1r. multicoloured .... 1·10　75

103 Mother and Child

(Des K. K. Karmacharya)

1971 (11 Dec). *25th Anniv of United Nations Children's Fund.*
P 14½ × 14.
268　**103**　1r. light blue .... 1·10　75

104 Mt. Everest   **105** Royal Standard

(Des K. K. Karmacharya)

1971 (28 Dec). *Tourism. Himalayan Peaks. T* **104** *and similar horiz designs.* P 13.

269	25p. blackish brn, orge-brn & greenish bl	35	15
270	1r. black, chestnut and new blue	75	50
271	1r.80 blackish grn, lt brn & greenish bl	1·30	95

Designs:—1r. Mt. Kanchenjunga; 1r.80, Mt. Annapurna I.

King Birendra
31 January 1972–2 June 2001

(Des K. K. Karmacharya)

1972 (19 Feb). *National Day.* P 13.
272	**105**	25p. black and red	45	30

106 Araniko and White Dagoba, Peking   **107** Open Book

(Des K. K. Karmacharya)

1972 (13 Apr). *Araniko (13th-century architect) Commemoration.* P 13.
273	**106**	15p. dp olive-brown & lt turquoise-bl	20	20

(Des K. K. Karmacharya)

1972 (8 Sept). *International Book Year.* P 14½ × 14.
274	**107**	2p. brown and buff	15	15
275		5p. black and pale drab	15	15
276		1r. black and light blue	90	75

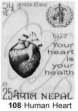 

108 Human Heart   **109** King Mahendra

(Des K. K. Karmacharya)

1972 (6 Nov). *World Heart Month.* P 13.
277	**108**	25p. crimson and grey-green	45	35

(Des K. K. Karmacharya)

1972 (15 Dec). *1st Death Anniv of King Mahendra.* P 13.
278	**109**	25p. black and chestnut	45	30

110 King Birendra   **111** Northern Border Costumes

(Des K. K. Karmacharya)

1972 (28 Dec). *King Birendra's 28th Birthday.* P 13.
279	**110**	50p. dull purple and yellow-ochre	50	45

(Des K. K. Karmacharya. Photo Govt Ptg Wks, Tokyo)

1973 (18 Feb). *National Costumes. T* **111** *and similar vert designs. Multicoloured.* P 13.

280	25p. Type **111**	35	15
	a. Block of 4. Nos. 280/3	2·40	
281	50p. Hill-dwellers	45	35
282	75p. Katmandu Valley	60	45
283	1r. Inner Terai	90	60
280/283 *Set of* 4		2·10	1·40

Nos. 280/3 were issued together in *se-tenant* blocks of four within the sheet of 16.

112 Sri Baburam Acharya   **113** Nepalese Family

(Des K. K. Karmacharya)

1973 (12 Mar). *85th Birth Anniv of Sri Baburam Acharya (historian).* P 13.
284	**112**	25p. drab and carmine	15	10

(Des K. K. Karmacharya)

1973 (7 Apr). *25th Anniv of World Health Organization.* P 14½ × 14.
285	**113**	1r. greenish blue and yellow-orange	90	75

114 Birthplace of Buddha, Lumbini

(Des K. K. Karmacharya)

1973 (17 May). *Tourism. T* **114** *and similar horiz designs. Multicoloured.* P 13.
286	25p. Type **114**	35	15
287	75p. Mt. Makalu	50	35
288	1r. Castle, Gurkha	75	75

115 Transplanting Rice

(Des K. K. Karmacharya)

1973 (29 June). *10th Anniv of World Food Programme.*
P 14½ × 14.
289 **115** 10p. olive-brown & dp bluish
violet 15 15

116 Interpol Headquarters,   **117** Shu Shom Nath
Paris   Sigdyal

(Des K. K. Karmacharya)

1973 (3 Sept). *50th Anniv of International Criminal Police
Organization (Interpol).* P 14½ × 14.
290 **116** 25p. new blue and ochre 35 20

(Des K. K. Karmacharya)

1973 (5 Oct). *1st Death Anniv of Shri Shom Nath Sigdyal
(scholar).* P 13.
291 **117** 1r.25 bluish violet 90 75

118 Cow

(Des K. K. Karmacharya)

1973 (25 Oct). *Domestic Animals. T* **118** *and similar horiz design.
Multicoloured.* P 13.
292 2p. Type **118** 15 15
    a. Brown-lake omitted . . . .
293 3r.25 Yak . . . . 1·60 1·10
The missing colour on No. 292a mainly affects the cows which
show only the underlying green colour.

119 King Birendra

(Des K. K. Karmacharya)

1973 (28 Dec)–**74**. *King Birendra's 29th Birthday.* P 13 × 14½. (5p.)
or 13½ × 14 (others).
294 **119** 5p. bistre-brown and black 15 15
295 15p. olive-brown and black
       (2.74) 20 15
296 1r. red-brown and black (2.74) . . 75 50

120 Text of National Anthem   **121** King Janak
                            seated on Throne

(Des K. K. Karmacharya)

1974 (18 Feb). *National Day. T* **120** *and similar horiz design.* P 13.
297 25p. claret 35 15
298 1r. bluish green 50 45
    Design:—1r. Anthem musical score.

(Des K. K. Karmacharya. Litho Pakistan Security Ptg Corp,
Karachi)

1974 (14 Apr). *King Janak Commemoration.* P 13½.
299 **121** 2r.50 multicoloured . . . . 1·80 1·50

122 Emblem and Village

(Des K. Karmacharya. Litho Pakistan Security Ptg Corp)

1974 (20 May). *25th Anniv of SOS Children's Village International.*
P 13.
300 **122** 25p. brown-red and new blue . . . 35 35

123 Football   **124** W.P.Y. Emblem

(Des K. Karmacharya. Litho Pakistan Security Ptg Corp)

1974 (1 July). *Nepalese Games. T* **123** *and similar vert design.
Multicoloured.* P 13.
301 2p. Type **123** 15 15
302 2r.75 Baghchal (diagram) . . . . . 1·10 90

(Des K. Karmacharya. Litho Pakistan Security Ptg Corp)

1974 (19 Aug). *World Population Year.* P 13.
303 **124** 5p. blue and ochre 20 15

125 U.P.U.
Monument, Berne

126 *Cethosia biblis*

(Des K. Karmacharya. Litho Pakistan Security Ptg Corp)

1974 (9 Oct). *Centenary of Universal Postal Union.* P 13.
304   **125**   1r. black and olive-yellow   75   50

(Des K. Karmacharya. Litho Pakistan Security Ptg Corp)

1974 (16 Oct). *Nepalese Butterflies. T* **126** *and similar horiz designs. Multicoloured.* P 13.
305   10p. Type **126**   15   15
306   15p. *Kallima inachus*   45   20
307   1r.25 *Kallima inachus* (underside)   . . .   1·10   75
308   1r.75 *Delias thysbe*   . . . .   1·30   1·10
305/308 *Set of 4*   . . . .   2·75   2·00

127 King Birendra

128 Muktinath

(Des K. Karmacharya. Litho Pakistan Security Ptg Corp)

1974 (28 Dec). *King Birendra's 30th Birthday.* P 13½ × 13.
309   **127**   25p. black and grey-green   20   20

(Des K. Karmacharya. Litho Pakistan Security Ptg Corp)

1974 (31 Dec). *Tourism. T* **128** *and similar multicoloured design.* P 13 × 13½ (25p.) or 13½ × 13 (1r.).
310   25p. Type **128**   35   15
311   1r. Peacock window, Bhaktapur
      (*horiz*)   75   45

129 Guheswari Temple

130 Tourism Year Emblem

(1r. to 2r.75, photo Courvoisier; 25p. litho, 50p. photo)

1975 (24 Feb). *Coronation of King Birendra. T* **129** *and similar multicoloured designs.* P 13 × 13½ (25p.), 14½ × 14 (50p.), or 11½ (others).
312   25p. Type **129**   35   15
313   50p. Lake Rara (37 × 30 *mm*)   35   15
314   1r. Throne and sceptre (46 × 26 *mm*)   .   50   35
315   1r.25 Royal Palace, Kathmandu (46 × 26
      mm)   . . . .   1·10   50
316   1r.75 Pashupatinath Temple (25 × 31
      mm)   75   75
317   2r.75 King Birendra and Queen
      Aishwarya (46 × 25 *mm*)   . . . . .   1·10   90
312/317 *Set of 6*   . . . .   3·75   2·50
MS318 143 × 105 mm. Nos. 314/15 and 317.
    Imperf   . . . .   4·00   4·00

(Des K. Karmacharya. Litho Pakistan Security Ptg Corp)

1975 (25 May). *South Asia Tourism Year. T* **130** *and similar multicoloured design.* P 12½ × 14 (2p.) or 14 × 12½ (25p.)
319   2p. Type **130**   15   15
320   25p. Temple stupa (*vert*)   35   35

131 Tiger

(Des K. Karmacharya. Litho Pakistan Security Ptg Corp)

1975 (17 July). *Wildlife Conservation. T* **131** *and similar multicoloured designs.* P 13.
321   2p. Type **131**   35   35
322   5p. Swamp deer (*vert*)   35   35
323   1r. Lesser panda   75   75

132 Queen Aishwarya and I.W.Y.
Emblem

133 Rupse Falls

(Des K. Karmacharya. Litho Pakistan Security Ptg Corp)

1975 (8 Nov). *International Women's Year.* P 13.
324   **133**   1r. multicoloured   50   35

(Des K. Karmacharya. Litho Pakistan Security Ptg Corp)

1975 (16 Dec). *Tourism. T* **133** *and similar multicoloured designs.* P 13½ × 13.
325   2p. Mt. Ganesh Himal (*horiz*)   15   15
326   25p. Type **133**   15   15
327   50p. Kumari ("Living Goddess")   . . .   50   35

134 King Birendra

136 Flag and Map

(Des K. Karmacharya)

1975 (28 Dec). *King Birendra's 31st Birthday.* P 13 × 13½.
328   **134**   25p. reddish violet and light
          mauve   20   15
No. 329 *is vacant.*

(Des K. Karmacharya)

1976 (19 Feb). *Silver Jubilee of National Democracy Day.* P 13.
330   **136**   2r.50 red and deep blue   90   75

137 Transplanting Rice

(Des K. Chitrakar. Litho Pakistan Security Ptg Corp)

1976 (11 Apr). *Agriculture Year.* P 13.
331 **137** 25p. multicoloured 20 15

 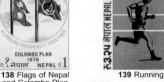

138 Flags of Nepal and Colombo Plan

139 Running

(Des K. Karmacharya)

1976 (1 July). *25th Anniv of Colombo Plan.* P 13 × 13½.
332 **138** 1r. multicoloured 50 45

(Des K. Karmacharya)

1976 (30 July). *Olympic Games, Montreal.* P 13 × 13½.
333 **139** 3r.25 black and light ultramarine . . 1·50 1·10

140 "Dove of Peace"

141 Lakhe Dance

(Des K. Karmacharya. Litho Pakistan Security Ptg Corp)

1976 (17 Aug). *Fifth Non-aligned Countries Summit Conference.* P 13½.
334 **140** 5r. blue, yellow and black . . . . . 1·90 1·30

(Des K. Karmacharya. Litho Pakistan Security Ptg Corp)

1976 (27 Sept). *Nepalese Dances.* T **141** *and similar horiz designs. Multicoloured.* P 13½.
335 10p. Type **141** 15 15
336 15p. Maruni dance 15 15
337 30p. Jhangad dance 35 20
338 1r. Sebru dance 50 35
335/338 *Set of 4* . . . . 1·00 75

142 Nepalese Lily

143 King Birendra

(Des K. Karmacharya. Litho Pakistan Security Ptg Corp)

1976 (7 Nov)–**77**. *Flowers.* T **142** *and similar multicoloured designs.* P 13.
339 30p. Type **142** 50 15
340 30p. *Meconopsis grandis* (24.1.77) . . . 50 15
341 30p. *Cardiocrinum giganteum* (*horiz*) (24.1.77) 50 15
342 30p. *Megacodon stylophorus* (*horiz*) (24.1.77) 50 15
339/342 *Set of 4* . . . . 1·80 50

(Des K. Karmacharya)

1976 (28 Dec). *King Birendra's 32nd Birthday.* P 14.
343 **143** 5p. bronze-green 15 10
344 30p. lake-brown, yellow-brown and greenish yellow 20 15

144 Liberty Bell

145 Kaji Amarsingh Thapa

(Des K. Karmacharya. Litho Pakistan Security Ptg Corp)

1976 (31 Dec). *Bicentenary of American Revolution.* P 13 × 13½.
345 **144** 10r. multicoloured . . . . 2·75 2·40

(Des K. Karmacharya)

1977 (18 Feb). *Kaji Amarsingh Thapa (19th-century warrior) Commemoration.* P 13½ × 13.
346 **145** 10p. brown-olive & pale reddish brn 15 15

146 Terracotta Figurine and Kapilavastu

147 Great Indian Hornbill (*Buceros bicornis*)

(Des K. Karmacharya)

1977 (3 May). *Tourism.* T **146** *and similar horiz design.* P 14½ × 14.
347 30p. deep blue-violet 15 15
348 5r. deep green and brown . . . . . 1·50 1·10
Design:—5r. Ashokan pillar, Lumbini.

(Des K. Karmacharya)

1977 (17 Sept). *Birds. T **147** and similar multicoloured designs.* P 13.

349	5p. Type **147**	45	20
350	15p. Cheer pheasant (*Catreus wellichii*) (horiz)	80	20
351	1r. Green magpie (*Cissa chinensis*) (horiz)	1·30	50
352	2r. Spiny babbler (*Turdoides nipalensis*)	2·40	75
349/352	*Set of 4*	8·50	4·50

148 Tukuche Himal and Police Flag

149 Map of Nepal and Scout Emblem

(Des K. Karmacharya)

1977 (2 Oct). *First Anniv of Ascent of Tukuche Himal by Police Team.* P 13½ × 13.

353	**148**	1r.25 multicoloured	20	15

(Des K. Karmacharya. Litho Pakistan Security Ptg Corp)

1977 (7 Nov). *25th Anniv of Nepal Scout Movement.* P 13½.

354	**149**	3r.50 multicoloured	45	30

150 Dhanwantari, the Health-giver

151 Map of Nepal and Flags

(Des K. Karmacharya)

1977 (9 Nov). *Health Day.* P 13.

355	**150**	30p. deep bluish green	20	15

(Des K. Karmacharya)

1977 (5 Dec). *26th Consultative Committee Meeting of Colombo Plan, Katmandu.* P 13 × 13½.

356	**151**	1r. multicoloured	35	20

152 King Birendra

153 General Post Office, Katmandu, and Seal

(Des K. Karmacharya)

1977 (28 Dec). *King Birendra's 33rd Birthday.* P 13.

357	**152**	5p. olive-brown	15	15
358		1r. red-brown	35	35

(Des K. Karmacharya)

1978 (14 Apr). *Centenary of Nepalese Post Office. T **153** and similar horiz design.* P 14½ × 14.

359	25p. orange-brown and agate	15	15
360	75p. brown-ochre and agate	35	35

Design:—75r. General Post Office, Kathmandu, and early postmark.

154 South-west Face of Mt. Everest

155 Sun, Ankh and Landscape

(Des K. Karmacharya)

1978 (29 May). *25th Anniv of First Ascent of Mt. Everest. T **154** and similar horiz design.* P 13½ × 13.

361	2r.30 greenish slate & purple-brown	90	50
362	4r. deep violet-blue and emerald	1·30	1·10

Design:—4r. South face of Mt. Everest.

(Des K. K. Karmacharya)

1978 (5 June). *World Environment Day.* P 13½ × 13.

363	**155**	1r. bluish green & reddish orange	35	20

156 Queen Mother Ratna

157 Rapids, Trishuli River

(Des K. K. Karmacharya)

1978 (20 Aug). *Queen Mother's 50th Birthday.* P 14.

364	**156**	2r.30 brown-olive	75	50

(Des K. K. Karmacharya. Litho Rosenbaum Bros, Vienna)

1978 (15 Sept). *Tourism. T **157** and similar multicoloured designs.* P 14.

365	10p. Type **157**	15	10
366	50p. Window, Nara Devi, Katmandu	20	15
367	1r. Mahakali dancer	45	35

158 Lapsi (*Choerospondias axillaris*)

159 Lamp and U.N. Emblem

(Des K. K. Karmacharya)

1978 (31 Oct). *Fruits. T* **158** *and similar multicoloured designs.*
P 13.
368	5p. Type **158**		20	10
369	1r. Katus (*Castanopsis indica*) (*vert*)		50	35
370	1r.25 Rudrakshya (*Elaeocarpus sphaericus*)		75	45

(Des K. K. Karmacharya. Litho Rosenbaum Bros, Vienna)

1978 (10 Dec). 30*th Anniv of Declaration of Human Rights.* P 13½.
371	**159**	25p. deep red-brown and vermilion	15	10
372		1r. chalky blue and vermilion	35	20

160 Wright Flyer I and Boeing 727-100

161 King Birendra

(Des K. K. Karmacharya)

1978 (17 Dec). *AIR. 75th Anniv of First Powered Flight.*
P 13½ × 13.
373	**160**	2r.30 blue and deep brown-ochre	90	75

(Des K. K. Karmacharya. Litho Rosenbaum Bros, Vienna)

1978 (28 Dec). *King Birendra's 34th Birthday.* P 14.
374	**161**	30p. deep violet-blue and red-brown	15	10
375		2r. deep olive-brown & bright violet	60	45

162 Red Machchhindranath and Kamroop and Patan Temples

163 "Buddha's Birth" (carving, Maya Devi Temple)

(Des K. K. Karmacharya)

1979 (27 Apr). *Red Machchhindranath (guardian deity) Festival, Patan.* P 14½ × 14.
376	**162**	75p. purple-brown and bronze-green	35	20

(Des K. K. Karmacharya)

1979 (12 May). *Lumbini Year.* P 13 × 13½.
377	**163**	1r. pale yellow and reddish brown	35	20

164 Planting a Sapling

165 Chariot of Red Machchhindranath

(Des M. N. S. Rana)

1979 (29 June). *Tree Planting Festival.* P 13 × 13½.
378	**164**	2r.30 reddish brown, deep yellow-green and pale yellow	90	75

(Des M. N. S. Rana. Litho Rosenbaum Bros, Vienna)

1979 (25 July). *Bhoto Jatra (Vest Exhibition) Festival.* P 13½.
379	**165**	1r. 25 multicoloured	45	35

166 Nepalese Scouts and Guides

167 Mount Pabil

(Des K. K. Karmacharya)

1979 (20 Aug). *International Year of the Child.* P 14.
380	**166**	1r. yellow-brown	45	35

(Des M. N. S. Rana)

1979 (26 Sept). *Tourism. T* **167** *and similar horiz designs.* P 13.
381		30p. deep bluish green	15	15
382		50p. deep carmine and greenish blue	15	15
383		1r.25 multicoloured	45	45

Designs:—50p. Yajnashala, Swargadwari; 1r.25, Shiva-Parbati (wood carving, Gaddi Baithak Temple).

168 Great Grey Shrike (*Lanius excubitor*)

169 Lichchhavi Coin (obverse)

(Des K. K. Karmacharya. Photo Harrison)

1979 (22 Nov). *International World Pheasant Association Symposium, Kathmandu. T* **168** *and similar multicoloured designs.* P 13½ × 14½ (3r.50) or 14½ × 13½ (others).

(a) POSTAGE.
384		10p. Type **168**	20	15
385		10r. Fire-tailed sunbird (*Aethopyga ignicauda*)	5·50	3·50

(b) AIR. Inscr "AIR MAIL".
386		3r.50 Himalayan monal pheasant (*Lophophorus impejanus*) (*horiz*)	1·90	1·60

(Des M. N. S. Rana. Photo Harrison)

1979 (16 Dec). *Coins.* T **169** *and similar square designs.* P 14½.

387	5p. salmon and chocolate		15	15
	a. Pair. Nos. 387/8		35	
388	5p. salmon and chocolate		15	15
389	15p. grey-blue and indigo		15	15
	a. Pair. Nos. 389/90		35	
390	15p. grey-blue and indigo		15	15
391	1r. slate-blue and deep grey-blue		45	45
	a. Pair. Nos. 391/2		95	
392	1r. slate-blue and deep grey-blue		45	45
387/392 *Set of 6*			1·30	1·30

Designs:—No. 388, Lichchhavi coin (reverse); 389, Malla coin (obverse); 390, Malla coin (reverse); 391, Prithvi Narayan Shah coin (obverse); 392, Prithvi Narayan Shah coin (reverse).

The two stamps of each value were issued together in *se-tenant* pairs within their sheets.

170 King Birendra

171 Samyak Pooja Festival

(Des K. K. Karmacharya. Litho Rosenbaum Bros, Vienna)

1979 (28 Dec). *King Birendra's 35th Birthday.* T **170** *and similar horiz design. Multicoloured.* P 14.

393	25p. Type **170**		15	10
394	2r.30 Reservoir		75	50

(Des K. K. Karmacharya. Litho Rosenbaum Bros, Vienna)

1980 (15 Jan). *Samyak Pooja Festival, Kathmandu.* P 13½.

395	**171**	30p. purple-brown, lt ol-grey & mar	15	15

172 Sacred Basil
(*Ocimum sanctum*)

173 Gyandil Das

(Des M. N. S. Rana. Photo Harrison)

1980 (24 Mar). *Herbs.* T **172** *and similar vert designs. Multicoloured.* P 14 × 14½.

396	5p. Type **172**		15	10
397	30p. Valerian (*Valeriana jatamansi Jones*)		20	10
398	1r. Nepalese pepper (*Zanthoxylum armatum*)		35	20
399	2r.30 Himalayan rhubarb (*Rheum emodi wall*)		75	50
396/399 *Set of 4*			1·30	80

(Des K. K. Karmacharya)

1980 (13 Apr). *Nepalese Writers.* T **173** *and similar horiz designs.* P 13.

400	5p. reddish lilac and ochre		10	10
401	30p. maroon and chestnut		15	10
402	1r. grey-olive and dull blue		30	20
403	2r.30 chalky blue and yellow-green		60	50
400/403 *Set of 4*			1·00	80

Designs:—30p. Siddhidas Amatya; 1r. Pahalman Singh Swanr; 2r.30, Jay Prithvi Bahadur Singh.

174 Everlasting Flame and Temple, Shirsasthan

175 Bhairab Dancer

(Des K. K. Karmacharya. Litho Secura, Singapore)

1980 (14 Sept). *Tourism.* T **174** *and similar vert designs. Multicoloured.* P 14.

404	10p. Type **174**		10	10
405	1r. Godavari Pond		35	20
406	5r. Mt. Dhaulagiri		1·20	90

(Des M. N. S. Rana. Litho Secura, Singapore)

1980 (29 Oct). *World Tourism Conference, Manila, Philippines.* P 14 × 13½.

407	**175**	25r. multicoloured	5·25	4·00

176 King Birendra

177 I.Y.D.P. Emblem and Nepalese Flag

(Des M. N. S. Rana. Litho Rosenbaum Bros, Vienna)

1980 (28 Dec). *King Birendras 36th Birthday.* P 14.

408	**176**	1r. multicoloured	35	20

(Des M. N. S. Rana. Litho Rosenbaum Bros, Vienna)

1981 (1 Jan). *International Year of Disabled Persons.* P 14.

409	**177**	5r. multicoloured	1·50	1·10

178 Nepal Rastra Bank

179 One Anna Stamp, 1881

(Des M. N. S. Rana. Litho Rosenbaum Bros, Vienna)

1981 (26 Apr). *25th Anniv of Nepal Rastra Bank.* P 14.

410	**178**	1r.75 multicoloured	45	35

(Des K. K. Karmacharya. Litho Rosenbaum Bros, Vienna)

1981 (16 July). *Nepalese Postage Stamp Centenary. T* **179** *and similar vert designs.* P 14.

411	10p. deep blue, olive-sepia and black		15	10
412	40p. purple, olive-sepia and black		15	10
413	3r.40 yellow-green, olive-sepia & black		90	75
MS414	117 × 77 mm. Nos. 411/13 (sold at 5r.)		2·20	2·20

Designs:—40p. Two anna stamp, 1881; 3r.40, Four anna stamp, 1881.

180 Nepalese Flag and Association Emblem

181 Hand holding Stamp

182 King Birendra

(Des K. K. Karmacharya. Litho Rosenbaum Bros, Vienna)

1981 (30 Oct). *70th Council Meeting of International Hotel Association, Kathmandu.* P 14.

415	**180**	1r.75 multicoloured	45	35

(Des K. K. Karmacharya. Litho Rosenbaum Bros, Vienna)

1981 (27 Dec). *"Nepal 81" Stamp Exhibition, Katmandu.* P 14.

416	**181**	40p. multicoloured	15	10

(Des M. N. S. Rana. Litho Rosenbaum Bros, Vienna)

1981 (28 Dec). *King Birendra's 37th Birthday.* P 14.

417	**182**	1r. multicoloured	30	20

183 Image of Hrishikesh, Ridi

184 Academy Building

(Des K. K. Karmacharya. Litho Rosenbaum Bros, Vienna)

1981 (30 Dec). *Tourism. T* **183** *and similar vert designs. Multicoloured.* P 14.

418	5p. Type **183**		10	10
419	25p. Tripura Sundari Temple, Baitadi		10	10
420	2r. Mt. Langtang Lirung		45	20

(Des M. N. S. Rana. Litho Carl Ueberreuter, Vienna)

1982 (23 June). *25th Anniv of Royal Nepal Academy.* P 14.

421	**184**	40p. multicoloured	15	15

185 Balakrishna Sama

186 "Intelsat V" and Dish Aerial

(Des K. K. Karmacharya. Litho Carl Ueberreuter, Vienna)

1982 (21 July). *First Death Anniv of Balakrishna Sama (writer).* P 13½.

422	**185**	1r. multicoloured	20	20

(Des K. K. Karmacharya. Litho Secura, Singapore)

1982 (7 Nov). *Sagarmatha Satellite Earth Station, Balambu.* P 14.

423	**186**	5r. multicoloured	1·30	75

187 Mt. Nuptse

188 Games Emblem and Weights

(Des K. K. Karmacharya. Litho Carl Ueberreuter, Vienna)

1982 (18 Nov). *50th Anniv of Union of International Alpinist Associations. T* **187** *and similar multicoloured designs.* P 14.

424	25p. Type **187**		15	15
	a. Horiz strip of 3. Nos. 424/6		1·40	
425	2r. Mt. Lhotse (31 × 31 *mm*)		50	35
426	3r. Mt. Everest (39 × 31 *mm*)		1·10	50

Nos. 424/6 were issued together in *se-tenant* strips of three, each strip forming a composite design.

(Des M. N. S. Rana. Litho Secura, Singapore)

1982 (19 Nov). *Ninth Asian Games, New Delhi.* P 14.

427	**188**	3r.40 multicoloured	90	75

189 Indra Sarobar Lake

190 King Birendra

(Des M. N. S. Rana. Litho Carl Ueberreuter, Vienna)

1982 (8 Dec). *Kulekhani Hydro-electric Project.* P 14.

428	**189**	2r. multicoloured	50	35

(Des M. N. S. Rana. Litho Secura, Singapore)

1982 (28 Dec). *King Birendra's 38th Birthday.* P 12½.

429	**190**	5p. multicoloured	15	15

191 N.I.D.C. Emblem   **192** Boeing 727 over Himalayas

(Des K. K. Karmacharya. Litho Carl Ueberreuter, Vienna)
1983 (15 June). *25th Anniv* (1984) *of Nepal Industrial Development Corporation.* P 14.
430   **191**   50p. multicoloured   15   15

(Des M. N. S. Rana. Litho Secura, Singapore)
1983 (1 Aug). *25th Anniv of Royal Nepal Airlines.* P 13½.
431   **192**   1r. multicoloured   45   20

193 W.C.Y. Emblem and Nepalese Flag   **194** Sarangi

(Des M. N. S. Rana. Litho Secura, Singapore)
1983 (30 Oct). *World Communications Year.* P 12.
432   **193**   10p. multicoloured   15   15

(Des K. K. Karmacharya. Litho Secura, Singapore)
1983 (3 Nov). *Musical Instruments. T* **194** *and similar vert designs. Multicoloured.* P 12.
433   5p. Type **194**   10   10
434   10p. Kwota (drum)   10   10
435   50p. Narashinga (horn)   20   20
436   1r. Murchunga   35   35
433/436 *Set of 4*   70   70

195 Chakrapani Chalise   **196** King Birendra and Doves

(Des M. N. S. Rana. Litho Secura, Singapore)
1983 (20 Dec). *Birth Centenary of Chakrapani Chalise (poet).* P 12.
437   **195**   4r.50 multicoloured   45   35

(Des K. K. Karmacharya. Litho Carl Ueberreuter, Vienna)
1983 (28 Dec). *King Birendra's 39th Birthday.* P 14.
438   **196**   5r. multicoloured   50   30

197 Barahkshetra Temple and Image of Barah   **198** Auditing Accounts

(Des M. N. S. Rana. Litho Carl Ueberreuter, Vienna)
1983 (30 Dec). *Tourism. T* **197** *and similar horiz designs. Multicoloured.* P 14.
439   1r. Type **197**   10   10
440   2r.20 Temple, Triveni   20   15
441   6r. Mt. Cho-oyu   50   35

(Des K. K. Karmacharya. Litho Carl Ueberreuter, Vienna)
1984 (28 June). *25th Anniv of Auditor General.* P 14.
442   **198**   25p. multicoloured   50   45

199 Antenna and Emblem   **200** University Emblem

(Des K. K. Karmacharya. Litho Carl Ueberreuter, Vienna)
1984 (1 July). *20th Anniv of Asia–Pacific Broadcasting Union.* P 14.
443   **199**   5r. multicoloured   1·30   1·10

(Des M. N. S. Rana. Litho Carl Ueberreuter, Vienna)
1984 (8 July). *25th Anniv of Tribhuvan University.* P 14.
444   **200**   50p. multicoloured   20   15

201 Boxing   **202** Family and Emblem

(Des K. K. Karmacharya. Litho Carl Ueberreuter, Vienna)
1984 (5 Aug). *Olympic Games, Los Angeles.* P 14.
445   **201**   10r. multicoloured   2·20   1·50

(Des K. K. Karmacharya. Litho Carl Ueberreuter, Vienna)
1984 (18 Sept). *25th Anniv of Nepal Family Planning Association.* P 14.
446   **202**   1r. multicoloured   20   15

203 National Flag and Emblem

204 Gharial (*Gavialis gangeticus*)

(Des M. N. S. Rana. Litho Carl Ueberreuter, Vienna)

1984 (22 Sept). *Social Service Day.* P 14.
447 **203** 5p. multicoloured 15 15

(Des K. K. Karmacharya. Litho Carl Ueberreuter, Vienna)

1984 (30 Nov). *Wildlife. T* **204** *and similar horiz designs. Multicoloured.* P 14.
448 10p. Type **204** 15 15
449 25p. Snow leopard (*Panthera uncia*) . . . 20 20
450 50p. Blackbuck (*Antilope cervicapra*) . . . 35 35

205 "Vishnu as Giant" (stone carving)

206 King Birendra

(Des M. N. S. Rana. Litho Carl Ueberreuter, Vienna)

1984 (21 Dec). *Tourism. T* **205** *and similar multicoloured designs.* P 14.
451 10p. Type **205** 10 10
452 1r. Temple of Chhinna Masta Bhagavati and sculpture (*horiz*) 20 15
453 5r. Mt. Api . . . . 1·30 80

(Des K. K. Karmacharya. Litho Carl Ueberreuter, Vienna)

1984 (28 Dec). *King Birendra's* 40*th Birthday.* P 14.
454 **206** 1r. multicoloured 20 15

207 Animals and Mountains

208 Shiva

(Des K. K. Karmacharya. Litho Carl Ueberreuter, Vienna)

1985 (6 May). *Sagarmatha (Mt. Everest) National Park.* P 14.
455 **207** 10r. multicoloured . . . . 4·00 1·50

(Des M. N. S. Rana. Litho Carl Ueberreuter, Vienna)

1985 (30 May). *Traditional Painting. T* **208** *and similar multicoloured designs showing details of cover of* Shiva Dharma Purana *(book).* P 14.
456 50p. Type **208** 20 20
     a. Horiz strip of 5. Nos. 456/60 . . . 1·20
457 50p. Multi-headed Shiva talking to woman 20 20
458 50p. Brahma and Vishnu making offering (15 × 22 *mm*) 20 20
459 50p. Shiva in single- and multi-headed forms 20 20
460 50p. Shiva talking to woman 20 20
456/460 Set of 5 . . . . 90 90

Nos. 456/60 were issued together in horizontal *se-tenant* strips of five within the sheet.
Nos. 456/60 were also issued in horizontal strips imperf between from a limited printing.

209 U.N. Flag

210 Lungs and Bacilli

(Des K. K. Karmacharya. Litho Carl Ueberreuter, Vienna)

1985 (24 Oct). 40*th Anniv of United Nations Organization.* P 13½.
461 **209** 5r. multicoloured . . . . 1·10 75

(Des K. K. Karmacharya. Litho State Ptg Wks, Vienna)

1985 (25 Nov). 14*th Eastern Regional Tuberculosis Conference, Kathmandu.* P 13½ × 14.
462 **210** 25r. multicoloured . . . . 5·25 3·75

211 Flags of Member Countries

212 Jaleshwar Temple

(Des M. N. S. Rana. Litho Carl Ueberreuter, Vienna)

1985 (8 Dec). *First South Asian Association for Regional Co-operation Summit.* P 14.
463 **211** 5r. multicoloured . . . . 1·10 75

(Des M. N. S. Rana. Litho Carl Ueberreuter, Vienna)

1985 (15 Dec). *Tourism. T* **212** *and similar horiz designs. Multicoloured.* P 13½.
464 10p. Type **212** 10 10
465 1r. Temple of Goddess Shaileshwari, Silgadi 20 15
466 2r. Phoksundo Lake 45 20

213 I.Y.Y. Emblem

214 King Birendra

(Des K. K. Karmacharya. Litho Carl Ueberreuter, Vienna)

1985 (21 Dec). *International Youth Year.* P 14.
467 **213** 1r. multicoloured 20 15

(Des M. N. S. Rana. Litho Carl Ueberreuter, Vienna)

1985 (28 Dec). *King Birendra's* 41*st Birthday.* P 14.
468 **214** 50p. multicoloured 15 15

215 Devi Ghat Hydro-
electric Project

216 Emblem

(Des M. N. S. Rana. Litho Carl Ueberreuter, Vienna)
1985 (28 Dec). P 14.
469 **215** 2r. multicoloured 50 35

(Des K. K. Karmacharya. Litho Carl Ueberreuter, Vienna)
1986 (10 Apr). *25th Anniv of Panchayat System (partyless government)*. P 13½.
470 **216** 4r. multicoloured 90 75

217 Royal
Crown

218 Pharping Hydro-electric
Station

(Photo Security Ptg Press, Nasik, India)
1986 (9 Oct)–**87**. *T* **217** *and similar vert designs.* P 13.
471 5p. brown and deep brown 10 10
472 10p. new blue 15 15
473 50p. turquoise-blue (14.4.87) 15 15
474 1r. light brown and ochre 20 20
471/474 Set of 4 . . . . 55 55
Designs:—5, 50p. Pashupati Temple; 10p. Mayadevi Temple of
Lumbini (Buddha's birthplace).

Nos. 475/9 are vacant.

(Des M. N. S. Rana. Litho Carl Ueberreuter, Vienna)
1986 (9 Oct). *75th Anniv of Pharping Hydro-electric Power Station.* P 13½.
480 **218** 15p. multicoloured 15 15

219 Emblem and Map

220 Mt. Pumori, Himalayas

(Des K. K. Karmacharya. Litho State Ptg Wks, Vienna)
1986 (26 Oct). *25th Anniv of Asian Productivity Organization.* P 13½ × 14.
481 **219** 1r. multicoloured 20 15

(Des M. N. S. Rana. Litho State Ptg Wks, Vienna)
1986 (26 Oct). *Tourism. T* **220** *and similar horiz design.* Multicoloured. P 13½ (60p.) or 13½ × 13 (8r.).
482 60p. "Budhanikantha" (sculpture of
reclining Vishnu), Kathmandu Valley
(38 × 22 *mm*) 15 10
483 8r. Type **220** . . . . 1·50 1·10

221 King Birendra

222 I.P.Y. Emblem

(Des M. N. S. Rana. Litho State Ptg Wks, Vienna)
1986 (28 Dec). *King Birendra's 42nd Birthday.* P 13 × 13½.
484 **221** 1r. multicoloured 20 15

(Des K. K. Karmacharya. Litho State Ptg Wks, Vienna)
1986 (28 Dec). *International Peace Year.* P 14.
485 **222** 10r. multicoloured . . . . . 1·60 1·30

223 National Flag and Council Emblem

(Des K. K. Karmacharya. Litho State Ptg Wks, Vienna)
1987 (22 Sept). *Tenth Anniv of National Social Service Co-ordination Council.* P 13½.
486 **223** 1r. multicoloured 20 15

224 Emblem and Forest

(Des K. K. Karmacharya. Litho State Ptg Wks, Vienna)
1987 (28 Oct). *First Nepal Scout Jamboree, Kathmandu.* P 14.
487 **224** 1r. reddish brown, reddish orge &
dp bl 45 15

225 Ashokan Pillar and Maya
Devi

226 Emblem

(Des M. N. S. Rana. Litho State Ptg Wks, Vienna)
1987 (28 Oct). *Lumbini (Buddha's birthplace) Development Project.* P 14.
488 **225** 4r. multicoloured 75 50

(Des M. N. S. Rana. Litho State Ptg Wks, Vienna)

1987 (2 Nov). *Third South Asian Association for Regional Co-operation Summit, Kathmandu.* P 14.
489   **226**   60p. gold and carmine-lake   15   15

227 Emblem

228 Kashthamandap,
Katmundu

(Des M. N. S. Rana. Litho State Ptg Wks, Vienna)

1987 (10 Nov). *25th Anniv of Rastriya Samachar Samiti (news service).* P 14.
490   **227**   4r. blackish purple, cobalt & carm-
red   75   50

(Des K. K. Karmacharya. Photo Security Ptg Press, Nasik, India)

1987 (21 Dec). *Tourism.* P 13 × 13½.
491   **228**   25p. multicoloured   15   15

229 Gyawali

230 Emblem

(Des K. K. Karmacharya. Photo Security Ptg Press, Nasik, India)

1987 (21 Dec). *89th Birth Anniv of Surya Bikram Gyawali (historian).* P 13 × 13½.
492   **229**   60p. multicoloured   15   15

(Des K. K. Karmacharya. Litho State Ptg Wks, Vienna)

1987 (21 Dec). *International Year of Shelter for the Homeless.* P 14.
493   **230**   5r. multicoloured   90   75

231 King Birendra

232 Mt. Kanjiroba

(Des K. K. Karmacharya. Litho State Ptg Wks, Vienna)

1987 (28 Dec). *King Birendra's 43rd Birthday.* P 14½ × 13½.
494   **231**   25p. multicoloured   15   15

(Des K. K. Karmacharya. Litho State Ptg Wks, Vienna)

1987 (30 Dec). *Tourism.* P 13½.
495   **232**   10r. multicoloured . . . .   1·60   1·10

233 Crown Prince
Dipendra

234 Baby in Incubator

(Des K. K. Karmacharya. Litho State Ptg Wks, Vienna)

1988 (28 Mar). *Crown Prince Dipendra's 17th Birthday.* P 14.
496   **233**   1r. multicoloured   20   15

(Des M. N. S. Rana. Litho State Ptg Wks, Vienna)

1988 (8 Apr). *25th Anniv of Kanti Children's Hospital, Kathmandu.* P 14.
497   **234**   60p. multicoloured   15   15

235 Swamp Deer

236 Laxmi, Goddess of
Wealth

(Des M. N. S. Rana. Litho State Ptg Wks, Vienna)

1988 (8 Apr). *12th Anniv of Royal Shukla Phanta Wildlife Reserve.* P 14.
498   **235**   60p. multicoloured   35   15

(Des K. K. Karmacharya. Litho State Ptg Wks, Vienna)

1988 (8 Apr). *50th Anniv of Nepal Bank Ltd.* P 14.
499   **236**   2r. multicoloured   35   20

237 Queen Mother

238 Hands protecting
Blood Drop

(Des K. K. Karmacharya. Litho State Ptg Wks, Vienna)

1988 (20 Aug). *60th Birthday of Queen Mother.* P 14 × 13½.
500   **237**   5r. multicoloured   90   75

(Des M. N. S. Rana. Litho State Ptg Wks, Vienna)

1988 (12 Sept). *25th Anniv of Nepal Red Cross Society.* P 14 × 13½.
501   **238**   1r. deep rose-red and red-brown . .   20   15

239 Temple and Statue   **240** King Birendra

(Des M. N. S. Rana. Litho Harrison)

1988 (16 Oct). *Temple of Goddess Bindhyabasini, Pokhara.* P 14½.

502   **239**   15p. multicoloured   15   15

(Des M. N. S. Rana. Litho State Ptg Wks, Vienna)

1988 (28 Dec). *King Birendra's 44th Birthday.* P 14.

503   **240**   4r. multicoloured   75   45

241 Temple   **242** Emblem   **243** S.A.A.R.C.
Emblem

(Des K. K. Karmacharya. Litho State Ptg Wks, Vienna)

1989 (3 Mar). *Pashupati Area Development Trust.* P 13½.

504   **241**   1r. multicoloured   20   15

(Des K. K. Karmacharya. Litho State Ptg Wks, Vienna)

1989 (5 Oct). *Tenth Anniv of Asia–Pacific Telecommunity.* P 14.

505   **242**   4r. emerald, black and bright
violet   45   30

(Des M. N. S. Rana. Litho State Ptg Wks, Vienna)

1989 (8 Dec). *South Asian Association for Regional Co-operation Year against Drug Abuse and Trafficking.* P 13 × 13½.

506   **243**   60p. multicoloured   15   15

244 King Birendra   **245** Child Survival
Measures

(Des M. N. S. Rana. Litho State Ptg Wks, Vienna)

1989 (28 Dec). *King Birendra's 45th Birthday.* P 13½ × 14½.

507   **244**   2r. multicoloured   35   15

(Des K. K. Karmacharya. Litho State Ptg Wks, Vienna)

1989 (31 Dec). *Child Survival Campaign.* P 13½.

508   **245**   1r. multicoloured   15   15

246 Lake Rara   **247** Mt. Amadablam

(Des M. N. S. Rana. Litho Harrison)

1989 (31 Dec). *Rara National Park.* P 14½ × 15.

509   **246**   4r. multicoloured   45   30

(Des M. N. S. Rana. Litho State Ptg Wks, Vienna)

1989 (31 Dec). *Tourism.* P 14.

510   **247**   5r. multicoloured   75   35

248 Crown Prince
Dipendra   **249** Temple of
Manakamana,
Gorkha

(Des K. K. Karmacharya. Litho State Ptg Wks, Vienna)

1990 (3 Jan). *Crown Prince Dipendra's Coming-of-Age.* P 14.

511   **248**   1r. multicoloured   15   15

(Des K. K. Karmacharya. Litho Harrison)

1990 (12 Apr). P 14½.

512   **249**   60p. grey-black and blackish
violet   15   15

250 Emblem and
Children   **251** Emblem

(Des K. K. Karmacharya. Litho State Ptg Wks, Vienna)

1990 (20 Aug). *25th Anniv of Nepal Children's Organization.* P 14.

513   **250**   1r. multicoloured   15   15

(Des K. K. Karmacharya. Litho State Ptg Wks, Vienna)

1990 (13 Sept). *Centenary of Bir Hospital.* P 14 × 13½.

514   **251**   60p. bright scarlet, dp brt blue &
yellow   15   15

252 Emblem

253 Goddess and Bageshwori Temple, Nepalgunj

(Des M. N. S. Rana. Litho Harrison)

1990 (9 Oct). *20th Anniv of Asian–Pacific Postal Training Centre, Bangkok.* P 14½.
515 **252** 4r. multicoloured 50 30

(Des K. K. Karmacharya (1r.), M. N. S. Rana (5r.). Litho State Ptg Wks, Vienna)

1990 (24 Dec). *Tourism. T 253 and similar horiz design. Multicoloured.* P 13½ (1r.) or 14 (5r.).
516 1r. Type **253** 15 15
517 5r. Mt. Saipal (36 × 27 *mm*) 60 35

254 Leisure Activities

255 King Birendra

(Des K. K. Karmacharya. Litho Harrison)

1990 (24 Dec). *South Asian Association for Regional Co-operation Girls' Year.* P 14½.
518 **254** 4r.60 multicoloured 25 15

(Des M. N. S. Rana. Litho State Ptg Wks, Vienna)

1990 (28 Dec). *King Birendra's 46th Birthday.* P 14.
519 **255** 2r. multicoloured 20 15

256 Koirala

257 Indian Rhinoceros and Lake

(Des K. K. Karmacharya. Litho State Ptg Wks, Viennna)

1990 (31 Dec). *76th Birth Anniv of Bisweswar Prasad Koirala (Prime Minister, 1959–60).* P 14.
520 **256** 60p. black, yellow-orange & brt carmine 10 10

(Des M. N. S. Rana. Litho Harrison)

1991 (10 Feb). *Royal Chitwan National Park.* P 14½.
521 **257** 4r. multicoloured 75 35

258 Flower and Crowd

259 Official and Villagers

260 Federation and Jubilee Emblems

(Des K. K. Karmacharya. Litho State Ptg Wks, Vienna)

1991 (9 Apr). *First Anniv of Abrogation of Ban on Political Parties.* P 14.
522 **258** 1r. multicoloured 15 15

(Des K. K. Karmacharya. Litho State Ptg Wks, Vienna)

1991 (3 May). *National Population Census.* P 14½ × 13½.
523 **259** 60p. multicoloured 15 15

(Des M. N. S. Rana. Litho State Ptg Wks, Vienna)

1991 (15 Aug). *25th Anniv of Federation of Nepalese Chambers of Commerce and Industry.* P 14 × 13½.
524 **260** 3r. multicoloured 35 20

261 Crosses

262 Delegates

(Des M. N. S. Rana. Litho State Ptg Wks, Vienna)

1991 (4 Sept). *25th Anniv (1990) of Nepal Junior Red Cross.* P 14½ × 14.
525 **261** 60p. carmine-red and brownish grey 10 10

(Des K. K. Karrnacharya. Litho Harrison)

1991 (10 Sept). *First Session of Revived Parliament.* P 14½.
526 **262** 1r. multicoloured 15 15

263 King Birendra making Speech

264 Rama and Janaki (statues) and Vivaha Mandap

(Des K. K. Karmacharya. Litho Harrison)

1991 (9 Nov). *Constitution Day.* P 15 × 14.
527 **263** 50p. multicoloured 10 10

(Des M. N. S. Rana. Litho Courvoisier)

1991 (11 Dec). *Fifth Anniv of Rebuilt Vivaha Mandap Pavilion, Janaki Temple.* P 11½.
528 **264** 1r. multicoloured 15 15

265 Mt. Kumbhakarna   **266** King Birendra

(Des M. N. S. Rana. Litho State Ptg Wks, Vienna)

1991 (11 Dec). *Tourism*. P 13½ × 14½.
529 **265** 4r.60 multicoloured 50   30

(Des K. K. Karmacharya. Litho State Ptg Wks, Vienna)

1991 (28 Dec). *King Birendra's 47th Birthday*. P 14½ × 13½.
530 **266** 8r. multicoloured 90   50

267 Houses   **268** Glass magnifying
Society Emblem

(Des M. N. S. Rana. Litho State Ptg Wks, Vienna)

1991 (28 Dec). *South Asian Association for Regional Co-operation Year of Shelter*. P 13½ × 14.
531 **267** 9r. multicoloured 90   60

(Des K. K. Karmacharya. Litho Pakistan Security Ptg Corp)

1992 (11 July). *25th Anniv* (1991) *of Nepal Philatelic Society*. P 13 × 13½.
532 **268** 4r. multicoloured 45   30

269 Rainbow over River   **270** Nutrition, Education
Valley   and Health Care

(Des K. K. Karmacharya. Litho Harrison)

1992 (24 Oct). *Environmental Protection*. P 12½ × 13.
533 **269** 60p. multicoloured 15   15

(Des M. N. S. Rana. Litho Pakistan Security Ptg Corp)

1992 (24 Oct). *Rights of the Child*. P 13½.
534 **270** 1r. multicoloured 15   15

271 Thakurdwara Temple,   **272** Bank
Bardiya   Emblem

(Des K. K. Karmacharya. Litho Courvoisier)

1992 (10 Nov). *Temples*. T **271** *and similar horiz designs. Multicoloured*. P 14½ × 14.

(a) POSTAGE.

535	75p. Type **271**		10	10
536	1r. Namo Buddha Temple, Kavre	. . .	10	10
537	2r. Narijhowa Temple, Mustang	. . . .	15	10

(b) AIR. Inscr "AIR MAIL".
538	11r. Dantakali Temple, Bijayapur	. . . .	1·00	65
535/538	*Set of 4*	. . . . . .	1·20	85

(Des M. N. S. Rana. Photo Security Ptg Press, Nasik, India)

1992 (20 Dec). *25th Anniv of Agricultural Development Bank*. P 13 × 13½.
539 **272** 40p. lake-brown and green 15   15

273 Pin-tailed Green   **274** King Birendra
Pigeon   exchanging Swords with
                      Goddess Sree Bhadrakali

(Des K. K. Karmacharya. Litho Courvoisier)

1992 (20 Dec). *Birds*. T **273** *and similar horiz designs. Multicoloured*. P 11½.
540	1r. Type **273**	. . . . .	10	10
541	3r. Bohemian waxwing	. . . . .	30	15
542	25r. Rufous-tailed desert (inscr "Finch") lark	. . . .	2·20	1·50

(Des M. N. S. Rana. Litho Harrison)

1992 (28 Dec). *King Birendra's 48th Birthday*. P 12½ × 13.
543 **274** 7r. multicoloured 60   35

275 Pandit Kulchandra   **276** Shooting and
Gautam   Marathon

(Des M. N. S. Rana. Litho Courvoisier)

1992 (31 Dec). *Poets*. T **275** *and similar vert designs. Multicoloured, frame colour given in brackets*. P 11½.
544	1r. Type **275**	. . . . .	15	10
545	1r. Chittadhar Hridaya (drab)	. . . . .	15	10
546	1r. Vidyapati (stone)	. . . . .	15	10
547	1r. Teongsi Sirijunga (grey)	. . . . .	15	10
544/547	*Set of 4*	. . . . . .	55	35

(Des K. K. Karmacharya. Litho Courvoisier)

1992 (31 Dec). *Olympic Games, Barcelona*. P 11½.
548 **276** 25r. multicoloured . . . . 2·20   1·50

277 Golden Mahseer (*Tor putitora*)

278 Antibodies attacking Globe

(Des K. K. Karmacharya. Photo Courvoisier)

1993 (6 Aug). *Fishes. T* **277** *and similar horiz designs. Multicoloured. Granite paper.* P 11½.
549   25p. Type **277** 10   10
550   1r. Marinka (*Schizothorax plagiostomus*) 10   10
551   5r. Indian eel (*Anguilla bengalensis*) . . 20   10
552   10r. False loach (*Psilorhynchus pseudecheneis*) 35   20
549/552 *Set of 4* 65   45
MS553 90 × 70 mm. Nos. 549/52 . . . . 1·80   1·80

(Des M. N. S. Rana. Litho State Ptg Wks, Vienna)

1993 (1 Dec). *World AIDS Day.* P 13½ × 14½.
554   **278**   1r. multicoloured 15   15

279 Tanka Prasad Acharya (Prime Minister, 1956–57)

280 Bagh Bairab Temple, Kirtipur

(Des M. N. S. Rana. Litho State Ptg Wks, Vienna)

1993 (2 Dec). *Death Anniversaries. T* **279** *and similar vert designs. Multicolorued.* P 13½.
555   25p. Type **279** (first anniv) 10   10
556   1r. Sungdare Sherpa (mountaineer) (fourth anniv) 10   10
557   7r. Siddhi Charan Shrestha (poet) (first anniv) 50   30
558   15r. Falgunanda (religious leader) (44th anniv) . . . . . 1·10   75
555/558 *Set of 4* . . . . 1·60   1·10

(Des K. K. Karmacharya. Litho State Ptg Wks, Vienna)

1993 (28 Dec). *Holy Places. T* **280** *and similar horiz designs. Multicoloured.* P 13½ × 14½.
559   1r.50 Halesi Mahadev cave (hiding place of Shiva), Khotang 10   10
560   5r. Devghat (gods' bathing place), Tanahun 35   20
561   8r. Type **280** 60   35

281 Tushahiti Fountain, Sundari Chowk, Patan

282 King Birendra

(Des M. N. S. Rana. Litho State Ptg Wks, Vienna)

1993 (28 Dec). *Tourism. T* **281** *and similar horiz design. Multicoloured.* P 13½ × 14½.
562   5r. Type **281** 35   20
563   8r. White-water rafting 60   35

(Des K. K. Karmacharya. Litho State Ptg Wks, Vienna)

1993 (28 Dec). *King Birendra's 49th Birthday.* P 14.
564   **282**   10r. multicoloured 75   45

283 Monument

284 Mt. Everest

1994 (17 May–Sept). *T* **283/4** *and similar designs. Photo.* P 14½ × 13½ (5r.) or 14½ (others).
565   **283**   20p. chocolate 10   10
566   —   25p. brown-red 10   10
567   —   30p. deep dull green 10   10
568   **284**   1r. multicoloured 15   15
569   —   5r. multicoloured (22.9) 35   20
565/569 *Set of 5* 75   60
Designs: 20 × 22 *mm*—25p. State arms. 22 × 20 *mm*—30p. Lumbini. 25 × 15 *mm*—5r. Map of Nepal, crown and state arms and flag.

285 Pasang Sherpa

286 Cigarette, Lungs and Crab's Claws

1994 (2 Sept). *First Death Anniv of Pasang Sherpa (mountaineer). Litho.* P 14.
570   **285**   10r. multicoloured 75   45

1994 (26 Sept). *Anti-smoking Campaign. Litho.* P 13½ × 14.
571   **286**   1r. multicoloured 15   15

287 Postal Delivery

288 Khuda

1994 (9 Oct). *Litho.* P 13 × 13½.
572   **287**   1r.50 multicoloured 15   15

1994 (9 Oct). *Weapons. T* **288** *and similar square designs. Multicoloured. Litho.* P 13½ × 14.
573   5r. Kukris (three swords and two scabbards) 35   20
   a. block of 4. Nos. 573/6 . . . . 2·10
574   5r. Type **288** 35   20
575   5r. Dhaal (swords and shield) . . . 35   20
576   5r. Katari (two daggers) 35   20
573/576 *Set of 4* . . . . 1·25   75

289 Workers and Emblem

1994 (9 Oct). *75th Anniv of International Labour Organization. Litho.* P 13.
577 **289** 15r. gold, bright blue & dp
ultramarine . . . . 1·10 75

290 Landscape

1994 (23 Oct). *World Food Day. Litho.* P 14.
578 **290** 25r. multicoloured . . . . . . 1·80 1·20

291 *Dendrobium densiflorum*   **292** Family

1994 (7 Nov). *Orchids.* T **291** *and similar vert designs. Litho.* P 14 × 13½.
579 10r. Type **291** 75 45
   a. Block of 4. Nos. 579/82 . . . . . 3·25
580 10r. *Coelogyne flaccida* 75 45
581 10r. *Cymbidium devonianum* 75 45
582 10r. *Coelogyne corymbosa* 75 45
579/582 *Set of 4* . . . . 2·75 1·60

1994 (5 Dec). *International Year of the Family. Litho.* P 12½ × 13.
583 **292** 9r. emerald, green and vermilion . . 65 45

293 Emblem and Airplane   **294** *Russula nepalensis*

1994 (7 Dec). *50th Anniv of International Civil Aviation Organization. Litho.* P 12½ × 13.
584 **293** 11r. bright blue, gold and deep
blue 80 50

1994 (20 Dec). *Fungi.* T **294** *and similar vert designs. Litho.* P 14.
585 7r. Type **294** 50 30
586 7r. *Morchella conica* 50 30
587 7r. *Amanita caesarea* 50 30
588 7r. *Cordyceps sinensis* 50 30
585/588 *Set of 4* . . . . 1·80 1·20

295 Dharanidhar koirala (poet)   **296** King Birendra, Flag, Map and Crown

1994 (23 Dec). *Celebrities.* T **295** *and similar multicoloured designs. Litho.* P 14 × 13½ (6r.) or 13½ × 14 (others).
589 1r. Type **295** 10 10
590 2r. Narayan Gopal Guruwacharya
(singer) 15 10
591 6r. Bahadur Shah (*vert*) 45 30
592 7r. Balaguru Shadananda 50 30
589/592 *Set of 4* . . . . 1·00

1994 (28 Dec). *King Birendra's 50th Birthday (1st issue). Litho.* P 14.
593 **296** 9r. multicoloured 65 45
See also No. 621.

297 Lake Tilicho, Manang   **298** Health Care

1994 (28 Dec). *Tourism.* T **297** *and similar multicoloured design. Litho.* P 13½ × 14 (9r.) or 14 × 13½ (11r.).
594 9r. Type **297** 65 45
595 11r. Taleju Temple, Katmandu (*vert*) . . 80 50

1994 (30 Dec). *Children's Activities.* T **298** *and similar square designs. Multicoloured. Litho.* P 14.
596 1r. Type **298** 10 10
   a. Block of 4. Nos. 596/9 . . . . . .
597 1r. Classroom 10 10
598 1r. Playground equipment 10 10
599 1r. Stamp collecting 10 10
596/599 *Set of 4* . . . . 1·10 75

299 Singhaduarbar

300 Crab on Lungs

1995 (29 May). *T 299 and similar design. Litho.* P 14 × 14½ (10p.) or 14½ × 14 (50p.).
600	10p. emerald	10	10
601	50p. deep violet-blue	10	10

Design: *Vert*—50p. Pashupati.

1995 (23 June). *Anti-cancer Campaign. Litho.* P 14½ × 13½.
602	**300** 2r. multicoloured	15	15

301 Chandra Man Singh Maskey (artist)

302 Bhakti Thapa (soldier)

1995 (11 July). *Celebrities. T 301 and similar vert designs. Multicoloured. Litho.* P 14.
603	3r. Type **301**	20	15
	a. Block of 4. Nos. 603/6	95	
604	3r. Parijat (writer)	20	15
605	3r. Bhim Nidhi Tiwari (writer)	20	15
606	3r. Yuddha Prasad Mishra (writer)	20	15

Nos. 603/6 were issued together in *se-tenant* blocks of four within the sheet.

1995 (1 Sept). *Celebrities. T 302 and similar vert designs. Multicoloured. Litho.* P 14 × 13½.
607	15p. Type **302**	10	10
608	1r. Madan Bhandari (politician)	10	10
609	4r. Prakash Raj Kaphley (human rights activist)	10	15

303 Gaur (*Bos gaurus*)

304 Anniversary Emblem

1995 (1 Sept). *"Singapore '95" International Stamp Exhibition. Mammals. T 303 and similar horiz designs. Multicoloured. Granite paper. Photo.* P 12.
610	10r. Type **303**	75	45
	a. Block of 4. Nos. 610/13	3·25	
611	10r. Lynx (*Felis lynx*)	75	45
612	10r. Assam macaque (*Macaca assamensis*)	75	45
613	10r. Striped hyena (*Hyaena hyaena*)	75	45

Nos. 610/13 were issued together in *se-tenant* blocks of four within the sheet.

1995 (16 Oct). *50th Anniv of Food and Agriculture Organization. Litho.* P 13½ × 14½.
614	**304** 7r. multicoloured	50	30

305 Figures around Emblem

306 Bhimeswor Temple, Dolakha

1995 (22 Oct). *50th Anniv of United Nations Organization. Granite paper. Photo.* P 12 × 11½.
615	**305** 50r. multicoloured	3·75	2·40

1995 (8 Nov–23 Dec). *Tourism. T 306 and similar multicoloured designs. Litho.* P 14½ × 13½ (1r.), 13½ × 14½ (5, 7r.), 13½ (18r.) or 14 (20r.).
616	1r. Type **306**	10	10
617	5r. Ugra Tara Temple, Dadeldhura (*horiz*)	35	20
618	7r. Mt. Nampa (*horiz*)	50	30
619	18r. Nrity Aswora (traditional Pauba painting) (27 × 39 *mm*)	1·30	90
620	20r. Lumbini (Buddha's birthplace) (28 × 28 *mm*) (23.12)	1·50	95

307 King Birendra

308 Anniversary Emblem

1995 (27 Dec). *King Birendra's 50th Birthday (1994) (2nd issue). Granite paper. Photo.* P 12.
621	**307** 1r. multicoloured	15	15

1995 (27 Dec). *Tenth Anniv of South Asian Association for Regional Co-operation. Litho.* P 13½.
622	**308** 10r. multicoloured	75	45

309 King Birendra

310 Karnali Bridge

1995 (28 Dec). *King Birendra's 51st Birthday. Litho.* P 13 × 13½.
623   **309**   12r. multicoloured   90   60

(Des M. N. S. Rana. Litho State Ptg Wks, Vienna)
1996 (13 May). P 14.
624   **310**   7r. multicoloured   50   30

311 State Arms

312 Kaji Kalu Pande (soldier and royal adviser)

1996 (2 Aug). *Litho.* P 14½ × 14.
625   **311**   25p. brown-red   15   15

(Des K. K. Karmacharya. Litho State Ptg Wks, Vienna)
1996 (6 Aug). *Political Figures. T* **312** *and similar horiz designs. Multicoloured.* P 13½ × 14.
626   75p. Type **312**   10   10
627   1r. Pushpa Lal Shrestha (Nepal Communist Party General-Secretary)   10   10
628   5r. Suvarna Shamsher Rana (founder of Nepal Democratic Congress Party)   35   20

313 Hem Raj Sharma (grammarian)

314 Runner and Track

(Des M. N. S. Rana. Litho State Ptg Wks, Vienna)
1996 (6 Aug). *Writers. T* **313** *and similar vert designs. Multicoloured.* P 14.
629   1r. Type **313**   10   10
630   3r. Padma Prasad Bhattarai (Sanskrit scholar)   20   15
631   5r. Bhawani Bhikshu (novelist)   35   20

1996 (9 Oct). *Olympic Games, Atlanta. Photo.* P 12.
632   **314**   7r. multicoloured   50   30

315 Kasthamandap, Kathmandu

316 Hindu Temple, Arjundhara

1996 (9 Oct). *Temples. T* **315** *and similar designs. Photo.* P 11½.
633   **315**   10p. black and brown-lake   10   10
634   50p. black and brown-lake   10   10
635   –   1r. brown-lake and new blue . . .   10   10
Design: *Vert*—1r. Nyata Pola temple, Bhaktapur.

1996 (20 Nov). *Tourism. T* **316** *and similar horiz designs. Multicoloured. Litho.* P 14.
636   1r. Type **316**   10   10
637   2r. Durbar, Nuwakot   15   10
638   8r. Gaijatra Festival, Bhaktapur . . .   65   45
639   10r. Lake Beganas, Kaski   90   60

317 Krishna Peacock

318 Ashoka Pillar

(Des K. K. Karmacharya. Litho State Ptg Wks, Vienna)
1996 (20 Nov). *Butterflies and Birds. T* **317** *and similar horiz designs. Multicoloured.* P 14.
640   5r. Type **317**   45   30
      a. Block of 4. Nos. 640/3 . . . .   1·80
641   5r. Great barbet ("Great Himalayan barbet")   45   30
642   5r. Sarus crane   45   30
643   5r. Northern jungle queen   45   30
    Nos. 640/3 were issued together in *se-tenant* blocks of four stamps, each block forming a composite design.

(Des M. N. S. Rana. Photo Courvoisier)
1996 (1 Dec). *Centenary of Rediscovery of Ashoka Pillar, Lumbini (birthplace of Buddha).* P 11½.
644   **318**   12r. multicoloured . . . .   1·00   65

319 King Birendra

1996 (28 Dec). *King Birendra's 52nd Birthday. Litho.* P 11½ × 12.
645 **319** 10r. multicoloured 60 60

320 Mt. Annapurna South and Mt. Annapurna I

1996 (28 Dec). *The Himalayas. T* **320** *and similar horiz designs. Litho.* P 14.
646 18r. Type **320** . . . . 1·10 75
   a. Horiz strip. Nos. 646/8 . . . 3·50
647 18r. Mt. Machhapuchhre and Mt.
   Annapurna I . . . . . . 1·10 75
648 18r. Mt. Annapurna IV and Mt. Annapurna
   II . . . . . . 1·10 75
Nos. 646/8 were issued together in *se-tenant* strips of three stamps, each strip forming a composite design.

321 King Birendra before Throne **322** Mountains and National Flags

1997 (1 Feb). *Silver Jubilee of King Birendra's Accession. Litho.* P 14.
649 **321** 2r. multicoloured 15 15

1997 (6 Apr). *40th Anniv of Nepal–Japan Diplomatic Relations. Phosphorescent, granite paper. Photo.* P 12.
650 **322** 18r. multicoloured . . . . 1·30 90

323 Postal Emblem **324** Campaign Emblem

1997 (12 Apr). *Litho.* P 14½ × 14.
651 **323** 2r. deep rose-red and yellow-
   brown 15 15

1997 (6 July). *National Tourism Year. T* **324** *and similar designs. Litho.* P 14.
652 2r. rosine and violet-blue 15 10
653 10r. multicoloured 75 45
654 18r. multicoloured . . . . 1·30 90

655 20r. multicoloured . . . . 1·50 95
Designs: *Horiz*—10r. Upper Mustang mountain peak; 18r. Rafting, River Sunkoshi. *Vert*—20r. Changunarayan.

325 Chepang Couple **326** National Flags and Handshake

1997 (30 Sept). *Ethnic Groups. T* **325** *and similar vert designs. Multicoloured. Litho.* P 14.
656 5r. Type **325** 35 20
657 5r. Gurung couple 35 20
658 5r. Rana Tharu couple 35 20

1997 (30 Sept). *50th Anniv of Nepal–United States Diplomatic Relations. Phosphorescent, granite paper. Photo.* P 11½ × 12.
659 **326** 20r. multicoloured . . . . 1·50 95

327 Riddhi Bahadur Malla (writer) **328** *Jasminum gracile*

1997 (6 Nov). *Celebrities. T* **327** *and similar vert design. Multicoloured. Phosphorescent, granite paper. Photo.* P 11½ × 12.
660 2r. Type **327** 15 10
661 2r. Dr. K. I. Singh (politician) 15 10

1997 (11 Dec). *Flowers. T* **328** *and similar horiz designs. Multicoloured. Litho.* P 14.
662 40p. Type **328** 10 10
663 1r. China aster (*Callistephus
   chinensis*) 10 10
664 2r. *Manglietia insignis* 15 10
665 15r. *Luculia gratissima* . . . . . 1·20 75

329 Dhiki (corn crusher) **330** King Birendra

1997 (29 Dec). *Traditional Technology. T* **329** *and similar multicoloured designs. Litho.* P 14.
666 5r. Type **329** . . . . 35 2·20
667 5r. Janto (mill stone) . . . . . 35 2·20
668 5r. Kol (oil mill) (*vert*) . . . . . 35 2·20
669 5r. Okhal (implement for pounding rice)
   (*vert*) . . . . 35 2·20

1997 (29 Dec). *King Birendra's 53rd Birthday. Phosphorescent, granite paper. Photo.* P 11½.
670 **330** 10r. multicoloured 75 45

| 331 Sunrise, Shree Antudanda, Ilam | 332 Ram Prasad Rai (nationalist) |

(Des K. K. Karmacharya. Photo Courvoisier)

1998 (8 May). *Tourism. T 331 and similar multicoloured designs. Granite paper.* P 11½.
671 2r. Type **331** 15 10
672 10r. Maitidevi Temple, Kathmandu . . . 75 45
673 18r. Great Renunciation Gate,
        Kapilavastu . . . . 1·30 90
674 20r. Mt. Cholatse, Solukhumbu (*vert*) . 1·50 95

(Des K. K. Karmacharya. Litho Austrian State Ptg Wks, Vienna)

1998 (26 June). *Personalities. T 332 and similar vert designs.* P 14 × 13½.
675 75p. slate-black and chestnut . . . 10 10
676 1r. slate-black and deep mauve 15 15
677 2r. slate-black and deep yellow-
        green 20 15
678 2r. slate-black and new blue 20 15
679 5r.40 slate-black and orange-red . . . 35 20
Designs:—No. 676, Imansing Chemjong (Kiranti language specialist); 677, Tulsi Meher Shrestha (social worker); 678, Maha Pundit Dadhi Ram Marasini (poet); 679, Mahananda Sapkota (educationalist and writer).

| 333 Match Scenes | 334 Ganesh Man Singh |

(Des M. N. S. Rana. Litho Austrian State Ptg Wks, Vienna)

1998 (26 June). *World Cup Football Championship, France.* P 14.
680 **333** 12r. multicoloured 90 60

(Des K. K. Karmacharya. Photo Courvoisier)

1998 (18 Sept). *First Death Anniv of Ganesh Man Singh (politician). Granite paper.* P 11½.
681 **334** 5r. multicoloured 35 20

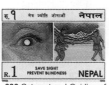

| 335 World Map and Nepalese Soldiers | 336 Cataract and Guiding of Blind Man |

(Des K. K. Karmacharya. Litho Austrian State Ptg Wks, Vienna)

1998 (9 Oct). *40 Years of Nepalese Army Involvement in United Nations Peace Keeping Missions.* P 13½ × 13.
682 **335** 10r. multicoloured 75 45

(Des M. N. S. Rana. Photo Courvoisier)

1998 (29 Nov). *Cataract Awareness Campaign. Granite paper.* P 11½ × 12.
683 **336** 1r. multicoloured 15 15

| 337 King Cobra | 338 Dove and Profile |

(Des M. N. S. Rana. Litho Austrian State Ptg Wks, Vienna)

1998 (29 Nov). *Snakes. T 337 and similar horiz designs. Multicoloured.* P 14.
684 1r.70 Type **337** 10 10
685 2r. Golden tree snake 15 10
686 5r. Asiatic rock python 35 20
687 10r. Karan's pit viper 75 45

(Des M. N. S. Rana. Litho Austrian State Ptg Wks, Vienna)

1998 (10 Dec). *50th Anniv of Universal Declaration of Human Rights.* P 14.
688 **338** 10r. multicoloured 75 45

| 339 Disabled Persons | 340 King Birendra |

(Des K. K. Karmacharya. Litho Austrian State Ptg Wks, Vienna)

1998 (27 Dec). *Asian and Pacific Decade of Disabled Persons.* P 14 × 13½.
689 **339** 10r. multicoloured 75 45

(Des M. N. S. Rana. Litho Austrian State Ptg Wks, Vienna)

1998 (29 Dec). *King Birendra's 54th Birthday.* P 13 × 13½.
690 **340** 2r. multicoloured 15 15

| 341 Dam and Power House | 342 Hospital and Emblem |

(Des M. N. S. Rana. Photo Courvoisier)

1998 (29 Dec). *River Marsyangdi Hydro-electric Power Station. Phosphorescent, granite paper.* P 11½.
691 **341** 12r. multicoloured 90 60

(Des M. N. S. Rana. Litho Austrian State Ptg Wks, Vienna)

1999 (8 Apr). *25th Anniv of Nepal Eye Hospital.* P 14.
692 **342** 2r. multicoloured 15 15

343 Kalika Bhagawati Temple, Baglung

344 Four-horned Antelope (*Tetracerus quadricornis*)

(Des K. K. Karmacharya. Litho Austrian State Ptg Wks, Vienna)

1999 (7 June). *Tourism. T* **343** *and similar multicoloured designs.* P 14 (697), 13½ × 13 (693, 695) or 13 × 13½ (others).
693	2r. Type **343**	15	10
694	2r. Chandan Nath Temple, Jumla (*vert*)	15	75
695	12r. Bajrayogini Temple, Sankhu (*vert*)	1·10	75
696	15r. Mt. Everest	1·30	90
697	15r. Ashokan Pillar, Lumbini, and English translation of its inscription (39 × 27 mm)	1·30	90

(Des K. K. Karmacharya. Photo Courvoisier)

1999 (7 June). *Mammals. T* **344** *and similar vert design. Multicoloured. Phosphorescent, granite paper.* P 12.
698	10r. Type **344**	90	60
699	10r. Argali (*Ovis ammon*)	90	60

345 Him Kanchha (mascot) and Games Emblem

346 U.P.U. Emblem and Cockerel

(Des K. K. Karmacharya. Litho Austrian State Ptg Wks, Vienna)

1999 (30 Sept). *Eighth South Asian Sports Federation Games, Kathmandu.* P 13½ × 14.
700	**345** 10r. multicoloured	90	60

(Des K. K. Karmacharya. Litho Austrian State Ptg Wks, Vienna)

1999 (9 Oct). *125th Anniv of Universal Postal Union.* P 13½.
701	**346** 15r. multicoloured	1·30	15

347 Ramnarayan Mishra (revolutionary, 1922–67)

348 Sorathi Dance

(Des M. N. S. Rana. Litho Austrian State Ptg Wks, Vienna)

1999 (20 Nov). *Personalities. T* **347** *and similar square designs.* P 14.
702	1r. deep grey-green and black	10	10
703	1r. brown-olive and black	10	10
704	1r. steel blue and black	10	10
705	2r. lake and black	15	10

706	2r. deep turquoise-blue and black	15	10
707	2r. buff and black	15	10

Designs:—No. 703, Master Mitrasen (writer, 1895–1946); 704, Bhupi Sherchan (poet, 1935–89); 705, Rudraraj Pandey (writer, 1901–87); 706, Gopalprasad Rimal (writer, 1917–73); 707, Mangaladevi Singh (revolutionary, 1924–96).

(Des M. N. S. Rana. Photo Courvoisier)

1999 (26 Dec). *Local Dances. T* **348** *and similar horiz designs. Multicoloured. Phosphorescent, granite paper.* P 12.
708	5r. Type **348**	45	30
709	5r. Bhairav dance	45	30
710	5r. Jhijhiya dance	45	30

349 Children working and writing

350 King Birendra

(Des K. K. Karmacharya. Litho Austrian State Ptg Wks, Vienna)

1999 (29 Dec). *Nepal's involvement in International Programme on the Elimination of Child Labour.* P 13½ × 14½.
711	**349** 12r. multicoloured	1·10	75

(Des K. K. Karmacharya. Litho Austrian State Ptg Wks, Vienna)

1999 (29 Dec). *King Birendra's 55th Birthday.* P 14 × 13½.
712	**350** 5r. multicoloured	45	30

351 Headquarters

352 Queen Aishwarya

2000 (2 Apr). *60th Anniv of Radio Nepal. Litho.* P 13½ × 14½.
713	**351** 2r. multicoloured	15	15

2000 (10 Apr). *Queen Aishwarya's 50th Birthday. Photo.* P 12.
714	**352** 15r. multicoloured	1·30	1·30

353 Front Page of Newspaper and Emblem

354 Tchorolpa Glacial Lake, Dolakha

2000 (5 May). *Centenary of Gorkhapatra (newspaper). Litho.* P 14.
715	**353** 10r. multicoloured	80	80

(Des K. K. Karmacharya. Litho Austrian State Ptg Wks, Vienna)

2000 (30 June). *Tourist Sights. T* **354** *and similar horiz designs. Multicoloured.* P 13½ × 14.

716	12r. Type **354**	1·00	1·00
717	15r. Dakshinkali Temple, Kathmandu	1·30	1·30
718	18r. Mount Annapurna (50th anniv of first ascent)	1·50	1·50

355 Ranipokhari Pagoda, Kathmandu   **356** Soldier and Child

2000 (7 July). *Photo.* P 11½.

719	**355**	50p. black and bright orange	10	10
720		1r. black and blue	10	10
721		2r. black and dull orange-brown	15	15

Nos. 722/724 are vacant.

(Des M. N. S. Rana. Litho Austrian State Ptg Wks, Vienna)

2000 (7 Sept). *50th Anniv of Geneva Convention.* P 13½ × 14.

725   **356**   5r. multicoloured   ·

357 Runners   **358** Hridayachandra Singh Pradhan (writer)

(Des M. N. S. Rana. Photo Courvoisier)

2000 (7 Sept). *Olympic Games, Sydney. Phosphorescent, granite paper.* P 12.

726   **357**   25r. multicoloured   2·20   2·20

(Des K. K. Karmacharya. Litho Austrian State Ptg Wks, Vienna)

2000 (7 Sept). *Personalities. T* **358** *and similar vert designs.* P 14.

727	2r. black and olive-yellow	15	15
728	2r. black and light brown	15	15
729	5r. black and grey-blue	45	45
730	5r. black and bright scarlet	45	45

Designs:—No. 728, Thir Barn Malla (revolutionary); 729, Krishna Prasad Koirala (social reformer); 730, Manamohan Adhikari (politician).

359 Indian Rhinoceros (*Rhinoceros unicornis*) (male)   **360** Orchid (Dactylorhiza hatagirea)

(Des K. K. Karmacharya. Photo Courvoisier)

2000 (14 Nov). *Wildlife. T* **359** *and similar horiz designs. Multicoloured. Phosphorescent, granite paper.* P 12.

731	10r. Type **359**	90	90
732	10r. Indian rhinoceros (*Rhinoceros unicornis*) (female)	90	90
733	10r. Lesser adjutant stork (*Leptoptilos javanicus*)	90	90
734	10r. Bengal florican (*Houbaropsis bengalensis*)	90	90

(Des M. N. S. Rana. Photo Courvoisier)

2000 (28 Dec). *Flowers. T* **360** *and similar multicoloured designs. Phosphorescent, granite paper.* P 12.

735	5r. Type **360**	45	45
736	5r. *Mahonia napaulensis* (*horiz*)	45	45
737	5r. *Talauma hodgsonii* (*horiz*)	45	45

361 King Birendra   **362** King Tribhuvana and Crowd

(Des M. N. S. Rana. Photo Courvoisier)

2000 (28 Dec). *King Birendra's 56th Birthday. Phosphorescent, granite paper.* P 12.

738   **361**   5r. multicoloured   45   45

(Des K. K. Karmacharya. Photo Courvoisier)

2001 (16 Feb). *50th Anniv of Constitutional Monarchy. Phosphorescent, granite paper.* P 12 × 11½.

739   **362**   5r. multicoloured   45   45

363 Crowd and Emblem   **364** Khaptad Baba (religious leader)

(Des K. K. Karmacharya. Photo Courvoisier)

2001 (17 Apr). *Population Census. Phosphorescent, granite paper.* P 12.

740   **363**   2r. multicoloured   15   15

**King Dipendra
2–4 June 2001**

**King Gyanendra
4 June 2001**

(Des M. N. S. Rana. Litho Austrian State Ptg Works, Vienna)

2001 (29 June). *Personalities. T* **364** *and similar vert designs.* P 14 × 13½.

741	2r. rose-pink and black	15	15
742	2r. mauve and black	15	15
743	2r. bright magenta and black	15	15
744	2r. lake and black	15	15
745	2r. greenish blue and black	15	15

Designs:—No. 742, Bhikkhu Pragyananda Mahathera (Buddhist writer and teacher); 743, Guru Prasad Mainali (author); 744, Tulsi Lal Amatya (politician); 745, Madan Lal Agrawal (industrialist).

365 Asiatic Coinwort (*Centella asiatica*)

366 Pipal Tree (*Ficus religiosa*)

(Des K. K. Karmacharya. Litho Austrian State Ptg Works, Vienna)

2001 (2 Nov). *Plants*. T **365** *and similar square designs. Multicoloured.* P 14.
746		5r. Type **365**		45	45
747		15r. *Bergenia ciliata*		1·50	1·50
748		30r. Himalayan yew (*Taxus baccata wallichania*)		3·00	3·00

(Des K. K. Karmacharya. Litho Austrian State Ptg Works, Vienna)

2001 (2 Nov). P 14 × 13½.
749 **366** 10r. multicoloured 90 90

367 Tents

368 National Flag

(Des K. K. Karmacharya. Litho Austrian State Ptg Works, Vienna)

2001 (2 Nov). *50th Anniv of United Nations High Commissioner for Refugees.* P 14.
750 **367** 20r. multicoloured . . . . . 1·80 1·80

2001 (28 Nov). *Litho.* P 14.
751 **368** 10p. vermilion and ultramarine . . . 15 15

369 Amargadi Fort

370 King Birendra

(Des M. N. S. Rana. Litho Austrian State Ptg Works, Vienna)

2001 (28 Dec). *Tourism.* T **369** *and similar multicoloured designs.* P 14 × 13½ (5r.) or 13½ × 14 (others).
752		2r. Type **369**		15	15
753		5r. Hiranyavarna Mahavihar (Golden Temple) (*vert*)		45	45
754		15r. Jugal mountain range		1·30	1·30

2001 (28 Dec). *57th Birth Anniv of King Birendra. Litho.* P 14½ × 13½.
755 **370** 15r. multicoloured . . . . . . 1·30 1·30

371 Children encircling Globe

372 Scout Emblem

(Des K. K. Karmacharya. Litho Austrian State Ptg Works, Vienna)

2001 (28 Dec). *United Nations Year of Dialogue among Civilizations.* P 14.
756 **371** 30r. multicoloured . . . . . . 2·50 2·50

(Des M. N. Rana. Litho Austrian State Ptg Wks, Vienna)

2002 (9 Apr). *50th Anniv of Nepalese Scouts.* P 14½ × 13½.
757 **372** 2r. chestnut and yellow-olive . . . 20 20

373 World Cup Emblem and Footballer

374 King Gyanendra

(Des K. K. Karmacharya. Litho Austrian State Ptg Wks, Vienna)

2002 (31 May). *World Cup Football Championship, Japan and South Korea.* P 13½ × 13.
758 **373** 15r. multicoloured . . . . . . 1·30 1·30

(Des M. N. Rana. Litho Austrian State Ptg Wks, Vienna)

2002 (5 June). *First Anniv of Accession of King Gyanendra.* P 13½.
759 **374** 5r. multicoloured 45 45

375 King Birendra and Queen Aishwarya

376 "Aryabalokiteshwor" (Siddhimuni Shakya)

(Des M. N. Rana. Litho Austrian State Ptg Wks, Vienna)

2002 (5 June). *King Birendra and Queen Aishwarya Commemoration.* P 14.
760 **375** 10r. multicoloured 45 45

(Des K. K. Karmacharya. Litho Austrian State Ptg Wks, Vienna)

2002 (29 July). *Paintings. T* **376** *and similar multicoloured design.*
P 14 × 13½ (761) or 13½ × 14 (762).
761   5r. Type **376**   45   45
762   5r. "Moti" (pearl) (King Birendra)
          (*horiz*)   45   45

377 Family encircled by   **378** Leaf Beetle
        barbed wire

2002 (6 Sept). *Social Awareness. T* **377** *and similar horiz design.*
Litho. P 14½ × 14.
763   1r. grey-black and brown   10   10
764   2r. grey-black and lilac   15   15
          Designs:—Type **377** (integration of untouchables); 2r. Children
leaving for school (treatment of girls).

(Des M. N. Rana. Litho Austrian State Ptg Wks, Vienna)

2002 (6 Sept). *Insects. T* **378** *and similar square design.*
Multicoloured. P 14.
765   3r. Type **378**   30   30
766   5r. Short Horn Grasshopper   45   45

379 Valley and   **380** Pathibhara Devisthan,
    Mountains   Taplejung

(Des M. N. Rana. Litho Austrian State Ptg Wks, Vienna)

2002 (9 Oct). *International Year of Mountains.* P 14.
767   **379**   5r. multicoloured   45   45

(Des K. K. Karmacharya. Litho Austrian State Ptg Wks, Vienna)

2002 (9 Oct). *Tourism. T* **380** *and similar horiz designs.*
Multicoloured. P 14.
768   5r. Type **380**   45   45
769   5r. Galeshwor Mahadevsthan, Myagdi . .   45   45
770   5r. Ramgram Stupa, Nawalparasi   45   45
771   5r. Mt. Nilgiri, Mustang   45   45

381 Dayabor Singh   **382** Members Flags and
    Kansakar   Organization Emblem
    (philanthropist)

2002 (8 Dec). *Personalities. T* **381** *and similar vert design.*
Multicoloured. Litho. P 13 × 13½.
772   2r. Type **381**   15   15
773   25r. Ekai Kawaguchi (first Japanese to
          visit Nepal) . . . .   2·20   2·20

2002 (8 Dec). *South Asian Association for Regional Co-operation
(SAARC) Charter Day.* P 13½ × 13.
774   **382**   15r. multicoloured . . . .   1·30   1·30

383 Anniversary   **384** FNCCI Emblem
    Emblem

(Des M. Rana. Litho Austrian State Ptg Wks, Vienna)

2003 (10 Apr). *50th Anniv of Chamber of Commerce.* P 14.
775   **383**   5r. multicoloured   10   10

(Des K. Karmacharya. Litho Austrian State Ptg Wks, Vienna)

2003 (11 Apr). *Industry and Commerce Day.* P 14.
776   **384**   5r. multicoloured   10   10

385 Mt. Everest

(Des K. Karmacharya. Litho Austrian State Ptg Wks, Vienna)

2003 (29 May). *50th Anniv of the First Ascent of Mount Everest.*
P 14.
777   **385**   25r. multicoloured   40   20

386 Babu Chiri Sherpa

(Des M. Rana. Litho Austrian State Ptg Wks, Vienna)

2003 (27 June). *Babu Chiri Sherpa (mountaineer)
Commemoration.* P 14.
778   **386**   5r. multicoloured   10   10

387 King Gyanendra

2003 (7 July). *57th Birth Anniv of King Gyanendra.* Litho.
P 14½ × 13½.
779   **387**   5r. multicoloured   10   10

388 Tea Garden

(Des M. Rana. Litho Austrian State Ptg Wks, Vienna)

2003 (7 July). *Eastern Nepal Tea Gardens.* P 14.
780　**388**　25r. multicoloured . . . .　40　20

389 Dilli Raman Regmi

(Des M. Rana. Litho Austrian State Ptg Wks, Vienna)

2003 (31 Aug). *Second Death Anniv of Dilli Raman Regmi (politician and historian).* P 14.
781　**389**　5r. bistre-brown and black . . . . .　10　10

390 Gopal Das Shrestha

(Des M. Rana. Litho Austrian State Ptg Wks, Vienna)

2003 (23 Sept). *Fifth Death Anniv of Gopal Das Shrestha (journalist).* P 14.
782　**390**　5r. olive-green and black . . . . .　10　10

391 Container, Crane and Emblem

(Des K. Karmacharya. Litho Austrian State Ptg Wks, Vienna)

2003 (9 Oct). *Export Year.* P 13½ × 14.
783　**391**　25r. multicoloured . . . .　40　20

392 Sankhadhar Sakhwaa (statue) and Celebrating Crowd

393 Ganesh (statue), Kageshwar

(Des K. Karmacharya. Litho Austrian State Ptg Wks, Vienna)

2003 (26 Oct). *Sankhadhar Sakhwaa (founder of Nepal calender).* P 13½ × 13.
784　**392**　5r. multicoloured . . . .　10　10

(Des M. Rana. Litho Austrian State Ptg Wks, Vienna)

2003 (23 Dec). *Tourist Sights. T* **393** *and similar multicoloured designs.* P 14.
785　　5r. Type **393** . . . .　10　10
786　　5r. Hydroelectric dam on Kali Gandaki
　　　river (*horiz*) . . . .　10　10
787　30r. Buddha (statue), Swayambhu
　　　(*horiz*) . . . .　50　25

394 Lotus

(Des K. Karmacharya. Litho Austrian State Ptg Wks, Vienna)

2003 (23 Dec). *Flowers. T* **394** *and similar vert designs. Multicoloured.* P 14 × 13½.
788　10r. Type **394** . . . .　20　10
　　　a. Block of 4. Nos. 787/90 . . . . . .　90
789　10r. Picrorhiza . . . .　20　10
790　10r. Himalayan rhubarb . . . . . .　20　10
791　10r. Jasmine . . . .　20　10
Nos. 788/91 were issued in *se-tenant* blocks of four stamps within the sheet.

INDIAN POST OFFICE IN NEPAL

A post office was opened in the British Residency at Kathmandu in 1816 following the end of the Gurkha War. Stamps of India were used from 1854, initially with "B137", "137" or "C-37" numeral cancellations. The Residency Post Office continued to provide the overseas mail service after Nepal introduced its own issues in 1881.

In 1920 the Residency Post Office became the British Legation Post Office. On the Independence of India in 1947 the service was transferred to the Indian Embassy and continued to function until 1965.

Philippines

1854. 20 Cuartos = 1 Real
8 Reales = 1 Peso Plata Fuerte
1864. 100 Céntimos = 1 Peso Plata Fuerte
1871. 100 Céntimos = 1 Escudo (= ½ Peso)
1872. 100 Céntimos = 1 Peseta (= 1/5 Peso)
1876. 1000 Milesimas = 100 Céntimos (or Centavos) = 1 Peso
1899. 100 Cents = 1 Dollar
1906. 100 Centavos = 1 Peso
1962. 100 Sentimas = 1 Piso

The first European to discover the islands (which in 1542 were named the Philippines) was Magellan, who was killed there in 1521 in a fight with the natives. In 1565 Miguel Lopez de Legazpi made a settlement in Cebu and in 1571 he founded Manila. The Moros of Mindanao and the Sulu archipelago, who were Moslems, fiercely resisted all Spanish attempts at domination until 1878, when they had to capitulate. Elsewhere missionary friars developed a Catholic civilization amongst the Filipinos, who intermarried with Spaniards and Chinese.

Queen Isabella II of Spain

29 September 1833–30 September 1868

1   2   3

Two plates of the 5 cuartos

(a) Head on ground of fine lines.
(b) Head on ground of coarse lines, farther apart.

(Eng on copper. Recess Plana, Jorba y Cia, Manila)

1854 (1 Feb). *Forty varieties on each plate.* Imperf.

1	**1**	5c. orange-red (a)	£1300	£225
2		5c. orange-red (b)	£1400	£250
3		10c. carmine	£425	£160
		a. Pale rose	£500	£160
5	**2**	1r. pale blue	£500	£170
		a. "CORROS"	£3250	£600
		b. Slate-blue	£600	£200
		ba. "CORROS"	£3500	£850
7		2r. bright green	£700	£130
		a. Dull green	£700	£170

Printed in sheets of 40 (5 × 8). The "CORROS" error occurs on position 26.

(Litho Plana, Jorba y Cia, Manila)

1855 (June). *Inner circle broken by outer frame at top and bottom. Four varieties.* Imperf.

9	**3**	5c. red	£1300	£275

(Litho Plana, Jorba y Cia, Manila)

1855 (Aug). *Inner circle smaller and unbroken. One type only.* Imperf.

10	**3**	5c. red	£5900	£600

USE OF STAMPS OF CUBA AND PUERTO RICO. Nos. 2a and 3 of the combined issues for Cuba and Puerto Rico were also issued for use in the Philippines from 1 January 1856. They may be included in a collection of this country if they have an identifiable Philippines cancellation, the most common being

Manila and Cavite. (*Prices for used copies with identifiable Philippines postmarks:* No. 2a, 1r. green/*bluish*, £70; No. 3, 2r. deep carmine/*bluish*, £95.)

11/12 *Catalogue numbers vacant*

4   5   6

(T **4/6** Litho M. Perez y Hijo, Manila)

1859 (1 Jan). *Four varieties.* Imperf.

(a) Thick wove paper.

13	**4**	5c. vermilion	13·50	6·25
		a. Scarlet	15·00	8·75
		b. Orange	25·00	10·00
14		10c. dull rose	12·50	13·50

(b) Thin paper.

15	**4**	5c. vermilion	13·50	4·25

(c) Thick, rough, ribbed paper.

16	**4**	5c. vermilion	39·00	13·50
		a. Pale red	39·00	13·50

1861. Imperf.

17	**5**	5c. vermilion	25·00	8·00

In T **5** the network is finer and the circle of pearls less clear than in T **4**.

1862 (Aug). *Coarse network. Period after "CORREOS".* Imperf.

18	**6**	5c. dull red	£100	42·00

7   8   9

(T **7/9** Litho M. Perez y Hijo, Manila)

1863 (Jan). *Fine network. Colon after "CORREOS".* Imperf.

19	**7**	5c. scarlet	10·00	4·25
20		10c. carmine	30·00	30·00
21		1r. rosy mauve	£550	£350
22		2r. blue	£425	£300

The 10c. was made from the plate of the 5c., and the 2 reales from the plate of the 1 real.

1863 (Feb (?)). *Inscr in Roman type.* Imperf.

23	**8**	1r. bottle-green	£250	£100
		a. Without stop before and after "CORREOS"	£250	
24		1r. grey-green	£180	£100
		a. Without stop before and after "CORREOS"	£180	

1863 (End). *Inscr in block letters.* Imperf.

25	**9**	1r. emerald-green	£110	38·00
		a. Yellow-green	£120	42·00

10

(Dies eng J. P. Varela. Typo Govt Ptg Works, Madrid)

1864 (1 Jan). *New Currency*. Imperf.

26	**10**	$3\frac{1}{8}$c. black/*buff*	2·75	1·50
27		$6\frac{2}{8}$c. green/*pale rose*	2·75	75
28		$12\frac{4}{8}$c. blue/*flesh*	5·50	60
29		25c. bright red/*pale rose*	10·50	4·25
30		25c. brown-red/*white*	7·50	2·50

The metric system was introduced in 1864, and the above four values were equal to the 5c. and 10c. and 1 and 2 reales of the preceding issue.

PROVISIONAL GOVERNMENT OF SPAIN

6 October 1868–15 June 1869

HABILITADO
POR LA
NACION.
(11)

1868 (Dec). *Handstamped with T* **11**.

31	**10**	$3\frac{1}{8}$c. black/*buff*	17·00	3·25
32		$6\frac{2}{8}$c. green/*pale rose*	17·00	3·25
33		$12\frac{4}{8}$c. blue/*flesh*	46·00	21·00
34		25c. brown-red	18·00	12·50

REGENCY, 15 June 1869–30 December 1870

Regent, Marshal Francisco Serrano (Duke de la Torre)

1870 (12 Apr). *Nos.* 24/5 *handstamped with T* **11**.

35	**8**	1r. grey-green	£110	21·00
36	**9**	1r. emerald-green	50·00	14·50

King Amadeo of Spain (Duke of Aosta)

30 December 1870–12 February 1873

12

(Die eng E. Juliá. Typo Govt Ptg Works, Madrid)

1871 (Mar). *New Currency*. P 14.

37	**12**	5c. blue	46·00	5·00
38		10c. deep green	6·75	4·25
39		20c. brown	50·00	29·00
40		40c. carmine	70·00	15·00

1872 (24 Jan). *Handstamped with T* **11**.

(a) Nos. 19 *and* 21/2.

41	**7**	5c. scarlet	50·00	35·00
42		1r. rosy mauve	£550	£325
43		2r. blue	£450	£180

(c) Nos. 2a/3 of Cuba and Puerto Rico.

44		1r. green/*bluish*	£150	80·00
45		2r. deep carmine/*bluish*	£180	70·00

13

(Dies eng H. Fernandez. Typo Govt Ptg Works, Madrid)

1872 (8 May–15 Oct). *New Currency*. P 14.

46	**13**	12c. rose (15 Oct)	10·00	4·25
47		16c. blue	£100	27·00
		a. Ultramarine	£120	60·00
48		25c. lilac-grey	8·50	3·75
		a. Grey	8·25	4·00
49		62c. pale mauve	25·00	7·25
50		1p.25 bistre-brown (15 Oct)	46·00	22·00
		a. Chestnut	46·00	22·00

The 12c. blue and the 62c. rose are colour trials.

FIRST SPANISH REPUBLIC

12 February 1873–31 December 1874

1873 (7 Oct). *No.* 18 *handstamped with T* **11**.

51	**6**	5c. dull red	60·00	38·00

1874 (Jan). *Nos.* 5 *and* 14 *handstamped with T* **11**.

52	**2**	1r. bright blue	£2000	£1000
		a. "CORROS"		
53	**4**	10c. dull rose	90·00	50·00

14

(Die eng E. Juliá. Typo Govt Ptg Works, Madrid)

1874. P 14.

54	**14**	12c. grey	11·50	3·50
		a. Lilac-grey	11·50	3·50
55		25c. ultramarine	4·25	1·50
56		62c. rose	35·00	3·50
57		1p.25 brown	£170	50·00

King Alfonso XII of Spain

(House of Bourbon restored)

31 December 1874–25 November 1885

15

16

(Die eng J. Garcia Moragó. Typo Govt Ptg Works, Madrid)

1875–77. *New Currency. Rosette on each side of* "FILIPINAS" *Value in centimos de peso*. P 14.

58	**15**	2c. rose (Aug 1875)	1·70	60
59		2c. blue (Dec 1877)	£150	70·00
60		6c. orange (Aug 1877)	8·00	1·80
61		10c. blue (Aug 1877)	2·10	50
62		12c. mauve (Jan 1876)	2·20	50
63		20c. deep purple-brown (Dec 1876)	11·00	2·50
64		25c. blue-green (Mar 1876)	8·00	50

1878–79. *Without rosettes. Value in milesimas de peso, block lettering*. P 14.

65	**16**	25m. black (Apr 1878)	2·10	35
66		25m. green (Jan 1879)	50·00	22·00
67		50m. dull purple (Jan 1878)	22·00	9·25
		a. Deep purple	22·00	9·25
68		($62\frac{1}{2}$m.) 0.0625 lilac (Jan 1878)	70·00	25·00
		a. Grey	42·00	14·50
69		100m. carmine (1879)	85·00	35·00
70		100m. yellow-green (1879)	7·50	2·10
71		125m. blue (Jan 1878)	3·75	35
72		200m. rose (1879)	25·00	5·00

73		200m. dull claret (1879)		£250	£120
74		250m. brown (Sept 1879)		9·25	2·10

Many stamps of T **15/16** may be found imperforate but they are proofs or from trial sheets.

(17)

1877–79. *Surch locally with T* **17.**

75	**15**	12c. on 2c. rose (Aug 1877)		70·00	22·00
		a. Surch inverted		£500	£225
		b. Surch double		£375	£225
76	**16**	12c. on 25m. black (Jan 1879)		70·00	21·00
		a. Surch inverted		£550	£425
77		12c. on 25m. black (B.) (Jan 1879)		£170	£130
		a. Surch Inverted		£650	£450

(18)   (19)

1879 (Sept). *Surch locally.*

(a) As T **18.**

78	**16**	2c. on 25m. green		38·00	8·50
		a. Surch double		—	£130
79		8c. on 100m. carmine		23·00	4·25
		a. "CORRZOS" for "CORREOS"		—	£150
		b. "COREROS" for "CORREOS"		75·00	38·00

(b) As T **19.**

80	**16**	2c. on 25m. green		£130	38·00
		a. "CONVINIO" for "CONVENIO"		—	£110
81		8c. on 100m. carmine		£140	34·00

No. 79b occurs on position 69.

20

PLATES OF TYPE 20. The plate for Type **20**, the Alfonso XII portrait design without year dates at top, was also used for contemporary issues of Cuba, Fernando Poo and Puerto Rico. It was retouched three times and the illustrations and notes which follow should enable collectors to distinguish the types easily.

Original state   *First retouch*

Second retouch   Third retouch

Original state. The medallion is surrounded by a heavy line of colour, of nearly even thickness, touching the horizontal line below the inscription in the upper label; the opening in the hair above the temple is narrow and pointed. Nos. 82/94 are all in this original state.

First retouch. The line above the medallion is thin, except at the upper right, and does not touch the horizontal line above it; the opening in the hair is slightly wider and a trifle rounded; the lock of hair above the forehead is shaped like a broad 'V', and ends in a point; there is a faint white line below it, which is not found in the original state.

Second retouch. The opening is still wider and more rounded; the lock of hair does not extend as far down on the forehead, is very slightly rounded, instead of being pointed, and the white line below it is thicker.

Third retouch. The opening in the hair forms a semicircle; the lock above the forehead has only a slight wave, and the white line is broader than before.

(Die eng E. Juliá. Typo Govt Ptg Works, Madrid)

1880 (19 Apr)**–89.** *Value in centimos de peso.* P 14.

82	**20**	2c. crimson		1·30	1·20
		a. Dull rose		75	1·30
83		2½c. sepia		6·25	1·30
84		2¾c. ultramarine (Feb 1882)		65	1·30
85		5c. grey (19 July 1882)		65	1·30
		a. Lavender		1·00	1·50
87		6⅛c. green (Mar 1882)		5·00	8·00
		a. Deep green		6·25	11·50
88		8c. chestnut		28·00	16·00
		a. Deep brown		28·00	16·00
89		10c. pale brown		2·75	1·30
		a. Brown-pink (Dec 1882)		2·75	1·30
90		10c. brown-purple (Dec 1882)		5·25	10·50
91		10c. green		£325	£180
92		12½c. rosine (19 July 1882)		1·50	1·20
		a. Pale pink		1·50	1·20
93		20c. grey-brown (19 July 1882)		2·10	1·00
94		25c. deep brown (19 July 1882)		2·75	1·00

Type **20** *retouched.* P 14.

First retouch (Nov 1883)

95	**20**	2¾c. dull blue		35	10
		a. Bright blue		35	10
		b. Deep ultramarine		35	10

Second retouch (1 Jan 1886)

96	**20**	2¾c. ultramarine		4·25	2·50

Third retouch. Value in milesimas de peso on 50m. (1887–89)

97	**20**	1c. grey-green (Jan 1888)		35	15
98		1c. brt yellow-green (1 May 1889)		35	15
99		50m. bistre (Apr 1887)		35	15
100		6c. brown (Jan 1888)		8·50	1·30

(21)   (22)

(23)

(24)

1881–86. *Various stamps diversely surcharged at Manila.*

I. POSTAGE STAMPS. *Issues of* 1880–89, *T* **20**.

(a) Black surch.

101	**21**	2c. on $2\frac{1}{2}$c. sepia (June 1881)	3·25	1·30
		a. Surch inverted	49·00	49·00
102	**22**	10c. on $2\frac{4}{8}$c. ultram (11 Sept 1886)	6·25	1·30
103	**23**	20c. on 8c. brown (22 Feb 1883)	8·50	2·75
		a. Surch inverted	16·00	14·50
		b. Surch double	16·00	16·00
104		1r. on 2c. dull rose (Oct 1883)	80·00	35·00
105		2r. on $2\frac{4}{8}$c. ultramarine (4 June 1883)	5·25	1·40
		a. Surch inverted	60·00	39·00
		b. Surch double	50·00	39·00

(b) Green surch.

106	**24**	8c. on 2c. crimson (4 June 1883)	6·25	1·50
		a. Surch inverted	23·00	18·00
		b. Surch double	27·00	24·00
107	**23**	10cuartos on 2c. crimson (Oct 1883)	3·75	1·30
		a. Surch inverted	15·00	15·00
		b. Surch double	36·00	36·00
		c. Surch double, one inverted	55·00	46·00
108		1r. on 2c. crimson (Oct 1883)	90·00	29·00
		a. Surch double	95·00	46·00
109		1r. on 5c. lavender (22 Feb 1883)	5·25	2·30
		a. Surch inverted	33·00	21·00
		b. Surch double	33·00	21·00
110		1r. on 8c. brown (22 Feb 1883)	10·00	3·75
		a. Surch inverted	37·00	18·00
		b. Surch double	46·00	35·00

(c) Red surch.

111	**22**	1c. on $2\frac{4}{8}$c. ultram (11 Sept 1886)	65	40
112	**23**	16cuartos on $2\frac{4}{8}$c. ultram (Oct 1883)	10·00	2·50
		a. Surch double	55·00	24·00
113		1r. on 2c. crimson (4 June 1883)	6·75	2·50
		a. Surch inverted	22·00	13·50
		b. Surch double	55·00	39·00
114		1r. on 5c. lavender (4 June 1883)	16·00	4·75
		a. Surch inverted	55·00	25·00

(25)

(26)

(27)

(28)

II. FISCAL STAMPS. *T* **25** *inscr* "DERECHO JUDICIAL" *(Judicature Fees).*

(a) Black surch.

115	**21**	2c. on 10 cuartos, bistre (Apr 1881)	22·00	14·00
		a. Surch inverted	50·00	55·00
116	**26**	$2\frac{4}{8}$c. on 10 cuartos, bistre (Jan 1881)	3·25	70
		a. Surch inverted	37·00	37·00
117		$2\frac{4}{8}$c. on 2r. blue (Jan 1881)	£160	70·00
118		8c. on 2r. blue (Apr 1881)	8·75	2·40
119		8c. on 10c. brown	£180	£140
120	**23**	1r. on 10 cuartos, bistre (Jan 1882)	12·50	4·00
		a. Surch double	30·00	27·00
121		1r. on $12\frac{4}{8}$c. lavender (Oct 1883)	8·00	3·75
		a. Surch inverted	55·00	49·00
		b. Surch double	80·00	80·00

(b) Blue opt.

122	**27**	10 cuartos, bistre (Jan 1881)	£160	70·00

(c) Yellow surch.

123	**23**	16cmos. on 2r. blue (4 June 1883)	6·00	2·50

(d) Red surch or opt.

124	**28**	$6\frac{2}{8}$c. on $12\frac{4}{8}$c. lavender (24 Feb 1885)	5·00	3·00
125	**23**	1r. on $12\frac{4}{8}$c. lavender (4 June 1883)	7·25	3·25
		a. Surch inverted	55·00	
		b. Surch double	60·00	
126	**27**	1r. green (Jan 1881)	90·00	65·00
		a. Surch inverted	£120	

(e) Green surch.

127	**23**	1r. on 10 cuartos, bis (22 Feb 1883)	12·00	4·25

(f) Surch with two different values, T **26** *and* **23**.

128		8c. on 2r. on 2r. blue (R.) (Oct 1883)	26·00	13·00

(29)

(30)

(31)

III. FISCAL STAMPS. *T* **29** *and T* **30** *inscr* "DERECHOS DE FIRMA" (Duty on Acknowledgments)

(a) Yellow surch, T **24**.

129	**29**	2c. on 200m. green (Jan 1882)	5·00	2·50
		a. Surch inverted	17·00	19·00
		b. Surch double	34·00	29·00

(b) Red surch, T **23**.

130	**29**	1r. on 200m. green (4 June 1883)	60·00	37·00
		a. Surch inverted	£100	£100
		b. Surch double	£120	£110
131		1r. on 1 peso, green (4 June 1883)	30·00	14·50
132	**30**	1r. on 10 pesetas, bis (4 June 1883)	44·00	23·00

IV. TELEGRAPH STAMPS. *Surch as T* **23**.

(a) Red surch.

133	**31**	2r. on 250m. ultram (22 Feb 1883)	10·00	3·25
		a. Surch double	42·00	42·00

(b) Black surch.

134	**31**	20c. on 250m. ultram (22 Feb 1883)	£110	90·00
		a. Surch inverted	£120	£120
135		2r. on 250m. ultram (4 June 1883)	13·50	4·25

(c) Surch with (a) and (b).

136	**31**	1r. in *red* and 20c. in *black* on 250m. ultramarine (22 Feb 1883)	10·50	4·50
		a. Red surch inverted	9·50	7·25
		b. Red surch double	18·00	15·00

(d) Yellow surch.

137	**31**	20c. on 150m. ultramarine	27·00	22·00

P 32

(Die eng E. Juliá. Typo Govt Ptg Works, Madrid)

1886–89. PRINTED MATTER. P 14.

P138	P **32**	1m. rose (1 May 1889)	25	15
		a. Carmine	25	15
P139		$\frac{1}{8}$c. green (1 Jan 1886)	25	15
P140		2m. blue (1 May 1889)	25	15
P141		5m. brown (1 May 1889)	25	15
P138/141		*Set of* 4	90	55

(32)

(33)

34

1887 (Dec)–**88**. *Various stamps surch with T* **32** *or* **33** *(No.* 142*), in magenta.*

I. POSTAGE STAMPS.

138	**20**	$2\frac{4}{8}$c. on 1c. grey-grn (27 June 1888)	2·10	1·20
		a. Surch inverted	7·50	7·50
		b. Surch double	7·50	7·50
139		$2\frac{4}{8}$c. on 5c. lavender (27 June 1888)	1·40	65
140		$2\frac{4}{8}$c. on 50m. bistre (27 Feb 1888)	1·90	1·30
141		$2\frac{4}{8}$c. on 10c. green (29 Aug 1888)	1·40	70
142		8c. on $2\frac{4}{8}$c. ultramarine	80	50
		a. Surch inverted	8·75	8·75
		b. Surch double	8·75	8·75

II. PRINTED MATTER STAMP.

143	P **32**	$2\frac{4}{8}$c. on $\frac{1}{8}$c. green (29 Sept 1888)	50	20

III. FISCAL STAMPS.

144	**29**	$2\frac{4}{8}$c. on 200m. grn (26 June 1888)	4·00	1·80
145		$2\frac{4}{8}$c. on 20c. brown (29 Sept 1888)	11·50	5·00

IV. TELEGRAPH STAMP.

146	**34**	$2\frac{4}{8}$c. on 1c. bistre (27 June 1888)	80	60
		a. Surch double	7·50	7·50

(35)

1889 (7 June). *Various provisional stamps used for postage.*

Surch "RECARGO DE CONSUMOS" (Extra Tax on Provisions), *as T* **35**.

I. POSTAGE STAMPS. *T* **20**.

147	$2\frac{4}{8}$c. on 1c. green	20	20
	a. Surch inverted		
	b. Surch double	4·75	4·75
	c. Surch double, one inverted	7·25	8·75
148	$2\frac{4}{8}$c. on 2c. crimson	15	15
	a. Surch inverted	4·75	5·25
	b. Surch double	5·00	5·50
149	$2\frac{4}{8}$c. on $2\frac{4}{8}$c. ultramarine	10	10
	a. Surch double	3·75	3·75
150	$2\frac{4}{8}$c. on 5c. lavender	15	15
	a. Surch double	5·75	6·00
151	$2\frac{4}{8}$c. on 50m. bistre	15	15
	a. Surch inverted	5·50	5·50
152	$2\frac{4}{8}$c. on $12\frac{4}{8}$c. rose	75	75

II. TELEGRAPH STAMPS. *T* **34**.

153	$2\frac{4}{8}$c. on 1c. bistre	40	40
154	$2\frac{4}{8}$c. on 2c. carmine	40	40
155	$2\frac{4}{8}$c. on $2\frac{4}{8}$c. brown	15	15
	a. Surch double	6·00	6·75
156	$2\frac{4}{8}$c. on 5c. blue	15	15
	a. Surch inverted	5·00	5·50
	b. Surch double	6·00	6·00
157	$2\frac{4}{8}$c. on 10c. green	15	15
	a. Surch double	9·25	9·25
158	$2\frac{4}{8}$c. on 10c. mauve	80	70
	a. Surch double	5·75	6·00
159	$2\frac{4}{8}$c. on 20c. mauve	30	30
	a. Surch double	7·00	6·75

III. PRINTED MATTER STAMP. *Type* P **32**.

160	$2\frac{4}{8}$c. on $\frac{1}{8}$c. green	20	20
	a. Surch double	1·80	1·80

IV. FISCAL STAMP. *Inscr* "DERECHO JUDICIAL" *(central motif as for T* **43** *of Spain). Magenta surch.*

161	$17\frac{4}{8}$c. on 5p. green	75·00	

In addition to the above, various telegraph and fiscal stamps without any surcharge were likewise used postally.

Varieties of many stamps from No. 101 to 161 are known with surcharges *sideways, omitted* (in pairs with normal), *triple*, etc. The surcharges in most cases also vary considerably in setting on the sheet.

King Alfonso XIII of Spain

17 May 1886–14 April 1931

36

P 37

(Die eng E. Juliá. Typo Govt Ptg Works, Madrid)

1890 (1 Jan). *Thin paper.* P 14.

162	**36**	2c. lake	15	15
163		$2\frac{4}{8}$c. deep blue	40	15
164		5c. slate-green	35	15
165		5c. indigo	40	15
166		8c. yellow-green	25	15
167		10c. blue-green	1·40	25
168		$12\frac{4}{8}$c. pale yellow-green	25	15
169		20c. pale rosine	60·00	30·00
170		25c. sepia	4·50	85
162/170		*Set of* 9	60·00	28·00

(Die eng E. Juliá. Typo Govt Ptg Works, Madrid)

1890. *PRINTED MATTER.* P 14.

P171	P **37**	1m. deep purple (1 Jan)	15	15
P172		$\frac{1}{8}$c. deep purple (12 June)	15	15
P173		2m. deep purple (12 June)	15	15
P174		5m. deep purple (12 June)	15	15
		a. Imperf (pair)	55·00	55·00

1891 (20 Apr). *Colours changed.* P 14.

171	**36**	5c. blue-green	65	20
172		10c. lilac-rose	65	15
173		$12\frac{4}{8}$c. deep yellow-green	20	15
174		20c. salmon	8·50	2·50
175		25c. indigo (*thin paper*)	1·70	20
171/175		*Set of* 5	10·50	2·75

1892 (1 Jan). *Colours changed and new values.* P 14.

176	**36**	1c. dull violet	85	25
177		2c. light violet	40	15
		a. Deep violet	45	15
178		$2\frac{4}{8}$c. olive-grey	25	15

179		5c. sage-green	65	15
180		5c. violet-black*	£550	£200
181		6c. brown-purple	25	15
182		8c. ultramarine	65	25
183		10c. light carmine	65	15
184		12½c. orange	65	15
185		15c. cinnamon	85	25
186		20c. olive-sepia	2·10	35
		a. Greyish brown	2·10	40
187		25c. blue (greyish paper)	2·20	35
176/187 (except 180) Set of 11			8·50	2·10

* Do not confuse this with No. 199.

1892 (1 Jan). *PRINTED MATTER. Colours changed.* P 14.
P188	P **37**	1m. pale green	2·00	50
P189		½c. pale green	90	20
P190		2m. pale green	2·40	50
P191		5m. pale green	£225	50·00

1893 (13 June). *PRINTED MATTER. Colours changed.* P 14.
P192	P **37**	1m. emerald-green	2·30	40
P193		½c. emerald-green	90	20
P194		2m. emerald-green	2·40	45

1894 (1 Jan)–**95**. *Colours changed. Thick paper.* P 14.
188	**36**	1c. rosine	13·50	7·25
		a. Carmine-lake (25 Apr 1895)	13·50	7·50
189		2c. carmine	15	15
190		2c. sepia	15	15
191		5c. pale-green	65	55
192		6c. orange-red	1·60	75
193		8c. brown-lake	80	25
194		10c. lake (greyish paper)	80	25
195		15c. rosine	1·70	80
196		20c. deep purple	14·00	7·25
188/196 Set of 9			30·00	15·00

1894 (1 Jan). *PRINTED MATTER. Colours changed. Thick paper.* P 14.
P197	P **37**	1m. olive-grey	20	20
P198		½c. red-brown	20	20
P199		2m. olive-grey	20	20
P200		5m. olive-grey	20	20

1896 (1 Jan). *Colours changed.* P 14.
197	**36**	1c. emerald	1·80	50
198		2c. ultramarine	25	15
199		5c. brown-violet	8·50	2·50
200		5c. bright blue-green	5·00	1·80
201		6c. rosine	5·00	2·50
202		10c. cinnamon	60	25
203		15c. blue-green	2·10	1·40
204		20c. orange	4·25	1·40
197/204 Set of 8			25·00	9·50

1896 (1 Jan). *PRINTED MATTER. Colours changed.* P 14.
P205	P **37**	1m. blue	25	15
P206		½c. blue	85	50
P207		2m. sepia	35	15
P208		5m. blue-green	2·50	1·30

1897. *New values.* P 14.
205	**36**	40c. deep purple	14·50	4·25
206		80c. carmine-lake	25·00	10·00

Imperforate stamps of Type **36** are from trial sheets.

1897. *Surch as T* **37**.

(a) In black.
207	**36**	5c. on 5c. pale green	21·00	12·50
208		15c. on 15c. rosine	2·50	1·40
		a. Surch inverted	12·00	10·50
209		20c. on 20c. deep purple	18·00	10·00
		a. Surch inverted	34·00	34·00
210		20c. on 25c. sepia	12·50	8·50
		a. Surch inverted	14·50	14·50

(b) In violet.
211	**36**	15c. on 15c. rosine	10·00	8·50

(c) In blue.
212	**36**	5c. on 5c. pale green	4·50	2·50
213		15c. on 15c. cinnamon	3·75	2·30
		a. Surch inverted	12·50	11·50
214		20c. on 20c. greyish brown	6·25	4·00
		a. Surch inverted	14·50	14·50

(d) In red.
215	**20**	5c. on 5c. lavender	5·00	2·40
		a. Surch in blackish red (mixed inks)	7·50	4·75
216	**36**	5c. on 5c. sage green	4·00	2·40

Other surcharges in violet-black are known but are believed to be reprints.

(Dies eng B. Maura. Typo Govt Ptg Works, Madrid)

1898 (Jan). P 14.
217	**38**	1m. chestnut	15	15
218		2m. chestnut	15	15
219		3m. chestnut	15	15
220		4m. chestnut	6·75	1·50
221		5m. chestnut	15	15
222		1c. deep purple	15	15
223		2c. blue-green	15	15
224		3c. brown	15	15
225		4c. orange	11·50	8·00
226		5c. rosine	25	15
227		6c. blue	65	35
228		8c. sepia	25	15
229		10c. orange-vermilion	1·70	60
230		15c. olive-slate	1·30	40
231		20c. maroon	1·30	60
232		40c. dull lilac	65	40
233		60c. black	3·00	1·40
234		80c. red-brown	3·00	1·40
235		1p. yellow-green	16·00	10·00
236		2p. Prussian blue	22·00	12·50
217/236 Set of 20			60·00	35·00

FILIPINO REVOLUTIONARY GOVERNMENT

The desire of the Filipinos for independence arose when Spain first became a republic in 1873. Dr. José Rizal became the propagandist of the movement but in 1892 he was deported from Manila after founding the Liga Filipino for the betterment of the people. On 26 August 1896 a revolt began and Rizal, who took no part in it, was later shot by the Spaniards. In March 1897 Emilio Aguinaldo was elected President of a Philippine Republic. After the Spanish–American War broke out on 21 April 1898. Aguinaldo proclaimed the independence of the Philippines on 12 June and co-operated with the Americans. Following the cession of the islands to the United States he revolted against American rule until, after his capture in March 1901, he took an oath of allegiance.

In the following designs the letters "KKK" are the initials of the Katipunan secret political society, which plotted for independence. They were adopted as part of the emblems of the Filipino Revolutionary Government.

(37)

38

39   40 (lines below value)   41 (no lines)

(Typo Litografia del Gómez, Santa Cruz)

1898–99. P 11½.

(a) POSTAGE.

237	**39**	2c. red	2·75	2·75
238	**40**	2c. red	21·00	21·00
239	**41**	2c. red	20	60
		a. Imperf (pair)	6·75	

R **42**   P **43**

(b) REGISTERED LETTER.

R240	R **42**	8c. green	1·00	9·75
		a. Imperf (pair)	9·75	

(c) PRINTED MATTER.

P241	P **43**	1m. black	30	60
		a. Imperf (pair)	2·75	

The stamps are inscribed for different classes of mail, but as no instructions were given as to their usage they were employed indiscriminately. 2c. and 50c. telegraph stamps and a 10c. revenue stamp (inscrbed "RECIBOS") were issued and are known used postally.

There were also a number of local provisional issues made under the auspices of local governments of islands and towns.

UNITED STATES ADMINISTRATION

The Spanish–American War, in which the Spanish fleet was destroyed off Manila, ended with the Treaty of Paris on 10 December 1898, by which Spain ceded the Philippines to the United States for $20,000,000. Military rule was followed by civil administration from 4 July 1901.

BOOKLET PANES. All booklet panes have their outer edges imperforate.

(**44**)

(T **44** optd by U.S. Bureau of Engraving and Printing)

FOR WELL CENTERED COPIES ADD:
50% for No. 251; 30% for Nos. 252/E283

1899 (30 June)–**1901**. *Stamps of United States optd with T* **44**.

(a) No wmk.

251	50c. orange		£325	£200

(b) Wmk double-lined "USPS", T **87**.

252	1c. yellow-green		2·40	50
	a. Opt inverted		£8500	
253	2c. carmine (III) (270)		1·60	70
254	2c. orange-red (III) (284b)		95	50
	a. Booklet pane of six (1900)		£250	
255	3c. violet		4·75	95
256	4c. yell-brn (285c) (30 Aug 1901)		19·00	4·00
257	5c. blue		4·75	70
	a. Opt inverted		—	£2500
258	6c. purple-lake (30 Aug 1901)		24·00	5·75
259	8c. violet-brown (30 Aug 1901)		24·00	6·00
260	10c. brown (I)		14·50	3·25

261	10c. orange-brown (II)		£160	24·00
262	15c. olive-green		26·00	6·50
263	50c. yellow-orange		£100	32·00
	a. Red-orange		£200	
264	$1 black (I) (R.) (30 Aug 1901)		£350	£225
265	$1 black (II) (R.) (30 Aug 1901)		£1800	£600
266	$2 deep blue (R.) (30 Aug 1901)		£400	£275
267	$5 deep green (R.) (30 Aug 1901)		£750	£700

Designs:—1c. Franklin; 2c. Washington; 3c. Jackson; 4c. Lincoln; 5c. Grant; 6c. Garfield; 8c. Sherman; 10c. Webster; 15c. Clay; 50c. Jefferson; $1 Perry; $2 Madison; $5 Marshall.

1899 (6 Aug)–**1901**. *POSTAGE DUE. Stamps of United States optd with T* **44**.

D268	1c. lake		5·25	1·20
D269	2c. lake		5·25	95
D270	3c. lake (31 Aug 1901)		14·50	5·75
D271	5c. lake		12·00	2·00
D272	10c. lake		16·00	4·50
D273	30c. lake (31 Aug 1901)		£190	90·00
D274	50c. lake		£160	80·00
D268/274	Set of 7		£375	£160

The 1c. was provisionally used for local postage from 5 to 19 Sept, 1902.

1901 (6 Sept). *SPECIAL DELIVERY. Stamps of United States optd as T* **44**.

E268	10c. indigo (R.)		95·00	80·00

1903 (20 Sept)–**04**. *U.S. Presidents optd with T* **44**.

268	1c. blue-green		3·25	30
269	2c. carmine		6·00	95
270	3c. bright violet (1 Nov 1904)		55·00	9·75
271	4c. brown (1 Nov 1904)		60·00	18·00
	a. Orange-brown		60·00	16·00
272	5c. blue (4 Jan 1904)		9·75	80
273	6c. brownish lake (1 Nov 1904)		65·00	18·00
274	8c. violet-black (1 Nov 1904)		36·00	12·00
275	10c. brown (1 Nov 1904)		16·00	2·00
	a. Pair, one without opt		—	£1100
276	13c. deep purple-brown (4 Jan 1904)		28·00	14·50
	a. Purple-brown		28·00	14·50
277	15c. olive-green (4 Jan 1904)		48·00	12·00
278	50c. orange		£100	28·00
279	$1 grey-black (R.) (4 Jan 1904)		£275	£160
280	$2 deep blue (R.) (1 Nov 1904)		£700	£700
281	$5 blue-green (R.) (1 Nov 1904)		£900	£800

Designs:—1c. Franklin; 2c. Washington; 3c. Jackson; 4c. Grant; 5c. Lincoln; 6c. Garfield; 8c. Martha Washington; 10c. Webster; 13c. Harrison; 15c. Clay; 50c. Jefferson; $1 Farragut; $2 Madison; $5 Marshall.

1904 (1 Nov). *U.S. President optd with T* **44**.

282	2c. scarlet (Washington)		4·75	2·20
	a. Carmine		4·50	1·80
	b. Booklet pane of six		£900	

45 Rizal   46 Arms of the   E 47 Messenger Running
              City of Manila

FOR WELL CENTERED COPIES ADD 30% (Nos. 283/303)

(Recess U.S. Bureau of Engraving and Printing)

1906 (8 Sept)–**10**. *T* **46** *(peso values) and portraits as T* **45**. *Wmk double-lined "PIPS" in sheet.* P 12.

283	2c. deep green (Type **45**)		25	15
	a. Yellow-green (1910)		30	15
	b. Booklet pane of six		£275	

284	4c. carmine-rose (McKinley)		25	15
	a. Carmine-lake (1910)		50	15
	b. Booklet pane of six		£350	
285	6c. violet (Magellan)		95	15
286	8c. brown (Legaspi)		2·00	55
287	10c. blue (Lawton)		1·50	15
	a. Deep blue		1·50	15
288	12c. crimson-lake (Lincoln)		4·00	1·60
289	16c. violet-black (Sampson)		3·25	25
290	20c. pale brown (Washington)		3·25	25
291	26c. deep sepia (Carriedo)		4·75	2·00
292	30c. olive-green (Franklin)		4·00	1·20
293	1p. orange		24·00	5·75
294	2p. black		30	1·20
295	4p. deep blue		90·00	12·00
296	10p. green		£180	55·00
283/296 Set of 14			£275	75·00

See also Nos. 297/303, 304/18, 319/36, 337/51 and 353/66.

(Recess U.S. Bureau of Engraving and Printing)

1906 (8 Sept). SPECIAL DELIVERY. Wmk double-lined "PIPS" in sheet. P 12.

E297	E **47**	20c. deep ultramarine	24·00	6·00
		a. Pale ultramarine	24·00	6·50

See also Nos. E319, E337, E353 and E367.

SPECIAL PRINTING. In 1907 there was a special printing of Nos. 268, 270/82 and D268/74 on very white paper for the Bureau of Insular Affairs. However, they are difficult to distinguish from the ordinary stamps. For the Special Delivery issue Type E **117** was overprinted instead of Type E **87**.

1907. SPECIAL DELIVERY. Special printing. United States stamp optd as T **44**.

E298	10c. ultramarine (R.)		£1500

Design:—10c. Washington.

1909–13. Colours changed. Wmk double-lined "PIPS". P 12.

297	12c. red-orange (1910)		7·25	2·00
298	16c. olive-green (1911)		2·75	95
299	20c. yellow		6·50	95
300	26c. blue-green		1·60	65
301	30c. ultramarine (1910)		8·00	2·75
302	1p. violet		24·00	4·00
303	2p. violet-brown (1913)		70·00	2·40
297/303 Set of 7			£110	12·00

FOR WELL CENTERED COPIES ADD 20%
(Nos. 304/E367)

1911–14. Types as before but wmk single-lined "PIPS" in sheet. P 12.

304	2c. yellow-green		55	15
	a. Booklet pane of six		£325	
305	4c. carmine-lake		2·00	15
	a. Carmine			
	b. Booklet pane of six		£325	
306	6c. deep violet		1·60	15
307	8c. brown		6·75	40
308	10c. blue		2·75	15
309	12c. orange		2·00	40
310	16c. olive-green		2·00	15
	a. Pale olive-green		2·00	15
311	20c. yellow		1·60	25
	a. Orange		1·60	25
312	26c. blue-green		2·40	25
313	30c. ultramarine		2·75	40
314	30c. grey (1914)		8·00	40
315	1p. violet		18·00	50
316	2p. purple-brown		23·00	70
317	4p. deep blue		£475	65·00
318	10p. deep green		£180	20·00
304/318 Set of 15			£650	80·00

1911 (Apr). SPECIAL DELIVERY. Wmk single-lined "PIPS" in sheet. P 12.

E319	E **47**	20c. deep ultramarine	16·00	1·50

1914–26. Types as before. Wmk single-lined "PIPS" in sheet.

(a) Perf 10 (1914–23).

319	2c. yellow-green		1·50	15
	a. Booklet pane of six		£275	
320	4c. carmine		1·50	15
	a. Booklet pane of six		£275	
321	6c. violet		32·00	7·25
	a. Deep violet		36·00	4·75
322	8c. brown		36·00	8·00
323	10c. blue		23·00	15
324	16c. olive-green		65·00	3·50
325	20c. orange		20·00	70
326	30c. grey		48·00	2·40
327	1p. violet		95·00	2·75
319/327 Set of 9 (cheapest)			£300	22·00

(b) Perf 11 (1918–26).

328	2c. yellow-green		16·00	3·50
	a. Booklet pane of six		£450	
329	4c. carmine		23·00	2·00
	a. Booklet pane of six		£800	
330	6c. deep violet		32·00	1·50
331	8c. light brown		£180	24·00
332	10c. blue		48·00	1·20
333	16c. olive-green		80·00	5·75
334	20c. orange		48·00	6·50
335	30c. grey		48·00	10·50
336	1p. violet		60·00	11·50
328/336 Set of 9			£475	60·00

1916. SPECIAL DELIVERY. Wmk single-lined "PIPS" in sheet. P 10.

E337	E **47**	20c. deep ultramarine	£140	60·00
		a. Pale ultramarine		

1917–28. Types as before and new portrait (No. 344). No wmk. P 11.

337	2c. yellow-green		15	15
	a. Deep green		15	15
	b. Green		15	15
	c. Booklet pane of six		20·00	
	d. Imperf between (horiz pair)		£1100	
	e. Imperf between (vert pair)		£1400	
338	4c. carmine-lake		15	15
	a. Light rose		15	15
	b. Booklet pane of six		13·50	
339	6c. violet		25	15
	a. Purple (1928)		30	15
	b. Booklet pane of six		£350	
340	8c. yellow-brown		15	15
	a. Orange-brown		15	15
341	10c. blue		25	15
342	12c. orange		25	25
343	16c. light olive-green (Sampson)		48·00	10
	a. Olive-bistre		48·00	30
344	16c. olive-bistre (Dewey) (1923)		80	15
	a. Olive-green		1·00	15
345	20c. orange-yellow		25	15
346	26c. orange		40	40
	a. Blue-green		50	25
347	30c. grey		50	25
	a. Grey-black		50	25
348	1p. violet		24·00	80
	a. Red-lilac		24·00	80
	b. Pale red-lilac		24·00	95
349	2p. purple-brown		24·00	65
350	4p. deep blue		19·00	40
351	10p. green (1926)		44·00	4·50
337/351 Set of 15 (cheapest)			£150	7·50

Coil stamp. Imperf × perf 11 (1928)

352	2c. green		6·00	12·00

1919. SPECIAL DELIVERY. No wmk. P 11.

E353	E **47**	20c. ultramarine	50	25
		a. Pale blue	65	25
		b. Dull violet	50	25

1925–31. Types as before. No wmk. Imperf.

353	2c. green		25	40
	a. Yellow-green (1931)		15	15
354	4c. carmine		30	80
	a. Carmine-rose (1931)		25	15

355	6c. deep violet	6·50	3·25
	a. Violet (1931)	80	80
356	8c. yellow-brown	4·75	2·40
	a. Brown (1931)	80	80
357	10c. deep blue	19·00	5·75
	a. Blue (1931)	1·50	1·20
358	12c. red-orange	19·00	5·75
	a. Deep orange (1931)	1·90	1·80
359	16c. olive-bistre (Dewey)	19·00	4·75
	a. Olive-green (1931)	1·60	1·20
360	20c. yellow	16·00	4·75
	a. Orange-yellow (1931)	1·60	1·20
361	26c. blue-green	19·00	5·75
	a. Green (1931)	1·60	1·20
362	30c. grey	19·00	5·75
	a. Light grey (1931)	1·90	1·50
363	1p. violet	65·00	32·00
	a. Light violet (1931)	3·25	3·25
364	2p. violet-brown	£160	60·00
	a. Brown-violet (1931)	9·75	9·75
365	4p. deep blue	£800	£325
	a. Blue (1931)	32·00	28·00
366	10p. deep green	£1600	£600
	a. Green (1931)	80·00	95·00
353/366	Set of 14 (cheapest)	£120	£130

1925–31. SPECIAL DELIVERY. Imperf.

E367	E **47**	20c. dull violet	16·00	40·00
		a. Violet-blue (1931)	32·00	24·00

(48)

49 Legislative Palace

FOR WELL CENTERED COPIES ADD 50%

1926 (13 May). AIR. Madrid–Manila Flight. Stamps of 1917–26 optd with T **48**, by Philippine Bureau of Printing.

(a) No wmk. P 11.

368	2c. yellow-green (R.)	6·50	6·50
369	4c. carmine-lake (V.)	9·75	9·75
	a. Opt inverted	£1300	
370	6c. violet (R.)	40·00	24·00
371	8c. orange-brown (V.)	40·00	24·00
372	10c. deep blue (R.)	40·00	24·00
373	12c. orange (V.)	40·00	40·00
374	16c. light olive-green (Sampson) (V.)	2500	£1300
	a. Olive-bistre (R.)	£4750	£2500
375	16c. olive-green (Dewey) (V.)	55·00	55·00
376	20c. orange-yellow (V.)	55·00	55·00
377	26c. blue-green (V.)	55·00	55·00
378	30c. grey (V.)	55·00	55·00
379	2p. purple-brown (R.)	£400	£250
380	4p. deep blue (R.)	£550	£375
381	10p. green (V.)	£950	£500

(b) Wmk single-lined "PIPS". P 12.

382	26c. blue-green (V.)	£3500	

(c) Wmk single-lined "PIPS". P 10.

383	1p. violet	£160	£140

FOR WELL CENTERED COPIES ADD 20%
(Nos. 384/D401)

(Recess Philippine Bureau of Printing)

1926 (20 Dec). Inauguration of Legislative Palace. P 12.

384	**49**	2c. black and green	40	25
		a. Imperf between (horiz pair)	£200	
		b. Imperf between (vert pair)	£325	
385		4c. black and rosine	40	25
		a. Imperf between (horiz pair)	£180	
		b. Imperf between (vert pair)	£300	
386		16c. black and olive-green	80	65
		a. Double impression of centre	£375	
		b. Imperf between (horiz pair)	£225	
		c. Imperf between (vert pair)	£325	
387		18c. black and red-brown	80	65
		a. Double impression of centre	£400	
		b. Imperf between (vert pair)	£325	
388		20c. black and orange	1·20	95
		a. Imperf (pair)	£350	
		b. Imperf between (vert pair)	£350	
		c. Error. Centre in brown	£375	
		ca. Imperf (pair)	£350	
389		24c. black and grey	2·40	65
		a. Imperf between (vert pair)	£325	
390		1p. black and mauve	36·00	26·00
		a. Imperf between (vert pair)	£375	
384/390	Set of 7		38·00	26·00

O.B.   O B

Most of the stamps, Nos. 251 to 366 and Nos. E268 and E297 exist handstamped or overprinted "OB" (as shown in the above illustrations), in *violet, yellow, green, blue, red*, or *black*, the letters standing for Official Business. These stamps were used by the various Government departments on official correspondence, each department or individual official applying the overprint by any convenient method. Many types of the overprint exist.

From December 1926, officially overprinted stamps were provided, as listed below.

OFFICIAL
(O **50**)

D 51 Post Office Clerk

1926 (20 Dec). OFFICIAL. Inauguration of Legislative Palace. Stamps of postage issue optd in red with Type O **50**, by Philippine Bureau of Printing.

O391	**49**	2c. black and green	2·00	80
O392		4c. black and rosine	2·00	95
		a. Imperf between (vert pair)	£475	
O393		18c. black and red-brown	6·50	3·25
O394		20c. black and orange	5·75	1·50
O391/394	Set of 4		14·50	6·00

(Recess U.S. Bureau of Engraving and Printing)

1928 (21 Aug). POSTAGE DUE. P 11.

D395	D **51**	4c. carmine-red	15	15
D396		6c. carmine-red	15	15
D397		8c. carmine-red	15	15
D398		10c. carmine-red	15	15
D399		12c. carmine-red	15	15
D400		16c. carmine-red	25	25
D401		20c. carmine-red	15	15
D395/401	Set of 7		1·00	1·00

L.O.F.

1923
(52)

O.B.
(O **53**)

1928 (9 Nov). *AIR. London–Orient Flight by British Squadron of Hydroplanes. Stamps of 1917–28 optd in red with T **52**, by Philippine Bureau of Printing.*

(a) No wmk. P 11.

402	2c. green		40	25
403	4c. carmine-lake		50	40
404	6c. purple		1·60	1·50
405	8c. orange-brown		1·90	1·60
406	10c. blue		1·90	1·60
407	12c. orange		2·50	2·40
408	16c. olive-green (Dewey)		1·90	1·60
409	20c. orange-yellow		2·50	2·40
410	26c. blue-green		8·00	5·25
411	30c. grey		8·00	5·25

(b) Wmk single-lined "PIPS". P 12.

412	1p. violet		40·00	30·00
402/412 *Set of 11*			60·00	47·00

1931 (18 May). *OFFICIAL. Stamps of 1917–28. No wmk. P 11. Optd with Type O **53**, by U.S. Bureau of Engraving and Printing.*

O413	2c. yellow-green		15	15
	a. No stop after "B"		10·50	3·00
O414	4c. carmine-lake		15	15
	a. No stop after "B"		10·50	3·00
O415	6c. violet		15	15
O416	8c. brown		15	15
O417	10c. blue		15	15
O418	12c. orange		25	15
	a. No stop after "B"		23·00	
O419	16c. olive-green (Dewey)		25	15
	a. Olive-bistre		1·60	25
O420	20c. orange-yellow		25	15
	a. No stop after "B"		14·50	11·00
O421	26c. green		30	25
	a. Blue-green		1·40	90
O422	30c. grey		25	25
O413/422 *Set of 10*			1·80	1·50

1931 (18 May). *OFFICIAL SPECIAL DELIVERY. No. E353b optd with Type O **53**, by U.S. Bureau of Engraving and Printing.*

EO423	E **47** 20c. dull violet		80	50
	a. No stop after "B"		18·00	14·00
	b. Opt double			

56 Pier No. 7, Manila Bay

57 Vernal Falls, Yosemite National Park, California, wrongly inscr "PAGSANJAN FALLS"

58 Rice Plantation

59 Rice Terraces

60 Baguio Zigzag

(61)

(Recess U.S. Bureau of Engraving and Printing)

1932 (3 May). P 11.

424	**54**	2c. green		40	55
425	**55**	4c. carmine		30	30
426	**56**	12c. orange		50	50
427	**57**	18c. vermilion		20·00	8·00
428	**58**	20c. yellow		65	65
429	**59**	24c. violet		1·20	70
430	**60**	32c. sepia		1·20	80
424/430 *Set of 7*				22·00	10·00

1932 (26 Sept). *No. 350 surch as T **61**, by U.S. Bureau of Engraving and Printing.*

431	1p. on 4p. deep blue (O.)		1·60	40
432	2p. on 4p. deep blue (C.)		2·75	65

ROUND-THE-WORLD FLIGHT
VON GRONAU
1932
(62)

F. REIN
MADRID-MANILA
FLIGHT-1933
(63)

1932 (27 Sept). *AIR. Von Gronau Round-the-World Flight. Nos. 424/30 optd with T **62**, (sideways on 18c.). in green, by Philippine Bureau of Printing.*

433	**54**	2c. green		30	30
434	**55**	4c. carmine		30	30
435	**56**	12c. orange		50	50
436	**57**	18c. vermilion		2·75	2·75
437	**58**	20c. yellow		1·50	1·50

54 Mayon Volcano

55 Post Office, Manila

438	**59**	24c. violet	1·50	1·50
439	**60**	32c. sepia	1·50	1·50
433/439		Set of 7	7·50	7·50

FOR WELL CENTERED COPIES ADD 40%

1933 (11 Apr). *AIR. Rein Madrid–Manila Flight. Stamps of 1917–28. optd with T* **63**. *No wmk.* P 11.

440		2c. green	30	30
441		4c. carmine	40	30
442		6c. purple	65	65
443		8c. brown	2·00	1·30
444		10c. blue	1·80	80
445		12c. orange	1·60	80
446		16c. olive-green (Dewey)	1·60	80
447		20c. yellow	1·60	95
448		26c. green	1·80	1·30
		a. Blue-green	2·40	1·60
449		30c. grey	2·40	1·60
440/449		Set of 10	12·50	8·00

(64)   (65)

FOR WELL CENTERED COPIES ADD 20%
(Nos. 450/569)

(Optd by Philippine Bureau of Printing)

1933 (26 May). *AIR.*

(a) No. 337b optd with T **64**.

450		2c. green	40	40

(b) Stamps of 1932 optd with T **65**.

451	**55**	4c. carmine	15	15
452	**56**	12c. orange	25	15
453	**58**	20c. yellow	25	15
454	**59**	24c. violet	30	25
455	**60**	32c. sepia	40	30
450/455		Set of 6	1·60	1·25

66 Baseball

67 Tennis   **68** Basketball

(Des F. Amorsolo. Typo Philippine Bureau of Printing)

1934 (14 Apr). *10th Far Eastern Championship Games.* P 12.

456	**66**	2c. brown	1·20	65
457	**67**	6c. blue	25	15
		a. Imperf between (vert pair)	£850	
458	**68**	16c. purple	40	40
		a. Imperf horiz (vert pair)	£850	

69 Dr. J. Rizal   **70** Woman, Carabao and Rice-stalks

71 Filipino Girl   **72** Pearl Fishing

73 Fort Santiago   **74** Salt Springs

75 Magellan's Landing   **76** "Juan de la Cruz"

77 Rice Terraces   **78** Blood Compact

79 Barasoain Church   **80** Battle of Manila Bay

81 Montalban Gorge

82 George Washington (after painting by John Faed)

(Recess U.S. Bureau of Engraving and Printing)

1935 (15 Feb). P 11.

459	69	2c. carmine	15	15
460	70	4c. green	15	15
461	71	6c. chocolate	15	15
462	72	8c. violet	15	15
463	73	10c. carmine	25	15
464	74	12c. black	25	15
465	75	16c. blue	25	15
466	76	20c. olive-bistre	25	15
467	77	26c. indigo	30	25
468	78	30c. vermilion	30	25
469	79	1p. black and orange	2·00	1·50
470	80	2p. black and brown	4·00	1·50
471	81	4p. black and blue	4·00	2·75
472	82	5p. black and green	8·00	2·00
459/472 *Set of 14*			18·00	8·50

1935 (14 Mar). OFFICIAL. Nos. 459/68 optd with Type O **53**. by U.S. Bureau of Engraving and Printing.

O473	69	2c. carmine	15	15
		a. No stop after "B"	10·50	3·50
O474	70	4c. green	15	15
		a. No stop after "B"	10·50	5·25
O475	71	6c. chocolate	15	15
		a. No stop after "B"	16·00	15·00
O476	72	8c. violet	15	15
O477	73	10c. carmine	15	15
O478	74	12c. black	15	15
O479	75	16c. blue	15	15
O480	76	20c. olive-bistre	15	15
O481	77	26c. indigo	25	25
O482	78	30c. vermilion	30	30
O473/482 *Set of 10*			1·60	1·60

COMMONWEALTH OF THE PHILIPPINES

On 15 November 1935 the Commonwealth of the Philippines was established, with a president and a national assembly. The United States kept control of defence and foreign relations. After the Japanese attack on China in 1937 the demands for complete independence lessened.

83 "The Temples of Human Progress"

(Des Fabian de la Rosa. Recess U.S. Bureau of Engraving and Printing)

1935 (15 Nov). Inauguration of Commonwealth of the Philippines. P 11.

483	**83**	2c. carmine	15	15
484		6c. violet	15	15
485		16c. blue	25	25

486		36c. yellow-green	30	30
487		50c. brown	50	50
483/487 *Set of 5*			1·20	1·20

P.I. U.S. INITIAL FLIGHT

December -1935
(84)

1935 (2 Dec). AIR. "China Clipper" Trans Pacific Air Mail Flight. Stamps of 1935, optd with T **84**, in gold.

488	**73**	10c. carmine	25	15
489	**78**	30c. vermilion	40	40

MANILA-MADRID ARNACAL FLIGHT–1936

6 CENTAVOS 6
(86)

85 José Rizal y Mercado

(Recess Philippine Bureau of Printing)

1936 (19 June). 75th Birth Anniv of Rizal. P 12.

490	**85**	2c. ochre	15	15
491		6c. grey-blue	15	15
		a. Imperf vert (horiz pair)	£900	
492		36c. red-brown	50	50

1936 (6 Sept). AIR. Madrid–Manila Flight by Arnaiz and Calvo. Stamps of 1917–28 surch as T **86**, by Philippine Bureau of Printing.

493		2c. on 4c. carmine-lake (B.)	15	15
494		6c. on 12c. orange (V.)	15	15
495		16c. on 26c. blue-green	25	25
		a. On 26c. green	95	65

COMMON-WEALTH
(87)

COMMONWEALTH
(88) (18¼ × 2¾ mm)

89 Manuel L. Quezon

1936 (7 Oct)–**37**. Nos. 459/72 optd with T **87** (2c., 6c., 20c.) or **88** (others), by U.S. Bureau of Engraving and Printing.

496	69	2c. carmine (28 Dec 1936)	15	15
		a. Booklet pane of six (15 Jan 1937)	3·75	
497	70	4c. green (29 Mar 1937)	40	40
498	71	6c. chocolate	25	15
499	72	8c. violet (29 Mar 1937)	25	15
500	73	10c. carmine (28 Dec 1936)	15	15
		a. "H" omitted		
501	74	12c. black (29 Mar 1937)	15	15
502	75	16c. blue	15	15
503	76	20c. olive-bistre (29 Mar 1937)	65	40
504	77	26c. indigo (29 Mar 1937)	40	30
505	78	30c. vermilion (28 Dec 1936)	30	15
506	79	1p. black and orange	65	40
507	80	2p. black and brown (29 Mar 1937)	4·50	2·40
508	81	4p. black and blue (29 Mar 1937)	16·00	4·00
509	82	5p. black and green (29 Mar 1937)	2·40	1·20
496/509 *Set of 14*			24·00	9·00

See also Nos. 524/37.

(Des I. R. Miranda. Recess U.S. Bureau of Engraving and Printing)

1936 (15 Nov). *First Anniv of Autonomous Government.* P 11.

510	**89**	2c. red-brown	15	15
511		6c. yellow-green	15	15
512		12c. ultramarine	25	25

90 Philippine Is

(D **91**)

3 CVOS. 3

92 Arms of Manila

(Des I. R. Miranda. Recess U.S. Bureau of Engraving and Printing)

1937 (3 Feb). *33rd International Eucharistic Congress.* P 11.

513	**90**	2c. green	15	15
514		6c. yellow-brown	15	15
515		12c. blue	15	15
516		20c. orange	25	15
517		36c. violet	40	40
518		50c. scarlet	55	30
513/518	*Set of 6*		1·30	1·20

1937 (10 Apr)–**38**. *OFFICIAL. Nos. 496 and 503 optd with Type* O **53**.

O519	**69**	2c. carmine	15	15
		a. No stop after "B"	4·00	2·30
O520	**76**	20c. olive-bistre (26 Apr 1938)	55	40

1937 (29 July). *POSTAGE DUE. No. D395 surch with Type* D **91**, *in blue.*

D521	D **51**	3c. on 4c. carmine-red	15	15

(Recess U.S. Bureau of Engraving and Printing)

1937 (27 Aug). P 11.

522	**92**	10p. slate-black	3·25	1·60
523		20p. red-brown	1·60	1·20

COMMON-WEALTH

(93)

COMMONWEALTH

(94) (18¾ × 1¾ mm)

1938–40. *Nos. 459/72 optd with T* **93** (2c., 6c.. 20c.) *or* **94** (*others*), *by U.S. Bureau of Engraving and Printing.*

524	**69**	2c. carmine (1939)	15	15
		a. Booklet pane of six	3·50	
		b. "WEALTH COMMON"	£2750	
		c. Hyphen omitted (from booklet panes)		
525	**70**	4c. green (1940)	95	2·40
526	**71**	6c. chocolate (12 May 1939)	15	15
		a. *Golden brown*	20	15
527	**72**	8c. violet (1939)	15	15
		a. "H" omitted	60·00	
528	**73**	10c. carmine (12 May 1939)	15	15
529	**74**	12c. black (1940)	15	15
530	**75**	16c. blue (1938)	15	15
531	**76**	20c. olive-bistre (27 Apr 1939)	15	15
532	**77**	26c. indigo (1940)	25	25
533	**78**	30c. vermilion (23 May 1939)	1·30	65
534	**79**	1p. black and orange (29 Aug 1938)	40	15
535	**80**	2p. black and brown (1939)	2·40	65
536	**81**	4p. black and blue (1940)	£110	£120
537	**82**	5p. black and green (1940)	4·75	2·75
524/537	*Set of 14*		£110	£110

No. 524c occurs in position 5 of some booklet panes.

O.   **B.**

O.   **B.**

COMMON-WEALTH

(O **95**)

COMMONWEALTH

(O **96**)

FIRST AIR MAIL EXHIBITION

Feb. 17 to 19, 1939

8 CENTAVOS 8

(**97**)

1938 (8 Sept)–**40**. *OFFICIAL. Stamps of 1935 optd as Types* O **95** (2c., 6c. and 20c.) *or* O **96** (*others*), *by U.S. Bureau of Engraving and Printing.*

O538	**69**	2c. carmine (1939)	15	15
		a. Hyphen omitted	14·50	14·50
		b. No stop after "B"	18·00	17·00
O539	**70**	4c. green	15	15
O540	**71**	6c. chocolate	15	15
O541	**72**	8c. violet	15	15
O542	**73**	10c. carmine	15	15
		a. No stop after "O"	23·00	23·00
O543	**74**	12c. black	15	15
O544	**75**	16c. blue	15	15
O545	**76**	20c. olive-bistre (1940)	25	25
O546	**77**	26c. indigo	30	30
O547	**78**	30c. vermilion	25	25
O538/547	*Set of 10*		1·60	1·70

1939 (17 Feb). *AIR. First Manila Air Mail Exhibition. Nos. 346/a and 522 surch as T* **97**, *by Philippine Bureau of Printing.*

548		8c. on 26c. green	1·30	50
		a. On 26c. *blue-green*	65	40
549		1p. on 10p. slate-black (R.)	2·40	2·00

1939 (27 Apr). *SPECIAL DELIVERY. No.* E353b *optd* "COMMONWEALTH" *as T* **94**. P 11.

E550	E **47**	20c. dull violet	25	25

FIRST FOREIGN

TRADE WEEK

2

MAY 21-27, 1939   CENTAVOS

(**98**)

FIRST FOREIGN TRADE WEEK

MAY 21-27, 1939

6 CENTAVOS 6

(**99**)

50 CENTAVOS 50

FIRST FOREIGN

TRADE WEEK

MAY 21-27, 1939

(**100**)

1939 (5 July). *First National Foreign Trade Week. Nos. 460, 346/a and 523 surch with T* **98/100**, *by Philippine Bureau of Printing.*

551		2c. on 4c. green (R.)	15	15
552		6c. on 26c. green (V.)	15	15
		a. On 26c. *blue-green*	25	20
553		50c. on 20p. red-brown	80	80

101 Triumphal Arch

102 Malacanan Palace

103 Pres. Quezon Taking Oath of
Office

(Recess U.S. Bureau of Engraving and Printing)

1939 (15 Nov)—**40.** *Fourth Anniv of National Independence.* P 11.

554	**101**	2c. green	15	15
555		6c. carmine	15	15
556		12c. blue	25	15
557	**102**	2c. green	15	15
558		6c. orange	15	15
559		12c. carmine	25	15
560	**103**	2c. orange (8 Feb 1940)	15	15
561		6c. green (8 Feb 1940)	15	15
562		12c. violet (8 Feb 1940)	25	15
554/562 *Set of 9*			1·50	1·20

104 José Rizal

105 Filipino Vinta and Boeing
314 Flying Boat

(Recess U.S. Bureau of Engraving and Printing)

1941 (14 Apr). P 11 × 10½.

Rotary Press printing. 19 × 22½ mm.

563	**104**	2c. yellow-green	15	15

1941. P 11.

Flat Plate printing. 18¾ × 22 mm.

564	**104**	2c. yellow-green	15	40
		a. Booklet pane of six	1·50	
		b. Pale yellow-green	25	40
		ba. Booklet pane of six	3·50	

Nos. 564/*b* only exist from booklet panes and with one or two
sides imperf.

1941 (14 Apr). OFFICIAL. Optd "O.B." *as in Type* O **96**, *by U.S.
Bureau of Engraving and Printing.*

O565	**104**	2c. yellow-green (563)	15	15

(Des O. Spirito. Recess U.S. Bureau of Engraving and Printing)

1941 (30 June). *AIR.* P 11.

566	**105**	8c. carmine-red	80	50
567		20c. ultramarine	95	40
568		60c. myrtle green	1·20	80
569		1p. blackish brown	65	40
566/569 *Set of 4*			3·25	1·90

JAPANESE OCCUPATION

In the Second World War, Japanese forces landed in Luzon on
10 December 1941 and captured Manila on 2 January 1942.
Resistance, except from Filipino guerrillas, ceased after the fall of
Corregidor on 6 May 1942. The Philippines were declared by the
Japanese to be a republic within their Greater East Asia Co-
Prosperity Sphere on 14 October 1943.

(J **1**)

50 **CENTAVOS** **50**

(J **2**)

1942–43. *Stamps of Philippine Islands variously optd or surch, by
Philippine Bureau of Printing.*

*(a) Nos. 563 and 529/30 optd with bars, as Type J **1**.*

J1	**104**	2c. yellow-green (4 Mar 1942)	15	30
		a. Pair, one without opt		
J2	**74**	12c. black (30 Apr 1943)	1·90	1·90
J3	**75**	16c. blue (4 Mar 1942)	4·75	4·50

*(b) Nos. 526/a, 533/4 and 508 variously surch as Type J **2**.*

J4	**71**	5c. on 6c. chocolate (1 Sept 1942)	30	65
		a. On 6c. *golden brown*	15	15
J5	**78**	16c. on 30c. vermilion (11 Jan 1943)	95	1·30
J6	**79**	50c. on 1p. blk & orge (30 Apr 1943)	3·75	3·75
		a. Surch double	—	£190
J7	**81**	1p. on 4p. black & bl (30 Apr 1943)	70·00	75·00
		a. "S" in "PESO" inverted	90·00	95·00
J1/7 *Set of 7*			75·00	80·00

No. J7a occurs in position 4.

CONGRATULATIONS
FALL OF
BATAAN AND
CORREGIDOR
1942

2

(J **3**)

1942 (18 May). *Fall of Bataan and Corregidor. No. 460 surch with
Type J **3**, by Philippine Bureau of Printing.*

J8	**70**	2c. on 4c. green	3·25	3·25

1942 (13 Oct). *POSTAGE DUE. No. D395 of Philippine Islands
surch as Type* D **91,** *but with addition of bar above, by Philippine
Bureau of Printing.*

JD9	D **51**	3c. on 4c. carmine-red (B.)	21·00	12·00

4c. Postage Due stamps with manuscript surcharge of 3c. were
used from 3 September 1942 until No. JD9 was issued.

J **4** Agricultural
Produce

(J **5**)

(Litho Coast and Geodetic Survey Office)

1942 (12 Nov). *Red Cross Fund.* P 12.
J9	J **4**	2c.+1c. violet			4·00	2·00
J10		5c.+1c. green			4·00	2·00
J11		16c.+2c. orange			£140	55·00

1942 (8 Dec). *First Anniv of "Greater East Asia War".* No. 460 of
Philippine Is. surch with Type J **5**, *by Philippine Bureau of
Printing.*
J12	**70**	5c. on 4c. green		1·60	1·60

(J **6**)

1943 (23 Jan). *First Anniv of Philippine Executive Commission.
Nos. 566 and 569 of Philippine Is. surch as Type* J **6**, *by
Philippine Bureau of Printing.*
J13	**105**	2c. on 8c. carmine-red		95	1·30
J14		5c. on 1p. blackish brown		1·30	1·60

J **7** Nipa Hut

J **8** Rice Planter

J **9** Mts Mayon
and Fuji

J **10** Morro
Vinta

W **81** of Japan

(Typo (2c., 6c. and 25c.). Recess (others). Govt Ptg Wks,
Tokyo)

1943–44. W **81** of Japan. P 13.
J15	J **7**	1c. red-orange (7 June 1943)		55	55
J16	J **8**	2c. light green (1 April 1943)		55	55
J17	J **7**	4c. slate-green (7 June 1943)		55	55
J18	J **9**	5c. chestnut (1 April 1943)		55	95
J19	J **8**	6c. carmine (14 July 1943)		55	70
J20	J **9**	10c. greenish blue (14 July 1943)		55	70
J21	J **10**	12c. grey-blue (14 July 1943)		95	1·20
J22		16c. sepia (14 July 1943)		55	55
J23	J **7**	20c. purple (16 Aug 1943)		1·00	1·20
J24	J **9**	21c. violet (16 Aug 1943)		70	95

J25	J **8**	25c. purple brown (16 Aug 1943)		80	55
J26	J **9**	1p. carmine (7 June 1943)		6·50	1·90
J27	J **10**	2p. slate-purple (16 Sept 1943)		16·00	4·75
J28		5p. olive-green (10 April 1944)		23·00	7·75
J15/28	*Set of 14*			48·00	20·00

(JO **11**)

J **11** Map of Manila Bay

1943 (7 Apr)–**44**. *OFFICIAL. Nos. 563, 526/a, 498 and 533 of
Philippine Is. variously optd or surch with bars and "(K.P.)", as
in Type* JO **11**, *by Philippine Bureau of Printing.*
JO29	**104**	2c. yellow-green		65	1·50
		a. Opt double		£325	
JO30	**71**	5c. on 6c. chocolate (526)		1·40	1·60
		a. On 6c. golden brown		1·40	1·60
JO31		5c. on 6c. chocolate (498) (26 June 1944)		27·00	27·00
JO32	**78**	16c. on 30c. vermilion		4·00	5·75

There are variations in the length of the bars and in the spacing
between them.

(Photo Govt Ptg Wks, Tokyo)

1943 (7 May). *First Anniv of Fall of Bataan and Corregidor.* P 13.
J29	J **11**	2c. carmine		1·40	1·40
J30		5c. emerald green		1·40	1·40

J **12** "Limbagan"
(*trans* "Printing
press")

J **13** Filipino Girl

1943 (20 June). *350th Anniv of Introduction of the Printing Press
into the Philippines. No. 531 of Philippine Is. surch with Type*
J **12**, *by Philippine Bureau of Printing.*
J31	**76**	12c. on 20c. olive-bistre		1·40	1·40
		a. Surch double			

(Photo Philippine Bureau of Printing)

1943 (14 Oct). *Japanese Declaration of the "Independence of the
Philippines".*

(a) Sheet stamps. A. P 12.
J32	J **13**	5c. blue		2·75	1·40
J33		12c. orange		2·75	1·40
J34		17c. carmine		2·75	1·40

B. Imperf (without gum).
J32	J **13**	5c. blue		1·40	1·40
J33		12c. orange		1·40	1·40
J34		17c. carmine		1·40	1·40

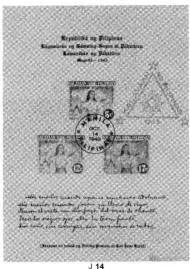

J 14

(b) *Miniature sheet, 127 × 177 mm containing Nos. J32/4B.*
MSJ35 J **14** (sold at 2p.50) . . . . 75·00 14·50

REPUBLIKA NG PILIPINAS
MAYNILA

Sa kapahintulutan ng **Kgg.** QUINTIN PAREDES, *Kagawad
ng mga Gawaing-Bayan at Pahatiran*

*Sa pagsilang ng makabayang
damdamin sa Pilipinas*

J 19

(b) *Miniature sheet.* 101 × 143 *mm containing Nos. J39/41B.
Without gum* (2 Sept).
MSJ42 J **19** (sold at 1p.) . . . . 3·25 5·25

**BAHÂ
1943

+21**

(J **15** "BAHA" (trans
"Flood"))

1943 (8 Dec). *Luzon Flood Relief Fund. Surch as Type* J **15**, *by
Philippine Bureau of Printing.*

J36	J **10**	12c.+21c. grey-blue	65	1·40
J37	J **7**	20c.+36c. purple	65	1·40
J38	J **9**	21c.+40c. violet	65	1·40

J **16** José Rizal   J **17** Rev José   J **18** A. Mabini
Burgos

(Litho Philippine Bureau of Printing)

1944 (17 Feb–2 Sept). *National Heroes.*

(a) *Sheet stamps.* A. P 12.

J39	J **16**	5c. blue	2·75	1·00
J40	J **17**	12c. carmine	1·50	1·00
J41	J **18**	17c. orange	1·50	1·00

B. Imperf.

J39	J **16**	5c. blue	2·00	1·00
J40	J **17**	12c. carmine	2·00	1·00
J41	J **18**	17c. orange	2·00	1·00

**REPÚBLIKA
NG PILIPINAS
5-7-44**

(J **20**)

1944 (7 May). *Second Anniv of Fall of Bataan and Corregidor.
Nos. 567/8 of Philippine Is, surch as Type* J **20**, *by Philippine
Bureau of Printing.*

J43	**106**	5c.on 20c. ultramarine	1·80	2·40
J44		12c.on 60c. myrtle green	2·40	3·25

**REPUBLIKA NG
PILIPINAS
(K. P.)**

(JO **21**)

K. P.

(JO **22**)

1944 (28 Aug). *OFFICIAL. Nos. 526/a of Philippine Is. surch with
Type* JO **21**, *by Philippine Bureau of Printing.*

JO45	**71**	5c.on 6c. chocolate	1·40	2·00
		a. On 6c. *golden-brown*	1·40	2·00

1944 (28 Aug). *OFFICIAL. No. O545 of Philippine Is. optd with
Type* JO **22**, *by Philippine Bureau of Printing.*

JO46	**76**	20c. olive-bistre	2·75	4·00

REPUBLIKA NG PILIPINAS

(K. P.)

(JO 23)

J 24 José P. Laurel

1944 (28 Aug). *OFFICIAL. No. 569 of Philippine Is. optd with Type JO 23, by Philippine Bureau of Printing.*
JO47 **105** 1p. blackish brown . . . . . . 6·75 8·00

(Litho Philippine Bureau of Printing)

1945 (12 Jan). *First Anniv of Republican Government. Imperf. No gum.*
J45 J **24** 5s. purple-brown . . . . . . 65 2·00
J46 7s. blue-green . . . . . 65 2·00
J47 20s. blue . . . . 65 2·00
Although prepared for issue on 14 October 1944, Nos. J45/7 were not released until 12 January 1945.

COMMONWEALTH RESTORED

After the destruction of the Japanese fleet in the Battle of Leyte Gulf on 24 to 26 October 1944, U.S. forces completed their landings on Leyte. After landings on Luzon, Manila was retaken on 4 March 1945 and the Japanese finally surrendered on 2 September.

VICTORY
(106)

VICTORY
(107)

Type **106**.   Curved opt 21 mm long. Normally shows broken "T". Issued at Tacloban.
Type **107**.   Straight opt 20 mm long. Issued at Palo.

1944. *Provisional issues for Leyte. Various stamps of Philippine Is. handstamped with T 106 or 107, in violet.*

(a) POSTAGE (8 Nov–28 Dec).
570	69	2c. carmine* (496) (3 Dec)	£200	£120
		a. Booklet pane of six	£1500	
571		2c. carmine (524) (14 Dec)	£1100	£1100
572	104	2c. yellow-green (563)	3·25	2·40
573	70	4c. green (460)	32·00	32·00
574	71	6c. chocolate (461) (14 Dec) . . .	£1400	£1300
575	89	6c. yellow-green (3 Dec)	£110	90·00
576	71	6c. chocolate (498) (28 Dec) . . .	£650	£650
577	101	6c. carmine (14 Dec)	£110	95·00
578	102	6c. orange (14 Dec)	£650	£550
579	103	6c. green	£160	£140
580	72	8c. violet (527)	13·00	19·00
581	73	10c. carmine (500)	95·00	65·00
582		10c. carmine (528)	£110	95·00
583	89	12c. ultramarine (3 Dec)	£550	£250
584	101	12c. blue (14 Dec)	£3250	£1800
585	103	12c. violet	£2000	£130
586	75	16c. blue (465) (3 Dec)	£650	
587		16c. blue (502)	£475	£325
588		16c. blue (530) (3 Dec)	£250	£140
589	76	20c. olive-bistre (531)	24·00	24·00
590	78	30c. vermilion (505) (3 Dec) . . .	£250	£180
591		30c. vermilion (533) (3 Dec) . . .	£350	£275
592	79	1p. black and orange (534) (3 Dec)	£4750	£3500

*No. 570 only comes from booklet panes and all examples have one or two straight edges.

(b) AIR (3 Dec).
593	**55**	4c. carmine (451)	£1900	£1900

(c) SPECIAL DELIVERY.
E594	E **47**	20c. dull violet (E353b)	£650	£450
E595		20c. violet (E550)	£180	£140

(d) POSTAGE DUE (3 Dec).
D596	D **51**	4c. carmine-red	£120
D597		6c. carmine-red	70·00
D598		8c. carmine-red	75·00
D599		10c. carmine-red	70·00
D600		12c. carmine-red	70·00
D601		16c. carmine-red	75·00
D602		20c. carmine-red	75·00

(e) OFFICIAL.
O603	69	2c. carmine (O538)	£190	£120
O604	104	2c. yellow-green (O565)	5·25	2·40
O605	70	4c. green (O474)	32·00	24·00
O606	71	6c. chocolate (O540)	£4000	
O607	73	10c. carmine (O542)	£110	
O608	76	20c. olive-bistre (O480)	£4750	
O609		20c. olive-bistre (O520)	£1300	

The above issues for the Island of Leyte were authorised by the Secretary of National Defence and Communications and were valid for international mail. It is believed that they were used indiscriminately on the various classes of mail according to availability.

FOR WELL CENTERED COPIES ADD 20%
(Nos. 610/O624)

VICTORY
(108)

VICTORY
(109)

1945 (19 Jan–1 May). *Victory issue. Nos. 524/31, 533/4 and 522/3 optd with T 108 (2c., 6c., 20c., 10p., 20p.) or 109 (others).*
610	69	2c. carmine	15	15
611	70	4c. green	15	15
612	71	6c. chocolate	25	15
613	72	8c. violet	25	15
614	73	10c. carmine	25	15
615	74	12c. black	15	15
616	75	16c. blue	30	15
617	76	20c. olive-bistre	40	15
618	78	30c. vermilion (1 May)	50	40
619	79	1p. black and orange	1·50	30
620	92	10p. slate-black (1 May) . . .	48·00	11·50
621		20p. red-brown (1 May) . . .	44·00	12·00
610/621 Set of 12		. . . . .	85·00	23·00

1945 (1 May). *SPECIAL DELIVERY. No. E550 optd with T 109.*
E622 E **47** 20c. violet 80 50

110 José Rizal

(Recess U.S. Bureau of Engraving and Printing)

1946 (28 May). *Rotary press printing. P 11 × 10½.*
623 **110** 2c. sepia 25 15

1946 (19 June). *OFFICIAL. Optd "O.B." as in Type O 96.*
O624 **110** 2c. sepia 15 15

INDEPENDENT REPUBLIC

The Philippines became an independent republic on 4 July 1946.

111 "Independence"

(112)

(Recess U.S. Bureau of Engraving and Printing)

1946 (4 July). *Proclamation of Independence.* P 11.
625	**111**	2c. carmine		30	30
626		6c. green		60	30
627		12c. blue		90	45

1946 (30 Dec). *Fiftieth Anniv of Martyrdom of Dr. José Rizal. No. 623 (Rizal) optd with T 112, by Philippine Bureau of Printing.*
628	**110**	2c. sepia		30	20

113 Bonifacio Monument   **114** Mayon Volcano   **115** M-a-nuel L. Quezon

(Recess A. B. N. Co)

1947 (23 Mar–1 Aug). *T 113/4 and similar designs.* P 12.
629		4c. black-brown (1 Aug)		15	15
630		10c. red		15	15
631		12c. blue (19 June)		20	15
632		16c. slate (19 June)		1·60	95
633		20c. reddish brown		45	15
634		50c. green (19 June)		1·20	10
635		1p. bright violet (1 Aug)		2·40	60
629/635 *Set of 7*				5·50	2·00

Designs: *Vert*—4c. Rizal Monument; 50c., 1p. Avenue of Palm Trees. *Horiz*—12c. Jones Bridge; 16c. Santa Lucia Gate.

(Typo Philippine Bureau of Printing)

1947 (1 May–28 Nov). P 11½ × 12.
636	**115**	1c. green		15	10
		a. Imperf between (vert pair)			
MS637 64 × 85 mm. No. 636 in block of four.					
Imperf (28 Nov)				1·50	1·50

116 President Roxas taking Oath of Office   **117** Presidents Quezon and Roosevelt

(Typo Philippine Bureau of Printing)

1947 (4 July). *First Anniv of Independence.* P 12.
638	**116**	4c. carmine		20	15
639		6c. green		50	50
640		16c. purple		1·20	80

(Recess A. B. N. Co)

1947 (19 Aug). *AIR.* P 12.
641	**117**	6c. green		60	60
642		40c. red-orange		1·30	1·30
643		80c. blue		3·25	3·25

D 118   **119** United Nations' Emblem

(Recess A. B. N. Co)

1947 (20 Oct). *POSTAGE DUE.* P 12.
D644	D **118**	3c. carmine		15	15
D645		4c. dull ultramarine		35	30
D646		6c. olive green		50	45
D647		10c. orange		80	60
D644/647 *Set of 4*				1·60	1·40

(Typo Philippine Bureau of Printing)

1947 (24 Nov). *Conference of Economic Commission in Asia and the Far East, Baguio.* Imperf.
648	**119**	4c. carmine and pink		1·60	1·60
		b. Perf 12½		1·80	1·80
649		6c. deep and pale violet		2·40	2·40
		b. Perf 12½		2·50	2·50
650		12c. bright and pale blue		2·75	2·75
		b. Perf 12½		2·75	2·75

E 120 Cyclist Messenger and Post Office   **121** General MacArthur

(Recess A. B. N. Co)

1947 (22 Dec). *EXPRESS LETTER.* P 12.
E651	E **120**	20c. reddish purple		60	45

(Recess A. B. N. Co)

1948 (3 Feb). *Third Anniv of Liberation.* P 12.
652	**121**	4c. violet		60	20
653		6c. carmine		1·10	75
654		16c. ultramarine		1·60	75

122 Threshing Rice

O. B. O. B.

(O **123**) 13 mm   (O **124**) 15 mm

(Typo Philippine Bureau of Printing)

1948 (23 Feb). *United Nations Food and Agriculture Organization Conference, Baguio.* P 12½.

(a) POSTAGE.

655	**122**	2c. green and olive-yellow	90	60
656		6c. light brown and yellow-ochre	1·10	80
657		18c. blue and light blue	3·00	2·40

(b) AIR. Inscr "AIR MAIL".

658	**122**	40c. carmine and pink	15·00	8·00
655/658		*Set of 4*	18·00	10·50

1948 (1–25 May). *OFFICIAL. Nos. 629/30 and 632 optd with Type O* **123** *(10c.) or O* **124** *(others).*

O659		4c. black-brown	15	10
	a.	Opt inverted	22·00	
	b.	Opt double	22·00	
O660		10c. red	20	10
O661		16c. slate (25 May)	2·20	80

No. O660 also exists with the overprint measuring 12½ instead of 13 mm, applied in New York, the others being overprinted in Manila.

125 Dr. José Rizal	**126** Pres. Manuel Roxas	**127** Scout and Badge

(Recess A. B. N. Co)

1948 (19 June)—**49**. P 12.

662	**125**	2c. emerald-green	20	15
	a.	Booklet pane of six (19 Aug 1949)	1·30	1·30

(Recess A. B. N. Co)

1948 (15 July). *President Roxas Mourning issue.* P 12.

663	**126**	2c. grey-black	20	15
664		4c. grey-black	35	20

(Typo Philippine Bureau of Printing)

1948 (31 Oct). *25th Anniv of Founding of Philippine Boy Scouts.* Imperf.

665	**127**	2c. green and sepia	1·10	60
	b.	Perf 11½	1·80	90
666		4c. pink and sepia	1·50	90
	b.	Perf 11½	2·20	1·30

128 Sampaguita, National Flower

O. B.

(O **129**) 14 mm

(Typo Philippine Bureau of Printing)

1948 (8 Dec). *Flower Day.* P 12½.

667	**128**	3c. blue-green and black	35	30

1948 (30 Dec). *OFFICIAL. No. 662 optd with Type O* **129**.

O668	**125**	2c. emerald-green	50	10

1949 (23 Jan–4 July). *OFFICIAL. Nos. 633/4 optd with Type O* **129** *(20c.) or 12 mm wide (50c.).*

O669		20c. reddish brown (4 July)	15	15
O670		50c. green	75	45

130 Santos, Tavera and Kalaw	**131** *Doctrina Christiana* (first book published in Philippines)

(Recess A. B. N. Co)

1949 (1 Apr). *Library Rebuilding Fund. T* **130/1** *and similar type.* P 12.

671	**130**	4c.+2c. sepia	1·10	80
672	**131**	6c.+4c. violet	3·25	2·20
673	–	18c.+7c. deep blue	4·50	3·75

Design: *Vert*—18c. Title page of Rizal's *Noli Me Tangere*.

132 U.P.U. Monument, Berne	**133** Gen. del Pilar at Tirad Pass

(T **132/3**. Recess A. B. N. Co)

1949 (10 Oct). *75th Anniv of Universal Postal Union.* P 12.

674	**132**	4c. green	20	10
675		6c. violet	20	15
676		18c. blue	80	30
MS677		106 × 92 mm. Nos. 674/6. Imperf	1·50	1·50

1949 (2 Dec). *50th Death Anniv of General Gregorio del Pilar.* P 12.

678	**133**	2c. brown-red	15	15
679		4c. green	35	30

134 Globe	**135** Red Lauan Tree

(Recess A. B. N. Co)

1950 (1–3 Mar). *Fifth International Congress of Junior Chamber of Commerce.* P 12.

(a) POSTAGE (3 Mar).

680	**134**	2c. violet	20	10
681		6c. deep green	30	15
682		18c. blue	65	20

(b) AIR. Inscr "AIR MAIL".

683	**134**	30c. orange	50	20
684		50c. rose-carmine	90	20
680/684		*Set of 5*	2·30	75

(Recess A. B. N. Co)

1950 (14 Apr). *50th Anniv of Forestry Service.* P 12.

685	**135**	2c. green	35	20
686		4c. violet	75	30

136
Franklin D. Roosevelt

137 Lions Emblem

(T **136/7**. Recess A. B. N. Co)

1950 (22 May). *25th Anniv of Philatelic Association.* P 12.

687	**136**	4c. sepia	30	20
688		6c. carmine-pink	60	35
689		18c. blue	1·30	95
MS690 61 × 51 mm. **136** 80c. grey-green. Imperf			2·50	2·50

1950 (4 June). *Lions International Convention, Manila.* P 12.

(a) POSTAGE.

691	**137**	2c. yellow-orange	65	65
692		4c. slate-lilac	1·00	1·00

*(b) AIR. Inscr "*AIR MAIL*".*

693	**137**	30c. emerald	1·00	75
694		50c. ultramarine	1·10	1·00
691/694 *Set of* 4			3·25	3·00
MS695 91 × 88 mm. Nos. 693/4			2·20	2·20

138 Pres. Quirino taking Oath of Office

ONE CENTAVO
(**139**)

(Recess A. B. N. Co)

1950 (4 July). *Inauguration of Pres. Quirino.* P 12.

696	**138**	2c. carmine	15	10
697		4c. purple	15	15
698		6c. blue-green	20	15

1950 (20 Sept). *No.* 662 *surch with T* **139**, *by Philippine Bureau of Printing.*

699	**125**	1c.on 2c. emerald-green	15	10

1950 (20 Sept). *OFFICIAL. No.* O668 *surch with T* **139**, *by Philippine Bureau of Printing.*

O700	**125**	1c.on 2c. emerald-green	10	10

140 Dove and Map

141 War Widow and Children

(T **140/1**. Recess A. B. N. Co)

1950 (23 Oct). *Baguio Conference.* P 12.

701	**140**	5c. green	30	20
702		6c. carmine	30	20
703		18c. ultramarine	75	50

1950 (30 Nov). *Aid to War Victims. T* **141** *and similar design.* P 12.

704	2c.+2c. vermilion	10	10
705	4c.+4c. violet (Disabled veteran)	45	45

142 Arms of Manila

143 Soldier and Peasants

(Recess A. B. N. Co)

1951 (3 Feb–26 Aug). *As T* **142** *(various arms and frames).* P 12.

(a) Arms inscr "MANILA", (3 Feb).

706	5c. violet	60	50
707	6c. grey	50	35
708	18c. ultramarine	60	50

(b) Arms inscr "CEBU", (27 Apr).

709	5c. scarlet	60	50
710	6c. brown	50	35
711	18c. violet	60	50

(c) Arms inscr "ZAMBOANGA", (19 June).

712	5c. blue-green	60	50
713	6c. red-brown	50	35
714	18c. pale blue	60	50

(d) Arms inscr "ILOILO", (26 Aug).

715	5c. bright green	60	50
716	6c. violet	50	35
717	18c. deep blue	60	50
706/717 *Set of* 12		6·25	4·75

(Litho Carmelo Bauerman Inc, Manila)

1951 (31 Mar). *Guarding Peaceful Labour.* Imperf.

718	**143**	5c. green	20	20
		b. Perf 12½	20	10
719		6c. brown-purple	35	35
		b. Perf 12½	35	35
720		18c. blue	1·00	1·00
		b. Perf 12½	90	90

144 Philippines Flag and U.N. Emblem

145 Statue of Liberty

146 Schoolchildren

(T **144/6**. Recess A. B. N. Co)

1951 (24 Oct). *United Nations Day.* P 12.

721	**144**	5c. vermilion	90	35
722		6c. blue-green	60	35
723		18c. ultramarine	1·60	1·10

1951 (10 Dec). *Human Rights Day.* P 12.

724	**145**	5c. green	50	30
725		6c. red-orange	75	50
726		18c. ultramarine	1·30	80

1952 (31 Jan). *50th Anniv of Philippine Educational System.* P 12.

727	**146**	5c. red-orange	60	50

147 M. L. Quezon

O.　B.

(O **148**) 15 mm

(Recess A. B. N. Co (1c., 5c., 2p.), Govt Ptg Wks, Tokyo (2c., 3c., 60c.), De La Rue (10c., 20c., 50c.), Toppan Ptg Co, Tokyo (25c.))

1952–60. *T* **147** *and similar portraits.* P 12 (1c., 5c., 2p.), 13 (2c., 3c., 60c.), 14 × 13½ (10c., 20c., 50c.) or 12 × 12½ (25c.).

728	1c. red-brown (30 Nov 1953)	15	15
729	2c. grey-black (26 May 1960)	15	15
730	3c. brown-red (13 May 1959)	15	15
731	5c. vermilion (17 Mar 1952)	15	15
732	10c. deep blue (*shades*) (1 Apr 1955)	15	15
733	20c. carmine-red (16 Aug 1955)	30	15
734	25c. yellow-green (29 Oct 1958)	45	20
735	50c. orange-red (2 Mar 1959)	90	30
736	60c. carmine (30 Nov 1958)	1·00	45
737	2p. violet (1 May 1952)	3·25	1·10
728/737	*Set of* 10	6·00	2·50

Portraits:—2c. J. Abad Santos; 3c. A. Mabini; 5c. M. H. del Pilar; 10c. Father José Burgos; 20c. Lapu-Lapu; 25c. Gen. A. Luna; 50c. C. Arellano; 60c. A. Bonifacio; 2p. G. L. Jaena.

1952–55. *OFFICIAL. Nos.* 728 *and* 731/3 *optd with Type* O **148**.

O738	1c. red-brown (30 Nov 1953)	15	10
O739	5c. vermilion (11 Mar 1952)	15	10
O740	10c. deep blue (1 Apr 1955)	20	15
O741	20c. carmine-red (16 Aug 1955)	50	15
O738/741	*Set of* 4	90	45

149 Aurora A. Quezon

150 Milkfish and Map of Oceania

(Recess A. B. N. Co)

1952 (19 Aug). *Fruit Tree Memorial Fund.* P 12.

742	**149**	5c.+1c. blue	15	15
743		6c.+2c. carmine-rose	45	45

(Recess Security Bank Note Co. Philadelphia)

1952 (23 Oct). *Indo-Pacific Fisheries Council.* P 12½.

744	**150**	5c. chestnut	1·20	75
		a. Imperf between (vert or horiz pair)		
745		6c. blue	75	60

151 "A Letter from Rizal"

152 Wright Park, Baguio City

(Recess Security Bank Note Co, Philadelphia)

1952 (16 Nov). *Pan-Asiatic Philatelic Exhibition, Manila.* P 12½.

(a) POSTAGE.

746	**151**	5c. blue	65	15
747		6c. brown	65	20

(b) AIR. Inscr "AIR MAIL".

748	**151**	30c. carmine	1·30	1·10

(Recess A. B. N. Co)

1952 (15 Dec). *Third Lions District Convention.* P 12.

749	**152**	5c. orange-red	95	95
750		6c. deep turquoise-green	1·30	1·10

153 F. Baltazar (poet)

154 "Gateway to the East"

155 Pres. Quirino and Pres. Sukarno

(T **153/4**. Recess A. B. N. Co)

1953 (27 Mar). *National Language Week.* P 12.

751	**153**	5c. olive-bistre	50	35

1953 (30 Apr). *International Fair, Manila.* P 12.

752	**154**	5c. blue-green	35	15
753		6c. vermilion	35	15

(Recess (black portion); litho (colours) A. B. N. Co)

1953 (5 Oct). *Visit of President Quirino to Indonesia.* P 12.

754	**155**	5c. multicoloured	20	10
755		6c. multicoloured	30	30

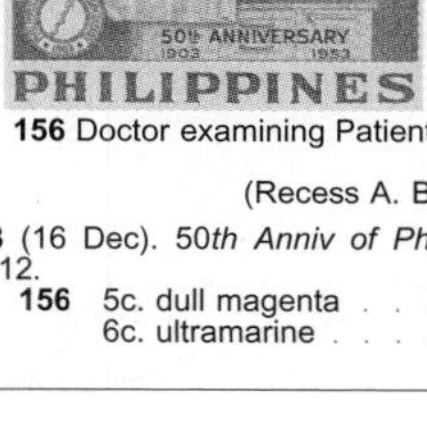

156 Doctor examining Patient

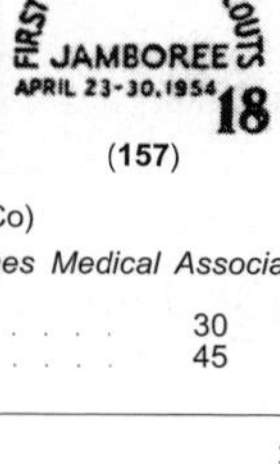

(**157**)

(Recess A. B. N. Co)

1953 (16 Dec). *50th Anniv of Philippines Medical Association.* P 12.

756	**156**	5c. dull magenta	30	30
757		6c. ultramarine	45	35

1954 (23 Apr). *First National Scout Jamboree. No.* 731 *optd as T* **157**, *but larger, without surch and No.* 634 *surch, with T* **157**, *by Philippine Bureau of Printing.*
758   5c. vermilion . . . . 1·30   1·10
759   18c.on 50c. green . . . . 2·20   1·60

158 Stamp of 1854, Magellan and Manila P.O.

159 Diving

(Recess De La Rue)

1954 (25 Apr). *Stamp Centenary.* P 13.
(a) POSTAGE.
760   **158**   5c. yellow-orange & dp reddish vio   80   60
761   18c. yellow-orange & dp bright blue   1·60   1·30
762   30c. yellow-orange and bluish green   3·75   2·40
(b) AIR. Inscr "AIR MAIL".
763   **158**   10c. yellow-orange and sepia   1·60   1·30
764   20c. yellow-orange and bronze-green   2·75   2·20
765   50c. yellow-orange and rose-red   5·50   4·75
760/765 *Set of 6* . . . . 14·50   11·25

(Recess De La Rue)

1954 (31 May). *Second Asian Games, Manila. T* **159** *and similar horiz designs.* P 13.
766   5c. dp blue/*blue* (Throwing the discus)   90   65
767   18c. deep green/*green* . . . . . .   1·50   1·10
768   30c. lake/*pink* (Boxing) . . . . . .   2·20   1·90

(160)

161 "Independence"

162 "The Immaculate Conception" (Murillo)

1954 (6 Sept). *Manila Conference. Nos.* 630 *and* 633 *surch as T* **160**, *in blue.*
769   **113**   5c.on 10c. red   20   15
770   **114**   18c.on 20c. reddish brown   80   75

(Recess De La Rue)

1954 (30 Nov). *Independence Commemoration.* P 13.
771   **161**   5c. carmine-red   30   20
772   18c. deep blue   95   60

(Recess A. B. N. Co)

1954 (30 Dec). *Marian Year.* P 12.
773   **162**   5c. blue   60   35

163 Mayon Volcano   **164** "Labour"

(T **163/4**. Recess De La Rue)

1955 (23 Feb). *50th Anniv of Rotary International.* P 13.
(a) POSTAGE.
774   **163**   5c. deep ultramarine   35   15
775   18c. carmine . . . .   1·30   65
(b) AIR. Inscr "AIR MAIL".
776   **163**   50c. blue-green . . . .   2·50   1·10

1955 (26 May). *Labour-Management Congress, Manila.* P 13 × 12½.
777   **164**   5c. sepia . . . .   1·50   60

165 President Magsaysay

166 Lt. J. Gozar and Boeing P-26A "Peashooter"

(Recess De La Rue)

1955 (4 July). *Ninth Anniv of Republic.* P 12½.
778   **165**   5c. deep blue   20   20
779   20c. scarlet   75   75
780   30c. deep emerald . . . .   1·30   1·30

(Recess Waterlow)

1955 (20 Oct–12 Dec). *AIR. Air Force Heroes. T* **166** *and similar horiz design.* P 13.
781   **166**   20c. deep violet   80   15
782   –   30c. scarlet (12 Dec) . . . . .   1·30   30
783   **166**   50c. deep bluish green . . . . .   1·10   20
784   –   70c. greenish blue (12 Dec) . . .   1·90   1·30
781/784 *Set of 4* . . . .   4·50   1·70
    Design:—30, 70c. Lt. C. F. Basa and Boeing P-26A "Peashooter".

167 Liberty Well   (168)

(Des D. F. Amorsolo. Recess Waterlow)

1956 (16 Mar). *Artesian Wells for Rural Areas.* P 12½ × 13½.
785   **167**   5c. violet   35   35
786   20c. myrtle-green   80   75

1956 (1 Aug). *Fifth Conference of World Confederation of Organizations of the Teaching Profession. No.* 731 *optd with T* **168**.
787   5c. vermilion   35   35

169 Nurse and War Victims

170 Monument (landing marker) in Leyte

(Recess A. B. N. Co)

1956 (30 Aug). *Fiftieth Anniv of Philippines Red Cross. Cross litho, in red. P* 12.
788   **169**   5c. violet   50   50
789   20c. black-brown   75   60

(Litho Philippine Bureau of Printing)

1956–57. *Liberation Commemoration. P* 12½ (20 Oct 1956)..
790   **170**   5c. carmine-red   15   15
            a. Printed double   . . . .   —   —
            b. Imperf (16 Feb 1957)   90   90

171 St. Thomas's University

172 Statue of the Sacred Heart

(Photo Courvoisier)

1956 (13 Nov). *University of St. Thomas. P* 11½.
791   **171**   5c. chocolate and Venetian red   . .   25   20
792   60c. red-brown and deep mauve   . .   1·10   1·00

(Recess A. B. N. Co)

1958 (28 Nov). *2nd National Eucharistic Congress, and Centenary of the Feast of the Sacred Heart. P* 12.
793   **172**   5c. deep sage-green   35   30
794   20c. deep rose   80   80

5   **5**

(173)

174 Girl Guide, Badge and Camp

1956 (7 Dec). *Surch with T* **173**.
795   5c.on 6c. brown (710) (B.)   15   15
796   5c.on 6c. red-brown (713) (B.)   15   15
797   5c.on 6c. violet (716)   15   15

(Litho Philippine Bureau of Printing)

1957 (19 Jan). *Girl Guides' Pacific World Camp, Quezon City, and Birth Centenary of Lord Baden-Powell. P* 12½.
798   **174**   5c. deep violet-blue   70   70
            b. Imperf   . . . .   3·80   3·80

175 President Ramon Magsaysay

176 Sergio Osmeña (Speaker), and First Philippine Assembly

(Recess A. B. N. Co)

1957 (31 Aug). *Death of President Magsaysay. P* 12.
799   **175**   5c. black   15   10

(Recess De La Rue)

1957 (16 Oct). *50th Anniv of First Philippine Assembly. P* 12½ × 13½.
800   **176**   5c. deep bluish green   15   15

177 "The Spoliarium," after Juan Luna

(178)

(Recess De La Rue)

1957 (23 Oct). *Birth Centenary of Luna (painter). P* 14 × 14½.
801   **177**   5c. lake   15   10

1957 (30 Dec). *Inauguration of President-elect C. P. Garcia and Vice-President-elect D. Macapagal. Nos.* 732/3 *surch as T* **178**, *by Philippine Bureau of Printing.*
802   5c.on 10c. deep blue (R.)   20   20
803   10c.on 20c. carmine-red   30   30

179 University of the Philippines

(Recess Govt Ptg Wks, Tokyo)

1958 (18 June). *Golden Jubilee of University of the Philippines. P* 13½.
804   **179**   5c. lake   35   15

180 President Garcia

181 Main Hospital Building, Quezon Institute

(Photo Courvoisier)

1958 (4 July). *Twelfth Anniv of Republic.* P 11½.
805	**180**	5c. multicoloured		15	15
806		20c. multicoloured		60	45

(Photo Govt Ptg Wks, Tokyo)

1958 (19 Aug). *OBLIGATORY TAX. T.B. Relief Fund.* P 13½.
807	**181**	5c.+5c. myrtle-green and red		20	20
		a. Perf 12		1·80	1·80
808		10c.+5c. violet and red		45	45
		a. Perf 12		4·75	4·75

For compulsory use on all mail between 19 August and 30 September 1958.

182 The Immaculate Conception and Manila Cathedral

(Recess Govt Ptg Wks, Tokyo)

1958 (8 Dec). *Inauguration of Manila Cathedral.* P 13½.
809	**182**	5c. multicoloured		20	15
		a. Perf 12		2·50	2·20

OneCentavo
(183)

O B
(O 184)

1959 (11 Jan). *No. 731 surch with T* **183**, *by Philippine Bureau of Printing.*
810	1c.on 5c. vermilion		15	10

1959 (11 Jan). *OFFICIAL. No.* 810 *optd with Type* O **184**, *by Philippine Bureau of Printing.*
O811	1c.on 5c. vermilion		15	10

(185)

186 Philippine Flag

1959 (3 Feb). *14th Anniv of Liberation. Nos. 704/5 surch as T* **185**, *by Philippine Bureau of Printing.*
812	1c.on 2c.+2c. vermilion		10	10
813	6c.on 4c.+4c. violet		15	15

(Photo Govt Ptg Wks, Tokyo)

1959 (8 Feb). *Adoption of Philippine Constitution.* P 13.
814	**186**	6c. carmine-red, brt blue & yellow		15	10
815		20c. carmine-red, brt blue & yellow		20	20

187 Bulacan Seal

188 Scout at Campfire

(Recess Govt Ptg Wks, Tokyo (816/7, 820/1); Toppan Ptg Co, Tokyo (818/9))

1959. *Provincial Seals. Various designs as T* **187**.

(a) Bulacan Seal and 60th Anniv of Malolos Constitution. P 13½ (2 Apr).
816	**187**	6c. yellow-green		15	10
817		20c. scarlet		30	20

(b) Capiz Seal (with inset portrait of Pres. Roxas) and 11th Anniv of Death of Roxas. P 12½ (15 Apr).
818	6c. brown		10	10
819	25c. deep reddish violet		30	30

(c) Bacolod Seal. P 13½ (1 Oct).
820	6c. blue-green		15	10
821	10c. deep claret		20	15
816/821	Set of 6		1·10	85

(Recess Govt Ptg Wks, Tokyo)

1959. *Tenth World Scout Jamboree, Manila. Various vert designs as T* **188**. P 13.

(a) POSTAGE (22 July).
822	6c.+4c. carmine-red/yellow		15	15
823	6c.+4c. carmine-red		35	35
	a. *Tête-bêche* pair Nos. 823 and 825		1·10	
824	25c.+5c. deep blue/yellow		60	60
825	25c.+5c. blue		75	75

(b) AIR (17 July).
826	30c.+10c. deep dull green		60	60
827	70c.+20c. chestnut		1·30	1·30
828	80c.+20c. reddish violet		1·90	1·90
822/828	Set of 7		5·00	5·00
MS829	171 × 90 mm. Nos. 823, 825/8 (sold at 4p.) (27 July)		12·50	12·50

Designs:—25c. Scout with bow and arrow; 30c. Scout cycling; 70c. Scout with model airplane; 80c. President Garcia with scout. Nos. 823 and 825 were issued together in *tête-bêche* pairs within the sheet.

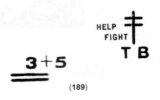
(189)

190 Bohol Sanatorium

(T **189** optd by and T **190** recess Toppan Ptg Co, Tokyo)

1959 (19 Aug). *OBLIGATORY TAX T.B. Relief Fund.*

*(a) Nos. 807/8 surch as T **189**, in red.*

830	**181**	3c.+5c. on 5c.+5c.	20	20
		a. "3+5" and bars omitted		
		b. Perf 12		
831		6c.+5c. on 10c.+ 5c.	20	20
		a. Perf 12		

(b) P. 12.

832	**190**	6c.+5c. deep yellow-green and red	20	20
833		25c.+5c. deep blue and red	45	35

For compulsory use on all mail between 19 August and 30 September 1959.

191 Pagoda and Gardens at Camp John Hay

(Recess Govt Ptg Wks, Tokyo)

1959 (1 Sept). *50th Anniv of Baguio.* P 13½.

834	**191**	6c. emerald	15	10
		a. Perf 12	1·50	1·30
835		25c. scarlet	35	20

6¢

UNITED
NATIONS
DAY

(**192**)

1959 (24 Oct). *United Nations Day. No. 676 surch with T **192** in red, by Philippine Bureau of Printing.*

836	**132**	6c.on 18c. blue	15	10

193 Maria Cristina Falls

One ≡

(**194**)

(Photo Govt Ptg Wks, Tokyo)

1959 (18 Nov). *World Tourist Conference, Manila.* P 13½.

837	**193**	6c. yellow-green and deep violet	15	15
		a. Perf 12	1·50	95
838		30c. emerald-green and sepia	60	45
		a. Perf 12	5·25	4·00

1959 (1 Dec). *No. 629 surch with T **194**, by Philippine Bureau of Printing*

839		1c.on 4c. black-brown	15	10

195   **196** Dr. José Rizal

(Recess Govt Ptg Wks, Tokyo)

1959 (10 Dec). *Centenary of Manila Athenaeum (school).* P 13½.

840	**195**	6c. bright blue	10	10
		a. Perf 12	1·10	1·10
841		30c. scarlet	50	35
		a. Perf 12	5·25	4·00

(Recess Waterlow)

1959 (30 Dec). P 14 × 12.

842	**196**	6c. grey-blue	15	10

1959 (30 Dec). *OFFICIAL. No. 842 optd as Type O **148** but measuring 16½ mm.*

O843	**196**	6c. grey-blue	15	10

197 Book of the Constitution

(Photo Govt Ptg Wks, Tokyo)

1960 (8 Feb). *25th Anniv of Philippines Constitution.* P 14 × 12½.

(a) POSTAGE.

844	**197**	6c. chocolate and gold	15	15

(b) AIR. Inscr "AIR MAIL".

845	**197**	30c. blue and silver	45	30

198 Congress Building

(Recess Waterlow)

1960 (Mar). *Fifth Anniv of Manila Pact.* P 12½.

846	**198**	6c. green	10	10
847		25c. orange	45	35

199 Sunset, Manila Bay

(Photo Govt Ptg Wks, Tokyo)

1960 (7 Apr). *World Refugee Year.* P 13.

848	**199**	6c. multicoloured	15	15
849		25c. multicoloured	45	30

200 North American F-86 Sabre and Boeing P-12 Bi-plane   **(201)**

(Recess De La Rue)

1960 (2 May). *AIR. 25th Anniv of Philippine Air Force.* P 14 × 14½.

850	**200**	10c. carmine-red	15	15
851		20c. ultramarine	45	30

1960 (4 July–Sept). *Various stamps surch as T* **201**, *by Carmelo Bauerman Inc, Manila.*

852	**134**	1c.on 18c. blue (R.)	20	15
853	**161**	5c.on 18c. deep blue (R.)		
		(15 Sept)	20	20
854	**163**	5c.on 18c. carmine	30	15
855	**158**	10c.on 18c. yell-orge & dp brt bl		
		(R.)	20	15
856	**140**	10c.on 18c. ultram (R.) (15 Sept)	30	20
852/856 *Set of 5*			1·10	75

202 Lorraine Cross   **(203)**

(Photo Govt Ptg Wks, Tokyo)

1960 (29 July). *50th Anniv of Philippine Tuberculosis Society. Lorraine Cross and wreath in red and gold.* P 13½.

857	**202**	5c. green	15	10
858		6c. blue	15	10

1960 (19 Aug). *OBLIGATORY TAX. T. B. Relief Fund No.* 807 surch with *T* **203** *in red, by Philippine Bureau of Printing.*

859	**181**	6c.+5c. on 5c.+ 5c. myrtle-grn &		
		red	35	15
		a. Perf 12	2·75	2·20

For compulsory use on all mail between 19 August and 30 September 1960.

204 Pres. Quezon   **205** Basketball

(Recess Bradbury Wilkinson)

1960 (15 Nov).

P 12½ × 13.

860	**204**	1c. deep olive	15	10

(Photo Govt Ptg Wks, Tokyo)

1960 (30 Nov). *Olympic Games, Rome. T* **205** *and similar designs.* P 13½ × 13.

(a) POSTAGE.

861		6c. brown and green	15	10
862		10c. chocolate & reddish pur		
		(Running)	20	15

(b) AIR. Inscr "AIR MAIL".

863		30c. sepia & red orange (Rifle		
		shooting)	60	50
864		70c. brown purple & lt blue		
		(Swimming)	1·30	1·10
861/864 *Set of 4*			2·00	1·60

206 Presidents Eisenhower and Garcia

207 "Mercury" and Globe

(Photo Govt Ptg Wks, Tokyo)

1960 (30 Dec). *Visit of President Eisenhower.* P 13½.

865	**206**	6c. multicoloured	20	15
866		20c. multicoloured	50	30

(Photo Govt Ptg Wks, Tokyo)

1961 (23 Jan). *Manila Postal Conference.* P 13½.

(a) POSTAGE.

867	**207**	6c. orange-brown, gold, blue &		
		blk	15	10

(b) AIR. Inscr "AIR MAIL".

868	**207**	30c. orange-brown, gold, green &		
		blk	35	30

20   **20**

(208)

1961 (16 Feb). *No.* 734 *surch with T* **208**, *by Philippine Bureau of Printing.*

869	20c.on 25c. yellow-green	30	15

2nd National Boy Scout Jamboree Pasonanca Park **10**

(209)

210 La Salle College

1961 (2 May). *Second National Scout Jamboree, Zamboanga.* Nos. 822/5 surch as T **209**, by Philippine Bureau of Printing.
870   10c.on 6c.+4c. carmine red/*yellow* . . . 15   15
871   10c.on 6c.+4c. carmine-red 50   50
   a. *Tête-bêche* pair. Nos. 871 and
   873 . . . . 1·10
872   30c.on 25c.+ 5c. deep blue/*yellow* (R.) . 35   35
873   30c.on 25c.+5c. blue 60   60
870/873 *Set of 4* . . . . 1·40   1·40
   Nos. 871 and 873 were issued together in *tête-bêche* pairs within the sheet.

(Photo Courvoisier)

1961 (16 June). *50th Anniv of La Salle College.* P 11½.
874   **210**   6c. multicoloured 15   10
875   10c. multicoloured 20   15

211 Rizal when student, School and University Buildings

(Photo Govt Ptg Wks, Tokyo)

1961 (19 June–31 Dec). *Birth Centenary of Dr. José Rizal.* T **211** and similar horiz designs. P 13½.
876   5c. multicoloured 10   10
877   6c. multicoloured 10   10
878   10c. brown and green 20   20
879   20c. turquoise and red-brown 30   30
880   30c. multicoloured (31 Dec) 50   35
876/880 *Set of 5* . . . . 1·10   95
   Designs:—6c. Rizal and birthplace at Calamba, Laguna; 10c. Rizal, mother and father; 20c. Rizal extolling Luna and Hidalgo at Madrid; 30c. Rizal's execution.

I K A **15** KAARAWAN Republika ng Pilipinas Hulyo 4, 1961
(212)

1961 (4 July). *15th Anniv of Republic.* Nos. 846/7 optd with T **212**, by Philippine Bureau of Printing.
881   **198**   6c. green 20   20
882   25c. orange 45   45

213 Roxas Memorial T. B. Pavilion

214 Globe, Plan Emblem and Supporting Hand

(Photo Courvoisier)

1961 (19 Aug). *OBLIGATORY TAX. T.B. Relief Fund. Cross in red.* P 11½.
883   **213**   6c.+5c. brown 35   15
   For compulsory use on all mail between 19 August and 30 September 1961.

(Photo J. Enschedé)

1961 (8 Oct). *Seventh Anniv of Admission of Philippines to Colombo Plan.* P 13 × 11½.
884   **214**   5c. orange, green, gold and
                violet 10   10
885   6c. orange, green, gold and deep
                blue 15   15

 6¢ **PAAF GOLDEN JUBILEE 1911 1961**
(215)

1961 (30 Nov). *Philippine Amateur Athletic Federation's Golden Jubilee.* No. 850 surch with T **215**, by Philippine Bureau of Printing.
886   **200**   6c.on 10c. carmine-red 20   20

216 Typist

(217)

(Photo Govt Ptg Wks, Tokyo)

1961 (9 Dec). *Government Employees' Association.* P 12½.
887   **216**   6c. violet and orange-brown . . . 20   10
888   10c. grey-blue and orange-brown . . 35   20

1961 (31 Dec). *Inauguration of Pres. Macapagal and Vice-Pres. Pelaez.* No. 819 surch with T **217**, by Philippine Bureau of Printing.
889   6c.on 25c. deep reddish violet 15   10

(218)

1962 (23 Jan). *No. 807 surch with T* **218**, *by Philippine Bureau of Printing.*

890	**181**	6s.on 5c.+ 5c. myrtle-green & red		15	15
		a. Perf 12			

E **219** G.P.O., Manila

220 Waling-Waling

(Recess Bradbury, Wilkinson)

1962 (23 Jan). *EXPRESS LETTER.* P 13½ × 13.

E891	E **219**	20c. deep magenta		35	30

(Photo J. Enschedé)

1962 (9 Mar). *Orchids. T* **220** *and similar vert designs. Multicoloured.* P 13½ × 14.

892	5c. Type **220**			15	15
	a. Block of 4. Nos. 892/5			90	
893	6c. White mariposa			15	15
894	10c. *Dendrobium sanderii*			20	20
895	20c. Sanggumay			35	35
892/895 *Set of 4*				75	75

Nos. 892/5 were issued together in *se-tenant* blocks of four stamps within the sheet.

G. O.

(O 222)

221 A. Mabini (statesman)

G. O. G. O.

(O 223) **(O 224)**
(17 × 3 mm)

(Recess De La Rue (1s.), Toppan Ptg Co, Tokyo (6s. choc), Govt Ptg Wks, Tokyo (6s. blue, 50s.), Bradbury, Wilkinson (others))

1962 (13 May)–**69**. *New Currency T* **221** *and similar vert portraits. Various perfs.*

896	1s. chestnut (p 14) (23 Sept 1963)		10	10
897	3s. carmine (p 13½)		10	10
898	5s. carmine-red (p 13½) (23 Sept 1963)		10	10
899	6s. chocolate (p 13 × 12) (19 June 1962)		15	10
900	6s. greenish blue (p 13) (19 June 1964)		15	10
901	10s. purple (p 13½) (24 Mar 1963)		15	10
902	20s. greenish blue (p 13½ × 13) (20 Oct 1963)		20	10
903	30s. vermilion (p 13½ × 13) (30 Nov 1962)		50	15
904	50s. violet (p 13) (1 May 1963)		90	15
905	70s. blue (p 13½) (10 Dec 1963)		1·10	50
906	1p. emerald (p 13½) (23 Jan 1963)		2·20	45
907	1p. red-orange (p 13½) (3 Feb 1969)		75	35
896/907 *Set of 12*			5·75	2·10

Portraits:—1s. M. L. Quezon; 5s. M. H. del Pilar; 6s. (2) José Rizal (*different*); 10s. Father J. Burgos; 20s. Lapu-Lapu; 30s. Rajah Soliman; 50s. C. Arellano; 70s. S. Osmeña; 1p. (906), E. Jacinto; 1p. (907), J. M. Panganiban.

(Optd by Bradbury, Wilkinson (O **222**), Toppan Ptg Co, Tokyo (O **223**), Govt Ptg Wks, Tokyo (O **224**))

1962 (19 June)–**64**. *OFFICIAL. Nos.* 898/904 *optd with Types* O **222**/4 *or similar type.*

O908	O **222**	5s. carmine-red (23 Sept 1963)		10	10
O909	O **223**	6s. chocolate		15	10
		a. Opt smaller (16½ × 2½ mm)			
O910	—	6s. greenish bl (19 June 1964)		15	10
O911	O **222**	10s. purple (24 Mar 1963)		20	15
O912		20s. greenish blue (20 Oct 1963)		30	15
O913		30s. vermilion (30 Nov 1962)		35	30
O914	O **224**	50s. violet (1 May 1963)		45	35
O908/914 *Set of 7*				1·50	1·10

The overprint on No. O910 is in the same fount as Type O **224** but with the letters spaced only 4 mm apart.

225 Pres. Macapagal taking Oath

226 Valdes Memorial T.B. Pavilion

(Photo Govt Wks, Tokyo)

1962 (4 July). *Independence Day. Centres multicoloured; background colours given.* P 13½.

915	**225**	6s. blue		15	10
916		10s. green		20	15
917		30s. lilac		35	20

The above stamps were postmarked "12 JUNE 1962" on issue, to "mark philatelically" the celebration of Independence Day (June 12th).

(Photo Courvoisier)

1962 (19 Aug). *OBLIGATORY TAX. T.B. Relief Fund. Cross in red.* P 11½.

918	**226**	6s.+5s. slate-purple		15	15
919		30s.+5s. ultramarine		45	30
920		70s.+5s. greenish blue		1·00	90

For compulsory use on all mail between 19 August and 30 September 1962.

227 Lake Taal

BICENTENNIAL
Diego Silang
Revolt
20

(228)

(Photo Courvoisier)

1962 (24 Oct). *Malaria Eradication.*P 11½.
921	**227**	6s. multicoloured		15	15
922		10s. multicoloured		20	15
923		70s. multicoloured		1·50	1·10

1962 (15 Nov). *Bicentenary of Diego Silang Revolt. No. 734 surch with T* **228** *in red, by Philippine Bureau of Printing.*
924	20s.on 25c. yellow-green		30	20

(229)   230 Dr. Rizal playing Chess

1962 (23 Dec). *No. 742 with "+1" premium obliterated with T* **229**, *by Philippine Bureau of Printing.*
925	**149**	5c. blue	20	15

(Recess Govt Ptg Wks, Tokyo)

1962 (30 Dec). *Rizal Foundation Fund T* **230** *and similar horiz design.* P 13 × 13½.
926	6s.+4s. emerald-green and magenta		20	20
927	30s.+5s. blue and reddish purple		50	50

Design:—30s. Dr. Rizal fencing.

(231)   (232)

1963 (19 Feb–12 Mar). *Nos. 897 and 899 surch as T* **231**, *by Philippine Bureau of Printing.*
928	1s.on 3s. carmine (12 Mar)		15	10
929	5s.on 6s. chocolate		15	15

1963 (12 June). *Diego Silang Bicentenary Art and Philatelic Exhibition, G.P.O., Manila. No. 737 surch as T* **232**, *by Philippine Bureau of Printing.*
930	6c.on 2p. violet		15	15
931	20c.on 2p. violet		30	30
932	70c.on 2p. violet		90	75

233 "We want to see . . ." (Pres. Roxas)   234 Lorraine Cross on Map

(Recess Bradbury, Wilkinson)

1963 (4 July). *Presidential Sayings (1st issue).* P 14 × 13½.
933	**233**	6s. blue and black	15	10
934		30s. brown and black	45	15

See also Nos. 959/60, 981/2, 1015/6, 1034/5, 1055/6, 1148/9 and 1292/3.

(Recess Bradbury, Wilkinson)

1963 (19 Aug). *OBLIGATORY TAX. T.B. Relief Fund. Cross in red.* P 13½.
935	**234**	6s.+5s. pink and violet		15	10
936		10s.+5s. pink and deep green		15	15
937		50s.+5s. pink and deep chocolate		75	50

For compulsory use on all mail between 19 August and 30 September 1963.

235 Globe and Flags   236 Centenary Emblem

(Photo Govt Ptg Wks, Tokyo)

1963 (26 Aug). *First Anniv of Asian–Oceanic Postal Union.* P 13½ × 13.
938	**235**	6s. multicoloured		15	15
939		20s. multicoloured		20	15

(Photo Courvoisier)

1963 (1 Sept). *Red Cross Centenary.* P 11½.
940	**236**	5s. red, grey and violet		15	10
941		6s. red, grey and ultramarine		15	15
942		20s. red, grey and green		45	20

237 Tinikling (dance)

(Photo De La Rue)

1963 (15 Sept). *Folk Dances. Horiz designs as T* **237**. *Multicoloured.* P 14 × 14½.
943	**237**	5s. Type 237		15	15
		a. Block of 4 Nos. 943/6		75	
944		6s. Pandanggo sa Ilaw		15	15
945		10s. Itik-Itik		15	15
946		20s. Singkil		30	30
943/946	*Set of 4*			70	70

Nos. 943/6 were issued together in *se-tenant* blocks of four stamps within the sheet.

238 Pres Macapagal and Philippine Family

(Photo De La Rue)

1963 (28 Sept). *President's Social-Economic Programme.* P 14.
947	**238**	5s. multicoloured		15	15
948		6s. multicoloured		15	15
949		20s. multicoloured		35	20

239 Presidents' Meeting

240 Bonifacio and Flag

243 A. Mabini (patriot)

244 Negros Oriental T.B. Pavilion

(Photo Govt Ptg Wks, Tokyo)

1963 (28 Sept). *Visit of President Mateos of Mexico.* P 13½ × 13.

950	**239**	6s. multicoloured	. . . . .	15	15
951		30s. multicoloured	. . . . .	45	15

(Photo Courvoisier)

1963 (30 Nov). *Birth Centenary of Andres Bonifacio (patriot).* P 11½.

952	**240**	5s. multicoloured	. . . . .	15	10
953		6s. multicoloured	. . . . .	15	15
954		25s. multicoloured	. . . . .	35	30

1963 (10 Dec). *15th Anniv of Declaration of Human Rights. Sheet No.* **MS**677 *optd* "UN ADOPTION OF HUMAN RIGHTS 15TH ANNIVERSARY DEC. 10, 1963", *by Philippine Bureau of Printing.*

MS955	106 × 92 mm. Imperf	. . . . .	1·30	1·30

241 Harvester

242 Bamboo Organ, Catholic Church, Las Piñas

(Photo Govt Ptg Wks, Tokyo)

1963 (20 Dec). *Freedom from Hunger.* P 13½ × 13.

(a) POSTAGE.

956	**241**	6s. multicoloured	. . . . .	15	10

(b) AIR. Inscr 'PANGHIMPAPAWID'.

957	**241**	30s. multicoloured	. . . . .	60	45
958		50s. multicoloured	. . . . .	95	75

(Recess Govt Ptg Wks, Tokyo)

1963 (30 Dec). *Presidential Sayings (2nd issue). As T* **233** *but with portrait and saying changed.* P 13½.

959	6s. black and light reddish violet	. . .	15	10
960	30s. black and dull green	. . . . .	35	15

Portrait and saying:—Pres. Magsaysay. "I believe . . ."

(Photo Govt Ptg Wks, Tokyo)

1964 (4 May). *Las Piñas Organ Commemoration.* P 13½.

961	**242**	5s. multicoloured	. . . . .	15	10
962		6s. multicoloured	. . . . .	15	15
963		20s. multicoloured	. . . . .	45	20

(Photo Harrison)

1964 (23 July). *Birth Centenary of A. Mabini. Wmk "Harrison & Sons, London" in script (W* **253** *of Thailand).* P 14½.

964	**243**	6s. multicoloured	. . . . .	15	10
965		10s. multicoloured	. . . . .	15	15
966		30s. multicoloured	. . . . .	35	15

(Photo De La Rue)

1964 (19 Aug). *OBLIGATORY TAX. T.B. Relief Fund. Cross in vermilion.* P 13½ × 14.

967	**244**	5s.+5s. purple	. . . . .	15	10
968		6s.+5s. ultramarine	. . . . .	15	10
969		30s.+5s. brown	. . . . .	45	30
970		70s.+5s. green	. . . . .	90	80
967/970	*Set of 4*	. . . . .		1·50	1·10

For compulsory use on all mail between 19 August and 30 September 1964.

245 S.E.A.T.O. Emblem and Flags

246 President signing the Land Reform Code

247 Basketball

(Photo De La Rue)

1964 (8 Sept). *Tenth Anniv of South-East Asian Treaty Organization.* P 13.

971	**245**	6s. multicoloured	. . . . .	15	10
972		10s. multicoloured	. . . . .	20	15
973		25s. multicoloured	. . . . .	30	15

(Photo Harrison)

1964 (21 Dec). *Agricultural Land Reform Code. President and Inscr at foot, orange-brown, rose and sepia.* W **253** *of Thailand.* P 14½.

(a) POSTAGE.

974	**246**	3s. green	. . . . .	15	10
975		6s. bright blue	. . . . .	15	15

(b) AIR. Inscr "PANGHIMPAPAWID".

976	**246**	30s. red-brown	. . . . .	35	20

(Photo Harrison)

1964 (28 Dec). *Olympic Games, Tokyo. T* **247** *and similar vert designs. Sport in chocolate.* W **253** *of Thailand.* P 15 × 14.

977		6s. pale blue and gold	. . . . .	15	15
		b. Imperf	. . . . .	30	30
978		10s. pink and gold	. . . . .	20	15
		b. Imperf	. . . . .	50	45
979		20s. lemon and gold	. . . . .	50	20
		b. Imperf	. . . . .	95	95

980	30s. light green and gold		65	50
	b. Imperf		1·40	1·20
977/980 *Set of* 4			1·40	90
977b/980b *Set of* 4			2·75	2·50

Sports—10s. Relay-racing; 20s. Hurdling; 30s. Football.

(Recess Bradbury, Wilkinson)

1965 (28 Feb). *Presidential Sayings (3rd issue). As T 233 but with portrait and saying changed.* P 13½.

981	6s. black and green		15	15
982	30s. black and reddish purple		35	15

Portrait and saying:—Pres. Quirino, "So live . . .".

248 Presidents Lübke and Macapagal

249 Meteorological Emblems

(Photo Govt Ptg Wks, Tokyo)

1965 (19 Apr). *Visit of President of German Federal Republic.* P 13½.

983	**248**	6s. multicoloured	15	10
984		10s. multicoloured	20	15
985		25s. multicoloured	35	30

(Photo Govt Ptg Wks, Tokyo)

1965 (22 May). *Centenary of Philippines Meteorological Services.* P 13½.

986	**249**	6s. multicoloured	15	15
987		20s. multicoloured	15	15
988		50s. multicoloured	60	30

250 Pres. Kennedy

251 King Bhumibol and Queen Sirikit, Pres. Macapagal and Wife

(Des N. Dimanlig. Photo Harrison)

1965 (29 May). *John F. Kennedy (U.S. President) Commemoration.* W **253** of Thailand. P 14½ × 14.

989	**250**	6s. multicoloured	15	15
990		10s. multicoloured	20	15
		a. Pink (on face) omitted		
991		30s. multicoloured	50	20
		a. Imperf (pair)	£300	
		b. Blue (tie) omitted		

The face in No. 990a is the same colour as the hair; the tie in No. 991b is coloured grey.

(Photo De La Rue)

1965 (12 June). *Visit of King and Queen of Thailand.* P 12½ × 13.

992	**251**	2s. multicoloured	10	10
993		6s. multicoloured	15	15
994		30s. multicoloured	50	20

252 Princess Beatrix and Mrs. Macapagal

(253)

(Photo De La Rue)

1965 (4 July). *Visit of Princess Beatrix of the Netherlands.* P 13.

995	**252**	2s. multicoloured	10	10
996		6s. multicoloured	15	15
997		10s. multicoloured	20	15

1965 (19 Aug). *OBLIGATORY TAX. T.B. Relief Fund. No.* 968 surch as T **253** *in red, by Philippine Bureau of Printing.*

998	**244**	1s.+5s. on 6s.+5s. ultramarine	15	10
999		3s.+5s. on 6s.+5s. ultramarine	20	15

For compulsory use on all mail between 19 August and 30 September 1965.

254 Hand holding Cross and Rosary

255 Baptism of Filipinos by Father Urdaneta, Cebu

(Photo Govt Ptg Wks, Tokyo)

1965 (4 Oct). *400th Anniv of Philippines Christianisation. Multicoloured designs inscr "1565–1965".* P 13½.

(a) POSTAGE. As T **254**.

1000	3s. Type **254**		15	10
1001	6s. Legaspi-Urdaneta Monument		20	10

(b) AIR. As T **255**.

1002	30s. Type **255**		50	30
1003	70s. "Way of the Cross"—ocean map of Christian voyagers' route, Spain to the Philippines		1·30	1·20
1000/1003 *Set of* 4			1·90	1·50
MS1004 170 × 105 mm. Nos 1000/3. Imperf			3·00	3·00

256 Signing Agreement

257 Cyclists and Globe

(Photo De La Rue)

1965 (25 Nov). *"MAPILINDO" Conference, Manila.* P 13 × 12½.

1005	**256**	6s. blue, red and yellow	15	15
1006		10s. red-brown, red, yellow & blue	15	15
1007		25s. green, red, yellow and blue	45	20

The above stamps depict President Sukarno of Indonesia, President Macapagal of the Philippines and Prime Minister Tunku Abdul Rahman of Malaysia.

(Photo Govt Ptg Wks, Tokyo)

1965 (5 Dec). *Second Asian Cycling Championships, Philippines.*
P 13½.

1008	**257**	6s. multicoloured		10	10
1009		10s. multicoloured		20	15
1010		25s. multicoloured		45	30

10s

MARCOS–LOPEZ
INAUGURATION
DEC. 30, 1965
(258)

259 Dr. A. Regidor

1965 (30 Dec). *Inauguration of President Marcos and Vice-President Lopez. Nos. 926/7 surch as T* **258**, *by Philippine Bureau of Printing.*

1011	10s.on 6s.+4s. emerald-green & mag		20	20
1012	30s.on 30s.+5s. blue & reddish			
	purple		50	50

(Recess Bradbury, Wilkinson)

1966 (21 Jan). *Regidor (patriot) Commemoration.* P 11½ × 11.

1013	**259**	6s. blue		15	15
1014		30s. deep red-brown		30	20

HELP ME STOP
SMUGGLING

Pres. MARCOS
(260)

261 Girl Scout

(Recess Bradbury, Wilkinson)

1966 (6 Feb). *Presidential Sayings (4th issue). As T* **233** *but with portrait and saying changed.* P 13½.

1015		6s. black and lake		15	10
1016		30s. black and blue		35	20

Portrait and saying:—Pres. Aguinaldo. "Have faith . . .".

1966 (1 May). *Campaign Against Smuggling. No.* 900 *optd with T* **260** *in red, by Philippine Bureau of Printing.*

1017		6c. greenish blue		20	15
		a. Opt inverted		16·00	
		b. Opt double			
		c. Opt double, one inverted			
		d. Opt double, both inverted			

No. 1017 also exists with black overprint. This is believed to be a trial printing.

(Photo and litho De La Rue)

1966 (26 May). *Silver Jubilee of Philippine Girl Scouts.* P 13.

1018	**261**	3s. multicoloured		15	10
1019		6s. multicoloured		15	15
1020		20s. multicoloured		45	20

262 Pres. Marcos taking Oath

(Litho De La Rue)

1966 (12 June). *Inauguration of President Marcos (in* 1965*).*
P 12½.

1021	**262**	6s. multicoloured		15	15
1022		20s. multicoloured		15	15
1023		30s. multicoloured		30	20

263 Manila Seal and Historical Scenes

(Litho De La Rue)

1966 (24 June). *Introduction of New Seal for Manila.* P 12½.

1024	**263**	6s. multicoloured		15	15
1025		30s. multicoloured		30	15

264 Bank Façade and 1-peso Coin

265 "Progress"

(Litho De La Rue)

1966 (22 July). *50th Anniv of Philippines National Bank.*

(a) T **264** *and similar horiz design.* P 14 × 13½.

1026		6s. black, silver, gold and blue		15	10
1027		10s. multicoloured		20	15

MS1028 157 × 70 mm. **265** 70s.
multicoloured . . . . 1·90 1·90
Design:—10s. Old and new Bank buildings.

266 Bank Building

(267)

(Photo Harrison)

1966 (1 Oct). *60th Anniv of Postal Savings Bank.* W **253** of Thailand. P 14½.

1029	**266**	6s. violet, lt yellow & blue-			
		green		15	10
1030		10s. claret, lt yellow & blue-			
		green		20	15
1031		20s. brt blue, lt yellow & blue-			
		green		45	20

1966 (24 Oct). *Manila Summit Conference. Nos.* 1021 *and* 1023 *optd with T* **267**, *by Philippine Bureau of Printing.*
1032 **262** 6s. multicoloured (G) 20 15
    a. Deep ultramarine (frame etc)
      of stamp printed double . . . .
1033   30s. multicoloured 30 30
    a. Opt inverted
   Imperforate copies of No. 1033 with green overprint have been seen but their status is unknown.

(Recess Govt Ptg Wks, Tokyo)

1966 (6 Nov). *Presidential Sayings (5th issue). As T* **233** *but with portrait and saying changed.* P 13½.
1034   6s. black and deep orange-brown . . . 15 10
1035   30s. black and new blue 35 15
   Portrait and saying:—Pres. Laurel. "No one can love the Filipinos better . . .".

50th **ANNIVERSARY**
LIONS INTERNATIONAL
1967

(268)   269 "Succour" (after painting
                       by F. Amorsolo)

1967 (14 Jan). *50th Anniv of Lions International. Nos.* 977/80B *optd as T* **268**, *by Philippine Bureau of Printing.* *Imperf.*
1036   6s. pale blue and gold 15 15
    a. Inverted surch on perf stamp . . .
1037   10s. pink and gold 20 15
1038   20s. lemon and gold 45 20
1039   30s. light green and gold 65 65

(Litho De La Rue)

1967 (15 May). *25th Anniv of Battle of Bataan.* P 14.
1040 **269** 5s. multicoloured 15 10
1041   20s. multicoloured 20 15
1042   2p. multicoloured . . . . 2·40 1·30

4s
(270)

1967 (7–10 Aug). *Nos.* 900 *and* 975 *surch as T* **270**, *by Philippine Bureau of Printing.*
1043   – 4s.on 6s. greenish blue
           (10 Aug) 15 10
1044 **246** 5s.on 6s. bright blue 15 10

271 Stork-billed
Kingfisher

272 Gen. MacArthur, and
Paratroopers landing on Corregidor

(Photo Govt Ptg Wks, Tokyo)

1967 (19 Aug). *OBLIGATORY TAX. T.B. Relief Fund. T* **271** *and similar vert bird designs. Multicoloured. Cross in red.* P 13½.
1045   1s.+5s. Type **271** 15 15
1046   5s.+5s. Rufous hornbill 20 20

1047   10s.+5s. Philippine (inscr "Monkey-
           eating") eagle 35 20
1048   30s.+5s. Great-billed parrot 75 50
1045/1048 *Set of 4* . . . . 1·30 95
   For compulsory use on all mail between 19 August and 30 September 1967.
   See also Nos. 1113/16.

(Litho De La Rue)

1967 (31 Aug). *25th Anniv of Battle of Corregidor.* P 14.
1049 **272** 6s. multicoloured 10 10
1050   5p. multicoloured . . . . 4·50 3·75

273 Bureau of Posts Building, Manila

(Litho De La Rue)

1967 (15 Sept). *65th Anniv of Philippines Bureau of Posts.* P 14.
1051 **273** 4s. multicoloured 20 20
1052   20s. multicoloured 20 15
1053   50s. multicoloured 60 45

274 Escaping from Eruption

(Photo Govt Ptg Wks, Tokyo)

1967 (28 Sept). *OBLIGATORY TAX. Taal Volcano Eruption (1965) (1st issue).* P 13½ × 13.
1054 **274** 70s. multicoloured 95 80
   For compulsory use on foreign air mail where the rate exceeded 70s. In aid of Taal Volcano Rehabilitation Committee.
   See also No. 1071.

(Recess Govt Ptg Wks, Tokyo)

1967 (15 Nov). *Presidential Sayings (6th issue). As T* **233** *but with portrait and saying changed.* P 13½.
1055   10s. black and light blue 15 10
1056   30s. black and violet 35 15
   Portrait and saying:—Pres. Quezon. "Social Justice is far more beneficial . . .".

275 "The Holy
Family" (Filipino
version)

276 Pagoda, Pres. Marcos and
Chiang Kai-shek

(Photo Govt Ptg Wks, Tokyo)

1967 (1 Dec). *Christmas.* P 13½.
1057	**275**	10s. multicoloured	20	15
1058		40s. multicoloured	50	45

(Photo Govt Ptg Wks, Tokyo)

1967 (30 Dec)–**68**. *China-Philippines Friendship.* T **276** *and similar horiz designs.* P 13½.
1059		5s. multicoloured	10	10
1060		10s. multicoloured (12 Mar 1968)	15	15
1061		20s. multicoloured	20	15

Designs: (with portraits of Pres. Marcos and Chiang Kaishek)–10s. Gateway, Chinese Garden, Rizal Park, Luneta; 20s. Chinese Garden, Rizil Park, Luneta.

277 Ayala Avenue, Manila, Inaugural Ceremony and Rotary Badge

(Litho De La Rue)

1968 (9 Jan). *First Anniv of Makati Centre Post Office, Manila.* P 14 × 13½.
1062	**277**	10s. multicoloured	15	15
1063		20s. multicoloured	20	20
1064		40s. multicoloured	60	60

(278)   (279)

1968 (8 Mar). *Surch as T* **278/9**, *by Philippine Bureau of Printing.*
1065	–	5s.on 6s. black and green (981)	15	10
1066	–	5s.on 6s. blk & dp orge brn (1034)	15	10
1067	**244**	10s.on 6s.+ 5s. ultramarine	15	10

In No. 1066 the obliterating bars are on the right of the figure of value and closely adjacent.

280 Calderon, Barasoain Church and Constitution

(Litho De La Rue)

1968 (4 Apr). *Birth Centenary of Felipe G. Calderon (lawyer and author of Malolos Constitution).* P 14.
1068	**280**	10s. multicoloured	15	10
1069		40s. multicoloured	60	45
1070		75s. multicoloured	1·20	1·10

281 Eruption

282 "Philcomsat" Earth Station and Globe

(Litho De La Rue)

1968 (1 Oct). *Taal Volcano Eruption (1965) (2nd issue).* P 14 × 13½.
1071	**281**	70s. multicoloured	95	95

In 1968 two sets were prepared by an American agency under contract with the Philippine postal authority but at the last moment this contract was cancelled by the Philippine Government. In the meanwhile the stamps had been put on sale in the U.S.A. but they were not issued in the Philippine Islands and they had no postal validity. Later attempts were made to have the stamps validated but in the event they were never put on sale at post offices. They comprise a set for the Mexican Olympic Games in the values 1s., 2s., 3s., 15s. postage, 50s., 75s., 1p., 2p. airmail and 5s. miniature sheets and a set in memory of J. F. Kennedy and Robert Kennedy in the values 1s., 2s., 3s. postage, 5p., 10p. airmail and 5s. and 10p. miniature sheets.

(Photo Govt Ptg Wks, Tokyo)

1968 (21 Oct). *Inauguration of "Philcomsat"–POTC Earth Station, Tanay, Rizal, Luzon.* P 13½.
1072	**282**	10s. multicoloured	20	15
1073		40s. multicoloured	60	45
1074		75s. multicoloured	1·00	90

283 "Tobacco Production" (mural)

(Photo Govt Ptg Wks, Tokyo)

1968 (15 Nov). *Philippines Tobacco Industry.* P 13½.
1075	**283**	10s. multicoloured	15	15
1076		40s. multicoloured	60	50
1077		70s. multicoloured	1·10	90

284 "Kudyapi"

285 Concordia College

(T **284/5**. Photo Govt Ptg Wks, Tokyo)

1968 (22 Nov). *St. Cecilia's Day. Musical Instruments.* T **284** *and similar horiz designs.* Multicoloured. P 13½.
1078		10s. Type **284**	10	10
1079		20s. "Ludag"	10	10
1080		30s. "Kulintangan"	25	20
1081		50s. "Subing"	35	35
1078/1081	*Set of 4*		70	65

1968 (8 Dec). *Centenary of Concordia Women's College.*
P 13 × 13½.
1082	**285**	10s. multicoloured	10	10
1083		20s. multicoloured	15	10
1084		70s. multicoloured	50	35

286 Children singing
Carols

287 Philippine Tarsier
(*Tarsius* sp.)

(T 286/7. Photo Govt Ptg Wks, Tokyo)

1968 (16 Dec). *Christmas.* P 13½.
1085	**286**	10s. multicoloured	15	15
1086		40s. multicoloured	50	45
1087		75s. multicoloured	95	80

1969 (8 Jan). *Philippines Fauna. T 287 and similar horiz designs.
Multicoloured.* P 13½.
1088		2s. Type **287**	15	15
1089		10s. Tamarau (*Bubalus mindorensis*)	15	15
1090		20s. Water buffalo (*Bubalus bubalis*)	20	20
1091		75s. Greater Malay chevrotain (*Tragulus nigricans*)	1·30	1·00
1088/1091 *Set of 4*			1·60	1·40

288 President Aguinaldo and Cavite
Building

(Litho De La Rue)

1969 (23 Jan). *Birth Centenary of President Emilio Aguinaldo.*
P 14.
1092	**288**	10s. multicoloured	20	15
1093		40s. multicoloured	60	35
1094		70s. multicoloured	1·00	80

289 Rotary Emblem and "Bastion of
San Andres"

290 Senator
C. M. Recto

(Litho and photo De La Rue)

1969 (29 Jan). *50th Anniv of Manila Rotary Club.* P 12½.

(a) POSTAGE.
1095	**289**	10s. multicoloured	15	15

(b) AIR. Inscr "PANGHIMPAPAWID".
1096	**289**	40s. multicoloured	45	30
1097		75s. multicoloured	95	75

(Photo Govt Ptg Wks, Tokyo)

1969 (8 Feb). *Recto Commemoration.* P 13½.
1098	**290**	10s. reddish purple	15	10

**PHILATELIC WEEK
NOV. 24-30. 1968**

(291)   **292** José Rizal College

1969 (14 Feb). *Philatelic Week. No. 1051 optd with T 291, by
Philippine Bureau of Printing.*
1099	**273**	4s. multicoloured	20	10

(Photo Govt Ptg Wks, Tokyo)

1969 (19 Feb). *50th Anniv of José Rizal College, Mandaluyong,
Rizal.* P 13 × 13½.
1100	**292**	10s. multicoloured	15	15
1101		40s. multicoloured	60	45
1102		50s. multicoloured	90	65

(293)   **294** Red Cross
Emblems and
Map

1969 (10 May). *Fourth National Boy Scout Jamboree, Palayan
City. No. 1019, surch with T 293, in red.*
1103	**261**	5s.on 6s. multicoloured	20	15

(Photo Harrison)

1969 (26 May). *50th Anniv of League of Red Cross Societies.*
P 12½.
1104	**294**	10s. scar, lt ultram & brownish grey	15	15
1105		40s. scarlet, indigo and cobalt	50	30
1106		75s. scarlet, olive-brown and buff	80	75

295 President and
Mrs. Marcos
harvesting Rice

296 "The Holy Child of Leyte"
(statue)

(Photo Harrison)

1969 (12 June). *"Rice for Progress".* P 14.
1107	**295**	10s. multicoloured	15	15
1108		40s. multicoloured	50	35
1109		75s. multicoloured	80	75

(Photo Govt Ptg Wks, Tokyo)

1969 (30 June). *80th Anniv of Return of the "Holy Child of Leyte"*
to Tacloban. P 13½.

(a) POSTAGE.

1110	**296**	5s. multicoloured	15	10
1111		10s. multicoloured	15	15

(b) AIR. Inscr "PANGHIMPAPAWID".

1112	**296**	40s. multicoloured	50	35

(Litho Govt Ptg Wks, Tokyo)

1969 (15 Aug). *OBLIGATORY TAX. T.B. Relief Fund. Vertical bird*
designs as T **271**. *Multicoloured.* P 14.

1113	1s.+5s. Common gold-backed			
	woodpecker		20	15
1114	5s.+5s. Philippine trogon		20	15
1115	10s.+5s. Johnstone's (inscr "Mt. Apo")			
	lorikeet		35	20
1116	40s.+5s. Scarlet (inscr "Johnstone's")			
	minivet		50	35
1113/1116 *Set of 4*			1·10	75

For compulsory use on all mail between 19 August and
30 September 1969.

297 Bank Building

(Photo Govt Ptg Wks, Tokyo)

1969 (12 Sept). *Inauguration of Philippines Development Bank,*
Makati, Rizal. P 13½.

1117	**297**	10s. black, bright green & steel-		
		blue	15	10
1118		40s. black, bright green & dp		
		claret	90	45
1119		75s. black, bright green and		
		brown	1·30	95

298 *Troides magellanus*   299 Children of the World

(Photo Govt Ptg Wks, Tokyo)

1969 (15 Sept). *Philippine Butterflies. T* **298** *and similar horiz*
designs. Multicoloured. P 13½.

1120	10s. Type **298**		20	15
1121	20s. *Graphium agamemnon (Papilio*			
	agammemnon)		30	20
1122	30s. *Papilio heleuus* (sp. *hystaspes*)		50	30
1123	40s. *Trogonptera trojana*		80	45
1120/1123 *Set of 4*			1·60	1·00

(Photo Harrison)

1969 (6 Oct). *15th Anniv of Universal Children's Day.* P 13.

1124	**299**	10s. multicoloured	15	10
1125		20s. multicoloured	20	15
1126		30s. multicoloured	20	20

300 Memorial and   301 Cultural Centre
Outline of Landing

(Litho De La Rue)

1969 (20 Oct). *25th Anniv of U.S. Forces' Landing on Leyte.*
P 13½ × 14.

1127	**300**	5s. multicoloured	15	10
1128		10s. multicoloured	20	15
1129		40s. multicoloured	50	30

(Photo Govt Ptg Wks, Tokyo)

1969 (4 Nov). *Cultural Centre, Manila.* P 13½.

1130	**301**	10s. bright blue	15	15
1131		30s. bright purple	35	20

1969 PHILATELIC WEEK
(302)

1969 (24 Nov). *Philatelic Week. Nos. 943/6 surch as T* **302**, *or*
optd only.

1132	**237**	5s. multicoloured	15	15
		a. Block of 4 Nos. 1132/5	80	
1133	–	5s.on 6s. multicoloured	15	15
1134	–	10s. multicoloured	20	20
1135	–	10s.on 20s. multicoloured	20	20
1132/1135 *Set of 4*			65	65

Nos. 1132/5 were issued together in *se-tenant* blocks of four
stamps within the sheet. They are listed in the same order as
Nos. 943/6.

303 Melchora Aquino

(Photo Harrison)

1969 (30 Nov). *50th Death Anniv of Melchora Aquino, "Tandang*
Sora" (Grand Old Woman of the Revolution). P 12½.

1136	**303**	10s. multicoloured	15	15
1137		20s. multicoloured	20	15
1138		30s. multicoloured	50	20

5s

PASINAYA, IKA-2 PANUNUNGKULAN
PANGULONG FERDINAND E. MARCOS
DISYEMBRE 30, 1969

(304) (serifed capitals)

5s

PASINAYA, IKA-2 PANUNUNGKULAN
PANGULONG FERDINAND E. MARCOS
DISYEMBRE 30, 1969

(304a) (no serifs, wider spacing)

1969 (30 Dec). *Second-term Inauguration of President Marcos.
No. 1021 surch with T 304a.*

1139	262	6s.on 6s. multicoloured (304)		20	10
		a. Surch double			
		b. Surch with T **304a**		60	30
		ba. "5s" omitted			
		c. Deep ultramarine (frame etc) of			
		stamp printed double			

No. 1139ba occurs on Row 4, stamp 3 of part of the printing
from T **304a**.

305 Ladle and Steel Mills

(Photo Govt Ptg Wks, Tokyo)

1970 (20 Jan). *Iligan Integrated Steel Mills.* P 12½.

1140	305	10s. multicoloured		15	15
1141		20s. multicoloured		35	20
1142		30s. multicoloured		65	30

4s

(306)

307 New U.P.U. Headquarters
Building

1970 (30 Apr). *Nos. 900, 962, 964 surch as T 306.*

1143	–	4s.on 6s. greenish blue		15	10
1144	242	5s.on 6s. multicoloured		15	10
1145	243	5s.on 6s. multicoloured		15	10
		a. Surch double			

(Photo Govt Ptg Wks, Tokyo)

1970 (20 May). *New Universal Postal Union Headquarters
Building, Berne.* P 13½.

1146	307	10s. dp ultram, lemon & lt grnsh			
		bl		15	15
1147		30s. dp ultram, lemon & pale			
		emer		60	30

(Recess Bradbury, Wilkinson)

1970 (12 June). *Presidential Sayings (7th issue). As T **233** but
with new portrait and saying.* P 13½.

1148	10s. black and purple		15	10
1149	40s. black and emerald		35	15

Portrait and saying:—Pres. Osmena. "Ante todo el bien de
nuestro pueblo" ("*The well-being of our nation comes above all*").

308 Dona Julia V. de Ortigas and T. B.
Society Headquarters

(Photo Govt Ptg Wks, Tokyo)

1970 (3 Aug). *OBLIGATORY TAX. T.B. Relief Fund.* P 13½.

1150	308	1s.+5s. multicoloured		15	10
1151		5s.+5s. multicoloured		20	20
1152		30s.+5s. multicoloured		75	50
1153		70s.+5s. multicoloured		95	65
1150/1153 *Set of 4*				1·80	1·30

For compulsory use on all mail between 19 August and
30 September 1970.

309 I.C.S.W. Emblem

(Photo Harrison)

1970 (6 Sept). *15th International Conference on Social Welfare.*
P 13½ × 14½.

1154	309	10s. multicoloured		15	15
1155		20s. multicoloured		30	20
1156		30s. multicoloured		60	20

310 "Crab" (after sculpture
by A. Calder)

311 *Tridacna squamosa*
(Scaled Tridacna)

(Photo Govt Ptg Wks, Tokyo)

1970 (5 Oct). *"Fight Cancer" Campaign.* P 13.

1157	310	10s. multicoloured		20	15
1158		40s. multicoloured		45	20
1159		50s. multicoloured		65	35

(Photo Govt Ptg Wks, Tokyo)

1970 (19 Oct). *Seashells.* T **311** *and similar horiz designs.
Multicoloured.* P 13½.

1160	5s. Type **311**		15	10
1161	10s. *Spondylus regius* (Royal thorny			
	spiny oyster)		15	10
1162	20s. *Murex pecten* (Venus comb			
	murex)		20	15
1163	40s. *Conus gloriamaris* (Glory of the sea			
	cone)		60	35
1160/1163 *Set of 4*			1·00	65

FOUR
(312)

313 The "Hundred Islands" and Ox-cart

1970 (26 Oct). *Nos. 986, 1024 and 1026 surch as T* **312**.
1164 **249** 4s.on 6s. multicoloured   15   10
1165 **263** 4s.on 6s. multicoloured   15   10
1166   –   4s.on 6s. multicoloured   15   10

(Photo Enschedé)

1970 (12 Nov). *Tourism (1st series).* T **313** *and similar horiz designs. Multicoloured.* P $12\frac{1}{2} \times 13\frac{1}{2}$.
1167   10s. Type **313**   15   15
1168   20s. Tree-house, Pasonanca Park,
       Zamboanga City   20   15
1169   30s. "Filipino" (statue) and sugar
       plantation, Negros Island   30   30
1170   2p. Calesa (horse-carriage) and Miagao
       Church, Iloilo   1·90   1·20
1167/1170 *Set of 4*   2·30   1·60
   See also Nos. 1186/9, 1192/5 and 1196/9.

UPU-AOPU
REGIONAL SEMINAR

NOV. 23 - DEC. 5, 1970

TEN   **10ˢ**

314 Map of the   (315)
Philippines

(Photo Govt Ptg Wks, Tokyo)

1970 (16 Nov). *Golden Jubilee of Philippine Pharmaceutical Association.* P $13\frac{1}{2}$.
1171 **314** 10s. multicoloured   15   10
1172   50s. multicoloured   75   35

1970 (22 Nov). *U.P.U./A.O.P.U Regional Seminar, Manila. No.* 938 *surch with T* **315**.
1173 **235** 10s.on 6s. multicoloured   15   15

1970 PHILATELIC WEEK

10ˢ
TEN

(316)

1970 (22 Nov). *Philatelic Week. No. 977A surch with T* **316**.
1174 **247** 10s.on 6s. choc, pale blue &
        gold   15   10
     a. On No. 977B

317 Pope Paul VI and Map

(Photo Harrison)

1970 (27 Nov). *Pope Paul's Visit to the Philippines.* P $13\frac{1}{2} \times 14\frac{1}{2}$.
(a) POSTAGE.
1175 **317** 10s. multicoloured   15   15
1176   30s. multicoloured   30   20
(b) AIR. Inscr "PANGHIMPAPAWID".
1177 **317** 40s. multicoloured   45   20

318 Mariano Ponce   **G.O.**
                      (O **319**)

(Recess Harrison (15s.), De La Rue (others))

1970 (30 Dec)–**73**. P $14 \times 14\frac{1}{2}$.
1178   10s. carmine   15   10
1179   15s. deep chocolate (31 May 1973)   15   10
1180   40s. carmine-red (10 July 1972)   35   10
1181   1p. steel-blue (26 June 1972)   95   35
1178/1181 *Set of 4*   1·40   60
   Designs:—15s. Josefa Llanes Escoda; 40s. Gen. Miguel Malvar; 1p. Julian Felipe.

1970 (30 Dec). *OFFICIAL. No. 1178 optd with Type O* **319**.
O1182 **318** 10s. carmine   15   10

320 "PATA" Horse and Carriage

(Photo Harrison)

1971 (21 Jan). *20th PATA Conference and Workshop, Manila.* P $14\frac{1}{2}$.
1183 **320** 5s. multicoloured   15   10
1184   10s. multicoloured   15   15
1185   70s. multicoloured   50   35

(Photo Enschedé)

1971 (15 Feb). *Tourism (2nd series). Horiz designs similar to T* **313**. *Multicoloured.* P $12\frac{1}{2} \times 13\frac{1}{2}$.
1186   10s. Nayong Pilipino resort   10   10
1187   20s. Fish-farm, Iloilo   15   10
1188   30s. Pagsanjan Falls   20   15
1189   5p. Watch-tower, Punta Cruz   1·80   1·60
1186/1189 *Set of 4*   2·00   1·75

321 Emblem and Family

(Photo Govt Ptg Wks, Tokyo)

1971 (21 Mar). *Regional Conference of International Planned Parenthood Federation for S.E. Asia and Oceania.* P 13½.

1190	**321**	20s. multicoloured	15	10
1191		40s. multicoloured	20	15

(Photo Enschedé)

1971 (19 Apr). *Tourism (3rd series). Horiz designs similar to T 313. Multicoloured.* P 12½ × 13½.

1192		10s. Aguinaldo pearl farm	15	15
1193		20s. Coral-diving, Davao	15	15
1194		40s. Taluksangay Mosque	20	20
1195		1p. Ifugao woman and Bananue rice-terraces	1·60	65
1192/1195	*Set of 4*		1·90	1·00

(Photo Enschedé)

1971 (3 May). *Tourism (4th series). Horiz designs similar to T 313. Multicoloured.* P 12½ × 13½.

1196		10s. Cannon and fishing-boats, Fort del Pilar	15	15
1197		30s. Magellan's Cross, Cebu City	15	15
1198		50s. "Big Jar", Calamba, Laguna (Rizal's birthplace)	30	20
1199		70s. Mayon Volcano and diesel train	1·60	45
1196/1199	*Set of 4*		2·00	85

FIVE 5ˢ
(322)

323 G. A. Malcolm (founder) and Law Symbols

1971 (10 June). *No. 1026 surch with T 322.*

1200	**264**	5s.on 6s. multicoloured	15	10

(Photo Govt Ptg Wks, Tokyo)

1971 (15 June). *60th Anniv of Philippines College of Law.* P 13½.

(a) POSTAGE.

1201	**323**	15s. multicoloured	15	15

(b) AIR. Inscr "PANGHIMPAPAWID".

1202	**323**	1p. multicoloured	80	75

324 Commemorative Seal

325 Arms of Faculties

(Photo Harrison)

1971 (24 June). *400th Anniv of Manila.* P 13 × 13½.

(a) POSTAGE.

1203	**324**	10s. multicoloured	15	15

(b) AIR. Inscr "PANGHIMPAPAWID".

1204	**324**	1p. multicoloured	1·20	80

The 1p. perf 12 is a forgery.

(Photo Govt Ptg Wks, Tokyo)

1971 (8 July). *Centenaries of Faculties of Medicine and Surgery, and of Pharmacy, Santo Tomas University.* P 13½.

(a) POSTAGE.

1205	**325**	5s. multicoloured	15	10

(b) AIR. Inscr "PANGHIMPAPAWID".

1206	**325**	2p. multicoloured	1·60	1·50

(326)

1971 (11 July). *World Congress of University Presidents, Manila. No. 1029 surch with T 326.*

1207	**266**	5s.on 6s. violet, lt yellow & bl-grn	15	10
		a. Surch inverted		
		b. Surch double		

327 "Our Lady of Guia"

(Photo Govt Ptg Wks, Tokyo)

1971 (16 Aug). *400th Anniv of "Our Lady of Guia", Ermita, Manila.* P 13½.

1208	**327**	10s. multicoloured	15	15
1209		75s. multicoloured	60	50

328 Bank and "Customers"

(Photo State Bank Note Ptg Wks, Helsinki)

1971 (14 Sept). *70th Anniv of First National City Bank.* P 12½.
1210	**328**	10s. multicoloured		15	15
1211		30s. multicoloured		30	20
1212		1p. multicoloured		75	60

5^S
FIVE

(329)   1971- PHILATELIC WEEK   **(330)**

1971 (24 Nov). *No. 1013 surch as T* **329**.
1213	**259**	4s.on 6s. blue		15	10
1214		5s.on 6s. blue		15	10

1971 (24 Nov). *Philatelic Week. No. 1029 surch with T* **330**.
1215	**266**	5s.on 6s. multicoloured		15	10

331 Dish Aerial and Events   **332** Fathers Burgos, Gomez and Zamora

(Photo Harrison)

1972 (29 Feb). *Sixth Asian Electronic Conference, Manila* (1971) *and Related Events.* P 14 × 14½.
1216	**331**	5s. multicoloured		15	10
1217		40s. multicoloured		60	35

(Photo State Bank Note Ptg Wks, Helsinki)

1972 (3 Apr). *Centenary of Martyrdom of Fathers Burgos, Gomez and Zamora.* P 13 × 12½.
1218	**332**	5s. multicoloured		10	10
1219		60s. multicoloured		45	45

333 Human Organs

(Photo State Bank Note Ptg Wks, Helsinki)

1972 (11 Apr). *4th Asian-Pacific Gastroenterological Congress, Manila.* P 12½ × 13.

(a) POSTAGE.
1220	**333**	20s. multicoloured		20	15

(b) AIR. Inscr "PANGHIMPAPAWID".
1221	**333**	40s. multicoloured		45	35

≡ 5^S
FIVE

(334)

1972 (20 Apr). *No. 1024 surch with T* **334**.
1222	**263**	5s.on 6s. multicoloured		15	10

1972 (16 May). *No. O914 with "G.O." opt cancelled, by short parallel bars, for ordinary postal use.*
1223	O **224**	50s. violet		45	20

≡ 10^S

(335)

1972 (29 May). *Various stamps surch as T* **335**.
1224	**245**	10s.on 6s. (No. 971)		15	10
		a. Error. 10s. on 25s.			
		(No. 973)			
		b. Surch inverted			
1225	**251**	10s.on 6s. (No. 993)		15	10
1226	–	10s.on 6s. (No. 1015)		15	10

336 Memorial Gardens, Manila

(Photo State Bank Note Ptg Wks, Helsinki)

1972 (31 May). *Tourism. "Visit Asean Lands" Campaign.* P 12½.
1227	**336**	5s. multicoloured		15	10
1228		50s. multicoloured		90	20
1229		60s. multicoloured		1·20	35

337 "KKK" Flag

(Photo Harrison)

1972 (12 June). *Evolution of Philippines' Flag. T* **337** *and similar horiz designs.* P 13.
1230	30s. bright rose-red and ultramarine			30	20
	a. Block of 10. Nos. 1230/9			3·25	
1231	30s. bright rose-red and ultramarine			30	20
1232	30s. bright rose-red and ultramarine			30	20
1233	30s. black and ultramarine			30	20
1234	30s. bright rose-red and ultramarine			30	20
1235	30s. bright rose-red and ultramarine			30	20
1236	30s. bright rose-red and ultramarine			30	20

1237	30s. bright rose-red and ultramarine		30	20
1238	30s. black, bright rose-red & ultramarine		30	20
1239	30s. lemon, brt rose-red & ultramarine		30	20
	a. Lemon (sun and stars) omitted			
1230/1239	Set of 10		2·75	1·80

Flags:—No. 1230, Type **337**; No. 1231, Three "K"'s in pyramid; No. 1232, Single "K"; No. 1233, "K", skull and crossbones; No. 1234, Three "K"'s and sun in triangle; No. 1235, Sun and three "K"'s; No. 1236, Ancient Tagalog "K" within sun; No. 1237, Face in sun; No. 1238, Tricolor; No. 1239, Present national flag—sun and stars within triangle, two stripes.

Nos. 1230/1239 were issued together *se-tenant* in two horizontal rows of five stamps within the sheet of 50.

338 Mabol, Santol and Papaya

(Photo Harrison)

1972 (1 Aug). *OBLIGATORY TAX. T.B. Relief Fund. Fruits. T* **338** *and similar horiz designs. Multicoloured.* P 13½ × 13.

1240	1s.+5s. Type **338**		10	10
1241	10s.+5s. Bananas, balimbang and mangosteen		15	15
1242	40s.+5s. Guava, mango, duhat and susongkalabac		30	30
1243	1p.+5s. Orange, pineapple, lanzones and sirhuelas		65	65
1240/1243	Set of 4		1·10	1·10

For compulsory use on all mail between 19 August and 30 September 1972.

339 Bridled Parrotfish (*Scarus frenatus*)

340 Bank Headquarters

(Photo Govt Ptg Wks, Tokyo)

1972 (14 Aug). *Fishes. T* **339** *and similar horiz designs. Multicoloured.* P 13½.

(a) POSTAGE.

1244	5s. Type **339**		15	10
1245	10s. Klein's Butterflyfish (*Chaetodon kleini*)		15	10
1246	20s. Moorish Idol (*Zanclus cornutus*)		20	15

(b) AIR. Inscr "PANGHIMPAPAWID".

1247	50s. Two-spined Angelfish (*Holacanthus bispinosus*)		75	35
1244/1247	Set of 4		1·10	65

(Photo Govt Ptg Wks, Tokyo)

341 Pope Paul VI

(Photo De La Rue)

1972 (26 Sept). *1st Anniv of Pope Paul's Visit to Philippines.* P 14.

(a) POSTAGE.

1251	**341**	10s. multicoloured		10	10
1252		50s. multicoloured		45	35

(b) AIR. Inscr "PANGHIMPAPAWID".

1253	**341**	60s. multicoloured		60	60

(Photo Govt Ptg Wks, Tokyo)

1972 (12 Sept). *25th Anniv of Philippines Development Bank.* P 13½.

1248	**340**	10s. multicoloured		15	10
1249		20s. multicoloured		15	15
1250		60s. multicoloured		60	35

10ˢ =

(342)

343 "La Barca de Aqueronte" (Hidalgo)

1972 (29 Sept). *Various stamps surch as T* **342**.

1254	**240**	10s.on 6s. (No. 953)		15	10
1255	–	10s.on 6s. (No. 959)		15	10
1256	**250**	10s.on 6s. (No. 989)		15	10
		a. Surch inverted		19·00	

(Photo Enschedé)

1972 (16 Oct). *25th Anniv of Stamps and Philatelic Division, Philippines Bureau of Posts. Filipino Paintings. T* **343** *and similar multicoloured designs.* P 14 × 13½ (30s.) or 14 × 13 (others).

1257	5s. Type **343**		10	10
	a. Silver (frame) omitted			
1258	10s. "Afternoon Meal of the Rice Workers" (Amorsolo)		15	15
1259	30s. "Espanay Filipinas" (Luna) (27 × 60 mm)		20	20
1260	70s. "The Song of Maria Clara" (Amorsolo)		60	60
1257/1260	Set of 4		95	95

344 Lamp, Emblem and Nurse

(Photo Enschedé)

1972 (22 Oct). *50th Anniv of Philippine Nurses' Association.*
P 12½ × 13½.

1261	**344**	5s. multicoloured	10	10
1262		10s. multicoloured	15	15
1263		70s. multicoloured	45	35

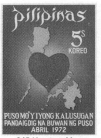

345 Heart on Map

(Photo Govt Ptg Wks, Tokyo)

1972 (24 Oct). *World Heart Month.* P 13½.

1264	**345**	5s. bright rose-red, bright emerald and bright reddish violet	10	10
1265		10s. bright rose-red, bright emerald and greenish blue	15	10
1266		30s. bright rose-red, light blue and pale blue-green	20	20

346 "The First Mass" (C.V. Francisco)

(Photo De La Rue)

1972 (31 Oct). *450th Anniv of First Mass in Limasawa* (1971).
P 14.

(a) POSTAGE.

1267	**346**	10s. multicoloured	15	15

(b) AIR. Inscr "PANGHIMPAPAWID".

1268	**346**	60s. multicoloured	50	45

ASIA PACIFIC SCOUT CONFERENCE
NOV, 1972

(347)

1972 (13 Nov). *Asian-Pacific Scout Conference, Manila. Various stamps surch as T 347.*

1269	**233**	10s.on 6s. (No. 933)	15	10
1270	**240**	10s.on 6s. (No. 953)	15	10
1271	**—**	10s.on 6s. (No. 981)	15	10

The inscription overprinted on No. 1270 is in three lines.

348 Olympic Emblems and Torch

(Photo Enschedé)

1972 (15 Nov). *Olympic Games. Munich.* P 12½ × 13½.

1272	**348**	5s. multicoloured	10	10
1273		10s. multicoloured	15	15
1274		70s. multicoloured	60	45

1972 PHILATELIC WEEK

TEN   10s

(349)

1972 (23 Nov). *Philatelic Week. Nos. 950 and 983 surch as T 349.*

1275	**239**	10s.on 6s. multicoloured	15	10
1276	**248**	10s.on 6s. multicoloured	15	10

350 Manunggul Burial Jar

(Photo Govt Ptg Wks, Tokyo)

1972 (29 Nov). *Philippine Archaeological Discoveries. T 350 and similar vert designs. Multicoloured.* P 13½.

1277		10s. Type **350**	15	10
1278		10s. Ritual earthenware vessel	15	10
1279		10s. Metal pot	15	10
1280		10s. Earthenware vessel	15	10
1277/1280	*Set of 4*		55	35

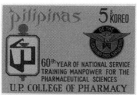

351 Emblems of Pharmacy and University of the Philippines

(Photo Enschedé)

1972 (11 Dec). *60th Year of National Training for Pharmaceutical Sciences, University of the Philippines.* P 12½ × 13½.
1281	**351**	5s. multicoloured		10	10
1282		10s. multicoloured		15	15
1283		30s. multicoloured		20	15

352 "The Lantern-makers" (J. Pineda)

(Photo Harrison)

1972 (14 Dec). *Christmas.* P 12½.
1284	**352**	10s. multicoloured		15	15
1285		30s. multicoloured		20	15
1286		50s. multicoloured		45	35

353 President Roxas and Wife

(Photo Enschedé)

1972 (21 Dec). *25th Anniv of Philippines Red Cross.* P 13½ × 12½.
1287	**353**	5s. multicoloured		15	10
1288		20s. multicoloured		15	15
1289		30s. multicoloured		20	20

(354)

355 University Building

1973 (22 Jan). *Various stamps surch as T* **354**.
1290	**238**	10s.on 6s. multicoloured		15	10
1291	**256**	10s.on 6s. blue, red and yellow		15	10

(Recess Govt Ptg Wks, Tokyo)

1973 (22 Feb). *Presidential Sayings (8th issue). Similar to T* **233** *but with portrait and saying changed.* P 13½.
1292	10s. black and olive-bistre		15	10
1293	30s. black and mauve		35	15

Portrait and saying:—Pres. Garcia. "I would rather be right than successful".

(Photo Harrison)

1973 (1 Mar). *60th Anniv of St. Louis University, Baguio City.* P 13½ × 14.
1294	**355**	5s. multicoloured		10	10
1295		10s. multicoloured		10	10
1296		75s. multicoloured		60	50

356 Col. J. Villamor, Boeing P-26A "Peashooter" and Mitsubishi A6M Zero-Sen Fighters

(Photo Harrison)

1973 (9 Apr). *Villamor Commemoration.* P 13½ × 14.
1297	**356**	10s. multicoloured		15	10
1298		2p. multicoloured		1·30	1·30

(357)   (358)

1973 (23 Apr). *Various stamps surch as T* **357/8**.
1299	**252**	5s.on 6s. multicoloured		15	10
1300	**266**	5s.on 6s. violet, lt yellow & bl-grn		15	10
1301	**318**	15s.on 10s. carmine		15	10

On No. 1301 the official overprint "G.O." is obliterated by bars.

359 Actor and Stage Performance   (360)

(Photo State Bank Note Ptg Wks, Helsinki)

1973 (15 May). *First "Third-World" Theatre Festival, Manila.* P 13 × 12½.
1302	**359**	5s. multicoloured		10	10
1303		10s. multicoloured		10	10
1304		50s. multicoloured		35	20
1305		70s. multicoloured		60	35
1302/1305		Set of 4		1·00	70

1973 (4 June). *Pres. Marcos's Anti-Smuggling Campaign. No. 1017 surch with T* **360**.
1306	5s.on 6s. greenish blue		15	10

15+5ˢ

5ˢ =   =

(361)   (362)

1973 (4 June). *Tenth Death Anniv of Pres. John F. Kennedy. No. 989 surch with T* **361**.
1307 **250** 5s.on 6s. multicoloured 15 10

1973 (15 June). *OBLIGATORY TAX. T.B. Relief Fund. Nos. 1241/2 surch as T* **362**.
1308 15s.+5s. on 10s.+ 5s. multicoloured . . 15 15
1309 60s.+5s. on 40s.+5s. multicoloured . . . 45 45
For compulsory use on all mail between 19 August and 30 September 1973.

363 Proclamation Scenes   **364** M. Agoncillo (maker of first national flag)

(Photo Enschedé)

1973 (24 Sept). *75th Anniv of Philippine Independence.* P 12½ × 13½.
1310 **363** 15s. multicoloured 15 15
1311 45s. multicoloured 20 20
1312 90s. multicoloured 65 65

(Litho Bureau of Printing, Manila)

1973 (24 Sept)–**74**. *T* **364** *and similar vert designs.* No watermark. P 12½.
1313 15s. violet (15 May 1974) 15 10
   a. Imperf 15 10
   b. Printed double . . . .
   c. Wmk **380** 15 10
1314 60s. lake-brown 35 35
   a. Imperf (16 April 1974) 60 60
   ab. Printed double . . . .
1315 90s. greenish blue (9 December 1974) 60 30
   a. Imperf 90 90
1316 1p.10 new blue (22 July 1974) 75 35
   a. Imperf 90 90
   b. Wmk **380** 75 35
1317 1p.50 brt carmine (25 October 1973) . . 95 80
   a. Imperf . . . . . . 1·80 1·80
1318 1p.50 chocolate (8 November 1974) . . 95 35
   a. Imperf . . . . . . 1·30 1·30
   b. Wmk **380** 95 35
   ba. Printed double . . . .
   bb. Printed on both sides . . . .
1319 1p.80 deep blue-green (27 Nov 1973) . . . . . . 1·10 1·00
   a. Imperf (10 June 1974) . . . 1·30 1·30
1320 5p. greenish blue (8 October 1973) . . 3·00 3·00
   a. Imperf (31 May 1974) . . . . 3·75 3·75
1313/1320 Set of 8 . . . . 7·00 5·50
1313a/1320a Set of 8 . . . . 9·50 9·50

Designs:—15s. Gabriela Silang (revolutionary); 90s. Teodoro Yangco (businessman); 1p.10, Pio Valenzuela (physician); 1p.50 (No. 1317), Pedro Paterno (revolutionary); 1p.50 (No. 1318), Teodora Alonso (mother of José Rizal); 1p.80, E. Evangelista (revolutionary); 5p. F. M. Guerrero (writer).
The watermark on No. 1318b exists both upright and sideways.
The 15s. and 1p.50 values with watermark exist on both ordinary and luminescent paper.

365 Sra Imelda Marcos

(Photo Govt Ptg Wks, Tokyo)

1973 (31 Oct). *Projects Inaugurated by Sra Imelda Marcos.* P 13½.
1321 **365** 15s. multicoloured 15 15
1322 50s. multicoloured 30 30
1323 60s. multicoloured 35 35

366 Malakanyang Palace

(Litho De La Rue)

1973 (15 Nov). *Presidential Palace, Manila.* P 14.

(a) POSTAGE.
1324 **366** 15s. multicoloured 15 15
1325 50s. multicoloured 20 20

(b) AIR. Inscr "PANGHIMPAPAWID".
1326 **366** 60s. multicoloured 35 35

367 Interpol Emblem   **368** Scouting Activities

(Photo State Bank Note Ptg Wks, Helsinki)

1973 (18 Dec). *50th Anniv of International Criminal Police Organization (Interpol).* P 13.
1327 **367** 15s. multicoloured 15 10
1328 65s. multicoloured 45 20

IMPERFORATE STAMPS. Many issues between 1973 and 1976 printed by the Bureau of Printing, Manila were also officially issued imperforate. This was done to prevent speculation in imperforate stamps which were known to be leaking out of the printing works.

(Litho Bureau of Printing, Manila)

1973 (28 Dec)–**74**. *Golden Jubilee of Philippine Boy Scouts. T* **368** *and similar vert designs.* P 12½.

1329	15s. olive-bistre & lt emerald	. . . .	15	15
	b. Imperf (4.2.74)	. . . . . .	20	20
1330	65s. brt new blue & ol-yell	. . . .	45	30
	b. Imperf (4.2.74)	. . . . . .	60	60

Design:—65s. Scouts reading brochure.

Although Nos. 1329B/1330B were issued on 4 February 1974, First Day covers received the postmark of 28 December 1973.

369 Bank Emblem, Urban and Agricultural Landscapes

(Photo Enschedé)

1974 (3 Jan). *25th Anniv of Central Bank of the Philippines. T* **369** *and similar horiz designs. Multicoloured.* P 12½ × 13½.

1331	15s. Type **369**	. . . .	15	10
1332	60s. Bank Building, 1949	. . . .	35	20
1333	1p.50 Bank complex, 1974	. . . .	95	60

370 "Maria Clara" Costume

(Photo State Bank Note Ptg Wks, Helsinki)

1974 (15 Jan). *Centenary of Universal Postal Union. Philippine Costumes. T* **370** *and similar vert designs. Multicoloured.* P 12½.

1334	15s. Type **370**	. . . . . .	15	15
1335	60s. "Balintawak"	. . . . . .	35	20
1336	80s. "Malong"	. . . . . .	60	30

1973
PHILATELIC
WEEK

15ˢ

———

(371)

1974 (4 Feb). *Philatelic Week* (1973). *No.* 1303 *surch with T* **371**, *in red.*

1337	**359**	15s.on 10s. multicoloured	. . . .	15	10

First Day Covers are dated 26 November 1973.

15ˢ
=

PHILIPPINE LIONISM 1949-1974
(372)

1974 (25 Mar). *25th Anniv of Philippine "Lionism". Nos.* 1297 *and* 1180 *surch as T* **372**.

1338	**356**	15s.on 10s. multicoloured	. . . .	15	10
1339	–	45s.on 40s. carmine-red	. . . .	20	20

On No. 1339 the Lions emblem is at the foot and the inscription is on the left, reading downwards.

373 Map of South-East Asia

(Litho Bureau of Printing, Manila)

1974 (30 Apr). *Asian Pediatrics Congress. Manila.* P 12½

1340	**373**	30s. bright rose-red and bright greenish blue	. . . .	20	15
		a. Rose-red (emblem and "PILIPINAS") omitted	. . . .	–	†
		b. Imperf	. . . .	20	15
1341		1p. rosine & dp turq-grn	. . . .	60	35
		b. Imperf	. . . .	80	60

374 Gen. Valdes and Hospital

(Litho Bureau of Printing, Manila)

1974 (8 July). *T.B. Relief Fund.* P 12½

1342	**374**	15s.+5s. dp bluish green and red	. . . .	15	15
		b. Imperf	. . . .	20	20
1343		1p.10+5s. ultramarine and red	. . . .	35	30
		b. Imperf	. . . .	60	35

Nos. 1342/3 were intended for use as Obligatory Tax stamps from 19 August until 30 September. The concession was repealed on 14 August, however, and use of the stamps was voluntary.

5ˢ   =   = **5ˢ**   = **5** ˢ
(375)   (376)   (377)

1974 (1 Aug). *Various stamps surch with T* **375/7**.

1344	**375**	5s.on 3s. green (No. 974)	. . . .	15	10
1345	**376**	5s.on 6s. multicoloured (No. 1024)	. . . .	15	10
1346	**377**	5s.on 6s. multicoloured (No. 1026)	. . . .	15	10

378 W.P.Y. Emblem   **379** Red Feather Emblem

(Des Nemesio Dimanlig. Litho Bureau of Printing, Manila)

1974 (15 Aug). *World Population Year.* No watermark. P 12½.

1347	**378**	5s. blk & brt yell-orge		15	15
		b. Imperf		15	15
1348		2p. royal bl & lt emer		1·10	60
		a. Wmk **380**		1·10	60
		b. Imperf		1·30	95

The watermark on No. 1348a exists upright or sideways.

380 "Republic of the Philippines, Bureau of Posts"
(¼-size illustration)

PAPERS AND WATERMARKS From 1975 onwards many issues are printed on phosphorescent and/or fluorescent papers as well as on non-luminescent papers. Due to the practice of printing most issues over a period of time rather than all at once the majority of issues are found on more than one type of paper. Those that can be distinguished only under a UV lamp are not listed separately. Similarly Wmk **380** is found upright, inverted, sideways, reversed etc., sometimes appearing different ways on the same issue. On the white paper with white gum used in the 1980s the watermark is slightly smaller.

(Litho Bureau of Printing, Manila)

1974 (5 Sept). *25th Anniv of Community Chest Movement in the Philippines.* W **380**. P 12½.

1349	**379**	15s. red and new blue		15	15
		b. Imperf		20	20
1350		40s. red and emerald		20	15
		b. Imperf		35	30
1351		45s. red and chestnut		35	15
		b. Imperf		35	30

381 Sultan Mohammad Kudarat, Map, Ships
and Order

(Photo Harrison)

1975 (13 Jan). *Sultan Kudarat of Mindanao Commemoration.* P 13 × 14.

1352	**381**	15s. multicoloured		15	10

382 Association Emblem   **383** Rafael Palma

(Litho Bureau of Printing, Manila)

1975 (20 Jan). *25th Anniv of Philippine Mental Health Association.* W **380** (sideways). P 12½.

1353	**382**	45s. emerald & yell-orge		20	15
		a. Yellow-orge omitted		—	—
		b. Imperf		35	35
1354		1p. emerald & brt purple		45	30
		b. Imperf		60	60

(Litho Bureau of Printing, Manila)

1975 (6 Feb). *Birth Centenary of Rafael Palma (educationalist and statesman).* No watermark. P 12½.

1355	**383**	15s. bright emerald		20	15
		a. Wmk **380**		20	15
		b. Imperf		20	20

Although No. 1355 was issued on 6 February 1975, First Day Covers were postmarked 24 October 1974, the date of the actual birth centenary.

No. 1355a exists on ordinary and luminescent paper.

See also No. 1436.

384 Heart Centre Emblem

(Litho Bureau of Printing, Manila)

1975 (14 Feb). *Inauguration of Philippine Heart Centre for Asia, Quezon City.* W **380**. P 12½.

1356	**384**	15s. scarlet & ultramarine		15	15
		b. Imperf		20	20
1357		50s. scarlet and emerald		20	20
		a. Scarlet (emblem) omitted		—	—
		b. Imperf		35	35

The watermark on No. 1356 exists upright or sideways.

385 Cadet in Full Dress, and Academy
Building

(Litho Harrison)

1975 (17 Feb). *70th Anniv of Philippine Military Academy.* P 13 × 14.

1358	**385**	15s. multicoloured		15	15
1359		45s. multicoloured		45	20

386/95 "Helping the Disabled"

(Illustration reduced in size, actual size of block of ten stamps 100 × 61 mm (design area). The stamps are numbered from top left to top right and then from bottom left to bottom right)

(Litho Bureau of Printing, Manila)

1975 (15 Mar). *25th Anniv of Philippines Orthopaedic Association (1974)*. W **380** (upright or sideways). Litho. P 12½.

1360	**386**	45s. bluish green	20	15
		a. Block of 10	3·00	
		b. Imperf	20	15
		ba. block of 10	3·00	
1361	**387**	45s. bluish green	20	15
		b. Imperf	20	15
1362	**388**	45s. bluish green	20	15
		b. Imperf	20	15
1363	**389**	45s. bluish green	20	15
		b. Imperf	20	15
1364	**390**	45s. bluish green	20	15
		b. Imperf	20	15
1365	**391**	45s. bluish green	20	15
		b. Imperf	20	15
1366	**392**	45s. bluish green	20	15
		b. Imperf	20	15
1367	**393**	45s. bluish green	20	15
		b. Imperf	20	15
1368	**394**	45s. bluish green	20	15
		b. Imperf	20	15
1369	**395**	45s. bluish green	20	15
		b. Imperf	20	15
1360/1369 *Set of 10*			1·80	1·30
1360b/1369b *Set of 10*			1·80	1·30

Nos. 1360/9 and 1360b/1369b were issued together in *se-tenant* blocks of ten within the sheet, forming the composite design illustrated.

The blocks exist with perf to perf measurements of 117 × 70 mm or 104 × 68 mm from different printings.

5$

(396)

397 Planting Sapling

398 Jade Vine

1975 (15 Apr). *Nos. 1153 and 1342/3 surch as T* **396**.

1370	**374**	5s.on 15s.+ 5s. deep bluish		
		green and red	10	10
1371	**308**	60s.on 70s.+ 5s. multicoloured	35	20
1372	**374**	1p.on 1p.10+ 5s. ultram & red	45	30
		a. Surch double	16·00	

(Litho Harrison)

1975 (19 May). *Forest Conservation. T* **397** *and similar vert design. Multicoloured.* P 14½.

1373	45s. Type **397**	20	15
	a. Horiz pair. Nos. 1373/4	55	
1374	45s. Sapling and tree trunks	20	15

Nos. 1373/4 were issued together in horizontal *se-tenant* pairs within the sheet.

(Litho Harrison)

1975 (9 June). P 14½.

1375	**398**	15s. multicoloured	15	10

399 Madame Imelda
Marcos and IWY
Emblem

400 Commission
Badge

1975 (2 July). *International Women's Year.* W **380**. P 12½.

1376	**399**	15s. black, new blue and deep		
		blue	15	15
		b. Imperf	20	20
		c. Wmk sideways	35	20
1377		80s. blk, new bl & pk	45	35
		ab. Pink (background) omitted	—	—
		b. Imperf	45	45
		c. Wmk sideways	65	35

The upright watermark is on ordinary paper and the sideways watermark on luminescent.

(Litho Bureau of Printing, Manila)

1975 (19 Sept). *75th Anniv of Civil Service Commission.* W **380** (sideways). P 12½.

1378	**400**	15s. multicoloured	15	15
		b. Imperf	15	15
1379		50s. multicoloured	30	20
		b. Imperf	30	30

The watermark on No. 1378 is also found upright.
Nos. 1378/9 exist on ordinary and luminescent paper.

401 Angat River Bridge

(Litho Bureau of Printing, Manila)

1975 (30 Sept). *25th Anniv of International Commission on Irrigation and Drainage.* W **380**. P 12½.

1380	**401**	40s. ultram & yell-orange	20	15
		a. Ultramarine (bridge and		
		emblem) printing only	—	—
		b. Imperf	20	20
1381		1p.50 ultram & magenta	60	45
		b. Imperf	75	75

Because the frame colour is omitted on No. 1380Aa, there is no value inscribed on the stamp.
Nos. 1380A/1A exist on ordinary and luminescent paper.

402 "Welcome to Manila"　　　**403** N. Romualdez (legislator and writer)

(Litho De La Rue)

1975 (4 Nov). *Centenary of Hong Kong and Shanghai Banking Corporation's Service in the Philippines.* P 13½.

1382	**402**	1p.50 multicoloured	1·30	35

(Litho Bureau of Printing, Manila)

1975 (7 Nov). *Birth Centenary of Romualdez.* W **380**. P 12½.

1383	**403**	60s. lilac	20	15
		b. Imperf	30	30

404 General G. del Pilar　　　**405** Boeing 747-100 Airliner and Martin M-130 Flying Boat

(Litho Bureau of Printing, Manila)

1975 (22 Nov). *Birth Centenary of Pilar.* W **380**. P 12½.

1384	**404**	90s. magenta	35	15
		b. Imperf	60	60

(Des and litho Asian Productivity Organization Press, Manila)

1975 (22 Nov). *40th Anniv of First Trans-Pacific China Clipper Airmail Flight from San Francisco to Manila. Multicoloured, background colours given.* W **380** (sideways). P 12½.

1385	**405**	60s. bright green	45	20
1386		1p.50 deep new blue	1·20	60
		a. Black (inscriptions and value) omitted		
		b. Blue printed both sides		

(406)　　　**407** APO Emblem

1975 (22 Nov). *Airmail Exhibition. Nos. 1314 and 1318b optd with T* **406**.

1387		60s. lake-brown	20	20
1388		1p.50 chocolate	65	65

The watermark on No. 1388 exists upright or sideways.

(Litho Bureau of Printing, Manila)

1975 (24 Nov). *25th Anniv of APO Philatelic Society.* W **380**. P 12½

1389	**407**	5s. multicoloured	15	15
		ab. Green (centre) omitted	—	†
		b. Imperf	15	15
		c. Wmk sideways	65	35
1390		1p. multicoloured	50	35
		b. Imperf	35	35
		c. Wmk sideways	95	45

The example seen of No. 1389 was also misperforated.
The upright watermark is on ordinary paper and the sideways watermark on luminescent paper.

408 E. Jacinto　　　**409** San Augustin Church

(Litho Bureau of Printing, Manila)

1975 (15 Dec). *Birth Centenary of Emilio Jacinto (military leader).* W **380**. P 12½.

1391	**408**	65s. mauve	20	15
		b. Imperf	25	25

No. 1391 exists on ordinary and luminescent paper.

(Litho Bureau of Printing, Manila)

1975 (23 Dec). *Holy Year. Churches. T* **409** *and similar designs.* W **380**. P 12½.

1392		20s. turquoise-blue	15	15
		b. Imperf	20	20
1393		30s. black & orange-yell	15	15
		b. Imperf	20	20
1394		45s. brn-red, rose & blk	20	15
		b. Imperf	25	20
1395		60s. bistre, greenish yellow and black	30	20
		a. Black ("PILIPINAS" and value) double	—	—
		b. Imperf	35	35
1392/1395	Set of 4		75	60
1392b/1395b	Set of 4		90	85

Designs: *Horiz*—30s. Morong Church; 45s. Taal Basilica. *Vert*—60s. San Sebastian Church.
The watermark on Nos. 1392/3 and 1395 exists upright or sideways.
Nos. 1392/5 exist on ordinary and luminescent paper.

410 "Conducting" Hands　　　**411** Douglas DC-3 and DC-10

(Des A. Chuidian. Litho Bureau of Printing, Manila)

1976 (27 Jan). *50th Anniv of Manila Symphony Orchestra. Multicoloured, background colour given.* W **380** (sideways). P 12½.

1396	**410**	5s. yellow-orange		10	10
1397		50s. greenish yellow		35	30
		a. Value omitted			

(Litho Neda, Manila)

1976 (14 Feb). *30th Anniv of Philippine Airlines (PAL).* W **380**. P 12½.

1398	**411**	60s. multicoloured		30	15
1399		1p.50 multicoloured		1·20	65
		a. Inverted impression in blue on back			

No. 1399a and similar listed errors accidentally received on the back a positive impression from the blanket of the first colour printed.

412 Felipe Agoncillo (statesman)

413 University Buildings

(Litho Bureau of Printing, Manila)

1976 (27 Feb). *Agoncillo Commemoration.* W **380**. P 12½.

1400	**412**	1p.60 black		95	20

(Litho Bureau of Printing, Manila)

1976 (30 Mar). *75th Anniv of National University.* W **380** (sideways). P 12½.

1401	**413**	45s. multicoloured		20	15
1402		60s. multicoloured		35	20

Nos. 1401/2 exist on ordinary and luminescent paper.

414 "Foresight Prevents Blindness"

415 Emblem on Book

(Litho APO-Neda, Manila)

1976 (7 Apr). *World Health Day.* W **380** (sideways). P 12½.

1403	**414**	15s. multicoloured		15	10

A used copy of No. 1403 with all inscriptions and value omitted has been seen.

(Litho Bureau of Printing, Manila)

1976 (24 May). *75th Anniv of National Archives.* W **380** (upright or sideways). P 12½.

1404	**415**	1p.50 multicoloured		80	75
		a. Imperf (pair)			

416 College Emblem and University Tower

(Litho Bureau of Printing, Manila)

1976 (7 June). *50th Anniv of Colleges of Education and Science, Saint Thomas' University.* W **380**. P 12½.

1405	**416**	15s. multicoloured		15	10
		a. Imperf (pair)			
1406		50s. multicoloured		20	20

417 College Building

(Litho Bureau of Printing, Manila)

1976 (26 July). *50th Anniv of Maryknoll College.* W **380** (upright or sideways). P 12½.

1407	**417**	15s. multicoloured		15	10
1408		1p.50 multicoloured		80	60

15ˢ

Montreal   1976

21st OLYMPICS
CANADA
(418)

1976 (30 July). *Olympic Games, Montreal.* No. 1273 surch with T **418**.

1409	**348**	15s.on 10s. multicoloured		15	10

419 Constabulary Headquarters, Manila

(Litho Neda, Manila)

1976 (8 Aug–14 Oct). *75th Anniv of Philippine Constabulary.* W **380**. Perf 12½.

1410	**419**	15s. multicoloured		15	15
		b. Imperf (14.10)		20	20
1411		60s. multicoloured		35	20
		b. Imperf (14.10)		60	60

420 Land and Aerial Surveying

(424)

5⁵

(421)

1976 (26 Nov). *Philatelic Week*. No. 1295 *surch with T* **424**.
| 1418 | **355** | 30s.on 10s. multicoloured | | 15 | 15 |

(Litho Bureau of Printing, Manila)

1976 (2 Sept). *75th Anniv of Lands Bureau*. W **380**. P 12½.
| 1412 | **420** | 80s. multicoloured | | 25 | 25 |
| | | a. Imperf (pair) | | | |

1976 (20 Sept). *AIR. Bicentenary of American Revolution. No.*
MS1004 *optd* "*U.S.A. BICENTENNIAL 1776–1976*" *and
individual stamps surch as T* **421**, *in black*.
MS1413 170 × 105 mm. 5s. on 3s., 5s. on 6s.,
15s. on 30s., 50s. on 70s. Imperf . . . . . . 3·75   3·75
This sheet also exists with the overprint in red but is believed
to be from a restricted printing.

425 "Going to Church"

1976 (1 Dec). *Christmas*. W **380**. P 12½.
| 1419 | **425** | 15s. multicoloured | | 10 | 10 |
| 1420 | | 30s. multicoloured | | 20 | 15 |

422 Badges of
Banking
Organizations

423 Virgin of Antipolo

426 "Facets of
Education"

Pl.20

(427)

1976 (13 Dec). *75th Anniv of Philippine Educational System*.
W **380** (*upright or sideways*). P 12½.
1421	**426**	30s. multicoloured		15	15
1422		75s. multicoloured		45	20
		a. Imperf (pair)			

(Litho Bureau of Printing, Manila)

1976 (4 Oct). *Joint Annual Meetings of Board of Governors of
International Monetary Fund and World Bank, Manila*. W **380**
(*upright or sideways*). P 12½.
1414	**422**	60s. multicoloured		20	20
		a. Imperf (pair)			
		ab. Do. and black omitted			
1415		1p.50 multicoloured		80	60
		a. Deep blue (centre of globes) omitted			

The effect of the missing colour (which is really magenta) on
No. 1415a is to leave the globes a greenish blue colour. The
apparent deep blue appearance of the normal is achieved by
laying magenta over the greenish blue, the two colours combining
to produce deep blue. Printings have been seen in which the
greenish blue was so weak that the final appearance is of a dull
purple; the latter should be regarded as a shade of the normal.

1977 (17 Jan). *Nos.* 1316b *and* 1320 *surch as T* **427**.
| 1423 | | 1p.20 on 1p.10 new blue | | 60 | 35 |
| 1424 | | 3p.on 5p. greenish blue | | 1·30 | 1·10 |

428 José Rizal

429 Flags, Map and Emblem

PRINTERS. From No. 1416 to 2156 all stamps were printed in
lithography by the Asian Productivity Organization Production Unit,
Inc.–NEDA, Manila (from May 1986 Quezon), *unless otherwise
stated*.

1977 (24 Jan). *Famous Filipinos. T* **428** *and similar vert design.
Multicoloured*. W **380**. P 12½.
1425		30s. Type **428** (16 Feb)		15	10
		a. Imperf vert (horiz pair)		48·00	
		b. Imperf between (horiz pair)			
1426		2p.30 Dr. Galicano Apacible		95	65

1976 (26 Nov). *350th Anniv of Virgin of Antipolo. Multicoloured,
colour of bottom panel given*. W **380** (*sideways*). P 12½.
1416	**423**	30s. new blue		15	15
1417		90s. cerise		35	35
		a. Value omitted		65·00	

1977 (1 Apr). *15th Anniv of Asian–Oceanic Postal Union. Multicoloured, colour of bottom line of inscription given.* W **380**. P 12½.

1427	**429**	50s. new blue	15	10
		a. Value omitted		
1428		1p.50 bright green	60	45
		a. Value omitted	33·00	
		b. Inverted positive impression in red on black		

Nos. 1427/8 exist on ordinary or luminescent paper.
See note after No. 1399.

430 Worker and Cogwheels

431 Commission Emblem

1977 (21 April). *Tenth Anniv of Asian Development Bank.* W **380** (*sideways*). P 12½.

1429	**430**	90s. multicoloured	45	35
1430		2p.30 multicoloured	95	80

1977 (14 May). *National Rural Credit Commission.* W **380** (*sideways*). P 12½.

1431	**431**	30s. multicoloured	15	10

432 Dutch Windmill and First Stamps of the Netherlands and the Philippines

(Litho Questa)

1977 (14 June). AIR. *"Amphilex 77" International Stamp Exhibition, Amsterdam. Sheet 73 × 90 mm.* P 14½.

MS1432 **432** 7p.50 × 3, multicoloured . . . . 11·00 11·00

This miniature sheet was also issued imperforate from a limited printing.

No. **MS**1432 was sold on 26 May at the exhibition. Unsold sheets were sold in the Philippines from 14 June.

433 Solicitor-General's Emblem

434 Conference Emblem

1977 (30 June). *75th Anniv of Office of Solicitor General.* W **380**. P 12½.

1433	**433**	1p.65 multicoloured	45	20

1977 (29 July). *World Law Conference, Manila.* W **380**. P 12½.

1434	**434**	2p.20 multicoloured	75	30

435 ASEAN Emblem

1977 (8 Aug). *Tenth Anniv of Association of South East Asian Nations (ASEAN).* W **380**. P 12½.

1435	**435**	1p.50 multicoloured	65	35
		a. Imperf vert (horiz pair)	£110	
		b. Inverted positive impression in new blue on back		

See note under No. 1399.

1977 (15 Aug). *As No. 1355a (Rafael Palma), but value and colour changed.*

1436	**383**	30s. chocolate	15	10

436 *Mercury* (cable ship) and Map

1977 (26 Aug). *Inauguration of OLUHO Cable (Okinawa–Luzon–Hong Kong).* W **380** (*upright or sideways*). P 12½.

1437	**436**	1p.30 multicoloured	60	35

437 President Marcos

1977 (11 Sept). *60th Birth Anniversary of President Marcos.* W **380**. P 12½.

1438	**437**	30s. multicoloured	15	10
1439		2p.30 multicoloured	1·00	65

438 People raising Flag

439 Bishop Gregorio Aglipay (founder)

1977 (21 Sept). *Fifth Anniv of "New Society". Multicoloured, colour of bottom panel given.* W **380**. P 12½.

1440	**438**	30s. blue	15	10
1441		2p.30 emerald	1·00	65
		a. Value omitted		

Nos. 1440/1 exist on ordinary and luminescent paper.

1977 (1 Oct). *75th Anniv of Aglipayan Church.* W **380** (*sideways* (30s.), *upright or sideways* (90s.)). P 12½.
1442	**439**	30s. multicoloured		15	10
1443		90s. multicoloured		35	20

440 Bull and early Spanish Stamps

1977 (7 Oct). *AIR. "Espamer '77" International Stamp Exhibition, Barcelona. Sheet* 75 × 90 *mm.* P 12½ × 13.
MS1444 **440** 7p.50 × 3, multicoloured . . . . 15·00 15·00
No. **MS**1444 also exists imperforate from a limited printing.

441 Fokker F.7 Trimotor *General New* and World Map

442 Eight-pointed Star and Children

1977 (28 Oct). *50th Anniv of First Pan-Am International Air Service.* W **380**. P 12½.
1445 **441** 2p.30 multicoloured 95 60

1977 (1 Dec). *Christmas.* W **380**. P 12½.
1446	**442**	30s. multicoloured		15	10
1447		45s. multicoloured		20	15

444 Scouts and Map of Philippines

1977 (Dec). *Philatelic Week. No.* 1390 *surch with T* **443**, *in red.*
1448 **407** 90s.on 1p. multicoloured 35 20

1977 (27 Dec). *National Scout Jamboree.* W **380**. P 12½.
1449 **444** 30s. multicoloured 50 15

445 University Badge

446 Sipa Player

1978 (26 Jan). *50th Anniv of Far Eastern University.* W **380** (*sideways*). P 12½.
1450 **445** 30s. multicoloured 15 10

1978 (28 Feb). *Sipa (Filipino ball game). T* **446** *and similar diamond-shaped designs showing sipa players.* W **380**. P 12½.
1451	5s. multicoloured		10	10
	a. Block of 4. Nos. 1451/4		90	
1452	10s. multicoloured		10	10
1453	40s. multicoloured		30	15
1454	75s. multicoloured		45	20
1451/1454 *Set of 4*			85	50

Nos. 1451/4 were issued together in *se-tenant* blocks of four within the sheet, each block forming a composite design.

447 José Rizal

448 Arms of Meycauayan

1978 (28 Mar–June). *T* **447** *and similar vert designs.* W **380**. P 12½.
1455	30s. deep ultramarine (11.4)		15	10
1456	30s. cerise (19.6)		15	10
1457	90s. deep green (26.4)		20	10
1458	1p.20 scarlet		35	15
1455/1458 *Set of 4*			75	60

Designs:—No. 1456, Rajah Kalantiaw (Panay chief); 90s. Lope K. Santos ("Father of Filipino grammar"); 1p.20, Gregoria de Jesus (patriot).
Nos. 1457/8 exist on ordinary and luminescent paper.

1978 (21 Apr). *400th Anniv of Meycauayan.* W **380** (*sideways*). P 12½.
1459 **448** 1p.05 multicoloured 35 20
a. Value omitted . . . .
No. 1459 exists on ordinary and luminescent paper.

449 Horse-drawn Mail Cart

(Litho Staderini SPA, Rome)

1978 (9 June). *"CAPEX 78" International Stamp Exhibition, Toronto. T* **449** *and similar horiz designs. Multicoloured.* P 13½.
1460	2p.50 Type **449**		1·10	75
	a. Pair. Nos. 1460/1		4·25	
1461	5p. Filipino vinta		3·00	1·90

MS1462 Two sheets, each 90 × 73 mm, each containing 4 × 7p.50. (a) P 12½ × 13, with blue backgrounds; (b) Imperf, with green backgrounds . . . . 18·00 18·00
Designs: 36 × 22 *mm*—7p.50, (i) As No. 1461; (ii) As No. 1460; (iii) Early steam locomotive; (iv) Schooner.
Nos. 1460/1 were issued together in *se-tenant* pairs within the sheet.

450 Andres Bonifacio Monument
(Guillermo Tolentino)

1978 (10 July). *Andres Bonifacio Monument.* W **380** (*upright or sideways*). P 12½.
1463	**450**	30s. multicoloured	15	10
		a. Imperf (pair)	43·00	

No. 1463 exists on ordinary and luminescent paper.

451 Knight, Rook and Globe

1978 (17 July). *World Chess Championship, Baguio City.* W **380**. P 12½.
1464	**451**	30s. orange-vermilion & blue-violet	15	10
1465		2p. orange-vermilion & blue-violet	60	35

The 2p. exists on ordinary and luminescent paper.

452 Miner

453 Pres. Quezon

1978 (12 Aug). *75th Anniv of Benguet Consolidated Mining Company.* W **380**. P 12½.
1466	**452**	2p.30 multicoloured	1·20	45
		a. Value omitted	80·00	

1978 (19 Aug). *Birth Centenary of Manuel L. Quezon (former President). Multicoloured, colour of bottom inscription given.* W **380** (*sideways*). P 12½.
1467	**453**	30s. black	15	10
1468		1p. new blue	35	15
		a. Positive impression in red on back		
		b. Value omitted		

The 1p. exists on ordinary and luminescent paper.
See note after No. 1399.

454 Law Association and
Conference Emblems

455 Pres. Osmeña

1978 (27 Aug). *58th International Law Association Conference, Manila.* W **380**. P 12½.
1469	**454**	2p.30 multicoloured	80	60

Exists on ordinary and luminescent paper.

1978 (8 Sept). *Birth Centenary of Sergio Osmeña (former President).* W **380** (*sideways*). P 12½.
1470	**455**	30s. multicoloured	15	10
1471		1p. multicoloured	35	20
		a. Positive impression in reddish purple on back		

See note after No. 1399.

456 Map of Cable Route and *Mercury*
(cable ship)

1978 (30 Sept). *Inauguration of Philippines–Singapore Submarine Cable.* W **380**. P 12½.
1472	**456**	1p.40 multicoloured	60	20
		a. Imperf (pair)		

Exists on ordinary and luminescent paper.

457 Basketball

1978 (1 Oct). *Eighth Men's World Basketball Championship, Manila.* W **380**. P 12½.
1473	**457**	30s. multicoloured	15	10
1474		2p.30 multicoloured	80	60

The 2p.30 exists on ordinary and luminescent paper.

458 Dr. Catalino Gavino and Hospital

459 Nurse vaccinating Child

1978 (13 Oct). *400th Anniv of San Lazaro Hospital.* W **380**. P 12½.
1475 **458** 50s. multicoloured 20 10
    a. Imperf horiz (vert pair) . . . .
1476   90s. multicoloured 35 20

1978 (24 Oct). *Global Eradication of Smallpox.* W **380** (*sideways*). P 12½.
1477 **459** 30s. multicoloured 10 10
1478   1p.50 multicoloured 65 35

(460)

461 Man on Telephone, Map and Satellite

1978 (23 Nov). *Philatelic Week. No. 1391A surch with T* **460**.
1479 **408** 60s.on 65s. mauve 20 10

1978 (28 Nov). *50th Anniv of Philippine Long Distance Telephone Company. T* **461** *and similar horiz design.* W **380**. P 12½.
1480   30s. Type **461** 10 10
    a. Horiz pair. Nos. 1480/1 95
    ab. Values omitted (pair) . . .
1481   2p. Woman on telephone and globe . 75 50
  Nos. 1480/1 were issued together in horizontal *se-tenant* pairs within the sheet, each pair forming a composite design.

462 Family travelling in Ox-drawn Cart

1978 (28 Nov). *Decade of Filipino Child.* W **380**. P 12½.
1482 **462** 30s. multicoloured 10 10
1483   1p.35 multicoloured 60 20
  The 30s. exists on ordinary and luminescent paper.

463 Spanish Colonial Church and Arms

464 Church and Arms

1978 (7 Dec). *400th Anniv of Agoo Town.* W **380**. P 12½.
1484 **463** 30s. multicoloured 10 15
1485   45s. multicoloured 15 20

1978 (8 Dec). *400th Anniv of Balayan Town. Multicoloured, colour of bottom panel given.* W **380**. P 12½.
1486 **464** 30s. reddish brown 15 10
    a. Value omitted . . . . . 80·00
1487   90s. new blue 35 15
    a. Value omitted . . . . . 37·00

465 Dr. Sison

466 Family and Houses

1978 (15 Dec). *Dr. Honoria Acosta Sison (first Filipino woman physician) Commemoration.* W **380**. P 12½.
1488 **465** 30s. multicoloured 15 10
  Exists on ordinary and luminescent paper.

1978 (28 Dec). *30th Anniv of Declaration of Human Rights.* W **380**. P 12½.
1489 **466** 30s. multicoloured 10 10
1490   3p. multicoloured . . . . . 1·30 75
  First Day Covers are dated 10 December.

467 Melon Butterflyfish (*Chaetodon trifasciatus*)

(Litho Questa)

1978 (29 Dec). *Fishes. T* **467** *and similar horiz designs. Multicoloured.* P 14.
1491 **467** 30s. Type **467** 15 10
1492   1p.20 Black triggerfish (*Balistoides niger*) 45 15
1493   2p.20 Picasso triggerfish (*Rhinecanthus aculeatus*) 80 35
1494   2p.30 Copper-banded butterflyfish (*Chelmon rostratus*) 80 45
1495   5p. Atoll butterflyfish (*Chaetodon mertensi*) . . . . . 1·80 1·00
1496   5p. Yellow-faced angelfish (*Euxiphipops xanthometapon*) . . . . . 1·80 1·00
1491/1496 *Set of 6* . . . . 5·25 2·75

468 Carlos P. Romulo

469 Cogwheel (Rotary emblem)

1979 (14 Jan). *80th Birthday of Carlos P. Romulo (first Asian president of United Nations Assembly).* W **380**. P 12½.
1497	**468**	30s. multicoloured	10	10
1498		2p. multicoloured	95	45

1979 (26 Jan). *60th Anniv of Manila Rotary Club. Multicoloured, background colour given.* W **380**. P 12½.
1499	**469**	30s. greenish yellow	10	10
1500		2p.30 blue-green	70	25
		a. Value omitted		

470 Rosa Sevilla de Alvero

471 Burning-off Gas and Map

1979 (4 Mar). *Birth Centenary of Rosa Sevilla de Alvero (writer and educator).* W **380**. P 12½.
1501	**470**	30s. magenta	10	10

1979 (21 Mar). *First Oil Production, Nido Complex, Palawan.* W **380**. P 12½.
1502	**471**	30s. multicoloured	15	10
1503		45s. multicoloured	20	10

472 Merrill's Fruit Dove

(Litho Questa)

1979 (16 Apr). *Birds.* T **472** *and similar horiz designs. Multicoloured.* P 14.
1504	30s. Type **472**		30	15
1505	1p. Brown tit-babbler		50	45
1506	2p.20 Mindoro zone-tailed (inscr "Imperial") pigeon		95	45
1507	2p.30 Steere's pitta		1·00	50
1508	5p. Koch's pitta and red-breasted pitta		2·20	1·20
1509	5p. Great eared nightjar		2·20	1·20
1504/1509 *Set of 6*			6·50	3·50

473 Association Emblem

1979 (30 Apr). *25th Anniv of Association of Special Libraries of the Philippines.* W **380**. P 12½.
1510	**473**	30s. yellowish green, black and greenish yellow	15	10
1511		75s. yellowish green, black and bright yellow-green	30	10
1512		1p. yellowish grn, blk & yell-orge	35	20

The 30s. on thin unwatermarked paper, perf or imperf, is a forgery.

474 Conference Emblem

1979 (3 May). *Fifth United Nations Conference on Trade and Development, Manila.* W **380**. P 12½.
1513	**474**	1p.20 multicoloured	35	15
1514		2p.30 multicoloured	95	35
		a. Inverted positive impression in red on back		

Nos. 1513/14 exist on ordinary and luminescent paper.
See note after No. 1399.

475 Malay civet (*Viverra tangalunga*)

476 Dish Aerial

(Litho Questa)

1979 (15 May). *Animals.* T **475** *and similar horiz. designs. Multicoloured.* P 14.
1515	30s. Type **475**		15	10
1516	1p.20 Crab-eating macaque (*Macaca philippinensis philippinensis*)		45	15
1517	2p.20 Javan pig (*Sas celebensis philippensis*)		80	35
1518	2p.30 Leopard cat (*Felis minuta*)		80	45
1519	5p. Oriental small-clawed otter (*Amblovx cinerea cinerea*)		1·80	1·00
1520	5p. Malayan pangolin (*Paramanis culionensis*)		1·80	1·00
1515/1520 *Set of 6*			5·25	2·75

First Day Covers are dated 14 May.

1979 (17 May). *World Telecommunication Day.* T **476** *and similar vert design. Multicoloured.* W **380** (*sideways*). P 12½.
1521	90s. Type **476**		30	10
1522	1p.30 Hemispheres		45	20

The 90s. exists on ordinary and luminescent paper.

477 Mussaenda "Dona Evangelina"

(Litho Questa)

1979 (13 June). *Cultivated Mussaendas. T 477 and similar horiz designs. Multicoloured.* P 14.

1523	30s. Type **477**		15	10
1524	1p.20 "Doña Esperanza"		45	15
1525	2p.20 "Doña Hilaria"		80	35
1526	2p.30 "Doña aurora"		80	45
1527	5p. "Gining Imelda"		1·80	1·00
1528	5p. "Doña Trining"		1·80	1·00
1523/1528 *Set of* 6			5·25	2·75

First Day Covers are dated 11 June.

478 Manila Cathedral

(Des A. Divina)

1979 (25 June). *400th Anniv of Archdiocese of Manila. Multicoloured, colour of frame given.* W **380** (sideways). P 12½.

1529	**478**	30s. orange-red	15	10
1530		75s. magenta	20	10
1531		a. Value omitted		
		90s. light green	35	20
		a. Value omitted		

Nos. 1529/31 exist on ordinary and luminescent paper.

479 *Bagong Lakas* (patrol boat)

1ST SCOUT PHILATELIC EXHIBITION

AIRMAIL 90⁵

JULY 4-14, 1979
QUEZON CITY
(480)

1979 (26 June). *Navy Foundation Day.* W **380**. P 12½.

1532	**479**	30s. multicoloured	20	10
1533		45s. multicoloured	30	15

1979 (4 July). *AIR. First Scout Philatelic Exhibition and 25th Anniv of First National Scout Jamboree. Nos. 822 and* **MS**829 *surch as T* **480**.

1534	**188**	90s.on 6c.+4c. carmine-red/ yellow	30	30

MS1535 171 × 90 mm. Nos. 823, 825/8 each surch 50s. ... 2·75 2·75

On No. **MS**1535 the surcharges are as T **480** but omitting the word "AIRMAIL"; there is also a commemorative overprint in the margin.

481 Drug Addict breaking Manacles

482 Afghan Hound

1979 (23 July). *"Fight Drug Abuse" Campaign.* W **380**. P 12½.

1536	**481**	30s. multicoloured	15	10
1537		90s. multicoloured	35	15
1538		1p.05 multicoloured	45	20

(Litho Questa)

1979 (3 Aug). *Cats and Dogs. T* **482** *and similar horiz designs. Multicoloured.* P 14.

1539	30s. Type **482**		10	10
1540	90s. Tabby cats		35	15
1541	1p.20 Dobermann pinscher		45	20
1542	2p.20 Siamese cats		80	20
1543	2p.30 German shepherd dog		95	80
1544	5p. Chinchilla cats		1·80	95
1539/1544 *Set of* 6			4·00	2·10

First Day Covers are dated 6 July.

483 Children flying Kites

484 Hands holding Emblems

1979 (31 Aug). *International Year of the Child. T* **483** *and similar horiz designs showing paintings by Rod Dayao. Multicoloured.* W **380**. P 12½.

1545	15s. Type **483**		10	10
1546	20s. Boys fighting with catapults		15	10
1547	25s. Girls dressing-up		15	15
1548	1p.20 Boy playing policeman		35	20
1545/1548 *Set of* 4			70	50

1979 (27 Sept). *80th Anniv of Methodism in Philippines.* W **380**. P 12½.

1549	**484**	30s. multicoloured	15	10
1550		1p.35 multicoloured	45	15

Nos. 1549/50 exist on ordinary and luminescent paper.

485 Anniversary Medal and 1868 Coin

1979 (15 Nov). *50th Anniv of Philippine Numismatic and Antiquarian Society.* W **380**. P 12½.

1551	**485**	30s. multicoloured	15	10

Exists on ordinary and luminescent paper.

486 Concorde over Manila and Paris

(487)

1979 PHILATELIC WEEK

1979 (22 Nov). *25th Anniv of Air France Service to Philippines. T* **486** *and similar horiz design. Multicoloured.* W **380**. P 12½.
1552 1p.05 Type **486** 50 30
1553 2p.20 Concorde over monument . . . 1·30 60

1979 (23 Nov). *Philatelic Week. No.* 1400 *surch with T* **487** *in red.*
1554 **412** 90s.on 1p.40 black 35 15

488 "35" and I.A.T.A. Emblem

489 Bureau of Local Government Emblem

1979 (27 Nov). *35th International Air Transport Association Annual Meeting, Manila.* W **380**. P 12½.
1555 **488** 75s. multicoloured 30 15
1556 2p.30 multicoloured 95 65

1979 (14 Dec). *Local Government Year.* W **380**. P 12½.
1557 **489** 30s. multicoloured 15 15
1558 45s. multicoloured 20 65
  A block of four of the 30s. has been seen imperf vertically at left margin and between, with the right-hand vertical perforations running at an angle through the designs.

490 Christmas Greetings

491 Rheumatism Victim

1979 (17 Dec). *Christmas. T* **490** *and similar vert design. Multicoloured.* W **380**. P 12½.
1559 30s. Type **490** 15 10
1560 90s. Stars 45 30
  a. Imperf (pair) . . . .

1980 (20 Jan). *Fourth Congress of Southeast Asia and Pacific Area League against Rheumatism, Manila.* W **380**. P 12½.
1561 **491** 30s. multicoloured 15 10
1562 90s. multicoloured 50 20

492 Birthplace and MacArthur Memorial Foundation

493 Columbus and Emblem

1980 (26 Jan). *Centenary of General Douglas MacArthur (U.S. Army Chief of Staff). T* **492** *and similar multicoloured designs.* W **380** (*sideways*). P 12½.
1563 30s. Type **492** 15 10
1564 75s. General MacArthur 35 15
1565 2p.30 Hat, pipe and glasses . . . . 1·30 75
MS1566 76 × 76 mm. 5p. Landing in the Philippines (*horiz*). Imperf . . . . . . 3·00 2·50
  A horizontally misperforated block of No. 1564 has been seen with the first two rows imperf, the second row of stamps being incomplete.

1980 (14 Feb). *75th Anniv of Knights of Columbus Organization in Philippines.* W **380** (*sideways*). P 12½.
1567 **493** 30s. multicoloured 15 10
1568 1p.35 multicoloured 80 45

494 Soldiers and Academy Emblem

495 Tirona, Benitez and University

1980 (17 Feb). *75th Anniv of Philippine Military Academy.* W **380**. P 12½.
1569 **494** 30s. multicoloured 15 10
1570 1p.20 multicoloured 75 30

1980 (21 Feb). *60th Anniv of Philippine Women's University.* W **380**. P 12½.
1571 **495** 30s. multicoloured 15 10
1572 1p.05 multicoloured 65 30
  Nos. 1571/2 exist on ordinary and luminescent paper.
  In the first printing of No. 1571 one stamp in the sheet had "PILIPINAS" omitted. This error was removed from the sheets before sale, having first been crossed through in ballpoint and handstamped "OB". The errors were reportedly destroyed but at least one example is known to exist.

496 Boats and Burning City

497 Mosque and Koran

1980 (23 Feb). *75th Anniv of Rotary International. T* **496** *and similar horiz designs showing details of Carlos Francisco's painting. Multicoloured.* W **380**. P 12½.
1573	30s. Type **496**		15	10
1574	30s. Priest with cross, swordsmen and soldier		15	10
1575	30s. "K K K" flag and group around table		15	10
1576	30s. Man in midst of spearmen and civilian scenes		15	10
1577	30s. Reading the Constitution, soldiers and U.S. and Philippines flags		15	10
	a. *Se-tenant* strip of 5 (Nos. 1573/7)		80	
1578	2p.30 Type **496**		1·30	60
1579	2p.30 As No. 1574		1·30	60
1580	2p.30 As No. 1575		1·30	60
1581	2p.30 As No. 1576		1·30	60
1582	2p.30 As No. 1577		1·30	60
	a. *Se-tenant* strip of 5 (Nos. 1578/82)		6·75	
	ab. Imperf horiz (block of 10)			
1573/1582 *Set of 10*			9·00	3·00

The five stamps of each value were issued together in *se-tenant* strips of five within the sheet, each strip forming a composite design.

1980 (28 Mar). *600th Anniv of Islam in Philippines.* W **380**. P 12½.
1583	**497**	30s. multicoloured	15	10
1584		1p.30 multicoloured	75	30

Nos. 1583/4 exist on ordinary and luminescent paper.

498 Hand stubbing-out Cigarette   499 Scouting Activities and Badge

1980 (11 Apr). *World Health Day. Anti-smoking Campaign.* W **380** (*sideways*). P 12½.
1585	**498**	30s. multicoloured	15	10
1586		75s. multicoloured	45	20

First Day Covers are dated 7 April.

1980 (26 May). *40th Anniv of Girl Scouting in Philippines.* W **380**. P 12½.
1587	**499**	30s. multicoloured	15	10
1588		2p. multicoloured	65	30

500 Jeepney   (501)

1980 (7 July). *Philippine Jeapneys (decorated jeeps). T* **500** *and similar horiz design. Multicoloured.* W **380**. P 12½.
1589	30s. Type **500**		15	10
1590	1p.20 Side view of jeepney		65	30

First Day Covers are dated 24 June.

1980 (23 July). *82nd Anniv of Independence. Nos.* 1400 *and* 1319 *surch as T* **501** *in red.*
1591	**412**	1p.35 on 1p.60 black	80	45
1592	–	1p.60 on 1p.80 deep blue-green	1·00	50
		a. Surch inverted	24·00	
		b. Surch inverted on No. 1319a		

First Day Covers are dated 12 June.

502 Association Emblem   503 Map and Emblems

1980 (1 Aug). *Seventh General Conference of International Association of Universities, Manila.* W **380**. P 12½.
1593	**502**	30s. multicoloured	15	10
1594		2p.30 multicoloured	1·30	1·30

1980 (18 Aug). *46th Congress of International Federation of Library Associations and Institutions, Manila.* W **380** (*sideways*). P 12½.
1595	**503**	30s. bright green and black	20	10
1596		75s. light blue and black	45	20
1597		2p.30 rose-red and black	1·50	80

504 Filipinos and Emblem   **40ˢ** (505)

1980 (19 Sept). *Fifth Anniv of Kabataang Barangay (national council charged with building the "New Society").* W **380**. P 12½.
1598	**504**	30s. multicoloured	20	10
1599		40s. multicoloured	20	15
1600		1p. multicoloured	65	30

1980 (26 Sept–Oct). *Provisionals. Nos.* 1501, 1536, 1557, 1559 *and* 1433 *surch as T* **505** *or with similar types.*
1601	**470**	40s.on 30s. magenta (B.)	20	10
		a. Surch inverted		
1602	**481**	40s.on 30s. multicoloured (13 Oct)	20	10
		a. Surch inverted		
		b. Surch double		
1603	**489**	40s.on 30s. multicoloured (B.) (14 Oct)	20	10
		a. Surch inverted		
		b. "40s" omitted		
1604	**490**	40s.on 30s. multicoloured (R.) (14 Oct)	20	10
		a. Surch inverted		
		b. Surch double		
1605	**433**	2p.on 1p.65 multicoloured (R.) (14 Oct)	1·30	65
		a. Surch inverted		
1601/1605 *Set of 5*			1·90	95

On No. 1603b the bars of the surcharge are misplaced.
First Day Covers for all values are dated 26 September.
See also Nos. 1624/40.

506 Sunset, Filipino Vinta and Conference Emblem

507 Stamps and Magnifying Glass

1980 (27 Sept). *World Tourism Conference, Manila.* W **380**. P 12½.
1606	**506**	30s. multicoloured	20	15
1607		2p.30 multicoloured	1·40	80

1980 (9 Oct). *Postage Stamp Day.* W **380** (*sideways*). P 12½.
1608	**507**	40s. multicoloured	20	15
1609		1p. multicoloured	65	30
1610		2p. multicoloured	1·30	65

508 U.N. Headquarters and Philippines Flag

509 *Murex alabaster*

1950 (20 Oct). *35th Anniv of United Nations Organization. T* **508** *and similar vert design. Multicoloured.* W **380**. P 12½.
1611		40s. Type **508**	30	15
1612		3p.20 U.N. Headquarters and U.N. and Philippines flags	1·90	1·30

1980 (2 Nov). *Shells. T* **509** *and similar horiz designs. Multicoloured.* W **380** (*sideways*). P 12½.
1613		40s. Type **509**	20	15
		a. Imperf vert (horiz pair)		
1614		60s. *Bursa bubo*	35	20
1615		1p.20 *Murex zamboi*	65	30
1616		2p. *Xenophora pallidula*	1·30	60
1613/1616 *Set of 4*			2·30	1·10

510 Interpol Emblem on Globe

1980 (17 Nov). *49th General Assembly of Interpol (International Police Organization), Manila.* W **380** (*sideways*). P 12½.
1617	**510**	40s. multicoloured	20	10
1618		1p. multicoloured	65	30
1619		3p.20 multicoloured	2·10	1·30
First Day Covers are dated 5 November.				

P1.20 ═══

511 University and Faculty Emblems

(**512**)

1980 (17 Nov). *75th Anniv of Central Philippine University. Multicoloured, background colour given.* W **380** (*sideways*). P 12½.
1620	**511**	40s. greenish blue	30	10
		a. Imperf horiz (vert pair)		
		b. Black (inscriptions and value) omitted		
1621		3p.20 yellowish green	1·20	1·30

1980 (10 Dec). *Philatelic Week. No. 1377A surch with T* **512**.
1622	**399**	1p.20 on 80s. black, new blue & pink	60	30
		a. Surch inverted		
First Day Covers are dated 21 November.				

10s

513 Christmas Tree and Presents

(**514**)

1980 (15 Dec). *Christmas.* W **380**. P 12½.
1623	**513**	40s. multicoloured	20	10

1981 (2 Jan)–*82. Various stamps surch as T* **505**, **514** *or with similar types.*
1624	**244**	10s.on 6s.+5s. ultramarine (15 Mar 1982)	15	10
1625	**462**	10s.on 30s. multicoloured (O.) (12 Jan 1981)	10	10
		a. Inscription and value (black) of stamp printed double		
		b. Surch inverted		
1626	**408**	40s.on 65s. mauve (1391A) (2 Apr 1981)	20	10
		a. Surch inverted		
		b. Surch double, one inverted	31·00	
1627	**458**	40s.on 90s. multicoloured (5 Mar 1981)	20	10
1628	**481**	40s.on 90s. multicoloured (26 Feb 1981)	20	10
		a. Double surch, one inverted		
1629	–	40s.on 90s. multicoloured (1560) (2 Apr 1981)	20	10
1630	**448**	40s.on 1p.05 multicoloured (25 Nov 1981)	20	10
1631	**462**	40s.on 1p.35 multicoloured (25 Nov 1981)	20	15
1632	**399**	85s.on 80s. blk, new bl & pk (1377A)	50	30
		a. Surch inverted		
1633	**408**	1p.on 65s. mauve (1391A) (24 Feb 1981)	75	30
1634	**401**	1p.on 1p.50 ultramarine and magenta (1381A) (4 Aug 1981)	75	30
1635	**422**	1p.on 1p.50 multicoloured (10 Feb 1981)	60	20

1636	–	1p.20 on 1p.50 chocolate (1318b) (25 Nov 1981)	75	35
1637	**433**	1p.20 on 1p.65 multicoloured (2 Apr 1981)	75	35
1638	–	1p.20 on 1p.80 deep blue-green (1319) (2 Apr 1981)	75	35
1639	**401**	2p.on 1p.50 ultramarine and magenta (1381A) (27 July 1981)	1·30	60
1640	**434**	3p.20 on 2p.20 multicoloured (19 Mar 1981)	1·90	1·00

No. 1636 exists on ordinary and luminescent paper.
First Day Covers of Nos. 1626, 1629 and 1637/8 are dated 26 March; of No. 1627, 26 February; of Nos. 1633, 1635 and 1640, 28 January; and of Nos. 1634 and 1639, 21 July.

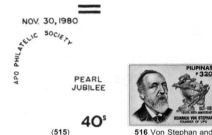

NOV. 30, 1980

APO PHILATELIC SOCIETY

PEARL JUBILEE

40ˢ

(515)

516 Von Stephan and U.P.U. Emblem

1981 (7 Jan). *30th Anniv of APO Philatelic Society. No. 1470 surch with T* **517**.
1641	**455**	40s.on 30s. multicoloured	20	10
		a. Surch inverted		

First Day Covers are dated 30 November.

1981 (3 Feb). *150th Birth Anniv of Heinrich von Stephan (founder of Universal Postal Union). W* **380** (*sideways*). P 12½.
1642	**516**	3p.20 multicoloured	1·90	95

First Day Covers are dated 30 January.

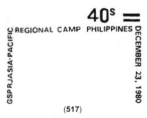

40ˢ

REGIONAL CAMP PHILIPPINES DECEMBER 23, 1980

GSP RJ ASIA-PACIFIC

(517)

1981 (5 Feb). *Girl Scouts' Camp. No. 1589 surch with T* **517**.
1643	**500**	40s.on 30s. multicoloured	20	10

First Day Covers are dated 2 January.

518 Pope John Paul II   **519** Parliamentary Debate

(Des N. Dimanlig and A. Chuidian. Litho Staderini SPA, Rome)

1981 (17 Feb). *Papal Visit. T* **518** *and similar multicoloured designs.* P 13½.
1644	90s. Type **518**	50	20
1645	1p.20 Pope and cardinals	65	30
1646	2p.30 Pope blessing crowd (*horiz*)	1·30	65
1647	3p. Pope and Manila Cathedral (*horiz*)	1·60	80
1644/1647 *Set of* 4		3·75	1·75
MS1648 75 × 91 mm. 7p.50, Pope and map of Philippines		6·00	3·00

1981 (21 Apr). *Interparliamentary Union Meeting, Manila.* W **380**. P 12½.
1649	**519**	2p. multicoloured	1·40	60
1650		3p.20 multicoloured	1·90	1·00

First Day Covers are dated 20 April.

520 Monument   **521** Pres. Aguinaldo's Car

1981 (8 June). *José Rizal Monument, Luneta Park. Granite paper.* W **380**. P 12½.
1651	**520**	40s. black, greenish yellow & brown	20	10
		a. Imperf horiz (vert pair)		

First Day Covers are dated 29 May.

1981 (17 June). *50th Anniv of Philippine Motor Association. T* **521** *and similar horiz designs. Multicoloured. Granite paper.* W **380** (*sideways*). P 12½.
1652	40s. Type **521**	20	10
	a. Block of 4. Nos. 1652/5	1·00	
1653	40s. 1930 Model car	20	10
1654	40s. 1937 Model car	20	10
1655	40s. 1937 Model car (*different*)	20	10
1652/1655 *Set of* 4		75	35

Nos. 1652/5 were issued together in *se-tenant* blocks of four within the sheet.
First Day Covers are dated 25 May.

522 Bubble Coral

1981 (25 June). *Corals. T* **522** *and similar horiz designs. Multicoloured. Granite paper.* W **380** (*sideways*). P 12½.
1656	40s. Type **522**		20	10
	a. Block of 4. Nos. 1656/9		1·00	
1657	40s. Branching corals		20	10
1658	40s. Brain coral		20	10
1659	40s. Table coral		20	10
1656/1659 *Set of 4*			75	35

Nos. 1656/9 were issued together in *se-tenant* blocks of four within the sheet.
First Day Covers are dated 22 May.

523 Pres. Marcos and Flag

1981 (30 June)–84. *Inauguration of President Marcos. Granite paper.* W **380** (*sideways on No. 1660*). P 12½.
1660	**523** 40s. multicoloured		20	10
	a. Imperf		20	10
	b. Fibreless paper (4 Oct 1983)		65	30
	c. Positive impression in black on back		—	—

MS1661 78 × 78 mm. 5p. As No. 1660 but design smaller with inscriptions below.
Imperf		3·00	1·30
a. Fibreless paper (18 Oct 1984)		7·75	7·75
b. Black (inscription and value) printed double		—	—

Nos. 1660/**MS**1661 also exist with the surface heavily varnished. It is understood these were mainly intended for use in presentation albums.
See note after No. 1399.

524 St. Ignatius de Loyola (founder)

525 F. R. Castro

1981 (31 July). *400th Anniv of Jesuits in Philippines. T* **524** *and similar horiz designs. Multicoloured. Granite paper.* W **380** (*sideways*). P 12½.
1662	40s. Type **524**		20	10
	a. Block of 4. Nos. 1662/5		1·00	
	ab. Imperf horiz (block of 4)		80·00	
1663	40s. José Rizal and Intramuros Ateneo		20	10

1664	40s. Father Federico Faura (director) and Manila Observatory		20	10
1665	40s. Father Saturnino Urios (missionary) and map of Mindanao		20	10
1662/1665 *Set of 4*			75	35

MS1666 89 × 89 mm. As Nos. 1662/5 but smaller. Imperf (sold at 2p.) . . . . 2·20 75

Nos. 1662/5 were issued together in *se-tenant* blocks of four within the sheet.

1981 (2 Sept)–82. *Chief Justice Fred Ruiz Castro. Granite paper.* W **380** (*sideways*). P 12½.
1667	**525** 40s. multicoloured		20	10
	a. Positive impression in black on back			
	b. Fibreless paper (1 June 1982)		1·20	45

See note after No. 1399.

526 Pres. Ramon Magsaysay

527 Man in Wheelchair

1981 (7 Sept). *T* **526** *and similar vert designs. Granite paper.* W **380**. P 12½.
1668	1p. red-brown and black (24 Sept)		65	30
	a. Imperf horiz (vert pair)			
	b. Inverted positive impression of red-brown on back			
1669	1p.20 reddish brown and black		75	35
1670	2p. maroon and black (15 Sept)		1·40	60
	a. Imperf horiz (vert pair)			

Designs:—1p. General Gregorio del Pilar; 2p. Ambrosio R. Bautista.
First Day Covers of No. 1668 are dated 18 September and those of No. 1669, 31 August.
See note after No. 1399.
See also Nos. 1699/1704, 1807/15, 1889/90, 1913/16, 1975, 2007 and 2031/4.

1981 (24 Oct). *International Year of Disabled Persons. Granite paper.* W **380**. P 12½.
1671	**527** 40s. multicoloured		30	15
	a. Imperf vert (horiz pair)			
1672	3p.20 multicoloured		1·90	1·00

528 Early Filipino Writing

529 Isabel II Gate, Manila

1981 (7 Nov)–83. *24th International Red Cross Conference, Manila. Granite paper.* W **380**. P 12½.
1673	**528** 40s. black, scarlet and bistre		15	10
1674	2p. black and rosine		1·30	50
1675	3p.20 black, rosine and mauve		1·90	90
	a. Fibreless paper (17 Feb 1983)		3·00	1·30

1981 (13 Nov)–**82**. *Granite paper*. W **380** (*sideways*). P 12½.
1676   **529**   40s. black 20   10
     a. Fibreless paper (2 Apr
        1982) 30   15
     b. Imperf horiz (vert pair) . . . .
     c. Printed double . . . .

530 Concert in Park

1981 (20 Nov)–**82**. *Opening of Concert at Park* 200. *Granite paper*. W **380** (*sideways*). P 12½.
1677   **530**   40s. multicoloured 20   10
     a. Fibreless paper (26 Apr
        1982) . . . . 2·30   50
     b. Imperf vert (horiz pair) . . . .

1981 PHILATELIC WEEK
(**531**)

1981 (24 Nov). *Philatelic Week. No. 1435 surch with T* **531**.
1678   **485**   1p.20 on 1p.50 multicoloured . . . 75   35
First Day Covers are dated 23 November.

532 Running

1981 (3 Dec). 11*th South-East Asian Games, Manila. T* **532** *and similar horiz designs. Granite paper.* W **380** (*sideways*). P 12½.
1679   40s. orange-yellow, yell-grn & dp
     ochre 20   10
1680   1p. multicoloured 75   30
1681   2p. multicoloured . . . . 1·50   60
1682   2p.30 multicoloured . . . . 1·50   65
1683   2p.80 multicoloured . . . . 1·80   80
1684   3p.20 bluish violet and greenish
     blue . . . . 1·90   1·00
1679/1684 *Set of 6* . . . . 6·75   3·00
Designs:—1p. Cycling; 2p. Pres. Marcos and Juan Antonio Samaranch (president, International Olympic Committee); 2p.30, Football; 2p.80, Shooting; 3p.20, Bowling.

533 Manila Film Centre

534 Carriedo Fountain

1982 (18 Jan). *Manila International Film Festival. T* **533** *and similar vert designs. Multicoloured. Granite paper.* W **380**. P 12½.
1685   40s. Type **533** 30   10
1686   2p. Front view of trophy . . . . . . 1·50   60
     a. Fibreless paper (3 Aug 1982) . . 2·00   65
     b. Imperf horiz (vert pair) . . .
1687   3p.20 Side view of trophy . . . . . . 1·90   1·00
     a. Fibreless paper (9 July 1982) . . 2·50   1·30
     b. Imperf horiz (vert pair) . . .

1982 (25 Jan). *Centenary of Manila Metropolitan Waterworks and Sewage System. Granite paper.* W **380** (*sideways*). P 12½.
1688   **534**   40s. new blue 20   10
     a. Imperf vert (horiz pair) . . . .
1689   1p.20 chocolate 75   35
     a. Printed both sides . . . .
First Day Covers are dated 22 January.

535 Lord Baden-Powell (founder)

536 Embroidered Banner

1982 (22 Feb)–**83**. *75th Anniv of Boy Scout Movement. T* **535** *and similar vert design. Granite paper.* W **380**. P 12½.
1690   40s. Type **535** 20   10
     a. Cream fibreless paper with chalk
        surface (8 June 1982) 20   10
     b. White fibreless paper (29 Sept
        1983) . . . . 5·75   35
     c. Black (inscriptions and value)
        omitted . . . .
1691   2p. Scout . . . . 1·50   60
     a. Fibreless paper (21 Oct 1982) . . 1·50   60
     b. Black ("PILIPINAS" and value)
        omitted . . . .
     c. Imperf horiz (vert pair) . . . .

1982 (25 Feb)–**84**. *25th Anniv of Children's Museum and Library Inc. T* **536** *and similar horiz design. Multicoloured. Granite paper.* W **380** (*sideways*). P 12½.
1692   40s. Type **536** 20   10
     a. Fibreless paper (29 Feb 1984) . . 20   10
     b. "PILIPINAS" and value omitted . .
1693   1p.20 Children playing 75   35
     a. Fibreless paper (3 Feb 1984) . . 90   45
     b. Positive impression in blk on
        back . . . .
See note after No. 1399.

537 Pres. Marcos presenting Sword of Honour

538 Soldier and Memorial

1982 (25 Mar). *Military Academy. Granite paper.* W **380** (*sideways*). P 12½.

1694	537	40s. multicoloured	20	15
		a. Fibreless paper	20	15
1695		1p. multicoloured	75	30
		a. Fibreless paper	85	30
		b. Black (inscriptions) omitted		

1982 (9 Apr)–**83**. *Bataan Day. T* **538** *and similar horiz designs. Cream chalk-surfaced paper.* W **380**. P 12½.

1696	40s. multicoloured	20	10
	a. White paper (13 Oct 1983)	80	10
1697	2p. multicoloured	1·50	60
	a. Imperf vert (horiz pair)		
MS1698	76 × 76 mm. 3p.20, brown-purple and black. Imperf	2·20	1·60
	a. White paper	2·20	1·60
	b. Black (Inscriptions and value) omitted		
	c. Inverted positive impression in red on back		

Design:—2p. Doves and rifle; 3p.20, Field gun and flag.
The 40s. on while paper exists with cream or white gum.
See note below No. 1399.

I.

II.

Two Types of 1p. (Quezon):
I. With long tilde over "N" of "DOA" full V of dress in design.
II. Tilde shorter; portrait cropped and enlarged

1982 (28 Apr)–**83**. *Vert designs as T* **526**. *Cream chalk-surfaced paper.* W **380**. P 12½.

1699	40s. turquoise-blue (7 May 1982)	20	10
	a. Printed double		
	b. Printed on both sides		
1700	1p. rose-red (I)	75	30
	a. Imperf vert (horiz pair)		
	b. Imperf horiz (vert pair)		
	c. Type II (*white paper*) (20 May 1983)	1·20	35
1701	1p.20 reddish brown (18 May 1982)	75	35
1702	2p. deep magenta (17 Aug 1982)	1·30	60
	a. White paper (4 Oct 1983)	1·60	50
1703	2p.30 maroon (3 Sept 1982)	1·50	60
1704	3p.20 chalky blue (22 Aug 1982)	1·90	1·00
	a. White paper (11 Oct 1983)	2·10	1·00
1699/1704	Set of 6 (*cheapest*)	8·25	3·50

Designs:—40s. Isabelo de los Reyes (founder of first workers' union); 1p. Aurora Aragon Quezon (social worker and former First Lady); 1p.20, Francisco Dagohoy; 2p. Juan Sumulong (politician); 2p.30, Professor Nicanor Abelardo (composer); 3p.20, General Vicente Lim.
No. 1700c exists with cream or white gum.
First Day Covers of No. 1699 are dated 4 May; of No. 1702, 10 August; and of No. 1703, 25 August.
For these designs in other values see Nos. 1811/15.

539 Worker with Tower Award (Type II) **540** Cogwheel and Tower Award (Type I)

Two types of T **539/40**:
I. With inscription below design; final word spelt "MANGGAGAWA" (as illus for T **540**)
II. With inscription incorporated in design; final word incorrectly spelt "MANGAGAWA" (as illus for T **539**).

1982 (5 May)–**84**. *Tower Awards (for best "Blue Collar" Workers). Cream chalk-surfaced paper.* W **380**. P 12½.

1705	539	40s. multicoloured (I)	20	10
		a. White paper (3 May 1984)	1·70	40
		b. Emerald (inscription) omitted		
		c. Emerald (inscription) double		
		d. Type II (24 Nov 1982)	20	10
1706	540	1p.20 multicoloured (I)	75	35
		a. White paper (4 Oct 1983)	1·80	65
		b. Type II (8 Nov 1982)	75	40

First Day Covers of Nos. 1705/6 are dated 1 May.

541 Green Turtle (*Chelonia mydas*) **542** K.K.K. Emblem

1982 (5 June)–**84**. *Tenth Anniv of United Nations Environment Programme. T* **541** *and similar horiz design. Multicoloured. Cream chalk-surfaced paper.* W **380**. P 12½.

1707	40s. Type **541**	30	15
	a. White paper (19 Jan 1984)	55	10
1708	3p.20 Philippine eagle (*Pithecophaga jefferyi*)	2·75	1·00
	a. White paper (24 Jan 1984)	3·50	1·00

1982 (12 June)–**83**. *Inauguration of Kilusang Kabuhayan at Kaunlaran (national livelihood movement). Cream chalk-surfaced paper.* W **380** (*sideways*). P 12½.

1709	542	40s. deep bluish green, yellowish green and black/*cream*	20	10
		a. Deep bluish green double		
		b. White paper (26 Feb 1983)	20	10
		c. Imperf vert (horiz pair)		
		d. Black quintuple		

The white paper comes with cream or white gum.
See also Nos. 1816/17.

543 Chemistry
Apparatus and
Emblem

544 Dr. Fernando G. Calderon
and Emblems

547 Emblem and
Flags forming Ear of
Wheat

548 St. Theresa of Avila

1982 (21 June)–**83**. *50th Anniv of Adamson University. Cream chalk-surfaced paper.* W **380** (*sideways*). P 12½.

1710	**543**	40s. multicoloured	20	10
		a. Gold omitted		
		b. White paper (22 Sept 1983)	3·50	35
1711		1p.20 multicoloured	75	35
		a. Gold omitted		

1982 (20 July)–**83**. *75th Anniv of College of Medicine, University of the Philippines. Cream chalk-surfaced paper.* W **380**. P 12½.

1712	**544**	40s. multicoloured	30	15
		a. White paper (29 Nov 1983)	45	10
1713		3p.20 multicoloured	1·90	1·00
		a. White paper (29 Nov 1983)	2·10	1·00

First Day Covers of Nos. 1712/13 are dated 10 June.

1982 (22 Sept)–**84**. *15th Anniv of Association of South-East Asian Nations. Cream chalk-surfaced paper.* W **380**. P 12½.

1719	**547**	40s. multicoloured	20	10
		a. White paper (12 Jan 1984)	45	10
		b. Black ("asean") omitted		

First Day Covers are dated 8 August.

1982 (15 Oct)–**83**. *400th Death Anniv of St. Theresa of Avila. T* **548** *and similar horiz design. Multicoloured. Cream chalk-surfaced paper.* P 13 × 13½.

1720		40s. Type **548**	20	10
1721		1p.20 St. Theresa and map of Europe, Africa and Asia	75	35
		a. Perf 12½ (1 Dec 1982)	90	50
		ab. Do. White paper (23 Nov 1983)	1·20	40
1722		2p. As No. 1721	1·50	60
		a. Perf 12½ (1 Dec 1982)	1·80	70
		b. White paper (13 June 1983)	1·70	50

545 Pres. Marcos

546 Hands supporting
Family

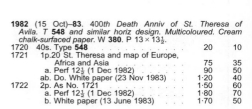

549 St. Isabel College

550 Pres. Marcos signing
Decree and Tenant Family

1982 (11 Sept)–**84**. *65th Birthday of President Ferdinand E. Marcos. Cream chalk-surfaced paper.* W **380** (*sideways*). P 13½ × 13.

1714	**545**	40s. multicoloured	20	10
		a. White paper (9 Sept 1983)	45	20
		b. Perf 12½ (*white paper*) (13 Oct 1983)	30	10
1715		3p.20 multicoloured	1·90	1·00
		a. White paper (8 Sept 1983)	1·90	1·00
		b. Perf 12½ (*white paper*) (14 Feb 1984)	1·90	1·00
MS1716	76 × 76 mm. Nos. 1714/15. Imperf		2·50	1·60
		a. White paper (14 Dec 83)	6·50	3·25
		b. Black (inscriptions and values) printed double		
		c. Positive impression in carmine on back		

Nos. 1714b and 1715b exist with cream or white gum. See note after No. 1399.

1982 (16 Sept). *25th Anniv of Social Security System.* W **380** (*sideways*). P 13½ × 13.

1717	**546**	40s. black, pale orange and blue	20	10
1718		1p.20 black, pale orange & emer	75	35
		a. Imperf (pair)		

First Day Covers are dated 1 September.

1982 (22 Oct). *350th Anniv of St. Isabel College.* W **380**. P 13 × 13½.

1723	**549**	40s. multicoloured	20	15
1724		1p. multicoloured	75	30

I.

II.

Two types of No. 1725:
I. Front edge of lectern and all of Pres. Marcos's right hand visible, design includes part of lower arms of children.
II. Foot of design cuts across lectern and right hand: children's arms cut off at elbows. Design is ¼ mm shorter.

1982 (25 Oct)–**83**. *Tenth Anniv of Tenant Emancipation Decree.*
W **380**.

		(a) Size 37 × 27–27¼ mm. P 13 × 13½.		
1725	**550**	40s. yellowish green, reddish brown and black (I)	20	10
		a. Type II	20	10
		(b) Size 32 × 22½ mm. P 13.		
1726	**550**	40s. yellowish green, reddish brown and black (10 Nov 1983)	20	10

First Day Covers of No. 1725 are dated 21 October.

551 "Reading Tree"

552 Helmeted Heads

1982 (4 Nov)–**84**. *Literacy Campaign. Cream chalk-surfaced paper.* W **380**. P 13 × 13½.

1727	**551**	40s. multicoloured	20	10
		a. White paper (14 Feb 1983)	65	10
		ab. Do. Perf 12½ (11 Oct 1983)	1·20	25
1728		2p.30 multicoloured	1·50	60
		a. White paper (19 Jan 1984)	1·60	60

No. 1728a exists with cream or white gum.
The 2p.30 exists perf 12½ with "SPECIMEN" overprint.

1982 (7 Nov)–**84**. *43rd World Congress of Skal Clubs, Manila.* T **552** *and similar horiz design. Multicoloured.* W **380**. P 13 × 13½.

1729	40s. Type **552**	20	10
	a. Perf 12½ (18 Jan 1984)	50	10
1730	2p. Head in feathered headdress	1·50	60
	a. Perf 12½ (12 Jan 1984)	1·50	50

553 Dancers with Parasols

554 Dr. Robert Koch and Bacillus

1982 (10 Nov)–**83**. *25th Anniv of Bayanihan Folk Arts Centre.* T **553** *and similar horiz design. Multicoloured. Cream chalk-surfaced paper.* W **380**. P 13 × 13½.

1731		40s. Type **553**	20	10
		a. Perf 12½ (white paper) (19 Dec 1983)	50	10
1732		2p.80 Dancers (*different*)	1·80	80
		a. White paper (7 Apr 1983)	2·10	75

1982 (7 Dec)–**83**. *Centenary of Tubercle Bacillus. Cream chalk-surfaced paper.* W **380**. P 13 × 13½.

1733	**554**	40s. vermilion, blue and black	20	10
		a. Imperf (pair)		
1734		2p.80 multicoloured	1·80	80
		a. White paper (10 June 1983)	2·40	90
		b. Red (bacilli) double		
		c. Positive impression in red on back		

See note after No. 1399.

555 Father Christmas in Sleigh

556 Presidental Couples and Flags

1982 (14 Dec)–**83**. *Christmas. Cream chalk-surfaced paper.* W **380**. P 13 × 13½.

1735	**555**	40s. multicoloured	20	15
		a. Black printed double		
		b. White paper (10 Jan 1983)	60	15
1736		1p. multicoloured	75	30
		a. White paper (10 Jan 1983)	1·20	25

1982 (24 Dec)–**83**. *State Visit of Pres. Marcos to United States. Cream chalk-surfaced paper.* W **380**. P 13 × 13½.

1737	**556**	40s. multicoloured	15	15
		a. White paper (22 Apr 1933)	30	15
1738		3p.20 multicoloured	1·30	90
		a. White paper (22 Apr 1983)	2·30	90
		b. Positive impression of yellow on back		
MS1739	76 × 75 mm. Nos. 1737/8. Imperf (27 Dec)		2·75	1·30
		a. White paper (24 Jan 1983)	3·00	1·40
		b. Silver (simulated perfs) omitted		

See note below No. 1399.
First Day Covers of Nos. 1737/8 are dated 18 December.

557 Woman with Sewing Machine

558 Stamp and Magnifying Glass

1982 (28 Dec)–**83**. *United Nations World Assembly on Ageing.* T **557** *and similar vert design. Cream chalk-surfaced paper.* W **380**. P 13½ × 13.

1740	1p.20 myrtle green and orange	75	35
	a. White paper (2 Feb 1983)	70	35
1741	2p. brown-rose and blue	1·50	60
	a. White paper (5 Apr 1983)	1·40	55

Design:—2p. man with carpentry tools.
No. 1740a exists with cream or white gum.
First Day Covers of Nos. 1740/1 are dated 24 December.

1983 (21 Jan). *Philatelic Week.* W **380**. P 13 × 13½.

1742	**558**	40s. multicoloured	20	10
		a. Perf 12½ (21 Oct 1983)	30	10
1743		1p. multicoloured	45	30
		a. Perf 12½ (10 Nov 1983)	90	30

No. 1743a exists with cream or white gum.
First Day Covers of Nos. 1742/3 are dated 28 November 1982.

559 Eulogio Rodriguez

560 Symbolic Figure and Film Frame

1983 (21 Jan)–**84**. *Birth Centenary of Eulogio Rodriguez (former President of Senate). Cream chalk-surfaced paper.* W **380** (*sideways*). P 13½.

1744	**559**	40s. multicoloured	20	10
		a. White paper	25	10
1745		1p.20 multicoloured	75	35
		a. White paper	75	40
		ab. Perf 12½ (2 May 1984)	1·70	40

Nos. 1744a and 1745a exist with cream or white gum.

1983 (24 Jan). *Manila International Film Festival. Cream chalk-surfaced paper.* W **380**. P 13 × 13½.

1746	**560**	40s. multicoloured	20	10
		a. White paper	20	10
		ab. Do. Perf 12½ (10 Nov 1983)	1·10	20
		b. Gold (inscription) omitted		
1747		3p.20 multicoloured	1·50	95
		a. White paper	1·60	90
		ab. Do. Perf 12½ (20 Oct 1983)	2·50	95
		b. Gold (inscription) omitted		

Nos. 1746a and 1747a exist with cream or white gum.

561 Monument

562 Early Printing Press

1983 (18 Feb)–**84**. *Second Anniv of Beatification of Lorenzo Ruiz.* W **380**. P 13 × 13½.

1748	**561**	40s. greenish yellow, carmine-vermilion and black	20	10
		a. Perf 12½ (22 June 1984)	60	10
		b. Imperf (pair)		
1749		1p.20 multicoloured	75	35
		a. Perf 12½ (26 Apr 1984)	1·60	40
		b. Imperf (pair)		
		c. Yellow printed both sides, inverted on back		

Nos. 1748 and 1749 exist with cream or white gum.

(Des C. Fajardo)

1983 (14 Mar). *390th Anniv of First Local Printing Press.* W **380**. P 13 × 13½.

1750	**562**	40s. light green and black	20	10

No. 1750 exists with cream or white gum.

563 Emblem and Ship

(564)

(Des A. T. Chuidian)

1983 (18 Mar). *25th Anniv of International Maritime Organization.* W **380** (*sideways*). P 13½ × 13.

1751	**563**	40s. orange-vermilion, blk & ultram	20	10

No. 1751 exists with cream or white gum.
First Day Covers are dated 17 March.

1983 (14 Apr). *Seventh National Scout Jamboree. No. 1709b optd with T 564 in red.*

1752	**542**	40s. dp bluish green, brt green & black	20	10

First Day Covers are dated 13 April.

=
40^s
(565)

566 Calculator Keys

1983 (15 Apr). *Nos. 1360A/9A surch with T 565 (inverted on Nos. 1758/62).*

1753	**386**	40s.on 45s. bluish green	20	10
		a. Block of 10. Nos. 1753/62	2·40	
1754	**387**	40s.on 45s. bluish green	20	10
1755	**388**	40s.on 45s. bluish green	20	10
1756	**389**	40s.on 45s. bluish green	20	10
1757	**390**	40s.on 45s. bluish green	20	10
1758	**391**	40s.on 45s. bluish green	20	10
1759	**392**	40s.on 45s. bluish green	20	10
1760	**393**	40s.on 45s. bluish green	20	10
1761	**394**	40s.on 45s. bluish green	20	10
1762	**395**	40s.on 45s. bluish green	20	10
1753/1762		*Set of 10*	1·80	90

(Des A. T. Chuidian and V. Castro)

1983 (19 Apr). *11th International Organization of Supreme Audit Institutions Congress. T 566 and similar horiz designs.* W **380** (*upright or sideways on* **MS**). P 13 × 13½.

1763		40s. royal blue, light new blue & silver	20	10
		a. Imperf (pair)		
1764		2p.80 multicoloured	1·80	80
MS1765		77 × 76 mm. Nos. 1763/4. Imperf	2·20	1·50
		a. Bright green (background of 2p.80) omitted		
		b. Red omitted		
		c. Yellow omitted		
		d. Silver omitted		

Design:—2p.80, Congress emblem.
Nos. 1763/**MS**1765 exist with cream or white gum.

567 Smiling Children

568 Detail of Statue

(Des Grafica)

1983 (9 May). *75th Anniv of Philippine Dental Association.* W **380** (*sideways*). P 13½ × 13.
| 1766 | **567** | 40s. lt green, dp magenta & orge- | | |
| | | brn | 20 | 15 |

No. 1766 exists with cream or white gum.

(Des R. S. Austria and E. Rivera)

1983 (17 June–Dec). *75th Anniv of University of Philippines.* T **568** *and similar vert design.* W **380** (*sideways*). P 13½ × 13½.
1767	40s. lake-brown and yellowish green		20	15
	a. Perf 12½ (2 Dec 1983)		75	20
1768	1p.20 multicoloured		65	30
	a. Perf 12½ (12 Dec 1983)		1·30	50

Design:—1p.20, Statue and diamond.

569 Yasuhiro Nakasone and Pres. Marcos

570 Agriculture and Natural Resources

(Des A. T. Chuidian)

1983 (5 July). *Visit of Japanese Prime Minister.* W **380**. P 13 × 13½.
| 1769 | **569** | 40s. multicoloured | 20 | 15 |

No. 1769 exists with cream or white gum.
First Day Covers are dated 20 June.

(Des A. T. Chuidian and A. Divina)

1983 (13 July–Nov). *25th Anniv of National Science and Technology Authority.* T **570** *and similar horiz designs.* *Multicoloured.* W **380**. P 13 × 13½.
1770	40s. Type **570**	30	15
	a. Block of 4. Nos. 1770/3	1·30	
	b. Perf 12½ (3.11)	55	15
	ba. Block of 4. Nos. 1770b/3b	2·30	
1771	40s. Heart, medical products and food (Health and nutrition)	30	15
	b. Perf 12½ (3.11)	55	15
1772	40s. Industrial complex and car (Industry and energy)	30	15
	b. Perf 12½ (3.11)	55	15
1773	40s. House, scientific equipment and book (Sciences and Social science)	30	15
	b. Perf 12½ (3.11)	55	15
1770/1773 *Set of 4*		1·10	55
1770b/1773b *Set of 4*		2·00	55

Nos. 1770/3 and 1770b/3b, respectively, were issued together in *se-tenant* blocks of four within the sheet.
First Day Covers of Nos. 1770/3 are dated 11 July.

571 Globes and W.C.Y. Emblem

572 Postman

(Des A. Chuidian, Jnr)

1983 (24 Oct). *World Communications Year.* W **380**. P 12½.
| 1774 | **571** | 3p.20 multicoloured | 1·90 | 90 |

(Des A. Chuidian, Jnr)

1983 (31 Oct). *Bicentenary of Philippine Postal System.* W **380**. P 12½.
| 1775 | **572** | 40s. multicoloured | 20 | 15 |

573 Woman with Tambourine

574 University Activities

(Des V. Castro)

1983 (15–18 Nov). *Christmas.* T **573** *and similar vert designs.* *Multicoloured.* W **380** (*sideways*). P 12½.
1776	40s. Type **573**	20	15
	a. Strip of 5. Nos. 1776/80	1·20	
	ab. Green ptd both sides. Strip of 5		
	ac. Imperf. Strip of 5		
1777	40s. Man turning spit (left side)	20	15
1778	40s. Pig on spit	20	15
1779	40s. Man turning spit (right side)	20	15
1780	40s. Man with guitar	20	15
1776/1780 *Set of 5*		90	70
MS1781	153 × 77 mm. Nos. 1776/80. Imperf (18 Nov)	1·80	1·80

Nos. 1776/80 were issued together in *se-tenant* strips of five within the sheet, each strip forming a composite design.
Nos. 1776/80 exist with cream or white gum.

1983 (1 Dec). *50th Anniv of Xavier University.* W **380**. P 12½.
| 1782 | **574** | 40s. multicoloured | 20 | 15 |
| 1783 | | 60s. multicoloured | 35 | 15 |

Nos. 1782/3 exist with cream or white gum.

575 Woman casting Vote

576 Workers

(Des A. T. Chuidian)

1983 (7 Dec). *50th Anniv of Female Suffrage.* W **380**. P 12½.
1784	**575**	40s. multicoloured		20	15
1785		60s. multicoloured		35	15

Nos. 1784/5 exist perf 13½ × 13 with "SPECIMEN" overprint.

(Des R. H. Asuncion)

1983 (8 Dec). *50th Anniv of Ministry of Labour and Employment.* W **380**. P 12½.
1786	**576**	40s. multicoloured		20	15
1787		60s. multicoloured		35	15

Nos. 1786/7 exist with cream or white gum.

577 Cutting Stamp from Envelope

578 Red-vented Cockatoo (*Kakatoe haematuropygia*)

1983 (20 Dec). *Philatelic Week.* T **577** and similar horiz designs. *Multicoloured.* W **380**. P 12½.
1788	50s. Type **577**		45	15
	a. Strip of five. Nos. 1788/92		2·40	
1789	50s. Sorting stamps		45	15
1790	50s. Soaking stamps		45	15
1791	50s. Hinging stamps		45	15
1792	50s. Mounting stamp in album		45	15
1788/1792	*Set of 5*		2·00	70

Nos. 1788/92 were issued together in *se-tenant* strips of five within the sheet.
Nos. 1788/92 exist with cream or white gum.
Nos. 1788/92 exist perf 13 × 13½ with "SPECIMEN" overprint.

(Litho Questa)

1984 (9 Jan). *Parrots.* T **578** and similar vert designs. *Multicoloured.* P 14.
1793	40s. Type **578**		60	30
1794	2p.30 Guaiabero (*Bolbopsittacus lunulatus*)		80	30
1795	2p.80 Mountain racket-tailed parrot (*Prioniturus montanus*)		95	35
1796	3p.20 Great-billed parrot (*Tanygnathus megalorynchos*)		1·20	35
1797	3p.60 Müllers's parrot (*Tanygnathus sumatranus*)		1·50	75
1798	5p. Philippine hanging parrot (*Loriculus philippinensis*)		1·30	65
1793/1798	*Set of 6*		5·75	2·40

579 Princess Tarhata Kiram

580 Nun and Congregation

(Des C. Fajardo)

1984 (16 Jan–Apr). *Fifth Death Anniv of Princess Tarhata Kiram.* W **380**. P 13.
1799	**579**	3p. deep green, yellowish grn & scar	75	30
		a. Perf 12½ (2 Apr 1984)	90	30
		b. Scarlet printed double		
		c. Frame printed double		
		d. Face printed double		

No. 1799a exists with cream or white gum.

(Des R. Asuncion)

1984 (23 Jan–Oct). *300th Anniv of Religious Congregation of the Virgin Mary.* W **380** (*sideways*). P 13½ × 13.
1800	**580**	40s. multicoloured	15	15
		a. Perf 12½ (16 Oct 1984)	30	15
1801		60s. multicoloured	15	15
		a. Perf 12½ (6 Mar 1984)	45	15

581 Dona Concha Felix de Calderon

60s
(582)

1984 (9 Feb–Mar). *Birth Centenary of Doña Concha Felix de Calderon.* W **380**. P 13.
1802	**581**	60s. blue-green and black	10	10
		a. Perf 12½ (12 Mar 1984)	30	10
1803		3p.60 blue-green and scarlet	50	15
		a. Perf 12½ (20 Feb 1984)	90	30
		b. Scarlet printed double		

No. 1802 and 1803/a exist with cream or white gum.

1984 (20–22 Feb). *Various stamps surch as T **582**.*
1804	**545**	60s.on 40s. multicoloured (*p* 13½ × 13) (R.)	15	15
		a. Perf 12½	15	15
		b. Inverted positive impression in black on back		
		c. Black of stamp printed double		
1805	**558**	60s.on 40s. multicoloured	15	15
1806	–	3p.60 on 3p.20 chalky blue (1704a) (O.) (22 Feb)	95	30

First Day Covers are dated 20 Feb.

1984 (22 Mar)–85. *As Nos. 1700/4 but values changed, and new designs as T **526**.* W **380**. P 12½ (1p.80, 3p.60, 4p.20) or 13 (others).
1807	60s. chestnut and black		15	10
1808	60s. reddish violet & black (31 Mar 1984)		15	10
1809	60s. black (14 June 1984)		15	10
1810	60s. dull blue (12 Sept 1984)		20	10
	a. Perf 12½ (18 Mar 1985)		35	10
	b. Imperf (pair)			
1811	1p.80 chalky blue (27 Mar 1984)		20	15
1812	2p.40 maroon (27 Mar 1984)		35	15
	a. Perf 12½ (2 May 1984)		45	15
1813	3p. dull brown (7 Sept 1984)		35	15
	a. Perf 12½ (3 Oct 1984)		45	15
1814	3p.60 rose-red (22 × 32 *mm*) (11 May 1984)		50	15
1815	4p.20 bright purple (11 May 1984)		60	20
1807/1815	*Set of 9*		2·40	1·10

Designs:—No. 1807, General Artemio Ricarte; 1808, Teodoro M. Kalaw (politician); 1809, Carlos P. Garcia (fourth President); 1810, Quintin Paredes (senator); 1811, General Vicente Lim; 1812, Professor Nicanor Abelardo; 1813, Francisco Dagohoy; 1814, Aurora Aragon Quezon; 1815, Juan Sumulong.
Nos. 1811, 1812a and 1814 exist with cream or white gum.
First Day Covers of Nos. 1811/12 are dated 26 March.

For Nos. 1810, 1813 (redrawn) and 1814 (size 22 × 30 mm), all with watermark of arms and inscription, see Nos. 1913 and 1915/16.

1984 (27 Mar)–**85**. W **380**. P 13.

1816	542	60s. blue-green, brt green & black		15	15
		a. Perf 12½ (1 Aug 1984)		15	15
		b. Blue-green double			
		c. Black double			
1817		60s. deep bluish green, rosine and black (19 Oct 1984)		15	15
		a. Perf 12½ (8 Mar 1985)		50	15
		ab. Do. Cream chalk-surfaced paper (8 Mar 1985)		1·80	50

On No. 1816c the second impression reads "60 s PILIPINAS"; this impression should be complete and not cut by the perforations.

583 Manila

584 "Lady of the Most Holy Rosary with St. Dominic" (C. Francisco)

1984 (25 Apr–Aug). *150th Anniv of Ayala Corporation.* W **380**. P 13 × 13½.

1818	583	70s. multicoloured		15	10
		a. Perf 12½ (14 Aug 1984)		50	15
1819		3p.60 multicoloured		35	15
		a. Positive impression of "PILIPINAS" on back			

1984 (18 May). *"España 84" International Stamp Exhibition, Madrid.* T **584** and similar horiz designs. Multicoloured. P 14.

1820	2p.50 Type **584**		35	15
	a. Horiz pair. Nos. 1820/1		1·30	60
1821	5p. "Spoliarum" (Juan Luna)		80	35

MS1822 99 × 73 mm. 7p.50, As No. 1821;
7p.50, Virgin of Manila and Spanish galleon;
7p.50, Illustrations from Rizal's *The Monkey and the Turtle*; 7p.50, As No. 1820.
P 14½ × 15 or imperf . . . . . . 8·00 8·00
Nos. 1820/1 were issued together in horizontal *se-tenant* pairs within the sheet.

585 Maria Paz Mendoza Guazon

586 *Euthalia satrapes* (*Adolias amlana*)

1984 (26 May). *Birth Centenary of Dr. Maria Paz Mendoza Guazon.* W **380**. P 13.

1823	585	60s. bright scarlet and new blue	15	10
1824		65s. bright scarlet, black & new blue	15	10
		a. Black printed double		

(Litho Questa)

1984 (10 July). *Butterflies.* T **586** and similar horiz designs. Multicoloured. P 14.

1825	60s. Type **586**		15	10
1826	2p.40 *Papilio daedalus*		50	20

1827	3p. *Prothoe frankii*		65	30
1828	3p.60 *Troides magellanus*		80	30
1829	4p.20 *Yoma sabina*		95	45
1830	5p. *Graphium idaeoides* (*Chilasa idaeoides*)		1·30	50
1825/1830 Set of 6			4·00	1·70

First Day Covers are dated 5 July.

(587)

1984 (18 July–2 Aug). *National Children's Book Day. Stamp from No.* **MS**1822 (*The Monkey and the Turtle*) *surch with* T **587**.

1831	7p.20 on 7p.50 multicoloured (perf)		15·00	8·75
	a. Surch in red on imperf stamp (2 Aug)		15·00	8·75

Nos. 1831, 1832, 1841 and 1846 with black overprint on the *imperforate* stamps come from a second printing, most of which was sent to an overseas agent and not placed on sale in post offices. This agent also received overprinted uncut miniature sheets.

(588)

1984 (3 Aug). *420th Anniv of Philippine–Mexican Friendship. Stamp from No.* **MS**1822 (*Virgin of Manila*) *surch with* T **588**.

1832	7p.20 on 7p.50 multicoloured (perf)		15·00	8·75
	a. Surch in red on imperf stamp		15·00	8·75

See note below No. 1831.

589 Running   **590** The Mansion

1984 (19 Aug). *Olympic Games, Los Angeles.* T **589** and similar vert designs. Multicoloured. P 14.

1833	60s. Type **589**		10	10
1834	2p.40 Boxing		45	20
1835	6p. Swimming		1·20	60
1836	7p.20 Windsurfing		1·50	80
1837	8p.40 Cycling		1·80	90
1838	20p. Running (woman athlete)		4·00	2·20
1833/1838 Set of 6			8·00	4·25

MS1839 87 × 129 mm. 6p. × 4, As Nos. 1834 and 1836/8 . . . . . . 4·75 4·75
Nos. 1833/**MS**1839 have red stars in the design. The stamps and miniature sheet also exist imperf with blue stars, and the stamps imperf with red stars, from limited printings.
First Day Covers are dated 27 July.

1984 (24 Aug). *75th Anniv of Baguio City.* W **380**. P 12½.

1840	590	1p.20 multicoloured	20	15

(591)

1984 (3 Sept). *300th Anniv of Our Lady of Holy Rosary Parish. Stamp from No. MS1822 ("Lady of the Most Holy Rosary with St. Dominic") surch with T 591.*

1841	7p.20 on 7p.50 multicoloured (perf)		30·00	26·00
	a. Surch in red on imperf stamp		30·00	26·00
	b. Error "LADY" for "HOLY" (perf)		48·00	55·00

First Day Covers are dated 1 September.
See note below No. 1831.

592 Electric Train on Viaduct   **593** Australian and Philippine Stamps and Koalas

(Des A Chuidian, Jnr)

1984 (10 Sept). *Light Railway Transit.* W **380**. P 13 × 13½.

1842	**592**	1p.20 multicoloured	45	15
		a. Positive impressions in brown and orange on back		

See note after No. 1399.

(Litho Questa)

1984 (21 Sept). *"Ausipex 84" International Stamp Exhibition, Melbourne.* P 14½ × 15.

1843	**593**	3p. multicoloured	60	30
1844		3p.60 multicoloured	75	30
MS1845	75 × 90 mm. **593** 20p. × 3 multicoloured		24·00	24·00

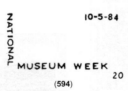

(594)

1984 (5 Oct). *National Museum Week. Stamp from No. MS1822 ("Spoliarum") Surch with T 594.*

1846	7p.20 on 7p.50 multicoloured (perf)		15·00	8·75
	a. Surch in red on imperf stamp		15·00	8·75
	ab. Surch double			

See note below No. 1831.

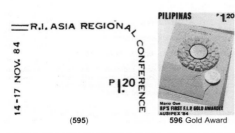

(595)   **596** Gold Award

1984 (14 Nov). *Asia Regional Conference of Rotary International. No. 1728a surch with T 595.*

1847	**551**	1p.20 on 2p.30 multicoloured	20	15

No. 1847 exists with cream or white gum.

1984 (22 Nov). *Philatelic Week. Gold Award at "Ausipec 84" to Mario Que. T 596 and similar vert design. Multicoloured.* W **380** (sideways). P 13½ × 13.

1848	1p.20 Type **596**		20	15
	a. Horiz pair, Nos. 1848/9		75	40
1849	3p. Page of Que's exhibit		45	15

Nos. 1848/9 were issued together in horizontal *se-tenant* pairs within the sheet.
See also Nos. 1879/80.

597 Caracao (canoes)   (598)

1984 (26 Nov). *Water Transport. T 597 and similar horiz designs. Multicoloured.* P 14.

1850	60s. Type **597**		20	15
1851	1p.20 Chinese junk		20	15
1852	6p. Spanish galleon		1·30	60
1853	7p.20 Casco (Filipino cargo prau)		1·50	75
1854	8p.40 Early paddle-steamer		1·60	90
1855	20p. Modern liner		4·00	1·90
1850/1855	Set of 6		8·00	4·00

1984 (28 Nov–7 Dec). *No. MS1666 surch with T 598.*

MS1856	89 × 89 mm. 3p. on 2p. multicoloured	90	90
	a. Surch "P3.00" (7 Dec)	90	90

The values on the stamps within the sheet have also been cancelled with bars.
First Day Covers are dated 20 November.

599 Anniversary Emblem   **600** Virgin and Child

1984 (7 Dec). *125th Anniv of Ateneo de Manila University.* W **380**. P 13 × 13½.

1857	**599**	60s. ultramarine and gold	20	15
1858		1p.20 ultramarine and silver	35	20

1984 (8 Dec). *Christmas. T 600 and similar vert design. Multicoloured.* W **380**. P 13½ × 13.

1859	60s. Type **600**		15	10
	a. Horiz pair. Nos. 1859/60		65	30
1860	1p.20 Holy Family		35	20

Nos. 1859/60 were issued in horizontal *se-tenant* pairs within the sheet.

601 Manila–Dagupan Steam Locomotive, 1892

602 Abstract

(Litho Questa)

1984 (18 Dec). *Rail Transport. T* **601** *and similar horiz designs. Multicoloured.* P 14.

1861	60s. Type **601**		20	15
1862	1p.20 Light Railway Transit train, 1984		20	15
1863	6p. Bicol express, 1955		1·30	60
1864	7p.20 Electric tram, 1905		1·50	75
1865	8p.40 Diesel commuter railcar, 1972		1·60	90
1866	20p. Horse-tram, 1898		4·00	1·90
1861/1866 *Set of 6*			8·00	4·00

1984 (19 Dec). *Tenth Anniv of Philippine Jaycees' Ten Outstanding Young Men Awards. T* **602** *and similar vert designs showing abstracts by Raul G. Isidro. Multicoloured.* W **380**. P 13½ × 13.

1867	60s. deep brown background in circle		15	10
	a. Strip of 10. Nos. 1867/76	3·25		
1868	60s. Type **602**		15	10
1869	60s. carmine-red background		15	10
1870	60s. blue and purple background		15	10
1871	60s. orange and drab background		15	10
1872	3p. As No. 1867		45	30
1873	3p. Type **602**		45	30
1874	3p. As No. 1869		45	30
1875	3p. As No. 1870		45	30
1876	3p. As No. 1871		45	30
1867/1876 *Set of 10*			2·75	1·80

Nos. 1867/76 were issued together in *se-tenant* strips of ten within the sheet.

Nos. 1867/76 exist with cream or white gum.

603 Tobacco Plant and Dried Leaf   (**604**)

Philatelic Week 1984

1985 (14 Jan). *25th Anniv of Philippine Virginia Tobacco Administration.* W **380**. P 13 × 13½.

1877	**603**	30s. multicoloured	15	10
1878		3p. multicoloured	60	30

1985 (25 Jan). *Philatelic Week, 1984. Nos. 1848/9 optd with T* **604**.

1879	1p.20 multicoloured		20	15
	a. Horiz pair. Nos. 1879/80		80	50
1880	3p. multicoloured		50	35

Nos. 1879/80 were issued in horizontal *se-tenant* pairs within the sheet.

605 National Research Council Emblem

606 *Carmona retusa*

1985 (3 Feb). *Fifth Pacific Science Association Congress.* W **380**. P 13 × 13½.

1881	**605**	60s. black, royal blue and new blue	15	10
1882		1p.20 black, royal blue & brt orge	45	20

1985 (18 Mar–Aug). *Medicinal Plants. T* **606** *and similar horiz designs. Multicoloured.* W **380**. P 12½.

1883	60s. Type **606** (18 Mar)		20	10
	a. Perf 13 × 13½		15	10
1884	1p.20 *Orthosiphon aristatus*		20	15
	a. Perf 13 × 13½ (2 Aug)		20	15
1885	2p.40 *Vitex negundo*		45	30
	a. Perf 13 × 13½ (2 Aug)		60	30
1886	3p. *Aloe barbadensis*		60	35
	a. Perf 13 × 13½ (30 July)		90	30
1887	3p.60 *Quisqualis indica* (18 Mar)		1·30	45
	a. Perf 13 × 13½		65	45
1888	4p.20 *Blumea balsamifera*		90	50
	a. Perf 13 × 13½ (7 Aug)		1·30	50
1883/1888 *Set of 6* (*cheapest*)			3·25	1·60

Nos. 1887/a exist with cream or white gum.

1985 (22 Mar–May). *Vert designs as T* **526**. W **380**. P 13.

1889	60s. blackish brown		20	10
	a. Perf 12½		20	10
1890	60s. deep rose-red (21 May)		20	10

Designs:—No. 1889, Dr. Deogracias V. Villadolid; 1890, Santiago Fonacier (former Senator and army chaplain).

For No. 1890 with watermark arms and inscription, see No. 1914.

Nos. 1891/5 are vacant.

607 "Early Bird" Satellite

1985 (8 Apr). *20th Anniv of International Telecommunications Satellite Organization.* W **380**. P 13 × 13½.

1896	**607**	60s. multicoloured	15	10
1897		3p. multicoloured	60	30

First Day Covers are dated 6 April.

608 Piebalds

609 Emblem

(Litho Format)

1985 (12 Apr). *Horses. T* **608** *and similar horiz designs. Multicoloured.* P 14.

1898	60s. Type **608**	20	15
1899	1p.20 Palominos	20	15
1900	6p. Bays	1·30	60
1901	7p.20 Browns	1·50	75
1902	8p.40 Greys	1·60	90
1903	20p. Chestnuts	4·00	1·90
1898/1903 *Set of 6*		8·00	4·00
MS1904 123 × 84 mm. 8p.40 × 4, As Nos. 1899/1901 and 1903		8·75	8·75

1985 (22 Apr). *25th Anniv of National Tax Research Centre.* W **380** (*sideways*). P 13½ × 13.

1905	**609** 60s. multicoloured	15	10

610 Transplanting Rice

611 Image of Holy Child of Cebu

1985 (27 May–Dec). *25th Anniv of International Rice Research Institute, Los Baños. T* **610** *and similar horiz design. Multicoloured.* W **380**. P 13 × 13½.

1906	60s. Type **610**	15	10
	a. Perf 12½ (16 Dec)	75	
1907	3p. Paddy fields	35	20

(Des A. Chuidian, Jnr)

1985 (4 June). *420th Anniv of Filipino–Spanish Treaty. T* **611** *and similar horiz design. Multicoloured.* W **380**. P 12½.

1908	1p.20 Type **611**	20	15
	a. Horiz pair. Nos. 1908/9	70	30
	ab. Imperf (pair)		
1909	3p.60 Rajah Tupas and Miguel Lopez de Legazpi signing treaty	45	15

Nos. 1908/9 were issued together in *se-tenant* pairs within sheets of forty stamps and ten half stamp-size labels depicting Cebu city seal.

10th ANNIVERSARY
PHILIPPINES
AND
PEOPLE'S REPUBLIC OF CHINA
DIPLOMATIC RELATIONS

1975 - 1985

(**612**) (¾-size illustration)

1985 (8–11 June). *Tenth Anniv of Diplomatic Relations with Chinese People's Republic. No.* **MS**1661 *optd with T* **612**.

MS1910 78 × 78 mm. 5p. multicoloured (apostrophe added by hand)	2·75	2·75
a. Apostrophe printed (11 June)	2·30	2·30

The first printing had the apostrophe in "People's" omitted and this was added by hand and thus varies. Later printings had the error corrected.

A limited quantity of the corrected overprint exist on heavily varnished paper.

613 Early Anti-TB Label

1985 (29 July). *75th Anniv of Philippine Tuberculosis Society. T* **613** *and similar horiz design. Multicoloured.* W **380**. P 13 × 13½.

1911	60s. Type **613**	15	10
	a. Pair. Nos. 1911/12	50	30
1912	1p.20 Screening for TB, laboratory work, health education and inoculation	30	20

Nos. 1911/12 were issued together in *se-tenant* pairs within the sheet.

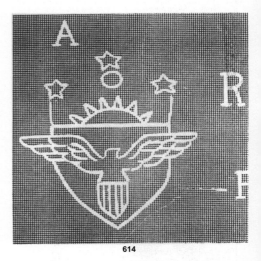

614

W **614**. With two groups of inscriptions (each side of arms) each in three lines: "REPUBLIKA NG PILIPINAS" and "KAWANIHAN NG KOREO"; and other spaced letters between each horizontal row of arms.

1985 (12 Aug)–**86**. *As Nos.* 1810, 1890 *and* 1813/14 *but* W **614**, *Nos.* 1915/16 *also redrawn.* P 13.

1913	60s. dull blue	20	10
	a. Perf 12½ (4 Sept 1986)	30	10
1914	60s. deep rose-red (26 Nov 1985)	20	15
1915	3p. brown (16 Dec 1985)	65	25
1916	3p.60 rose-red (22 × 30 *mm*) (14 Feb 1986)	1·00	35
1913/1916 *Set of 4*		1·90	75

The 3p.60 on unwatermarked paper is a postal forgery.

ANNIVERSARY GIRL SCOUT CHARTER
(615)

1985 (19 Aug). *45th Anniv of Girl Scout Charter. No. 1409 surch as T* **615**, *in gold and black.*

1917	**348**	2p.40 on 15s. on 10s. multicoloured	30	20
1918		4p.20 on 15s. on 10s. multicoloured	60	30
		a. Gold opt double		
1919		7p.20 on 15s. on 10s. multicoloured	95	45

616 "Our Lady of Fatima"

617 Family planting Tree

(Des M. Melchor. Litho)

1985 (8 Sept). *Marian Year. 2000th Birth Anniv of Virgin Mary. T* **616** *and similar vert designs. Multicoloured.* W **380** (*sideways*). P 13½ × 13.

1920	**616**	1p.20 Type **616**	20	15
		a. Gold (frame) omitted		
1921		2p.40 "Our Lady of Beaterio" (Juan Bueno Silva)	30	15
1922		3p. "Our Lady of Peñafrancia"	35	20
1923		3p.60 "Our Lady of Guadalupe"	60	30
1920/1923	*Set of 4*		1·30	75

(Des A. Chuidian, Jnr)

1985 (9 Sept). *Tree Week. International Year of the Forest.* W **380** (*sideways*). P 13½ × 13.

1924	**617**	1p.20 multicoloured	20	15
		a. Perf 12½ (wmk upright)	2·10	1·20

The initial delivery, perforated 12½, was mainly used for presentation purposes including First Day Covers dated 9 June. Remaining stock was sold with the later delivery, perforated 13½ × 13, in September.

618 Battle of Bessang Pass

619 Vicente Orestes Romualdez

1985 (19 Sept–Dec). *40th Anniv of Bessang Pass Campaign.* W **380** (*upright or sideways*). P 13 × 13½.

1925	**618**	1p.20 multicoloured	20	15
		a. Perf 12½ (13 Dec)	1·60	25

First Day Covers are dated 14 June.

(Des C. Fajardo. Litho)

1985 (19 Sept). *Birth Centenary of Vicente Orestes Romualdez (lawyer).* W **380**. P 13.

1926	**619**	60s. deep turquoise-blue	90	15
		a. Perf 12½	25	10
1927		2p. bright magenta	1·20	35
		a. Perf 12½	30	15

First Day Covers are dated 19 September.

620 Fishing

621 Banawe Rice Terraces

1985 (23 Sept). *International Youth Year. T* **620** *and similar horiz design showing children's paintings. Multicoloured.* W **380**. P 13 × 13.

1928		2p.40 Type 620	30	15
		a. Imperf (pair)		
1929		3p.60 Picnic	50	15

The watermark on No. 1929 exists upright or sideways.

1985 (30 Sept–Dec). *World Tourism Organization Congress, Sofia, Bulgaria.* W **380**. P 13 × 13½.

1930	**621**	2p.40 multicoloured	30	20
		a. Perf 12½ (9 Dec)	95	10

First Day Covers are dated 26 September.

622 Export Graph and Crane lifting Crate

(623) (bars 4 mm long)

1985 (8 Oct). *Export Promotion Year.* W **380** (*sideways*). P 13½ × 13.

1931	**622**	1p.20 multicoloured	20	15

1985 (21 Oct)–**86**. *No. 1815 surcharged with T* **623**.

1932		3p.60 on 4p.20 bright purple	75	35
		a. Bars 6 mm long (27 Nov 1985)	80	35
		ab. Perf 13 (10 Jan 1986)	4·00	90

The 4 mm long bars are found extended by hand.
No. 1932ab is not knuwn to exist unsurcrarged.

624 Emblem and Dove with Olive Branch

625 Martin M-130 Flying Boat *China Clipper*

1985 (24 Oct). *40th Anniv of United Nations Organization.* W **380** (sideways). P 13½ × 13.
1933 **624** 3p.60 multicoloured 45 20
    a. Imperf (pair) . . . .

(Des A. Chuidian and A. Divina)

1985 (22 Nov). *50th Anniv of First Trans-Pacific Commercial Flight (San Francisco–Manila). T* **625** *and similar horiz design. Multicoloured.* W **380**. P 13 × 13½.
1934 3p. Type **625** 35 20
1935 3p.60 Route map, *China Clipper* and
    anniversary emblem 50 20

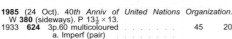

60ˢ

(626)

1985 (24 Nov). *Philatelic Week. Nos. 1863/4 surch as T* **626**.

(a) POSTAGE.
1936 60s.on 6p. multicoloured 15 10

(b) AIR. Additionally optd "AIRMAIL".
1937 3p.on 7p.20 multicoloured 60 30

627 Bible and Churches

628 Panuluyan (enactment of search for an inn)

(Des D. Laurente and M. David)

1985 (3 Dec). *National Bible Week.* W **380**. P 12½.
1938 **627** 60s. multicoloured 15 10
1939 3p. multicoloured 60 30

(Des R. Asuncion)

1985 (9 Dec). *Christmas. T* **628** *and similar horiz design. Multicoloured.* W **380**. P 13 × 13½.
1940 60s. Type **628** 15 10
    a. Perf 12½ . . . . 1·50 35
1941 3p. Pagdalaw (nativity) 60 30
    a. Perf 12½ . . . . 2·50 90
First Day Covers are dated 8 December.

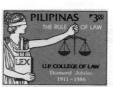

629 Justice holding Scales

630 Rizal and *Noli Me Tangere*

(Des R. Asuncion)

1986 (12 Jan). *75th Anniv of College of Law. T* **629** *and similar horiz designs.* W **380**. P 13 × 13½.
1942 **629** 60s. magenta and black 15 10
1943 3p. brt yellowish green, dp clar &
    blk 60 30
  See also No. 2009.

1986 (21 Feb–July). *Centenary of Publication of Noli Me Tangere (José Rizal's first book). T* **630** *and similar vert design.* W **614**. P 13.
1944 60s. deep reddish violet 10 10
1945 1p.20 deep bluish green 30 20
1946 3p.60 red-brown (14 July) 65 30
  Design:—1p.20, 3p.60, Rizal, *To the Flowers of Heidelberg* (poem) and Heidelberg University.
  Nos. 1944/5 exist on paper with watermark **380** from a limited printing. First Day Covers of No. 1946 are dated 10 July.

631 Douglas DC-3, 1946

632 Oil Refinery, Manila Bay

1986 (15 Mar). *45th Anniv of Philippine Airlines. T* **631** *and similar horiz designs, each scarlet, black and deep ultramarine.* W **614** *(sideways).* P 13.
1947 60s. Type **631** 15 15
    a. Block of 4. Nos. 1947/50 . . 75
1948 60s. Douglas DC-4, 1946 . . . . . . 15 15
1949 60s. Douglas DC-6, 1948 . . . . . . 15 15
1950 60s. Vickers Viscount 784, 1957 . . . 15 15
1951 2p.40 Fokker F.27 Friendship, 1960 . . 50 20
    a. Block of 4. Nos. 1951/4 . . 2·20
1552 2p.40 Douglas DC-8-50, 1962 . . . . 50 20
1953 2p.40 B.A.C. One Eleven 500, 1964 . . 50 20
1954 2p.40 Douglas DC-10-30, 1974 . . . . 50 20
1955 3p.60 Beech 18, 1941 . . . . . . 75 35
    a. Pair. Nos. 1955/6 . . . . 1·60 75
1956 3p.60 Boeing 747/200, 1980 . . . . 75 35
1947/1956 *Set of* 10 . . . . . . 3·75 1·90
  Nos. 1947/50 and 1951/4 were issued together in *se-tenant* blocks of four stamps and Nos. 1955/6 in *se-tenant* pairs within their respective sheets.
  Nos. 1947/56 on paper with watermark **380** were used for presentation purposes.
  The 3p.60 on unwatermarked paper is a postal forgery.
  See also No. 2013.

(Des Graphic Atelier)

1986 (12 Apr–July). *25th Anniv of Bataan Refinery Corporation. T* **632** *and similar design.* W **380** (*sideways on* 60s.). P 13½ × 13 (60s.) or 13 × 13½ (3p.).

1957	60s. silver and emerald		15	10
	a. Wmk **614** (23 July)		25	10
1958	3p. silver and blue (*horiz*)		50	20
	a. Wmk **614** (23 July)		60	20

Design: *Horiz*—3p. Refinery (*different*).

633 Emblem

634 Emblem and Industrial and Agricultural Symbols

1986 (2 May). *"Expo 86" World's Fair, Vancouver.* W **614**. P 13 × 13½.

1959	**633**	60s. multicoloured	15	10
1960		3p. multicoloured	60	30

Nos. 1959/60 on paper with watermark **380** were used to prepare special folders for sale at the exhibition.

(Des Maria Carmela Escasa)

1986 (15 May–July). *25th Anniv of Asian Productivity Organization.* W **614**.

(a) Size 37 × 27 mm. P 13 × 13½.

1961	**634**	60s. grey-black, brt green & yell-orge	15	10
1962		3p. black, brt green & reddish orge	60	30

(b) Size 30 × 22 mm. P 13 (14 July).

1963	**634**	3p. light brown	65	30

First Day Covers of No. 1963 are dated 10 July.
Nos. 1961/2 on paper with watermark **380** were used for presentation purposes.

636 (½-*size illustration*)

1986 (22 May). *"Ameripex 86" International Stamp Exhibition, Chicago. T* **635** *and similar vert design.* W **614** (*sideways*). P 13½ × 13.

1964	60s. yellowish green, blk & greenish yell		15	10
1965	3p. olive-bistre, black and apple green		60	30

Design:—3p. 1935 20c. stamp.
Nos. 1964/5 exist on paper with watermark **380** from a limited printing.
See also No. 2006.

(Des R. Asuncion and A. Chuidian, Jnr)

1986 (27 May–Aug). *"People Power". T* **637** *and similar multicoloured designs.* W **380** (*sideways*). P 13½ × 13.

1966	60s. Type **637**		15	10
	a. Wmk **636** (15 Aug)		15	10
1967	1p.20 Radio antennae, helicopter and people		20	15
	a. Wmk **636** (15 Aug)		35	15
1968	2p.40 Religious procession		45	20
	a. Wmk **636** (15 Aug)		50	15
1969	3p. Crowds around soldiers in tanks		50	20
	a. Wmk **636** (15 Aug)		65	15
1966/1969	*Set of 4* (*cheapest*)		1·20	60

MS1970 76 × 76 mm. 7p.20, Crowd, Pres. Aquino and Vice-Pres. Laurel (42 × 32 *mm*).

	Imperf	2·20	2·20
	a. W **636** (*sideways*) (15 Aug)	2·20	2·20

First Day Covers are dated 25 May.

635 1906 2c. Stamp

637 Corazon Aquino, Salvador Laurel and Hands

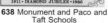

638 Monument and Paco and Taft Schools

639 Aquino praying

1986 (16 June). *75th Anniv of First La Salle School in Philippines. T* **638** *and similar horiz designs.* W **614**. P 13 × 13½.

1971	60s. brownish black, rose-lilac & emerald		15	15
	a. Emerald printed double			
1972	2p.40 brownish black, new bl & emer		45	20
	a. Emerald printed double			

1973   3p. brownish black, olive-yellow &
      emer 50   20
MS1974 75 × 75 mm. 7p.20, brownish black and
      emerald. Imperf . . . . 4·50   4·50
      Designs:—2p.40, St. Miguel Febres Cordero and Paco school;
3p. St. Benilde and Taft school; 7p.20, Founding brothers of Paco
school.

(Des A. Chuidian and R. Asuncion)

1986 (21 Aug). *Third Death Anniv of Benigno S. Aquino,
Jnr. T* **639** *and similar horiz designs and vert design as T* **526**.
W **636** (*sideways on* 1975/6). P 13½ × 13 (vert) or 13 × 13½
(horiz).
1975   60s. deep bluish green 15   15
1976   2p. multicoloured 30   15
1977   3p.60 multicoloured 65   30
MS1978 75 × 75 mm. 10p. multicoloured.
      Imperf . . . . 2·50   2·50
      Designs: 27 × 36 *mm* (*as T* **526**)—60s. Aquino. *Horiz* (*as T*
639)—3p.60, Aquino (*different*); 10p. Crowd and Aquino.
      See also No. 2007.

640 *Vanda sanderiana*   **641** "Christ carrying
                             the Cross"

1986 (28 Aug). *Orchids. T* **640** *and similar vert designs.
Multicoloured.* W **636** (*sideways*). P 13½ × 13.
1979   60s. Type **640** 15   10
1980   1p.20 *Epigeneium lyonii* . . . 50   15
1981   2p.40 *Paphiopedilum philippinense* . 90   20
1982   3p. *Amesiella philippinense* . . 1·10   20
1979/1982 *Set of 4* . . . . 2·40   60

1986 (29 Aug). *400th Anniv of Quiapo District. T* **641** *and similar
design.* W **614** (*sideways on* 60s.). P 13½ × 13 (60s.) or 13 × 13½
(3p.60).
1983   60s. carmine-lake, black and
      magenta 15   10
1984   3p.60 dull ultramarine, black & brt
      grn 60   30
      Design: *Horiz*—3p.60, Quiapo Church.

642 Hospital   **643** Comet and Earth

1986 (1 Sept). *75th Anniv or Philippine General Hospital.* W **614**
(*sideways*). P 13.
1985   **642**   60s. multicoloured 15   15
1986   3p. multicoloured 50   20
      See also No. 2012.

1986 (25 Sept). *Appearance of Halley's Comet. T* **643** *and similar
horiz design. Multicoloured.* W **636**. P 13 × 13½.
1987   60s. Type **643** 10   10
1988   2p.40 Comet, Moon and Earth . . . 45   30

644 Handshake   **645** Emblem

(Des A. Chuidian and R. Asuncion)

1986 (10 Nov). *74th International Dental Federation Congress,
Manila. T* **644** *and similar horiz design. Multicoloured.* W **636**
(*sideways on* 60s.). P 13 × 13½.
1989   60s. Type **644** 15   10
1990   3p. Jeepney, Manila 75   35
      See also Nos. 2008 and 2011.

(Des A. Chuidian and R. Asuncion)

1986 (28 Nov). *75th Anniv of Manila Young Men's Christian
Association.* W **614**. P 13.
1991   **645**   2p. new blue 45   15
1992   3p.60 scarlet 65   35
      See also Nos. 2010 and 2058.

646 Old and New Buildings   **647** Butterfly and Beetles

(Des A. Chuidian)

1986 (12 Dec). *85th Anniv of Philippine Normal College. T* **646**
and similar horiz design. W **636**. P 13 × 13½.
1993   60s. multicoloured 15   10
      a. Imperf (pair) . . . .
1994   3p.60 bright lemon, deep yellow brown
      and dull ultramarine 90   45
      Design:—3p.60, Old and new buildings (*different*).

(Des A. Chuidian and R. Asuncion)

1986 (20 Dec). *Philatelic Week and International Peace
Year. T* **647** *and similar designs.* W **636**. P 13½ × 13 (1p.) or
13 × 13½ (others).
1995   60s. multicoloured 15   10
1996   1p. new blue and black 20   15
1997   3p. multicoloured 75   35
      Designs: *Vert*—1p. Peace Year emblem. *Horiz*—3p.
Dragonflies.
      First Day Covers are dated 21 November.

648 Mother and Child   (**649**)

(Des R. Asuncion)

1986 (20 Dec). *Christmas. T* **648** *and similar multicoloured designs.* W **636** (*sideways on 60s.*). P 13½ × 13 (vert) or 13 × 13½ (horiz).

1998		60s. Type **648**	15	10
1999		60s. Couple with child and cow	15	10
2000		60s. Mother and child with doves	15	10
2001		1p. Mother and child receiving gifts (*horiz*)	30	15
2002		1p. Mother and child beneath arch (*horiz*)	30	15
2003		1p. Madonna and shepherd adoring child (*horiz*)	30	15
2004		1p. Shepherds and animals around child in manger (*horiz*)	30	15
1998/2004		*Set of 7*	1·50	80

First Day Covers are dated 15 December.

1987 (6 Jan). *No.* 1944 *surch with T* **649**.

2005	**630**	1p.on 60s. deep reddish violet	15	10

1987 (16 Jan–30 Mar). *As previous issues but values changed and smaller,* 22 × 30 *mm or* 32 × 22 *mm* (5p.50). W **614** (*sideways on horiz designs*).

2006	–	75s. yell-grn (as No. 1965) (30 Mar)	15	10
2007	–	1p. new blue (as No. 1975) (5 Feb)	20	15
2008	**644**	3p.25 deep bluish green (30 Mar)	75	15
2009	**629**	3p.50 lake-brown (5 Mar)	80	15
2010	**645**	4p. new blue (20 Jan)	75	15
2011	–	4p.75 dull yellowish green (as No. 1990)	1·10	15
2012	**642**	5p. drab (5 Mar)	1·10	15
2013	–	5p.50 deep blue (as No. 1956)	1·10	20
2006/2013		*Set of 8*	5·25	1·10

First Day Covers for all values are dated 16 January.

Nos. 2007, 2010 and 2013 perf 11½ without watermark or with papermaker's sheet watermark are postal forgeries.

No. 2010 has an imprint date "1-1-87" at foot. For slightly smaller version without imprint date see No. 2058.

650 Manila Hotel, 1912

651 Emblem

(Des A. Chuidian)

1987 (30 Jan). *75th Anniv of Manila Hotel. T* **650** *and similar horiz designs.* W **636** (*sideways*). P 13 × 13½.

2014		1p. olive-bistre and black	20	15
2015		4p. multicoloured	75	35
2016		4p.75 multicoloured	90	45
2017		5p.50 multicoloured	1·10	50
2014/2017		*Set of 4*	2·75	1·30

Designs:—4p. Hotel; 4p.75, Lobby; 5p.50, Staff in ante-lobby.

(Des R. Asuncion)

1987 (9 Feb). *50th Anniv of International Eucharistic Congress, Manila. T* **651** *and similar multicoloured design.* W **636** (*sideways on 1p.*). P 13½ × 13 (75s.) or 13 × 13½ (1p.)

2018		75s. Type **651**	15	10
2019		1p. Emblem (*different*) (*horiz*)	30	15

First Day Covers are dated 7 February.

652 Pres. Cory Aquino taking Oath

653 Dr. José Laurel (founder) and Tower

1987 (4 Mar). *Ratification of New Constitution. T* **652** *and similar design.* W **636** (*sideways on 1p.*). P 13 × 13½ (1p.) or 13½ × 13 (5p.50).

2020		1p. multicoloured	20	15
2021		5p.50 new blue and orange brown	1·20	60

Design: *Vert*—5p.50, Constitution on open book and dove.

Stamps as No. 2021 but rouletted and without watermark are postal forgeries.

See also No. 2060.

1987 (7 Mar). *35th Anniv of Lyceum.* W **636** (*sideways*). P 13 × 13½.

2022	**653**	1p. multicoloured	20	10
2023		2p. multicoloured	60	15

654 City Seal, Man with Philippine Eagle and Woman with Fruit

655 Salary and Policy Loans

1987 (16 Mar). *50th Anniv of Davao City.* W **636** (*sideways*). P 13 × 13½.

2024	**654**	1p. multicoloured	15	10

1987 (1 June). *50th Anniv of Government Service Insurance System. T* **655** *and similar vert designs. Multicoloured.* W **636**. P 13½ × 13.

2025		1p. Type **655**	20	15
2026		1p.25 Disability and medicare	20	15
2027		2p. Retirement benefits	35	20
2028		3p.50 Survivorship benefits	65	35
2025/2028		*Set of 4*	1·25	75

656 Emblem and People in Hand

657 Woman, Ballot Box and Map

1987 (13 July). *50th Anniv of Salvation Army in Philippines.* W **636**. P 13½ × 13.

2029	**656**	1p. multicoloured	30	10

First Day Covers are dated 5 June.

1987 (15 July). *50th Anniv of League of Women Voters.* W **636**. P 13½ × 13.

2030	**657**	1p. blue and magenta	15	10

1987 (31 July–Dec). *Vert designs as T* **526**. W **614**. P 12½ (2032) or 13 (others).

2031	1p. olive-green			15	10
2032	1p. greenish blue (9 Sept)			15	10
	a. Perf 13 (16 Nov)			1·20	15
2033	1p. Venetian red (11 Oct)			15	10
2034	1p. dp reddish purple & brt carm				
	(17 Dec)			15	10
2031/2034 *Set of* 4				55	35

Designs:—No. 2031, Gen. Vicente Lukban; 2032, Wenceslao Q. Vinzons; 2033, Brigadier-General Mateo Capinpin; 2034, Jesus Balmori.

First Day Covers of No. 2033 are dated 15 October and of 2034, 28 December.

658 Map and Flags as Leaves

659 Man with Outstretched Arm

1987 (7 Aug). *20th Anniv of Association of South-East Asian Nations.* W **636**. P 13 × 13½.

2035	**658**	1p. multicoloured	30	10

1987 (11 Aug). *Exports. T* **659** *and similar horiz design.* W **614** (*sideways*). P 13.

2036	1p. multicoloured		15	10
2037	2p. brt green, orange-yellow & red-brown		30	15

Design:—2p. Man, cogwheel and factory.
See also No. 2059.

660 Nuns, People and Crucifix within flaming Heart

661 Statue and Stained Glass Window

1987 (21 Aug). *125th Anniv of Daughters of Charity in the Philippines.* W **636**. P 13½ × 13.

2038	**660**	1p. blue, bright rose-red and black	20	10

First Day Covers are dated 22 July.

1987 (15 Oct). *Canonization of Blessed Lorenzo Ruiz de Manila (first Filipino saint). T* **661** *and similar vert design. Multicoloured.* W **636** (*sideways*). P 13½ × 13.

2039	1p. Type **661**	20	15
2040	5p.50 Lorenzo Ruiz praying before execution	1·30	35
MS2041 56 × 56 mm. 8p. As No. 2040. Imperf		1·80	1·80
	a. Gold printed double		

First Day Covers are dated 10 October.

P4.75
——
(662)

663 Nun and Emblem

1987 (12 Oct). *No. 2012 surch with T* **662**.

2042	**642**	4p.75 on 5p. drab	95	15

1987 (27 Oct). *75th Anniv of Good Shepherd Sisters in Philippines.* W **636**. P 13 × 13½.

2043	**663**	1p. multicoloured	20	10

664 Founders

665 Family with Stamp Album

1987 (29 Oct). *50th Anniv of Philippines Boy Scouts.* W **636**. P 13 × 13½.

2044	**664**	1p. multicoloured	20	10

First Day Covers are dated 28 October.

1987 (7 Nov). *50th Anniv of Philippines Philatelic Club.* W **636**. P 13 × 13½.

2045	**665**	1p. multicoloured	20	10

666 Monks, Church and Wrecked Galleon

667 Flags

(Des J. Pullilo)

1987 (11 Nov). *400th Anniv of Dominican Order in Philippines. T* **666** *and similar designs.* W **636** (*sideways on* 1p.). P 13½ × 13 (1p.) or 13 × 13½ (others).

2046	1p. black, greenish blue & bright orange		15	15
2047	4p.75 multicoloured		80	30
2048	5p.50 multicoloured		1·30	45

Designs: *Horiz*—4p.75, J. A. Jeronimo Guerrero, Diego de Sta. Maria and Letran Dominican College; 5p.50, Pope and monks.

1987 (10 Dec). *Third Association of South-East Asian Nations Summit Meeting.* W **636**. P 13 × 13½.

2049	**667**	4p. multicoloured	95	10

First Day Covers are dated 5 December.

Philippine Postal Service
Pasko 1987

668 Dove with Letter

669 Emblem, Headquarters and Dr. Rizal

1987 (8 Dec). *Christmas. T* **668** *and similar vert designs. Multicoloured.* W **636** (*sideways*). P 13½ × 13.

2050	1p. Type **668**		15	15
2051	1p. People and star decoration		15	15
2052	4p. Crowd going to church		80	20
2053	4p.75 Mother and children exchanging gifts		80	30
2054	5p.50 Children and bamboo cannons		1·20	30
2055	8p. Children at table bearing festive fare		1·50	50
2056	9p.50 Woman at table		1·60	65
2057	11p. Woman having Christmas meal		1·90	65
2050/2057 *Set of 8*			7·25	2·50

1987 (17 Dec). *As previous issues but redrawn (4p.), new value and colour (4p.75) or smaller, 22 × 31 mm, and changed colour (5p.50).* W **614**. P 13.

2058	**645**	4p. new blue (21½ × 29 *mm*)	70	45
2059	–	4p.75 new blue & blk (as No. 2037)	65	15
2060	–	5p.50 bright green and yellow-brown (as No. 2021)	80	15

No. 2058 has the value redrawn, the imprint date omitted and vertical instead of diagonal dots as background shading.
First Day Covers of Nos. 2059/60 are dated 16 December.
The 5p.50 rouletted is a postal forgery.

1987 (19 Dec)–**88**. *75th Anniv of Grand Lodge of Philippine Masons.* W **636**. P 13 × 13½.

2061	**669**	1p. multicoloured	30	10
		a. Wmk **380** (1 Aug 1988)	1·60	15

670 Foodstuffs in Split Globe

671 Official Seals and Gavel

1987 (28 Dec). *40th Anniv of United Nations Organization. T* **670** *and similar horiz designs. Multicoloured.* W **636**. P 13 × 13½.

2062	1p. Type **670** (International Fund for Argricultural Development)		20	15
	a. Horiz strip. Nos. 2062/5 plus label			
	ab. Blue printed double (strip)			
2063	1p. Means of transport and communications (Asian and Pacific Transport and Communications Decade)		20	15
2064	1p. Family and hands holding houses (International Year of Shelter for the Homeless)		20	15
2065	1p. Happy children playing musical instruments (World Health Day: child vaccination campaign)		20	15
2062/2065 *Set of 4*			70	55

Nos. 2062/5 were issued together in horizontal *se-tenant* strips of four stamps plus one label bearing the U.N. emblem.
First Day Covers are dated 22 December.
Nos. 2062/5 exist imperforate from a limited printing.

1988 (25 Jan). *Opening Session of* 1987 *Congress. T* **671** *and similar multicoloured design.* W **636** (*sideways on* 1p.). P 13½ × 13 (1p.) or 13 × 13½ (5p.50).

2066	1p. Type **671**	20	10
2067	5p.50 Congress in session and gavel (*horiz*)	1·40	45

672 Children and Bosco

673 Emblem

1988 (1 Feb–Aug). *Death Centenary of St. John Bosco (founder of Salesian Brothers).* W **636**. P 13 × 13½.

2068	**672**	1p. multicoloured	15	10
		a. wmk **380** (13 July)	60	20
2069		5p.50 multicoloured	1·20	45
		a. Wmk **380** (1 Aug)	85	55

First Day Covers of Nos. 2068/9 are dated 31 January.

1988 (1 Feb–June). *Buy Philippine-Made Movement Month.* W **636** (*sideways*). P 13½ × 13.

2070	**673**	1p. multicoloured	15	15
		a. Wmk **380** (sideways) (3 June)	15	15
		ab. Red printed double		

P 3.00 ═══
(674)

675 Envelope with Coded Addresses

1988 (15 Feb–2 Mar). *Various stamps surch as T* **674**.

2071	–	3p.on 3p.60 brown (No. 1946)	50	20
2072	**645**	3p.on 3p.60 scarlet	60	20
2073	–	3p.on 3p.60 multicoloured (No. 1977) (17 Feb)	75	30
2074	–	3p.on 3p.60 dull ultramarine, black & bright green (No. 1984) (17 Feb)	50	20
2075	**646**	3p.on 3p.60 brt lemon, dp yellow-brown & dull ultramarine (2 Mar)	75	30
2071/2075 *Set of 5*			2·75	1·10

First Day Covers are dated 14 February.

(Des A. Divina)

1988 (25 Feb). *Postal Codes.* W **614** (*sideways*). P 13.

2076	**675**	60s. multicoloured	15	10
2077		1p. multicoloured	20	15

676 *Vesbius purpureus*   **677** Solar Eclipse

1988 (11 Mar). *Insect Predators. T* **676** *and similar vert designs. Multicoloured.* W **614**. P 13.

2078	1p. Type **676**		15	10
2079	5p.50 *Campsomeris aurulenta*		1·10	45

(Des E. Aguirre and Imelda Joson)

1988 (18 Mar–4 Apr). W **636**. P 13 × 13½.

2080	**677**	1p. multicoloured	15	10
		a. Wmk **380** (4 Apr)	30	10
2081		5p.50 multicoloured	1·20	45
		a. Wmk **380** (4 Apr)	1·50	45

678 Teodoro   **679** Emblem

(Des I. Fajardo)

1988 (27 Apr). *101st Birth Anniv of Toribio Teodoro (industrialist).* W **614** (*sideways*). P 13.

2082	**678**	1p. cinnamon, yell-brn & rose-carm	15	10
2083		1p.20 turq-blue, agate & rose-carm	20	15

(Des R. Asuncion)

1988 (22 May). *75th Anniv of College of Holy Spirit. T* **679** *and similar vert design.* W **380** (*sideways*). P 13½ × 13.

2084	1p. lake-brown, gold and black		15	10
2085	4p. lake-brown, olive-green and black		80	30

Designs:—4p. Arnold Janssen (founder) and Sister Edelwina (director, 1920–47).
Each issued both in sheets of 50 and sheetlets of 15 stamps.

680 Emblem   **681** Luna and Hidalgo

(Des A. Divina)

1988 (4 June). *Newly Restored Democracies International Conference.* W **380** (*sideways*). P 13½ × 13.

2086	**680**	4p. brt new blue, dp ultramarine & blk	95	30

Issued in sheets of 50 and sheetlets of 15 stamps.

1988 (15 June). *National Juan Luna and Felix Resurrection Hidalgo Memorial Exhibition.* W **614**. P 13.

2087	**681**	1p. black, greenish yellow & yell-brn	15	10
2088		5p.50 black, cinnamon & yellow-brn	1·00	35

682 Magat Dam, Ramon, Isabela   **683** Scuba Diving, Siquijor

(Des A. Divina)

1988 (22 June). *25th Anniv of National Irrigation Administration.* W **380** (*sideways*). P 13½ × 13.

2089	**682**	1p. multicoloured	1·10	1·10
2090		5p.50 multicoloured	1·20	50

Issued in sheets of 50 and sheetlets of 15 stamps.

1988 (11 July). *Olympic Games, Seoul. T* **683** *and similar horiz designs. Multicoloured.* W **380**. P 13 × 13½.

2091	1p. Type **683**		15	15
	a. Horiz strip. Nos. 2091 and 2093/5 plus label		20	10
	b. Imperf		15	15
	ba. Horiz strip. Nos. 2091b and 2093b/5b plus label		5·75	—
2092	1p.20 Big game fishing, Aparri Cagayan		20	15
	b. Imperf		30	20
2093	4p. Yachting, Manila Central		75	45
	b. Imperf		1·00	60
2094	5p.50 Mountain climbing, Mt. Apo, Davao		1·10	65
	b. Imperf		1·50	90
2095	8p. Golfing, Cebu City		1·50	95
	b. Imperf		2·00	1·30
2096	11p. Cycling (Tour of Mindanao), Marawi City		2·20	1·30
	b. Imperf		3·00	1·80
2091/2096	*Set of 6*		5·25	3·25
2091b/2096b	*Set of 6*		7·00	4·50

The 1p., 5p.50, 4 and 8p. values were issued both in separate sheets and together in horizontal *se-tenant* strips of four stamps and central label commemorating Philippine Olympic Week.

684 Headquarters, Plaza Santa Cruz, Manila   (**685**)

(Des A. Divina, Bunag, A. Luzon, R. Goco)

1988 (15 July–8 Aug). *Banking Anniversaries. T* **684** *and similar horiz design. Multicoloured.* W **380**. P 13 × 13½.

2097	1p. Type **684** (50th anniv of Philippine International Commercial Bank)		15	15
2098	1p. Family looking at factory and countryside (25th anniv of Land Bank) (8 Aug)		15	15

2099   5p.50 Type **684**   95   50
2100   5p.50 As No. 2098 (8 Aug)   95   50
2097/2100 Set of 4 . . . .   2·00   1·20
   The two designs of each value were issued together both in
sheets of 50 and in sheetlets of 12. The sheets of 50 were divided
into blocks of 25 stamps of each design, giving vertical *se-tenant*
pairs from the middle horizontal rows (complete sheets were not
issued until August). The sheetlets of 12 contained blocks of 6
stamps of each design divided by a gutter. (*Prices for se-tenant
pairs*: Nos. 2097/8, 45p. *un*; Nos. 2099/2100, £2·10 *un*.)

1988 (1 Aug). *Various stamps surch as T* **685**.
2101   1p.90 on 2p.40 multicoloured
          (No. 1968a)   45   15
2102   1p.90 on 2p.40 brownish black, new
          blue and emerald (No. 1972)   45   15
2103   1p.90 on 2p.40 multicoloured
          (No. 1981)   45   15
2104   1p.90 on 2p.40 multicoloured (No. 1988)
          (Gold)   45   15
2101/2104 Set of 4 . . . .   1·60   55

686 Balagtas

687 Hospital

(Des R. Goco)

1988 (13 Aug). *Birth Bicentenary of Francisco Balagtas Baltasco
(writer). T* **686** *and similar vert design. Each deep olive, light
brown and greenish yellow.* W **614**. P 13.
2105   1p. Type **686**   15   10
          a. Horiz pair. Nos. 2105/6   35   20
2106   1p. As Type **686** but details reversed . 15   10
   Nos. 2105/6 were issued together in horizontal *se-tenant* pairs
within the sheet.

(Des R. Goco)

1988 (18 Aug). *50th Anniv of Quezon Institute (tuberculosis
hospital).* W **380**. P 13 × 13½.
2107   **687**   1p. multicoloured   15   15
2108   5p.50 multicoloured . . . . .   1·00   60
   Each issued in sheets of 50 and sheetlets of 15 stamps.

688 *Lentinus
edodes*

689 Archery

(Des A. Divina, R. Goco and A. Luzon)

1988 (13 Sept). *Fungi. T* **688** *and similar vert designs.
Multicoloured.* W **614**. P 13.
2109   60s. Type **688**   15   10
2110   1p. *Auricularia polytricha*   20   15
2111   2p. *Lentinus sajor-caju (Pleurotus sajor-
          caju)*   35   20
2112   4p. *Volvariella volvacea*   90   45
2109/2112 Set of 4 . . . .   1·40   80

(Des R. Asuncion and A. Chuidian)

1988 (17 Sept). *Olympic Games, Seoul. T* **689** *and similar vert
designs. Multicoloured.* W **380** *(sideways).* P 13½ × 13.
2113   1p. Type **689**   20   15
          b. Imperf   20   15
2114   1p.20 Tennis   20   15
          b. Imperf   20   15
2115   4p. Boxing   60   30
          b. Imperf   60   30
2116   5p.50 Athletics   90   45
          b. Imperf   90   45
2117   8p. Swimming . . . . . .   1·30   60
          b. Imperf . . . .   1·30   60
2118   11p. Cycling . . . . . .   1·80   95
          b. Imperf . . . .   1·80   95
2113/2118 Set of 6 . . . . . .   4·50   2·25
2113b/2118b Set of 6 . . . . . .   4·50   2·30
MS2119 101 × 76 mm. 5p.50, Weightlifting;
   5p.50, Basketball; 5p.50, Judo, 5p.50,
   Shooting. Imperf . . . . . .   4·50   4·50

690 Department of Justice

691 Red Cross Work

(Des A. Luzon)

1988 (26 Sept). *Law and Justice Week.* W **380**. P 13 × 13½.
2120   **690**   1p. multicoloured   15   10
   Issued in sheets of 50 and sheetlets of 6 stamps.

(Des A. Divina)

1988 (30 Sept). *125th Anniv of Red Cross.* W **380** *(sideways).*
   P 13½ × 13.
2121   **691**   1p. multicoloured   15   15
2122   5p.50 multicoloured . . . . .   1·00   50
   Each issued in sheets of 50 and sheetlets of 6 stamps.

692 Girl and Boy

693 Map and Shrimps

(Des C. Fajardo)

1988 (6 Oct). *50th Anniv of Christian Children's Fund.* W **380**
   (sideways). P 13½ × 13.
2123   **692**   1p. multicoloured   15   10
   Issued in sheets of 50 and sheetlets of 6 stamps.

1988 (19 Oct). *50th Anniv of Bacolod City Charter.* W **380**.
   P 13 × 13½.
2124   **693**   1p. multicoloured   15   10
   Issued in sheets of 50 and sheetlets of 6 stamps.

694 Breastfeeding

695 A. Aragon
Quezon

1988 (24 Oct). *Child Survival Campaign. T* **694** *and similar vert designs. Multicoloured.* W **380** *(sideways).* P 13½ × 13.

2125	1p. Type **694**		15	10
	a. Vert strip of 5. Nos. 2125/9		80	
2126	1p. Growth monitoring		15	10
2127	1p. Immunization		15	10
2128	1p. Oral rehydration		15	10
2129	1p. Access for the disabled (U.N. Decade of Disabled Persons)		15	10
2125/2129 *Set of 5*			70	45

Nos. 2125/9 were issued together in vertical *se-tenant* strips of five within sheets of 50 and sheetlets of 15 stamps.

1988 (7 Nov). *Birth Centenary of Aurora Aragon Quezon.* W **614**. P 13.

2130	**695**	1p. multicoloured	15	10
2131		5p.50 multicoloured	90	60

696 Post Office

697 Sampaloc Branch
Transmitter

1988 (24 Nov)–**89**. *Philatelic Week. T* **696** *and similar vert designs. Multicoloured.* W **614**. P 13.

2132	1p. Type **696** (inscr "1938")		20	15
	a. Block of 4. Nos. 2132/5		90	
	b. Inscr "1988" (2 May 1989)		35	20
	ab. Block of 4. Nos. 2132a and 2133/b		1·10	
2133	1p. Stamp counter		20	15
2134	1p. Fern and stamp displays		20	15
2135	1p. People looking at stamp displays		20	15
2132/2135 *Set of 4 (cheapest)*			75	55

Nos. 2132/5 were issued together in *se-tenant* blocks of four within the sheet.

The initial printing had the erroneous date on No. 2132 throughout the sheet. It was corrected in subsequent printings.

(Des Design Systemat)

1988 (28 Nov). *Ten Years of Technological Improvements by Philippine Long Distance Telephone Company.* W **380** *(sideways).* P 13½ × 13.

2136	**697**	1p. multicoloured	15	10
		a. "YOUR LINE TO THE TIMES" omitted		

The inscription in the right hand corner of the design, below "50 60", is found in various positions or omitted.

Issued in sheets of 50 and sheetlets of 6 stamps.

698 Clasped Hands
and Dove

699 Crowd with Banners

1988 (2 Dec). *Christmas. T* **698** *and similar multicoloured designs.* W **614** *(sideways on horiz designs).* P 13.

2137	75s. Type **698**		15	15
2138	1p. Children making decorations (horiz)		15	15
2139	2p. Man carrying decorations on yoke (horiz)		30	20
2140	3p.50 Christmas tree		60	30
2141	4p.75 Candle and stars		80	35
2142	5p.50 Reflection of star forming heart (horiz)		95	45
2137/2142 *Set of 6*			2·75	1·40

(Des A. Divina)

1988 (9 Dec). *Commission on Human Rights* (2143) *and 40th Anniv of Universal Declaration of Hunan Rights* (2144). *T* **699** *and similar horiz design. Multicoloured.* W **380**. P 13 × 13½.

2143	1p. Type **699**		15	10
2144	1p. Doves escapng from cage		15	10

Nos. 2143/4 were issued together in sheets of 50 stamps consisting of blocks of 25 of each value (giving 5 *se-tenant* pairs) and in sheetlets of 12 stamps consisting of blocks of 6 of each value, the blocks separated by a gutter. (*Price of se-tenant pare* 40p. *un.*)

700 Church, 1776

701 Statue and School

(Des A. Luzon)

1988 (19 Dec). *400th Anniv of Malate. T* **700** *and similar horiz designs. Multicoloured.* W **614** *(sideways).* P 13.

2145	1p. Type **700**		15	10
	a. Block of 4. Nos. 2145/8		75	
2146	1p. Our Lady of Remedies Church anniversary emblem and statue of Virgin (Eduardo Castrillo)		15	10
2147	1p. Church, 1880		15	10
2148	1p. Church, 1988		15	10
2145/2148 *Set of 4*			55	35

Nos. 2145/8 were issued together in *se-tenant* blocks of four within the sheet.

First Day Covers are dated 16 December.

1988 (20 Dec). *50th Anniv of University of Santo Tomas Graduate School.* W **380** *(sideways).* P 13½ × 13.

2149	**701**	1p. multicoloured	15	10

Issued in sheets of 50 and sheetlets of 6 stamps.

702 Order's Activities

703 Miguel Ver (first leader)

1989 (17 Feb). *50th Anniv of Oblates of Mary Immaculate.* W **380** (*sideways*). P 13½ × 13.
2150 **702** 1p. multicoloured 15 10
Issued in sheets of 50 and sheetlets of 6 stamps.

1989 (18 Feb). *47th Anniv of Recognition of Hunters ROTC Guerrilla Unit (formed by Military Academy and University students).* T **703** *and similar vert design. Multicoloured.* W **614**. P 13.
2151 1p. Type **703** 15 10
   a. Horiz pair. Nos. 2151/2 . . . . . 35 25
2152 1p. Eleuterio Adevoso (leader after Ver's death) 15 10
Nos. 2151/2 were issued together in horizontal *se-tenant* pairs within the sheet, each pair forming a composite design.

704 Foodstuffs and Paulino Santos

705 Sinulog

1989 (27 Feb). *50th Anniv of General Santos City.* W **380**. P 13 × 13½.
2153 **704** 1p. multicoloured 15 10

1989 (1 Mar). *"Fiesta Islands '89" (1st series).* T **705** *and similar vert designs. Multicoloured.* W **614**. P 13.
2154 4p.75 Type **705** 95 35
2155 5p.50 Cenaculo (Lenten festival) 95 45
2156 6p.25 Iloilo Paraw Regatta 95 65
See also Nos. 2169/71, 2177/9, 2194/6 and 2210.

PRINTERS. From No. 2157 all stamps were printed in lithography by Amstar Co Inc, Quezon, *unless otherwise stated.*

706 Tomas Mapúa

707 Adventure Pool

1989 (18 May). *Birth Centenaries.* T **706** *and similar vert designs. Multicoloured.* W **380** (*sideways*). P 14 × 13½.
2157 1p. Type **706** 15 10
   a. Horiz strip of 5. Nos. 2157/61 . . . 80
2158 1p. Carnilo Osias 15 10
2159 1p. Dr. Olivia Salamanca 15 10
2160 1p. Dr. Francisco Santiago 15 10
2161 1p. Leandro Fernandez 15 10
2157/2161 *Set of 5* 70 45

Nos 2157/61 were issued together in horizontal *se-tenant* strips of five within the sheet.

1989 (31 May). *26th International Federation of Landscape Architects World Congress, Manila.* T **707** *and similar horiz designs. Multicoloured.* W **614** (*sideways*). P 14 × 13½.
2162 1p. Type **707** 15 10
   a. Block of 4. Nos. 2162/5 75
2163 1p. Paco Park 15 10
2164 1p. Street improvements in Malacañang area 15 10
2165 1p. Erosion control on upland farm . . . 15 10
2162/2165 *Set of 4* 55 35
Nos. 2162/5 were issued together in *se-tenant* blocks of four within the sheet.

708 Palawan Peacock-pheasant (*Polyplectron emphanum*)

709 Entrance and Statue of Justice

1989 (5 June). *Environment Month.* T **708** *and similar vert designs. Multicoloured.* W **614**. P 13½ × 14.
2166 1p. Type **708** 15 10
   a. Horiz pair. Nos. 2166/7 . . . . . 35 25
2167 1p. Palawan bear cat (*Arctictis whitei*) . . 15 10
Nos. 2166/7 were issued together in horizontal *se-tenant* pairs within the sheet, each pair forming a composite design.

1989 (11 June). *Supreme Court.* W **380** (*sideways*). P 14.
2168 **709** 1p. multicoloured 30 15
Issued in sheets of 50 and sheetlets of 6 stamps.

PHOSPHORESCENT SECURITY MARKING. From No. 2169 all issues (except for surcharges on previous issues) have a phosphorescent security marking once on each stamp, *unless otherwise stated.* At first this consisted of the letters "PPS", from June 1992 it was "PPC".

1989 (28 June). *"Fiesta Islands '89" (2nd series).* Vert designs as T **705**. *Multicoloured.* W **614**. P 13½ × 14.
2169 60s. Turumba 15 10
2170 75s. Pahiyas 15 15
2171 3p.50 Independence Day 50 30
The 60 and 75s. exist on both ordinary and luminescent paper.

710 Birds, Quill, *Noli Me Tangere* and Flags

711 Graph

1989 (1 July). *Bicentenary of French Revolution and Decade of Philippine Nationalism.* W **380**. P 14.
2172 **710** 1p. multicoloured 15 15
2173 5p.50 multicoloured 90 60
   a. Red printed double . . . . .
Each issued in sheets of 50 and sheetlets of 6 stamps.

1989 (14 July). *National Science and Technology Week. T* **711** *and similar vert design. Multicoloured.* W **380** (*sideways*). P 14.

2174	1p. Type **711**	15	10
	a. Horiz pair. Nos. 2174/5	35	25
2175	1p. "Man" (Leonardo da Vinci) and emblem of Philippine Science High School	15	10

Nos. 2174/5 were issued together in horizontal *se-tenant* pairs, each pair forming a composite design, within sheets of 50 and sheetlets of 4 stamps.

₱4**75**

(712)

713 Monument, Flag, Civilian and Soldier

(Surch APO-NEDA, Quezon)

1989 (21 Aug). *No. 2060 surch with T* **712**.

2176	4p.75 on 5p.50, brt green & yellow-brn	75	50
	a. Surch inverted		

1989 (1 Sept). *"Fiesta Islands 89" (3rd series). Vert designs as T* **705**. *Multicoloured.* W **614**. P 13½ × 14.

2177	1p. Pagoda Sa Wawa (carnival float)	15	15
	a. Imperf (pair)		
2178	4p.75 Cagayan de Oro Fiesta	80	35
2179	5p.50 Peñafrancia Festival	95	45

The 4p.75 exists on both ordinary and luminescent paper.

(Des R. Asuncion)

1989 (23 Oct). *50th Anniv of National Defence Department.* W **380** (*sideways*). P 14.

2180	**713** 1p. multicoloured	20	10

Issued in sheets of 50 and sheetlets of 6 stamps.

714 Map and Satellite

715 The Annunciation

(Des A. Divina)

1989 (30 Oct). *Tenth Anniv of Asia–Pacific Telecommunity.* W **380**. P 14.

2181	**714** 1p. multicoloured	30	15

Issued in sheets of 50 and sheetlets of 6 stamps.

(Des N. Ferrariz (60s.), J. Enriquez (75s.), C. Cruz (1p.), E. Cuevas (2p.), R. Aguilar (4p.), F. Geronimo (4p.75)

1989 (10 Nov). *Christmas. T* **715** *and similar vert designs. Multicoloured.* W **380**. P 13½ × 14.

2182	60s. Type **715**	10	10
2183	75s. Mary and Elizabeth	15	10

2184	1p. Mary and Joseph travelling to Bethlehem	15	10
2185	2p. Search for an inn	30	20
2186	4p. Wise men and star	65	45
2187	4p.75 Adoration of shepherds	75	50
2182/2187	*Set of 6*	1·90	1·30

First Day Covers are dated 8 November.

716 Lighthouse, Ship and Lifebelt

717 Spanish Philippines 1854 and Revolutionary Govt 1898 2c. Stamps

(Des A. Divina)

1989 (13 Nov). *International Maritime Organization.* W **380**. P 14.

2188	**716** 1p. multicoloured	20	10

Issued in sheets of 50 and sheetlets of 6 stamps.

(Des A. Divina)

1989 (17 Nov). *"World Stamp Expo '89" International Stamp Exhibition, Washington D.C. T* **717** *and similar horiz designs. Multicoloured.* W **380**. P 14.

2189	1p. Type **717**	15	10
2190	4p. U.S. Administration 1899 50c. and Commonwealth 1935 6c. stamps	75	50
2191	5p.50 Japanese Occupation 1942 2c. and Republic 1946 6c. stamps	90	60

Each issued in sheets of 50 and sheetlets of 6 stamps.

718 Teacher using Stamp as Teaching Aid

719 Heart

(Des R. Goco and R. Manalili)

1989 (20 Nov). *Philatelic Week. Philately in the Classroom. T* **718** *and similar horiz design. Multicoloured.* W **380** (*sideways*). P 14 × 13½.

2192	1p. Type **718**	15	10
2193	1p. Children working with stamps	15	10

(Des A. Luzon, R. Naval and C. Fajardo)

1989 (4 Dec). *"Fiesta Islands '89" (4th series). Vert designs as T* **705**. W **614**. P 13½ × 14.

2194	1p. Masked festival, Negros	15	15
2195	4p.75 Grand Cañao, Baguio	80	35
	a. Imperf (pair)		
2196	5p.50 Fireworks	95	45

First Day Covers are dated 1 December.
The 5p.50 exists on both ordinary and luminescent paper.

1990 (12 Feb). *11th World Cardiology Congress, Manila.* W **614** (*sideways*). P 14.

2197	**719** 5p.50 scarlet, dull ultramarine & black	95	45

720 Glasses of Beer

721 Houses and Family

(Des R. David and H. Reyes)

1990 (16 Apr). *Centenary of San Miguel Brewery.* W **614**. P 14.
2198	**720**	1p. multicoloured	. . . . .	15	15
2199		5p.50 multicoloured	. . . . .	95	45

(Des Mandy Labayen)

1990 (30 Apr). *Population and Housing Census.* T **721** *and similar vert design. Multicoloured, colours of houses given.* W **614**. P 14.
2200	**721**	1p. dull ultramarine	. . . .	15	10
		a. Horiz pair. Nos. 2200/1	. . .	35	25
2201		1p. flesh	. . . . .	15	10

Nos. 2200/1 were issued together in horizontal *se-tenant* pairs within the sheet, each pair forming a composite design.

722 Scouts

723 Claro Recto (politician)

1990 (21 May). *50th Anniv of Philippine Girl Scouts.* W **614** (*sideways*). P 14.
2202	**722**	1p. multicoloured	. . . .	35	10
2203		1p.20 multicoloured	. . . .	35	15

1990 (1 June). *Birth Centenaries.* T **723** *and similar vert designs. Multicoloured.* W **380** (*sideways*). P 14 × 13½.
2204		1p. Type **723**	. . . .	15	10
		a. Strip of 5. Nos. 2204/8	. . .	80	
2205		1p. Manuel Bernabe (poet)	. . .	15	10
2206		1p. Guillermo Tolentino (sculptor)	. . .	15	10
2207		1p. Elpidio Quirino (President, 1948–53)	. . .	15	10
2208		1p. Dr. Bienvenido Gonzalez (University President, 1937–51)	. . .	15	10
2204/2208		*Set of 5*	. . . .	70	45

Nos. 2204/8 were issued together in *se-tenant* strips of five within the sheet.

724 Badge and Globe

725 Torch

1990 (21 July). *50th Anniv of Legion of Mary.* W **614**. P 14.
2209	**724**	1p. multicoloured	. . . . .	15	10

1990 (6 Aug). *"Fiesta Islands '89" (5th series). As No. 2179 but new value.* W **614**. P 13½ × 14.
2210		4p. multicoloured		95	35

1990 (10 Sept). *20th Anniv of Asian–Pacific Postal Training Centre.* W **614**. P 14.
2211	**725**	1p. multicoloured	. . . .	15	15
2212		4p. multicoloured	. . . .	65	35

726 Catechism Class

727 Waling Waling Flowers

1990 (28 Sept). *National Catechetical Year.* W **614**. P 14.
2213	**726**	1p. multicoloured	. . . .	15	10
2214		3p.50 multicoloured	. . . .	60	35

1990 (3–18 Oct). *29th Orient and South-East Asian Lions Forum, Manila.* T **727** *and similar vert design. Multicoloured.* W **614**. P 14.
2215		1p. Type **727**	. . . .	20	15
2216		4p. Sampaguita flowers (18 Oct)	. . .	65	30

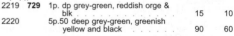

728 Areas for Improvement

729 Letters of Alphabet

1990 (24 Oct). *40th Anniv of United Nations Development Programme.* W **614**. P 14.
2217	**728**	1p. multicoloured	. . . .	15	10
2218		5p.50 multicoloured	. . . .	90	60

1990 (24 Oct). *International Literacy Year.* W **614** (*sideways*). P 14.
2219	**729**	1p. dp grey-green, reddish orge & blk	. . .	15	10
2220		5p.50 deep grey-green, greenish yellow and black	. . .	90	60

730 "Laughter"
(A. Magsaysay-Ho)

731 Star

1990·(16 Nov). *Philatelic Week.* T **730** *and similar multicoloured designs.* W **614**. P 14.
2221		1p. "Family" (F. Amorsolo) (*horiz*)	. . .	20	15
2222		4p.75 "The Builders" (V. Edades)	. . .	1·20	60
2223		5p.50 Type **730**	. . . .	1·40	75

1990 (3 Dec). *Christmas. T* **731** *and similar vert designs. Multicoloured.* W **614** (*sideways*). P 14.

2224	1p. Type **731**		15	10
	a. Strip of 4. Nos. 2224/7		80	
2225	1p. Stars within stars (Prussian blue background)		15	10
2226	1p. Red and white star		15	10
2227	1p. Gold and red star (deep green background)		15	10
2228	5p.50 Geometric star (Paskuhan Village, San Fernando)		15	10
2224/2228 *Set of 5*			70	45

Nos. 2224/7 were issued together in *se-tenant* strips of four stamps within the sheet.

732 Figures

733 La Solidaridad in 1990 and 1890 and Statue of Rizal

1990 (7 Dec). *International White Cane Safety Day.* W **614** (*sideways*). P 14.

2229	**732** 1p. black, greenish yellow & dp ultram		20	15

1990 (17 Dec). *Centenary of Publication of* Filipinas Dentro de Cien Años *by José Rizal.* W **614** (*sideways*). P 14.

2230	**733** 1p. multicoloured		20	15

734 Crowd before Figure of Christ

735 Tailplane and Stewardess

1991 (30 Jan). *Second Plenary Council of the Philippines.* W **614** (*sideways*). P 14.

2231	**734** 1p. multicoloured		20	15

1991 (15 Mar). *50th Anniv of Philippine Airlines.* W **614** (*sideways*). P 14.

(a) POSTAGE.

2232	**735** 1p. multicoloured		15	15

(b) AIR. Inscr "AIRMAIL".

2233	**735** 5p.50 multicoloured		95	60

736 Gardenia

737 Sheepshank

1991 (1 Apr–Nov). *Flowers. T* **736** *and similar designs. Multicoloured.* W **614** (*sideways*). P 14 × 13½.

2234	60s. Type **736** (I) (11 Apr)		10	10
	a. Type II (29 July)		10	10
2235	75s. Yellow bell (I) (11 Apr)		10	10
	a. Type II (12 Nov)		50	20
2236	1p. Yellow plumeria (I)		15	15
	a. Block of 4. Nos. 2236/9		65	
	b. Type II (1 Aug)		15	15
	ba. Block of 4. Nos. 2236b and 2237a/9a		65	
2237	1p. Red plumeria (I)		15	15
	a. Type II (1 Aug)		15	15
2238	1p. Pink plumeria (I)		15	15
	a. Type II (1 Aug)		15	15
2239	1p. White plumeria (I)		15	15
	a. Type II (1 Aug)		15	15
2240	1p.20 Nerium (7 June)		15	10
2241	3p.25 Ylang-ylang (I) (11 Apr)		60	35
	a. Type II (29 Oct)		80	35
2242	4p. Pink ixora (7 June)		60	35
	a. Block of 4. Nos. 2242/5		2·50	
2243	4p. White ixora (7 June)		60	35
2244	4p. Yellow ixora (7 June)		60	35
2245	4p. Red ixora (7 June)		60	35
2246	4p.75 Orange bougainvillea (7 June)		65	45
	a. Block of 4. Nos. 2246/9		2·75	
2247	4p.75 Purple bougainvillea (7 June)		65	45
2248	4p.75 White bougainvillea (7 June)		65	45
2249	4p.75 Red bougainvillea (7 June)		65	45
2250	5p. Canna (7 June)		75	45
2251	5p.50 Red hibiscus (I)		95	65
	a. Block of 4. Nos. 2251/4		3·75	
	b. Type II (2 Sept)		95	65
	ba. Block of 4. Nos 2251b and 2252a/4a		3·75	
2252	5p.50 Yellow hibiscus (I)		95	65
	a. Type II (2 Sept)		95	65
2253	5p.50 White hibiscus (I)		95	65
	a. Type II (2 Sept)		95	65
2254	5p.50 Pink hibiscus (I)		95	65
	a. Type II (2 Sept)		95	65
2234/2254 *Set of 21* (*cheapest*)			10·00	6·75

The 60s. and 1p., both Type II, exist with imprint dates "1991" and "1992". The 1992 version of the 1p. exists with both versions of the phosphorescent security marking.

Differences in Types are as follows:

60s.: I. Distance between "PILIPINAS" and "date" is 2¼ mm; II. Distance is 1 mm.

75s.: I. Distance between date and "PILIPINAS" is 4 mm; II. Distance is 2½ mm.

1p.: I. "p" of face value and first "1" of "1991" do not align; II. Do align.

3p.25: I. Side inscription and "1991" do not align; II. Do align.

5p.50: I. Distance between "PILIPINAS" and "1991" is 3½ mm; II. Distance is 2 mm.

See also Nos. 2322/41 and 2475.

1991 (22 Apr). *12th Asia–Pacific and Ninth National Boy Scouts Jamboree. T* **737** *and similar horiz designs. Multicoloured.* W **614** (*sideways on MS*2258). P 14.

2255	1p. Reef knot		20	15
2256	4p. Type **737**		60	30
2257	4p.75 Granny knot		65	30
MS2258 88 × 82 mm. Nos. 2255/7. Imperf (sold at 16p.50)			3·00	3·00

738 Jorge Vargas

739 "Antipolo" (Carlos Francisco) and Score

1991 (3 June). *Birth Centenaries. T* **738** *and similar vert designs. Multicoloured.* W **614** (*sideways*). P 14 × 13½.

2259	1p. Type **738**		15	10
	a. Horiz strip of 5. Nos. 2259/63		80	
2260	1p. Ricardo Paris		15	10
2261	1p. José Laurel		15	10

2262	1p. Vicente Fabella	15	10
2263	1p. Maximo Kalaw	15	10
2259/2263	Set of 5	70	45

Nos. 2259/63 were issued together in horizontal *se-tenant* strips of five stamps within the sheet.

1991 (25 June). *400th Anniv of Antipolo.* W **614**. P 14.

2264	**739**	1p. multicoloured	20	15

740 Philippine Eagle   **741** Emblem

1991 (31 July). *Endangered Species. The Philippine Eagle (Pithecophaga jefferyi).* T **740** *and similar horiz designs. Multicoloured.* W **614**. P 14.

2265	1p. Type **740**	45	30
2266	4p.75 Eagle on branch	1·90	1·30
2267	5p.50 Eagle in flight	2·20	1·50
2268	8p. Eagle feeding chick	3·25	2·20
2265/2268	*Set of 4*	7·00	4·75

(Des G. Bautista)

1991 (20 Aug). *Centenary of Founding of Society of Lawyers (from 1904 Philippine Bar Association).* W **614**. P 14.

2269	**741**	1p. multicoloured	20	15

742 Flags and Induction   **743** First
Ceremony   Regular
Division
Emblem

(Des A Divina (1, 16p.). Raquel Torregrosa (others))

1991 (29 Aug–Dec). *50th Anniv of Induction of Philippine Reservists into United States Army Forces in the Far East.*

(a) T **742**. W **614**. P 14.

2270	**742**	1p. multicoloured	20	15
MS2271	82 × 88 mm. **742** 16p. multicoloured.			
	Imperf		2·75	2·75

(b) T **743** *and similar vert designs showing Divisional emblems. Background colours given where necessary in brackets.* W **614** (*sideways*). P 14 × 13½ (8 Dec).

2272	2p. dp rose-red, blk & lemon (1st Regular)	20	15
	a. Block of 32. Nos. 2272/2303	7·50	
2273	2p. multicoloured (lemon) (2nd Regular)	20	15
2274	2p. multicoloured (lemon) (11th)	20	15
2275	2p. new blue, lemon & blk (lemon) (21st)	20	15
2276	2p. deep rose-red and black (1st Regular)	20	15
2277	2p. black, new blue and deep rose-red (2nd Regular)	20	15
2278	2p. multicoloured (white) (11th)	20	15
2279	2p. new blue, lemon & blk (white) (21st)	20	15
2280	2p. multicoloured (lemon) (31st)	20	15
2281	2p. multicoloured (lemon) (41st)	20	15
2282	2p. multicoloured (lemon) (51st)	20	15
2283	2p. multicoloured (lemon) (61st)	20	15
2284	2p. dp rose-red, new blue & black (31st)	20	15

2285	2p. multicoloured (white) (41st)	20	15
2286	2p. new blue, black & dp rose-red (51st)	20	15
2287	2p. multicoloured (white) (61st)	20	15
2288	2p. multicoloured (lemon) (71st)	20	15
2289	2p. multicoloured (lemon) (81st)	20	15
2290	2p. multicoloured (lemon) (91st)	20	15
2291	2p. multicoloured (lemon) (101st)	20	15
2292	2p. multicoloured (white) (71st)	20	15
2293	2p. multicoloured (white) (81st)	20	15
2294	2p. multicoloured (white) (91st)	20	15
2295	2p. multicoloured (white) (101st)	20	15
2296	2p. new blue, blk & lemon (Bataan Force)	20	15
2297	2p. lemon, deep rose-red & black (lemon) (Philippine)	20	15
2298	2p. multicoloured (lemon) (Air Corps)	20	15
2299	2p. black, new blue and lemon (Offshore Patrol)	20	15
2300	2p. new blue and black (Bataan Force)	20	15
2301	2p. lemon, deep rose-red and black (white) (Philippine)	20	15
2302	2p. multicoloured (white) (Air Corps)	20	15
2303	2p. black and new blue (Offshore Patrol)	20	15
2272/2303	*Set of 32*	5·75	4·25

Nos. 2272/2303 were issued together in *se-tenant* blocks of 32 stamps within the sheet.

744 Basilio   **745** St. John of the
Cross

(Des R. Alejandro)

1991 (18 Sept). *Centenary of Publication of El Filibusterismo by José Rizal.* T **744** *and similar vert designs showing characters from the novel. Each crimson, turquoise-blue and black.* W **614** (*sideways*). P 14.

2304	1p. Type **744**	15	15
	a. Block of 4. Nos. 2304/7	75	
2305	1p. Simoun	15	15
2306	1p. Father Florentino	15	15
2307	1p. Juli	15	15
2304/2307	*Set of 4*	55	55

Nos. 2304/7 were issued together in vertical *se-tenant* blocks of four stamps within the sheet.

(Des R. Asuncion)

1991 (15 Oct). *400th Death Anniv of St. John of the Cross.* W **614** (*sideways on 1p.*). P 14.

2308	**745**	1p. multicoloured	20	15
MS2309	59 × 59 mm. 16p. St. John praying, signature and Type **745**. Imperf		4·50	4·50

746 Faces (Children's Fund)

(Des A. Divina)

1991 (24 Oct). *United Nations Agencies. T* **746** *and similar horiz designs.* W **614**. P 14.

2310	1p. multicoloured	15	15
2311	4p. multicoloured	60	20
2312	5p.50 black, orange-red & dull ultram	80	35

Designs:—4p. Hands supporting boatload of people (High Commissioner for Refugees); 5p.50, 1951 15c. and 1954 3c. U.N. stamps (40th anniv of Postal Administration).

747 "Bayanihan" (Carlos "Botong" Francisco)

1991 (20 Nov). *Philatelic Week. T* **747** *and similar horiz designs. Multicoloured.* W **614**. P 14.

2313	2p. Type **747**	30	15
2314	7p. "Sari-Sari Vendor" (Mauro Malang Santos)	1·00	50
2315	8p. "Give Us This Day" (Vicente Manansala)	1·20	60

748 Gymnastics   (749)

(Des R. Goco and A. Luzon)

1991 (22 Nov). *16th South-East Asian Games, Manila. T* **748** *and similar designs. Multicoloured.* W **614** (*sideways on Nos.* 2318/ MS2320). P 14.

2316	2p. Type **748**	30	15
	a. Vert pair. Nos. 2316/17	65	35
2317	2p. Gymnastics (emblem at bottom)	30	15
2318	6p. Arnis (martial arts) (emblem at left) (*vert*)	65	15
	a. Horiz pair. Nos. 2318/19	1·50	35
2319	6p. Arnis (emblem at right) (*vert*)	65	15
2316/2319 *Set of 4*		1·70	55

MS2320 Two sheets. (a) 90 × 60 mm. Nos. 2318/19. Imperf; (b) 65 × 98 mm. Nos. 2316/19 . . . . . . 3·00 3·00

Designs of the same value were issued together in *se-tenant* pairs within their sheets, each pair forming a composite design.

Only the upper right-hand stamp in each miniature sheet has the security marking.

1991 (28 Nov). *First Philippine Philatelic Convention, Manila. No.* **MS**1698 *surch with T* **749** *in bright scarlet.*

MS2321 brown-purple and black . . . . 1·10 1·10

No. **MS**2321 is also overprinted in the margin "1st Philippine Philatelic Convention NOVEMBER 27 - 29, 1991" within a frame.

1991 (1 Dec)–*92. Flowers. Vert designs as T* **736**. *Multicoloured.* W **614**. P 14 × 13½.

2322	1p.50 Type **736** (13 Dec 1991)	15	15
2323	2p. Yellow plumeria	20	20
	a. Block of 4. Nos. 2323/6	95	
2324	2p. Red plumeria	20	20
2325	2p. Pink plumeria	20	20
2326	2p. White plumeria	20	20
2327	3p. Nerium (13 Dec 1991)	30	30
2328	5p. Ylang-ylang (I) (13 Dec 1991)	50	50
	a. Type II (1992)	50	50
2329	6p. Pink ixora	60	60
	a. Block of 4. Nos. 2329/32	60	60
2330	6p. White ixora	60	60
2331	6p. Yellow ixora	60	60
2332	6p. Red ixora	75	75
2333	7p. Orange bougainvillea	75	75
	a. Block of 4. Nos. 2333/6	3·00	
2334	7p. Purple bougainvillea	75	75
2335	7p. White bougainvillea	75	75
2336	7p. Red bougainvillea	80	80
2337	8p. Red hibiscus	80	80
	a. Block of 4. Nos. 2337/40	3·25	
2338	8p. Yellow hibiscus	80	80
2339	8p. White hibiscus	80	75
2340	8p. Pink hibiscus	80	80
2341	10p. Canna (13 Dec 1991)	1·00	1·00
2322/2341 *Set of 20*		12·25	11·50

Stamps of the same value were issued together in *se-tenant* blocks of four within their sheets.

All values except 5p. Type II exist with imprint dates "1991" (security marking "PPS") and "1992". Of the 1992 dated examples the 5p. Type I exists with marking "PPC" only, the 1p.50 and 10p. with "PPS" only, the other values (including 5p. Type II) come with both versions.

In Type I of the 5p. the side inscription roughly aligns with the end of the date. In Type II the right-hand edge of the inscription aligns with the second "9" in "1992".

750 Church

751 Player

(Des A. N. Arandela, A. R. Arandela, L. Aranal and R. Domingo)

1991 (4 Dec). *Christmas. Children's Paintings. T* **750** *and similar vert designs. Multicoloured.* W **614** (*sideways*). P 14.

2342	2p. Type **750**	20	15
2343	6p. Christmas present	65	45
2344	7p. Santa Claus and tree	75	50
2345	8p. Christmas tree and star	90	60
2342/2345 *Set of 4*		2·25	1·50

(Des Catherine Cuenca)

1991 (19 Dec). *Centenary of Basketball. T* **751** *and similar multicoloured designs.* W **614** (*sideways on* 2, 8p.). P 14.

2346	2p. Type **751**	35	15
2347	6p. Player and map (issue of first basketball stamp, 1934) (*horiz*)	90	30
2348	7p. Girls playing basketball (introduction of basketball in Philippines, 1904) (*horiz*)	1·00	35
2349	8p. Players	1·30	50
2346/2349 *Set of 4*		3·50	1·20

MS2350 Two sheets. (a) 60 × 60 mm. Match scene. Imperf; (b) 73 × 101 mm. Nos. 2346/9 . . . . . . 4·00 4·00

ba. Inverted positive impression of black on back

In **MS**2350b only the 6p. stamp has the security marking.

752 Monkey firing Cannon

(Des R. Guco)

1991 (27 Dec). *New Year. Year of the Monkey. T* **752** *and similar horiz design.* W **614**. P 14.

2351	**752**	2p. multicoloured	45	15
2352		6p. multicoloured	1·30	30

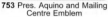

753 Pres. Aquino and Mailing Centre Emblem

754 *Curcuma longa*

(Des A. Divina)

1992 (15 Jan). *Kabisig Community Projects Organization. T* **753** *and similar horiz designs. Multicoloured.* W **614**. P 14.

2353	2p. Type **753**		20	20
2354	6p. Housing		65	30
2355	7p. Livestock		80	35
2356	8p. Handicrafts		95	45
2353/2356 *Set of 4*			2·30	1·20

(Des L. Baluyot)

1992 (7 Feb). *Asian Medicinal Plants Symposium, Los Baños, Laguna. T* **754** *and similar vert designs. Multicoloured.* W **614** (*sideways*). P 14.

2357	2p. Type **754**		35	20
2358	6p. *Centella asiatica*		75	30
2359	7p. *Cassia alata*		90	35
2360	8p. *Ervatamia pandacaqui*		1·00	45
2357/2360 *Set of 4*			2·75	1·20

755 "Mahal Kita", Envelopes and Map

756 Philippine Pavilion and Couple Dancing

(Des D. Dujunco)

1992 (10 Feb). *Greetings Stamps. T* **755** *and similar horiz designs. Multicoloured.* W **614**. P 14.

2361	2p. Type **755**		20	15
	a. Pair. Nos. 2361/2		50	35
2362	2p. As No. 2361 but inscr "I Love You"		20	15
2363	6p. Heart and doves ("Mahal Kita")		75	35
	a. Pair. Nos. 2363/4		1·60	75
2364	6p. As No. 2363 but inscr "I Love You"		75	35
2365	7p. Basket of flowers ("Mahal Kita")		80	35
	a. Pair. Nos. 2365/6		1·70	80
2366	7p. As No. 2365 but inscr "I Love You"		80	35
2367	8p. Cupid ("Mahal Kita")		1·60	45
	a. Pair. Nos. 2367/8		3·25	90
2368	8p. As No. 2367 but inscr "I Love You"		1·60	45
2361/2368 *Set of 8*			6·00	2·30

Stamps of the same value were issued together in *se-tenant* pairs within their sheets.

(Des Mandy Labayen and A. Divina)

1992 (27 Mar). *"Expo '92" World's Fair, Seville. T* **756** *and similar multicoloured designs.* W **614** (*sideways on* 2369/70). P 14.

2369	2p. Type **756**		20	15
2370	8p. Pavilion, preacher and conquistador holding globe		95	45
MS2371 63 × 76 mm. 16p. Pavilion (*horiz*).				
	Imperf		1·90	1·90

757 "Our Lady of the Sun" (icon)

758 Fish Farming

(Des R. Asuncion)

1992 (12 Apr). *300th Anniv of Apparition of Our Lady of the Sun at Vaga Gate, Cavite.* W **614** (*sideways*). P 14.

2372	**757**	2p. multicoloured	20	15
2373		8p. multicoloured	95	45

(Des A. Luzon)

1992 (4 May). *75th Anniv of Department of Agriculture. T* **758** *and similar horiz designs. Multicoloured.* W **614** (*sideways*). P 14.

2374	2p. Type **758**		20	15
	a. Strip of 3. Nos. 2374/6		70	
2375	2p. Pig farming		20	15
2376	2p. Sowing seeds		20	15

Nos. 2374/6 were issued together in *se-tenant* strips of three within the sheet.

759 Race Horses and Emblem

760 Manuel Roxas (President, 1946–48)

(Des Mandy Labayen and A. Divina)

1992 (14 May). *125th Anniv of Manila Jockey Club.* W **614** (*sideways on* **MS**2378). P 14.

2377	**759**	2p. multicoloured	20	15
MS2378 74 × 63 mm. **759** 8p. multicoloured.				
	Imperf		95	95

(Des A. Divina, R. Naval and Raquel Torregrosa)

1992 (1 June). *Birth Centenaries. T* **760** *and similar vert designs. Multicoloured.* W **614** (*sideways*). P 14 × 13½.

2379	2p. Type **760**		20	15
	a. Strip of 5. Nos. 2379/83		1·20	
2380	2p. Natividad Almeda-Lopez (judge)		20	15
2381	2p. Roman Ozaeta (jurist)		20	15
2382	2p. Engracia Cruz-Reyes (women's rights campaigner and environmentalist)		20	15
2383	2p. Fernando Amorsolo (artist)		20	15
2379/2383 *Set of 5*			90	70

Nos. 2379/83 were issued together in *se-tenant* strips of five within the sheet.

761 King, Queen and 1978 30s. Stamp

762 Bataan Cross

(Des Mandy Labayen and A. Divina)

1992 (7 June). *30th Chess Olympiad, Manila. T* **761** *and similar horiz design. Multicoloured.* W **614** (*sideways on* MS2386). P 14.

2384	2p. Type **761**	20	15
2385	6p. King, Queen and 1962 6s.+4s. stamp	65	45
MS2386 89×63 mm. 8p. Type **761**; 8p. As No. 2385. Imperf		1·80	1·80

In the miniature sheet only the right-hand stamp has the security marking.

(Des Mandy Labayen and Raquel Torregrosa)

1992 (26 June). *50th Anniv of Pacific Theatre in Second World War. T* **762** *and similar vert designs. Multicoloured.* W **614** (*upright on* MS2390a, *sideways on others*). P 14.

2387	2p. Type **762**	20	15
2388	6p. Map inside "W"	65	45
2389	8p. Corregidor eternal flame	95	65
MS2390 Two sheets. Imperf. (a) 63×75 mm. 16p. Map of Bataan and cross; (b) 76×63 mm. 16p. Map of Corregidor and Eternal Flame		3·00	3·00

763 Pres. Aquino and Pres.-elect Ramos

(Des A. Divina)

1992 (30 June). *Election of Fidel Ramos to Presidency.* W **614**. P 14.

2391	**763** 2p. multicoloured	30	15

764 "Dapitan Shrine" (César Legaspi)

1992 (17 July). *Centenary of Dr. José Rizal's Exile to Dapitan. T* **764** *and similar multicoloured design.* W **614** (*sideways on* 2393). P 14.

2392	2p. Type **764**	20	15
2393	2p. Portrait (after Juan Luna) (*vert*)	20	15

765 "Spirit of ASEAN" (Visit Asean Year)

766 Member of the Katipunan

(Des J. Joya)

1992 (18 July). *25th Anniv of Association of South-East Asian Nations. T* **765** *and similar horiz design. Multicoloured.* W **614**. P 14.

2394	2p. Type **765**	20	15
2395	2p. "ASEAN Sea" (25th Ministerial Meeting and Postal Ministers' Conference)	20	15
2396	6p. Type **765**	65	45
2397	6p. As No. 2395	65	45
2394/2397 *Set of 4*		1·50	1·10

(Des C. Francisco)

1992 (27 July). *Centenary of Founding of Katipunan* ("KKK") *(revolutionary organization). T* **766** *and similar multicoloured designs.* W **614** (*sideways on* 2398/9). P 14.

2398	2p. Type **766**	20	15
	a. Pair. Nos. 2398/9	50	35
2399	2p. Revolutionaries	20	15
2400	2p. Plotting (*horiz*)	20	15
	a. Pair. Nos. 2400/1	50	40
2401	2p. Attacking (*horiz*)	20	15
2398/2401 *Set of 4*		70	55

Nos. 2398/9 and 2400/1 respectively were issued together in *se-tenant* pairs within their sheets.

767 Dr. José Rizal, Text and Quill

(Des A. Divina)

1992 (31 July). *Centenary of Founding of La Liga Filipina.* W **614**. P 14.

2402	**767** 2p. multicoloured	20	15

768 Swimming

769 School, Emblem and Students

(Des A. Luzon)

1992 (4 Aug). *Olympic Games, Barcelona. T* **768** *and similar horiz designs.* W **614** (*sideways on* MS2406). P 14.

2403	2p. Type **768**	20	15
2404	7p. Boxing	75	50
2405	8p. Hurdling	90	60
MS2406 87×85 mm. 1p. Type **768**; 7p. No. 2404; 8p. No. 2405. Imperf		4·50	4·50
	a. Magenta printed double		

In the miniature sheet only the 7p. value has the security marking.

(Des A. Divina (2407), R. Asuncion (2408))

1992 (15 Aug). *Centenaries. T* **769** *and similar multicoloured design.* W **614** (*sideways on No.* 2408). P 14.

2407	2p. Type **769** (Sisters of the Assumption in the Philippines)	20	15
2408	2p. San Sebastian's Basilica, Manila (centenary (1991) of blessing of fifth construction) (*vert*)	20	15

770 Masonic Symbols   **771** Ramos taking Oath

(Des R. Naval)

1992 (31 Aug). *Centenary of Nilad Lodge (first Filipino Masonic Lodge). T* **770** *and similar vert designs.* W **614** (*sideways*). P 14.

2409	2p. black and yellow-green	20	15
2410	6p. multicoloured	65	45
2411	8p. multicoloured	90	60

Designs:—6p. Antonio Luna and symbols; 8p. Marcelo del Pilar ("Father of Philippine Masonry") and symbols.

(Des R. Naval)

1992 (31 Aug). *Swearing in of President Fidel Ramos. T* **771** *and similar horiz design. Multicoloured.* W **614**. P 14.

2412	2p. Type **771**	20	15
2413	8p. President taking oath in front of flag	95	45

772 Flamingo Guppy

(Des D. Dujunco)

1992 (9 Sept). *Freshwater Aquarium Fishes (1st series). T* **772** *and similar horiz designs. Multicoloured.* W **614**. P 14.

2414	1p.50 Type **772**	15	10
	a. Strip of 5. Nos. 2414/18	90	
2415	1p.50 Neon tuxedo guppy	15	10
2416	1p.50 King cobra guppy	15	10
2417	1p.50 Red-tailed guppy	15	10
2418	1p.50 Tiger lace-tailed guppy	15	10
2419	2p. Pearl-scaled goldfish	30	15
	a. Strip of 5. Nos. 2419/23	1·60	
2420	2p. Red-capped goldfish	30	15
2421	2p. Lion-headed goldfish	30	15
2422	2p. Black moor goldfish	30	15
2423	2p. Bubble-eyed goldfish	30	15
2424	4p. Delta topsail platy	60	60
	a. Sheetlet of 4. Nos. 2424/7	2·40	

2425	4p. Orange-spotted hi-fin platy	60	60
2426	4p. Red lyre-tailed swordtail	60	60
2427	4p. Bleeding heart hi-fin platy	60	60
2414/2427 *Set of 14*		4·25	3·25

MS2428 Two sheets. (a) 132 × 78 mm. 6p. Green discus; 6p. Brown discus; 7p. Red discus; 7p. Harald's blue discus; (b) 88 × 61 mm. 8p. Golden arowana. Imperf   2·50   2·50

Nos. 2414/18 and 2419/23 respectively were issued together in *se-tenant* strips of five within their sheets; Nos. 2424/7 were issued in *se-tenant* sheetlets of four stamps.

The stamps in No. **MS**2428a are arranged in two vertical pairs with a gutter between. The sheet exists with the gutter horizontally imperforate or perforated.

See also Nos. 2543/**MS**2557.

"PHILIPPINE STAMP EXHIBITION 1992 — TAIPEI"
(**773**) (¾-*size illustration*)

1992 (12 Sept). *Philippines Stamp Exhibition, Taipeh, Taiwan. No.* **MS**2428 *optd with T* **773**.

MS2429 Two sheets. (a) 132 × 79 mm. 6p. × 2, 7p. × 2 multicoloured; (b) 88 × 61 mm. 8p. multicoloured   4·50   4·50

On No. **MS**2429a the overprint is vertical in both the left and right margins; on No. **MS**2429b it is horizontal in the bottom margin.

774 Couple   **775** Melon, Beans, Tomatoes and Potatoes

(Des F. Manalang and T. Daquioag)

1992 (28 Sept). *Greetings Stamps. "Happy Birthday". T* **774** *and similar vert design. Multicoloured.* W **614** (*sideways*). P 14.

2430	2p. Type **774**	20	15
2431	6p. Type **774**	65	45
2432	7p. Balloons and candles on birthday cake	75	50
2433	8p. As No. 2432	95	60
2430/2433 *Set of 4*		2·30	1·50

(Des A. Divina)

1992 (14 Oct). *500th Anniv of Discovery of America by Columbus. T* **775** *and similar horiz designs. Multicoloured.* W **614**. P 14.

2434	2p. Type **775**	20	15
2435	6p. Maize and sweet potatoes	65	45
2436	8p. Pineapple, cashews, avocado and water melon	90	60

Second National Philatelic Convention

780 Family and Canoe

781 Damaged Trees

(Des A. Luzon)

1992 (15 Nov). *Anti-drugs Campaign. T **780** and similar vert design. Multicoloured.* W **614** (*sideways*). P 14.
2444	2p. Type **780**	20	15
2445	8p. Man carrying paddle, children and canoe	90	60

Cebu, Philippines, Oct. 22-24, 1992

(776)

1992 (15 Oct). *Second National Philatelic Convention. No. **MS**2271 optd with T **776** in blue.*
MS2437	**742** 16p. multicoloured	3·00	3·00

1992 (16 Nov). *Mt. Pinatubo Fund (for victims of volcanic eruption). T **781** and similar horiz designs. Multicoloured.* W **614**. P 13½.
2446	25s. Type **781**	10	10
2447	1p. Mt. Pinatubo erupting	10	10
	a. Block of 4. Nos. 2447/50	35	
2448	1p. Cattle in ash-covered field	10	10
2449	1p. Refugee settlement	10	10
2450	1p. People shovelling ash	10	10
2446/2450	*Set of 5*	45	45

Nos. 2447/50 were issued together in *se-tenant* blocks of four within the sheet.

777 Figures around World Map

778 Mother and Child

(Des A. Divina)

1992 (27 Oct). *International Nutrition Conference, Rome.* W **614**. P 14.
2438	**777** 2p. multicoloured	20	15

(Des J. Joya)

1992 (5 Nov). *Christmas. T **778** and similar vert designs showing mothers and children.* W **614** (*sideways*). P 14.
2439	2p. multicoloured	20	15
2440	6p. multicoloured	65	45
2441	7p. multicoloured	75	50
2442	8p. multicoloured	95	60
2439/2442	*Set of 4*	2·30	1·50

INAUGURATION OF THE PHILIPPINE POSTAL MUSEUM AND PHILATELIC LIBRARY. NOVEMBER 10 1992

(779)

1992 (10 Nov). *Inauguration of Postal Museum and Philatelic Library. No. **MS**1566 optd with T **779** in red.*
MS2443	76 × 76 mm. 5p. multicoloured	1·80	1·80

782 Red Junglefowl

(Des R. Asuncion)

1992 (27 Nov). *New Year. Year of the Cock. T **782** and similar horiz design. Multicoloured.* W **614**. P 14.
2451	2p. Type **782**	20	15
2452	6p. Maranao Sarimanok (mythical bird)	65	45
MS2453	98 × 87 mm. Nos. 2451/2 plus two labels. Perf or imperf	90	90

(783) (½-size illustration)

1992 (1 Dec). *Philippine Stamp Exhibition, Taipeh. No. **MS**2453 optd with T **783** in the margin. Perf or imperf.*
MS2454	98 × 87 mm. 2, 6p. multicoloured	1·80	1·80

784 Badges of 61st and 71st Divisions, Cebu Area Command

785 "Family" (César Legaspi) (family ties)

(Des Raquel Torregrosa)

1992 (7 Dec). *Philippine Guerrilla Units of Second World War (1st series). T 784 and similar vert designs. Multicoloured. W 614 (sideways). P 14.*

2455	2p. Type **784**	20	15
	a. Block or strip of 4. Nos. 2455/8	95	
2456	2p. Vinzons Guerrillas and badges of 48th Chinese Guerrilla Squadron and 101st Division	20	15
2457	2p. Anderson's Command, Luzon Guerrilla Army Forces and badge of Bulacan Military Area	20	15
2458	2p. President Quezon's Own Guerrillas and badges of Marking's Fil-American Troops and Hunters ROTC Guerrillas	20	15
2455/2458 *Set of 4*		75	55

Nos. 2455/8 were issued together in *se-tenant* blocks of four within the sheet.

First Day Covers are dated 5 December.

See also Nos. 2594/7.

1992 (7 Dec). *Philatelic Week. T 785 and similar vert designs. Multicoloured. W 614 (sideways). P 14.*

2459	2p. Type **785**	20	15
2460	6p. "Pounding Rice" (Nena Saguil) (hard work and industry)	65	45
2461	7p. "Fish Vendors" (Romeo Tabuena) (flexibility and adaptability)	75	50

First Day Covers are dated 24 November.

786 Black Shama

(Des A. Divina)

1992 (15 Dec). *Endangered Birds. T 786 and similar horiz designs. Multicoloured. W 614 (sideways on Nos. 2467/70). P 14.*

*(a) As Type **786**.*

2462	2p. Type **786**	20	15
	a. Strip of 5. Nos. 2462/6	1·20	
	ab. *Tête-bêche* strip or block of 10	2·30	
2463	2p. Blue-headed fantail	20	15
2464	2p. Mindoro zone-tailed (inscr "Imperial") pigeon	20	15
2465	2p. Sulu hornbill	20	15
2466	2p. Red-vented (inscr "Philippine") cockatoo	20	15

(b) Size 29 × 39 mm.

2467	2p. Philippine trogon	20	20
	a. Sheetlet of 4. Nos. 2467/70	95	
2468	2p. Rufous hornbill	20	20
2469	2p. White-bellied black woodpecker	20	20
2470	2p. Spotted wood kingfisher	20	20

(c) Size 36 × 26½ mm.

2471	2p. Brahminy kite	20	20
	a. Sheetlet of 4. Nos. 2471/4	95	
2472	2p. Philippine falconet	20	20
2473	2p. Reef heron	20	20
2474	2p. Philippine duck (inscr "Mallard")	20	20
2462/2474 *Set of 13*		2·30	1·90

Nos. 2462/6 were issued together in vertical and horizontal *se-tenant* strips of five within sheets of 50 stamps with the lower block of 25 inverted. Nos. 2467/70 and 2471/4 respectively were issued in *se-tenant* sheetlets of four stamps.

First Day Covers are dated 25 November.

1993 (23 Jan). *As No. 2235 but value changed. W **614** (sideways). P 14 × 13½.*

2475	1p. multicoloured	10	10

787 Flower (Jasmine)

788 Flower (Jasmine)

(Des A. Divina and Raquel Torregrosa)

1993 (29 Apr)–**94**. *National Symbols. T 787/8 and similar vert designs. Multicoloured. Dated "1993". W **614** (sideways). P 13½.*

*(a) As T **787** with "Pilipinas" in ochre at top of design.*

2476	1p. Type **787**	15	10
2477	2p. Flag ("(watawat)" 6½ mm long)	20	15
2478	6p. Leaf (palm)	65	45
2479	7p. Costume	75	50
2480	8p. Fruit (mango)	90	60

*(b) As T **788** with "Pilipinas" in red at foot of design (9 July 1993–1994).*

2481	60s. Tree	15	10
2482	1p.50 Fish	15	10
2483	2p. Flag (distance between face value and "1993" 15 mm) (10 Feb 1994)	15	10
2484	3p. Animal (water buffalo)	30	20
2485	5p. Bird (finches)	50	35
2486	8p. Fruit (4 October 1993)	1·00	60
2487	10p. House	1·10	75
2476/2487 *Set of 12*		5·50	3·50

For 1 and 2p. values on watermarked paper and dated "1993" (including Type **788** and both types of flag but redrawn) see Nos. 2512/21 and 2565/78. For values dated "1994" or later and on unwatermarked paper, see Nos. 2641/9.

789 *Euploea mulciber dufresne*

1993 (28 May). *Butterflies. Multicoloured. W **614** (sideways on Nos. 2493/6). P 14.*

*(a) T **789** and similar horiz designs.*

2488	2p. Type **789**	20	15
	a. Strip of 5. Nos. 2488/92	1·20	
	ab. *Tête-bêche* (strip or block of 10)	2·40	
2489	2p. *Cheritra orpheus*	20	15
2490	2p. *Delias henningia*	20	15
2491	2p. *Mycalesis ita*	20	15

2492	2p. *Delias diaphana*	20	15

(b) Size 28 × 35 mm.

2493	2p. *Papilio rumanzobia*	20	20
	a. Sheetlet of 4. Nos. 2493/6	95	
2494	2p. *Papilio palinurus*	20	20
2495	2p. *Trogonoptera trojana*	20	20
2496	2p. Tailed jay (*Graphium*		
	agamemnon)	20	20
2488/2496 *Set of 9*		2·75	1·50

(c) Sheet 140 × 70 mm.

MS2497 10p. *Papilio iowi, Valeria boebera* and
Delias themis (116 × 27 mm) . . . . 1·50 1·50
Nos. 2488/92 were issued together in vertical and horizontal *se-tenant* strips of five within sheets of 50 stamps with the lower block of 25 inverted. Nos. 2493/6 were issued together in *se-tenant* sheetlets of four stamps, forming a composite design.

(790) (⅔-size illustration)

1993 (29 May). *"Indopex '93" International Stamp Exhibition, Surabaya. No.* MS2497 *optd with T* 790 *in the margin.*
MS2498 140 × 70 mm. 10p. multicoloured . . . 2·20 2·20
No. 2493a was also overprinted in the margin as T 790.

791 Nicanor Abelardo

792 Boxing and Judo

1993 (10 June). *Birth Centenaries. T* 791 *and similar vert designs. Multicoloured. W* 614. P 14 × 13½.

2499	2p. Type 791	20	15
	a. Horiz strip of 5. Nos. 2499/2503	1·20	
2500	2p. Pilar Hidalgo-Lim	20	15
2501	2p. Manuel Viola Gallego	20	15
2502	2p. Maria Ylagan-Orosa	20	15
2503	2p. Eulogio B. Rodriguez	20	15
2499/2503 *Set of 5*		2·00	70

Nos. 2499/2503 were issued together in *se-tenant* strips of five stamps within the sheet.

1993 (23 June). *17th South-East Asian Games, Singapore. T* 792 *and similar multicoloured designs. Phosphorescent security marking* (2504/9). *W* 614 (*sideways on* MS2510). P 14.

2504	2p. Weightlifting, archery, fencing and shooting (79 × 29 mm)	20	15
	a. Horiz strip of 3. Nos. 2504/6	75	
2505	2p. Type 792	20	15
2506	2p. Athletics, cycling, gymnastics and golf (79 × 29 mm)	20	15
2507	6p. Table tennis, football, volleyball and badminton (79 × 29 mm)	65	45
	a. With additional inscr "June 12–20 1993"		
	b. Horiz strip of 3. Nos. 2507/9	2·10	
2508	6p. Billiards and bowling	65	45
2509	6p. Swimming, water polo, yachting and diving (79 × 29 mm)	65	45
2504/2509 *Set of 6*		1·90	95

MS2510 84 × 96 mm. 10p. Basketball (*vert*) 2·25 1·60
Stamps of the same value were issued together in horizontal *se-tenant* strips of three within their sheets.
No. 2507a occurs on row 4, stamp 1.

Towards the Year 2000

46th PAF Anniversary 1 July 1993
(793) (½-size illustration)

1993 (1 July). *46th Anniv of Philippine Air Force. No.* MS2497 *optd in the margin with T* 793 *in royal blue.*
MS2511 140 × 70 mm. 10p. multicoloured . . . 7·50 7·50

1993 (9 July). *Centenary of Declaration of Philippine Independence (1st issue). Vert designs as T* 788 *showing National Symbols. Multicoloured. W* 614 (*sideways*). P 13½.

2512	1p. Flag	10	10
	a. Sheetlet. Nos. 2512/21 plus 2 labels	95	
2513	1p. House	10	10
2514	1p. Costume	10	10
2515	1p. Tree	10	10
2516	1p. Type 788	10	10
2517	1p. Fruit	10	10
2518	1p. Leaf	10	10
2519	1p. Fish	10	10
2520	1p. Animal	10	10
2521	1p. Bird	10	10
2512/2521 *Set of 10*		90	90

Nos. 2512/21 were issued together in *se-tenant* sheetlets of 10 stamps and 2 labels showing the state arms. The foot of the sheetlet contains bars and lyrics from the national anthem.
See also Nos. MS2663, 2717/19, MS2753, 2818/20, MS2906, 2973/5, MS3010, 3017/19, 3089/MS3092, 3093/7, 3103/5, MS3106, 3107/21, MS3178, 3200/9.

794 *Spathoglottis chrysantha*

(795) (½-size illustration)

1993 (14 Aug). *Orchids. T* 794 *and similar vert designs. Multicoloured.* P 14.

2522	2p. Type 794	20	15
	a. Block of 5. Nos. 2522/6	1·30	
2523	2p. *Arachnis longicaulis*	20	15
2524	2p. *Phalaenopsis mariae*	20	15
2525	2p. *Coelogyne marmorata*	20	15
2526	2p. *Dendrobium sanderae*	20	15
2527	3p. *Dendrobium serratilabium*	30	20
	a. Block of 5. Nos. 2527/31	1·60	
2528	3p. *Phalaenopsis equestris*	30	20
2529	3p. *Vanda merrillii*	30	20

2530	3p. *Vanda luzonica*	30	20
2531	3p. *Grammatophyllum martae*	30	20
2522/2531	Set of 10	2·25	1·60

MS2532 Two sheets, each 58 × 99 mm. (a) 8p.
Aerides' quinquevulnera (27 × 77 mm). Perf;
(b) 8p. *Vanda lamellata* (27 × 77 mm).
Imperf 90   90
Stamps of the same value were issued together in *se-tenant*
blocks of five stamps within the sheet.

1993 (14 Aug). *"Taipei '93" Asian Stamp Exhibition. No.* **MS**2532
optd with T **795** *in the margin.*
MS2533 Two sheets, each 58 × 99 mm. (a) 8p.
multicoloured. Perf; (b) 8p. multicoloured.
Imperf 90   90

796 Dog in Window
("Thinking of You")

797 Palms and
Coconuts

1993 (20 Aug). *Greetings Stamps. T* **796** *and similar horiz
designs. Multicoloured. W* **614**. P 14.

2534	2p. Type **796**	20	15
	a. Pair. Nos. 2534/5	50	35
2535	2p. As No. 2534 but inscr "Naalala Kita"	20	15
2536	6p. Dog looking at clock ("Thinking of You")	65	45
	a. Pair. Nos. 2536/7	1·40	90
2537	6p. As No. 2536 but inscr "Naalala Kita"	65	45
2538	7p. Dog looking at calendar ("Thinking of You")	75	50
	a. Pair. Nos. 2538/9	1·60	1·10
2539	7p. As No. 2538 but inscr "Naalala Kita"	75	50
2540	8p. Dog with pair of slippers ("Thinking of You")	90	60
	a. Pair. Nos. 2540/1	1·80	
2541	8p. As No. 2540 but inscr "Naalala Kita"	90	60
2534/2541	Set of 8	4·50	3·00

Stamps of the same value were issued together in *se-tenant*
pairs within their sheets.

1993 (24 Aug). *"Tree of Life". W* **614** *(sideways). P* 14.

| 2542 | **797** | 2p. multicoloured | 20 | 15 |

798 Albino Ryukin Goldfish

799 Map and Emblem

(Des D. Dujunco)

1993 (9 Sept). *Freshwater Aquarium Fishes (2nd series). P 14.*

(a) T **798** *and similar horiz designs.*

2543	2p. Type **798**	20	15
	a. Strip of 5. Nos. 2543/7	1·20	
2544	2p. Black oranda goldfish	20	15

2545	2p. Lion-headed goldfish	20	15
2546	2p. Celestial goldfish	20	15
2547	2p. Pompon goldfish	20	15
2548	2p. Paradise fish	20	15
	a. Strip of 5. Nos 2548/52	1·20	
2549	2p. Pearl gourami	20	15
2550	2p. Red-tailed black shark	20	15
2551	2p. Tiger barb	20	15
2552	2p. Cardinal tetra	20	15

(b) Size 29 × 39 mm (Nos. 2553/6) or 39 × 29 mm (stamps in No.
MS2557a).

2553	2p. Pearl-scaled angel fish	20	15
	a. Sheetlet of 4. Nos. 2553/6	95	
2554	2p. Zebra freshwater angelfish	20	20
2555	2p. Marble freshwater angelfish	20	20
2556	2p. Black freshwater angelfish	20	20
2543/2556	Set of 14	2·50	2·00

MS2557 Two sheets. (a) 138 × 78 mm. 3p.
Neon siamese fighting fish; 3p. Libby
Siamese fighting fish; 3p. Split-tailed Siamese
fighting fish; 3p. Butterfly Siamese fighting
fish. Perf; (b) 87 × 60 mm. 6p. Albino oscar.
Imperf
Nos. 2543/7 and 2548/52 respectively were issued together in
se-tenant strips of 5 within their sheets and Nos. 2553/6 in *se-tenant* sheetlets of four stamps.

1993 (20 Sept). *Basic Petroleum and Minerals Inc. "Towards Self-sufficiency in Energy". W* **614**. P 14.

| 2558 | **799** | 2p. multicoloured | 20 | 15 |

(800) (⅖-*size illustration*)

1993 (20 Sept). *"Bangkok 1993" International Stamp Exhibition,
Thailand. No.* **MS**2557 *optd as T* **800**.
MS2559 Two sheets. (a) 3p. × 4 multicoloured;
(b) 6p. multicoloured . . . . 7·50   7·50
The overprint on No. **MS**2559b is smaller.

801 Globe, Scales, Book
and Gavel

802 "Our Lady of La Naval"
(statue) and Galleon

1993 (30 Sept). *16th International Law Conference, Manila. T* **801**
and similar multicoloured designs. P 14.

2560	2p. Type **801**	20	15
2561	6p. Globe, scales, gavel and conference emblem on flag of Philippines (*vert*)	65	45
2562	7p. Woman holding scales, conference building and globe	80	50
2563	8p. Fisherman pulling in nets and emblem (*vert*)	95	65
2560/2563	Set of 4	2·30	1·60

1993 (18 Oct). *400th Anniv of Our Lady of La Naval. W* **614**. P 14.

| 2564 | **802** | 2p. multicoloured | 20 | 15 |

1993 (28 Oct). *National Symbols. Vert designs as T **787** (No. 2571) or T **788** (others). Multicoloured.* W **614** (sideways). P 13½.

2565	2p. Hero (Dr. José Rizal)	20	15
	a. Block of 14. Nos. 2565/78	3·00	
2566	2p. House	20	15
2567	2p. Costume	20	15
2568	2p. Dance ("Tinikling")	20	15
2569	2p. Sport (Sipa)	20	15
2570	2p. Bird	20	15
2571	2p. Flag (as No. 2477 but with "(watawat)" 4½ mm long)	20	15
2572	2p. Animal	20	15
2573	2p. Type **788**	20	15
2574	2p. Tree	20	15
2575	2p. Fruit	20	15
2576	2p. Leaf	20	15
2577	2p. Fish	20	15
2578	2p. Flag (as No. 2483 but with distance between face value and "1993" 17 mm)	20	15
2565/2578	*Set of 14*	2·50	1·90

Nos. 2565/78 were issued together in *se-tenant* blocks within sheets of 200 stamps containing 10 blocks of 14 and 5 blocks of 12 stamps (without the two flag designs).

803 Woman and Terraced Hillside

804 Trees

1993 (29 Oct). *International Year of Indigenous Peoples. T **803** and similar vert designs showing women in traditional costumes. Multicoloured.* P 14.

2579	2p. Type **803**	20	15
2580	6p. Woman, plantation and mountain	65	45
2581	7p. Woman and mosque	80	50
2582	8p. Woman and vintas (canoes)	95	65
2579/2582	*Set of 4*	2·30	1·60

1993 (22 Nov). *Philatelic Week. "Save the Earth". T **804** and similar horiz designs. Multicoloured.* P 14.

2583	2p. Type **804**	20	15
2584	6p. Marine flora and fauna	65	45
2585	7p. Bird and irrigation system	80	50
2586	8p. Effects of industrial pollution	95	65
2583/2586	*Set of 4*	2·30	1·60

805 1949 6c.+4c. Stamp and Symbols

806 Moon-buggy and Society Emblem

1993 (30 Nov). *400th Anniv of Publication of Doctrina Christiana (first book published in Philippines).* P 14.

2587	**805** 2p. multicoloured	20	15

1993 (30 Nov). *50th Anniv of Filipino Inventors Society. T **806** and similar vert design.* P 14.

2588	2p. Type **806**	20	15
	a. Horiz pair. Nos. 2588/9	50	35
2589	2p. Rice-harvesting machine	20	15

Nos. 2588/9 were issued together in *se-tenant* pairs within the sheet, each pair forming a composite design.

807 Holy Family

808 Northern Luzon

1993 (1 Dec). *Christmas. T **807** and similar vert designs. Multicoloured.* P 14.

2590	2p. Type **807**	20	15
2591	6p. Church goers	65	45
2592	7p. Cattle and baskets of food	80	50
2593	8p. Carol-singers	95	65
2590/2593	*Set of 4*	2·30	1·60

1993 (10 Dec). *Philippine Guerrilla Units of Second World War (2nd series). T **808** and similar vert designs. Multicoloured.* P 14.

2594	2p. Type **808**	20	15
	a. Block or strip of 4. Nos. 2594/7	95	
2595	2p. Bohol Area Command	20	15
2596	2p. Leyte Area Command	20	15
2597	2p. Palawan Special Battalion and Sulu Area Command	20	15
2594/2597	*Set of 4*	70	55

Nos. 2594/7 were issued together in *se-tenant* blocks and strips of four stamps within the sheet.

809 Dove over City (peace and order)

810 Shih Tzu

1993 (14 Dec). *"Philippines 2000" (development plan). T **809** and similar horiz designs. Multicoloured.* P 14.

2598	2p. Type **809**	20	15
2599	6p. Means of transport and communications	65	45
2600	7p. Offices, roads and factories (infrastructure and industry)	80	50
2601	8p. People from different walks of life (people empowerment)	95	65
2598/2601	*Set of 4*	2·30	1·60
MS2602	110 × 85 mm. 8p. Various motifs on themes of peace, transport and communication, infrastructure and industry and people power. Imperf	2·20	2·20

1993 (15 Dec). *New Year. Year of the Dog. T **810** and similar horiz design. Multicoloured.* P 14.

2603	2p. Type **810**	20	15
2604	6p. Chow	65	45
MS2605	98 × 88 mm. Nos. 2603/4 plus two labels. Perf or imperf	1·50	1·50

811 Jamboree Emblem and Flags   **812** Club Emblem on Diamond

1993 (28 Dec). *First Association of South-East Asian Nations Scout Jamboree, Makiling. T* **811** *and similar vert design. Multicoloured. P* 14.

2606	2p. Type **811**	20	15
2607	6p. Scout at camp-site, flags and emblem	65	45
MS2608	86 × 86 mm. Nos. 2606/7	1·80	1·80

1994 (19 Jan). *75th Anniv of Manila Rotary Club. P* 14.

2609	**812** 2p. multicoloured	20	15

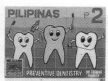 

813 Teeth and Dental Hygiene Products   **814** *Acropora micropthalma*

1994 (3 Feb). *17th Asian–Pacific Dental Congress, Manila. T* **813** *and similar multicoloured design. P* 14.

2610	2p. Type **813**	20	15
2611	6p. Flags of participating countries and teeth over globe with Philippines circled (*vert*)	65	45

1994 (15 Feb). *Corals. T* **814** *and similar multicoloured designs. P* 14.

2612	2p. Type **814**	20	15
	a. Block of 10. Nos. 2612/21	2·40	
2613	2p. *Seriatopora hystrix*	20	15
2614	2p. *Acropora latistella*	20	15
2615	2p. *Millepora tenella*	20	15
2616	2p. *Millepora tenella* (*different*)	20	15
2617	2p. *Pachyseris valenciennesi*	20	15
2618	2p. *Pavona decussata*	20	15
2619	2p. *Galaxea fascicularis*	20	15
2620	2p. *Acropora formosa*	20	15
2621	2p. *Acropora humilis*	20	15
2622	2p. *Isis* sp. (*vert*)	20	20
	a. Sheetlet of 4. Nos. 2622/5	95	
2623	2p. *Plexaura* sp. (*vert*)	20	20
2624	2p. *Dendronepthya* sp. (*vert*)	20	20
2625	2p. *Heteroxenia* sp. (*vert*)	20	20
2612/2625	Set of 14	2·50	2·10

MS2626 135 × 78 mm. 3p. *Xenia puertogalerae*; 3p. *Plexaura* sp. (*different*); 3p. *Dendrophyllia gracilis*; 3p. *Plerogyra sinuosa*   95   95

Nos. 2612/21 were issued together in blocks of ten stamps within the sheet and Nos. 2622/5 in *se-tenant* sheetlets of four stamps.

For sheet as No. **MS**2626 but with additional inscription for "Naphilcon '94", see No. **MS**2631.

815 New Year Stamps of 1991 and 1992 and Exhibition Emblem   **816** Class of 1944 Emblem

1994 (18 Feb). *"Hong Kong '94" Stamp Exhibition. T* **815** *and similar horiz design. Multicoloured. P* 14.

2627	2p. Type **815**	20	15
2628	6p. 1993 New Year stamps	65	45
MS2629	Two sheets, each 98 × 72 mm. (a) Nos. 2627/8 (pale blue margin); (b)		
	Nos. 2627/8 (bright yellow-green margin)	90	90

1994 (20 Feb). *50th Anniv of Philippine Military Academy Class of 1944. P* 14.

2630	**816** 2p. multicoloured	20	15

1994 (21 Feb). *"Naphilcon '94" First National Philatelic Congress. As No.* **MS**2626 *but with additional inscription in the central gutter.*

MS2631 135 × 78 mm. 3p. × 4, multicoloured   1·40   1·40

817 Airplane over Harbour, Man, Cogwheel and Emblem   **818** Stork carrying Baby ("Binabati Kita")

1994 (1 Mar). *Federation of Filipino–Chinese Chambers of Commerce and Industry. P* 14.

2632	**817** 2p. multicoloured	20	15

1994 (15 Apr). *Greetings Stamps. T* **818** *and similar vert designs. Multicoloured. P* 14.

2633	2p. Type **818**	20	15
	a. Pair. Nos. 2633/4	50	35
2634	2p. As No. 2633 but inscr "Congratulations"	20	15
2635	2p. Bouquet ("Binabati Kita")	20	15
	a. Pair. Nos. 2635/6	50	35
2636	2p. As No. 2635 but inscr "Congratulations"	20	15
2637	2p. Mortar board, scroll and books ("Binabati Kita")	20	15
	a. Pair. Nos. 2637/8	50	35
2638	2p. As No. 2637 but inscr "Congratulations"	20	15
2639	2p. Bouquet, doves and heads inside heart ("Binabati Kita")	20	15
	a. Pair. Nos. 2639/40	50	35
2640	2p. As No. 2639 but inscr "Congratulations"	20	15
2633/2640	Set of 8	1·40	1·10

Stamps of the same design were issued together in *se-tenant* pairs within their sheets.

1994 (19 Apr)–**95**. *National Symbols. As T* **788** *but on unwatermarked paper. Dated "1994" or "1995". P* 13½.

2641	1p. Type **788** (3 May 1994)	15	15
2642	1p.50 Fish (6 Feb 1995)	15	15
2644	3p. Animal (19 Apr 1994)	15	15
2645	5p. Bird (19 Apr 1994)	30	20
2646	6p. Leaf (1 Dec 1994)	35	15
2647	7p. Costume (6 July 1994)	40	25
2649	10p. House (19 Apr 1994)	55	30
2641/2649 *Set of 7*		1·80	1·20

The 1, 3 and 5p. exist dated both "1994" and "1995". Numbers have been left for additions to this series.

819 Gloria Diaz (Miss Universe 1969)

820 Antonio Molina (composer)

1994 (5 May). *Miss Universe Beauty Contest. T* **819** *and similar vert designs. Multicoloured.* P 14.

2653	2p. Type **819**	20	15
	a. Pair. Nos. 2653 and 2655	95	65
2654	2p. Margie Moran (Miss Universe 1973)	20	15
	a. Pair. Nos. 2654 and 2656	1·10	80
2655	6p. Crown	65	45
2656	7p. Contestant	80	60
2653/2656 *Set of 4*		1·60	1·20
MS2657 90 × 80 mm. 8p. As No. 2653; 8p. As No. 2654		1·80	1·80

Nos. 2653 and 2655 were issued together in *se-tenant* pairs within the sheet, as were also Nos. 2654 and 2656.

(Des R. Naval and Raquel Torregrosa)

1994 (1 June). *Birth Centenaries. T* **820** *and similar vert designs. Multicoloured.* P 14 × 13½.

2658	2p. Type **820**	20	15
	a. Strip of 5. Nos. 2658/62	1·20	80
2659	2p. José Yulo (Secretary of Justice)	20	15
2660	2p. Josefa Jara-Martinez (social worker)	20	15
2661	2p. Nicanor Reyes (accountant)	20	15
2662	2p. Sabino Padilla (judge)	20	15
2658/2662 *Set of 5*		90	65

Nos. 2658/62 were issued in *se-tenant* strips of five within the sheet.

1994 (13 June). *Centenary of Declaration of Philippine Independence (2nd issue). National Landmarks. Sheet* 100 × 80 mm *containing vert designs as T* **788**. *Multicoloured.* P 13½.

MS2663 2p. Aguinaldo Shrine; 2p. Barasoain Shrine; 3p. Rizal Shrine; 3p. Mabini Shrine ... 1·20 1·20

821 Map, Forest and Emblem (Baguio City)

822 Cross through "ILLEGAL RECRUITMENT"

1994 (4 July). *Export Processing Zones. T* **821** *and similar horiz designs. Multicoloured.* P 14.

2664	2p. Type **821**	20	15
	a. Block of 4. Nos. 2664/7	90	
2665	2p. Cross on hilltop (Bataan)	20	15
2666	2p. Octagonal building (Mactan)	20	15
2667	2p. Aguinaldo Shrine (Cavite)	20	15
2668	7p. Map and products	80	50
	a. Horiz pair. Nos. 2668/9	1·80	1·30
2669	8p. Globe and products	95	65
2664/2669 *Set of 6*		2·30	1·60

Nos. 2264/9 were issued together in *se-tenant* blocks of four stamps and Nos. 2668/9 in horizontal *se-tenant* pairs within their sheets, each block and pair forming composite designs.

1994 (15 July). *Anti-illegal Recruitment Campaign.* P 14.
2670 **822** 2p. multicoloured ... 20 15

823 Palawan Bearcat (*Arctictis whitei*)

824 *Conus gloriamaris* (Glory of the Sea Cone)

1994 (15 Aug). *Mammals. T* **823** *and similar horiz designs. Multicoloured.* P 14.

2671	6p. Type **823**	75	45
	a. Block of 4. Nos. 2671/4	3·25	
2672	6p. Philippine tarsier (*Tarsius syrichta*)	75	45
2673	6p. Malayan pangolin (inscr "Scaly Anteater") (*Manis javanica*)	75	45
2674	6p. Indonesian ("Palawan") porcupine (*Thecurus pumilus*)	75	45
2671/2674 *Set of 4*		2·75	1·60
MS2675 96 × 67 mm. 12p. Visayan spotted deer (*Cervus alfredi*) (79 × 29 mm)		1·50	1·50

Nos. 2671/4 were issued together in *se-tenant* blocks of four stamps within the sheet.
See also No. **MS**2681.

1994 (16 Aug). *"Philakorea 1994" International Stamp Exhibition, Seoul. Shells. T* **824** *and similar horiz designs. Multicoloured.* P 14.

2676	2p. Type **824**	20	15
	a. Block of 4. Nos. 2676/9	90	
2677	2p. *Conus striatus* (Striate cone)	20	15
2678	2p. *Conus geographus* (Geography cone)	20	15
2679	2p. *Conus textile* (Textile cone)	20	15
2676/2679 *Set of 4*		75	55
MS2680 Two sheets, each 88 × 78 mm. (a) 6p. Striate cone; 6p. *Conus marmoreus* (Marble cone). (b) 6p. Marble cone; 6p. Geography cone		1·50	1·50

Nos. 2676/9 were issued together in *se-tenant* blocks of four stamps within the sheet.

1994 (31 Aug). *"Singpex '94" National Stamp Exhibition, Singapore. As No.* **MS**2675 *but additionally inscribed "Singpex '94 31 August–3 September 1994" and emblem.* P 14.
MS2681 96 × 67 mm. 12p. multicoloured ... 1·50 1·50

825 Sergio Osmeña, Snr.

826 Family (International Year of the Family)

1994 (15 Sept). *50th Anniv of Leyte Gulf Landings. T* **825** *and similar horiz designs. Multicoloured.* P 14.
2682	2p. Type **825**	20	15
	a. Block of 4. Nos. 2682/5	90	
2683	2p. Soldiers landing at Palo	20	15
2684	2p. "Peace – A Better World" emblem	20	15
2685	2p. Carlos Romulo	20	15
2682/2685 *Set of 4*		75	55

Nos. 2682/5 were issued together in *se-tenant* blocks of four stamps, each block forming a composite design.

(Des M. Malto)

1994 (24 Oct). *Anniversaries and Event. T* **826** *and similar horiz designs. Multicoloured.* P 14.
2686	2p. Type **826**	20	15
2687	6p. Workers (75th anniv of International Labour Organization)	75	45
2688	7p. Aircraft and symbols of flight (50th anniv of International Civil Aviation Organization)	90	60

827 Blue-naped Parrot (*Tanygnathus lucionensis*)	**828** Presidents Fidel Ramos and W. Clinton

(Des A. Divina)

1994 (8 Nov). *"Aseanpex '94" Stamp Exhibition, Penang, Malaysia. Birds. T* **827** *and similar multicoloured designs.* P 14.
2689	2p. Type **827**	20	15
	a. Block of 4. Nos. 2689/92	90	
2690	2p. Luzon bleeding heart (*Gallicolumba luzonica*)	20	15
2691	2p. Palawan peacock-pheasant (*Polyplectron emphanum*)	20	15
2692	2p. Koch's pitta (*Pitta kochi*)	20	15
2689/2692 *Set of 4*		75	55
MS2693 69 × 55 mm. 12p. Philippine eagle (*Pithecophaga jefferyi*) (*vert*)		1·50	1·50

Nos. 2689/92 were issued in *se-tenant* blocks of four within the sheet.

(Des R. Naval)

1994 (12 Nov). *Visit of United States President William Clinton to Philippines.* P 14.
2694	**828**	2p. multicoloured	20	15
2695		8p. multicoloured	1·00	65

829 Convention Emblem	**830** "Soteranna Puson y Quintos de Ventenilla" (Dionisio de Castro)

(Des Cheryl Tabo and V. Secuya)

1994 (15 Nov). *Association of South-East Asian Nations Eastern Business Convention, Davao City.* P 14.
2696	**829**	2p. multicoloured	30	15
2697		6p. multicoloured	75	50

The convention was originally planned for May 1995 but was postponed. Nos. 2696/7 are overprinted with the amended date; stamps with the original date were not issued.

(Des Cheryl Tabo)

1994 (21 Nov). *Philatelic Week. Portraits. T* **830** *and similar vert designs. Multicoloured.* P 14.
2698	2p. Type **830**	30	1·70
2699	6p. "Quintina Castor de Sadie" (Simon Flores y de la Rosa)	75	50
2700	7p. "Portrait of the Artist's Mother" (Felix Hidalgo y Padilla)	90	60
2701	8p. "Una Bulaqueña" (Juan Luna y Novicio)	1·00	65
2698/2701 *Set of 4*		2·75	3·00
MS2702 60 × 100 mm. 12p. "Cirilo and Severina Quiason Family" (Simon Flores y de la Rosa) (28½ × 79 *mm*)		1·50	1·50

831 Wreath	**832** Piggy Bank

(Des A. Divina and Cheryl Tabo)

1994 (25 Nov). *Christmas. T* **831** *and similar vert designs. Multicoloured.* P 14.
2703	2p. Type **831**	30	15
2704	6p. Angels	75	50
2705	7p. Bells	90	60
2706	8p. Christmas basket	1·00	65
2703/2706 *Set of 4*		2·75	1·70

1994 (5 Dec). *New Year. Year of the Pig. T* **832** *and similar horiz design. Multicoloured.* P 14.
2707	2p. Type **832**	30	15
	a. Black double		
2708	6p. Pig couple	75	50
MS2709 98 × 88 mm. Nos. 2707/8 plus two labels. Perf or imperf		1·10	1·10

The imperforate miniature sheet was re-issued with a change of colour, from green to blue, to the pig's hat on the top label.

833 Raid on Prison	**834** East Central Luzon Guerrilla Area

1994 (8 Dec). *50th Anniversaries of Raid by Hunters ROTC Guerrillas on Psew Bilibi Prison and of Mass Escape by Inmates. T* **833** *and similar horiz design. Multicoloured.* P 14.
2710	2p. Type **833**	20	15
	a. Horiz pair. Nos. 2710/11	50	35
2711	2p. Inmates fleeing	20	15

Nos. 2710/11 were printed together in horizontal *se-tenant* pairs within the sheet, each pair forming a composite design.

(Des J. de los Santos)

1994 (8 Dec). *Philippine Guerrilla Units of Second World War (3rd series). T **834** and similar vert designs. Multicoloured. P 14.*
2712 2p. Type **834** 20 15
    a. Block of 4. Nos. 2712/15 90
2713 2p. Mindoro Provincial Battalion and
    Marinduque Guerrilla Force 20 15
2714 2p. Zambales Military District and
    Masbate Guerrilla Regiment 20 15
2715 2p. Samar Area Command 20 15
2712/2715 *Set of 4* 75 55
Nos. 2712/15 were issued together in *se-tenant* blocks of four within the sheet.

835 Ribbon on Globe

836 Flag

1994 (12 Dec). *National AIDS Awareness Campaign. P 14.*
2716 **835** 2p. multicoloured 20 15

(Des A. Divina)

1994 (15 Dec). *Centenary of Declaration of Philippine Independence (3rd issue). T **836** and similar vert designs. Multicoloured. P 14.*
2717 2p. Type **836** 20 15
    a. Horiz strip of 3. Nos. 2717/19 75
2718 2p. Present state flag 20 15
2719 2p. Anniversary emblem 20 15
Nos. 2717/19 were issued together in horizontal *se-tenant* strips of three stamps within the sheet, forming a composite design.

837 Pope John Paul II and Manila Cathedral

(Des A. Divina, R. Naval, Cheryl Tabo, Raquel Torregrosa and J. de los Santos)

1995 (2 Jan). *Papal Visit. T **837** and similar horiz designs. Multicoloured. P 14.*
2720 2p. Type **837** (400th anniv of Manila
    Archdiocese) 20 15
    a. Block of 4. Nos. 2720/3 90
2721 2p. Pope and Cebu Cathedral (400th
    anniv of Diocese) 20 15
2722 2p. Pope and Caceres Cathedral (400th
    anniv of Diocese) 20 15
2723 2p. Pope and Nueva Segovia Cathedral
    (400th anniv of Diocese) 20 15
2724 2p. Pope, globe and Pope's arms . . . 30 20
2725 6p. Pope and Federation of Asian
    Bishops emblem (sixth Conference,
    Manila) 75 50
2726 8p. Pope, youths and emblem (tenth
    World Youth Day) . . . . 1·00 65
2720/2726 *Set of 7* . . . . 2·50 1·75
MS2727 81 × 60 mm. 8p. Pope and President
   Fidel Ramos . . . . 1·00 1·00
Nos. 2720/3 were issued together in *se-tenant* blocks of four within the sheet.

Nos. 2724/6 were each issued in sheets of 36 stamps and 14 labels, one in each sheet showing the Pope and the others the emblem appropriate to each value.

CHRISTYPEX '95
JANUARY 4-16, 1995
University of Santo Tomas, Manila
PHILIPPINE PHILATELIC FEDERATION
(838)

1995 (4 Jan). *"Christypex '95" Philatelic Exhibition, Manila. No. **MS**2727 optd with T **838** in the margin.*
MS2728 81 × 60 mm. 8p. multicoloured . . . . 1·00 1·00

839 Landing Craft and Map

(Des J. de los Santos)

1995 (7 Jan). *50th Anniv of Lingayen Gulf Landings. T **839** and similar horiz design. Multicoloured. P 14.*
2729 2p. Type **839** 20 15
    a. Horiz pair. Nos. 2729/30 . . . . 50 35
2730 2p. Map and emblems of 6th, 37th, 40th
    and 43rd army divisions 20 15
Nos. 2729/30 were issued together in horizontal *se-tenant* pairs within the sheet, each pair forming a composite design.

840 Monument (Peter de Guzman) and Ruins of Intramuros (½-size illustration)

(Des R. Naval and Cheryl Tabo)

1995 (3 Feb). *50th Anniv of Battle for the Liberation of Manila. T **840** and similar horiz design. Multicoloured. P 14.*
2731 2p. Type **840**
2732 8p. Monument and ruins of Legislative
    Building and Department of
    Agriculture . . . .

841 Diokno

842 Anniversary Emblem and Ethnic Groups

(Des R. Naval)

1995 (27 Feb). *Eighth Death Anniv of José Diokno (politician). P 14.*
2733 **841** 2p. multicoloured 20 15

1995 (4 Mar). *75th Anniv of International School, Manila. T **842** and similar horiz design. Multicoloured. P 14.*
2734 2p. Type **842** 20 15
2735 8p. Globe and cut-outs of children . . . 1·00 65

843 Greater Malay Mouse Deer

1995 (30 Mar). *Mammals. T* **843** *and similar horiz designs. Multicoloured.* P 14.

2736	2p. Type **843**	20	15
	a. Block of 4. Nos. 2736/9	90	
2737	2p. Tamarau	20	15
2738	2p. Visayan warty pig	20	15
2739	2p. Palm civet	20	15
2736/2739	*Set of 4*	75	55

MS2740 Sheet 89 × 80 mm. 8p. Flying lemur;
8p. Philippine deer . . . . 2·10 2·10
Nos. 2736/9 were issued together in *se-tenant* blocks of four stamps within the sheet.

844 Nasugbu Landings

845 Memorial

1995 (10 Apr). *50th Anniversaries. T* **844** *and similar horiz designs. Multicoloured.* P 14.

2741	2p. Type **844**	20	15
	a. Horiz pair. Nos. 2741/2	50	35
2742	2p. Tagaytay Landings	20	15
2743	2p. Battle of Nichols Airbase and Fort McKinley	20	15

Nos. 2741/2 were issued together in *se-tenant* horizontal pairs within the sheet, each pair forming a composite design.

1995 (27 Apr). *50th Anniv of Liberation of Baguio.* P 14.
2744 **845** 2p. multicoloured 20 15

846 Cabanatuan Camp

847 Victorio Edades (artist)

1995 (28 May). *50th Anniv of Liberation of Internment and Prisoner of War Camps. T* **846** *and similar horiz designs. Multicoloured.* P 14.

2745	2p. Type **846**	20	15
2746	2p. Entrance to U.S.T. camp	20	15
2747	2p. Los Baños camp	20	15

Nos. 2746/7 are wrongly inscribed "Interment".

(Des A. Divina, R. Naval, Cheryl Tabo, Raquel Torregrosa and J. de los Santos)

1995 (1 June). *Birth Centenaries. T* **847** *and similar vert designs. Multicoloured.* P 13½.

2748	2p. Type **847**	20	15
	a. Strip of 5. Nos. 2748/52	1·10	
2749	2p. Jovita Fuentes (opera singer)	20	15
2750	2p. Candido Africa (medical researcher)	20	15
2751	2p. Asuncion Arriola-Perez (politician)	20	15
2752	2p. Eduardo Quisumbing (botanist)	20	15
2748/2752	*Set of 5*	90	70

Nos. 2748/52 were issued together in *se-tenant* strips of five stamps within the sheet.

1995 (12 June). *Centenary of Declaration of Philippine Independence (3rd issue). 123rd Anniv of Cavite Mutiny. Sheet* 100 × 80 *mm containing vert designs as T* **788**. P 13½.
MS2753 2p. Cavite shipyard; 2p. Centenary memorial; 3p. San Felipe fortress; 3p. Crisanto de los Reyes y Mendoza (death centenary) . . . . 1·30 80

848 Emblems and Bible

849 Ferrer

(Des R. Tiama)

1995 (22 July). *50th Anniv of Philippine Catholic Bishops' Conference, Manila.* P 14.
2754 **848** 2p. multicoloured 20 15

(Des J. de los Santos)

1995 (2 Aug). *Eighth Death Anniv of Jaime Ferrer (administrator).* P 14.
2755 **849** 2p. multicoloured 20 15

850 Neolithic Burial Jar, Manunggul

851 Philippine Eagle

(Des A. Divina and Cheryl Tabo)

1995 (4 Aug). *Archaeology. T* **850** *and similar multicoloured designs.* P 14.

2756	2p. Type **850**	20	15
	a. Block of 4. Nos. 2756/59	90	
2757	2p. Iron age secondary burial jar, Ayub Cave, Mindanao	20	15
2758	2p. Iron age secondary burial jar (*different*), Ayub Cave	20	15
2759	2p. Neolithic ritual drinking vessel, Leta-Leta Cave, Palawan	20	15
2756/2759	*Set of 4*	75	55

MS2760 100 × 70 mm. 12p. 14th–15th-century double-spouted vessel and presentation tray, Laurel, Batangas (80 × 30 *mm*) . . . . 1·60 1·60
Nos. 2756/9 were issued together in *se-tenant* blocks of four stamps within the sheet.
See also No. **MS**2767.

(Des A. Divina)

1995 (8 Aug). *Adoption of the Philippine Eagle as National Bird. Sheet* 69 × 55 *mm.* P 14.
MS2761 **851** 16p. multicoloured . . . . . . 2·20 2·20

852 Right Hand
supporting Wildlife

853 Anniversary Emblem,
Buildings and Trolley

(Des J. de los Santos)

1995 (10 Aug). *Association of South-East Asian Nations Environment Year. T **852** and similar vert designs. Multicoloured.* P 14.

2762	2p. Type **852**		20	15
	a. Horiz pair. Nos. 2762/3		50	35
2763	2p. Left hand supporting wildlife		20	15
MS2764 89 × 78 mm. 6p. Type **852**; 6p. As				
No. 2766			1·60	1·60

Nos. 2762/3 were issued together in horizontal *se-tenant* pairs within the sheet, each pair forming a composite design.

(Des Mercury Drug Art Dept and DQA Industrial Design)

1995 (15 Aug). *50th Anniv of Mercury Drug Corporation.* P 14.

2765	**853**	2p. multicoloured	20	15

854 Parish Church

855 Instructor and Pupils

(Des A. Divina)

1995 (18 Aug). *400th Anniv of Parish of Saint Louis Bishop, Lucban.* P 14.

2766	**854**	2p. multicoloured	20	15

(Des A. Divina and Cheryl Tabo)

1995 (19 Aug). *"Jakarta '95" Asian Stamp Exhibition. As No. **MS**2760 but with additional inscription at foot.* P 14.

MS2767 100 × 70 mm. 12p. multicoloured		1·60	1·60

(Des Raquel Torregrosa)

1995 (1 Sept). *25th Anniv of Asian–Pacific Postal Training Centre, Bangkok.* P 14.

2768	**855**	6p. multicoloured	80	50

856 Crops and Child
drinking from Well

857 Carlos Romulo

(Des A. Divina)

1995 (25 Sept). *50th Anniv of Food and Agriculture Organization.* P 14.

2769	**856**	8p. multicoloured	1·10	75

(Des Raquel Torregrosa and R. Naval)

1995 (26 Sept–9 Oct). *50th Anniv of United Nations Organization. T **857** and similar vert designs. Multicoloured.* P 14.

(a) Subject's name in small letters (26 Sept)

2770	2p. José Bengzon (inscr "Cesar Bengzon")		55	55
	a. Block of 4. Nos. 2770/3		2·30	
2771	2p. Rafael Salas (Assistant Secretary General) (*inscr 12 mm*)		55	55
2772	2p. Salvador Lopez (Secretary) (*inscr 15 mm*)		55	55
2773	2p. Jose Ingles (Under-secretary) (inscr 10 mm)		55	55
2770/2773 Set of 4			2·00	2·00
MS2774 71 × 57 mm. 16p. Carlos Romulo (President of General Assembly)			2·20	2·20

(b) Subject's name in larger letters (9 Oct)

2775	2p. Type **857**		20	15
	a. Block of 4. Nos. 2775/8		90	
2776	2p. Rafael Salas (*inscr 13 mm*)		20	15
2777	2p. Salvador Lopez (*inscr 16 mm*)		20	15
2778	2p. Jose Ingles (*inscr 12 mm*)		20	15
2775/2778 Set of 4			75	55

No. 2770 depicts José Bengzon in error for his brother César and was withdrawn from issue after two days, although the remaining stamps in the sheet continued to be sold. A revised block with Carlos Romulo substituted for the Bengzon stamp, but with the subjects names redrawn on all the stamps, was placed on sale in October.

858 Anniversary
Emblem

859 Eclipse

(Des Admakers)

1995 (5 Oct). *50th Anniv of Manila Overseas Press Club.* P 14.

2779	**858**	2p. multicoloured	20	15

(Des R. Ortega)

1995 (24 Oct). *Total Solar Eclipse.* P 14.

2780	**859**	2p. multicoloured	20	15

860 Flag

861 "Two Igorot Women"
(Victorio Edades)

(Des A. Divina, Raquel Torregrosa, R. Naval, A. Luzon and R. Goco)

1995 (2 Nov). *National Symbols. T **860** and similar vert designs, with pale blue barcode at top. Multicoloured.* P 13½.

2781	2p. Flag ("Pilipinas" at top)		20	15
	a. Block of 14. Nos. 2781/94			
2782	2p. Hero (José Rizal)		20	15
2783	2p. House		20	15
2784	2p. Costume		20	15
2785	2p. Dance		20	15
2786	2p. Sport		20	15
2787	2p. Bird (Philippine eagle)		20	15
2788	2p. Type **860**		20	15

2789	2p. Animal (water buffalo)	20	15
2790	2p. Flower (jasmine)	20	15
2791	2p. Tree	20	15
2792	2p. Fruit (mango)	20	15
2793	2p. Leaf (palm)	20	15
2794	2p. Fish	20	15
2781/2794	Set of 14	2·50	1·90

Nos. 2781/94 were issued together in *se-tenant* blocks of 14 stamps within the sheet.

(Des A. Divina. Litho)

1995 (6 Nov). *National Stamp Collecting Month (1st issue). Paintings by Filipino artists. T **861** and similar horiz designs. Multicoloured.* P 14.

2795	2p. Type **861**	30	15
2796	6p. "Serenade" (Carlos Francisco)	90	50
2797	7p. "Tuba Drinkers" (Vicente Manansala)	95	65
2798	8p. "Genesis" (Hernando Ocampo)	1·00	80
2795/2798	Set of 4	2·75	1·90
MS2799	99 × 70 mm. "The Builders" (Victorio Edades) (79 × 29 mm)	1·60	1·60

See also No. **MS**2805.

862 Tambourine

863 Abacus and Anniversary Emblem

(Des A. Divina)

1995 (22 Nov). *Christmas. T **862** and similar vert designs showing musical instruments and lines from carols. Multicoloured.* P 14.

2800	2p. Type **862**	20	15
2801	6p. Maracas	75	50
2802	7p. Guitar	95	65
2803	8p. Drum	1·20	80
2800/2803	Set of 4	2·75	1·90

(Des D. Doplan)

1995 (27 Nov). *50th Anniv of Sycip Gorres Velayo & Co. (accountants).* P 14.

2804	**863**	2p. multicoloured	20	15

864 Pres. Ramos signing Stamp Month Proclamation

865 Rat and Fireworks

(Des R. Naval)

1995 (29 Nov). *National Stamp Collecting Month (2nd issue). Sheet 80 × 60 mm.* P 14.

MS2805	**864** 8p. multicoloured	1·10	1·10

(Des C. Sangco, G. Lopez and B. Dones)

1995 (1 Dec). *New Year. Year of the Rat. T **865** and similar horiz design. Multicoloured.* P 14.

2806	2p. Type **865**	30	20
2807	6p. Model of rat	80	50
MS2808	98 × 88 mm. Nos. 2806/7 plus 2 greetings labels. Perf or imperf	1·20	1·20

866 Badge of Fil-American Irregular Troops Veterans Legion

867 Liberation of Panay and Romblon

(Des Raquel Torregrosa. Litho)

1995 (8 Dec). *50th Anniv of Guerrilla Units of Second World War (4th issue). T **866** and similar vert designs. Multicoloured.* P 14.

2809	2p. Type **866**	20	15
	a. Block of 4. Nos. 2809/12	90	
2810	2p. Badge of Bicol Brigade Veterans	20	15
2811	2p. Map of Fil-American Guerrilla forces (Cavite) and Hukbalahap unit (Pampanga)	20	15
2812	2p. Map of South Tarlac military district and Northwest Pampanga	20	15
2809/2812	Set of 4	75	55

Nos. 2809/12 were issued together in *se-tenant* blocks of four stamps within the sheet.

(Des A. Divina, R. Naval, Cheryl Tabo, Raquel Torregrosa and J. de los Santos)

1995 (15 Dec). *50th Anniversaries. T **867** and similar horiz designs. Multicoloured.* P 14.

2813	2p. Type **867**	20	15
	a. Strip of 5. Nos. 2813/17	1·10	
2814	2p. Liberation of Cebu	20	15
2815	2p. Battle of Ipo Dam	20	15
2816	2p. Battle of Bessang Pass	20	15
2817	2p. Surrender of General Yamashita	20	15
2813/2817	Set of 5	90	70

Nos. 2813/17 were issued together in *se-tenant* strips of five stamps within the sheet.

868 José Rizal

(Des A. Divina, R. Naval and J. de los Santos)

1995 (27 Dec). *Centenary of Declaration of Philippine Independence (5th issue). Revolutionaries. T **868** and similar vert designs. Multicoloured.* P 14.

2818	2p. Type **868**	20	15
	a. Strip of 3. Nos. 2818/20	65	
2819	2p. Andres Bonifacio	20	15
2820	2p. Apolinario Mabini	20	15

Nos. 2818/20 were issued together in *se-tenant* strips of three stamps within the sheet.

869 Top detail of Map of Islands (½-*size illustration*)

1995 (27 Dec). *50th Anniv of End of Second World War. Dated "1995". Two sheets containing new designs as T* **869** *and previous designs. Multicoloured.* P 14.
MS2821 Two sheets. (a) 177 × 139 mm. 2p. × 8,
Nos. 2682/5, 2729/30 and 2741/2; 2p. × 4,
As T **869** forming composite design of map of
Philippine Islands (blue background). (b)
179 × 199 mm. 2p. × 13, Nos. 2710/11, 2731,
2743/7 and 2813/17; 2p. × 4, As T **869**
forming composite design of map of
Philippine Islands (green background); 2p. As
No. 2732 . . . . 8·00   8·00

1996 (8 Jan)–*97. National Symbols. As T* **860** *(with bar code). Multicoloured.* P 13½.
2822	1p. Flower (jasmine) (12 Feb)	15	10
2823	1p.50, Fish (12 Feb)	20	15
2823a	2p. Flower (jasmine) (15 Apr 1997)	30	30
2824	3p. Animal (water buffalo) (12 Feb)	35	30
2825	4p. Flag ("Pilipinas" at top)	50	35
	a. Block of 14. Nos. 2825/38 (dated "1995")	7·25	5·25
	b. Block of 14. Nos. 2825/32 and 2834/9 (dated "1996") (12 Feb)	7·25	5·25
2826	4p. Hero (José Rizal)	50	35
2827	4p. House	50	35
2828	4p. Costume	50	35
2829	4p. Dance	50	35
2830	4p. Sport	50	35
2831	4p. Bird (Philippine eagle)	50	35
2832	4p. Type **860**	50	35
2833	4p. Animal (head of water buffalo) (dated "1995")	50	35
2834	4p. Flower (jasmine)	50	35
2835	4p. Tree	50	35
2836	4p. Fruit (mango)	50	35
2837	4p. Leaf (palm)	50	35
2838	4p. Fish	50	35
2839	4p. Animal (water buffalo) (dated "1996") (12 Feb)	50	35
2840	5p. Bird (Philippine eagle) (12 Feb)	75	1·20
2841	6p. Leaf (palm) (21 Nov 1996)	80	50
2842	7p. Costume (19 Apr 1996)	90	60
2843	8p. Fruit (mango) (19 Apr 1996)	1·10	75
2844	10p. House (19 Apr 1996)	1·40	90
2822/2844 *Set of* 24		12·00	9·50

No. 2833 is dated "1995" and Nos. 2822/4 and 2839/40 "1996".
Nos. 2825/38 were issued in blocks of 14 stamps dated "1995". Nos. 2825/32 and 2834/9 were also issued in blocks of 14 stamps dated "1996".
The 3, 5, 7, 8 and 10p. values were issued in 1997 with date imprint "1997".

Nos. 2845/55 are vacant.

870 "Treating Patient" (Manuel Baldemor)

871 Walled City of Intramuros

(Des Cheryl Tabo)

1996 (10 Jan). *23rd International Congress of Internal Medicine, Manila.* P 14.
2856	**870**	2p. multicoloured	20	15

(Des R. Olbes)

1996 (26 Jan). *Centenary of Sun Life of Canada (insurance company). T* **871** *and similar horiz design. Multicoloured.* P 14.
2857	2p. Type **871**	20	15
2858	8p. Manila Bay sunset	1·10	75

872 Pair of Lovebirds on Branch ("I Love You")

873 University Building and Map of Islands on Grid

(Des A. Divina and J. de los Santos)

1996 (9 Feb). *Greetings Stamps. T* **872** *and similar horiz designs. Multicoloured.* P 14.
2859	2p. Type **872**	20	15
	a. Pair. Nos. 2859/60	45	35
2860	2p. Pair of lovebirds ("Happy Valentine")	20	15
2861	6p. Cupid holding banner ("I Love You")	75	50
	a. Horiz pair. Nos. 2861/2	1·60	1·10
2862	6p. Cupid holding banner ("Happy Valentine")	75	50
2863	7p. Box of chocolates ("I Love You")	95	65
	a. Pair. Nos. 2863/4	2·00	1·40
2864	7p. Box of chocolates ("Happy Valentine")	95	65
2865	8p. Butterfly and roses ("I Love You")	1·20	80
	a. Pair. Nos. 2865/6	2·50	1·70
2866	8p. Butterfly and roses ("Happy Valentine")	1·20	80
2859/2866 *Set of* 8		5·50	3·75

Stamps of the same value were issued together in *se-tenant* pairs within their sheets, Nos. 2861/2 forming a composite design.

1996 (5 Mar). *50th Anniv of Gregorio Araneta University Foundation.* P 14.
2867	**873**	2p. multicoloured	20	15

874 Hospital

875 Racoon Butterflyfish

(Des D. Nacario)

1996 (5 Mar). *50th Anniv of Santo Tomas University Hospital.* P 14.
2868	**874**	2p. multicoloured	20	15

(Des A. Divina, R. Naval, Raquel Torregrosa and J. de los Santos)

1996 (12–21 Mar). *Fishes (1st series). T* **875** *and similar horiz designs. Multicoloured.* P 14.
2869	4p. Type **875**	50	35
	a. Strip of 5. Nos. 2869/73	2·75	
2870	4p. Clown triggerfish	50	35

2871	4p. Regal angelfish	50	35
2872	4p. Mandarin fish	50	35
2873	4p. Emperor angelfish	50	35
2874	4p. Powder-brown tang	50	35
	a. Strip of 5. Nos. 2874/8	2·75	
2875	4p. Blue-girdled angelfish	50	35
2876	4p. Palette surgeonfish	50	35
2877	4p. Moorish idol	50	35
2878	4p. Yellow-tailed anemonefish	50	35
2869/2878	Set of 10	4·50	3·25

MS2879 Two sheets. (a) 140 × 81 mm. 4p.
Clown triggerfish; 4p. Blue and red angelfish;
4p. Regal angelfish; 4p. Yellow-tailed
anemonefish. (b) 82 × 61 mm. 12p.
Lionfish. 2·20 2·20

MS2880 Two sheets. No. **MS**2879 additionally
inscr in right margin for "Indonesia '96" World
Youth Stamp Exhibition, Bandung
(21 Mar) . . . . 1·60 1·60

Nos. 2869/73 and 2874/8 respectively were issued together in
se-tenant strips of five stamps within their sheets.
No. **MS**2879 commemorates "ASEANPEX '96".
See also Nos. 2885/**MS**2895.

PALARONG '96
PAMBANSA
SOCSARGEN

(SOUTH COTABATO, SARANGANI & GENERAL SANTOS CITY)
APRIL 14-21, 1996

(876) (½-size illustration)

1996 (14 Apr). *Basketball Championship. No.* **MS**2510 *trimmed to*
85 × 85 mm (to remove inscr at foot) and optd in bottom margin
with T **876** in red. P 14.
MS2881 10p. multicoloured . . . . 1·30 1·30

877 Francisco Ortigas

878 Mother Francisca and
Convent

1996 (30 Apr). P 14.
2882 **877** 4p. multicoloured 50 35

(Des A. Divina)

1996 (30 Apr). *300th Anniv of Dominican Sisters of St. Catherine*
of Siena. P 14.
2883 **878** 4p. multicoloured 50 35

879 Nuclear Reactor

(880)

(Des D. Jacinto)

1996 (30 Apr). *Centenary of Discovery of Radioactivity by Antoine*
Henri Becquerel. P 14.
2884 **879** 4p. multicoloured 50 35

(Des A. Divina, R. Naval, Raquel Torregrosa and R. Goco)

1996 (10 May). *Fishes (2nd series). Horiz designs as* T **875**.
Multicoloured. P 14.

2885	4p. Spotted boxfish	50	35
	a. Strip of 5. Nos. 2885/9	2·75	
2886	4p. Saddleback butterflyfish	50	35
2887	4p. Sail-finned tang	50	35
2888	4p. Harlequin tuskfish	50	35
2889	4p. Clown wrasse	50	35
2890	4p. Yellow-faced angelfish	50	35
	a. Strip of 5. Nos. 2890/4	2·00	
2891	4p. Long-horned cowfish	50	35
2892	4p. Queen angelfish	50	35
2893	4p. Forceps butterflyfish	50	35
2894	4p. Yellow tang	50	35
2885/2894	Set of 10	4·50	3·25

MS2895 Two sheets. (a) 133 × 80 mm.
Nos. 2888, 2890 and 2892/3; (b)
136 × 74 mm. 4p. Purple fire goby; 4p. Yellow
seahorse; 4p. Dusky batfish; 4p. Long-nosed
hawkfish . . . . 4·50 4·50

Nos. 2885/9 and 2890/4 respectively were issued together in
se-tenant strips of five stamps within their sheets.
No. **MS**2895 commemorates "ASEANPEX '96".

1996 (16 May). *No.* **MS**2895 *additionally inscr in margin "CHINA*
'96–9th Asian International Exhibition" in English and Chinese
and with exhibition emblem.
MS2896 Two sheets. (a) 133 × 80 mm. 4p. × 4
multicoloured; (b) 136 × 74 mm. 4p. × 4
multicoloured . . . . 4·50 4·50

1996. *Tenth Anniv of Young Philatelists' Society. Nos. 2471/4 optd*
with T **880** *in green.*

2897	2p. multicoloured	20	20
	a. Sheetlet of 4. Nos. 2897/2900	1·10	
2898	2p. multicoloured	20	20
2899	2p. multicoloured	20	20
2900	2p. multicoloured	20	20
2897/2900	Set of 4	75	75

Nos. 2897/2900 were issued together in *se-tenant* sheetlets of
four stamps.

881 Carlos
Garcia
(President,
1957–61)

882 Satellite, Dish Aerial,
Cock and Map

(Des A. Divina, R. Naval, R. Goco and J. de los Santos)

1996 (1 June). *Birth Centenaries.* T **881** *and similar vert designs.*
P 13½.

2901	4p. Type **881**	50	35
	a. Strip of 5. Nos. 2901/5	2·75	1·80
2902	4p. Casimiro del Rosario (physicist)	50	35
2903	4p. Geronima Pecson (first woman senator)	50	35
2904	4p. Cesar Bengson (member of International Court of Justice)	50	35
2905	4p. José Corazon de Jesus (writer)	50	35
2901/2905	Set of 5	2·30	1·60

Nos. 2901/5 were issued together in *se-tenant* strips of five
stamps within the sheet.

1996 (12 June). *Centenary of Declaration of Philippine*
Independence (6th issue). Centenary of Philippine Revolution.
Sheet 100 × 80 mm containing vert designs as T **860** but with
bar code sideways at right. P 13½.
MS2906 4p. Cry of Pugadlawin; 4p. Battle of
Pinaglabanan; 4p. Cry of Nueva Ecija; 4p.
Battle of Binakayan . . . . 2·20 2·20

(Des D. Batallones and C. Saliendra)

1996 (13 June). *50th Anniv of ABS–CBN Broadcasting Services in Philippines.* T **882** *and similar horiz designs. Multicoloured.* P 14.

2907	4p.	Type **882**	50	35
2908	8p.	Cock, satellite and hemispheres	1·10	75

883 "M" and Heart

884 Cojuangco

(Des Art Zone)

1996 (24 June). *"Convention City Manila".* P 14.

2909	**883**	4p. multicoloured	50	35

(Des Raquel Torregrosa)

1996 (3 July). *Birth Centenary of José Cojuangco (entrepreneur and Corazon Aquino's father).* P 14.

2910	**884**	4p. multicoloured	50	35

885 Brass Helmet and Top Hat

886 Boxing

1996 (4 July). *50th Anniv of Republic Day. Philippine–American Friendship Day.* T **885** *and similar horiz design. Multicoloured.* P 14.

2911	4p.	Type **885**	50	35
2912	8p.	Philippine eagle and American bald eagle	1·10	75
MS2913	60 × 80 mm. 16p. American and Philippine flags (27 × 37 *mm*)		2·20	2·20

1996 (19 July). *Centenary of Modern Olympic Games.* T **886** *and similar horiz designs. Multicoloured.* P 14.

2914	4p.	Type **886**	50	35
2915	6p.	Athletics	80	50
2916	7p.	Swimming	95	65
2917	8p.	Equestrian	1·10	75
2914/2917	*Set of 4*		3·00	2·00
MS2918	119 × 80 mm. 4p. × 4, Motifs as in Nos. 2914/17 but with different backgrounds and inscriptions differently arranged.		2·20	2·20

887 Alma Mater (statue, Guillermo Tolentino) and Manila Campus (after Florentino Concepcion)

888 *Dendrobium anosmum*

(Des J. de los Santos)

1996 (15 Aug). *50th Anniv of University of the East, Manila and Kalookan City.* P 14.

2919	**887**	4p. multicoloured	50	35

(Des A. Divina)

1996 (20 Sept). *Orchids.* T **888** *and similar multicoloured designs.* P 14.

2920	4p.	Type **888**	50	35
		a. Block or strip of 4. Nos. 2920/3	2·10	
2921	4p.	*Phalaenopsis equestris-alba*	50	35
2922	4p.	*Aerides lawrenceae*	50	35
2923	4p.	*Vanda javierii*	50	35
2924	4p.	*Renanthera philippinensis*	50	35
		a. Block or strip of 4. Nos. 2924/7	2·10	
2925	4p.	*Dendrobium schuetzei*	50	35
2926	4p.	*Dendrobium taurinum*	50	35
2927	4p.	*Vanda lamellata*	50	35
2920/2927	*Set of 8*		3·50	2·50
MS2928	141 × 64 mm. 4p. *Coelogyne pandurata* (*vert*); 4p. *Vanda merrilii* (*vert*); 4p. *Cymbidium aliciae* (*vert*); 4p. *Dendrobium topaziacum* (*vert*)		2·20	2·20

No. **MS**2928 commemorates "ASEANPEX '96".

889 Emblem and Globe

890 Children's Activities

(Des R. Valenciano)

1996 (30 Sept). *Sixth Asia–Pacific International Trade Fair, Manila.* P 14.

2929	**889**	4p. multicoloured	50	35

1996 (9 Oct). *50th Anniv of United Nations Children's Fund.* T **890** *and similar vert designs. Multicoloured.* P 14.

2930	4p.	Type **890**	50	35
		a. Block of 4. Nos. 2930/3	2·10	
2931	4p.	Windmills, factories, generator, boy with radio and children laughing	50	35
2932	4p.	Mother holding "sun" baby and children gardening	50	35
2933	4p.	Wind blowing toy windmills, boy with electrical fan and children playing	50	35
2930/2933	*Set of 4*		1·80	1·25
MS2934	91 × 58 mm. 16p. Boy with anemometer, girl with test tubes, boy with magnifying glass and girl with windmill (39 × 29 *mm*)		2·20	2·20

Nos. 2930/3 were issued together in *se-tenant* blocks of four stamps within the sheet.

891 Fran's Fantasy "Aiea"

892 Communications

(Des A. Divina, R. Naval, Raquel Torregrosa and P. de los Santos)

1996 (21 Oct). *"Taipeh 96" Asian Stamp Exhibition. Orchids. T* **891** *and similar multicoloured designs.* P 14.

2935	4p. Type **891**	50	35
	a. Block of 4. Nos. 2935/8	2·10	
2936	4p. Malvarosa Green Goddess "Nani"	50	35
2937	4p. Ports of Paradise "Emerald Isle"	50	35
2938	4p. Mem. Conrada Perez "Nani"	50	35
2939	4p. Pokai Tangerine "Lea"	50	35
	a. Block of 4. Nos. 2939/42	2·10	
2940	4p. Mem. Roselyn Reisman "Diana"	50	35
2941	4p. C. Moscombe × Toshie Aoki	50	35
2942	4p. Mem. Benigno Aquino "Flying Aces"	50	35
2935/2942	*Set of 8*	3·50	2·50

MS2943 97 × 65 mm.12p. Pamela Hetherington "Coronation", Living Gold "Erin Treasure" and Eleanor Spicer "White Bouquet" (79 × 29 mm) . . . . 1·60 1·60
No. **MS**2943 also commemorates "ASEANPEX '96"

1996 (30 Oct). *Fourth Asia–Pacific Economic Co-operation Summit Conference, Subic. T* **892** *and similar multicoloured designs.* P 14.

2944	4p. Type **892**	50	35
2945	6p. Open hands reaching towards sun (*horiz*)	80	50
2946	7p. Grass and buildings (*horiz*)	95	65
2947	8p. Members' flags lining path leading to emblem, city and sun	1·10	75
2944/2947	*Set of 4*	3·00	2·00

PILIPINAS P4

893 Philippine Nativity (Gilbert Miraflor)

EUGENIO P. PEREZ

894 Perez

(Des A. Divina)

1996 (5 Nov). *Christmas. T* **893** *and similar multicoloured designs showing stamp design competition winning entries.* P 14.

2948	4p. Type **893**	50	35
2949	6p. Church (Stephanie Miljares) (*horiz*)	80	50
2950	7p. Carol singer with guitars (Mark Sales) (*horiz*)	95	65
2951	8p. Carol singers and statue of buffalo (Lecester Glaraga)	1·10	75
2948/2951	*Set of 4*	3·00	2·00

(Des R. Naval)

1996 (11 Nov). *Birth Centenary of Eugenio Perez (politician).* P 14.
2952	**894**	4p. multicoloured	50	35

895 Carabao

PILIPINAS P4

896 Rizal (aged 14)

(Des Raquel Torregrosa and R. Pando)

1996 (1 Dec). *New Year. Year of the Ox. T* **895** *and similar horiz design. Multicoloured.* P 14.

2953	4p. Type **895**	50	35
2954	6p. Tamaraw	80	50

MS2955 97 × 88 mm. Nos. 2953/4. Perf or imperf . . . . 1·30 1·30

(Des A. Divina, R. Naval, R. Goco, Raquel Torregrosa, P. de los Santos and M. Malto)

1996 (14–17 Dec). *"Aseanpex '96" Association of South-East Asian Nations Stamp Exhibition, Manila. Death Centenary of Dr. José Rizal (1st issue). T* **896** *and similar multicoloured designs.* P 14.

2956	4p. Type **896**	50	35
	a. Block of 4. Nos. 2956/9	2·10	
2957	4p. Rizal (aged 18)	50	35
2958	4p. Rizal (aged 25)	50	35
2959	4p. Rizal (aged 31)	50	35
2960	4p. Title page of *Noli Me Tangere* (first novel) (15 Dec)	50	35
	a. Block of 4. Nos. 2960/3	2·10	
2961	4p. Gomburza and associates (15 Dec)	50	35
2962	4p. "Oyang Dapitana" (sculpture by Rizal) (15 Dec)	50	35
2963	4p. Bust by Rizal of Ricardo Carnicero (commandant of Dapitan) (15 Dec)	50	35
2964	4p. Rizal's house at Calamba (*horiz*) (16 Dec)	50	35
	a. Block of 4. Nos. 2964/7	2·10	
2965	4p. University of Santo Tomas, Manila (*horiz*) (16 Dec)	50	35
2966	4p. Hotel de Oriente, Manila (*horiz*) (16 Dec)	50	35
2967	4p. Dapitan during Rizal's exile (*horiz*) (16 Dec)	50	35
2968	4p. Central University, Madrid (*horiz*) (17 Dec)	50	35
	a. Block of 4. Nos. 2968/71	2·10	
2969	4p. British Museum, London (*horiz*) (17 Dec)	50	35
2970	4p. Botanical Garden, Madrid (*horiz*) (17 Dec)	50	35
2971	4p. Heidelberg, Germany (*horiz*) (17 Dec)	50	35
2956/2971	*Set of 16*	7·75	5·00

MS2972 Four sheets, each 97 × 70 mm. (a) 12p. Cooking equipment and portrait as in T **896**; (b) 12p. Cooking equipment and portrait as in No. 2957 (15 Dec); (c) 12p. Cooking equipment and portrait as in No. 2958 (16 Dec); (d) 12p. Cooking equipment and portrait as in No. 2959 (17 Dec) . . . . . . 6·50 6·50
See also No. 2976.

PILIPINAS P4

897 Father Mariano Gomez

PILIPINAS P4

898 Rizal (poster)

(Des R. Naval and P. de los Santos)

1996 (20 Dec). *Centenary of Declaration of Philippine Independence (7th issue). Execution of Secularist Priests, 1872. T* **897** *and similar vert designs. Multicoloured.* P 14.

2973	4p. Type **897**	50	35
	a. Horiz strip of 3. Nos. 2973/5	1·60	1·10
2974	4p. Father José Burgos	50	35
2975	4p. Father Jacinto Zamora	50	35

Nos. 2973/5 were issued together in horizontal *se-tenant* strips of three stamps within the sheet.

(Des A. Divina)

1996 (30 Dec). *Death Centenary of Dr. José Rizal (2nd issue).* P 14.
2976 **899** 4p. multicoloured 50 35

PHOSPHORESCENT MARKINGS. From No. **MS**2977 the phosphorescent markings on all issues (except for surcharges and overprints on previous designs) consist of "PCC" and "PHILIPPINE POSTAL CORPORATION", the latter in small letters forming a band.

(Des Raquel Torregrosa)

1997 (12 Feb). *"Hong Kong 97" Stamp Exhibition. Chinese Zodiac. Two sheets* 161 × 100 *mm containing previous New Year issues (some with changed face values). Multicoloured. One phosphor band.* P 14.
MS2977 Two sheets. (a) 4p. × 6, As Nos. 2351, 2452, 2603, 2707, 2806 and 2953; (b) 6p. × 6, As Nos. 2352, 2451, 2604, 2708, 2807 and 2954 . . . . 8·00 8·00

899 Soldier, Dove and National Colours

900 Ordination, Seminary, Priest prostrate before Altar and Priest at Devotions

(Des A. Burgos and P. de los Santos)

1997 (18 Feb). *Centenary of Philippine Army. One phosphor band.* P 14.
2978 **899** 4p. multicoloured 50 45

(Des R. Pando)

1997 (21 Feb). *Bicentenary of Holy Rosary Seminary, Naga City.* P 14.
2979 **900** 4p. multicoloured 50 45
First Day Covers are dated 18 February.

1997 (26 Feb–10 Mar). *National Symbols. Vert designs as T* **788** *(no barcode). Multicoloured. "Pilipinas" in blue.* P 13½.
2980	1p.	Flower (jasmine) (27 Feb)	30	15
2981	5p.	Bird (Philippine eagle)	1·30	45
2982	6p.	Leaf (palm) (10 Mar)	1·50	60
2983	7p.	Costume (7 Mar)	1·80	65
2984	8p.	Fruit (mango) (6 Mar)	2·10	80
2985	10p.	House (27 Feb)	2·50	1·00
2980/2985 *Set of 6*			8·50	3·25

901 Volunteers attending Patient

902 Insurance Services

(Des F. Cinco and A. Devina)

1997 (8 Apr). *50th Anniv of Philippine National Red Cross.* P 14.
2986 **901** 4p. multicoloured 50 45

(Des M. Villanoy)

1997 (8 Apr). *50th Anniv of Philippine American Life Insurance Company.* P 14.
2987 **902** 4p. multicoloured 50 45

903 Columns

904 Signatures and Globe

(DOF-CAG Design Staff and Friends)

1997 (8 Apr). *Centenary of Department of Finance.* P 14.
2988 **903** 4p. multicoloured 50 45

(Des J. Pastor)

1997 (18 Apr). *50th Anniv of J. Walter Thompson (Philippines) Inc. (advertising agency).* P 14.
2989 **904** 4p. multicoloured 50 45

World Philatelic Exhibition

May 29 – June 8, 1997
San Francisco, California U.S.A.
(905)

1997 (29 May). *"Pacific 97" International Stamp Exhibition, San Francisco. No.* **MS**2913 *optd with T* **905** *in the right margin and with exhibition emblem in the left margin.* P 14.
MS2990 16p. multicoloured . . . . 3·00 3·00

(Des R. Naval)

1997 (10 June). *National Symbol. As T* **860** *(with bar code). "Pilipinas" in black at foot. Multicoloured.* P 13½.
2991 4p. Gem (South Sea pearls) 50 45

PHOSPHORESCENT SECURITY MARKINGS. From No. 2992 all stamps have a phosphorescent "PPC" and bar code.

906 Visayan Warty Pig (*Sus cebifrons*)

907 Founding Signatories

1997 (24 July). *Endangered Animals. T* **906** *and similar horiz designs. Multicoloured.* P 14.
2992	4p.	Type **906**	60	50
		a. Strip or block of 4. Nos. 2992/5	2·50	
2993	4p.	Sow and young Visayan warty pig	60	50
2994	4p.	Visayan spotted deer (*Cervus alfredi*) buck	60	50
2995	4p.	Roe and young Visayan spotted deer	60	50
2992/2995 *Set of 4*			2·10	1·80

Nos. 2992/5 were issued together in *se-tenant* blocks or strips of four within large sheets and also separately in sheetlets of eight stamps with an enlarged margin at right giving details of the animal featured.
First Day Covers are dated 15 July.

(Des A. Divina, R. Naval, Raquel Torregrosa and P. de los Santos)

1997 (7 Aug). *30th Anniv of Association of South-East Asian Nations. T* **907** *and similar horiz designs. Multicoloured.* P 14.
2996	4p.	Type **907**		60	50
	a.	Pair. Nos. 2996/7		1·30	1·10
2997	4p.	Flags of founding member nations		60	50
2998	6p.	Members' flags as figures forming circle around ASEAN emblem		90	75
	a.	Pair. Nos. 2998/9		1·80	1·60
2999	6p.	Members' flags encircling globe		90	75
2996/2999	*Set of 4*			3·50	2·25

Stamps of the same value were issued together in *se-tenant* pairs within the sheet.

908 Symbols of Education and Law, University Building and Graduate

909 Assembly Emblem

(Des P. de los Santos)

1997 (19 Aug). *50th Anniv of Manuel L. Quezon University.* P 14.
3000	**908**	4p. multicoloured		50	45

(Des Alma Tuazon)

1997 (20 Aug). *Second World Scout Parliamentary Union General Assembly, Manila.* P 14.
3001	**909**	4p. multicoloured		50	45

First Day Covers are dated 17 August.

910 Isabelo Abaya

911 Roberto Regala (diplomat and lawyer)

1997 (24 Sept). *Battle of Candon. T* **910** *and similar multicoloured design.* P 14.
3002	4p.	Type **910**		50	45
3003	6p.	Abaya rallying revolutionaries (*horiz*)		75	65

(Des A. Divina, R. Naval, R. Goco and Raquel Torregrosa)

1997 (15 Oct). *Birth Centenaries. T* **911** *and similar vert designs. Multicoloured.* P 14 × 13½.
3004	4p.	Type **911**		50	45
	a.	Strip of 5. Nos. 3004/8		2·75	
3005	4p.	Doroteo Espiritu (dentist)		50	45
3006	4p.	Elisa Ochoa (nurse, first Congresswoman and 1930s' national tennis champion)		50	45
3007	4p.	Mariano Marcos (politician)		50	45
3008	4p.	José Romero (politician)		50	45
3004/3008	*Set of 5*			2·25	2·00

Nos. 3004/8 were issued together in *se-tenant* strips of five stamps within the sheet.
First Day Covers are dated 1 June.

912 St. Theresa

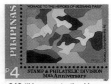

913 "Homage to the Heroes of Bessang Pass" (Hernando Ruiz Ocampo)

(Des R. Asuncion)

1997 (16 Oct). *Death Centenary of St. Theresa of Lisieux.* P 14.
3009	**912**	6p. multicoloured		75	65

1997 (7 Nov). *Centenary of Declaration of Philippine Independence (8th issue). Revolutionaries. Sheet* 100 × 80 *mm containing vert designs as T* **860** *but with barcode sideways at right.* P 13½.
MS3010 Edilberto Evangelista and battle of Zapota Bride; 4p. Vicente Alvarez; 4p. Fracisco del Castillo; 4p. Pantaleon Villegas   2·20   2·20

The stamps in No. **MS**3010 have phosphorescent "PPC" only.
First Day Covers are dated 12 June.

PHOSPHORESCENT SECURITY MARKINGS. From No. 3011 the phosphorescent markings consisted of Philpost's emblem, "PPC" and barcode.

1997 (21 Nov). *50th Anniv of Stamp and Philatelic Division. Modern Art. T* **913** *and similar multicoloured designs.* P 14.
3011	4p.	Type **913**		45	45
3012	6p.	"Jardin III" (Fernando Zobel)		75	65
3013	7p.	"Abstraction" (Nena Saguil) (*vert*)		80	75
3014	8p.	"House of Life" (Jose Joya) (*vert*)		95	90
3011/3014	*Set of 4*			2·75	2·50

MS3015 120 × 69 mm. 16p. "Dimension of Fear" (Jose Joya) (79 × 30 *mm*)   1·90   1·90
First Day Covers are dated 16 October.

914 Man painting with Feet

915 Bonifacio writing

1997 (21 Nov). *Asian and Pacific Decade of Disabled Persons.* P 14.
3016	**914**	6p. multicoloured		75	75

First Day Covers are dated 24 October.

1997 (2 Dec). *Centenary of Declaration of Philippine Independence (9th issue). Statues of Andres Bonifacio. T* **915** *and similar vert designs. Multicoloured.* P 14.
3017	4p.	Type **915**		45	45
	a.	Horiz strip of 3. Nos. 3017/19		1·40	
3018	4p.	Bonifacio holding flag		45	45
3019	4p.	Bonifacio holding sword		45	45

Nos. 3017/19 were issued together in horizontal *se-tenant* strips of three within the sheet.
First Day Covers are dated 30 November.

916 Von Stephan

1997 (11 Dec). *Death Centenary of Heinrich von Stephan (founder of Universal Postal Union).* P 14.
3020 **916** 4p. multicoloured 50 50
First Day Covers are dated 24 October.

917 Underwater Scene (½-*size illustration*)

1997 (11 Dec). *International Year of the Reef.* P 14.
3021 **917** 8p. multicoloured . . . . . . 1·00 1·00
MS3022 100 × 69 mm. **917** 16p.
multicoloured . . . . 2·10 2·10
First Day Covers are dated 24 October.

918 "Adoration of the Magi"   919 Tiger

1997 (17 Dec). *Christmas.* T **918** *and similar vert designs showing stained glass windows. Multicoloured.* P 14.
3023 4p. Type **918** 45 45
3024 6p. Mary, Jesus and Wise Men . . 75 75
3025 7p. Mary on donkey and Nativity . . . 80 80
3026 8p. "Nativity" 95 95
3023/3026 *Set of 4* . . . . 2·75 2·75
First Day Covers are dated 7 November.

1997 (22 Dec). *New Year. Year of the Tiger.* T **919** *and similar horiz design. Multicoloured.* P 14.
3027 4p. Type **919** 45 45
3028 6p. Head of tiger and tiger climbing
rockface 65 65
MS3029 98 × 90 mm. Nos. 3027/8 plus two
labels . . . . 1·10 1·10
First Day Covers are dated 1 December.

920 "Dalagang Bukid"   921 Hatch Grey
(Fernando Amorsolo)

1997 (23–24 Dec). *Stamp Collecting Month. Paintings.* T **920** *and similar multicoloured designs.* P 14.
3030 4p. Type **920** 45 45
3031 6p. "Bagong Taon" (Arturo Luz)
(24.12) 75 75
3032 7p. "Jeepneys" (Vicente Manansala)
(*horiz*) (24.12) 80 80
3033 8p. "Encounter of the *Nuestra Señora de
Cavadonga* and the *Centurion*"
(Alfredo Carmelo) (*horiz*) . . 95 95
3030/3033 *Set of 4* . . . . 2·75 2·75
MS3034 102 × 60 mm. 16p. "Pista sa Nayon"
(Carlos Francisco) (77 × 27 *mm*) . . 2·10 2·10
First Day Covers are dated 4 November.

PHOSPHORESCENT SECURITY MARKINGS. From No. 3035 these consisted of "PHILPOST" and its emblem, printed upright, inverted and sideways throughout the sheet. The barcode occurs below each horizontal "PHILPOST".

1997 (24 Dec). *Gamecocks.* T **921** *and similar multicoloured designs.* P 14.
3035 4p. Type **921** 30 30
a. Block or horiz strip of 4.
Nos. 3035/8 . . . . . . 1·30
3036 4p. Spangled roundhead 30 30
3037 4p. Racey mug 30 30
3038 4p. Silver grey 30 30
3039 4p. Grey (*vert*) 30 30
a. Block or horiz strip of 4.
Nos. 3039/42 . . . . . . 1·30
3040 4p. Kelso (*vert*) 30 30
3041 4p. Brunner roundhead (*vert*) . . . 30 30
3042 4p. Democrat (*vert*) 30 30
3035/3042 *Set of 8* . . . . 2·10 2·10
MS3043 Two sheets. (a) 55 × 69 mm. 12p.
Cocks fighting (*vert*); (b) 99 × 59 mm. 16p.
Cocks preparing to fight (79 × 29 *mm*) . . . 2·10 2·10
Nos. 3035/8 and 3039/42 respectively were issued together in *se-tenant* blocks and horizontal strips of four within their sheets.
First Day Covers are dated 18 December.

922 Philippine Eagle   923 Flag and Stars
(*Pithcophaga jefferyi*)

1997 (24 Dec)–**98**. *National Symbols.* T **922** *and similar horiz designs. Multicoloured.* P 14.
3044 20p. Type **922** . . . . 1·50 1·50
3045 30p. Philippine eagle (*different*) . . . 2·20 2·20
3046 50p. Philippine eagle (*different*)
(13.1.98) . . . . 3·75 3·75
First Day Covers of Nos. 3044/5 are dated 5 December and No. 3046, 10 December 1997.

(Des C. Gabuco, N. Parma and A. Divina)

1998 (20 Feb). *50th Anniv of Art Association of the Philippines.* T **923** *and similar horiz design. Multicoloured.* P 14.
3047 4p. Type **923** 45 45
a. Pair. Nos. 3047/8 . . . . 1·00 1·00
3048 4p. Hand clasping paintbrushes . . . 50 50
Nos. 3047/8 were issued together in *se-tenant* pairs within the sheet.
First Day Covers are dated 14 February.

924 Mother Philippine, Club Building and Emblem

925 Marie Eugenie

928 Mt. Apo, Bagobo Woman, Orchids and Fruit

929 School and Emblem

(Des A. Perez)

1998 (25 Feb). *Centenary of Club Filipino (social club).* P 14.
3049 **924** 4p. multicoloured 45 45

(Des A. Davina)

1998 (20 Mar). *50th Anniv of Apo View Hotel, Davao City.* P 14.
3070 **928** 4p. multicoloured 45 45

(Des A. Perez)

1998 (25 Feb). *Death Centenary of Blessed Marie Eugenie (founder of the Sisters of the Assumption).* P 14.
3050 **925** 4p. multicoloured 45 45

(Des S. Lee)

1998 (5 May). *75th Anniv of Philippine Cultural High School.* P 14.
3071 **929** 4p. multicoloured 35 35

926 Philippine and United States Flag

927 Emilio Jacinto

930 Old and Present School Buildings

931 Lighthouse, Warship and Past and Present Uniforms

(Des N. and P. Vinluan and A. Divina)

1998 (25 Feb). *50th Anniv of Fulbright (student exchange) Program.* P 14.
3051 **926** 4p. multicoloured 45 45

(Des P. de los Santos)

1998 (5 May). *75th Anniv of Victorino Mapa High School, San Rafael.* P 14.
3072 **930** 4p. multicoloured 35 35

(Des R. Naval, Raquel Torregrosa, P. de los Santos and, A. Divina)

1998 (4 Mar–20 July). *Heroes of the Revolution. T* **927** *and similar vert designs, with pale blue barcode at foot. Multicoloured.* P 13½.
3052		2p. Type **927** (9 Sept 1998)	20	15
	a.	Booklet pane. Nos. 3052, 3184a ×2, 3057a, 3059a ×2, 3060a ×2 and 3188a ×2 (15 Dec 1998) . . .	6·00	
3054		4p. Melchora Aquino	45	35
3055		4p. José Rizal (18 May 1998)	35	30
3056		5p. Antonio Luna (30 Apr 1998) . .	45	35
3057		8p. Marcelo del Pilar (20 July 1998) . .	60	50
	a.	Barcode shorter. Booklets (15 Dec 1998)	60	50
3058		10p. Gregorio del Pilar (18 May 1998)	75	65
3059		11p. Andres Bonifacio (24 Mar 1998) . .	80	75
	a.	Barcode shorter. Booklets (15 Dec 1998)	80	75
3060		13p. Apolinario Mabini (24 Mar 1998) . .	95	90
	a.	Barcode shorter. Booklets (15 Dec 1998) . . .	95	90
3061		15p. Emilio Aguinaldo (24 Mar 1998) . .	1·10	1·00
3062		18p. Juan Luna (11 June 1998) . .	1·30	1·20

Numbers have been left for additions to this series.
First Day Covers for No. 3054 are dated 3 March.
Nos. 3057/61 were re-issued with "1999" imprint date.
On Nos. 3057a, 3059a and 3060a the left end of the barcode aligns with the subject's shoulder.

(Des C. Panda)

1998 (5 May). *Centenary of Philippine Navy.* P 14.
3073 **931** 4p. multicoloured 35 35

932 University and Igorot Dancer

933 Training Ship and Emblem

(Des Raquel Torregrosa)

1998 (5 May). *50th Anniv of University of Baguio.* P 14.
3074 **932** 4p. multicoloured 35 35

(Des A. Divina)

1998 (7 May). *50th Anniv of Philippine Maritime Institute.* P 14.
3075 **933** 4p. multicoloured 35 35

934 Forest, Palawan   **935** Climbing Ilang-ilang

(Des F. Manosa (**MS**3078), Rosario Garcia (others))

1998 (22 May). *"EXPO '98" World's Fair, Lisbon.* T **934** *and similar multicoloured designs. Phosphorescent markings.* P 14.

3076	4p. Type **934**	35	35
3077	15p. Filipino vinta (sail canoe), Zamboanga (*horiz*)	1·10	1·10
MS3078 102 × 81 mm. 15p. Main Lobby of Philippine Pavilion (*79 × 29 mm*)		1·10	1·10

(Des A. Divina)

1998 (29 May). *"Florikultura '98" International Garden Festival, San Fernando, Pampanga. Illustrations from* Flowers of the Philippines *by Manuel Blanco.* T **935** *and similar multicoloured designs. Phosphorescent markings.* P 14.

3079	4p. Type **935**	30	30
	a. Block of 4. Nos. 3079/82	1·30	
3080	4p. *Hibiscus rosa-sinensis*	30	30
3081	4p. *Nerium oleander*	30	30
3082	4p. Arabian jasmine (*Jasminum sambac*)	30	30
3083	4p. *Gardenia jasminoides* (*vert*)	30	30
	a. Block of 4. Nos. 3083/6	1·30	
3084	4p. Flame-of-the-Forest (*Ixora coccinea*) (*vert*)	30	30
3085	4p. Indian coral bean (*Erythrina indica*) (*vert*)	30	30
3086	4p. *Abelmoschus moschatus* (*vert*)	30	30
3079/3086 *Set of 8*		2·20	2·20
MS3087 61 × 70 mm. 15p. *Medinilla magnifica* (*vert*)		3·00	3·00

Nos. 3079/82 and 3083/6 respectively were issued together in *se-tenant* blocks of four stamps within their sheets.

936 City and International Airport (½-*size illustration*)

(Des B. Reyes)

1998 (1 June). *Clark Special Economic Zone. Phosphorescent markings.* P 14.

3088	**936** 15p. multicoloured	1·10	1·10

First Day Covers are dated 28 May.

937 Manila Galleon   **938** "Spoliarium" (Juan Luna)

(Des R. Naval. Photo)

1998 (3 June). *Centenary of Declaration of Philippine Independence (10th issue). Philippines–Mexico–Spain Friendship.* T **937** *and similar horiz designs. Multicoloured. Phosphorescent markings.* P 14.

3089	15p. Type **937**	1·10	1·10
	a. Horiz strip of 3. Nos. 3089/91	3·50	

3090	15p. Philippine woman with flag, Legaspi-Urdaneta Monument and galleon	1·10	1·10
3091	15p. Spanish and Philippine flags, Cebú Basilica (after M. Miguel) and "Holy Child" (statuette)	1·10	1·10
MS3092 145 × 90 mm. Nos. 3089/91 plus three labels		3·25	3·25

Nos. 3089/91 were issued together in horizontal *se-tenant* strips of three stamps within the sheet.

(Litho Questa)

1998 (3 June). *Centenary of Declaration of Philippine Independence (11th issue). Booklet stamps.* T **938** *and similar horiz designs. Multicoloured.* P 14.

3093	4p. Type **938**	20	20
	a. Booklet pane. No. 3093 × 4	90	
3094	8p. General Emilio Aguinaldo introducing Philippine national flag at Cavite	35	35
	a. Booklet pane. No. 3094 × 4	1·50	
3095	16p. Execution of José Rizal, 1896	2·75	2·75
	a. Booklet pane. No. 3095	3·00	
3096	16p. Andres Bonifacio and Katipunan monument	2·75	2·75
	a. Booklet pane. No. 3096	3·00	
3097	20p. Barasoain Church (venue of first Philippine Congress, 1898)	3·25	3·25
	a. Booklet pane. No. 3097	3·50	

The booklet containing the five panes was sold at 150p.

939 Andres Soriano (accountant)   **940** Melchora Aquino

(Des A. Divina, R. Naval, Raquel Torregrosa and P. de los Santos)

1998 (4 June). *Birth Centenaries.* T **939** *and similar vert designs. Multicoloured. Phosphorescent markings.* P 13½.

3098	4p. Type **939**	35	35
	a. Strip of 5. Nos. 3098/3102	1·80	
3099	4p. Tomas Fonacier (University dean and historian)	35	35
3100	4p. Josefa Escoda (founder of Filipino Girl Scouts and social reformer)	35	35
3101	4p. Lorenzo Tañada (politician)	35	35
3102	4p. Lazaro Francisco (writer)	35	35
3098/3102 *Set of 5*		1·60	1·60

Nos. 3098/3102 were issued together in *se-tenant* strips of five stamps within the sheet.

First Day Covers are dated 1 June.

(Des A. Divina, R. Naval and R. Goco)

1998 (9 June). *Centenary of Declaration of Philippine Independence (12th issue). Women Revolutionaries.* T **940** *and similar vert designs. Multicoloured. Phosphorescent markings.* P 14.

3103	4p. Type **940**	20	20
	a. Strip of 3. Nos. 3103/5	65	
3104	4p. Nazaria Lagos	20	20
3105	4p. Agueda Kahabagan	20	20

Nos. 3103/5 were issued together in *se-tenant* strips of three stamps within sheets of 50 which contained 15 such strips plus five extra examples of No. 3103.

(Des A. Divina, Raquel Torregrosa and C. Pando)

1998 (12 June). *Centenary of Philippine Independence (13th issue). Events of 1898. Sheet 100 × 80 mm containing vert designs as T* **860** *but with barcode sideways at right. Phosphorescent markings.* P 13½.
MS3106 Cebu uprising; 4p. Negros uprising; 4p.
Iligan uprising; 4p. Centenary emblem . . . . . 1·20   1·20

(941)

1998 (12 June–July). *Centenary of Declaration of Philippine Independence (14th issue). Nos.* 2644, 2825/32 *and* 2834/9 *optd with T* **941** *in gold.*

3107	3p. Animal (head of water buffalo) (7 July)		30	30
3108	4p. Flag ("Pilipinas" at top)		30	30
	a. Block of 14. Nos. 3108/21		4·50	
3109	4p. Hero (José Rizal)		30	30
3110	4p. House		30	30
3111	4p. Costume		30	30
3112	4p. Dance		30	30
3113	4p. Sport		30	30
3114	4p. Bird (Philippine eagle)		30	30
3115	4p. Type **860**		30	30
3116	4p. Animal (water buffalo)		30	30
3117	4p. Flower (jasmine)		30	30
3118	4p. Tree		30	30
3119	4p. Fruit (mango)		30	30
3120	4p. Leaf (palm)		30	30
3121	4p. Fish		30	30
3107/3121	*Set of 15*		4·00	4·00

Only the "1995" dated issue of No. 2644 was overprinted.
Nos. 3108/21 were issued together in *se-tenant* blocks of 14 stamps within the sheet.

942 River Pasig   **943** Bottle-nosed ("Bottlenose") Dolphin

(Des V. Larosa)

1998 (19 June). *River Pasig Environmental Campaign. Phosphorescent markings.* P 14.
3122 **942** 4p. multicoloured 35   35

(Des A. Divina, R. Naval, R. Goco, P. de los Santos and C. Pando)

1998 (19 June). *Marine Mammals. T* **943** *and similar horiz designs. Multicoloured. Phosphorescent markings.* P 14.

3123	4p. Type **943**		30	30
	a. Sheetlet of 20. Nos. 3123/42		6·25	
3124	4p. Humpback whale		30	30
3125	4p. Fraser's dolphin		30	30
3126	4p. Melon-headed whale		30	30
3127	4p. Minke whale		30	30
3128	4p. Striped dolphin		30	30
3129	4p. Sperm whale		30	30
3130	4p. Pygmy killer whale		30	30
3131	4p. Cuvier's beaked whale		30	30
3132	4p. Killer whale		30	30
3133	4p. Bottle-nosed ("Bottlenose") dolphin (different)		30	30
3134	4p. Spinner dolphin ("Long-snouted spinner dolphin")		30	30
3135	4p. Risso's dolphin		30	30
3136	4p. Finless porpoise		30	30
3137	4p. Pygmy sperm whale		30	30
3138	4p. Pantropical spotted whale		30	30
3139	4p. False killer whale		30	30
3140	4p. Blainville's beaked whale		30	30
3141	4p. Rough-toothed dolphin		30	30
3142	4p. Bryde's whale		30	30
3123/3142	*Set of 20*		5·50	5·50
MS3143	83 × 60 mm. 15p. Dugong		1·80	1·80

944 Coconuts and Products   **945** Grapes, Emblem and Nun

1998 (9 Oct). *Centenary of Philippine Coconut Industry. Phosphorescent markings.* P 14.
3144 **944** 4p. multicoloured 30   30

1998 (9 Oct). *75th Anniv of Holy Spirit Adoration Sisters in the Philippines. Phosphorescent markings.* P 14.
3145 **945** 4p. multicoloured 30   30

946 Child posting Letter   **947** Holly Wreath

1998 (4 Nov). *Centenary of Postal Service. T* **946** *and similar vert designs. Multicoloured. Phosphorescent markings.* P 14.

3146	6p. Type **946**		45	45
	a. Block of 4. Nos. 3146/9		1·90	
3147	6p. Globe and handshake		45	45
3148	6p. Philippine stamp, globe, airplane, galleon and building		45	45
3149	6p. Flags, dove and letters floating down to girl		45	45
3146/3149	*Set of 4*		1·60	1·60
MS3150	102 × 60 mm. 15p. Boy holding letter and letters encircling globe (75 × 30 *mm*)		1·00	1·00

Nos. 3146/9 were issued in *se-tenant* blocks of four stamps within the sheet.

1998 (5 Nov). *Christmas. T* **947** *and similar vert designs. Multicoloured. Phosphorescent markings.* P 14.

3151	6p. Type **947**		45	45
3152	11p. Star wreath		75	75
3153	13p. Flower wreath		90	90
3154	15p. Bell wreath		1·00	1·00
3151/3154	*Set of 4*		2·75	2·75

948 2c. Postage Stamps (½-*size illustration*)

1998 (5–9 Nov). *"Philipas '98" International Stamp Exhibition, Mandaluyong City. Six sheets, each 121 × 60 mm, containing horiz designs as T **948** showing 1898 Filipino Revolutionary Government stamps. Multicoloured. Phosphorescent markings.* P 14.

MS3155 Six sheets. (a) 15p. Type **948** (blue background); (b) 15p. Postage and 1m. imperforate and perforate Printed Matter ("IMPRESOS") stamps; (c) 15p. 2 and 5c. Telegraph stamps; (d) 15p. 8c. Registered Letter ("CERTIFICADO") and 10c. Revenue ("RECIBOS") stamps; (e) 15p. Local issue and 5p. "LIBERTAD" stamp; (f) 15p. As No. MS3154a but imperforate and with green background . . . . 13·50 13·50

The five perforated sheets were originally sold in order on successive days of the exhibition; a smaller number of the imperforate sheets was sold at 100p. each. Subsequently a further printing of all six sheets was made and sold at a stamp exhibition in Pampanga, the imperforate sheet at 15p. The second printing of the imperforate sheet was in a larger quantity and 5000 sheets were later sold at face value at Manila central Post Office.

949 Person gagged with Barbed Wire | **950** Papal Mitre (*Mitra papalis*)

1998 (6 Nov). *50th Anniv of Universal Declaration of Human Rights. Phosphorescent markings.* P 14.
3156 **949** 4p. multicoloured 35 35
First Day Covers are dated 24 October.

1998 (7 Nov). *Shells. T **950** and similar horiz designs. Multicoloured. Phosphorescent markings.* P 14.
3157 **950** 4p. Type **950** 30 30
    a. Block of 4. Nos. 3157/60 . . . 1·30
3158 4p. *Vexillum citrinum* 30 30
3159 4p. Rugose mitre (*Vexillum rugosum*) . . 30 30
3160 4p. *Volema carinifera* 30 30
3161 4p. *Teramachia dalli* 30 30
    a. Block of 4. Nos. 3161/4 . . . 1·30
3162 4p. *Nassarius vitiensis* 30 30
3163 4p. *Cymbiola imperialis* 30 30
3164 4p. *Cymbiola aulica* 30 30
3157/3164 Set of 8 . . . . . . 2·20 2·20
MS3165 97 × 70 mm. 8p. *Nassarius papillosus*; 8p. Trapezium horse conch (*Fasciolaria trapezium*) . . . . . . 2·10 2·10
Nos. 3157/60 and 3161/4 respectively were issued together in *se-tenant* blocks of four stamps within the sheet.
First Day Covers are dated 6 November.

951 Sea Creatures (¼-size illustration)

1998 (7 Nov). *International Year of the Ocean. Phosphorescent markings.* P 14.
3166 **951** 15p. multicoloured 70 70
MS3167 101 × 71 mm. No. 3166 . . . . 1·80 1·80
First Day Covers are dated 24 October.

952 Taking Oath | **953** Rabbit

1998 (10 Nov). *Inauguration of President Joseph Ejercito Estrada. T **952** and similar horiz design. Multicoloured. Phosphorescent markings.* P 14.
3168 6p. Type **952** 45 45
3169 15p. Inaugural speech . . . . . 1·00 1·00

1998 (1 Dec). *New Year. Year of the Rabbit. T **953** and similar horiz design. Multicoloured. Phosphorescent markings.* P 14.
3170 4p. Type **953** 30 30
3171 11p. Two rabbits 75 75
MS3172 97 × 89 mm. Nos. 3170/1 plus two labels. Perf or imperf . . . . . 2·00 2·00

954 Dyesebel | **955** Noli Me Tangere (José Rizal) (Pride in the Citizenry)

1998 (1 Dec). *National Stamp Collecting Month. Film Posters. T **954** and similar vert designs. Phosphorescent markings.* P 14.
3173 6p. blue and black 45 45
3174 11p. brown and black 75 75
3175 13p. deep mauve and black 90 90
3176 15p. blue-green and black . . . . 1·00 1·00
3173/3176 Set of 4 . . . . . . 2·75 2·75
MS3177 58 × 101 mm. 15p. black . . . . 1·80 1·80
Designs: As T **954**—11p. *Ang Sawa sa Lumang Simboryo*; 13p. *Prinsipe Amante*; 15p. (3176) *Anak Dalita. 26 × 76 mm*—15p. (MS3177) *Siete Infantes de Lara*.
First Day Covers are dated 25 November.

1998 (1 Dec). *Centenary of Declaration of Philippine Independence (15th issue). The Six Prides. Six sheets, each 84 × 90 mm, containing vert designs as T **955**. Multicoloured. Phosphorescent markings. Imperf.*
MS3178 Six sheets. (a) 15p. Type **955**; (b) 15p. Banaue Rice Terraces (engineering); (c) 15p. Monument and woman holding national flag (Filipino people); (d) 15p. Malay woman in traditional costume (heritage); (e) 15p. Woman decorating pot and scripts (literature); (f) 15p. Woman with eagle on arm (resources) . . . . . . 6·00 6·00
The sheets have simulated perforations.
First Day Covers are dated 20 November.

1998 (15 Dec). *Heroes of the Revolution. Vert designs as T **927**. Multicoloured. Phosphorescent markings.* P 13½.

(a) Yellow backgrounds.
3179 6p. Melchora Aquino 50 50
    a. Booklet pane. Nos. 3179/88 . . . 5·25
3180 6p. Andres Bonifacio 50 50

3181	6p. Apolinario Mabini	50	50
3182	6p. Emilio Aquinaldo	50	50
3183	6p. Antonio Luna	50	50
3184	6p. José Rizal ("P6" 3 mm from flag)	50	50
	a. "P6" 1½ mm from flag	50	50
3185	6p. Gregorio del Pilar	50	50
3186	6p. Juan Luna	50	50
3187	6p. Type **927**	50	50
3188	6p. Marcelo del Pilar	50	50

(b) Green backgrounds

3189	15p. Type **927**	1·10	1·10
	a. Booklet pane. Nos. 3189/98	11·50	
3190	15p. Melchora Aquino	1·10	1·10
3191	15p. José Rizal	1·10	1·10
3192	15p. Antonio Luna	1·10	1·10
3193	15p. Marcelo del Pilar	1·10	1·10
3194	15p. Gregorio del Pilar	1·10	1·10
3195	15p. Andres Bonifacio	1·10	1·10
3196	15p. Apolinario Mabini	1·10	1·10
3197	15p. Emilio Aquinaldo ("15" ½ mm below top of flag)	1·10	1·10
	a. "15" level with top of flag	1·10	1·10
3198	15p. Juan Luna	1·10	1·10

956 Old and New Bank Emblems

957 Anniversary Emblem

(Des B. Rumbaoa)

1999 (4 Jan). *50th Anniv of Central Bank of the Philippines. Phosphorescent security markings.* P 14.

3199	**956**	6p. multicoloured	35	35

First Day Covers are dated 3 January.

(Des Luisa Macasaet)

1999 (11 Jan). *Centenary of Declaration of Philippine Independence (16th issue). T **957** and similar vert designs. Multicoloured. Phosphorescent security markings.* P 14.

3200	6p. Type **957**	35	35
	a. Sheetlet of 10. Nos. 3200/9	3·75	
3201	6p. General Emilio Aguinaldo's house (site of declaration, June 1898)	35	35
3202	6p. Malolos Congress, Barasoain Church, Bulacan (ratification by regions of declaration, September 1898)	35	35
3203	6p. House in Western Negros (uprising of 5 November 1898)	35	35
3204	6p. Cry of Santa Barbara, Iloilo (inauguration of government, 17 November 1898)	35	35
3205	6p. Cebu City (Victory over Colonial Forces of Spain, December 1898)	35	35
3206	6p. Philippine flag and emblem (declaration in Butaan City of sovereignty over Mindanao, 17 January 1899)	35	35
3207	6p. Fa ade of Church (Ratification of Constitution, 22 January 1899)	35	35
3208	6p. Carnival procession, Malolos (Inauguration of Republic, 23 January 1899)	35	35
3209	6p. Barosoain Church and anniversary emblem	35	35
3200/3209	*Set of 10*	3·25	3·25

Nos. 3200/9 were issued together in *se-tenant* sheetlets of 10 stamps.

958 Scouts and Guides

959 Cruise Liner

1999 (16 Jan). *1995 Savings Bank stamps used as postage. T **958** and similar vert design. Phosphorescent security markings ("PPC") (No. 3211).* P 13½.

3210	5p. Type **958**	1·10	1·10
3211	5p. Children gardening	1·10	1·10

(Des A. Divina)

1999 (20 Jan). *Centenary of Department of Transportation and Communication. T **959** and similar vert designs. Multicoloured. Phosphorescent security markings.* P 14.

3212	6p. Type **959**	35	35
	a. Block of 4. Nos. 3212/15	1·50	
3213	6p. Airplane	35	35
3214	6p. Air traffic control tower	35	35
3215	6p. Satellite dish aerial and bus	35	35
3212/3215	*Set of 4*	1·25	1·25
MS3216	114 × 70 mm. 15p. Globe, stamps, Philpost headquarters and letters (79 × 27 mm)	1·80	1·80

Nos. 3212/15 were issued together in *se-tenant* blocks of four stamps within the sheet, each block forming a composite design.

960 San Juan del Monte Bridge

961 General Emilio Aguinaldo and Academy Arms

(Des R. Naval)

1999 (4 Feb). *Centenary of American–Filipino War. Phosphorescent security markings.* P 14.

3217	**960**	5p. multicoloured	35	35

(Des J. Gammad)

1999 (4 Feb). *Centenary (1998) of Philippine Military Academy. Phosphorescent security markings.* P 14.

3218	**961**	5p. multicoloured	35	35

962 Green-backed Heron

963 Man holding Crutches

(Des R. Naval, R. Goco and J. de los Santos)

1999 (22 Feb). *Birds. T **962** and similar horiz designs. Multicoloured. Phosphorescent security markings.* P 14.

3219	5p. Type **962**	35	35
	a. Block of 4. Nos. 3219/22	1·50	
3220	5p. Common tern	35	35
3221	5p. Greater crested tern	35	35
3222	5p. Ruddy turnstone	35	35
3223	5p. Black-winged stilt	35	35
	a. Block of 4. Nos. 3223/6	1·50	
3224	5p. Asiatic dowitcher	35	35
3225	5p. Whimbrel	35	35
3226	5p. Reef heron	35	35
3219/3226	*Set of 8*	2·50	2·50

MS3227 84 × 71 mm 8p. Spotted greenshank; 8p.Tufted duck . . . . 3·00 3·00

MS3228 84 × 71 mm. As No. **MS**3227 but with different margin and with emblem and inscription for "Australia '99" World Stamp Exhibition, Melbourne . . . . . 80 1·20

Nos. 3219/22 and 3223/6 respectively were issued together in *se-tenant* blocks of four stamp within their sheets.

1999 (12 Mar). *Heroes of the Revolution. As No. 3055 but with pink background and value changed. Phosphorescent security markings.* P 13½.

3229 5p. multicoloured 35 35

(Des M. Paz)

1999 (20 Mar). *50th Anniv of Philippine Orthopaedic Association. Phosphorescent security markings.* P 14.

3230 **963** 5p. multicoloured 35 35

964 Francisco Ortigas and Emblem

965 Entrance to Garden

(Des A. Divina)

1999 (20 Mar). *50th Anniv of Manila Lions Club. Phosphorescent security markings.* P 14.

3231 **964** 5p. multicoloured 35 35

(Des A. Divina)

1999 (20 Mar). *La Union Botanical Garden, San Fernando. T **965** and similar horiz design. Multicoloured. Phosphorescent security markings.* P 14.

3232	5p. Type **965**	35	35
	a. Horiz pair. Nos. 3232/3	80	80
3233	5p. Kiosk	35	35

Nos. 3232/3 were issued together in horizontal *se-tenant* pairs within the sheet, each pair forming a composite design.

966 Gliding Tree Frog

967 Manta Ray

(Des A. Divina)

1999 (5 Apr). *Frogs. T **966** and similar horiz designs. Multicoloured. Phosphorescent security markings.* P 14.

3234	5p. Type **966**	35	35
	a. Block or strip of 4. Nos. 3234/7	1·50	
3235	5p. Common forest frog	35	35
3236	5p. Woodworth's frog	35	35
3237	5p. Giant Philippine frog	35	35
3234/3237	*Set of 4*	1·25	1·25

MS3238 108 × 86 mm. 5p. Spiny tree frog; 5p. Truncate-toed chorus frog; 5p. Variable-backed frog . . . . . . 3·00 3·00

Nos. 3234/7 were issued together in *se-tenant* blocks and strips of four stamps within the sheet.

(Des A. Divina)

1999 (11 May). *Marine Life. T **967** and similar horiz designs. Multicoloured. Phosphorescent security markings.* P 14.

3239	5p. Type **967**	35	35
	a. Block or horiz strip of 4. Nos. 3239/42	1·50	
3240	5p. Painted rock lobster	35	35
3241	5p. Sea squirt	35	35
3242	5p. Banded sea snake	35	35
3239/3242	*Set of 4*	1·25	1·25

MS3243 111 × 88 mm. 5p. Sea grapes; 5p. Branching coral; 5p. Sea urchin . . . . 4·00 4·00

Nos. 3239/42 were issued together in *se-tenant* blocks and strips of four stamps within the sheets.

968 Nakpil

969 Child writing Letter and Globe

(Des R. Naval)

1999 (25 May). *Birth Centenary of Juan Nakpil (architect). Phosphorescent security markings.* P 14.

3244 **968** 5p. multicoloured 35 35

(Des R. Pando)

1999 (26 May). *125th Anniv of Universal Postal Union. T **969** and similar horiz designs. Multicoloured. Phosphorescent security markings.* P 14.

3245	5p. Type **969**	35	35
3246	15p. Girl with stamp album	1·10	1·10

970 Waling-Waling and Cattleya "Queen Sirikit"

971 Child writing

(Des A. Divina)

1999 (13 June). *50 Years of Philippines–Thailand Diplomatic Relations. T **970** and similar vert design. Multicoloured. Phosphorescent security markings.* P 14.

3247	5p. Type **970**	35	35
3248	11p. As Type **970** but with flowers transposed	80	80

(Des Geraldine Castillo)

1999 (5 July). *150th Anniv of Mongol Pencils. Phosphorescent security markings.* P 14.

3249 **971** 5p. multicoloured 35 35

972 Emblem and Handicapped Children

973 Sampaguita and Rose of Sharon

(Des A. Divina)

1999 (5 July). *75th Anniv of Masonic Charities for Handicapped Children. Phosphorescent security markings.* P 14.
3250 **972** 5p. multicoloured 35 35

(Des A. Divina)

1999 (9 Aug). *50 Years of Philippines–South Korea Diplomatic Relations. T* **973** *and similar vert design. Multicoloured. Phosphorescent security markings.* P 14.
3251 5p. Type **973** 35 35
3252 11p. As Type **973** but with flowers transposed 80 80

974 Teachers, Nurses and Machinists

975 Dove, Fishes, Bread and Quotation from Isaiah

(Des A. Divina)

1999 (30 Aug). *50th Anniv of Community Chest Foundation. Phosphorescent security markings.* P 14.
3253 **974** 5p. multicoloured 35 35

(Des Vee Torrevillas)

1999 (30 Aug). *Centenary of Philippine Bible Society. Phosphorescent security markings.* P 14.
3254 **975** 5p. multicoloured 35 35

976 Score, Jose Palma (lyricist) and Julian Felipe (composer)

977 St. Francis of Assisi and Parish Church

(Des R. Naval)

1999 (3 Sept). *Centenary of National Anthem. Phosphorescent security markings.* P 14.
3255 **976** 5p. multicoloured 35 35

(Des A. Divina)

1999 (3 Sept). *400th Anniv of St. Francis of Assisi Parish, Sariaya, Quezon. Phosphorescent security markings.* P 14.
3256 **977** 5p. multicoloured 35 35

25th ANNIVERSARY IPPS
(978)

1999 (24 Sept). *25th Anniv of International Philippine Philatelic Society. No.* **MS**3092 *optd on each stamp with T* **978** *and in the margins with anniversary inscr and emblems, in silver.*
MS3257 145 × 90 mm. Nos. 3089/91 plus three labels . . . . 3·50 3·50

979 Flags and Official Seal

980 New Business, Arts and Sciences Faculty Building

(Des A. Divina)

1999 (15 Oct). *The Senate. Phosphorescent security markings.* P 14.
3258 **979** 5p. multicoloured 35 35

(Des A. Divina)

1999 (20 Oct). *60th Anniv of Chiang Kai Shek College, Manila. Phosphorescent security markings.* P 14.
3259 **980** 5p. multicoloured 45 45

981 School Building

982 St. Agustin Church, Paoay (World Heritage Day)

(Des B. Aricayos)

1999 (25 Oct). *50th Anniv of Tanza National High School. Phosphorescent security markings.* P 14.
3260 **981** 5p. multicoloured 45 45

(Des R. Pando (3262))

1999 (25 Oct). *United Nations Day. T* **982** *and similar horiz designs. Multicoloured. Phosphorescent security markings.* P 14.
3261 5p. Type **982** 45 45
3262 11p. Elderly couple (International Year of the Elderly) 90 90
3263 15p. "Rizal Learns the Alphabet and Prayers from his Mother" (Miguel Galvez) (World Teachers' Day) . . 1·20 1·20

983 Angel

984 Tamaraw and Polar Bear

(Des A. Divina, R. Naval, P. de los Santos and C. Pando)

1999 (27 Oct). *Christmas. T* **983** *and similar vert designs. Multicoloured. Phosphorescent security markings.* P 14.

3264	5p. Type **983**		45	45
3265	11p. Angel holding star		90	90
3266	13p. Angel holding ribbon		1·10	1·10
3267	15p. Angel holding flowers		1·30	1·30
3264/3267 *Set of 4*			3·50	3·50
MS3268 141 × 95 mm. Nos. 3264/7			35	35

1999 (15 Nov). *50 Years of Philippines–Canada Diplomatic Relations. T* **984** *and similar vert design. Multicoloured. Phosphorescent security markings.* P 14.

3269	5p. Type **984**		45	45
3270	15p. As Type **984** but with animals transposed		1·30	1·30

985 Coliseum

986 Sunrise

(Des C. Trinidad, Dy. and R. Alcantara)

1999 (19 Nov). *Renovation of Araneta Coliseum. Phosphorescent security markings.* P 14.

3271	**985**	5p. multicoloured	45	45

(Des V. Gaje)

1999 (19 Nov). *Third Informal Summit of Association of Southeast Asian Nations, Manila. T* **986** *and similar vert design. Phosphorescent security markings.* P 14.

3272	**986**	5p. multicoloured	45	45
3273		11p. multicoloured	95	95

987 "Kristo" (Arturo Luz)

988 Dragon

1999 (29 Nov). *National Stamp Collecting Month. Modern Sculptures. T* **987** *and similar multicoloured designs. Phosphorescent security markings.* P 14.

3274	5p. Type **987**		45	45
3275	11p. "Homage to Dodgie Laurel" (J. Elizalde Navarro)		90	90
3276	13p. "Hilojan" (Napoleon Abueva)		1·10	1·10
3277	15p. "Mother and Child" (Napoleon Abueva)		1·30	1·30
3274/3277 *Set of 4*			3·50	3·50
MS3278 100 × 90 mm. 5p. "Mother's Revenge" (Jose Rizal) (*horiz*); 15p. "El Ermitaño" (Jose Rizal) (*horiz*)			2·50	2·50

1999 (1 Dec). *New Year. Year of the Dragon. T* **988** *and similar horiz design. Multicoloured. Phosphorescent security markings.* P 14.

3279	5p. Type **988**		45	45
3280	15p. Dragon amongst clouds		90	90
MS3281 98 × 88 mm. Nos. 3279/80 plus two labels. Perf or imperf			1·50	1·50

989 Gen. Gregorio H. del Pilar

990 *Paphiopedilum urbanianum*

(Des R. Naval)

1999 (2 Dec). *Centenary of the Battle of Tirad Pass. Phosphorescent security markings.* P 14.

3282	**989**	5p. multicoloured	45	45

(Des A. Divina)

1999 (3 Dec). *Orchids. T* **990** *and similar multicoloured designs. Phosphorescent security markings.* P 14.

3283	5p. Type **990**		45	45
	a. Block or strip of 4. Nos. 3283/6		1·90	
3284	5p. *Phalaenopsis schilleriana*		45	45
3285	5p. *Dendrobium amethystoglossum*		45	45
3286	5p. *Paphiopedilum barbatum*		45	45
3283/3286 *Set of 4*			1·60	1·60
MS3287 132 × 83 mm. 5p. *Paphiopedilum haynaldianum* (*horiz*); 5p. *Phalaenopsis stuartiana* (*horiz*); 5p. *Trichoglottis brachiata* (*horiz*); 5p. *Ceratostylis rubra* (*horiz*)			1·80	1·80

Nos. 3283/6 were issued together in *se-tenant* blocks or horizontal strips of four stamps within the sheet.

991 General Licerio Geronimo

992 Crowds around Soldiers in Tanks

(Des R. Naval)

1999 (21 Dec). *Centenary of Battle of San Mateo. Phosphorescent security markings.* P 14.

3288	**991**	5p. multicoloured	45	45

First Day Covers are dated 19 December.

(Des A. Divina)

1999 (31 Dec). *New Millennium (1st series). "People Power". T* **992** *and similar horiz designs. Multicoloured. Phosphorescent security markings.* P 14.
3289   5p. Type **992**   45   45
           a. Horiz strip of 3. Nos. 3289/91 . . .   1·40
3290   5p. Radio antennae, helicopters and
           people   45   45
3291   5p. Religious procession   45   45
     Nos. 3289/91 were issued together in horizontal *se-tenant* strips of three stamps within the sheet, each strip forming a composite design.
     See also Nos. 3311/13, 3357/9 and 3394/6.

993 Woman holding Gender Signs

994 Newspaper Headline and Headquarters

(Des Rica Braña-Alvis)

2000 (7 Jan). *25th Anniv of National Commission on Role of Filipino Women. Phosphorescent security markings.* P 14.
3292   **993**   5p. multicoloured   45   45

(Des M. Dizon)

2000 (2 Feb). *Centenary of the Manila Bulletin (newspaper). Phosphorescent security markings. Imprint date at left.* P 14.
3293   **994**   5p. multicoloured   45   45
                      a. Imprint date at right
                         (7 June)   45   45

995 Manuel Roxas (1946–48)

996 Golfer, Sailing Boat and Swimmers

(Des R. Naval and R. Pando)

2000 (6 Feb). *Presidential Office. T* **995** *and similar vert design. Multicoloured. Phosphorescent security markings.* P 13½.
3294   5p. Type **995**   45   45
           a. Pair. Nos. 3294/5   95   95
3295   5p. Elpidio Quirino (1948–53)   45   45

(Des R. Goco)

2000 (2 Mar). *150th Anniv of La Union Province. T* **996** *and similar horiz designs. Multicoloured. Phosphorescent security markings.* P 14.
3296   5p. Type **996**   45   45
           a. Block of 4. Nos. 3296/9 . . . .   1·90
3297   5p. Tractor, building and worker   45   45
3298   5p. Government building   45   45
3299   5p. Airplane, bus, satellite dish, workers
           and bus   45   45
3296/3299 *Set of 4* . . . .   1·60   1·60
     Nos. 3296/9 were issued together in *se-tenant* blocks of four stamps within the sheet.

997 Joseph Ejercito Estrada (1998–2000)

998 Workers and Emblem

2000 (13 Mar). *Presidential Office. T* **997** *and similar vert designs, with pale blue barcode at foot. Multicoloured. Phosphorescent security markings.* P 13½.
3300   5p. Presidential seal (face value at top
           left)   35   35
           a. Block of ten. Nos. 3300/9 . . . . .   3·75
3301   5p. Type **997**   35   35
3302   5p. Fidel V. Ramos (1992–98)   35   35
3303   5p. Corazon C. Aquino (1986–92)   35   35
3304   5p. Ferdinand E. Marcos (1965–86) . . .   35   35
3305   5p. Diosdado Macapagal (1961–65) . . .   35   35
3306   5p. Carlos P. Garcia (1957–61)   35   35
3307   5p. Ramon Magsaysay (1953–57)   35   35
3308   5p. Elpidio Quirino (1948–1953)   35   35
3309   5p. Manuel Roxas (1946–1948)   35   35
3300/3309 *Set of 10* . . . .   3·25   3·25
     Nos. 3300/9 were issued together in *se-tenant* blocks of ten stamps within the sheet.

(Des E. Santiago)

2000 (20 Mar). *Centenary of the Civil Service Commission. Phosphorescent security markings.* P 14.
3310   **998**   5p. multicoloured   45   45

999 Golden Garuda, Palawan

1000 Outrigger Canoe, Boracay Island

(Des C. Pando, B. Aricayos and A. Divina)

2000 (7 Apr). *New Millennium (2nd series). Artefacts. T* **999** *and similar horiz designs. Phosphorescent security markings. Multicoloured.* P 14.
3311   5p. Type **999**   75   75
           a. Horiz strip of 3. Nos. 3311/13 . . . .   2·50
3312   5p. Sunrise at Pusan Point, Davao
           Oriental   75   75
3313   5p. Golden Tara, Agusan   75   75
     Nos. 3311/13 were issued together in *se-tenant* strips of three stamps within the sheet.

(Des A. Divina and E. Patricio)

2000 (14 Apr). *Tourist Sites. T* **1000** *and similar horiz designs. Multicoloured. Phosphorescent security markings.* P 14.
3314   5p. Type **1000**   35   35
           a. Strip of 4. Nos. 3314/17 . . . .   1·50
3315   5p. Chocolate Hills, Bohol   35   35
3316   5p. El Nido Forest, Palawan   35   35
3317   5p. Vigan House, Ilocos Sur   35   35
3314/3317 *Set of 4* . . . .   1·25   1·25
MS3318 99 × 59 mm. 15p. Banaue rice
     terraces, Ifugao (79 × 29 *mm*) . . . .   1·80   1·80
     Nos. 3314/17 were issued together in *se-tenant* strips of four stamps within the sheet.

1001 Great Wall of China and Chinese Phoenix

1002 Television and Emblem

(Des J. Malinis and E. Patricio)

2000 (8 May). *25th Anniv of Diplomatic Relations with Republic of China. T* **1001** *and similar vert design. Multicoloured. Phosphorescent security markings.* P 14.

3319	5p. Type **1001**	35	35
3320	11p. Banaue rice terraces and Philippine Sarimanok	80	80
MS3321	98 × 60 mm. 5p. Great Wall of China (39 × 29 *mm*); 11p. Banaue rice terraces (39 × 29 *mm*)	1·20	1·20

(Des E. Divino)

2000 (1 June). *50th Anniv of GMA Television and Radio Network. Phosphorescent security markings.* P 14.

3322	**1002** 5p. multicoloured	45	45

1003 Church Building

1004 Carlos P. Garcia

(Des A. Divina)

2000 (1 June). *400th Anniv of St. Thomas de Aquinas Parish, Mangaldan. Phosphorescent security markings.* P 14.

3323	**1003** 5p. multicoloured	45	45

(Des A. Divina)

2000 (19 June–4 Aug). *Presidential Office. T* **1004** *and similar vert designs. Multicoloured. Phosphorescent security markings.* P 13½.

3324	10p. Type **1004** (4 Aug)	90	90
	a. Pair. Nos. 3324/5	1·90	1·90
3325	10p. Ramon Magsaysay (4 Aug)	90	90
3326	11p. Ferdinand E. Marcos (4 Aug)	95	95
	a. Pair. Nos. 3326/7	2·00	2·00
3327	11p. Diosdado Macapagal (4 Aug)	95	95
3328	13p. Corazon C. Aquino	1·00	1·00
	a. Pair. Nos. 3328/9	2·10	2·10
3329	13p. Fidel V. Ramos	1·00	1·00
3330	15p. Joseph Ejercito Estrada	1·20	1·20
	a. Pair. Nos. 3330/1	2·50	2·50
3331	15p. Presidential seal (face value at top right)	1·20	1·20
3324/3331	*Set of 8*	7·25	7·25

Nos. 3324/5, 3326/7, 3328/9 and 3330/1 respectively were issued in *se-tenant* pairs within the sheets.

1005 Memorial and Map

1006 Joseph Ejercito Estrada

(Des A. Divina)

2000 (19 June). *Battle Centenaries. T* **1005** *and similar multicoloured designs. Phosphorescent security markings.* P 14.

3332	5p. Type **1005** (Battle of Pulang Lupa)	45	45
3333	5p. Memorial and soldiers (Battle of Mabitac)	45	45
3334	5p. Sun and soldiers (Battles of Cagayan, Agusan Hill and Makahambus Hill) (*vert*)	45	45
3335	5p. Map, memorial and bamboo signalling device (Battle of Paye) (*vert*)	45	45
3332/3335	*Set of 4*	1·60	1·60

(Des A. Divina, R. Naval, J. de los Santos and R. Pando)

2000 (3 July). *Presidential Office (1st series). T* **1006** *and similar vert designs. Multicoloured. Phosphorescent security markings.* P 13½.

3336	5p. Presidential seal	45	45
	a. Block of ten. Nos. 3336/45	4·75	
3337	5p. Type **1006**	45	45
3338	5p. Fidel V. Ramos	45	45
3339	5p. Corazon C. Aquino	45	45
3340	5p. Ferdinand E. Marcos	45	45
3341	5p. Diosdado Macapagal	45	45
3342	5p. Carlos P. Garcia	45	45
3343	5p. Ramon Magsaysay	45	45
3344	5p. Elpidio Quirino	45	45
3345	5p. Manuel Roxas	45	45
3336/3345	*Set of 10*	4·00	4·00

Nos. 3336/45 were issued together in *se-tenant* blocks of ten stamps within the sheet.

See also Nos. 3489/98.

1007 Ornate Chequered Beetle

1008 St. Ferdinand Cathedral, Map and Emblem

(Des A. Divina, R. Goco, R. Pando and E. Patricio)

2000 (21 July). *Insects. T* **1007** *and similar horiz designs. Multicoloured. Phosphorescent security markings.* P 14.

3346	5p. Type **1007**	35	35
	a. Block of 4. Nos. 3346/9	1·50	
3347	5p. Sharpshooter bug	35	35
3348	5p. Milkweed bug	35	35
3349	5p. Spotted cucumber beetle	35	35
3350	5p. Green June beetle	35	35
	a. Block of 4. Nos. 3350/3	1·50	
3351	5p. Convergent ladybird beetle	35	35
3352	5p. Eastern hercules beetle	35	35
3353	5p. Harlequin cabbage bug	35	35
3346/3353	*Set of 8*	3·25	3·25
MS3354	Two sheets, each 99 × 91 mm. (a) Nos. 3346/9; (b) Nos. 3350/3	4·50	4·50

Nos. 3346/9 and 3350/3 respectively were issued together in *se-tenant* blocks of four stamps within the sheets.

(Des E. Patricio)

2000 (30 Aug). *50th Anniv of Lucena Diocese. Phosphorescent security markings.* P 14.
3355 **1008** 5p. multicoloured 50 50

1009 Nurses and Patients

1010 Balanghai

(Des A. Divina and E. Patricio)

2000 (30 Aug). *50th Anniv of Occupational Health Nurses' Association. Phosphorescent security markings.* P 14.
3356 **1009** 5p. multicoloured 50 50

(Des P. de los Santos and Nellie Tolentino)

2000 (22 Sept). *New Millennium (3rd series). Traditional Sea Craft. T* **1010** *and similar horiz designs. Multicoloured. Phosphorescent security markings.* P 14.
3357 5p. Type **1010** 45 45
   a. Horiz strip of 3. Nos. 3357/9 . . 1·40
3358 5p. Vinta 45 45
3359 5p. Caracoa 45 45
Nos. 3357/9 were issued together in horizontal *se-tenant* strips of three stamps within the sheet.

1011 Jars, Bank Note, Circuit Board, Computer Mouse and Emblem

1012 Ship, Globe, Airplane and Workers

(Des R. Ticsay)

2000 (26 Sept). *50th Anniv of Equitable PCI Bank. Phosphorescent security markings.* P 14.
3360 **1011** 5p. multicoloured 50 50

(Des E. Santiago)

2000 (29 Sept). *Year of Overseas Filipino Workers. Phosphorescent security markings.* P 14.
3361 **1012** 5p. multicoloured 50 50

1013 Pedro Poveda (founder), Buildings and Emblem

1014 Congress in Session

(Des R. Asuncion)

2000 (10 Oct). *50th Anniv of the Teresian Association (international lay preacher association) in the Philippines. Phosphorescent security markings.* P 14.
3362 **1013** 5p. multicoloured 50 50

(Des C. Sarte)

2000 (18 Oct). *House of Representatives. Phosphorescent security markings.* P 14.
3363 **1014** 5p. multicoloured 45 45

1015 Soldiers, Tank and Emblem

1016 Running

(Des R. Pando and R. Goco)

2000 (18 Oct). *50th Anniv of Philippine Marine Corps. Phosphorescent security markings.* P 14.
3364 **1015** 5p. multicoloured 45 45

(Des A. Divina)

2000 (18 Oct). *Olympic Games, Sydney. T* **1016** *and similar multicoloured designs. Phosphorescent security markings.* P 14.
3365 5p. Type **1016** 45 45
   a. Block of 4. Nos. 3365/8 . . 1·90
3366 5p. Archery 45 45
3367 5p. Rifle shooting 45 45
3368 5p. Diving 45 45
3365/3368 *Set of 4* . . . . . . 1·60 1·60
MS3369 100 × 85 mm. 5p. Boxing (*horiz*); 5p. Show jumping (*horiz*); 5p. Rowing (*horiz*); 5p. Taekwondo (*horiz*) . . . . . . 3·00 3·00
Nos. 3365/8 were issued together in *se-tenant* blocks of four stamps within sheets of 16.

1017 Boy, Envelopes and Statue of Postman

(Des A. Divina and E. Patricio)

2000 (6 Nov). *Postal Services. Sheet* 100 × 60 *mm.* P 14.
MS3370 **1017** 15p. multicoloured . . . . . . 1·20 1·20

1018 B'laan Woman's House, Davao del Sur

1019 Angel cradling Sunflowers

(Des A. Divina and E. Patricio)

2000 (15 Nov). *"Sheer Realities: Clothing and Power in 19th-century Philippines" Exhibition, Manila. T* **1018** *and similar multicoloured designs showing exhibits. Phosphorescent security markings.* P 14.
3371 5p. Type **1018** 45 45
   a. Horiz pair. Nos. 3371/2 . . 95 95
3372 5p. T'boli T'nalak abaca cloth, South Cotabato 45 45

3373	5p. Kalinga/Gaddang cotton loincloth, Cordilleras (*vert*)	45	45
	a. Horiz pair. Nos. 3373/4	95	95
3374	5p. Portrait of Leticia Jimenez (anon) (*vert*)	45	45
3371/3374	*Set of 4*	1·60	1·60

MS3375 101 × 70 mm. 5p. Portrait of Teodora Devera Ygnacio (Justiniano Asunción); 15p. Tawsug silk sash, Sulu Archipelago . . . . . 2·50 2·50

Nos. 3371/2 and 3373/4 were each issued together in horizontal *se-tenant* pairs within the sheet.

(Des A. Divina, J. de los Santos and E. Patricio)

2000 (22 Nov). *T* **1019** *and similar vert designs. Phosphorescent security markings. Multicoloured.* P 14.

3376	5p. Type **1019**	45	45
3377	5p. As No. 3376 but inscribed "CHRISTMAS 2000 JUBILEUM"	45	45
3378	11p. Angel with basket of fruit and swag of leaves	90	90
3379	13p. Angel with basket of fruit on shoulders	1·00	1·00
3380	15p. Angel with garland of flowers	1·30	1·30
3376/3380	*Set of 5*	3·75	3·75

1020 1955 5c. Labour Management Congress Stamp

(Des A. Divina, J. Ang, A. Claro and E. Patricio)

2000 (23 Nov). *50th Anniv of Amateur Philatelists Organization Philatelic Society. T* **1020** *and similar multicoloured designs. Phosphorescent security markings.* P 14.

3381	5p. Type **1020**	35	35
3382	5p. 1957 5c. Juan Luna birth centenary stamp (*horiz*)	35	35
3383	5p. 1962 5c. orchid stamp	35	35
3384	5p. 1962 6+4c. Rizal Foundation Fund stamp (*horiz*)	35	35
3381/3384	*Set of 4*	1·25	1·25

(1021)

2000 (24 Nov). *No. 1977 surcharged in red.*

3385 5p. on 3p.60 multicoloured 35 35

The surcharge was applied in two operations using two different handstamps, one for the obliterating bars and one for the face value. Various differences have been noted, some of which may be due to wear of the handstamps.

No. 3385 was first sold on 24th November 2000 for use on domestic mail. It was withdrawn from sale on 27th November 2000 but sales were resumed on 27th December 2001. It was only available from Manila Central Post Office.

1022 "Portrait of an Unknown Lady" (Juan Novicio Luna)

1023 Snake

(Des A. Divina, R. Orlina and E. Patricio)

2000 (30 Nov). *Modern Art. T* **1022** *and similar multicoloured designs. Phosphorescent security markings.* P 14.

3386	5p. Type **1022**	35	35
3387	11p. "Nude" (Jose Joya) (*horiz*)	80	80
3388	13p. "Lotus Odalisque" (Rodolfo Paras-Perez) (*horiz*)	90	90
3389	15p. "Untitled (Nude)" (Fernando Amorsolo) (*horiz*)	1·00	1·00
3386/3389	*Set of 4*	2·75	2·75

MS3390 100 × 80 mm. 15p. "The Memorial" (Cesar Legaspi) (*79 × 29 mm*) . . . . . 2·50 2·50

No. **MS**3390 was issued with a *se-tenant* stamp-size label showing the designs from Nos. 3386/9.

(Des R. Goco, A. Divina and E. Patricio)

2000 (1 Dec). *New Year. Year of the Snake. T* **1023** *and similar horiz design. Multicoloured. Phosphorescent security markings.* P 14.

3391	5p. Type **1023**	35	35
3392	11p. Snake	80	80

MS3393 98 × 88 mm. Nos. 3391/2 plus two labels. Perf or imperf . . . . . 2·20 2·20

1024 Ships in Port (Trade and Industry)

1025 Pesos Fuertes (1st Philippines Banknote)

(Des A. Divina, J. de los Santos and V. Serevo)

2000 (28 Dec). *New Millennium (4th series). T* **1024** *and similar horiz designs. Multicoloured. Phosphorescent security markings.* P 14.

3394	5p. Type **1024**	35	35
	a. Strip of 3. Nos. 3394/6	1·20	
3395	5p. Pupils and teacher (Education and Knowledge)	35	35
3396	5p. Globe, satellite, family using computer and woman using telephone (Communications and Technology)	35	35

Nos. 3394/6 were issued together in horizontal *se-tenant* strips of three stamps within the sheet.

(Des R. Daniel and A. Divina)

2001 (30 Jan). *150th Anniv of Philippines Bank. Phosphorescent security markings.* P 14.

3397 **1025** 5p. multicoloured 35 35

AGILA
1026 Eagle

1027 Rizal
General PACIANO RIZAL
150th Birth Anniversary 1851-2001

(Des A. Divina, R. Goco and V. Serevo)

2001 (1 Feb). *"Hong Kong 2001" International Stamp Exhibition. Flora and Fauna.* T **1026** *and similar horiz designs. Multicoloured. Phosphorescent security markings.* P 14.

3398	5p. Type **1026**		35	35
	a. Horiz or vert strip of 5.			
	Nos. 3398/3402		1·80	
3399	5p. Philippine tarsier		35	35
3400	5p. "Talisman Cove" (flower)		35	35
3401	5p. Turtle		35	35
3402	5p. Tamaraw		35	35

MS3403 Five sheets, each 80 × 71 mm. (a) 11p.
As Type **1026**; (b) 11p. As No. 3399; (c) 11p.
As No. 3400; (d) 11p. As No. 3401; (e) 11p.

As No. 3402	7·50	7·50

Nos. 3398/3402 were issued together in *se-tenant* strips of five stamps within sheets of 25.

Nos. **MS**3403a and **MS**3403c were also issued on 30 June 2001 with "PHILIPPINE CHINESE PHILATELIC SOCIETY 1951 GOLDEN JUBILEE 2001" additionally inscribed in the margin.

(Des V. Serevo)

2001 (7 Mar). *150th Birth Anniv of General Paciano Rizal. Phosphorescent security markings.* P 14.

3404	**1027**	5p. multicoloured	35	35

1028 Façade

1029 High Altar,
St. Peter's Basilica,
Rome

(Des J. de los Santos)

2001 (9 Mar). *Centenary of San Beda College. Phosphorescent security markings.* P 14.

3405	**1028**	5p. multicoloured	35	35

(Des E. Patricio and A. Divina)

2001 (14 Mar). *50th Anniv of Diplomatic Relations with Vatican City.* T **1029** *and similar vert designs. Multicoloured. Phosphorescent security markings.* P 14.

3406	5p. Type **1029**		35	35
3407	15p. High altar, San Agustin Church, Manila		1·10	1·10

MS3408 90 × 71 mm. 15p. Adam; 15p. God   2·20   2·20

The two stamps in No. **MS**3408 form the composite design of "Creation of Adam" (Michaelangelo).

1030 Presidential
Seal

1031 Our Lady of
Manaoag

Our Lady of Manaoag
1926 *Diamond Jubilee* 2001
Canonical Coronation

(Des A. Divina)

2001 (5 Apr). *Multicoloured, background colour given. Phosphorescent security markings.* P 14 × 13½.

3409	**1030**	5p. greenish yellow	35	35
3410		10p. green (1.3.02)	80	80
3411		11p. carmine-vermilion (1.3.02)	90	90
3412		13p. black (1.3.02)	1·10	1·10
3413		15p. new blue	1·30	1·30
3409/3413 *Set of 5*			4·00	4·00

(Des R. Barrientos)

2001 (22 Apr). *75th Anniv of Canonical Coronation of Our Lady of the Rosary of Manaoag. Phosphorescent security markings.* P 14.

3414	**1031**	5p. multicoloured	35	35

1032 Pres. Macapagal-
Arroyo taking
Presidential Oath

1033 Sydney Opera
House and Philippines
Cultural Centre

(Des A. Divina and E. Patricio)

2001 (29 Apr). *President Gloria Macapagal-Arroyo.* T **1032** *and similar vert design. Multicoloured. Phosphorescent security markings.* P 14.

3415	5p. Type **1032**	35	35
3416	5p. Pres. Macapagal-Arroyo waving	35	35

(Des A. Divina and E. Patricio)

2001 (28–31 May). *Philippine–Australia Diplomatic Relations.* T **1033** *and similar multicoloured designs. Phosphorescent security markings.* P 14.

3417	5p. Type **1033**	35	35
3418	13p. As Type **1033** but with subjects transposed	1·10	1·10

MS3419 96 × 60 mm. 13p. Philippines Cultural Centre and Sydney Opera House (79 × 29 mm) (31 May)   1·10   1·10

PHILIPPINE NORMAL UNIVERSITY
Centennial 1901 - 2001

Pagiingkod at Pamumuno sa Edukasyong Pangguro

SUPREME COURT
1901 *Centennial* 2001
KATARUNGAN AT BAYAN MAGPAKAILANMAN

1034 Philippine Normal
University

1035 Scales of Justice and
Court Building

(Des V. Serevo and E. Patricio (3420), E. Lozada, L. de Jesus, A. Divina and E. Patricio (3421))

2001 (1 June). *University Centenaries. T* **1034** *and similar horiz design. Multicoloured. Phosphorescent security markings.* P 14.
3420   5p. Type **1034** 35   35
3421   5p. Façade of Silliman University 35   35

(Des J. de los Santos and E. Patricio)

2001 (1 June). *Centenary of Supreme Court. Phosphorescent security markings.* P 14.
3422   **1035**   5p. multicoloured 35   35

1036 Joaquin J. Ortega

 **1037** Visayan Couple

(Des V. Serevo and E. Patricio)

2001 (12 July). *Anniversaries. T* **1036** *and similar vert designs. Multicoloured. Phosphorescent security markings.* P 14.
3423   5p. Type **1036** (centenary of appointment as first Civil Governor of the Province of La Union) 35   35
3424   5p. Eugenio H. Lopez (businessman, birth centenary) 35   35

(Des A. Divina and E. Patricio)

2001 (1 Aug). *"PHILANIPPON '01" International Stamp Exhibition, Japan. Boxer Codex (manuscript depicting Philippine lifestyle during first century of Spanish contact). T* **1037** *and similar vert designs. Multicoloured. Phosphorescent security markings.* P 14.
3425   5p. Type **1037** 45   45
       a. Horiz strip or block of 4.
          Nos. 3425/8 . . . . 1·90
3426   5p. Tagalog couple 45   45
3427   5p. Moros of Luzon (man wearing red tunic) 45   45
3428   5p. Moros of Luzon (woman wearing blue dress) 45   45
3425/3428 *Set of 4* . . . . 1·60   1·60
MS3429 82 × 107 mm. 5p. Tattooed Pintados; 5p. Pintados wearing costumes; 5p. Cagayan woman; 5p. Zambal . . . . . . 1·80   1·80
Nos. 3425/8 were issued together in *se-tenant* horizontal strips or blocks of four stamps within the sheet.

1038 Teachers and Thomas (transport)

 **1039** Emblem

(Des A. Divina and E. Patricio)

2001 (25 Aug). *Centenary of Arrival of American Teachers. T* **1038** *and similar horiz design. Multicoloured. Phosphorescent security markings.* P 14.
3430   5p. Type **1038** 45   45
3431   15p. Pupils and school building . . . . 1·30   1·30

(Des J. del Valle, R. Ignacio and E. Patricio)

2001 (14 Sept). *Centenary of Technology University, Manila. Phosphorescent security markings.* P 14.
3432   **1039**   5p. multicoloured 45   45

1040 Museum Artefacts

1041 1901 Lands Management Charter, Modern Surveyors and Emblems

(Des N. Escultura and E. Patricio)

2001 (17 Sept). *Centenary of National Museum. Phosphorescent security markings.* P 14.
3433   **1040**   5p. multicoloured 45   45

(Des V. Serevo and E. Patricio)

2001 (17 Sept). *Centenary of Lands Management Bureau. Phosphorescent security markings.* P 14.
3434   **1041**   5p. multicoloured 45   45

1042 Statue of St. Joseph and Seminary Building

1043 Makati City Financial District

(Des A. Divina)

2001 (3 Oct). *400th Anniv of San Jose Seminary. Phosphorescent security markings.* P 14.
3435   **1042**   5p. multicoloured 45   45

(Des E. Fernandez)

2001 (3 Oct). *Phosphorescent security markings.* P 14.
3436   **1043**   5p. multicoloured 45   45

1044 Trumpet

1045 Off Shore Production Platform

(Des J. De Los Santos, V. Serevo and R. Goco)

2001 (8 Oct). *Musical Instruments. T* **1044** *and similar multicoloured designs. Phosphorescent security markings.* P 14.
3437   5p. Type **1044** 45   45
       a. Block of 4. Nos. 3440/3 . . . . 1·90
3438   5p. Tuba 45   45

3439　5p. French horn .... 45　45
3440　5p. Trombone .... 45　45
3437/3440 Set of 4 .... 1·60　1·60
MS3441 81 × 106 mm. Vert:—5p. × 4 Bass
　　drum; Clarinet and oboe; Xylophone;
　　Sousaphone .... 1·80　1·80
Nos. 3437/40 were issued in se-tenant blocks of four stamps
within the sheet.

(Des Jenny Rivera)

2001 (16 Oct). *Malampaya Deep Water Gas to Power
　Project. T* **1045** *and similar horiz design. Multicoloured.
　Phosphorescent security markings.* P 14.
3442　5p. Type **1045** .... 45　45
3443　15p. As No. 3442 but with gold
　　border .... 1·30　1·30

1046 Two Stylized Figures

1047 Children surrounding globe

(Des G. Medina)

2001 (24 Oct). *International Year of Volunteers. Phosphorescent
　security markings.* P 14.
3444　**1046**　5p. multicoloured .... 45　45

(Micole Divina)

2001 (24 Oct). *United Nations Year of Dialogue among
　Civilizations. Phosphorescent security markings.* P 14.
3445　**1047**　15p. multicoloured .... 1·30　1·30

1048 Girls and Singers ("Herald Angels")

1049 William Tell Monument

(Des Pepper Roxas, Abigail Goy, Jill Posadas and Conrad
　Raquel)

2001 (30 Oct). *Christmas. T* **1048** *and similar horiz designs.
　Phosphorescent security markings.* P 14.
3446　5p. Type **1048** .... 45　45
3447　11p. Boy and Christmas baubles
　　("Kumukutikutitap") .... 90　90
3448　13p. Children and lanterns ("Pasko ni
　　Bitoy") .... 1·00　1·00
3449　15p. Children blowing trumpets ("Pasko
　　na naman") .... 1·30　1·30
3446/3449 Set of 4 .... 3·25　3·25

(Des Nathalie Fajardo, A. Divina and E. Patricio)

2001 (26 Nov). *150th Anniv of Philippines–Switzerland Diplomatic
　Relations. T* **1049** *and similar multicoloured designs.
　Phosphorescent security markings.* P 14.
3450　5p. Type **1049** .... 45　45
3451　15p. Jose P. Rizal Monument .... 1·30　1·30
MS3452 98 × 62 mm. 15p. Mayon volcano and
　　Matterhorn (80 × 30 mm) .... 1·30　1·30

1050 St. George and Dragon

1051 "Puj" (Antonio Austria)

(Des A. Divina, C. dela Cruz and E. Patricio)

2001 (7 Dec). *Centenary of Solicitor General's Office.
　Phosphorescent security markings.* P 14.
3453　**1050**　5p. multicoloured .... 45　45

(Des A. Divina, R. Orlina and E. Patricio)

2001 (7 Dec). *National Stamp Collecting Month. Art. T* **1051** *and
　similar multicoloured designs. Phosphorescent security
　markings.* P 14.
3454　5p. Type **1051** .... 45　45
3455　17p. "Hesus Nazareno" (Angelito
　　Antonio) .... 1·40　1·40
3456　21p. "Three Women with Basket" (Anita
　　Magsaysay-Ho) (vert) .... 1·60　1·60
3457　22p. "Church with Yellow background"
　　(Mauro Santos) .... 1·80　1·80
MS3458 102 × 74 mm. 22p. "Komedya ng
　Pakil" (Danilo Dalena) (80 × 30 mm) ....

1052 Couple (woman wearing brown apron)

(Des A. Divina, A. De Viana and E. Patricio)

2001 (12 Dec)–02. *Inhabitants of Manila drawn by Jean
　Mallet. T* **1052** *and similar vert designs. Phosphorescent
　security markings. Multicoloured.* P 13½.
3462　5p. Couple in riding dress (1.3.02) .. 45　45
3468　17p. Type **1052** .... 1·40　1·40
3469　21p. Couple (woman wearing blue
　　apron) .... 1·60　1·60
3470　22p. Couple using pestles and mortar 1·80　1·80
3462/3470 Set of 4 .... 4·75　4·75
Numbers have been left for additions to this series.

1053 Red Horse

1054 "Sanctification in Ordinary Life" (Godofredo F. Zapanta)

(Des V. Serevo, A. Divina, R. Orlina and E. Patricio)

2001 (14 Dec). *New Year. Year of the Horse. T* **1053** *and similar horiz design. Multicoloured. Phosphorescent security markings.* P 14.

3471	5p. Type **1053**		45	
3472	17p. White horse		1·40	1·40

MS3473 100 × 89 mm. As Nos. 3471/2 plus 2
labels. . . . . 1·80   1·80

No. **MS**3473 also exists imperforate.

2002 (9 Jan). *Birth Centenary of Josémaria Escrivá de Balaguer (founder of Opus Dei religious order). Phosphorescent security markings.* P 14.

3474   **1054**   5p. multicoloured 45   45

1055 St. Paul's Metropolitan Cathedral	1056 Salvador Araneta

2002 (22 Jan). *UNESCO World Heritage Sites, Vigan City, Ilocos Sur Province. T* **1055** *and similar horiz design. Multicoloured. Phosphorescent security markings.* P 14.

3475	5p. Type **1055**		45	45
3476	22p. Calee Crisologo		1·90	1·90

(Des J. De Los Santos)

2002 (31 Jan). *Birth Centenary of Salvador Araneta (nationalist politician and philanthropist). Phosphorescent security markings.* P 14.

3477   **1056**   5p. multicoloured 45   45

1057 "Manila Customs" (painting, Auguste Nicolas Vaillant)	1058 Envelope and "I Love You"

(Des R. Pablo)

2002 (1 Feb). *Centenary of Customs Bureau. Phosphorescent security markings.* P 14.

3478   **1057**   5p. multicoloured 45   45

(Des A. Divina, R. Goco, V. Serevo and P. De Los Santos)

2002 (8 Feb). *St. Valentine's Day. T* **1058** *and similar vert designs. Multicoloured. Phosphorescent security markings.* P 14.

3479	5p. Type **1058**		45	45
	a. Strip or block of 4. Nos. 3473/6		1·90	
3480	5p. Couple enclosed in heart		45	45
3481	5p. Cat and dog		45	45
3482	5p. Air balloon		45	45
3479/3482 *Set of 4*			1·60	1·60

Nos. 3479/82 were issued in *se-tenant* strips or blocks of four stamps within sheetlets of 16.

1059 "Image of the Resurrection" (detail, Fernando Amorsolo) and Hospital Façade	1060 Pedro Calungsod

(Des V. Serevo)

2002 (22 Mar). *Centenary of Baguio General Hospital and Medical Centre. Phosphorescent security markings.* P 14.

3483   **1059**   5p. multicoloured 45   45

(Des A. Divina)

2002 (2 April). *330th Death Anniv of Pedro Calungsod. T* **1060** *and similar vert design. Multicoloured. Phosphorescent security markings.* P 14.

3484   5p. Type **1060** 45   45

MS3485 102 × 72 mm. 22p. Pedro Calungsod
holding crucifix. Imperf. . . . . . . 1·80   1·80

1061 Virgin and Child (painting) and School Façade	1062 College Façade

(Des J. A. Divina and De Los Santos)

2002 (12 Apr). *Centenary of Negros Occidental High School. Phosphorescent security markings.* P 14.

3486   **1061**   5p. multicoloured 45   45

(Des Norma Compuesto, A. Divina and E. Patricio)

2002 (12 Apr). *Centenary of La Consolacion College, Manila. Phosphorescent security markings.* P 14.

3487   **1062**   5p. multicoloured 45   45

1063 Stupa, Buddha and Lotus Blossom	1064 Gloria Macapagal-Arroyo (2001–)

2002 (24 May). *Vesak Day. Phosphorescent security markings.* P 14.

3488   **1063**   5p. multicoloured 45   45

2002 (13 June). *Presidential Office (2nd series). T* **1064** *and similar vert designs, with pale blue barcode at foot. Multicoloured. Phosphorescent markings.* P 13½.

3489	5p. Type **1064**		45	45
	a. Block of ten. Nos. 3300/9		4·75	
3490	5p. Joseph Ejercito Estrada (1998–2000)		45	45
3491	5p. Fidel V. Ramos (1992–98)		45	45
3492	5p. Corazon C. Aquino (1986–92)		45	45
3493	5p. Ferdinand E. Marcos (1965–86)		45	45
3494	5p. Diosdado Macapagal (1961–65)		45	45
3495	5p. Carlos P. Garcia (1957–61)		45	45
3496	5p. Ramon Magsaysay (1953–57)		45	45
3497	5p. Elpidio Quirino (1948–1953)		45	45
3498	5p. Manuel Roxas (1946–1948)		45	45
3489/3498 *Set of 10*			4·00	4·00

Nos. 3489/98 were issued together in *se-tenant* blocks of ten stamps within the sheet.

1065 National Flag and School Façade

1066 Emblem and Cathedral Façade

(Des V. Serevo)

2002 (19 June). *Centenary of Cavite National High School. Phosphorescent security markings.* P 14.

3499	**1065**	5p. multicoloured	45	45

(Des R. Goco)

2002 (4 July). *Centenary Iglesia Filipina Independiente (religious movement). Phosphorescent security markings.* P 14.

3500	**1066**	5p. multicoloured	45	45

1067 Fish

1068 Edge of Mangrove Swamp

(Des J. Serrano)

2002 (10 July). *Marine Conservation. T* **1067** *and similar horiz designs. Multicoloured. Phosphorescent security markings.* P 14.

3501	5p. Type **1067**		45	45
3502	5p. Fish laid head to head		45	45
3503	5p. Edge of mangrove swamp		45	45
3504	5p. Hands holding minnows		45	45
3501/3504 *Set of 4*			1·60	1·60

MS3505 90 × 77 mm. 5p. × 4, Man using binoculars from catamaran (no fishing); Mangrove swamp (reforestation of mangroves); Divers (reef monitoring); Rows of seaweed (seaweed farming) . . . . . 1·80 1·80

No. **MS**3505 has a brief description of each stamp in the lower margin.

(Des A. Divina)

2002 (2 Aug). *Philakorea 2002 International Stamp Exhibition, Seoul. Two sheets, each 97 × 86 mm containing T* **1068** *and similar vert design. Multicoloured. Phosphorescent security markings.* P 14 (**MS**3506a) or imperf (**MS**3506b).

MS3506a 5p. Type **1068**; 17p. As No. 3488 . . 1·60 1·60

MS3506b As No. **MS**3506a but with gold horizontal band . . . . 5·25 5·25

(1069)

1070 Participating Countries' Flags surrounding Communication Mast

2002 (15 Aug). *No. 2476 optd with T* **1069** *in black. Phosphorescent security markings.*

3507	3p. on 60s. multicoloured	35	35

(Des E. Patricio)

2002 (22 Aug). *TELMIN, TELSOM and ATRC Telecommunications Meetings held in Manila. Phosphorescent security markings.* P 14.

3508	**1070**	5p. multicoloured	45	45

1071 Kapitan Moy Building and Giant Shoe

1072 Gerardo de Leon

(Des A. Devina)

2002 (15 Oct). *Shoe Manufacture in Marikina City. Phosphorescent security markings.* P 14.

3509	**1071**	5p. multicoloured	45	45

(Des A. Divina)

2002 (4 Nov). *National Stamp Collecting Month. Personalities. T* **1072** *and similar horiz designs. Multicoloured. Phosphorescent security markings.* P 14.

3510	5p. Type **1072** (filmmaker)		45	45
3511	17p. Francisca Reyes Aquino (folk dance researcher)		1·40	1·40
3512	21p. Pablo Antonio (architect)		1·60	1·60
3513	22p. Jose Garcia Villa (writer)		1·80	1·80
3510/3513 *Set of 4*			4·75	4·75

MS3514 100 × 74 mm. 22p. Honorata de la Rama (singer and actress). Imperf. . . . . 1·80 1·80

1073 Kutsinta (rice cakes)

1074 Dove, Family and Crucifix

(Des P. De Los Sanyos and R. Goco)

2002 (15 Nov). *Christmas. T* **1073** *and similar vert designs. Multicoloured. Phosphorescent security markings.* P 14.
3515	5p. Type **1073**		45	45
3516	17p. Sapin-sapin (multilayered cake)		1·40	1·40
3517	21p. Bibingka (rice and coconut cake)		1·60	1·60
3518	22p. Puto bumbong (cylindrical rice cakes)		1·80	1·80
3515/3518	*Set of* 4		4·75	4·75

(Des A. Divina)

2002 (25 Nov). *Fourth World Meeting of Families (papal initiative), Manila (1st issue). Phosphorescent security markings.* P 14.
3519 **1074** 11p. multicoloured 90 90
See also No. 3528.

1075 Antonio Pigafetta

1076 Female Goat

(Des A. Claro)

2002 (2 Dec). *480th Anniv of First Circumnavigation of the Globe (1st issue). T* **1075** *and similar horiz designs. Multicoloured. Phosphorescent security markings.* P 14.
3520	5p. Type **1075**		45	45
	a. Strip of 4. Nos. 3520/3		1·90	
3521	5p. Ferdinand Magellan		45	45
3522	5p. Charles I coin and *Vitoria*		45	45
3523	5p. Sebastian Eleano and *Vitoria*		45	45
3520/3523	*Set of* 4		1·60	1·60

Nos. 3520/3 were issued in *se-tenant* strips of four stamps within the sheet.

(Des V. Serevo and R. Goco)

2002 (2 Dec). *Year of the Goat. T* **1076** *and similar horiz design. Multicoloured. Phosphorescent security markings.* P 14.
3524	5p. Type **1076**		45	45
3525	17p. Male goat		1·40	1·40
MS3526	99 × 88 mm. Nos. 3524/5. Perf or imperf		1·80	1·80

1077 Lyceum Building and Bust of Jose Laurel (founder)

1078 Holy Family

2002 (5 Dec). *50th Anniv of Philippines Lyceum. Phosphorescent security markings.* P 14.
3527 **1077** 5p. multicoloured 45 45

(Des A. Divina)

2002 (10 Dec). *Fourth World Meeting of Families, Manila (2nd issue). Phosphorescent security markings.* P 14.
3528 **1078** 5p. multicoloured 45 45

1079 Mt. Guiting ($\frac{1}{2}$-size illustration)

(Des A. De Los Santos)

2002 (10 Dec). *International Year of Mountains. Sheet* 96 × 70 *mm. Phosphorescent security markings.* P 14.
MS3529 **1079** 22p. multicoloured . . . . . . 1·80 1·80

1080 Charles I Coin and 16th-century Map ($\frac{1}{2}$-size illustration)

(Des A. Claro)

2002 (10 Dec). *480th Anniv of First Circumnavigation of the Globe (2nd issue). Sheet* 104 × 85 *mm. Phosphorescent security markings.* Imperf.
MS3530 **1080** 22p. multicoloured . . . . . . 1·80 1·80

1081 *Geodorum densiflorum*

(Des A. Claro)

2002 (19 Dec). *Orchids. T* **1081** *and similar multicoloured designs. Phosphorescent markings.* Imperf (**MS**3534) or p 14 (others).
3531	5p. Type **1081**		45	45
	a. Strip or block of 4. Nos. 3531/4		1·90	
3532	5p. *Nervilia plicata*		45	45
3533	5p. *Luisia teretifolia*		45	45
3534	5p. *Dendrobium Victoria-reginae*		45	45
3531/3534	*Set of* 4		1·60	1·60
MS3535	101 × 87 mm. 22p. *Grammatophylum scriptum*		1·80	1·80

Nos. 3531/4 were issued in *se-tenant* strips or blocks of four stamps within the sheet.

Thailand

1883. 32 Solot = 16 Atts = 8 Peinung (Sio) =
4 Songpy (Sik) = 2 Fuang = 1 Salung
4 Salungs = 1 Tical
1909. 100 Satangs = 1 Tical
1912. 100 Satangs = 1 Baht

The Thai people originated in China and moved south to form a number of small states in the lands between what are now Assam and North Vietnam. In the 13th century Thai chieftains created the larger states of Sukhothai and Chiangmai at the expense of Khmer rulers. After King Rama Khamheng of Sukhothai (1283–1317) had expanded his kingdom to the south and adopted an alphabet, a stronger kingdom arose at Ayuthia, the founder of which was crowned in 1350 as Ramadhipati, first King of Siam, as the land was now called. Sukhothai became a vassal state. A long series of wars between Siam and Burma, Cambodia. Chiangmai and Laos occupied the next four centuries. Burma was the most powerful rival. From 1569 to 1584 Siam was under Burmese suzerainty and in 1767 the Burmese captured Ayuthia and brought the Siamese dynasty to an end. P'ya Taksin drove out the Burmese in 1776 but overstrain made him insane and in 1782 General Chakri was called to the throne, as first king of the present dynasty, and made Bangkok his capital.

During the 19th and early 20th centuries pressure was exerted on Siam to cede territory in the east to France and in the west and south to the United Kingdom, though in 1876 these two powers agreed to leave central Siam as a buffer state between Burma and Indo-China. France forced Siam to cede the territory which is now Laos in 1893 and the south-eastern provinces of Battambang and Siemreap in 1907. By a treaty of 10 March 1909 Siam transferred to the United Kingdom her rights in Kedah, Kelantan, Perlis and Trengganu.

Thai Numerals

๑	๒	๓	๔	๕	๖	๗	๘	๙	๐
1	2	3	4	5	6	7	8	9	0

SIAM

**King Chulalongkorn (Rama V)
11 November 1868–23 October 1910**

The portrait on all stamps of Siam until 1910 is that of King Chulalongkorn.

1   2   3

(Des and eng W. Ridgway. Recess Waterlow)

1883 (4 Aug)–**85**. P 14½–15 and compound.
1	**1**	1solot (½a.) indigo	6·50	6·50
		a. Imperf (pair)	£3250	£3250
		b. Imperf horiz (vert pair)	£3250	£3250
		c. Imperf between (horiz strip of 3)	£5500	
		d. Prussian blue	6·50	6·50
		e. Dull blue	6·50	6·50
2		1att rose-carmine	8·50	7·50
3		1sio (2a.) red	16·00	16·00
4	**2**	1sik (4a.) yellow-ochre	7·50	8·50
		a. Yellow	7·50	8·50
5	**3**	1salung (16a.*) brown-ochre	26·00	26·00
		a. Brown-orange (1885)	26·00	26·00
1/5 Set of 5 (cheapest)			60·00	60·00

There are three plates of the 1 solot:—
(a) Oval at top containing Siamese characters has solid blue background, only found in shades of indigo.
(b) Oval with lined background, found in indigo, Prussian blue and dull blue.
(c) Oval with lined background, with dot outside the outer frame line at top corners and at the bottom right-hand corner, found in indigo and Prussian blue.
The type previously listed with lines passing through the white Siamese characters, is a re-entry of Type (c).

*On joining the U.P.U. on 1 July 1885, the 1 salung was revalued at 12 atts but the stamp was not surcharged.

A 1 fuang (8a.) deep vermilion was prepared but delivered too late to be issued; it was included in the remainder stocks which were disposed of in 1900.

1 TICAL
(4)

1 Tical
(5) (13½ mm long)

1 Tic a l
(6) (15½ mm long)

1 Tical
(7) (Small serifs on "1")

1 Tical
(8) (Large serifs on "1")

1885 (1 July)–**87**. No. 1 handstamped in red.
6	**4**	1t.on 1 solot indigo	£2500	£1700
7	**5**	1t.on 1 solot indigo	£225	£225
		b. Figure "1" inverted	£2200	£2000
		d. Handstamp double (Bk.+R.)		
		e. T **5** in black and T **4** in red	£3000	
		f. Pair, one without handstamp		
8	**6**	1t.on 1 solot, indigo (1887)	£1300	£1300

Type **5** in black is a proof which was not issued because the value did not show clearly. This accounts for the extra surcharge in red and the use of Type **4** in red.
No. 7 exists with the handstamp either inverted or double.
There are numerous forgeries of these handstamps, some postally used.
Some time after 1887 there was an official reprint using Types **7** and **8** which were type-set to surcharge sheets of 80. These were not authorized for postal use but copies are known cancelled with earlier dates. (Prices unused, T **7** £200, T **8** £150.)

9   10   (11)

(Typo De La Rue)

1887 (1 Apr)–**91**. W **10**. P 14.
11	**9**	1a. green (2.91)	2·10	65
12		2a. green and carmine	3·25	65
13		3a. green and blue	7·50	2·50
14		4a. green and brown	6·50	2·10
15		8a. green and yellow	6·50	1·70
16		12a. purple and carmine	10·50	85
17		24a. purple and blue	15·00	1·10
18		64a. purple and brown	55·00	16·00
11/18 Set of 8			95·00	23·00

The 1a. differs in minor details from Type **9**.

1889 (Aug). No. 3 handstamped with T **11**.
19	**1**	1a.on 1 sio red	13·00	13·00
		b. Handstamp omitted (in pair with normal)	£1100	

Three handstamps were used, each varying slightly in the second character.
Examples exist showing the handstamp double or inverted.

(12) (13) (14) (15)

(16) (17) (18)

1889 (Nov)–**91**. *Nos. 12 and 13 surcharged.*

A. *Handstamped as T* **12** *(with varieties of "1" as T* **13/15)** *and T* **16/18.**

20	**12**	1a.on 2a. green and carmine		2·50	2·10
		a. Pair, one without handstamp		£650	
		b. Thai numeral omitted		£650	
		c. Figure "1" omitted		£225	
		d. Thai central inscr omitted		£650	
		e. Figure "1" and Thai numeral both omitted			
21	**13**	1a.on 2a. green and carmine		£250	£250
22	**14**	1a.on 2a. green and carmine		£130	55·00
23	**15**	1a.on 2a. green and carmine		£1100	£650
24	**12**	1a.on 3a. green and blue (9.90)		4·25	3·75
		a. Pair, one without handstamp		£2500	£900
		b. Thai central inscr omitted			
25	**16**	1a.on 3a. green and blue (9.90)		£14000	£11000
26	**17**	2a.on 3a. green and blue (1.90)		39·00	32·00
27	**18**	2a.on 3a. green and blue (1.90)		26·00	21·00
		a. Figure "2" omitted		£200	£200

No. 24 further handstamped with T **18.**

28	**18**	2a.on 1a. on 3a. green and blue (2.90)		£1300	£1100

There were at least eight handstamps as Type **12**. Originally the surcharge was applied as three separate operations, but subsequently the handstamp applied all three elements at once. All other surcharges, with the exception of Type **15**, were applied in one operation. There are two sub-types of Type **13**. Type **15** only exists as a three-part handstamp.

Most handstamps exist either double or inverted.

For the 2a. surcharges there are two recognized sub-types of Type **17** and three of Type **18**.

(19) (20) (21)

B. *Type-set surch with T* **19/20** *by Post and Telegraph Dept (Mar 1891).*

29	**19**	2a.on 3a. green and blue		39·00	36·00
30	**20**	2a.on 3a. green and blue		£350	£250

There are two sub-types each of Type **19** and Type **20**.

The stamp formerly listed as surcharged as T **21** has not been seen other than in used singles and is made from a handstamp so that it was never part of the setting of Nos. 29/30. Experts believe that it was produced unofficially some years later. Forgeries also exist.

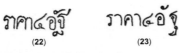

(22) (23)

1892 (Oct). *No. 17 surch in Siamese only.*

(a) *With four wooden handstamps showing first two characters joined.*

31	**22**	4a.on 24a. purple and blue		26·00	26·00

(b) *With three metal handstamps showing first two characters separate.*

32	**23**	4a.on 24a. purple and blue		21·00	17·00

Both Nos. 31 and 32 exist with the handstamp double and the former with handstamp inverted.

---

4 atts 4 atts 4 atts. 4 atts.
(24) (25) (26) (26a)

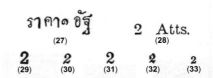

R. A. R. A. R. A.

(Roman (R) and Antique (A) lettering)

(Surch by Siam Mercantile Press, Bangkok)

1892 (Nov). *Nos. 31/2 further surch with English value in Roman lettering, type-set in panes of 120.*

33	**24**	4a.on 24a. purple and blue (31)		6·50	4·25
		c. Thai surch omitted		£750	£750
		d. English surch double		£225	£225
		e. Antique "a" (R.1/3, 1/5, 3/5, 4/2, 6/4 and one other)		32·00	32·00
		f. Antique second "t" (R.7/11, 9/4)		32·00	32·00
		g. Antique "s"		43·00	43·00
		h. Inverted "s" (R.4/4)		32·00	32·00
34	**25**	4a.on 24a. purple and blue (32)		9·75	5·25
		b. Thai surch omitted		£375	£375
		c. Antique first "t" (R.4/1)		43·00	43·00
35	**26**	4a.on 24a. purple and blue (32)		7·50	7·50
		b. Thai surch omitted		£1100	£1100
		d. Stop omitted (in pair with normal) (R.7/8)		60·00	60·00
		e. Comma in place of stop (R.3/2, 4/9–10)		19·00	19·00
		f. Antique "a" (R.1/4)		25·00	25·00
		g. Antique first "t" (R.10/10)		43·00	43·00
		h. Antique second "t" (R.1/6)		43·00	43·00
		i. Antique "s" (R.1/12)		43·00	43·00
		j. Inverted "s" (R.1/10)		43·00	43·00
36	**26a**	4a.on 24a. purple and blue (32)		9·75	5·25
		b. Thai surch omitted		£1100	£1100
		c. Type **26a** double		£300	£300

No. 34 is said to exist in pairs, from one stamp of which the surcharge "4 atts" has been omitted.

1 Atts.

ราคา๑ อัฐ   2 Atts.
(27)   (28)

2   2   2   2   2
(29) (30) (31) (32) (33)

(Surch by Post & Telegraph Department)

1894 (12–26 July). *No. 18 surch as T* **27**, *with variations of the English portions as T* **28/33**. *"Atts" in Roman. Heavy impressions.*

37	**27**	1a.on 64a. purple and brown (*English surch 14½ mm*)		2·10	2·10
		a. Surch double		£1400	£1400
		b. Pair, one without "s" (R.1/2, 8/2)		£500	£500
		c. Italic "s" (5 pos. per sheet)		85·00	85·00
		d. Italic "1" (R.9/9, 10/9)		£170	£170
		e. Inverted "s" (R.1/5, 2/5)		32·00	32·00
		f. Inverted (raised) stop (R.2/6)		43·00	43·00
38		1a.on 64a. purple and brown (*English surch 16½ mm*) (26.7)		1·10	85
		a. Surch inverted		£425	£425
39	**28**	2a.on 64a. purple and brown		10·50	10·50
		a. Inverted "s" (R.1/5, 2/5)		65·00	65·00
		b. Inverted (raised) stop (R.2/6)		£110	£110
40	**29**	2a.on 64a. purple and brown		43·00	43·00
41	**30**	2a.on 64a. purple and brown		17·00	17·00
42	**31**	2a.on 64a. purple and brown		£1500	£1600
43	**32**	2a.on 64a. purple and brown		26·00	26·00

44	33	2a.on 64a. purple and brown		85	85
		a. Narrow "A" (R.7/6)		11·00	11·00
		b. "Att.s" (R.1/5, 1/7)		50·00	50·00

The English portions of these surcharges vary considerably in length.

There were two settings of No. 37. Nos. 37b/d occur from the first setting and the remaining positional varieties from the second.

There were also two settings for the 2a. surcharge, both of 120 (12 × 10). The first setting contained thirty-eight examples of Type **28**, eight of Type **29**, eighteen of Type **30**, one of Type **31**, eleven of Type **32** and forty-four of Type **33** (including No. 44a). The second setting, issued 4 August 1894, consisted entirely of Type **33** and included the two examples of No. 44b.

1 Att.   1 Att.

ราคา๑อัฐ   ราคา๑อัฐ
(34)   (34a)

1894 (2 Aug). *No. 18 surch with T* **34**, *by Post & Telegraph Department. Heavy impression.*

45	34	1a.on 64a. purple and brown		1·00	1·00
		a. "AttS"		55·00	55·00
		b. "Atts"			
		c. Inverted (raised) stop (R.2/6)		50·00	50·00
		d. Narrow "A" (R.7/6)		13·00	13·00

Nos. 45a/b show the "S" or "s" applied by separate handstamp.

1894 (26 Aug). *No. 18 surch with T* **34a**, *by Vacharindr Printing Office.*

45e	34a	1a.on 64a. purple and brown		1·00	1·00
		ea. Stop omitted		32·00	32·00

1 Att.

ราฑา ๑ อัฐ
(35)

1 Att.
(36)

2 Atts.   10 Atts.

ราคา ๒ อัฐ   2 Atts.   ราคา๑๐อัฐ
(37)   (38)   (39)

(Surch by Siam Mercantile Press)

1894 (12 Oct)–**95**. *T* **9** *surch as T* **35** ("*Atts*" *in Roman*) *with variations in length of the English portion as T* **36/39**.

46	35	1a.on 64a. purple & brn (10 *mm* long)		1·10	85
		a. Surch inverted		£425	£425
		b. Surch both sides		£110	
		c. Surch double, second surch 2½ mm wider		£250	£250
47	36	1a.on 64a. pur & brn (8 *mm*) (29.12.94)		1·70	1·10
		a. Surch both sides		£180	
		b. Surch both sides, that on back inverted		£180	
		c. Surch both sides, that on back double		£275	
48	37	2a.on 64a. purple and brown (12 *mm*)		1·30	1·30
		a. Surch double, one inverted		£325	£325
		b. Surch double		£170	£170
		c. "s" omitted (R.5/5, 6/5)		32·00	32·00
		d. "s" Inverted (R2/4, 7/4 or R.2/6, 7/6)		17·00	17·00

49	38	2a.on 64a. purple and brown (10 *mm*) (29.12.94)		1·70	85
		a. Surch inverted		£300	£300
		b. Surch double		£325	£325
		c. Surch double, one inverted		£500	£500
		d. Surch both sides		£110	£110
		e. Surch both sides, that on back inverted		£110	£110
		f. Surch both sides, that on back double		£170	£170
		g. Surch inverted, surch on back normal		£650	
		h. Surch *tete-beche* (vert pair)		£650	
		i. "s" inverted (R.1/12, 6/12)		17·00	17·00
50	39	10a.on 24a. purple and blue (23.7.95)		5·00	85
		a. Surch both sides		£225	£225
		b. Surch both sides, that on back inverted		£225	£225
		c. Inverted "s" (R.1/12, 6/12)		26·00	13·00
		d. Inverted "0" (R.3/11, 8/11)		13·00	6·50

4 Atts.   4 Atts.
(40)   (41)

1896 (Jan). *No. 16 surch in English with T* **40** (*Roman*) *and in Siamese as T* **39**, *by Vacharindr Printing Press.*

51	40	4a.on 12a. purple and carmine		10·50	2·10
		a. English surch omitted		£110	£110
		b. Stop omitted			
		c. Surch inverted		£425	£425
		d. English surch double		£110	£110
		e. Surch both sides		£120	£120
		f. Inverted "s" (R.1/6, 6/6)		32·00	26·00

1897 (Jan). *No. 16 surch in English with T* **41** (*Roman*) *and in Siamese as T* **39**, *by Siam Mercantile Press.*

52	41	4a. on 12a. purple and carmine		14·00	2·50
		a. Surch double		85·00	85·00
		b. English surch double			
		c. Siamese surch double		£190	£190
		d. Surch inverted			
		e. Stop omitted (R.5/7)		65·00	50·00
		f. Comma in place of stop		65·00	50·00
		g. Antique first "t" (R.9/11)		32·00	21·00
		h. Antique second "t" (R.9/12, 10/4)		32·00	21·00
		i. Both "t's" antique (R.7/8)		32·00	21·00
		j. Antique "s" (R.3/2, 10/3)		65·00	32·00

1 Att.

ราคา ๑ อัฐ
(42)

1 Atts.
(43)

2 Atts.
(44)

3 Atts.   4 Atts.   10 Atts.
(45)   (46)   (46a)

(Surch by Rajatiptai Printing Press, Bangkok)

1898 (22 Feb)–**99**. *T* **9** *surch with T* **42** ("*Atts*" *in Antique letters*) *with English portion as T* **43/6a.**

53	42	1a.on 12a. purple and carmine (112 *mm*) (4,6 98)		10·50	4·25
		a. Roman "A" (R 1/5)		65·00	43·00
		b. Roman first "t" (R.2/6)		55·00	32·00
		c. Roman second "t" (R.2/1, 6/2)		43·00	32·00

54	**43**	1a.on 12a. purple and carmine (1899)	£250	£250
		a. Roman "A" (R.7/11)	£425	£425
		b. Roman first "t" (R.2/4, 9/11)	£425	£425
		e. Roman "s" (R. 4/9, 5/1, 7/2)	£425	£425
		f. Roman "ts" (R.7/1)	£425	£425
		g. Roman "tts" (R. 10/12)	£425	£425
		h. Roman "Atts" (17 positions)	£325	£325
55	**42**	1a.on 12a. pur & carm (9½ mm) (1899)	6·50	1·70
		a. Roman "A" (R.7/11)	32·00	21·00
		b. Roman first "t" (R.2/4, 9/11)	32·00	21·00
		c. Roman second "t" (R.7/1)	43·00	21·00
		d. Roman "tt" (R.10/12)	32·00	21·00
		h. Roman "Att" (17 positions)	32·00	13·00
56	**44**	2a.on 64a. purple and brown (1899)	21·00	3·25
		a. Surch double		
		b. Roman "A" (R.7/11)	43·00	21·00
		ba. Roman "A" and "s" (R.7/11)	£325	95·00
		c. Roman first "t" (R.2/4 (1st setting), 9/11 (both settings))	43·00	21·00
		ca. Roman 1st "t" and "s" (R.2/4)	£275	80·00
		d. Roman second "t" (R.2/3, 7/1, 10/4)	£275	85·00
		e. Roman "s" (R.4/9, 5/1, 7/2 or 95 positions)	43·00	21·00
		f. Roman "ts" (R.7/1)	43·00	21·00
		g. Roman "tts" (R.10/12)	43·00	21·00
		h. Roman "Atts" (17 positions)	50·00	24·00
57	**45**	3a.on 12a. purple & carmine (13½ mm)	8·50	2·10
		a. Surch double	£325	£325
		b. Roman "A" (R.1/5)	43·00	21·00
		c. Roman first "t" (R.2/6)	43·00	21·00
		d. Roman second "t" (R.2/1, 6/2)	43·00	21·00
		e. Roman "s" (R.2/b, 8/7)	43·00	21·00
58		3a.on 12a. purple and carmine (11½–11¾ mm) (1899)	8·50	2·10
		a. Surch double	£275	£200
		b. Roman "A" (R.1/5)	43·00	21·00
		ba. Roman "A" and "s" (R.7/11)	65·00	50·00
		c. Roman first "t" (R.2/6, 9/11)	43·00	21·00
		ca. Roman first "t" and "s" (R.2/4)	60·00	33·00
		d. Roman second "t" (R.2/1, 6/2)	43·00	21·00
		e. Roman "tt" (R.10/12)	65·00	60·00
		f. Roman "ts" (R.2/3, 7/1, 10/4)	65·00	38·00
		g. Roman "s" (R.4/4, 9/8 or 95 positions)	43·00	21·00
		h. Roman "Atts" (17 positions)	65·00	65·00
59	**46**	4a.on 12a. purple & carmine (8 mm)	21·00	5·25
		a. Surch double	£300	£160
		b. Comma in place of stop (R.5/9, 8/10, 9/10)	30·00	16·00
		c. Roman "A" (R.1/5)	75·00	32·00
		d. Roman first "t" (R.2/6)	75·00	32·00
		e. Roman second "t" (R.2/1, 6/2)	75·00	32·00
		f. Roman "s" (R.4/4, 9/8)	75·00	32·00
60		4a.on 12a. purple and carmine (8½ × 9 mm) (1898)	10·50	2·10
		a. Surch double	£225	£225
		b. Roman "A" (R.7/11)	32·00	17·00
		d. Roman first "t" (R.2/4, 9/11)	32·00	17·00
		e. Roman "s" (R.3/1, 4/9, 7/1, 9/1, 9/3)	32·00	17·00
		h. Roman "ts" (R.1/2, 4/12, 10/1)	32·00	17·00
		j. Roman "Atts" (17 positions)	32·00	17·00
61		4a.on 24a. purple and blue (3.10.99)	26·00	5·25
		c. Roman "A" and "s" (R.7/11)	65·00	32·00
		d. Roman first "t" (R.9/11)	65·00	32·00
		da. Roman first "t" and "s" (R.2/4)	65·00	32·00
		g. Roman "s" (95 positions)	45·00	8·00
		h. Roman "ts" (R.2/3, 7/1, 10/12)	65·00	32·00
		i. Roman "tts" (R.10/12)	65·00	32·00
		j. Roman "Atts" (17 positions)	43·00	21·00

62	**46a**	10a.on 24a. purple and blue (3.10.99)	£500	£600
		a. Roman "A" and "s" (R.7/11)	£650	£750
		b. Roman first "t" (R.9/11)	£650	£750
		ba. Roman first "t" and "s" (R.2/4)	£650	£750
		c. Roman "s" (95 positions)	£600	£700
		d. Roman "ts" (R.2/3, 7/1, 10/4)	£650	£750
		e. Roman "tts" (R.10/12)	£650	£550
		f. Roman "Atts" (17 positions)	£650	£750

Types **42** and **45** show variations in the length of the English surcharge as indicated in brackets.

The measurements given for Type **46** are the distance between the English and Thai surcharges.

There were two settings of the 2a. surcharge, Type **44**. The first contained Nos. 56b, 56c, 56e (3) and 56f/h. The second contained Nos. 56ba, 56c/ca, 56d, 56e (95) and 56g. There were also two settings for the 3a., No. **58**. The first contained Nos. 58b/c, 58d and 58g (2) and the second contained Nos. 58ba, 58c/ca, 58f, 58g (95) and 58h.

1 Att. (47)   1 Att. (47a)

2 Atts. (48)   2 Atts. (48a)

(Surch by Vacharindr Printing Press, Bangkok)

1899 (14 Feb). T **9** surch in English (Roman) and Siamese. Light impressions.

63	**47**	1a.on 12a. purple and carmine	16·00	3·25
64	**47a**	1a.on 12a. purple and carmine	16·00	3·25
		a. Figure "1" inverted (R.3/7)	£225	£170
		b. Second "t" inverted (R.1/9, 1/11)	£170	£150
65	**48**	2a.on 64a. purple and brown	21·00	4·25
66	**48a**	2a.on 64a. purple and brown	21·00	4·25
		a. Figure "1" instead of "2" (T **47a**) (R.1/7)	£250	£225

T **47** and **48** are found on vertical rows 1 to 6 and T **47a** and **48a** on vertical rows 7 to 12 of the sheets.

49   A   B

Two Types of 1a.:
Type A. Siamese characters wide.
Type B. Siamese characters narrow.

(Typo Giesecke & Devrient, Leipzig)

1899 (Sept)–**1904**. P 13½ × 14.

67	**49**	1a. olive-green (Type A)	1·10	45
68		b. Type B (1.1.04)	3·00	1·10
		2a. grass-green	1·10	45
69		2a. scarlet and pale blue (1.1.04)	4·25	1·10
70		3a. red and blue	2·10	65
71		3a. deep green (1.1.04)	5·25	3·00
72		4a. carmine	5·25	1·30
73		4a. chocolate and pink (1.1.04)	15·00	1·50
74		6a. carmine (1.1.04)	60·00	10·00
75		8a. deep green and orange	25·00	2·50
76		10a. ultramarine	4·25	1·10
77		12a. brown-purple and carmine	12·00	70
78		14a. dull blue (1.1.04)	13·00	6·50
79		24a. brown-purple and blue	70·00	6·50
80		28a. chocolate and blue (1.1.04)	21·00	7·50
81		64a. brown-purple and chestnut	20·00	6·00
67/81		Set of 15	£250	38·00

50   **(50a)**   **(50b)**

(Typo Giesecke & Devrient, Leipzig)

1899 (Oct). P 13½x14.

82	**50**	1a. green	£110	65·00
83		2a. green and red	£170	£110
84		3a. carmine and blue	£250	£150
85		4a. black and green	£2000	£550
86		10a. rose and green	£2000	£750
82/86 Set of 5			£4000	£1500

Stamps of this type arrived in 1897 but were rejected. The above five values were supplied in error to offices at Puket, Battambang, Kedah, Korat and Sisophon and put on sale. As soon as the error was discovered the issue was withdrawn and all stocks were destroyed. Postally used examples of the three lowest values are known.

1902 (31 Aug). *Provisionals for Battambang. Nos. 70 and 77 with typewritten surch as T 50a/b, in violet.*

87	**50a**	2a.on 3a. red and blue	£3250	£3500
88	**50b**	10a.on 12a. brown-purple and carmine	£3250	£3500
		a. Surch Type **50a** and Type **50b**	—	£7500

These provisionals were issued by the Postmaster with the authority of the Governor. It is understood that the original intention of the Postmaster was to surcharge alternate stamps of the 12a. value with 2a. and 10a. and one sheet or part sheet was done in this way. He then realised that this would create problems and decided to resurcharge the 2a. values with 10a. and to make a separate issue of the required 2a. value by surcharging the 3a. stamps.

1 Att.   **2 Atts.**

(51)   **(52)**   **53** Wat Cheng "Temple of Light"

1905 (Feb). *Surch with T 51/2, by Götte & Co, Bangkok.*

90	**49**	1a.on 14a. dull blue	5·25	4·25
		a. Surch double	£170	£170
		b. Stop omitted	21·00	21·00
		c. Figure "1" thicker and ¼ mm shorter	17·00	17·00
		d. Antique first "t" (R.7/4)		
		e. Antique second "t" (R.1/8)		
91		2a.on 28a. chocolate and blue	6·50	5·25
		a. Surch double	£110	£110
		b. Stop omitted (R.8/9)	21·00	21·00
		c. "2 Atts." measures 13½ mm	£110	£100
		d. Antique first "t" (R.7/4)		
		e. Antique second "t" (R.1/8)		

(Des C. Ferro. Recess Giesecke & Devrient, Leipzig)

1905 (Dec)–**09.** P 14.

92	**53**	1a. green and orange-yellow	1·10	45
		a. Green and orange (1908)	1·10	45
93		2a. grey and deep violet	1·10	45
94		2a. pale yellow-green (1.4.08)	4·25	2·50
95		3a. yellow-green	2·10	85
		a. Deep green (1908)	2·20	1·00
96		3a. grey and deep violet (1.4.08)	8·50	3·75
97		4a. pale red and sepia	4·25	45
98		4a. pale scarlet (1.4.08)	4·25	65
		a. Deep scarlet (1909)	4·25	65
99		5a. carmine	4·25	1·10

100		8a. olive-bistre and dull black	6·50	65
101		9a. blue (1.4.08)	13·00	4·75
102		12a. blue	8·50	1·50
103		18a. red-brown (1.4.08)	39·00	10·50
104		24a. red-brown	17·00	3·25
105		1t. bistre and deep blue	26·00	2·75
92/105 Set of 14			£130	31·00

Nos. 95/a, 98a, 99 and 101/4 were printed from single combined plates and the remainder from separate key and duty plates.

On the sheets of 100 of the 1t. the 4th and 9th vertical rows were in a darker blue owing to deeper engraving on the plates.

Siam.

Postage

10

Ticals

54   **(55)**

1907 (24 Apr). *Fiscal stamps optd as T 55, by Götte & Co, Bangkok. Typo. P 14.*

106	**54**	10t. olive-green	£425	65·00
		a. Comma in place of stop (R.5/1–4)	£500	£130
107		20t. olive-green	£4750	£250
		a. Comma in place of stop (R.5/1–4)	£4750	£350
108		40t. olive-green	£3500	£425
		a. Comma in place of stop (R.5/1–4)	£4250	£750

The values inscribed in Siamese correspond with the values overprinted in English.

Nos. 106/8 were primarily intended to pay postage on "Clubbed packets" (letters in bulk) sent to China.

Owing to a shortage of 1 att stamps in Bangkok, each local Postmaster was authorized to frank covers by manuscript, handstamp or label "1 Att stamps run short, postage paid" or similar wording and his signature and datestamp during the period from 11 to 16 December 1907.

1 att.

(56)

1907 (16 Dec). *No. 17 surch with T 56, by Götte & Co, Bangkok.*

109	**9**	1a.on 24a. purple and blue	1·30	65
		a. Surch double	£250	£250
		b. Surch double, one sideways or diagonal	£550	£550

2 Atts.   **(57)**   **(58)**   **4**   **9 Atts** **(59)**

No. 112c. Error (= "Hatt")

1908 (Sept). *Various stamps surch with T **57/9**, by Götte and Co, Bangkok.*

110	9	2a.on 24a. purple and blue	1·10	65
		a. Surch inverted	£250	£250
111	53	4a.on 5a. carmine	6·50	2·10
		a. Surch 17 instead of 18½ mm long (vert row 10)	32·00	26·00
112	49	9a.on 10a. ultramarine	7·50	2·75
		a. Surch inverted	£325	£325
		b. Surch double	£275	£275
		c. Error in Siamese character (R.7/6)	£150	£150
		d. Small "9" (R.8/6)	55·00	55·00
		e. Small first "t" (R.10/6)	50·00	50·00

រ័ชมังคลา

ภิเศก

๔(๗–๑๒๗.

Jubilee
1868-1908
(60)

61 Statue of King Chulalongkorn, Bangkok

1908 (11 Nov). *40th Anniv of Reign of King Chulalongkorn. Optd with T **60**, by Götte and Co, Bangkok.*

113	53	1a. green and yellow	1·10	65
		a. Opt omitted (in pair with normal)	£1100	£1100
		b. Small "i" (R.2/9, 4/6)	8·50	8·50
		c. Error in Siamese date (R.4/8)	£750	£750
		ca. Error corrected by hand	£650	£650
114		3a. deep green	2·10	1·50
		a. Small "i" (R.2/9, 4/6) (No. 111)	21·00	21·00
115		4a.on 5a. carmine	3·25	2·10
		a. Imperf three sides (pair)	£1700	£1700
		b. Surch 17 instead of 18½ mm long (vert row 10)	16·00	13·00
		c. Small "i" (R.2/9, 4/6)	26·00	21·00
116		8a. olive-bistre and dull black (R.)	15·00	15·00
		a. Small "i" (R.2/9, 4/6)	£130	£130
117		18a. red-brown	21·00	13·00
		a. Imperf three sides (pair)	£1700	£1700
		b. Small "i" (R.2/9, 4/6)	65·00	55·00
113/117	Set of 5		38·00	29·00

It is believed that 200 sheets of the 1a. were issued before the error, No. 113c, was noticed.

๖ สตางค์

๒ สตางค์

2 Satang

6 Satang

(62) (63) 64

1909 (15 Aug). *New Currency. Various stamps surch by Robert Götte, Bangkok.*

*(a) As T **62**.*

125	53	2s.on 1a. green and yellow	85	45
		a. Large "S" (R.9/6)	43·00	43·00
126		2s.on 2a. grey and deep violet	34·00	34·00
		a. Large "S" (R.9/6)	£225	£225
127		2s.on 2a. pale yellow-green	43·00	10·50
		a. *Deep green*	85	45
		b. English "2" omitted	£550	£550
		c. Large "S" (R.9/6)	10·50	10·50
129		3s.on 3a. yellow-green	1·50	1·30
		a. English "6" for "3"		
		b. Large "S" (R.9/6)	21·00	21·00
130		3s.on 3a. grey and deep violet	1·50	45
		a. English "6" for "3"		
		b. English "3" inverted	£650	£650
		c. Siamese "3" inverted	£650	£650
		d. Large "S" (R.9/6)	17·00	17·00
131		6s.on 4a. pale red and sepia	36·00	32·00
		a. Large English "6" (R.6/6)	£325	£325
		b. English "6" omitted	£500	£500
132		6s.on 4s. pale scarlet	65·00	55·00
		a. *Deep scarlet*	2·10	65
		b. English "6" inverted	£650	£650
		c. Large English "6" (R.6/6)	43·00	43·00
134		6s.on 5a. carmine	1·70	1·50
		a. Large English "6" (R.6/6)	55·00	55·00
135		12s.on 8a. olive-bistre and dull black	4·25	65
		a. Large "S" (R.9/6)	70·00	70·00
136		14s.on 9a. blue	6·50	1·10
137		14s.on 12a. blue	13·00	13·00
125/137	Set of 11 (*cheapest*)		90·00	75·00

It is believed that the 2a. in deep green was not issued without the surcharge. It was printed at the same time as the 4a. deep scarlet, No. 98a.

*(b) As T **63**.*

138	49	6s.on 6a. carmine	1·10	1·10
		a. Spaced "Sa tan g" (R.9/1)	£120	£120
139	9	14s.on 12a. purple and carmine	75·00	75·00
140	49	14s.on 14a. dull blue	9·75	9·75

There are two settings of Nos. 138 and 140, the second having a longer accent over the last Siamese character. No. 138a occurred in the second setting.

(Des C. Tamagno. Recess Giesecke & Devrient, Leipzig)

1908 (11 Nov). P 13½.

118	61	1t. violet and green	21·00	2·10
119		2t. orange and purple	43·00	7·50
120		3t. ultramarine and olive-green	65·00	9·75
121		5t. sage-green and deep lilac	85·00	17·00
122		10t. rose-carmine and brownish olive	£950	50·00
123		20t. brown and greyish slate	£225	60·00
124		40t. black-brown and greenish blue	£325	£190
118/124	Set of 7		£1500	£275

(Des C. Tamagno. Eng and recess Giesecke & Devrient, Leipzig)

1910 (5 May–15 June). P 14 × 14½.

141	64	2s. green and orange	1·10	45
142		3s. green	1·10	45
		a. Imperf horiz (vert pair)	£1100	£1100
143		6s. carmine	2·10	45
144		12s. olive-brown and black (15.6)	6·50	85
145		14s. blue	13·00	1·10
146		28s. red-brown	24·00	5·25
141/146	Set of 6		43·00	7·50

No. 142a occurs on the right-hand vertical row of one sheet and is also imperforate between stamp and margin.

King Vajiravudh (Rama VI)
23 October 1910–26 November 1925

65 King Vajiravudh   **66** King Vajiravudh

(Des C. Tamagno. Eng and recess Imperial Ptg Wks, Vienna.)

1912 (15 Oct). P 14 × 14½.

147	**65**	2s. brown	85	20
		a. Imperf between (vert pair)	£500	£425
		b. Imperf between (horiz pair)	£500	
148		3s. green	85	20
		a. Imperf between (vert pair)	£500	£425
		b. Imperf between (horiz pair)	£500	£425
149		6s. rose-carmine	1·30	30
150		12s. sepia and black	1·70	30
		a. Imperf between (vert pair)	£550	£550
151		14s. ultramarine	2·75	65
152		28s. chocolate	10·50	4·75
153	**66**	1b. sepia and blue	13·00	85
		a. Imperf between (vert pair)	£1100	£1100
		b. Imperf between (horiz pair)	£1100	£1100
154		2b. sepia and rose	17·00	1·30
155		3b. slate and green	19·00	2·10
156		5b. greyish black and violet	30·00	3·25
157		10b. purple and olive	£200	34·00
158		20b. brown and greenish blue	£300	39·00
147/158 *Set of 12*			£500	80·00

For London printings, see Nos. 166/76.

(67)   (68)

(Surch litho K. Oyama & Co, Bangkok)

1914–15. *Surch as T* **67.**

159	**65**	2s.on 14s. ultramarine (R.) (6.15)	1·10	20
		a. Imperf between (horiz pair)	£425	£425
		b. Imperf between (vert pair)	£425	£425
		c. Surch double	£325	£325
		d. Surch both sides	65·00	65·00
160		5s.on 6s. rose-carmine (B.) (4.14)	2·10	20
		a. Imperf between (horiz pair)	£500	£500
		b. Surch double	£225	£325
		c. Surch double, one sideways	£225	
161		10s.on 12s. sepia & black (R.) (3.14)	2·10	30
		a. Imperf between (horiz pair)	£425	£425
		b. Imperf between (vert pair)	£425	£425
		c. Surch double	£225	£225
162		15s.on 28s. chocolate (B.) (4.14)	4·25	55
		a. Imperf between (vert pair)	£475	£475

There are three types of surcharge of the 2s., five of the 5s., seven of the 10s. and six of the 15s. Minor varieties occur in some of these.

For 10s. on 28s., see No. 251.

(Surch litho K. Oyama & Co, Bangkok)

1915 (3 Apr)–**16.** *Surch as T* **68.**

163	**53**	2s.on 1a. green and yellow	4·25	2·10
		a. Pair, one without surch	£325	£325
164		2s.on 2a. grey and deep violet	4·25	2·10
165	**64**	2s.on 14s. ultramarine (R.) (10.16)	1·70	1·10
		a. Pair, one without surch	£325	£325

Waterlow Printings

In addition to differing from the Vienna print in perforation the 2s. and 3s. may be distinguished by the four clear lines on the chin in place of indistinct shading, and a white line between the shading of the collar and background at right.

In the baht values there are nine beads in the section of the inner frame below the crown, immediately above the King's head, instead of only seven in the Vienna printing.

The cross-bar of the "H" of "BAHT" is very slightly above the centre of the letter in the London printing but markedly so in the Vienna printing.

1917 (1 Jan). *T* **65/6** *redrawn and printed by Waterlow & Sons, London.* P 13½–15.

166	**65**	2s. yellow-brown	45	20
		a. Imperf between (horiz pair)	£650	£650
167		3s. bright green	65	30
		a. Imperf between (horiz pair)	£575	£575
		b. Imperf between (vert pair)	£650	£650
168		5s. carmine	1·70	20
		a. Imperf between (horiz pair)	£650	£650
		b. Imperf between (vert pair)	£500	£500
169		10s. olive-brown and black	1·10	20
		a. Imperf between (horiz pair)	£475	£475
		b. Imperf between (vert pair)	£500	£500
170		15s. blue	2·50	45
171	**66**	1b. sepia and blue	18·00	1·80
172		2b. brown and carmine	47·00	24·00
173		3b. grey-black and green	£275	£225
174		5b. greyish black and violet	85·00	75·00
175		10b. purple and olive	£250	7·50
		a. Perf 12½	£325	21·00
176		20b. brown and blue-green	£325	32·00
		a. Perf 12½	£375	43·00
166/176 *Set of 11*			£900	£225

(69)   (70)

1918 (11 Jan). *Red Cross Fund. Nos.* 166/76 *optd with T* **69,** *in red, by K. Oyama & Co, Bangkok.*

177	**65**	2s.(+3s.) yellow-brown	65	65
178		3s.(+2s.) bright green	65	65
179		5s.(+5s.) carmine	2·10	2·10
180		10s.(+5s.) olive-brown and black	2·50	2·50
181		15s.(+5s.) blue	2·50	2·50
182	**66**	1b.(+25s.) sepia and blue	13·00	10·50
183		2b.(+30s.) brown and carmine	17·00	13·00
184		3b.(+35s.) grey-black and green	26·00	21·00
185		5b.(+40s.) grey-black and violet	£110	75·00
		a. Opt double	£800	£400
186		10b.(+1b.) purple and olive	£250	£190
187		20b.(+1b.) brown and blue-green	£1300	£1200
177/187 *Set of 11*			£1600	£1400

1918 (2 Dec). *Victory in Great War. Nos.* 166/74 *optd in red, with T* **70,** *by K. Oyama & Co, Bangkok.*

188	**65**	2s. yellow-brown	45	45
		a. Opt double	£110	£110
189		3s. bright green	65	65
		a. Opt double	£110	£110
190		5s. carmine	1·10	1·10
		a. Opt double	£160	£160
191		10s. olive-brown and black	1·10	1·10
192		15s. blue	2·10	2·10
193	**66**	1b. sepia and blue	16·00	13·00
194		2b. brown and carmine	32·00	26·00
195		3b. grey-black and green	75·00	60·00
196		5b. grey-black and violet	£225	£200
188/196 *Set of 9*			£350	£275

A second printing made in 1919 was overprinted in vermilion.

&5   ⃝0 10
(71)   (72)

1919 (11 Nov)–**20**. *Nos. 149/50 surch with T **71/2**, by K. Oyama & Co, Bangkok.*

197	**65**	5s.on 6s. rose-carmine (G.)	1·10	20
198		10s.on 12s. sepia & black (R.)		
		(1.1.20)	2·10	30
		a. Imperf between (horiz pair)	£425	£425
		b. Siamese figure omitted	£425	£425
		c. Surch inverted	£425	£425
		d. Surch double	£160	£160

(72a)   (72b)

1920 (Feb). *Scouts' Fund. Various stamps handstamped locally.*

*(a) As T **72a**.*

199	**65**	2s.(+3s.) yellow-brown (166)	21·00	21·00
200		3s.(+2s.) bright green (148)	21·00	21·00
201		5s.on 6s. (+5s.) carmine	32·00	32·00
202		10s.on 12s. (+5s.) sepia and black	32·00	32·00
203		15s.(+5s.) blue (170)	65·00	65·00
204	**53**	1t.(+25s.) bistre and deep blue	£250	£250
199/204 *Set of 6*			£375	£375

Imperforate between varieties exist, in both horizontal and vertical pairs.

*(b) As T **72b**.*

205	**65**	2s.(+3s.) yellow-brown (166)	8·50	8·50
206		3s.(+2s.) bright green (148)	8·50	8·50
		a. Imperf between (horiz pair)		
207	**73**	5s.(+5s.) carmine/*pink*	65·00	65·00
		a. Imperf between (horiz pair)		
208	**65**	10s.on 12s. (+5s.) sepia and black	13·00	13·00
209		15s.(+5s.) blue (170)	13·00	13·00
210	**53**	1t.(+25s.) bistre and deep blue	£225	£225
205/210 *Set of 6*			£300	£300

These stamps were sold in aid of the "Wild Tiger" Scouts organization at the premium stated.

บำรุงเสือป่า

SCOUT'S FUND
73   **(73a)**

(Eng and recess Waterlow)

1920 (11 Mar)–**25**. P 13½–15.

211	**73**	2s. chocolate/*yellow* (6.8.21)	65	20
		a. Imperf between (vert pair)	£325	£325
		b. Imperf between (horiz pair)	£325	£325
212		3s. green/*green* (6.8.21)	1·10	30
213		3s. red-brown (21.7.24)	85	20
		a. Imperf between (horiz pair)	£325	£325
214		5s. carmine/*pink*	1·30	20
		a. Imperf between (vert pair)	£325	£325
215		5s. green (16.8 22)	15·00	1·90
216		5s. deep violet/*mauve* (p 12½) (1926)	3·25	20

217		10s. yellow-brown and black (6.8.21)	2·50	20
		a. Imperf between (vert pair)	£325	£325
218		15s. blue/*blue* (21.6.21)	4·25	20
		a. Imperf between (vert pair)	£325	£325
		b. Imperf between (horiz pair)	£325	£325
		c. Perf 12½ (1925)	£225	1·10
219		15s. carmine (16.8.22)	24·00	2·50
		a. Imperf between (horiz pair)	£425	£425
220		25s. chocolate (21.6.21)	10·50	1·30
221		25s. indigo (16.8.22)	18·00	1·10
222		50s. black and ochre-brown (6.8.21)	26·00	75
		a. Imperf between (vert pair)	£425	£425
		b. Imperf between (horiz pair)	£425	£425
		c. Perf 12½ (1925)	85·00	1·10
211/222 *Set of 12*			98·00	8·25

There are numerous shades in this issue.

1921 (17 Dec). *Scouts' Fund. Nos. 211/12, 214, 217/18, 220 and 222 optd with T **73a** by K. Oyama & Co, Bangkok.*

223	**73**	2s.(+3s.) chocolate/*yellow* (B.)	6·50	6·50
224		3s.(+2s.) green/*green* (R.)	6·50	6·50
225		5s.(+5s.) carmine/*pink* (B.)	6·50	6·50
226		10s.(+5s.) yellow-brown & black (R.)	6·50	6·50
227		15s.(+5s.) blue/*blue* (R.)	10·50	10·50
228		25s.(+25s.) chocolate (B.)	39·00	39·00
229		50s.(+30s.) black & ochre-brown (R.)	£180	£180
223/229 *Set of 7*			£225	£225

74 "Garuda" Bird

(Eng and recess Waterlow)

1925 (3 Jan)–**37**. *AIR.*

(a) P 13½–15.

230	**74**	2s. chocolate/*yellow* (21.4.25)	55	20
		a. Imperf between (horiz pair)	£425	£425
231		3s. chocolate	55	20
232		5s. green	5·25	30
233		10s. orange and black	10·50	30
234		15s. carmine	2·10	55
235		25s. deep blue	4·25	55
236		50s. black and orange-brown (21.4.25)	21·00	4·25
237		1b. brown and deep blue	19·00	5·25
230/237 *Set of 8*			55·00	10·50

(b) P 12½ (1930–37).

238	**74**	2s. chocolate/*yellow*	4·25	55
239		5s. green	55	20
240		10s. orange and black	55	20
241		15s. carmine	18·00	3·75
242		25s. deep blue (1937)	1·10	65
		a. Imperf between (vert pair)	£425	£425
243		50s. black and orange-brown (1937)	1·10	75
238/243 *Set of 6*			23·00	5·50

Stamps of this issue, perf 13½–15, with Siamese overprint reading "Government Museum 2468" were overprinted in connection with a fair in aid of the Government Museum, which was to have been held in 1925. Owing to the King's death, the fair was cancelled and the stamps were not issued for postal purposes.

The stock was used up during 1928 for interdepartmental accounting purposes and some post offices cancelled them with their ordinary datestamps.

King Prajadhipok (Rama VII)
26 November 1925–2 March 1935

75 Coronation Stone	**76** King Prajadhipok	**77** King Prajadhipok

(Recess Waterlow)

1926 (5 Mar). P 12½.

244	**75**	1t. green and lilac	6·50	1·10
245		2t. vermilion and carmine	15·00	3·25
246		3t. blue and olive-green	32·00	15·00
247		5t. olive-green and violet	39·00	10·50
248		10t. olive brown and scarlet	£160	13·00
249		20t. brown and grey-blue	£180	43·00
244/249 *Set of 6*			£400	80·00

This issue was intended to commemorate the 15th year of the reign of King Vajiravudh, but owing to the death of that monarch they were put on sale as ordinary postage stamps.

1928 (Jan). *Surch as T 67 by K. Oyama and Co, Bangkok, with single bar obliterating original value.*

250	**73**	5s.on 15s. carmine	2·50	1·60
251	**65**	10s.on 28s. chocolate (R.)	6·00	55

(Des Khun Thep Laksanlehka and Capt. M. C. Gunvudhi Prija. Recess Waterlow & Sons)

1928 (15 Apr–15 Nov). P 12½.

252	**76**	2s. chocolate (1.5)	45	10
253		3s. green (1.5)	55	20
		a. Imperf between (vert pair)	£250	£250
254		5s. violet	45	10
		a. Imperf between (horiz pair)	£200	£200
		b. Imperf between (vert pair)	£200	£200
255		10s. carmine	55	10
		a. Imperf between (vert pair)	£250	£250
256		15s. blue (1.5)	65	20
		a. Imperf between (vert pair)	£325	
257		25s. orange and black (1.5)	2·50	45
258		50s. black and orange (1.5)	1·30	65
259		80s. black and light blue (15.11)	2·10	55
260	**77**	1b. black and blue (1.6)	4·25	65
261		2b. brown and carmine	7·50	1·30
262		3b. black and yellow-green	6·50	2·10
263		5b. grey-brown and violet	13·00	3·25
264		10b. purple and olive-green	26·00	5·25
265		20b. red-brown and blue-green	55·00	10·50
266		40b. sepia and green	95·00	43·00
252/266 *Set of 15*			£200	60·00

(78)	79

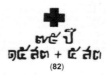

80 Kings Prajadhipok and Chao Phya Chakri	**81** Chao Phya Chakri (Rama I)

1930. *Surch as T 78 by K. Oyama and Co, Bangkok.*

267	**64**	10s.on 12s. olive-brown & black		
		(R.)	4·25	85
		a. Surch inverted	£225	£225
268		25s.on 28s. red-brown (B.)	17·00	1·30

(Des Prince Narisara. Recess Waterlow)

1932 (1 Apr). *150th Anniv of Chakri Dynasty and of Bangkok as Capital; Opening of Memorial Bridge over Menam.* P 12½.

269	**79**	2s. brown-red	85	20
270		3s. green	1·30	45
271		5s. violet	85	20
272	**80**	10s. black and carmine	1·30	20
273		15s. black and blue	5·25	65
274		35s. black and mauve	7·50	85
275		50s. black and claret	34·00	1·70
276	**81**	1b. indigo	50·00	10·50
269/276 *Set of 8*			95·00	13·00

A black commemorative cancellation representing two bowls standing one upon another on which rests the Sacred Book of the Constitution, was applied from 8–12 December 1933, at a Government Fair at Bangkok, to Nos. 252/8. 260 and corresponding values of the above set on the occasion of the First Anniversary of the Constitution.

King Ananda Mahidol (Rama VIII)
2 March 1935–9 June 1946

(82)	**83** National Assembly Hall

1939 (6 Apr). *Red Cross Fund. 75th Anniv of Membership of the International Red Cross. Nos. 171/3 surch as T 82, in red, by Boon Krong Bhanich, Bangkok.*

277		5+5s. on 1b. sepia and blue	7·50	7·50
278		10+5s. on 2b. brown and carmine	17·00	17·00
279		15+5s. on 3b. grey black and green	14·00	14·00

(Litho Royal Survey Dept, Bangkok)

1939 (24 June). *Seventh Anniv of Constitution and National Day (1st issue).* P 11, 11½, 12, 12½ and compound.

280	**83**	2s. purple-brown	2·10	65
		a. Imperf between (horiz pair)	75·00	75·00
		b. Imperf horiz (vert pair)	85·00	85·00
		c. Imperf vert (horiz pair)	85·00	85·00
281		3s. green	4·25	1·70
		a. Imperf between (horiz pair)	£120	£110
		b. Imperf horiz (vert pair)	£110	95·00
		c. Imperf vert (horiz pair)	£110	95·00
282		5s. dull purple	2·10	10
		a. Imperf between (horiz pair)	85·00	85·00
		b. Imperf horiz (vert pair)	85·00	85·00
		c. Imperf vert (horiz pair)	85·00	85·00
283		10s. carmine	8·50	15
		a. Imperf between (vert pair)	85·00	85·00
		b. Imperf horiz (vert pair)	85·00	85·00
		c. Imperf vert (horiz pair)	85·00	85·00
284		15s. blue	21·00	65
		b. Imperf horiz (vert pair)	£130	£110
		c. Imperf vert (horiz pair)	£130	£110
280/284 *Set of 5*			35·00	3·00

THAILAND

In June 1939 it was decreed that Siam, known to its inhabitants as Muang Thai ("the land of the free"), should be officially called Thailand.

84 Chakri Palace and "Garuda" Bird

(Des Fine Arts Dept. Litho Survey Dept, Defence Ministry,Bangkok)

1940 (13–30 May). *National Day (2nd issue).* P 12½.
285	**84**	2s. chocolate		2·10	65
286		3s. green		4·25	1·70
		a. Imperf between (vert pair)			
		b. Error. 5s. green (R.6/7)		£600	£450
287		5s. deep purple (24.5)		3·25	10
288		10s. carmine (30.5)		12·00	10
		a. Printed on both sides		£110	
289		15s. blue (28.5)		26·00	65
285/289	*Set of 5*			43·00	2·75

No. 286b was caused by a cliché of the 5s. being included in the plate of the 3s.

In June 1940 the Thai nationalist leader Luang Pibul Songgram made a pact with Japan. After the Japanese occupation of IndoChina and a short war between Thailand and the Vichy French authorities, Japan "mediated" and the lost provinces of Battambang and Siemreap and Laos west of the Mekong were perforce returned to Thailand by France on 9 May 1941. On 25 January 1942 Thailand declared war on the United Kingdom and the U.S.A. and on 19 October 1943, after the Japanese had taken Malaya, Japan returned to Thailand the states of Kedah, Kelantan, Perlis and Trengganu. For the stamps issued under Thai rule in these states see Part 1 Commonwealth & British Empire 1840–1952 catalogue. All these territories were returned to Indo-China and Malaya after the defeat of Japan.

85 King Ananda Mahidol

86 Ploughing Rice Field

87 Ban Pa'im Palace, Ayuthia

88 Monument of Democracy, Bangkok

(Des Fine Arts Dept, Bangkok. Recess Waterlow)

1941 (17 Apr). P 12½.
290	**85**	2s. brown		65	20
291		3s. green		1·10	65
292		5s. violet		65	20
293		10s. red		65	20
294	**86**	15s. grey and blue		65	30
295		25s. orange and slate		65	30
296		50s. grey and orange		65	45
297	**87**	1b. grey and ultramarine		2·50	65
298		2b. grey and carmine		7·50	1·30
299		3b. grey and green		13·00	3·25

300		5b. red and black		39·00	12·00
		a. Imperf between (horiz pair)			
301		101b. yellow and deep olive-green		55·00	34·00
290/301	*Set of 12*			£110	48·00

The 1941 printing was on toned paper; the set was later printed on white, thinner paper, the satang values being delivered in 1946 and the baht values in 1948.

(Recess Survey Dept, Defence Ministry, Bangkok)

1942 (1 Oct)–**43**. *AIR. With or without gum.* P 10½, 11, 12½ and compound.
302	**88**	2s. brown (15.2.43)		2·10	2·10
303		3s. green (24 6.43)		21·00	21·00
		a. Imperf between (vert pair)		£130	£130
304		5s. purple		2·10	45
		a. Imperf between (horiz pair)		65·00	65·00
		b. Imperf between (vert pair)		65·00	65·00
305		10s. carmine (15.3.43)		14·00	65
		a. Imperf between (vert pair)		95·00	95·00
306		15s. blue (15.12.43)		3·25	1·10
		a. Imperf between (vert pair)		85·00	85·00
302/306	*Set of 5*			38·00	23·00

There are numerous shades in this issue.

89 King Ananda Mahidol

90 Indo-China War Monument, Bangkok

91 Bangkaen Monument and Ears of Rice

(T **89/91** printed by Survey Dept, Defence Ministry, Bangkok)

1943 (1 May)–**48**.

(a) Recess. With or without gum. P 11.
307	**89**	1b. indigo		13·00	1·10
		a. Imperf between (horiz pair)		65·00	65·00
		b. Imperf between (vert pair)		65·00	65·00
		c. Imperf (pair)		65·00	65·00

(b) Litho. P 11 or 12½ × 11 (1.48).
308	**89**	1b. grey-blue		39·00	6·50
		a. Imperf between (horiz pair)		£110	£110

1943 (1 June–2 Nov).

(a) Recess. P 11 or 12½.
309	**90**	3s. deep green		13·00	13·00

(b) Litho. With or without gum. P 12½ × 11 (2.11).
310	**90**	3s. light greyish green		2·10	85

1943 (25 Nov)–**48**. *Tenth Anniv of Failure of* 1933 *Revolt. Litho. No gum or with gum (later printings).* P 11, 12½ × 11 or 12½.
311	**91**	2s. brown-orge (*shades*) (20 × 24½ mm)		1·70	1·30
		a. Imperf horiz (vert pair)		50·00	50·00
		b. Printed on both sides		21·00	
312		10s. carmine (*shades*) (20½ × 25 mm) (25.12.43)		2·50	30
		a. Imperf between (horiz pair)		50·00	50·00
		b. Imperf between (vert pair)		50·00	50·00
		c. Printed on both sides		£200	
		d. Design 19 × 24 mm (1948)		5·25	3·25

For stamps in similar design to Type **91** but with value in cents for use in Kedah, Kelantan, Perlis and Trengganu, see under Malaysia (Thai Occupation) in Commonwealth & British Empire 1840–1952 catalogue.

SIAM

From September 1945 to 10 May 1949 the country was again called Siam.

King Bhumibol Adulyadej (Rama IX), 9 June 1946

92 King Bhumibol   **93** King Bhumibol

(Recess Waterlow)

1947 (15 Nov)–**49**. P 12½.

(a) Size 19½ × 25 mm.

313	**92**	5s. violet	45	10
314		10s. scarlet (3.1.49)	1·10	10
315		20s. purple-brown	3·00	10
316		50s. olive-green (3.1.49)	3·00	10

(b) Size 21½ × 27 mm (1.11.48).

317	**92**	1b. blue and violet	6·50	20
318		2b. green and blue	14·00	85
319		3b. black and vermilion	21·00	1·70
320		5b. vermilion and blue-green	50·00	3·25
321		10b. violet and sepia	£180	1·10
322		20b. reddish purple and black	£225	4·25
313/322	*Set of 10*		£450	10·50

(Litho Survey Dept, Defence Ministry, Bangkok)

1947 (5 Dec)–**48**. *Coming of Age of King Bhumibol. Without gum or with gum (*10, 50s.*).* P 12½ × 11–11½.

323	**93**	5s. orange	1·10	1·10
		a. Perf 11 × 11–11½	4·00	1·40
324		10s. olive-brown	49·00	48·00
325		10s. sage-green (1948)	1·10	1·10
326		20s. blue	4·25	1·10
		a. Perf 11 × 11–11½	5·25	1·10
327		50s. green	8·50	2·10
		a. Perf 11 × 11–11½	10·00	3·25
323/327a	*Set of 5*		55·00	48·00

THAILAND

On 11 May 1949 the name of the country was changed back to Thailand.

94 King Bhumibol and Palace   **95** King Bhumibol   **96** United Nations Emblem

(Recess Waterlow)

1950 (5 May–Oct). *Coronation of King Bhumibol.* P 12½.

328	**94**	5s. purple	45	20
329		10s. scarlet (1.10)	45	20
330		15s. violet (1.10)	2·10	2·10
331		20s. brown	65	10
332		80s. green (15.8)	5·25	2·75
333		1b. blue (1.10)	1·70	20
334		2b. yellow (1.10)	10·50	85
335		3b. grey (1.10)	55·00	7·50
328/335	*Set of 8*		70·00	12·50

(Recess Waterlow)

1951–60. P 12½.

336	**95**	5s. bright purple (4.6.51)	20	10
337		10s. green (4.6.51)	20	10
338		15s. red-brown (15 2.52)	65	10
339		20s. chocolate (1960)	65	10
340		25s. carmine (15.2.51)	20	10

341		50s. grey-olive (15.10.56)	65	10
342		1b. blue (4.6.51)	85	10
343		1b.15 deep blue (1.9.53)	20	10
344		1b.25 brown-red (1.10.54)	3·25	20
345		2b. blue-green (1.12.51)	3·75	20
346		3b. grey (1.12.51)	6·50	30
347		5b. scarlet & dull turq-bl (1.2.55)	26·00	45
348		10b. violet and sepia (1.2.55)	£200	75
349		20b. olive-green & grey-black (1.2.55)	£180	10·50
336/349	*Set of 14*		£375	12·00

For 1961 De La Rue printings, perf 13 × 12½, see Nos. 412/21.

(Recess Waterlow)

1951 (24 Oct). *United Nations Day.* P 12½.

350	**96**	25s. deep ultramarine	2·50	2·10

   1952

97 "Garuda" Bird   **(97a)**   **(98)**

(Recess Waterlow*)

1952 (15 June)–**53**. *AIR.* P 13 × 12½.

351	**97**	1b.50 purple (15.9.53)	3·25	65
352		2b. blue	9·75	1·30
353		3b. grey (15.9.53)	13·00	85

*In 1961 the 1b.50 was printed by De La Rue from Waterlow plates in the same perforation.

1952 (24 Oct). *United Nations Day. Optd with T* **97a**.

354	**96**	25s. deep ultramarine (R.)	1·70	1·30

1952 (8 Dec). *20th Anniv of Constitution. Surch locally with T* **98**.

355	**76**	80s.+20s. black and light blue (R.)	14·00	10·50

99 Dancer over Cross   **(99a)**   **(100)**   **(101)**

(Typo (cross lithe) State Lottery Printing Press)

1953 (6 Apr). *60th Anniv of Thai Red Cross Society. Wmk characters between wavy lines.* P 11.

356	**99**	25s.+25s. dp bl, scar, cream & yell-grn	4·25	3·25
357		50s.+50s. dp bl, scar, cream & rose	13·00	10·50
358		1b.+1b. scar, cream & greenish bl	17·00	15·00

1953 (23 Oct). *United Nations Day. Optd with T* **99a**.

359	**96**	25s. deep ultramarine (R.)	1·10	85

1954 (24 Oct). *United Nations Day. Optd with T* **100**.

360	**96**	25s. deep ultramarine (R.)	3·25	2·75

Types **99a** and **100** double or inverted are forgeries.

1955 (4 Jan). *Optd with T* **101**.

361	**76**	5s. violet	5·25	6·50
362		10s. carmine	5·25	6·50

5 สต.
(102)

103 Processional Elephant

24
(104)

98

1955 (5 Jan). *Surch as T* **102**.
363 **92** 5s.on 20s. purple-brown . . . . 1·30 55
364 10s.on 20s. purple-brown (R.) . . . 1·90 55

(Recess Waterlow)

1955 (15 Feb–1 Apr). *400th Birth Anniv of King Naresuan.* P 13½.
365 **103** 25s. carmine . . . . 1·10 10
366 80s. purple (1.4) . . . . . 12·00 3·25
367 1b.25 bronze-green (1.4) . . 32·00 1·10
368 2b. deep blue (1.4) . . . . 7·50 85
369 3b. lake-brown (1.4) . . . . 21·00 75
365/369 *Set of 5* . . . . 65·00 5·50

1955 (3 Apr). *Red Cross Fair. Nos. 356/8 optd with T* **104**.
370 **99** 25s.+25s. dp bl, scar, cream & yell-
grn . . . . 17·00 10·50
371 50s.+50s. dp bl, scar, cream &
rose . . . . 80·00 65·00
372 1b.+1b. scar, cream & greenish
bl . . . . £120 95·00

105 Tao Suranari

106 Equestrian Statue

1
9
5
5
(106a)

(Recess Waterlow)

1955 (15 Apr). *Tao Suranari Commemoration.* P 12½ × 13½.
373 **105** 10s. deep lilac . . . . 1·30 30
374 25s. emerald 85 10
375 1b. bistre-brown . . . . . 21·00 1·70

(Recess Waterlow)

1955 (1 May). *King Taksin Commemoration.* P 13 × 12.
376 **106** 5s. ultramarine 65 30
377 25s. deep turquoise-green . . . 6·75 10
378 1b.25 deep rose-red . . . . . 18·00 1·80

1955 (24 Oct). *United Nations Day. Optd with T* **106a**.
379 **96** 25s. deep ultramarine (R.) . . . 3·25 2·75
Double and inverted overprints are forgeries.

107 Don Chedi Pagoda

1
9
5
6
(107a)

(Recess Waterlow)

1956 (1 Feb). P 13½ × 13.
380 **107** 10s. emerald . . . . 2·10 2·10
381 50s. reddish brown . . . . . 10·50 85
382 75s. violet . . . . 3·25 65
383 1b.50 brown-red . . . . . 13·00 1·10
380/383 *Set of 4* . . . . 26·00 4·25

1956 (24 Oct). *United Nations Day. Optd with T* **107a**.
384 **96** 25s. deep ultramarine (R.) . . . . 1·10 1·10

PRINTERS. All stamps up to No. 789 were printed by the Government Printing Works, Tokyo, *except where otherwise stated*.

108 Dharmachakra and Sambar

109

1957 (13 May). *2,500th Anniv of Buddhism. T* **108** *and similar vert designs. Photo.* W **109**. P 13½.
385 **108** 5s. sepia 45 10
386 10s. claret 45 10
387 15s. emerald . . . . . . 1·10 85
388 — 20s. red-orange . . . . 1·10 85
389 — 25s. brown 20 10
390 — 50s. magenta 85 25
391 — 1b. histre-brown . . . . 1·30 30
392 — 1b.25 slate-blue . . . . 17·00 3·50
393 — 2b. reddish purple . . . 3·25 45
385/393 *Set of 9* . . . . 23·00 6·00
Designs:—20s. to 50s. Hand of Peace and Dharmachakra; 1b. to 2b. Nakon Phatom pagoda.

110 U.N. Emblem and Laurel Sprays

111 Gateway to Grand Palace

112 Pagoda

1957 (24 Oct). *United Nations Day. Photo.* W **109**. P 13½.
394 **110** 25s. olive 55 20

1958 (24 Oct). *United Nations Day. Photo.* W **109**. P 13½.
395 **110** 25s. yellow-brown 55 20
See also No. 400.

1959 (15 Oct). *First South-East Asia Peninsula Games. T* **111** *and similar vert designs. Photo.* W **109**. P 13½.
396 10s. orange 20 10
397 25s. carmine-lake 30 10
398 1b.25 blue-green . . . . 2·00 30
399 2b. new blue . . . . 2·10 55
396/399 *Set of 4* . . . . 4·00 95
Designs:—25s. Royal parasols; 1b.25, Bowman; 2b. Wat Arun (temple) and prow of royal barge.

1959 (24 Oct). *United Nations Day. Photo.* W **109**. P 13½.
400 **110** 25s. indigo 65 20

1960 (7 Apr). *World Refugee Year. Photo.* W **109**. P 13½.
401	**112**	50s. brown		20	10
402		2b. yellow-green		1·10	65

113 Wat Arun Temple

114 Indian Elephant

115 S.E.A.T.O. Emblem

1960 (10 Aug). *Leprosy Releif Campaign. Photo.* W **109**. P 13½.
403	**113**	50s. carmine		20	10
404		2b. ultramarine		1·90	65

1960 (29 Aug). *Fifth World Forestry Congress, Seattle. Photo.* W **109**. P 13½.
405	**114**	25s. bright yellow-green		55	10

1960 (8 Sept). *South-East Asia Treaty Organization Day. Photo.* W **109**. P 13½.
406	**115**	50s. purple-brown		65	10

116 Siamese Child

117 Letter-writing

118 U.N. Emblem and Globe

1960 (3 Oct). *Children's Day. Photo.* W **109**. P 13½.
407	**116**	50s. reddish purple		45	10
408		1b. orange-brown		3·50	65

1960 (3 Oct). *International Correspondence Week. Photo.* W **109**. P 13½.
409	**117**	50s. magenta		45	10
410		2b. blue		1·90	65

1960 (24 Oct). *United Nations Day. Photo.* W **109**. P 13½.
411	**118**	50s. violet		55	20

See also Nos. 446 and 467.

1961. *As Nos. 336/47 but printed by De La Rue and perf* 13 × 12½.
412	**95**	5s. bright purple		65	20
413		10s. greyish green		65	20
414		15s. red-brown		6·50	1·10
415		20s. chocolate		4·25	85
416		25s. carmine		65	10
417		50s. grey-olive		1·30	20
418		1b. blue		4·25	45
419		2b. blue-green		7·50	65
420		3b. grey		17·00	85
421		5b. scarlet and dull turquoise-blue		£110	2·10
412/421 *Set of 10*				£140	6·00

119 King Bhumibol

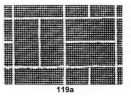

119a

(Recess De La Rue)

1961 (3 July)–**68**. W **119a**. P 13½ × 13.
422	**119**	5s. reddish purple (1962)		10	10
423		10s. bluish green (1962)		10	10
424		15s. red-brown (1962)		20	10
425		20s. deep brown (1962)		10	10
426		25s. carmine-red (1963)		20	10
427		50s. brown-olive (1962)		20	10
428		80s. orange (1962)		1·10	60
429		1b. brown and ultramarine		75	10
430		1b.25 yellow-ol & verm (15.1.65)		2·10	75
431		1b.50 yell-grn & bluish vio (6.8.61)		65	20
432		2b. violet and carmine-red (6.8.61)		85	10
433		3b. blue and brown		2·10	20
434		4b. black and yellow-bistre (1 2.68)		2·10	85
435		5b. green and blue (6.8.61)		9·75	25
436		10b. black and orange-red (6.8.61)		50·00	45
437		20b. blue and emerald (23.8.61)		43·00	2·10
438		25b. blue and deep green (23.8.61)		14·00	1·10
439		40b. black and yellow (15.1.65)		43·00	2·50
422/439 *Set of 18*				£150	9·00

120 Children in Garden

121 Pen, Letters and Globe

1961 (2 Oct). *Children's Day. Photo.* W **109**. P 13½.
440	**120**	20s. indigo		45	20
441		2b. deep reddish violet		2·50	65

1961 (9 Oct). *International Correspondence Week. Photo.* W **109**. P 13½.
442	–	25s. grey-green		45	10
443	–	50s. reddish purple		20	10
444	**121**	1b. bright rose-red		1·30	45
445		2b. ultramarine		1·90	55
442/445 *Set of 4*				3·50	1·10

Design:—25, 50s. Pen, and map on envelope.

1961 (24 Oct). *United Nations Day. Photo.* W **109**. P 13½.
446	**118**	50s. brown-lake		45	20

See also No. 467.

122 Thai Scout Badge and Saluting Hand

123 Campaign Emblem and Temple

1961 (1 Nov). *50th Anniv of Thai Scout Movement.* T **122** *and similar designs. Photo.* W **109**. P 13½.

447	50s. carmine	20	10
448	1b. bluish green	1·10	45
449	2b. blue	1·30	55

Designs: *Vert*—1b. Scout camp and scout saluting flag; 2b. King Vajiravudh in uniform, and scout, guide and cub marching.

1962 (7 Apr). *Malaria Eradication.* T **123** *and similar vert design. Photo.* W **109**. P 13½.

450	**123**	5s. orange-brown	20	10
451		10s. brown	20	10
452		20s. light blue	20	10
453		50s. carmine	20	10
454	–	1b. green	85	15
455	–	1b.50 brown-purple	1·50	55
456	–	2b. deep blue	1·10	20
457	–	3b. deep violet	3·25	1·90
450/457	*Set of 8*		6·75	3·00

Design:—Nos. 454/7, Hanuman fighting mosquitoes.

124 Bangkok

125 Thai Child with Doll

1962 (21 Apr). *"Century 21" Exhibition, Seattle. Photo.* W **109**. P 13½.

458	**124**	50s. purple	45	10
459		2b. ultramarine	3·75	65

1962 (1 Oct). *Children's Day. Photo.* W **109**. P 13 × 13½.

460	**125**	25s. turquoise-green	45	20
461		50s. yellow-brown	45	10
462		2b. magenta	3·75	65

126 Correspondence Symbols

127 Exhibition Emblem

1962 (8 Oct). *International Correspondence Week.* T **126** *and similar vert design. Photo.* W **109**. P 13 × 13½.

463	**126**	25s. bright reddish violet	45	20
464		50s. bright scarlet	45	10
465	–	1b. olive-bistre	2·10	45
466	–	2b. pale grey-green	3·75	55
463/466	*Set of 4*		5·25	1·20

Design:—1, 2b. Quill pen.

1962 (24 Oct). *United Nations Day. Photo.* W **109**. P 13½.

467	**118**	50s. carmine-red	45	20

1962 (1 Nov). *Students' Exhibition, Bangkok. Photo.* W **109**. P 13½.

468	**127**	50s. bistre	65	10

128 Harvesting

129 "Temple Guardian"

(Recess De La Rue)

1963 (21 Mar). *Freedom from Hunger.* W **119a**. P 14.

469	**128**	20s. green	75	20
470		50s. yellow-brown	55	10

1963 (1 Apr). *First Anniv of Asian-Oceanic Postal Union. Recess.* W **109**. P 13½.

471	**129**	50s. green and light brown	55	10

130 Centenary Emblem

131 G.P.O., Bangkok, and (inset) old Post Office

(Litho De La Rue)

1963 (1 Apr). *Centenary of Red Cross.* W **119a**. P 13½.

472	**130**	50s.+10s. brt scar & brownish grey	20	10
		a. Pair. Nos. 472/3	45	25
473	–	50s.+10s. brt scar & brownish grey	20	10

In No. 473 the positions of the emblem and inscriptions are reversed.

Nos. 472/3 were issued together in *se-tenant* pairs within the sheet.

(Recess De La Rue)

1963 (4 Aug). *80th Anniv of Post and Telegraph Department.* W **119a**. P 14.

474	**131**	50s. bronze-green, orge & slate-vio	45	10
475		3b. sepia, bronze-green & carm-red	4·75	1·20

132 King Bhumibol

O **133** (Trans "For Government Service Statistical Research")

133 Children with Dolls

1963 (22 Aug)–**71**. *Photo.* W **109**. P 13 × 13½.

476	**132**	5s. magenta	10	10
477		10s. green	10	10
478		15s. light brown	10	10
479		20s. olive-brown	10	10
480		25s. carmine	10	10
481		50s. deep olive	10	10
482		75s. bright lilac (22.12.71)	20	10
483		80s. orange	65	35

484	1b. brown and deep blue (1964)	65	20
485	1b.25 yellow-bistre and yellow-brown (15.1.65)	3·25	85
486	1b.50 yellow-green and deep bluish violet (1964)	65	45
487	2b. violet and carmine (1964)	45	10
488	3b. blue and yellow-brown (1964)	1·10	15
489	4b. black and yellow-bistre (1.2.68)	1·30	20
490	5b. green and blue (1964)	7·50	20
491	10b. black and orange-red (1964)	13·00	45
492	20b. grey-blue and green (1964)	75·00	2·75
493	25b. blue and bronze-green (1964)	5·25	45
494	40b. black & lt olive-yellow (15.1.65)	75·00	3·50
476/494	Set of 19	£170	9·50

(Des Nai Chao Thongma. Typo)

1963 (1 Oct)–64. *OFFICIAL.*

(a) Printed by Religious Printing Press. Rough perf about 11.

O495	O 133	10s. carmine-red and rose-pink	45	45
		a. Rose-pink frame omitted		
O496		20s. carmine and emerald-green	45	45
O497		25s. carmine-red and bright blue	45	45
		a. Blue frame omitted	18·00	
		b. Blue frame omitted (in pair with normal)		
O498		1b. carmine and silver-grey	45	45
O499		2b. carmine and bronze	45	45
O495/499	Set of 5		2·00	2·00

Imperforate between varieties exist, both horizontal and vertical pairs.

In No. O497a the frame is omitted on every stamp in the sheet. Further sheets are known, however, with frame omitted on stamp 2 of row 7 only and this is No. O497b. It needs to be in pair with normal to distinguish it from No. O497a.

(b) Printing in one colour by Infantry Printing Centre, Saraburi. Rough perf about 11 (Jan 1964).

O500	O 133	20s. green	45	45
O501		25s. greenish blue	45	45
O502		50s. scarlet	45	45
O503		1b. silver-grey	45	45
O504		2b. bistre	45	45
O500/504	Set of 5		2·00	2·00

The above were used compulsorily by Government Departments between 1 October 1963 and 31 January 1964 to determine the amount of mail sent out by the different departments for the purpose of charging them in the future. They were postmarked in the usual way.

1963 (7 Oct). *Children's Day. Litho.* W **109**. P 13½.

505	133	50s. carmine-red	45	10
506		2b. Prussian blue	3·75	55

134 "Garuda" Bird with Scroll in Beak

135 U.N. Emblem

1963 (7 Oct). *International Correspondence Week.* T **134** *and similar horiz design.* Litho. W **109**. P 13½.

507	134	50s. brown-purple and turquoise	65	10
508		1b. maroon and yellow-green	3·25	55

509	–	2b. slate-blue and yellow-brown	18·00	65
510	–	3b. yellow-green and orange-brown	6·75	1·90
507/510	Set of 4		26·00	3·00

Design:—2b., 3b. Women writing letters.

1963 (24 Oct). *United Nations Day. Litho.* W **109**. P 13½.

511	135	50s. greenish blue	45	10

136 King Bhumibol

137 Mother and Child

1963 (5 Dec). *King Bhumibol's 36th Birthday. Photo.* W **109**. P 13½.

512	136	1b.50 indigo, yellow and blue	2·10	45
513		5b. indigo, yellow and cerise	14·00	2·10

1964 (13 Jan). *17th Anniv of United Nations Children's Fund. Litho.* W **109**. P 13½.

514	137	50s. dull blue	45	10
515		2b. olive-green	3·50	55

138 "Hand" of Flags, Pigeon and Globe

139 Globe and U.N. Emblem

(Des S. Claychinda (50s.), N. Saraniyavongse (1b.), P. Chavananon (2b.), V. Masmondana (3b.). Litho)

1964 (5 Oct). *International Correspondence Week.* T **138** *and similar horiz designs.* W **109**. P 13½.

516		50s. deep mauve and green	20	10
517		1b. purple-brown and deep blue-green	3·25	55
518		2b. violet-blue and lemon	8·25	65
519		3b. olive-brown and new blue	1·70	55
516/519	Set of 4		14·50	2·75

Designs:—1b. Thai girls and map; 2b. Map, pen and pencil; 3b. Hand with quill pen, and Globe.

1964 (24 Oct). *United Nations Day. Photo.* W **109**. P 13½.

520	139	50s. olive-grey	75	10

140 King Bhumibol and Queen Sirikit

141 I.T.U. Emblem and Symbols

1965 (28 Apr). *15th Royal Wedding Anniversary. Photo.* W **109**. P 13½.

521	140	2b. multicoloured	8·50	20
522		5b. multicoloured	17·00	1·90

1965 (17 May). *Centenary of International Telecommunications Union. Photo.* W **109**. P 13½.
523 **141** 1b. emerald . . . . 3·25 30

142 Goddess, Letters and Globes

1965 (3 Oct). *International Correspondence Week. T* **142** *and similar horiz design. Multicoloured. Photo.* W **109**. P 13½.
524 50s. Type **142** 20 10
525 1b. Type **142** . . . . 1·90 45
526 2b. Handclasp, letters and world map . . 7·50 45
527 3b. As 2b. . . . . 12·00 2·50
524/527 *Set of 4* . . . . 19·00 3·25

143 Grand Palace, **144**
Bangkok

(Recess and litho Bradbury, Wilkinson)

1965 (24 Oct). *International Co-operation Year and 20th Anniv of U.N.* W **144**. P 13½ × 14.
528 **143** 50s. slate-blue, yellow and blue . . 85 10

145 U.P.U. **146** Child and Lotus
Monument,
Berne, and Map
of Thailand

1965 (1 Nov). *80th Anniv of Thailand's Admission to Universal Postal Union. Litho.* W **109**. P 13½.
529 **145** 20s. grey-blue and mauve . . . 20 10
530 50s. black and greenish blue . . . 65 20
531 1b. orange-brown and violet-
blue . . . . . . 3·50 55
532 3b. green and ochre . . . . . . 7·50 1·70
529/532 *Set of 4* . . . . 10·50 2·30

(Litho De La Rue)

1968 (8 Jan). *Children's Day. T* **146** *and similar horiz design.* W **119a**. P 13.
533 50s. chestnut and black 20 10
534 1b. green and black . . . . . 2·40 65
Design:—1b. Child climbing stairs.

147 Cycling **148** Emblem and
Fair Buildings

(Des Mrs. P. Srivibhata. Photo)

1966 (4 Aug). *Publicity for Fifth Asian Games, Bangkok. T* **147** *and similar horiz designs.* W **109**. P 13½.
535 20s. lake (Type **147**) 45 10
536 25s. reddish violet (Tennis) . . . 65 20
537 50s. rosine (Running) 45 10
538 1b. ultramarine (Weightlifting) . . 1·70 55
539 1b.25 black (Boxing) . . . . 2·50 2·10
540 2b. turquoise-blue (Swimming) . . 5·00 45
541 3b. chestnut (Basketball) . . . 9·75 3·00
542 5b. maroon (Football) . . . . 27·00 9·75
535/542 *Set of 8* . . . . 43·00 15·00
See also Nos. 553/6

(Des C. Singhsenee. Litho)

1966 (1 Sept). *First International Trade Fair, Bangkok.* W **109**. P 13½.
543 **148** 50s. purple 85 45
544 1b. chestnut . . . . . . 1·70 65

149 "Reading and Writing" **150** U.N.
Emblem

(Des P. Chaovananonda (545/6), Mrs. P. Srivibhata (547/8). Photo)

1966 (9 Oct). *International Correspondence Week. T* **149** *and similar horiz design.* W **109**. P 13½.
545 – 50s. rosine 20 10
546 1b. orange-brown . . . . 1·50 45
547 **149** 2b. violet . . . . . . 7·50 45
548 3b. turquoise-green . . . . 4·75 1·60
545/548 *Set of 4* . . . . 12·50 2·30
Design:—50s., 1b. "Map" envelopes representing the five continents, and pen.

(Des K. Saengkhooto. Litho De La Rue)

1966 (24 Oct). *United Nations Day.* W **119a**. P 13½.
549 **150** 50s. ultramarine 65 10

151 Pra Buddha **152** "Goddess of Rice"
Bata (monastery)

(Des Mrs. P. Srivibhata. Photo)

1966 (4 Nov). *20th Anniv of United Nations Educational, Scientific and Cultural Organization.* W **109**. P 13½.
550 **151** 50s. yellow-olive and black . . . 45 10

(Des K. Saeng-xuto and S. Khanboon. Recess)

1966 (25 Nov). *International Rice Year.* W **109**. P 13½.
| 551 | **152** | 50s. turquoise-blue and blue | 1·10 | 65 |
| 552 | | 3b. rosine and deep reddish purple | 10·50 | 3·00 |

153 Thai Boxing

154 Chevron Snakehead (*Channa striatus*)

(Des Mrs. P. Srivibhata. Photo)

1966 (9 Dec). *Fifth Asian Games, Bangkok.* T **153** and similar horiz designs, each in black, red and brown. W **109**. P 13.
553	50s. Type **153**	65	10
554	1b. Takraw (ball game)	2·50	95
555	2b. "Kite fighting"	14·00	2·10
556	3b. "Cudgel play"	13·00	7·50
553/556 *Set of 4*		27·00	9·50

(Des S. Swangchan (1b.), Mrs. P. Srivibhata (2b., 5b.),A. Kaewsawarng (3b.). Photo)

1967 (1 Jan). *Fishes.* T **154** and similar designs. Multicoloured. W **109**. P 13½.
557	1b. Type **154**	3·25	1·10
558	2b. Short mackerel (*Rastrelliger brachysomus*) (45 × 26 mm)	16·00	1·70
559	3b. Siamese barb (*Puntius gonionotus*) (45 × 26 mm)	7·50	4·25
560	5b. Siamese fighting fish (*Betta splendens*)	9·75	4·75
557/560 *Set of 4*		33·00	10·50

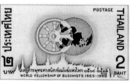

155 Djarmachakra and Globe

156 Great Indian Hornbill

(Des Mrs. P. Srivibhata. Litho)

1967 (15 Jan). *Establishment of Buddhist World Fellowship Headquarters in Thailand.* W **109**. P 13½.
| 561 | **155** | 2b. black and yellow | 3·50 | 55 |

(Des A. Kaewsawarng. Photo)

1967 (1 Feb). *Birds.* T **156** and similar vert designs. Multicoloured. W **109**. P 13½.
562	20s. Type **156**	45	45
563	25s. Southern grackle	65	65
564	50s. White-rumped shama	1·10	20
565	1b. Siamese fireback pheasant	2·75	85
566	1b.50 Spotted-necked dove	2·75	1·10
567	2b. Sarus crane	14·00	1·10
568	3b. White-throated kingfisher	7·50	5·25
569	3b. Asian open-bill stork	14·00	5·25
562/569 *Set of 8*		39·00	10·50

157 *Vandopsis parishii*

158 House

1967 (1 Apr). *Thai Orchids.* T **157** and similar vert designs. Multicoloured. Photo. W **109**. P 13½.
570	20s. Type **157**	45	30
571	50s. Ascocentrum curvifolium	65	20
572	80s. Rhynchostylis retusa	1·10	95
573	1b. Rhynchostylis gigantea	3·25	85
574	1b.50 Dendrobium alconeri	2·10	85
575	2b. Paphiopedilum callosum	12·00	1·10
576	3b. Dendrobium formosum	7·50	5·25
577	5b. Dendrobium primulinum	12·00	4·25
570/577 *Set of 8*		35·00	12·50

(Des G. Saeng-xuto and S. Khanboon. Recess)

1967 (6 Apr). *Thai Architecture.* T **158** and similar horiz designs. W **109**. P 13½.
578	50s. violet and greenish blue	1·10	45
579	1b.50 orange-brown and yellow-brown	3·25	1·70
580	2b. blue and turquoise	13·00	1·70
581	3b. sepia and orange-yellow	8·50	5·75
578/581 *Set of 4*		23·00	8·50
Buildings:—1b.50; Pagodas, 2b. Temple bell-tower; 3b. Temple.

159 *Sri Suphanahong* (royal barge) and Palace

(Des G. Saeng-xuto and S. Khanboon. Recess)

1967 (15 Sept). *International Tourist Year.* W **109**. P 13½.
| 582 | **159** | 2b. sepia and blue | 3·75 | 85 |

160 Dove, Globe, People and Letters

161 U.N. Emblem

(Des S. Khanhoon. Photo)

1967 (8 Oct). *International Correspondence Week.* T **160** and similar horiz design. W **109**. P 13½.
583	**160**	50s. multicoloured	45	15
584		1b. multicoloured	1·70	45
585		2b. black and yellow-green	4·25	55
586		3b. black and reddish brown	6·50	2·10
583/586 *Set of 4*			11·50	3·00
Design:—2b., 3b., Handclasp, globe and doves.

(Des G. Saeng-xuto and S. Khanboon. Photo)

1967 (24 Oct). *United Nations Day.* W **109**. P 13½.
| 587 | **161** | 50s. multicoloured | 45 | 10 |

162 National Flag

(Des G. Saeng-xuto and S. Khanboon. Photo)

1967 (5 Dec). *50th Anniv of Thai National Flag.* W **109**. P 13½.
588 **162** 50s. red, blue and turquoise-blue 45 10
589 2b. red, blue and olive-green . . . 4·75 85

163 Elephant carrying Teak Log   **164** Satellite and Thai Tracking Station

(Des G. Saeng-xuto and S. Khanboon. Recess)

1968 (1 Mar). *Export Promotion.* W **109**. P 13½.
590 **163** 2b. olive-brown and carmine . . . . 3·25 45

(Des G. Saeng-xuto and S. Khanboon. Photo)

1968 (1 Apr). *Satellite Communications.* W **109** (*sideways*). P 13.
591 **164** 50s. multicoloured 20 10
592 3b. multicoloured . . . . 3·00 1·20

165 "Goddess of the Earth"

(Des Mrs. P. Srivibhata Litho)

1968 (1 May). *International Hydrological Decade.* W **109** (*sideways*). P 13½.
593 **165** 50s. multicoloured 55 10

166 Snakeskin Gourami (*Trichogaster pectoralis*)

(Des A. Kaewsawarng. Photo)

1968 (1 June). *Thai Fishes. T* **166** *and similar horiz designs. Multicoloured.* W **109**. P 13½.
594 10s. Type **166** 20 10
595 20s. Red-tailed Black Shark (*Labeo bicolour*) 20 10
596 25s. Thai mahseer (*Tor tambroides*) 45 20
597 50s. Giant pangasius (*Pangasius sanitwangsei*) 65 10

598 80s. Bumblebee catfish (*Leiocassis siamensis*) . . . . 1·70 95
599 1b.25 Rambaia goby (*Vaimosa rambaiae*) . . . . 3·25 2·10
600 1b.50 Giant barb (*Catlocarpio siamensis*) . . . . 10·50 1·70
601 4b. Clown knifefish (*Notopterius chitala*) . . . . 26·00 10·50
594/601 *Set of 8* . . . . 39·00 14·00

167 *Papilio arcturus*   **168** Queen Sirikit

(Des G. Saeng-xuto and S. Khanboon. Photo)

1968 (1 July). *Thai Butterflies. T* **167** *and similar horiz designs. Multicoloured.* W **109**. P 13½.
602 50s. Type **167** 65 20
603 1b. *Papilio aecus* . . . . 3·75 85
604 3b. *Papilio memnon* . . . . 12·00 4·25
605 4b. *Papilio palinurus* . . . . 16·00 6·50
602/605 *Set of 4* . . . . 30·00 10·50

(Des P. Tiramantana. Recess and photo D.L.R.)

1968 (12 Aug). *Queen Sirikit's "Third Cycle" Anniversary (36th Birthday). T* **168** *and similar vert designs showing Queen Sirikit in different Thai costumes.* W **119a**. P 14.
606 50s. multicoloured 45 10
607 2b. multicoloured . . . . 1·70 75
608 3b. multicoloured . . . . 4·25 2·10
609 5b. multicoloured . . . . 8·50 2·40
606/609 *Set of 4* . . . . 13·50 4·75

169 W.H.O. Emblem and Medical Equipment

(Des G. Saeng-xuto and S. Khanboon. Photo D.L.R.)

1968 (1 Sept). *20th Anniv of World Health Organization.* W **119a**. P 13 × 12½.
610 **169** 50s. black and yellow-olive 45 10

170 Globe, Letter and Pen   **171** U.N. Emblem and Flags

(Des S. Khanboon (50s., 2b.), V. Buranahiran (1b., 3b.). Photo)

1968 (6 Oct). *International Correspondence Week. T* **170** *and similar horiz designs. Multicoloured.* W **109**. P 13½.

611	50s. Type **170**		20	10
612	1b. Globe on pen nib		85	20
613	2b. Type **170**		2·10	30
614	3b. Globe on pen nib		4·25	1·50
611/614 *Set of 4*			6·75	1·90

(Des S. Khanboon. Photo)

1968 (24 Oct). *United Nations Day.* W **109**. P 13½.

615	**171**	50s. multicoloured	45	10

172 Human Rights Emblem and Sculpture   **173** King Rama II

(Des G. Saeng-xuto and S. Khanboon. Photo)

1968 (10 Dec). *20th Anniv of Human Rights Year.* W **109**. P 13½.

616	**172**	60s. violet, carmine-red & blackish grn	55	10

1968 (30 Dec). *Bicentenary of Birth of King Rama II. Recess.* W **109**. P 13½.

617	**173**	50s. yellow and olive-brown	65	10

174 National Assembly Building

(Des S. Sukhanetr. Recess and photo)

1969 (10 Feb). *First Election Day under New Constitution.* W **109**. P 13½.

618	**174**	50s. multicoloured	45	10
619		2b. multicoloured	2·75	65

175 I.L.O. Emblem within Cogwheels

(Des G. Saeng-xuto and S. Khanboon. Photo)

1969 (1 May). *50th Anniv of International Labour Organization.* W **109**. P 13½.

620	**175**	50s. steel-blue, black and light violet	30	10

176 Ramwong Dance

(Des A. Kaewsawarng. Photo)

1969 (15 July). *Thai Classical Dances. T* **176** *and similar horiz designs. Multicoloured.* W **109**. P 13½.

621	50s. Type **176**		20	10
622	1b. Candle dance		85	45
623	2b. Krathop Mai dance		1·90	30
624	3b. Nohra dance		3·25	1·30
621/624 *Set of 4*			5·50	1·90

177 "Letters by Post"   **178** Globe in Hand

(Des S. Disatabandhu. Photo De La Rue)

1969 (5 Oct). *International Correspondence Week. T* **177** *and similar horiz design. Multicoloured.* W **119a**. P 13½.

625	50s. Type **177**		20	10
626	1b. Type **177**		65	20
627	2b. Writing and posting a letter		1·30	30
628	3b. As 2b.		2·10	75
625/628 *Set of 4*			3·75	1·20

(Des S. Khanboon. Photo)

1969 (24 Oct). *United Nations Day.* W **109**. P 13½.

629	**178**	50s. multicoloured	30	10

179 Tin Mine

(Des S. Khanboon. Recess)

1969 (18 Nov). *Export Promotion and 2nd Technical Conference of the International Tin Council, Bangkok.* W **109**. P 13½.

630	**179**	2b. grey-blue, purple-brown & pale bl	2·50	20

180 Loy Krathong Festival

(Des Mrs. P. Pongdam. Photo)

1969 (23 Nov). *Thai Ceremonies and Festivals. T* **180** *and similar horiz designs. Multicoloured.* W **109**. P 13½.

631	50s. Type **180**		20	10
632	1b. Marriage ceremony		65	20
633	2b. Khwan ceremony		85	30
634	5b. Songkran Festival		3·00	95
631/634 *Set of* 4			4·25	1·40

181 Breguet 14 Biplane

182 "Phra Rama"

(Des S. Khanboon. Recess)

1969 (10 Dec). *50th Anniv of Thai Airmail Services.* W **109**. P 13½.

635	**181**	1b. chestnut, green and blue	85	20

(Des P. Suvarnapunya. Recess and photo)

1969 (18 Dec). *Nang Yai Shadow Theatre. T* **182** *and similar vert designs, showing character figures. Multicoloured.* W **109**. P 13½.

636	50s. Type **182**		20	10
637	2b. "Ramasura"		2·10	20
638	3b. "Mekhala"		1·70	75
639	5b. "Ongkhot"		2·40	85
636/639 *Set of* 4			5·75	1·70

183 "Improvement of Productivity"

(Des S. Khanboon. Photo)

1970 (1 Jan). *Productivity Year.* W **109**. P 13½.

640	**183**	50s. multicoloured	30	10

184 Thai Temples within I.C.W. Emblem

185 Dish Aerials

(Des Mrs. P. Srivibhata. Litho)

1970 (31 Jan). *19th Triennial Conference of International Council of Women, Bangkok.* W **109**. P 13½.

641	**184**	50s. black and light blue	45	10

(Des C. Prasong. Litho Bradbury, Wilkinson)

1970 (1 Apr). *3rd Anniv of Thai Satellite Communications.* W **144**. P 14½.

642	**185**	50s. multicoloured	30	10

186 Households and Data

(Des A. Tularaks. Photo)

1970 (1 Apr). *7th Population Census.* W **109**. P 13½.

643	**186**	1b. multicoloured	45	10

187 New Headquarters Building

(Des Miss S. Rochanasupote. Recess and litho D.L.R)

1970 (15 June). *Inauguration of New U.P.U. Headquarters Building, Berne.* W **119a**. P 13½.

644	**187**	50s. multicoloured	30	10

188 Khun Ram Kamhang as Teacher

(Litho D.L.R.)

1970 (1 July). *International Education Year.* W **119a**. P 13½.

645	**188**	50s. multicoloured	55	20

189 Swimming Stadium

1970 (1 Sept). *6th Asian Gaines, Bangkok. T* **189** *and similar horiz designs. Recess and litho.* W **109**. P 13.

646	50s. reddish lilac, red and light yellow		30	10
647	1b.50 green, red and light violet-blue		75	30
648	3b. black, red and bronze		1·10	45
649	5b. ultramarine, brown-red & lt emerald		2·10	65
646/649 *Set of* 4			3·75	1·40

Designs:—1b.50, Velodrome; 3b. Subhajalasaya Stadium; 5b. Kittikachorn Indoor Stadium.
See also No. 660.

190 Children writing and Letter

191 U.N. Emblem Royal Palace, Bangkok

(Des Mrs. P. Pongdam. Photo)

1970 (4 Oct). *International Correspondence Week. T* **190** *and similar horiz designs. Multicoloured.* W **109**. P 13½.
650	50s. Type **190**		20	10
651	1b. Woman writing letter	55	20
652	2b. Women reading letters	1·30	20
653	3b. Man reading letter	1·80	75
650/653 *Set of* 4		3·50	1·10

(Des Miss S. Rochanasupote. Photo)

1970 (24 Oct). *25th Anniv of United Nations.* W **109** (*sideways*). P 13½.
654	**191**	50s. multicoloured	65	10

192 Rubber Plantation

(Des Miss S. Rochanasupote. Recess)

1970 (1 Nov). *Export Promotion.* W **109**. P 13½.
655	192	2b. light brown, carmine and emerald	1·70	20

193 The Heroes of Bangrachan

194 King Bhumibol lighting Flame

(Des Mrs. P. Srivibhata (50s.), Mrs. P. Pongdam (1b.), S. Dlsatabandhu (2b.), S. Sookphuen (3b.). Recess)

1970 (20 Nov). *Heroes and Heroines of Thai History. T* **193** *and similar horiz designs. Multicoloured.* W **109**. P 13½.
656	50s. reddish violet and vermilion	20	10
657	1b. brown-purple and reddish violet	45	45
658	2b. chocolate and magenta	2·10	55
659	3b. yellow-green and light blue	1·70	65
656/659 *Set of* 4		4·00	1·60

Designs:—1b. Thao Thepkrasatri and Thao Srisunthorn on ramparts; 2b. Queen Suriyothai riding elephant; 3b. Phraya Phichaidaphak and battle scene.

(Des S. Disatabandhu. Photo)

1970 (9 Dec). *Inauguration of 6th Asian Games, Bangkok.* W **109** (*sideways*). P 13½.
660	**194**	1b. multicoloured	65	10

195 Woman playing So Sam Sai

(Des Mrs. P. Srivibhata. Photo)

1970 (20 Dec). *Classical Thai Musical Instruments. T* **195** *and similar horiz designs. Multicoloured.* W **109**. P 13½.
661	50s. Type **195**	30	10
662	2b. Khlui phiang-o (flute)	75	20
663	3b. Krachappi (guitar)	1·70	45
664	5b. Thon rammana (drums)	3·25	75
661/664 *Set of* 4		5·50	1·40

196 Chocolate-pointed Siamese

197 Pagoda, Nakhon Si Thammarat

(Des Mrs. P. Srivibhata. Litho Bradbury, Wilkinson)

1971 (15 Mar). *Siamese Cats. T* **196** *and similar horiz designs. Multicoloured.* W **144**. P 13½ × 14.
665	50s. Type **196**	20	10
666	1b. Blue-pointed cat	1·50	45
667	2b. Seal-pointed cat	2·50	45
668	3b. Pure White cat and kittens	3·75	1·60
665/668 *Set of* 4		7·25	2·30

1971 (30 Mar). *Buddhist Holy Places in Thailand. T* **197** *and similar vert designs, showing pagodas. Recess and litho.* W **109** (*sideways*). P 13½.
669	50s. black, deep brown and cerise	30	10
670	1b. yellow-brown, reddish vio & yell-grn	55	20
671	3b. sepia, orange-brown & yellow-orge	1·30	30
672	4b. orange-brown, sepia and blue	2·50	1·50
669/672 *Set of* 4		4·25	1·90

Designs:—1b. Nakhon Phanom; 3b. Nakhom Pathom; 4b. Chiang Mai.

198 Corncob and Field

(Des M. Supanam. Recess)

1971 (20 Apr). *Export Promotion.* W **109**. P 13½.
673 **198** 2b. multicoloured . . . . 1·30 20

199 Buddha's Birthplace, Lumbini, Nepal

200 King Bhumibol and Thai People

1971 (9 May). *20th Anniv of World Fellowship of Buddhists.* T **199** and similar horiz designs. *Recess.* W **109**. P 13½.
674 50s. black and dull ultramarine . . . 30 10
675 1b. black and deep green 75 30
676 2b. black and ochre . . . . . . 1·70 45
677 3b. black and scarlet . . . . . 1·70 85
674/677 *Set of 4* . . . . 4·00 1·50
Designs:—1b. "Place of Enlightenment", Buddha Gaya, Bihar; 2b. "Place of First Sermon", Sarnath, Banaras; 3b. "Place of Final Passing Away", Kusinara.

(Litho D.L.R.)

1971 (9 June). *25th Anniv of Coronation. No wmk.* P 13½.
678 **200** 50s. multicoloured 65 10

201 Floating Market, Wat San

202 King and Queen in Scout Uniform

(Des Miss P. Salayachevin. Photo)

1971 (20 June). *Visit ASEAN Year (ASEAN = Association of South East Asian Nations).* W **109** (*sideways*). P 13½.
679 **201** 4b. multicoloured . . . . . . 1·30 30

(Des Mrs. P. Srivibhata. Litho)

1971 (1 July). *60th Anniv of Thai Boy Scout Movement.* W **109** (*sideways*). P 13½.
680 **202** 50s. black, red and orange-
yellow 65 10

203 Exhibition Emblem

1971 (4 Aug). *"THAILANDPEX 71" National Stamp Exhibition, Bangkok.* Nos. 428 and 483 optd as T **203**, *in deep blue, each opt extending over a block of four stamps.*
681 **119** 80s. orange . . . . 3·25 2·10
682 **132** 80s. orange . . . . 3·25 2·10
Prices are for blocks of four stamps showing the entire overprint. The overprint on No. 682 is smaller, 23 × 26 mm.

204 Two Girls writing a Letter

(Des Prayat Pongdam. Litho D.L.R.)

1971 (3 Oct). *International Correspondence Week.* T **204** and similar horiz designs. *Multicoloured.* W **119a**. P 13½.
683 50s. Type **204** 20 10
684 1b. Two girls reading letters 45 20
685 2b. Women with letter on veranda . . 1·10 20
686 3b. Man handing letter to woman . . . 2·10 75
683/686 *Set of 4* . . . . 3·50 1·10

205 Marble Temple, Bangkok

(Litho Bradbury, Wilkinson)

1971 (24 Oct). *United Nations Day. No wmk.* P 13½ × 14.
687 **205** 50s. multicoloured 45 10

206 Raising Ducks

(Des P. Chavananon. Photo)

1971 (15 Nov). *Rural Life.* T **206** and similar horiz designs. *Multicoloured.* W **109**. P 13½.
688 50s. Type **206** 20 10
689 1b. Growing tobacco seedlings 65 30

690	2b. Cooping fish	1·10	20
691	3b. Cleaning rice-seed	1·90	65
688/691	*Set of* 4	3·50	1·10

207 Mother and Child

(Des Mrs. P. Srivibhata. Photo D.L.R.)

1971 (11 Dec). *25th Anniv of United Nations Children's Fund.*
W **119a**. P 13½.

692	**207**	50s. multicoloured	30	10

208 Costumes from Chiang Saen Period
(17th Century)

(Des S. Disatabandhu. Litho Bradbury, Wilkinson)

1972 (12 Jan). *Historical Costumes. T* **208** *and similar horiz
designs. Multicoloured. No wmk. P* 13½ × 14.

693	50s. Type **208**	20	10
694	1b. Sukhothai period (13th–14th centuries)	65	20
695	1b.50 Ayudhya period (14th–17th centuries)	1·30	45
696	2b. Bangkok period (18th–19th centuries)	2·10	45
693/696	*Set of* 4	3·75	1·10

209 Globe and A.O.P.U. Emblem   **210** King
Bhumibol

(Des Miss W. Bumroongraj. Photo D.L.R.)

1972 (1 Apr). *10th Anniv of Asian-Oceanic Postal Union.* W **119a**.
P 13½.

697	**209**	75s. ultramarine	30	10

(Des S. Disatabandhu. Litho (Nos. 698/702) or recess (others))

1972 (28 Apr)–**79**. *Size* 21 × 26 *mm.* W **109** (*sideways on Nos.
698/702). P* 13.

698	**210**	10s. apple-green	10	10
699		20s. blue	10	10
700		25s. carmine-red	10	10
701		50s. grey-olive (23.12.79)	15	10
702		75s. lilac	10	10
703		1b.25 rose and bronze-green (15.11.72)	45	15
704		2b. reddish violet and orange-red (23.12.79)	45	10
705		2b.75 turquoise and purple	45	10
706		3b. blue and sepia (3.6.74)	1·70	15
707		4b. brown-red and blue (1.8.73)	65	15
708		5b. chestnut and reddish violet	65	10

709		6b. reddish violet and myrtle-green	1·70	15
710		10b. black and red	95	10
711		20b. yellow-green & orange (15.11.72)	2·10	20
712		40b. reddish violet & yell-brn (3.4.74)	18·00	4·75
712a		50b. deep bluish green and blackish purple (5.12.77)	21·00	95
713		100b. dp bl & reddish orge (5.12.77)	37·00	1·80
698/713	*Set of* 17		75·00	8·00

See also Nos. 898a/d.

211 Two Women, Iko Tribe

(Des Mrs. P. Pongdam. Photo D.L.R.)

1972 (11 May). *Hill Tribes of Thailand. T* **211** *and similar horiz
designs. Multicoloured.* W **119a**. P 13½.

714	50s. Type **211**	20	10
715	2b. Musician and children, Musoe tribe	85	20
716	4b. Woman embroidering, Yao tribe	3·75	2·10
717	5b. Woman with chickens, Maeo tribe	4·75	55
714/717	*Set of* 4	8·50	2·75

212 Ruby   **213** Prince
Vajiralongkorn

(Des P. Tiranan. Litho D.L.R.)

1972 (7 June). *Precious Stones. T* **212** *and similar horiz designs.*
W **119a**. P 13½.

718	75s. multicoloured	20	10
719	2b. multicoloured	3·50	55
720	4b. black and turquoise-green	6·50	2·40
721	6b. lake-brown, black and scarlet	6·00	2·10
718/721	*Set of* 4	14·50	4·50

Designs:—2b. Yellow sapphire; 4b. Zircon; 6b. Star sapphire.

(Des Miss P. Salayachevin. Photo)

1972 (28 July). *Prince Vajiralongkorn's 20th Birthday.* W **109**
(*sideways). P* 13½.

722	**213**	75s. multicoloured	45	10

214 Thai Ruan-ton Costume   **215** Rambutan

(Des S. Disatabandhu. Litho Bradbury, Wilkinson)

1972 (12 Aug). *Thai Women's National Costumes. T* **214** *and similar vert designs. Multicoloured.* W **144**. P 14 × 13½.

723	75s. Type **214**	20	10
724	2b. Thai Chitrlada	45	20
725	4b. Thai Chakri	2·10	1·80
726	5b. Thai Borompimarn	2·75	45
723/726 *Set of 4*		5·00	2·00
MS727 120 × 160 mm. Nos. 723/6 (sold at 20b.)		21·00	17·00

(Des A. Tularaks. Litho D.L.R.)

1972 (7 Sept). *Thai Fruits. T* **215** *and similar horiz designs. Multicoloured.* W **119a**. P 13½.

728	75s. Type **215**	20	10
729	1b. Mangosteen	85	45
730	3b. Durian	2·10	75
731	5b. Mango	7·50	1·30
728/731 *Set of 4*		9·50	2·40

216 Princess–Mother with Old People

(Des Miss W. Bumroongraj. Photo)

1972 (21 Oct). *Princess–Mother Sisangwan's 72nd Birthday.* W **109**. P 13½.

732	**216** 75s. myrtle-green and pale orange	1·70 20

217 Lod Cave, Phangnga   **218** Globe on U.N. Emblem

(Des P. Taotong (75s.), S. Simalai (1b.25), P. Chimpibul (2b.75), P. Sirisuwan (3b.). Litho D.L.R.)

1972 (15 Nov). *International Correspondence Week. T* **217** *and similar horiz designs, showing views. Multicoloured.* W **119a**. P 13½.

733	75s. Type **217**	20	10
734	1b.25 Kang Kracharn Reservoir, Phetchaburi	65	45
735	2b.75 Erawan Waterfall, Kanchanaburi	3·50	20
736	3b. Nok-kaw Mountain, Loei	2·50	75
733/736 *Set of 4*		6·25	1·40

(Des Miss P. Salayachevln. Litho D.L.R.)

1972 (15 Nov). *25th Anniv of U.N. Economic Commission for Asia and Far East.* W **119a**. P 14.

737	**218**	75s. multicoloured	30	10

219 Watphrajetubon Vimolmanklaram Rajvaramahaviharn (ancient University)   **220** Crown Prince Vajiralongkorn

(Des Miss W. Bumroongraj. Litho D.L.R.)

1972 (8 Dec). *International Book Year.* W **119a**. P 13½.

738	**219**	75s. multicoloured	30	10

(Des Miss P. Salayachevin and Miss W. Bumvoongraj. Photo)

1972 (28 Dec). *Investiture of Crown Prince.* W **109** (*sideways*). P 13½.

739	**220**	2b. multicoloured	85	20

221 Servicemen and Flag   **(222)**

(Des P. Suvarnapunya. Photo D.L.R.)

1973 (2 Feb). *25th Anniv of Veterans' Day.* W **119a**. P 13½.

740	**221**	75s. multicoloured	30	10

1973 (15 Feb). *Red Cross Fair. Nos. 472/3 surch with T* **222**.

741	**130**	75s.+25s. on 50s.+10s. bright scarlet and brownish grey	65	55
		a. Pair. Nos. 741/2	1·40	1·20
742	—	75s.+25s. on 50s.+10s. bright scarlet and brownish grey	65	55

223 Emblem, Bank and Coin-box   **224** "Celestial Being" and Emblem

(Des Government Savings Bank. Photo)

1973 (1 Apr). *60th Anniv of Government Savings Bank.* W **109**. P 13½.

743	**223**	75s. multicoloured	30	10

(Des Mrs. P. Srivibhata. Photo)

1973 (7 Apr). *25th Anniv of World Health Organization.* W **109**.
P 13½.
744 **224** 75s. multicoloured 30 10

225 *Nymphaea pubescens*

227 King
Bhumibol

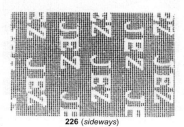
226 (*sideways*)

(Des S. Sothornboon (75s.), P. Sirisuwan (1b.50), C. Bunyasak
(2b.), U. Upalakalin (4b.). Litho Enschedé)

1973 (15 May). *Lotus Flowers. T 225 and similar horiz designs.*
Multicoloured. W **226** (*sideways*). P 11 × 13.
745 75s. Type **225** 20 10
746 1b.50 *Nymphaea pubescens*
 (*different*) 65 30
747 2b. *Nelumbo nucifera* . . . . 1·90 30
748 4b. *Nelumbo nucifera* (*different*) . 4·75 1·80
745/748 *Set of 4* . . . . 6·00 2·30

(Des S. Disatabandhu. Photo (Nos. 749/52) or recess (others)
D.L.R.)

1973 (15 June). W **119a**. P 13½ (Nos. 749/52) or 13 (others).
749 **227** 5s. plum 20 10
750 20s. steel blue 20 10
751 25s. carmine-red 20 10
752 75s. bluish violet 20 10
753 5b. red-brown and bluish
 violet . . . . 3·50 50
754 6b. slate-violet and myrtle-
 green . . . . 2·10 55
755 10b. blackish brown and rosine . 6·50 65
755a 20b. apple green and red-
 orange . . . . 65·00 5·50
749/755a *Set of 8* . . . . 70·00 7·00
See also Nos. 1031/2a.

228 Silverware

(Des Miss W. Bumroongraj (75s.), P. Chavananon
(2b.75), S. Sothornboon (4b.), C. Bunyasak (5b.). Litho D.L.R.)

1973 (15 June). *Thai Handicrafts. T 228 and similar horiz designs.*
Multicoloured. W **119a**. P 13½.
756 75s. Type **228** 20 10
757 2b.75 Lacquerware 85 20

758 4b. Pottery . . . . 3·50 1·40
759 5b. Paper umbrellas . . . . . 3·00 65
756/759 *Set of 4* . . . . 6·75 2·10
 Postal forgeries exist of Nos. 758 and 759, distinguishable by
being on unwatermarked paper.

229 King Janaka's Procession

(Des Miss P. Salayachevin. Photo)

1973 (17 July). *"Ramayana" Mural, Temple of Emerald Buddha,*
Bangkok. T 229 and similar horiz designs, each showing a
different detail from the mural. Multicoloured. W **109** (*sideways*).
P 13½.
760 25s. Type **229** 20 10
761 75s. Contest for Sita's hand . . . 20 10
762 1b.50 Monkey prince toppling portico . 1·30 1·10
763 2b. Monkey king breaking umbrella . 2·10 1·10
764 2b.75 Maleenarj as Court chief . . . 1·50 30
765 3b. Sprinkling holy water . . . 5·25 1·60
766 5b. Tapansura fighting Rama . . 8·50 4·25
767 6b. Bharata on march . . . . 2·10 1·10
760/767 *Set of 8* . . . . 19·00 8·75

230 "Postal Services"

(Des P. Payakanithi (75s.), Miss W. Bumroongraj (2b.). Photo)

1973 (4 Aug). *90th Anniv of Thai Post and Telegraph*
Department. T 230 and similar horiz design. Multicoloured.
W **109**. P 13½.
768 75s. Type **230** 20 10
769 2b. "Telecommunication Services" . . 1·10 45

231 1 Solot Stamp of 1883

(Des P. Payakanithi Recess and photo)

1973 (4 Aug). *"THAIPEX 73" National Stamp Exhibition. T 231*
and similar horiz designs. W **109**. P 13½.
770 75s. deep blue and carmine . . . 20 10
771 1b.25 rose-red and new blue . . . 1·10 55
772 1b.50 slate-purple and yellow-olive . 2·10 65
773 2b. dull green and yellow-orange . 2·50 65
770/773 *Set of 4* . . . . 5·25 1·70
MS774 191 × 97 mm. Nos. 770/3. Imperf (sold
 at 8b.) . . . . 8·50 7·50
 Designs:—1b.25, 6s. stamp of 1912; 1b.50, 5s. stamp of 1928;
2b. 3s. stamp of 1941.

232 Interpol Emblem

(Des Mrs. P. Srivibhata. Photo)

1973 (3 Sept). *50th Anniv of International Criminal Police Organization (Interpol).* W **109**. P 13½.
775 **232** 75s. multicoloured   30   10

233 "Lilid Pralaw"

234 Wat Suan Dok Temple, Chiangmai

(Des A. Tularaks (1b.50), C. Posayakrit (others). Litho Enschedé)

1973 (7 Oct). *International Correspondence Week.* T **233** and similar horiz designs, showing characters from Thai literature. Multicoloured. W **226**. P 11 × 13.
776	75s. Type **233**	20	10
777	1b.50 "Khun Chang Khun Phan"	85	45
778	2b. "Sang Thong"	2·10	65
779	5b. "Pha Apai Manee"	4·25	95
776/779 *Set of 4*		6·75	1·90

MS780 166 × 104 mm. Nos. 776/9. P 13½. (sold at 15b.)   17·00   16·00

(Des Miss P. Salayachevln. Litho Enschedé)

1973 (24 Oct). *United Nations Day.* W **226**. P 13 × 11.
781 **234** 75s. multicoloured   45   10

235 Schomburgk's Deer

(Des S. Disatabandhu. Photo)

1973 (14 Nov). *Protected Wild Animals.* T **235** and similar horiz designs. Multicoloured. W **109**. P 13½.
782	20s. Type **235**	20	20
783	25s. Kouprey	20	20
784	75s. Common gorals	65	20
785	1b.25 Water buffaloes	65	65
786	1b.50 Javan rhinoceros	2·50	1·70
787	2b. Thamin	7·50	1·70
788	2b.75 Sumatran rhinoceros	3·75	65
789	4b. Mainland serows	4·75	4·25
782/789 *Set of 8*		18·00	8·50

236 Flame Emblem

238 Children within Flowers

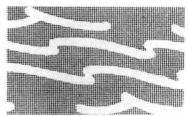

237 (This wmk is made up of a combination of dark and light lines.)

(Des Miss P. Salayachevin. Litho State Bank Note Printing Works, Helsinki)

1973 (10 Dec). *25th Anniv of Declaration of Human Rights.* W **237**. P 12½.
790 **236** 75s. multicoloured   65   10

(Des Mrs. P. Srivibhata. Litho State Bank Note Printing Works, Helsinki)

1974 (12 Jan). *Children's Day.* W **237** (sideways). P 13.
791 **238** 75s. multicoloured   65   10

75+25

1
9
7
3

๒๕๑๖
(239)

240 Statue of Krom Luang Songkia Nakarin

1974 (14 Feb). *Red Cross Fair. Nos. 472/3 surch as T* **239**.
792	**130**	75s.+25s. on 50s.+10s. bright scarlet and brownish grey	30	30
		a. Pair. Nos. 792/3	65	65
793	—	75s.+25s. on 50s.+10s. bright scarlet and brownish grey	30	30

(Des Miss W. Bumroongraj. Photo Enschedé)

1974 (17 Mar). *84th Anniv of Siriraj Hospital.* W **226** (sideways). P 13½.
794 **240** 75s. multicoloured   45   10

241 "Pha la Phiang Lai" **242** World's Largest Teak Amphur Nam-Pad

(Des Prayat Pongdam. Litho D.L.R.)

1974 (25 June). *Thai Classical Dance. T* **241** *and similar vert designs, showing characters. Multicoloured.* W **119a**. P 14.
795	75s. Type **241**		20	10
796	2b.75 "Phra Lak Phlaeng Rit"		1·10	20
797	4b. "Chin Sao Sai"		2·75	1·30
798	5b. "Charot Phra Sumen"		2·75	55
795/798	*Set of 4*		6·00	1·90

(Des Miss W. Bumroongraj. Litho State Bank Note Printing Works, Helsinki)

1974 (5 July). *15th Anniv of Arbor Day.* W **237** (*sideways*). P 12½.
799	**242**	75s. multicoloured	30	10

243 "Increasing Population"

(Des S. Klumnoi. Litho Enschedé)

1974 (19 Aug). *World Population Year.* W **226** (*sideways*). P 11 × 13.
800	**243**	75s. multicoloured	30	10

244 Royal Chariot

(Des Mrs. P. Srivibhata. Litho State Bank Note Printing Works, Helsinki)

1974 (19 Sept). *Centenary of National Museum. T* **244** *and similar horiz designs. Multicoloured.* W **237** (*sideways*). P 12½.
801	75s. Type **244**		20	20
802	2b. Ban Chiang painted pottery vase		85	45
803	2b.75 Avalokitesavara Bodhisattva statue		1·70	30
804	3b. King Mongkut Rama IV		1·90	55
801/804	*Set of 4*		4·25	1·30

Nos. 802/4 have the face values incorrectly shown as "BATH".

245 *Cassia fistula*

(Des P. Korn (75s.), A. Tularaks (2b.75), C. Bunyasak (3b.), P. Ching-chai (4b.). Litho Enschedé)

1974 (6 Oct). *International Correspondence Week. T* **245** *and similar horiz designs, showing tropical plants. Multicoloured.* W **226** (*sideways*). P 11 × 13.
805	75s. Type **245**		20	10
806	2b.75 *Butea superba*		65	20
807	3b. *Jasminum sambac*		2·50	45
808	4b. *Lagerstroemia speciosa*		1·30	95
805/808	*Set of 4*		4·25	1·50
MS809	169 × 100 mm. Nos. 805/8. P 13 × 13½			
	(sold at 15b.)		15·00	13·00

246 "UPU 100"

(Des S. Udomtharak. Litho State Bank Note Printing Works, Helsinki)

1974 (9 Oct). *Centenary of Universal Postal Union.* W **237**. P 12½.
810	**246**	75s. multicoloured	30	10

247 Wat Suthat Thepvararam

(Des Miss W. Bumroongraj. Photo Govt Ptg Wks, Tokyo)

1974 (24 Oct). *United Nations Day.* W **109**. P 13½.
811	**247**	75s. multicoloured	30	10

248 Elephant Round-up

(Des Miss P. Salayachevin. Recess and litho State Bank Note Printing Works, Helsinki)

1974 (16 Nov). *Tourism.* W **237**. P 12½.
812	**248**	4b. multicoloured	1·70	65

249 *Vanda coerulea*

(Des P. Pipitpiyapakorn. Photo Enschedé)

1974 (5 Dec). *Thai Orchids (1st series).* T **249** *and similar horiz designs. Multicoloured.* W **226** (*sideways*). P 11 × 13.
813	75s. Type **249**		20	10
814	2b.75 *Dendrobium aggregatum*		85	20
815	3b. *Dendrobium scabrilingue*		2·40	65
816	4b. *Aerides falcata var houlletiana*		1·30	85
813/816 *Set of 4*			4·25	1·60
MS817 138 × 105 mm. Nos. 813/16. P 13 × 13½				
(sold at 15b.)			21·00	17·00

See also Nos. 847/**MS**851.

250 Boy riding Toy Horse   **251**

(Des Mrs. P. Srivibhata. Litho State Printing Works, Berlin)

1975 (11 Jan). *Children's Day.* W **251**. P 13½.
818	**250**	75s. multicoloured		65	10

252 Democracy Monument   (252a)

253

(Des S. Klamnoi and P. Salayacheevin. Litho Harrison)

1975 (26 Jan). *Campaign for Democratic Institutions.* T **252** *and similar horiz designs. Multicoloured.* W **253**. P 14 × 14½.
819	75s. Type **252**		20	10
820	2b. "Rights and Liberties"		75	30
821	2b.75 "Freedom to choose work"		1·60	20
822	5b. Top of monument and text		2·10	65
819/822 *Set of 4*			4·50	1·10

1975 (11 Feb). *Red Cross Fair* (1974). *Nos.* 472/3 *surch as* T **252a**.
823	**130**	75s.+25s. on 50s.+10s. bright scarlet and brownish grey		65	45
		a. Pair. Nos. 823/4		1·40	95
824	—	75s.+25s. on 50s.+10s. bright scarlet and brownish grey		65	45

254 Marbled Cat   **255** White-eyed River Martin (*Pseudochelidon sirintarae*)

(Des P. Sripvat. Litho De La Rue)

1975 (5 Mar). *Protected Animals (1st series).* T **254** *and similar horiz designs. Multicoloured.* W **119a**. P 13½.
825	20s. Type **254**		20	10
826	75s. Gaur		65	10
827	2b.75 Indian elephant		4·75	65
828	3b. Clouded leopard		3·00	1·30
825/828 *Set of 4*			7·75	1·90

See also Nos. 913/16.

(Des W. Bumroongraj and P. Salayacheevin, Litho State Bank Note Ptg Works, Helsinki)

1975 (2 Apr). *Thailand Birds.* T **255** *and similar vert designs. Multicoloured.* W **237** (*sideways*). P 12½.
829	75s. Type **255**		30	10
830	2b. Asiatic paradise flycatcher (*Terpsiphone paradise*)		1·50	65
831	2b.75 Long-tailed broadbill (*Psarisomus dalhousiae*)		1·70	30
832	5b. Sultan tit (*Melanchlora sultanea*)		3·75	1·10
829/832 *Set of 4*			6·50	1·90

256 King Bhumibol and Queen Sirikit

(Des S. Udomtharak. Photo Enschedé)

1975 (28 Apr). *Royal Silver Wedding.* T **256** *and similar horiz design. Multicoloured.* W **226** (*sideways*). P 11 × 13.
833	75s. Type **256**		45	10
834	3b. Portraits as 75s. but different background		1·30	20

257 "Roundhouse Kick"

(Des V. Sodprasert. Litho State Bank Note Ptg Works, Helsinki)

1975 (20 May). *Thai Boxing.* T **257** *and similar horiz designs. Multicoloured.* W **237** (*sideways*). P 12½.
835	75s. Type **257**		30	10
836	2b.75 "Reverse elbow"		1·40	30
837	3b. "Flying knee"		1·70	85
838	5b. "Ritual homage"		5·25	1·30
835/838 *Set of 4*			7·75	2·20

258 Toskanth   **259** "Thaipex 75" Emblem

(Des G. Saeng-xuto. Litho State Bank Note Ptg Works, Helsinki)

1975 (10 June). *Thai Culture. Masks. T **258** and similar vert designs.* W **237** . Multcoloured. P 12½.

839	75s. Type **258**		30	10
840	2b. Kumbhakarn		1·80	30
841	3b. Rama		2·40	65
842	4b. Hanuman		6·50	2·10
839/842 *Set of 4*			10·00	2·75

(Des S. Udomtharak. Litho State Bank Note Ptg Works, Helsinki)

1975 (4 Aug). *"Thaipex 75" National Stamp Exhibition, Bangkok. T **259** and similar hertz designs. Multicoloured.* W **237** (*sideways*). P 12½.

843	75s. Type **259**		30	10
844	2b.75 Stamp designer		95	20
845	4b. Stamp printing works		1·30	85
846	6b. "Stamp collecting"		1·70	45
843/846 *Set of 4*			3·75	1·50

(Des P. Pipitpiyapakorn. Photo Enschedé)

1975 (12 Aug). *Thai Orchids (2nd series). Horiz designs as T **249**. Multicoloured.* W **226** (*sideways*). P 11 × 13.

847	75s. *Dendrobium cruentum*		30	10
848	2b. *Dendrobium parishii*		75	30
849	2b.75 *Vanda teres*		1·10	30
850	5b. *Vanda denisoniana*		2·50	75
847/850 *Set of 4*			4·25	1·30
MS851 138 × 105 mm. Nos. 847/50.				
P 13½ × 14			19·00	16·00

260 Perna viridis (*Mytillus smaragdinus*)

260a

(Des A Tularak. Litho Harrison)

1975 (5 Sept). *Sea Shells. T **260** and similar horiz designs. Multicoloured.* W **260a** (*sideways*). P 14 × 15.

852	75s. Type **260**		85	65
853	1b. *Turbo marmoratus* (Great Green Turban)		65	10
854	2b.75 *Oliva mustelina*		2·40	55
855	5b. *Cypraea moneta* (Money Cowrie)		6·00	1·90
852/855 *Set of 4*			8·50	3·00

261 Yachting

(Des P. Pipitpiyapakorn. Litho Enschedé)

1975 (20 Sept). *Eighth South-East Asian Peninsula Games, Bangkok (1st issue). T **261** and similar horiz designs.* W **226** (*sideways*). P 11 × 13.

856	75s. black and blue		20	10
857	1b.25 black and cerise		65	30
858	1b.50 black and bright scarlet		1·50	65
859	2b. black and bright apple green		1·90	65
856/859 *Set of 4*			3·75	1·50
MS860 118 × 133 mm. Nos 856/9.				
P 13½ × 14			16·00	13·00

Designs:—1b.25, Badminton; 1b.50, Volleyball; 2b. Rifle and pistol shooting.

Forgeries of No. 856 exist, distinguishable by being perf 11 all round.

See also Nos. 878/**MS**882.

262 Pataya Beach

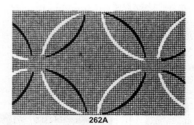

262A

(Des P. Pipitpiyapakorn. Litho State Bank Note Ptg Works, Helsinki)

1975 (5 Oct). *International Correspondence Week. T **262** and similar horiz designs. Multicoloured.* W **262a**. P 12½.

861	75s. Type **262**		30	10
862	2b. Samila Beach		95	55
863	3b. Prachuap Bay		1·90	30
864	5b. Laem Singha Bay		2·10	75
861/864 *Set of 4*			5·25	1·20

263 Children within Letters "U N"

(Des. P. Salayacheevin. Litho State Bank Note Pug Works, Helsinki)

1975 (24 Oct). *United Nations Day.* W **262a**. P 11½.
865 **263** 75s. multicoloured 30 10

264 Early Telegraphs

(Des M. Chaikrachang and S. Klamnoi. Litho Harrison)

1975 (4 Nov). *Centenary of Telegraph Service.* T **264** *and similar horiz designs. Multicoloured.* W **260a**. P 14 × 14½.
866 75s. Type **264** 45 20
867 2b.75 Teleprinter and dish aerial 85 20

265 *Sukhrip Khrong Muang*

(Litho State Bank Note Ptg Works, Helsinki)

1975 (18 Nov). *Thai Ceremonial Barges.* T **265** *and similar horiz designs. Multicoloured.* W **237** (*sideways*). P 12½.
868 75s. Type **265** 45 10
869 1b. Royal barge *Anekchat Phuchong* . . 1·30 45
870 2b. Royal barge *Anantanakarat* . . . . 1·90 55
871 2b.75 *Krabi Ran Ron Rap* . . . . . 2·10 45
872 3b. *Asura Wayuphak* . . . . 3·25 85
873 4b. *Asura Paksi* . . . . 2·50 1·90
874 5b. Royal Barge *Sri Suphanahong* . . . 6·00 3·25
875 6b. *Phali Rang Thawip* . . . . . . 3·75 2·10
868/875 *Set of 8* . . . . 19·00 8·75

266 King's Cipher and Thai Crown

267 Putting the Shot

(Des P. Pipitpiyapakorn. Litho Harrison)

1976 (5 Dec). *King Bhumibol's 48th Birthday.* T **266** *and similar vert design. Multicoloured.* W **260a** (*sideways*). P 15 × 14.
876 75s. Type **266** 30 10
877 5b. King Bhumibol in uniform . . . . 1·80 45

(Des P. Pipitpiyapakorn. Litho Enschedé)

1975 (9 Dec). *Eighth South-East Asian Peninsula Games, Bangkok (2nd issue).* T **267** *and similar horiz designs.* W **226**. P 11 × 13.
878 1b. black and red-orange 30 10
879 2b. black and light blue-green 55 65
880 3b. black and yellow . . . . . . 1·30 30
881 4b. black and bluish violet . . . . . 1·70 65
878/881 *Set of 4* . . . . 3·50 1·50
MS882 118 × 130 mm. Nos. 878/81.
  P 13½ × 14 . . . . 16·00 13·00
Designs:—2b. Table tennis; 3b. Cycling; 4b. Relay-running.

268 IWY Emblem on Globe   **269** Children writing

(Des S. Klamnoi. Litho Harrison)

1975 (20 Dec). *International Women's Year.* W **260a** (*sideways*). P 14 × 15.
883 **268** 75s. deep violet-blue, yellow-orange and black 30 10

(Des S. Rodboon. Litho Enschedé)

1976 (10 Jan). *Children's Day.* W **226** (*sideways*). P 13½ × 14.
884 **269** 75s. multicoloured 65 10

270 *Macrobrachium rosenbergii*   **(270a)**

(Des P. Pipitpiyapakorn. Litho Enschedé)

1976 (18 Feb). *Thai Lobsters and Shrimps.* T **270** *and similar horiz designs.* W **226** (*sideways*). *Multicoloured.* P 11 × 13.
885 75s. Type **270** 20 10
886 2b. *Panaeus merguiensis* . . . . . 2·50 65
887 2b.75 *Panulirus ornatus* . . . . . 1·90 20
888 5b. *Penaeus monodon* . . . . . . 6·00 1·60
885/888 *Set of 4* . . . . 9·50 2·30

1976 (26 Feb). *Red Cross Fair* (1975). *Nos. 472/3 surch as* T **270a**.
889 **130** 75s.+25s. on 50s.+10s. bright scarlet and brownish grey . . 30 30
       a. Pair. Nos. 889/90 . . . . . 65 65
890   — 75s.+25s. on 50s.+10s. bright scarlet and brownish grey . . 30 30

271 Common Golden-
backed Woodpecker
(*Dinopium javanense*)

272 Ben Chiang Pot

(Des W. Bumroongraj and P. Salayacheevin. Litho State Bank
Note Ptg Works, Helsinki)

1976 (2 Apr). *Thailand Birds. T* **271** *and similar vert designs.
Multicoloured.* W **237**. P 12½.

891	1b. Type **271**		20	10
892	1b.50 Greater green-billed malcoha			
	(*Phaenicophaeus tristis*)		45	30
893	3b. Long-billed scimitar babbler			
	(*Pomatorhinus hypoleucos*)		3·50	1·00
894	4b. Green magpie (*Cissa chinensis*)		1·30	50
891/894 *Set of 4*			5·00	1·70

(Des S. Disatabandhu. Litho Harrison)

1976 (5 May). *Ben Chiang Pottery. T* **272** *and similar vert designs
showing pottery.* W **260a**. P 14½ × 14.

895	1b. multicoloured		20	10
896	2b. multicoloured		3·25	30
897	3b. multicoloured		1·90	20
898	4b. multicoloured		2·10	1·50
895/898 *Set of 4*			6·75	1·90

(Litho (20, 75s.) or recess (others) State Bank Note Ptg
Works,Helsinki)

1976 (June–Oct). *As Nos.* **699** *etc. but larger,* 21 × 27 *mm.*
W **262a**. P 12½ × 13.

898*a*	**210**	20s. steel blue	1·60	10
898*b*		75s. reddish lilac	1·60	10
898*c*		10b. brownish blk & dull verm		
		(Sept)	26·00	95
898*d*		40b. reddish purp & brn-ochre		
		(Oct)	3·25	55
898*a*/898*d* *Set of 4*			30·00	1·50

As well as the differences in size, watermark etc., Nos. 898*a*/*d*
differ from Nos. 698/713 in details of design, particularly in the
figures of value which are taller and thinner.

273 Postman of 1883

274 Kinnari

(Des A. Daroonsart. Litho State Bank Note Ptg Works, Helsinki)

1976 (4 Aug). *Postmen's Uniforms. T* **273** *and similar vert designs.
Multicoloured.* W **262a**. P 12½.

899	1b. Type **273**		20	10
900	3b. Postman of 1935		1·30	20

901	4b. Postman of 1950		1·70	1·30
902	5b. Postman of 1974		3·25	55
899/902 *Set of 4*			5·50	1·90

(Des A. Tularak (1b., 2b.), A. Sripojnard (4b., 5b.). Photo
Enschedé)

1976 (3 Oct). *International Correspondence Week. Deities. T* **274**
and similar horiz designs. Multicoloured. W **226** (*sideways*).
P 11 × 13.

903	1b. Type **274**		3·25	75
904	2b. Suphan-Mat-Cha		45	10
905	4b. Garuda		85	20
906	5b. Naga		1·50	20
903/906 *Set of 4*			5·50	1·10

275 "Drug
Addictions"

276 Early and Modern Telephones

(Des P. Sangamuang. Photo Govt Ptg Wks, Tokyo)

1976 (24 Oct). *United Nations Day.* W **109** (*sideways*). P 13½.

907	**275**	1b. multicoloured	30	10

(Des P. Pipitpiyapakorn. Litho Harrison)

1976 (10 Nov). *Telephone Centenary.* W **260a**. P 14 × 14½.

908	**276**	1b. multicoloured	30	10

277 Sivalaya

278 "From Child
to Adult"

(Des P. Pipitpiyapakorn. Litho Harrison)

1976 (5 Dec). *Thai Royal Halls. T* **277** *and similar horiz designs.
Multicoloured.* W **260a** (*sideways*). P 14 × 14½.

909	1b. Type **277**		20	10
910	2b. Cakri		4·25	35
911	4b. Mahisra		1·90	1·10
912	5b. Dusit		2·10	65
909/912 *Set of 4*			7·50	2·00

(Des Prane Nimsamur)

1976 (26 Dec). *Protected Animals (2nd series). Horiz designs
as T* **254**. *Multicoloured.*

(a) W **119a**. P 13½. *Litho De La Rue.*

913	1b. Banteng		2·10	65
914	2b. Malayan tapir		2·50	85

(b) W **226** (*sideways*). P 11 × 13. *Photo Enschedé.*

915	4b. Sambar		75	20
916	5b. Hog-deer		95	20
913/916 *Set of 4*			5·75	1·70

(Des A. Daroonsart. Photo Govt Ptg Wks, Tokyo)

1977 (8 Jan). *Children's Day.* W **109**. P 13½.

917	**278**	1b. multicoloured	45	10

279 Alsthom Diesel-Electric Locomotive
No. 4101

(Des P. Sangamuang (1, 4b.), S. Klamnoi (others). Litho
Enschedé)

1977 (26 Mar). *80th Anniv of Thai State Railway. T* **279** *and similar horiz designs. Multicoloured.* W **226** (*sideways*). P 11 × 13.
918	1b.	Type **279**	45	10
919	2b.	Davenport diesel electric locomotive No. 577	2·00	30
920	4b.	Pacific steam locomotive No. 825, Japan	5·25	3·25
921	5b.	George Egestoff's steam locomotive	8·50	2·40
918/921		*Set of 4*	14·50	5·50

280 University Building

(Des Miss Maliwan Chaikrachang. Photo Enschedé)

1977 (29 Apr). *60th Anniv of Chulalongkorn University.* W **226** (*sideways*). P 11 × 13.
922	**280**	1b. multicoloured	55	10

281 Flags of A.O.P.U. Countries

(Des P. Salayacheevin. Litho State Bank Note Ptg Wks,
Helsinki)

1977 (1 Apr). *15th Anniv of Asian-Oceanic Postal Union.* W **282a**. P 12½.
923	**281**	1b. multicoloured	45	10

282 Crippled Ex-Serviceman

75·25

2520-1977
(**283**)

(Des P. Sangamuang. Photo Govt Ptg Wks, Tokyo)

1977 (2 Apr). *Sai-Jai-Thai Foundation Day.* W **109**. P 13½.
924	**282**	5b. multicoloured	85	15

1977 (6 Apr). *Red Cross Fair. No. 472/3 surch as T* **283**.
925	**130**	75s.+25s. on 50s.+10s. bright scarlet and brownish grey	30	30
		a. Pair. Nos. 925/6	65	65
926	—	75s.+25s. on 50s.+10s. bright scarlet and brownish grey	30	30

284 Phra Aphai Mani and Phisua Samut

285 Drum Dance

(Des A. Tularak. Photo Enschedé)

1977 (16 June). *Puppet Shows. T* **284** *and similar horiz designs. Multicoloured.* W **226** (*sideways*). P 11 × 13.
927	2b.	Type **284**	45	10
928	3b.	Rusi and Sutsakhon	1·10	20
929	4b.	Nang Vali and Usren	65	20
930	5b.	Phra Aphai Mani and Nang Laweng's portrait	1·10	30
927/930		*Set of 4*	3·00	70

(Des S. Disatabandhu. Photo Enschedé)

1977 (14 July). *Thai Folk Dances. T* **285** *and similar vert designs. Multicoloured.* W **226**. P 13 × 11.
931	2b.	Type **285**	30	15
932	3b.	Dance of Dip-nets	1·20	15
933	4b.	Harvesting dance	45	20
934	5b.	Kan dance	65	20
931/934		*Set of 4*	2·30	65

286 1b. Stamp of 1972

(Des Maliwan Chaikrachang. Litho State Bank Note Ptg Wks,
Helsinki)

1977 (4 Aug). *"THAIPEX 77" National Stamp Exhibition.* W **262**. P 12 × 12½.
935	**286**	75s. multicoloured	65	10

287 "Pla Bu Thong"

(Des A. Tularak. Photo Enschedé)

1977 (5 Oct). *International Correspondence Week. T* **287** *and similar horiz designs showing scenes from Thai literature. Multicoloured.* W **226** (*sideways*). P 11 × 13.
936	75s.	Type **287**	65	10
937	2b.	"Krai Thong"	1·10	55

938	5b. "Nang Kaew Na Ma"	1·70	20
939	6b. "Pra Rot Mali"	1·90	45
936/939	Set of 4	4·75	1·20

288 U.N. Building, Bangkok

(Des P. Siriprayoon. Litho Enschedé)

1977 (24 Oct). *United Nations Day.* W **226** (*sideways*). P 11 × 13.

940	**288**	75s. multicoloured	55	10

289 King Bhumibol in Scout Uniform, and Camp Fire

(Des P Nimsamur. Photo Enschedé)

1977 (21 Nov). *Ninth National Scout Jamboree.* W **226** (*sideways*). P 11 × 13.

941	**289**	75s. multicoloured	85	10

290 Map of A.S.E.A.N. Countries

(Des. P. Sangamuang. Litho State Bank Note Ptg Wks, Helsinki)

1977 (1 Dec). *Tenth Anniv of Association of South East Asian Nations.* W **262a.** P 12.

942	**290**	5b. multicoloured	95	30

291 Elbow and Wrist Joints

(Des. P. Sangamuang. Photo Enschedé)

1977 (20 Dec). *World Rheumatism Year.* W **226** (*sideways*). P 11 × 13.

943	**291**	75s. multicoloured	45	10

292 Children with Thai Flag

(Des Pranee Nimsamur. Photo Govt Ptg Wks, Tokyo)

1978 (9 Jan). *Children's Day.* W **109.** P 13.

944	**292**	75s. multicoloured	65	10

293 *Dendrobium heterocarpum*

(Des P. Pipitpiyapakorn. Photo Enschedé)

1978 (18 Jan). *Ninth World Orchid Conference, Thailand.* T **293** and similar horiz designs. Multicoloured. W **226** (*sideways*). P 11 × 13.

945	75s. Type **293**	65	45
946	1b. *Dendrobium pulchellum*	1·10	45
947	1b.50 *Doritis pulcherrima* var. buyssoniana	1·50	85
948	2b. *Dendrobium hercoglossum*	45	10
949	2b.75 *Aerides odorata*	3·25	10
950	3b. *Trichoglottis fasciata*	45	10
951	5b. *Dendrobium wardianum*	65	20
952	6b. *Dendrobium senile*	65	30
945/952	Set of 8	8·00	2·30

294 Agricultural Scenes and Rice Production Graph

295 Blood Donation and Red Cross

(Des Maliwan Chaikrachang. Litho State Bank Note Ptg Wks, Helsinki)

1978 (1 Mar). *Agricultural Census.* W **262a.** P 12½.

953	**294**	75s. multicoloured	20	10

(Des P. Sangamuang. Photo Govt Ptg Wks, Tokyo)

1978 (6 Apr). *Red Cross.* W **109.** P 13½.

954	**295**	2b.75+25s. multicoloured	65	65

296 Climbing Perch (*Anabas testudineus*)

(Des P. Pipitpiyapakorn. Photo Enschedé)

1978 (13 Apr). *Fishes. T* **296** *and similar horiz designs. Multicoloured.* W **226** (*sideways*). P11 × 13.

955	1b. Type **296**	1·30	65
956	2b. Siamese tigerfish (*Datnioides microlepis*)	30	10
957	3b. Glass catfish (*Kryptopterus apogon*)	55	10
958	4b. Esok (*Probarbus jullieni*)	85	30
955/958 *Set of 4*		2·75	1·00

297 "Birth of Prince Siddhartha"

(Des A. Tularak. Photo Govt Ptg Wks, Tokyo)

1978 (15 June). *"Buddha's Story" Mural, Puthi Savan Hall National Museum. T* **297** *and similar horiz designs showing details of mural. Multicoloured.* W **109** (*sideways*). P 13½.

959	2b. Type **297**	45	20
960	3b. "Prince Siddhartha cuts his hair"	1·30	45
961	5b. "Buddha descends from Tavatimsa Heaven"	5·25	1·30
962	6b. "Buddha enters Nirvana"	2·50	1·30
959/962 *Set of 4*		8·50	3·00

298 Bhumibol Dam

(Des Maliwan Chaikrachang. Litho Harrison)

1978 (28 July). *Dams. T* **298** *and similar horiz designs. Multicoloured.* W **253** (*sideways*). P 14 × 14½.

963	75s. Type **298**	65	20
964	2b. Sirikit Dam	65	20
965	2b.75 Vajiralongkorn Dam	1·30	20
966	6b. Ubolratana Dam	1·70	1·10
963/966 *Set of 4*		4·00	1·50

299 *Idea lynceus*

300 Phra Chedi Chai Mongkhon, Ayutthaya

(Des Maliwan Chaikrachang. Litho Enschedé)

1978 (25 Aug). *Butterflies. T* **299** *and similar horiz designs.* W **226** (*sideways*). P 11 × 13.

967	2b. black, pale violet and carmine-red	65	30
968	3b. multicoloured	1·10	30

969	5b. multicoloured	3·75	65
970	6b. multicoloured	2·10	1·30
967/970 *Set of 4*		6·75	2·30

Designs:—3b. *Sephisa chandra,* 5b. *Charaxes durnfordi;* 6b. *Cethosia penthesilea.*

(Des T. Thongkambai. Litho Enschedé)

1978 (8 Oct). *International Correspondence Week. Pagodas. T* **300** *and similar vert designs. Multicoloured.* W **226**. P 13 × 11.

971	75s. Type **300**	30	20
972	2b. Phra That Hariphunchai, Lamphun	55	20
973	2b.75 Phra Borom That Chaiya, Surat Thani	2·50	20
974	5b. Phra That Choeng Chum, Sakon Nakhon	1·10	65
971/974 *Set of 4*		4·00	1·10

301 Mother and Children

302 Basketball, Hockey and Boxing

(Des T. Monyakula. Litho Harrison)

1978 (24 Oct). *United Nations Day.* W **260a**. P 14½ × 14.

975	**301**	75s. multicoloured	45	10

(Des T. Monyakula. Litho Harrison)

1978 (9 Dec). *Eighth Asian Games, Bangkok. T* **302** *and similar horiz designs. Multicoloured.* W **253** (*sideways*). P 14 × 14½.

976	75s. Silhouettes of boxers, footballer and pole-vaulter	20	10
977	2b. Silhouettes of javelin-thrower, weightlifter and runner	30	10
978	3b. Football, shuttlecock, yacht and table-tennis bat and ball	75	20
979	5b. Type **302**	1·90	65
976/979 *Set of 4*		3·00	95

303 World Map and Different Races holding Hands

304 Children and S.O.S. Village, Tambol Bangpu

(Des P. Sangamuang. Litho Harrison)

1978 (20 Dec). *International Anti-apartheid Year.* W **253** (*sideways*). P 14 × 14½.

980	**303**	75s. multicoloured	30	10

(Des Pranee Nimsamur (981), T. Monyakula (982). Litho Harrison)

1979 (1 Jan). *International Year of the Child. T* **304** *and similar horiz design. Multicoloured.* W **253** (*sideways on No. 981*). P 14 × 14½ (981) or 14½ × 14 (982).

981	75s. Children painting Thai flag		75	20
982	75s. Type **304**		30	10

305 *Matuta lunaris*

306 Eye and Blind People

(Des P. Pipitpiyapakorn. Litho State Bank Note Ptg Wks, Helsinki)

1979 (22 Mar). *Crabs. T* **305** *and similar horiz designs. Multicoloured.* W **262a**. P 12½.

983	2b. Type **305**		65	30
984	2b.75 *Matuta planipes*		2·50	30
985	3b. *Portunus pelagicus*		1·10	45
986	5b. *Scylla serrata*		3·25	1·10
983/986	*Set of 4*		6·75	1·90

(Des P. Sangamuang. Litho Enschedé)

1979 (6 Apr). *Red Cross.* W **226**. P 13½.

987	**306**	75s.+25s. multicoloured	30	30

307 Sugar Apples

308 Planting Sapling

(Des P. Pipitpiyapakorn. Litho State Bank Note Ptg Wks, Helsinki)

1979 (25 June). *Fruits. T* **307** *and similar vert designs. Multicoloured.* W **262a**. P 12½.

988	1b. Type **307**		85	20
989	2b. Pineapple		65	20
990	5b. Bananas		2·10	85
991	6b. Longans		1·70	1·10
988/991	*Set of 4*		4·75	2·10

(Des P. Pipitpiyapakorn. Litho Enschedé)

1979 (10 July). 20*th Arbor Day.* W **226**. P 13 × 11.

992	**308**	75s. multicoloured	25	10

309 Pencil, Brush and Colours

310 Baisi Pak Cham

(Des Maliwan Sriluang-on. Litho Enschedé)

1979 (4 Aug). *"Thaipex 1979" National Stamp Exhibition, Bangkok. T* **309** *and similar horiz designs. Multicoloured.* W **226** (*sideways*). P 11 × 13.

993	75s. Type **309**		20	10
994	2b. Envelopes		30	15
995	2b.75 Stamps stockbook		75	15
996	2b. Tweezers, stamps and magnifying glass		1·90	65
993/996	*Set of 4*		2·75	90

(Des S. Taothong. Litho Harrison)

1979 (7 Oct). *International Correspondence Week. Traditional Flower Arrangements. T* **310** *and similar vert designs. Multicoloured.* W **253**. P 14½ × 14.

997	75s. Kruai upatcha (used at Buddhist ordination ceremony)		20	10
998	2b. Type **310** (used at Braminical ceremonies)		45	15
999	2b.75 Krathong dokmai (for paying respects to elders or superiors)		65	15
1000	5b. Phum dokmai (altar decoration)		1·90	65
997/1000	*Set of 4*		3·00	90

311 U.N.O. Emblem, Farmer, Cattle and Wheat

312*Makutrajakumarn* (frigate)

(Des T. Monyakula. Litho Harrison)

1979 (24 Oct). *United Nations Day.* W **253**. P 14½ × 14.

1001	**311**	75s. multicoloured	25	10

(Des T. Thongkambai. Photo Govt Ptg Wks, Tokyo)

1979 (20 Nov). *Ships of the Royal Thai Navy. T* **312** *and similar horiz designs. Multicoloured.* W **109**. P 13½.

1002	2b. Type **312**		45	20
1003	3b. *Tapi* (frigate)		65	20
1004	5b. *Prabparapak* (missile craft)		3·25	85
1005	6b. T 91 (patrol boat)		3·75	1·10
1002/1005	*Set of 4*		6·50	1·90

313 Order of the Rajamitrabhorn

314 Transplanting Rice

(Des T. Thongkambai. Litho Enschedé)

1979 (5 Dec). *Royal Decorative Orders. T* **313** *and similar vert designs. Multicoloured.* W **226**. P 13 × 11.

1006	1b. Type **313**		65	30
	a. Horiz pair. Nos. 1006/7		1·40	65
1007	1b. Rajamitrabhorn ribbon		65	30
1008	2b. Order of Royal House of Chakri		65	20
	a. Horiz pair. Nos. 1008/9		1·40	45
1009	2b. Royal House of Chakri ribbon		65	20
1010	5b. Order of the Nine Gems		1·30	45
	a. Horiz pair. Nos. 1010/11		2·75	95
1011	5b. Nine Gems ribbon		1·30	45
1012	6b. Knight Grand Cross of Order of Chula Chom Klao		1·50	65
	a. Horiz pair. Nos. 1012/13		3·00	1·10
1013	6b. Chula Chom Klao ribbon		1·50	65
1006/1013	*Set of* 8		7·50	2·00

The two stamps of each value were issued together in horizontal *se-tenant* pairs within their sheets.

(Des S. Charoen (1014), P. Somchuawieng (1015). Litho Enschedé)

1980 (12 Jan). *Children's Day. T* **314** *and similar vert design showing children's paintings. Multicoloured.* W **226**. P 13 × 11.

1014	75s. Type **314**		30	10
1015	75s. Harvesting rice		30	10

315 Family, House and Map of Thailand

316 Gold-fronted Leafbird (*Chloropsis aurifrons*)

(Des P. Sangamuang. Litho Harrison)

1980 (1 Feb). *Population and Housing Census.* W **253**. P 14½ × 14.

1016	**315** 75s. multicoloured		20	10

(Des M. Wongkalasin. Litho Enschedé)

1980 (26 Feb). *Ninth Conference of International Commission for Bird Preservation (Asian Section), Chiang Mai. T* **316** *and similar vert designs. Multicoloured.* W **226**. P 13 × 11.

1017	75s. Type **316**		20	10
1018	2b. Chinese yellow tit (*Parus spilonotus*)		30	15

1019	3b. Chestnut-tailed minla (*Minla strigula*)		75	20
1020	5b. Scarlet minivet (*pericrocotus flammeus*)		1·30	65
1017/1020	*Set of* 4		2·30	1·00

317 Extracting Snake Venom

(Des P. Sangamuang. Litho Enschedé)

1980 (6 Apr). *Red Cross.* W **226** (*sideways*). P 11 × 13.

1021	**317** 75s.+25s. multicoloured		30	30

318 Smokers and Diagram of Lungs

319 Garuda and Rotary Emblem

(Des P. Pipitpiyapakorn. Photo Govt Ptg Wks, Tokyo)

1980 (7 Apr). *Anti-smoking Campaign.* W **109** (*sideways*). P 13.

1022	**318** 75s. multicoloured		20	10

(Des P. Klaheng-ngarn. Litho Enschedé)

1980 (6 May). *75th Anniv of Rotary International.* W **226**. P 13 × 11.

1023	**319** 5b. multicoloured		85	15

320 Sai Yok Falls, Kanchanaburi

(Des P. Pipitpiyapakorn. Litho Harrison)

1980 (1 July). *Waterfalls. T* **320** *and similar horiz designs. Multicoloured.* W **253** (*sideways*). P 14 × 14½.

1024	1b. Type **320**		20	10
1025	2b. Punyaban Falls, Ranong		30	10
1026	5b. Heo Suwat Falls. Nakhon Ratchasima		1·10	45
1027	6b. Siriphum Falls, Chiang Mai		95	65
1024/1027	*Set of* 4		2·30	1·20

321 Family and Reverse of F.A.O. Medal

(Des P. Teeranandha; photo Govt Ptg Wks, Tokyo (75s.).
Des P. Pipitpiyapakorn; litho Enschedé (5b.))

1980 (12 Aug). *Queen Sirikit's "Fourth Cycle" Anniv (48th
birthday)*. *T* **321** *and similar multicoloured designs.* W **109** (75s.)
or **226** (*sideways*) (5b.). P 13 (75s.) or 11 × 13 (5b.).
1028	75s. Queen Sirikit (*vert*)		20	10
1029	5b. Type **321**		85	45
1030	5b. Craft workers and obverse of F.A.O. medal		85	45

(Photo Harrison)

1980 (1 Sept)–81. W **253**. P 14½.
1031	**227**	20s. deep blue	20	10
1031*a*		25s. brown-lake (5.12 81)	20	10
1032		50s. blackish olive (5.12.81)	1·10	10
1032*a*		75s. violet	20	10
1031/1032*a* Set of 4			1·50	35

322 Khao Phanomrung Temple, Buri Ram   **323** Princess Mother

(Des T. Thongkambai. Litho Enschedé)

1980 (5 Oct). *International Correspondence Week.
Temples. T* **322** *and similar horiz designs. Multicoloured.* W **226**
(*sideways*). P 11 × 13.
1033	75s. Type **322**		10	10
1034	2b. Prang Ku Temple Chaiyaphum		30	15
1035	2b.75 Phimai Temple, Nakhon Ratchasima		45	15
1036	5b. Sikhoraphum Temple, Surin		1·10	60
1033/1036 *Set of 4*			1·80	90

(Des D. Pongdam. Litho Harrison)

1980 (21 Oct). *80th Birthday of Princess Mother.* W **253**.
P 14½ × 14.
1037	**323**	75s. multicoloured	1·10	25

324 Golden Mount Temple, Bangkok   **325** King Bhumibol

(Des T. Thongkambai. Litho Harrison)

1980 (24 Oct). *United Nations Day.* W **253**. P 14½ × 14.
1038	**324**	75s. multicoloured	20	10

Original   Redrawn

The December 1983 issues had a blemish on the King's upper
lip. A redrawn plate was used for later printings of the 3, 5 and
6b.

1980 (5 Dec)–**86**.

(a) W **226** (*sideways*). *Litho Enschedé.* P 11 × 13.
1039	**325**	25s. dull scarlet	55	10
1039*a*		50s. olive-green (5.12.81)	2·10	10
1040		75s. bright reddish violet	10	10
1040*a*		1b.25 bright green (7.9.81)	10	10

(b) W **109** (*sideways on* 1b.). *Litho* (1b.) *or recess* (*others*) *Govt
Ptg Wks, Tokyo.* P 13½ × 13.
1041	**325**	1b. turquoise-blue (25 1.84)	10	10
1041*a*		2b. slate-pur & Indian red (5.12.84)	3·25	10
1042		3b. Prussian blue and deep yellow-brown (5.12.83)	5·25	10
		a. Redrawn (1985)	20	10
1042*b*		4b. chestnut & dp turq-bl (5.12.84)	20	10
1043		5b. reddish brn & dp lilac (5.12.83)	6·50	15
		a. Redrawn (1985)	45	10
1044		6b. deep reddish-lilac and deep green (5.12.83)	6·50	10
		a. Redrawn (1985)	45	10
1044*b*		6b.50 brown-olive and yellowish green (5.12.84)	45	15
1044*c*		7b. blackish brn & red-brn (5.12.84)	55	10
1044*d*		7b.50 royal blue and dull vermilion (25.1.85)	45	20
1044*e*		8b. dp olive & purple-brn (5.12.83)	45	10
1045		8b.50 orge-brn & emer (5.12.83)	45	20
1045*a*		9b. yellow-brn & dp vio-bl (25.1.85)	45	15
1046		9b.50 dp grn & yell-olive (5.12.83)	45	20
1047		10b. blackish olive and Indian red (5.12.84)	65	10
1048		20b. yellow-green and reddish orange (5.12.86)	1·10	15
1049		50b. dp blue-grn & dp lilac (5.12.84)	3·25	30
1050		100b. indigo & reddish orge (5.12.84)	5·25	65
1039/1050 *Set of 21* (*cheapest*)			19·00	2·00

See also Nos. 1179/80*b*.

326 "King Rama VII
signing Constitutional
Document"

327 Bowl

331 Palm Leaf Fish Mobile

332 Scout aiding
Cripple

(Des P. Pipitpiyapakorn. Litho Harrison)

1980 (10 Dec). *Monument to King Prajadhipok (Rama VII).* W **253**.
P $14\frac{1}{2} \times 14$.
1051 **326** 75s. multicoloured 20 10

(Des P. Chingchai (2b.). C. Boonyasakdi
(3b.), P. Pipitpiyapakorn (others). Litho Enschedé)

1980 (15 Dec). *Bencharong Ware. T* **327** *and similar horiz
designs. Multicoloured.* W **226** (*sideways*). P 11 × 13.
1052 2b. Type **327** 45 20
1053 2b.75 Covered bowls 45 20
1054 3b. Covered jar 85 30
1055 5b. Stem-plates 85 55
1052/1055 *Set of 4* . . . . . . 2·30 1·10

(Des P. Pipitpiyapakorn. Litho Enschedé)

1981 (6 Feb). *International Handicraft Exhibition. T* **331** *and similar
horiz designs. Multicoloured.* W **226** (*sideways*). P $13\frac{1}{2}$.
1059 75s. Type **331** 20 10
1060 75s. Carved teakwood elephant 20 10
1061 2b.75 Basketwork 55 25
1062 2b.75 Thai folk dolls 55 25
1059/1062 *Set of 4* . . . . 1·40 65

(Des P. Sangamuang. Litho Enschedé)

1981 (28 Feb). *International Year of Disabled Persons. T* **332** *and
similar vert design. Multicoloured.* W **226**. P 13 × 11.
1063 75s. Type **332** 20 10
1064 5b. Disabled person cutting
gemstones 85 30

328 King Vajiravudh

329 "Youth in
Electronics Age"
(V. Maichun)

(Des Pranee Nimsamur. Litho Harrison)

1981 (1 Jan). *Birth Centenary of King Vajiravudh.* W **253**.
P14$\frac{1}{2}$ × 14.
1056 **328** 75s. multicoloured 45 10

(Des and litho Enschedé)

1981 (16 Jan). *Children's Day.* W **226**. P 13 × 11.
1057 **329** 75s. multicoloured 30 10

330 Mosque, Pattani Province

(Des K. Pongpibool. Litho State Bank Note Ptg Wks, Helsinki)

1981 (18 Jan). *1400th Anniv of Hegira.* W **262a**. P $12\frac{1}{2}$.
1058 **330** 5b. multicoloured . . . . . . 1·30 45

333 Red Cross Volunteer aiding
Refugee

334 Ongkhot

(Des Maliwan Chaikrachang. Litho State Bank Note Ptg Wks,
Helsinki)

1981 (6 Apr). *Red Cross.* W **262a**. P $12\frac{1}{2}$.
1065 **333** 75s.+25s. deep green and red . . 65 65

(Des P. Pongdam. Litho Enschedé)

1981 (1 July). *Khon (Thai classical dance) Masks. T* **334** *and
similar vert designs. Multicoloured.* W **226**. P 13 × 11.
1066 75s. Type **334** 20 10
1067 2b. Maiyarab 30 15
1068 3b. Sukrip 75 20
1069 5b. Indrajit 85 65
1066/1069 *Set of 4* . . . . . . 1·90 1·00

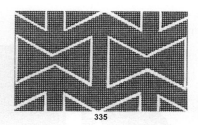

335

336 8a. Stamp, 1899

337 Luang Praditphairo

(Des C. Boonyasakdi. Litho J.W.)

1981 (4 Aug). *"Thaipex '81" National Stamp Exhibition, Bangkok.* T **336** and similar horiz designs. Multicoloured. W **335**. P 12.

1070	75s.	Type **336**	20	10
1071	75s.	28s. stamp, 1910	20	10
1072	2b.75	50s. stamp, 1921	55	30
1073	2b.75	3s. stamp, 1932	55	30
1070/1073 Set of 4			1·40	70

1981 (26 Aug). *Birth Centenary of Luang Praditphairo (musician).* W **253**. P 14½ × 14.

1074	**337**	1b.25 multicoloured	30	10

338 Mai Hok-Hian

339 Food Produce

(Des C. Boonyasakdi. Litho Govt Ptg Wks, Tokyo)

1981 (4 Oct). *International Correspondence Week. Dwarf Trees.* T **338** and similar vert designs. Multicoloured. W **109** (sideways). P 13½.

1075	75s.	Type **338**	20	10
1076	2b.	Mai Kam-Mao-Lo	30	20
1077	2b.75	Mai Khen	55	15
1078	5b.	Mai Khabuan	1·30	65
1075/1078 Set of 4			2·10	1·00

(Des C. Boonyasakdi. Litho J.W.)

1981 (16 Oct). *World Food Day.* W **335**. P 12.

1079	**339**	75s. multicoloured	25	10

340 Samran Mukhamat Pavilion, Bangkok

(Des T. Thongkambai. Litho Enschedé)

1981 (24 Oct). *United Nations Day.* W **226** (sideways). P 13½.

1080	**340**	1b.25 multicoloured	25	10

341 Expressway at Klongtoey

(Des Thailand Expressway and Rapid Transit Authority. Litho Enschedé)

1981 (29 Oct). *Inauguration of First Thai Expressway, Dindaeng–Tarua.* T **341** and similar horiz design. W **226** (sideways). P 13½.

1081	1b.	Type **341**	10	10
1082	5b.	Expressway interchange	1·10	35

342 King Cobra

343 Girl carrying Child

(Des C. Boonyasakdi. Litho Govt Ptg Wks, Tokyo)

1981 (1 Dec). *Snakes.* T **342** and similar horiz designs. Multicoloured. W **109**. P 13½.

1083	75s.	Type **342**	10	10
1084	2b.	Banded krait	65	30
1085	2b.75	Thai cobra	65	15
1086	5b.	Malayan pit viper	1·20	55
1083/1086 Set of 4			2·30	1·00

(Des P. Pongdam. Litho J.W.)

1982 (9 Jan). *Children's Day.* W **335** (sideways). P 12.

1087	**343**	1b.25 multicoloured	25	30

344 Scouts reaching for Peace

345 King Buddha Yod-Fa (Rama I)

(Des V. Vorachat-udompongse. Litho J.W.)

1982 (22 Feb). *75th Anniv of Boy Scout Movement.* W **335** (*sideways*). P 12.
1088 **344** 1b.25 multicoloured 25 10

(Des P. Pipitpiyapakorn. Litho J.W.)

1982 (4 Apr). *Bicentenary of Chakri Dynasty and of Bangkok. T* **345** *and similar vert designs. Multicoloured.* W **335**. P 12½ × 12.
1089 1b. Type **345** 20 10
1090 1b.25 Aerial view of Bangkok . . . 20 10
1091 2b. King Buddha Lert La Naphalai (Rama II) 45 10
1092 3b. King Nang Klao (Rama III) . . . . 1·30 20
1093 4b. King Mongkut (Rama IV) 85 30
1094 5b. King Chulalongkorn (Rama V) . . 1·70 65
1095 6b. King Vajiravudh (Rama VI) . . . 1·70 65
1096 7b. King Prajadhipok (Rama VII) . . 2·10 1·10
1097 8b. King Ananda Mahidol (Rama VIII) 1·10 65
1098 9b. King Bhumipol Adulyadej (Rama IX) . . . . 1·10 45
1089/1098 *Set of 10* . . . . 9·50 3·75
MS1099 Two sheets (a) 205 × 145 mm. Nos. 1089/98, (b) 195 × 180 mm. Nos. 1089/98 (sold at 130b. pair) . . . . 43·00 34·00

346 Dr. Robert Koch and Cross of Lorraine

(Des Ministry of Public Health. Litho Enschedé)

1982 (7 Apr). *Centenary of Discovery of Tubercle Bacillus.* W **226** (*sideways*). P 13½.
1100 **346** 1b.25 multicoloured 20 10

347*Quisqualis indica*

(Des T. Thongkambai. Litho Harrison)

1982 (30 June). *Flowers. T* **347** *and similar horiz designs. Multicoloured.* W **253** (*sideways*). P 14 × 15.
1101 1b.25 Type **347** 15 10
1102 1b.50 *Murraya paniculata* 25 15

1103 6b.50 *Mesua ferrea* 95 45
1104 7b. *Desmos chinensis* 75 30
1101/1104 *Set of 4* . . . . 1·90 90

348 Wat Bowon Sathan Sutthawat
349 "Landsat" Satellite

(Des N. Kaeosawang (4b.25), T. Thongkambai (others). Litho Enschedé)

1982 (4 Aug). *"Bangkok 1983" International Stamp Exhibition (1st issue). Temples. T* **348** *and similar horiz designs.* W **226** (*sideways*). P 13½.
1105 1b.25 Type **348** 20 10
1106 4b.25 Wat Phra Chetuphon Wimon Mangkhalaram 55 20
1107 6b.50 Wat Mahathat Yuwarat Rangsarit 65 40
1108 7b. Wat Phra Sri Rattana Satsadaram . . . . 1·10 30
1105/1108 *Set of 4* . . . . 2·30 90
MS1109 160 × 140 mm. Nos. 1105/8. P 12½ (sold at 30b.) . . . . 32·00 26·00
See also Nos. 1133/**MS**1135 and 1142/**MS**1146.

(Des N. Kaeosawang. Litho J.W.)

1982 (9 Aug). *Second United Nations Conference on the Exploration and Peaceful Uses of Outer Space, Vienna.* W **335** (*sideways*). P 12.
1110 **349** 1b.25 multicoloured 20 10

350 Prince Purachatra
351 Covered Jar

(Des Pranee Nimsamur. Litho Harrison)

1982 (14 Sept). *Birth Centenary of Prince Purachatra.* W **253**. P14.
1111 **350** 1b.25 multicoloured 20 10

(Des T. Thongkambai (1b.25), N. Kaeosawang (3b.), Achara Livisith (4b.25), C. Boonyasakdi (7b.). Litho Govt Ptg Wks, Tokyo)

1982 (3 Oct). *International Correspondence Week. Sangalok Pottery. T* **351** *and similar horiz designs. Multicoloured.* W **109** (*sideways*). P 13½.
1112 1b.25 Type **351** 20 10
1113 3b. Small jar 65 20
1114 4b.25 Celadon plate 45 30
1115 7b. Plate with fish design 85 45
1112/1115 *Set of 4* . . . . 1·90 95

352 Loha Prasat, Bangkok

353 Chap and Ching

356 Child sweeping

357 Postcodes

(Des T. Thongkambai. Litho Govt Ptg Wks, Tokyo)

1982 (24 Oct). *United Nations Day.* W **109**. P 13½.

1116	**352**	1b.25 multicoloured	20	10

(Des P. Pongdam. Litho Harrison)

1983 (8 Jan). *Children's Day.* W **253**. P 15 × 14.

1130	**356**	1b.25 multicoloured	20	10

(Des Niramol Ruangsom. Litho J.W.)

1982 (30 Nov). *Thai Musical Instruments. T* **353** *and similar horiz designs. Multicoloured.* W **335**. P 12.

1117	50s. Type **353**		10	10
1118	1b. Pi nok and pi nai (pipes)		30	10
1119	1b.25 Klong that and taphon (drums)		20	10
1120	1b.50 Khong mong (gong) and krap (wooden sticks)		20	15
1121	6b. Khong wong yai (glockenspiel)		2·10	75
1122	7b. Khong wong lek (glockenspiel)		85	30
1123	8b. Ranat ek (xylophone)		75	30
1124	9b. Ranat thum (xylophone)		75	30
1117/1124	Set of 8		5·25	1·90

(Des C. Boonyasakdi. Litho Govt Ptg Wks, Tokyo)

1983 (25 Feb). *First Anniv of Postcodes. T* **357** *and similar horiz design. Multicoloured.* W **109** (*sideways on No.* 1131). P 13½.

1131	1b.25 Type **357**		25	10
1132	1b.25 Postcoded envelope		25	10

358 Old General Post Office

(Des T. Thongkambai. Litho Enschedé)

1983 (25 Feb). *"Bangkok 1983" International Stamp Exhibition* (2nd issue). W **226** (*sideways*). P 13½.

1133	**358**	7b. multicoloured	85	15
1134		10b. multicoloured	1·30	25
MS1135	142 × 100 mm. Nos. 1133/4. P 12½ (sold at 30b.)		9·75	8·50

354 Pileated Gibbon

355 Emblem and Flags of Member Countries

(Des C. Boonyasakdi. Litho J.W.)

1982 (26 Dec). *National Wild Animal Preservation Day. Monkeys. T* **354** *and similar vert designs. Multicoloured.* W **335** (*sideways*). P 12.

1125	1b.25 Type **354**		20	10
1126	3b. Pigtail macaque		1·10	15
1127	5b. Slow loris		65	40
1128	7b. Silvered leaf monkey		85	45
1125/1128	Set of 4		2·25	1·20

359 Junks

360 Civil Servant's Shoulder Strap

(Des C. Boonyasakdi. Litho Harrison)

1983 (17 Mar). *25th Anniv of International Maritime Organization.* W **253** (*sideways*). P 14 × 15.

1136	**359**	1b.25 multicoloured	20	10

(Des C. Boonyasakdi. Litho Harrison)

1982 (26 Dec). *15th Anniv of Association of South-East Asian Nations.* W **253**. P 15 × 14.

1129	**355**	6b.50 multicoloured	85	20

(Des P Pongdam Litho J.W.)

1983 (1 Apr). *Civil Servants' Day.* W **335** (*sideways*). P 12.

1137	**360**	1b.25 multicoloured	20	10

361 Giving and Receiving Aid and Red Cross

362 Prince Sithiporn Kridakara

(Des U. Tikasub. Litho Govt Ptg Wks, Tokyo)

1983 (6 Apr). *Red Cross.* W **109**. P 13½.

1138	**361**	1b.25+25s. multicoloured	. . . .	45	45

(Des U. Tikasub. Litho Harrison)

1983 (11 Apr). *Birth Centenary of Prince Sithiporn Kridakara (agriculturalist).* W **253**. P 15 × 14.

1139	**362**	1b.25 multicoloured	. . . . . .	20	10

363 Satellite, Map and Dish Aerial

364 Prince Bhanurangsi

(Des C. Boonyasakdi. Litho Enschedé)

1983 (4 Aug). *Domestic Satellite Communications System.* W **226** (*sideways*). P 13½.

1140	**363**	2b. multicoloured	. . . . . .	30	10

(Des U. Tikasub. Litho Harrison)

1983 (4 Aug). *Prince Bhanurangsi (founder of Thai postal service) Commemoration.* W **253**. P 15 × 14.

1141	**364**	1b.25 multicoloured	. . . . . .	30	10

365 Post Box Clearance

366 Cable Map of A.S.E.A.N. Countries and Cable Ship

(Des P. Pipitpiyapakorn. Litho J.W.)

1983 (4 Aug). *"Bangkok 1983" International Stamp Exhibition (3rd issue).* T **365** and similar horiz designs. Multicoloured. W **335**. P 12.

1142	1b.25 Type **365**		10	10
1143	7b.50 Post Office counter	. . . . .	75	25
1144	8b.50 Mail transporter	. . . . . .	55	30
1145	9b. 50 Mail delivery	. . . . .	55	30
1142/1145 *Set of 4*			1·80	85

MS1146 162 × 140 mm. Nos. 1142/5. Perf (sold at 50b.) . . . . 10·50 9·75

The miniature sheet exists imperforate with fluorescent security markings "CAT" from a limited printing (*Price £85*).

(Des Maliwan Chaikrachang. Litho J.W.)

1983 (27 Sept). *Inauguration of Malaysia–Singapore–Thailand Submarine Cable.* T **366** and similar vert design. Multicoloured. W **335** (*sideways*). P 12.

1147	1b.25 Type **366**	. . . .	10	10
1148	7b. Map of new cable	. . . .	65	30

367 Flower Coral (*Acropora asper*)

(Des S. Chongthanapaithoon (2b.), C. Boonyasakdi (3b.), S. Kangtan (4b.), T. Monyakul (7b.). Litho Govt Ptg Wks, Tokyo)

1983 (6 Oct). *International Correspondence Week. Coral.* T **367** and similar horiz designs. Multicoloured. W **109** (*sideways*). P 13½.

1149	2b. Type **367**	. . . .	30	10
1150	3b. Lesser valley coral (*Platygyra lamellina*)	65	10
1151	4b. Mushroom coral (*Danafungia* sp.) . . .	30	30
1152	7b. Common lettuce coral (*Pectinia lactuca*)	95	55
1149/1152 *Set of 4*			2·00	95

368 Satellite and Submarine Cable Communications Equipment

(Des T. Thongkambai. Litho Harrison)

1983 (24 Oct). *World Communications Year.* T **368** and similar horiz design. Multicoloured. W **253** (*sideways*). P 14 × 15.

1153	2b. Type **368**	. . . .	30	10
1154	3b. Telephone and telegraph service equipment	30	10

369 Fishing for Skipjack   **370** Buddha
(sculpture)

(Des C. Boonyasakdi. Litho Harrison)

1983 (24 Oct). *United Nations Day.* W **253** (*sideways*). P 14 × 15.
1155   **369**   1b.25 multicoloured   20   10

(Des Pranee Nimsamur. Litho J.W.)

1983 (17 Nov). *700th Anniv of Thai Alphabet. T* **370** *and similar
designs.* W **335** (*sideways on* 8, 9b.). *Fluorescent security
marking* (7b.). P 12.
1156   3b. multicoloured   55   15
1157   7b. black and orange-brown   95   20
1158   8b. multicoloured   55   25
1159   9b. multicoloured   55   25
1156/1159 *Set of* 4 . . . .   2·30   75
Designs: *Horiz*—3b. Sangkhalok pottery; 7b. Thai characters.
Vert—9b. Mahathat Temple.
The security marking is "CAT" repeated four times.

371 Prince Mahidol   **372** Lotus Blossoms within Heads
of Songkhla

(U. Tikasub. Litho J.W.)

1983 (8 Dec). *60th Anniv of Co-operation between Siriraj Hospital
and Rockefeller Foundation.* W **335** (*sideways*). P 12.
1160   **371**   9b.50 multicoloured   85   45

(Des P. Nirun. Litho Govt Ptg Wks, Tokyo)

1984 (14 Jan). *Children's Day.* W **109** (*sideways*). P 13½.
1161   **372**   1b.25 multicoloured   25   10

373 Running

(Des Maliwan Chaikrachang. Litho Govt Ptg Wks, Tokyo)

1984 (22 Jan). *17th National Games. Phitsanulok Province. T* **373**
and similar horiz design. Multicoloured. W **109** (*sideways*).
P 13½.
1162   1b.25 Type **373**   30   10
1163   3b. Football   20   15

374 Skeletal Joints, Globe and   **375** Statue of King
Emblem   Naresuan and
                             Modern Armed
                             Forces

(Des U. Tikasub. Litho Harrison)

1984 (22 Jan). *Fifth South East Asia and Pacific Area League
Against Rheumatism Congress.* W **253** (*sideways*). P 14 × 15.
1164   **374**   1b.25 multicoloured   30   10

(Des T. Thongkambai. Litho Harrison)

1984 (25 Jan). *Armed Forces Day.* W **253**. P 15 × 14.
1165   **375**   1b.25 multicoloured   30   10

376 Royal Institute
Emblem in Door Arch

บำรุงกาชาด
๒๕๒๗

3.25+0.25
――――――――
(377)

(Des Niramon Ruangsom. Litho Harrison)

1984 (31 Mar). *50th Anniv of Royal Institute.* W **253**. P 15 × 14.
1166   **376**   1b.25 multicoloured   20   10

1984 (6 Apr). *Red Cross. No.* 954 *surch with T* **377**.
1167   **295**   3b.25+25s. on
          2b.75+25s. multicoloured . . .   85   85

378 King and Queen examining Land
Development Project

(Des P. Pipitpiyapakorn. Litho J.W.)

1984 (5 May). *Royal Initiated Projects. T* **378** *and similar horiz designs. Multicoloured.* W **335**. P 12.

1168	1b.25 Type **378**	25	10
	a. Strip of 5. Nos. 1168/72	1·40	
1169	1b.25 Improving barren area	25	10
1170	1b. 25 Dam, terrace farming and rain-making aircraft	25	10
1171	1b.25 Crops, fish and farm animals	25	10
1172	1b.25 King and Queen of Thailand	25	10
1168/1172 *Set of* 5		1·30	55

Nos. 1168/72 were issued together in *se-tenant* strips of five within the sheet.

379 Dome Building and University Emblem

(Des P. Pongdam. Litho Harrison)

1984 (27 June). *50th Anniv of Thammasat University.* W **253** (*sideways*). P 14 × 15.

1173	**379**	1b.25 multicoloured	20	10

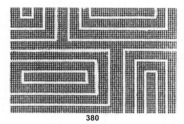

380

381 A.B.U. Emblem and Map

382 Chiang Saen Style Buddha

(Des C. Boonyasakdi. Litho J.W.)

1984 (1 July). *20th Anniv of Asia–Pacific Broadcasting Union.* W **380**. P 12.

1174	**381**	4b. multicoloured	55	15

(Des U. Tikasub (1b.25, 9b.50), Pranee Nimsamur (others). Litho Harrison)

1984 (12 July). *Thai Sculptures of Buddhas. T* **382** *and similar vert designs. Multicoloured.* W **253**. P 15 × 14.

1175	1b.25 Type **382**	10	10
1176	7b. Sukhothai style	95	35
1177	8b.50 Thong style	45	45
1178	9b.50 Ayutthaya style	45	45
1175/1178 *Set of* 4		1·80	1·20

(Litho Harrison)

1984–85. W **253** (*sideways*). P 14 × 15.

1179	**325**	50s. yellow-olive	1·70	10
1180		1b.25 yellow-green	2·10	10
1180*a*		1b.50 yellow-orange (6.4.85)	85	85
1180*b*		2b. brown-red (4.8.85)	45	10
1179/1180*b Set of* 4			4·50	1·00

383

384 *Alocasia indica* var. *metallica*

385 Princess Mother

(Des C. Boonyasakdi (1b.50, 4b.), S. Cherchaibhum (2b.) and N. Phuwanatnurak (10b.). Litho Cartor)

1984 (7 Oct). *International Correspondence Week. Medicinal Plants. T* **384** *and similar vert designs. Multicoloured.* W **383**. P 13½.

1181	1b.50 Type **384**	15	10
1182	2b. *Aloe barbadensis*	25	10
1183	4b. *Gynura pseudo-china*	45	20
1184	10b. *Rhoeo spathacea*	1·30	65
1181/1184 *Set of* 4		1·90	95

(Des P. Pongdam. Litho Harrison)

1984 (21 Oct). *84th Birthday of Princess Mother.* W **253**. P 15 × 14.

1185	**385**	1b.50 multicoloured	15	10

386 Threshing Rice

387 *Bhutanitis lidderdalei*

(Des N. Kaeosawang. Litho Harrison)

1984 (24 Oct). *United Nations Day.* W **253**. P 15 × 14.

1186	**386**	1b.50 multicoloured	15	10

(Des N. Kaeosawang. Photo Govt Ptg Wks, Tokyo)

1984 (27 Nov). *Butterflies. T* **387** *and similar horiz designs. Multicoloured.* W **109**. P 13½.

1187	2b.	Type **387**	20	10
1188	3b.	*Stichophthalma louisa*	20	10
1189	5b.	*Parthenos sylvia*	45	30
1190	7b.	*Stichophthalma godfreyi*	75	30
1187/1190	*Set of 4*		1·50	75

388 "Crossing the Road by Flyover" (U-Tai Raksorn)

389 Bangkok Mail Centre

(Litho Cartor)

1985 (12 Jan). *Children's Day. T* **388** *and similar horiz design showing children's drawings. Multicoloured.* W **383** (*sideways* on No. 1192). P 13½.

1191	1b.50	Type **388**	15	10
1192	1b.50	"Crossing the Road by Flyover" (Sravudh Charoennawee)	15	10

(Des C. Boonyasakdi. Litho Cartor)

1985 (25 Feb). *Inauguration of Bangkok Mail-sorting Centre.* W **383** (*sideways*). P 13½.

1193	**389**	1b.50 multicoloured	15	10

390 Monument to Tao-Thep-Krasattri and Tao-Sri-Sundhorn

2 +.25 บาท BAHT
(**391**)

(Des C. Boonyasakdi. Litho Harrison)

1985 (13 Mar). *Heroines of Phuket Bicentennial Ceremony.* W **253**. P 15 × 14.

1194	**390**	2b. multicoloured	30	10

1985 (30 Mar). *Red Cross. No.* 987 *surch with T* **391**.

1195	**306**	2b.+25s. on 75s.+25s. multicoloured	65	65

392 Bank Headquarters, Bangkok, and King Vajiravudh (Rama VI)

(Des S. Rungcharoenkitkul. Litho Harrison)

1985 (1 Apr). *72nd Anniv of Government Savings Bank.* W **253** (*sideways*). P 14 × 15.

1196	**392**	1b.50 multicoloured	15	10

393 Satellite over Thai Buildings

(Des Pranee Nimsamur. Litho J.W.)

1985 (6 Apr). *20th Anniv of International Telecommunications Satellite Organization.* W **380**. P 12.

1197	**393**	2b. multicoloured	25	10

394 Douglas DC-6 and Loi Krathong Festival

395 U.P.U. Emblem

(Des P. Pipitpiyapakorn. Litho Cartor)

1985 (1 May). *25th Anniv of Thai Airways. T* **394** *and similar horiz designs. Multicoloured.* W **383** (*sideways*). P 13½.

1198	2b.	Type **394**	10	10
1199	7b.50	Douglas DC-10-30 and Thai classical dancing	55	30
1200	8b.50	Airbus Industrie A300 and Thai buildings	65	35
1201	9b.50	Boeing 747-200 and world landmarks	65	40
1198/1201	*Set of 4*		1·80	1·00

(Litho J.W. (2b.), Cartor (10b.))

1985 (1 July). *Centenary of Membership of Universal Postal Union and International Telecommunications Union. T* **395** *and similar vert design. Multicoloured.* W **380** (2b.) or **383** (10b.). P 12 (2b.) or 13½ (10b.).

1202	2b.	Type **395**	10	10
1203	10b.	I.T.U. emblem	55	25

396 Pigeon   **397** Aisvarya Pavilion

400 Boxing   **401** Golden Trumpet (*Allemanda cathartica*)

(Des C. Boonyasakdi. Litho Govt Ptg Wks, Tokyo)

1985 (4 Aug). *National Communications Day.* W **109** (*sideways*). P 13½.

1204	**396**	2b. greenish blue, red & dp ultram	20	10

(Des C. Boonyasakdi. Litho J.W.)

1985 (1 Oct). *13th South-East Asia Games, Bangkok* (*1st issue*) *T* **400** *and similar horiz designs. Multicoloured.* W **380**. P 12.

1212	2b. Type **400**	25	10
	a. Strip of 5. Nos. 1212/16	1·30	
1213	2b. Putting the shot	25	10
1214	2b. Badminton	25	10
1215	2b. Throwing the javelin	25	10
1216	2b. Weightlifting	25	10
1212/1216 *Set of 5*		1·20	45

MS1217 186 × 127 mm. Nos. 1212/16 (sold at 20b.) . . . . . 13·00 10·50

Nos. 1212/16 were issued together in *se-tenant* strips of five within the sheet.

See also Nos. 1229/**MS**1233.

(Des T. Thongkambai. Litho Cartor)

1985 (4 Aug). *"Thaipex '85" National Stamp Exhibition. T* **397** *and similar multicoloured designs.* W **383** (*sideways on* 3, 7b.). P 13½.

1205	2b. Type **397**		20	10
1206	3b. Varopas Piman Pavilion (*horiz*)		30	10
1207	7b. Vehas Camrun Pavilion (*horiz*)		55	25
1208	10b. Vitoon Tassana Tower		65	45
1205/1208 *Set of 4*			1·50	85

MS1209 155 × 179 mm. Nos. 1205/8 . . . . . 26·00 21·00

No. **MS**1209 exists imperforate from a limited printing.

(Des P. Chingchai, S. Chongsanapaitoon and T. Thongkambai. Litho Cartor)

1985 (6 Oct). *International Correspondence Week. Climbing Plants. T* **401** *and similar vert designs. Multicoloured.* W **383**. P 13½.

1218	2b. Type **401**	30	10
1219	3b. *Jasminum auriculatum*	45	10
1220	7b. Passion flower (*Passiflora laurifolia*)	65	30
1221	10b. Coral-vine (*Antigonon leptopus*)	75	45
1218/1221 *Set of 4*		1·90	85

398 King Mongkut, Eclipsed Sun and Telescope

(Des P. Pipitpiyapakorn. Litho J.W.)

1985 (18 Aug). *National Science Day.* W **380**. P 12.

1210	**398**	2b. multicoloured	25	30

402 Mothers and Children at Clinic   **403** Prince Dhani Nivat

(Des N. Kaewsawang. Litho Cartor)

1985 (24 Oct). *United Nations Day.* W **383**. P 13½.

1222	**402**	2b. multicoloured	20	10

399 Department Seals, 1885 and 1985

(Des U. Tikasub. Litho Harrison)

1985 (3 Sept). *Centenary of Royal Thai Survey Department.* W **253** (*sideways*). P 14 × 15.

1211	**399**	2b. multicoloured	20	10

I

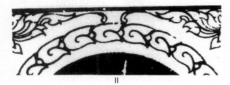

II

Type I: The "hooks" in the flower border around the portrait point in a clockwise direction.
Type II: The hooks point anti-clockwise.

(Des S. Prasong. Litho Cartor)

1985 (7 Nov). *Birth Centenary of Prince Dhani Nivat, Kromamun Bidyalabh Bridhyakorn.* W **383**. P 13½.
1223	**403**	2b. multicoloured (I)		20	10
		a. Type II		1·90	45
		b. Horiz *se-tenant* pair. Types I and II		13·00	10·50

Printed in sheets containing two panes of 50 stamps. Type II occurs in the first 5 vertical rows (i.e. 25 stamps) of pane 1.

404 Prince of Jainad

405 Emblem and Buildings

(Des Niramon Ruangsom. Litho Harrison)

1985 (12 Nov). *Birth Centenary of Rangsit, Prince of Jainad (Minister of Health).* W **253**. P 15 × 14.
1224	**404**	1b.50 multicoloured		15	10

(Des C. Boonyasakdi. Litho Cartor)

1985 (25 Nov). *Fifth Asian–Pacific Postal Union Congress.* T **405** and similar design. W **383** (*sideways*). P 13½.
1225		2b. multicoloured		10	10
1226		10b. multicoloured		55	25

Design:—10b. As Type **405** but different buildings.

406 Emblem

(Des C. Chumtap. Litho Harrison)

1985 (26 Nov). *International Youth Year.* W **253** (*sideways*). P 14 × 15.
1227	**406**	2b. multicoloured		55	20

407 Dentist and Nurse tending Patient

408 Volleyball

(Des T. Thongkambai and P. Naewboonnien. Litho Harrison)

1985 (5 Dec). *12th Asian–Pacific Dental Congress.* W **253** (*sideways*). P 14 × 15.
1228	**407**	2b. multicoloured		20	10

(Des S. Bhansani and N. Mongkolvisuth. Litho J.W.)

1985 (8 Dec). *13th South-East Asia Games, Bangkok (2nd issue).* T **408** and similar vert designs. Multicoloured. W **380**. P 12.
1229	1b. Type **408**		20	10
1230	2b. Sepak-takraw (kick-ball)		20	10
1231	3b. Gymnastics		20	10
1232	4b. Bowls		30	20
1229/1232 *Set of 4*			80	45
MS1233 186 × 129 mm. Nos. 1229/32 plus label (sold at 20b.)			13·00	10·50

409 Chevalier de Chaumont presenting message from Louis XIV to King Narai the Great, 1685

410 Emblem

(Des S. Poonsawat. Litho Cartor)

1985 (12 Dec). *300th Anniv of Franco–Thai Relations.* T **409** and similar multicoloured designs. W **383** (*sideways on 8b.50*). P 13½.
1234	2b. Type **409**		10	10
1235	8b.50 Siamese emissaries carrying reply from King Narai to King Louis XIV (*horiz*)		65	35

(Litho Leigh-Mardon Ltd, Melbourne, Australia (1235c), J.W. (others))

1985–87. W **380**. *Fluorescent security marking* (1235a/b). P 11 × 13.
1235a	**325**	1b. 25 yellow-green	65	10
1235b		2b. chestnut	1·30	10
		c. Perf 14½ × 14 (19.6.87)	45	10

The security marking is "CAT" repeated twice.

(Des C. Boonyasakdi. Litho Cartor)

1986 (1 Jan). *Third Anniv of International and Inauguration of Domestic Express Mail Services.* W **383** (*sideways*). P 13½.
1236 **410** 2b. multicoloured 15 10

411 Green Turtle (*Chelonia mydas*)   412 "Family picking Lotus" (Areeya Makarabhundhu)

(Des P. Pipitpiyapakorn. Litho Govt Ptg Wks, Tokyo).

1986 (8 Jan). *Turtles.* T **411** *and similar horiz designs. Multicoloured.* W **109**. P 13½.
1237   1b.50 Type **411** 20 10
1238   3b. Hawksbill turtle (*Eretmochelys imbricata*) 45 10
1239   5b. Leatherback turtle (*Dermochelys coriacea*) . . . . 1·30 20
1240   10b. Olive turtle (*Lepidochelys olivacea*) . . . . 1·10 30
1237/1240 *Set of 4* . . . . 2·75 65

(Litho Cartor)

1986 (11 Jan). *Children's Day.* W **383**. P 13½.
1241 **412** 2b. multicoloured 20 10

บำรุงกาชาด

๒๕๒๙   1986

2+.25 ฿BAHT

(413)

414 Statue of Sunthon Phu (Sukij Laidej), Amphoe Klaeng

1986 (5 Apr). *Red Cross. No. 1021 surch with* T **413**.
1242 **317** 2b.+25s. on 75s.+25s. multicoloured . . . 65 65

(Des Suntharee Prasong. Litho Cartor)

1986 (26 June). *Birth Bicentenary of Sunthon Phu (poet).* W **383**. P 13½.
1243 **414** 2b. multicoloured 20 10

415 Watermelon (*Citrullus lanatus*)

(Des S. Chongthanapaithoon. Litho Cartor)

1986 (26 June). *Fruit.* T **415** *and similar horiz designs. Multicoloured.* W **383** (*sideways*). P 13½.
1244   2b. Type **415** 55 10
1245   2b. Malay apple (*Eugenia malaccensis*) 55 10
1246   6b. Pomelo (*Citrus maxima*) 75 30
1247   6b. Papaya (*Carica papaya*) 75 30
1244/1247 *Set of 4* . . . . 2·30 70

416 Trees on Grid and Water Line

(Des C. Pongsang. Litho Cartor)

1986 (21 July). *National Tree Year.* W **383** (*sideways*). P 13½.
1248 **416** 2b. multicoloured 15 10

417 Pigeon flying from Man's Head to Transmission Masts   418 Chalom

(Des U. Tikasub. Litho Cartor)

1986 (4 Aug). *National Communications Day.* W **383** (*sideways*). P 13½.
1249 **417** 2b. multicoloured 15 10

(Des S. Sae-So (1250), P. Manastrong (1251), Achara Livisidhi (1252), N. Kaewsawang (1253). Litho Cartor)

1986 (5 Oct). *International Correspondence Week. Bamboo Baskets.* T **418** *and similar vert designs. Multicoloured.* W **383**. P 13½.
1250   2b. Type **418** 20 10
1251   2b. Krabung 20 10
1252   6b. Kratib 45 15
1253   6b. Kaleb 45 15
1250/1253 *Set of 4* . . . . 1·20 45

(419)   420 Emblem and War Scenes

1986 (5 Oct). *No. 1031 optd with* T **419** *in gold.*
1254 **227** 1b.on 20s. deep blue 10 10

(Des U Tikasub. Litho Cartor)

1986 (24 Oct). *International Peace year.* W **383** (*sideways*). P 13½.
1255 **420** 2b. slate blue, bright blue and rosine 20 10

421 Industrial and Agricultural Scenes within Emblem

(Des D. Tuchinda. Litho Govt Ptg Wks, Tokyo)

1986 (24 Oct). *Productivity Year.* W **109** (*sideways*). P 13½.
1256 **421** 2b. multicoloured 15 10

422 Scouts saluting and Scout helping Blind Man across Road

423 Vanda "Varavuth"

(Des Pranee Nimsamur. Litho Cartor)

1986 (7 Nov). *75th Anniv of Thai Scouting. T* **422** *and similar horiz designs. Multicoloured.* W **383** (*sideways*). P 13½.
1257 2b.+50s. Type **422** 15 15
1258 2b.+50s. Scouting activities . . . 15 15
1259 2b.+50s. King and Queen making
  presentations to scouts 15 15
1260 2b.+50s. 15th Asia–Pacific Scout
  Conference, Thailand 15 15
1257/1260 *Set of 4* 55 55

(Des W. Niyomsmarn. Litho Cartor)

1986 (7 Nov). *Sixth ASEAN Orchid Congress, Thailand. T* **423** *and similar multicoloured designs.* W **383** (*sideways on* 4, 5b.).
  P 13½.
1261 2b. Type **423** 20 10
1262 3b. Ascocenda "Emma" 20 15
1263 4b. Dendrobium "Sri-Siam" (*horiz*) . . 45 30
1264 5b. Dendrobium "Ekapol Panda"
  (*horiz*) 45 20
1261/1264 *Set of 4* . . . . . . 1·20 70
MS1265 116 × 99 mm. Nos. 1261/4 . . 55·00 43·00

424 *Volvariella volvacea*

(Des W. Niyomsmarn. Photo Govt Ptg Wks, Tokyo)

1986 (26 Nov). *Edible Fungi. T* **424** *and similar horiz designs. Multicoloured.* W **109**. P 13½.
1266 2b. Type **424** 20 10
1267 2b. *Pleurotus ostreatus* 20 10
1268 6b. *Auricularia polytricha* . . . 55 25
1269 6b. *Pleurotus cystidiosus* . . . 55 25
1266/1269 *Set of 4* . . . . . . 1·40 65

425 Black Sharkminnow *Morulius chrysophekadion*)

426 Children in Playground

(Des S. Poonsawat. Litho Cartor)

1986 (19 Dec). *60th Anniv of Fisheries Department. T* **425** *and similar horiz designs. Multicoloured.* W **383** (*sideways*). P 13½.
1270 2b. Type **425** 20 10
1271 2b. Blanc's knifefish (*Notopterus
  blanci*) 20 10
1272 7b. Asian boneytongue (*Scleropages
  formosus*) 45 25
1273 7b. Giant catfish (*Pangasianodon
  gigas*) 45 25
1270/1273 *Set of 4* . . . . . . 1·20 55

(Litho Leigh-Mardon Ltd, Melbourne)

1987 (10 Jan). *Children's Day. T* **426** *and similar vert design. Multicoloured.* W **380**. P 14½ × 15.
1274 2b. Type **426** 30 10
  a. Horiz pair. Nos. 1274/5 . . . 65 20
1275 2b. Children in and around swimming
  pool 30 10
Nos. 1274/5 were issued together in *se-tenant* pairs within the sheet, each pair forming a composite design showing "Our School" by Lawan Maneenetr.

427 General Dynamics F-16 Fighting Falcon and Northrop F-5 Tiger II Fighters and Pilot

(Des S. Donavanik and N. Aungsuwattakakul. Litho Cartor)

1987 (27 Mar). *72nd Anniv of Royal Thai Air Force.* W **383** (*sideways*). P 13½.
1276 **427** 2b. multicoloured 30 10

428 King Rama III and Temples

(Des Sriwarn Janehuttakarnkit. Litho Leigh-Mardon Ltd, Melbourne)

1987 (31 Mar). *Birth Bicentenary of King Rama III.* W **380**. P 15 × 14½.
1277 **428** 2b. multicoloured 25 10

2+0.50
บาท BAHT

429 Communications and
Transport Systems

(430)

(Des C. Boonyasakdi. Litho Leigh-Mardon Ltd, Melbourne)

1987 (1 Apr). *75th Anniv of Ministry of Communications.* W **380**.
P 15 × 14½.
1278 **429** 2b. multicoloured 15 10

1987 (4 Apr). *Red Cross. No.* 1065 *surch with T* **430**.
1279 **333** 2b.+50s. on 75s.+25s. deep green
and red 65 65

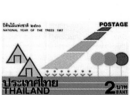

431 Tree-lined Street

432 Gold Peacock

(Des C. Pongsang. Litho Cartor)

1987 (11 July). *National Tree Year.* W **383** (*sideways*). P 13½.
1280 **431** 2b. multicoloured 15 10

(Des N. Kaewsawang. Litho Cartor)

1987 (4 Aug). *"Thaipex '87". National Stamp Exhibition.
Handicrafts.* T **432** *and similar multicoloured designs.* W **383**
(*sideways on Nos.* 1283/4). P 13½.
1281 2b. Type **432** 10 10
1282 2b. Gold hand-mirrors 10 10
1283 6b. Gold lustre water urn and finger
bowls with trays (*horiz*) 30 15
1284 6b. Gold swan vase (*horiz*) 30 15
1281/1284 *Set of 4* 80 45
MS1285 160 × 175 mm. Nos. 1281/4 (sold at
40b.)
. . . . 26·00 21·00
No. **MS**1285 exists imperforate from a limited printing.

433 Flying Bird and Animal Horn (Somsak
Junthavorn)

(Des C. Boonyasakdi. Litho Cartor)

1987 (4 Aug). *National Communications Day.* W **383** (*sideways*).
P 13½.
1286 **433** 2b. multicoloured 15 10

434 King Rama IX at Presentation
Ceremony, King Rama V and Emblem

(Des C. Boonyasakdi. Litho Cartor)

1987 (5 Aug). *Centenary of Chulachomklao Royal Military
Academy, Khao Cha-Ngok.* W **383** (*sideways*). P 13½.
1287 **434** 2b. multicoloured 15 10

435 Spiral Ropes leading to
Member Countries' Flags

436 People and Open
Book

(Des C. Boonyasakdi. Litho Cartor)

1987 (8 Aug). *20th Anniv of Association of South-East Asian
Nations.* W **383** (*sideways*). P 13½.
1288 **435** 2b. multicoloured 10 10
1289 3b. multicoloured 20 10
1290 4b. multicoloured 20 15
1291 5b. multicoloured 30 15
1288/1291 *Set of 4* 70 45

(Des Benjaporn Patapinyoboon. Litho Cartor)

1987 (8 Sept). *International Literacy Day.* W **383**. P 13½.
1292 **436** 2b. multicoloured 15 10

437 Flower-offering
Ceremony, Saraburi

438 Ministry Building

(Des S. Rodboon. Litho Cartor)

1987 (18 Sept). *Visit Thailand Year.* T **437** *and similar vert
designs.* W **383**. P 13½.
1293 2b. Type **437** 10 10
1294 3b. Duan Sib Festival (honouring
ancestors), Nakhon Si
Thammarat 20 10
1295 5b. Bang Fai (rain) Festival,
Yasothon 20 15
1296 7b. Loi Krathong, Sukhothai 30 15
1293/1296 *Set of 4* 70 45

(Des D. Toochinda. Litho Cartor)

1987 (18 Sept). *72nd Anniv of Auditor General's Office*. W **383** *(sideways)*. P 13½.
1297 **438** 2b. multicoloured 15 10

439 Temple of Dawn and *Sri Suphanahong* (royal barge) and Mt. Fuji within "100"

440 Tasselled Garland

(Des C. Boonyasakdi. Litho Govt Ptg Wks, Tokyo)

1987 (26 Sept). *Centenary of Thailand–Japan Friendship Treaty*. W **109** *(sideways)*. P 13½.
1298 **439** 2b. multicoloured 20 10

(Des P. Chingchai (2b.), S. Poonsawat (3b.), S. Chongthanapaithoon (5, 7b.). Litho Cartor)

1987 (4 Oct). *International Correspondence Week. Ceremonial Floral Garlands*. T **440** and similar vert designs. Multicoloured. W **383**. P 13½.
1299 2b. Floral tassle 10 10
1300 3b. Type **440** 20 10
1301 5b. Wrist garland 25 15
1302 7b. Double-ended garland 40 20
1299/1302 *Set of 4* 85 50

2 บาท
BAHT
(441)

442 Thai Pavilion

1987 (4 Oct). *No. 1180a surch with T* **441**.
1303 **325** 2b.on 1b.50 yellow-orange 15 10

(Des Niramol Ruaengsom. Litho Leigh-Mardon Ltd, Melbourne)

1987 (9 Oct). *Inauguration of Social Education and Cultural Centre*. W **380**. P 15 × 14½.
1304 **442** 2b. multicoloured 15 10

443 King Bhumibol Adulyadej as a Boy

444 "Teacher's Day" (Nutchaliya Suddhiprasit)

(Des P. Pipitpiyapakorn)

1987 (5 Dec). *King Bhumibol Adulyadej's* 60*th Birthday*. T **443** and similar horiz designs.

(a) Multicoloured. W **109**. *Photo Govt Ptg Wks, Tokyo*. P 13½.
1305 2b. Type **443** 20 10
1306 2b. Wedding photograph of King
Bhumibol Adulyadej and Queen
Sirikit, 1950 . . . . 20 10
1307 2b. King on throne during Accession
ceremony at Paisan Hall, 1950 . . . 20 10
1308 2b. King as monk on alms round 20 10
1309 2b. Elderly woman greeting King 20 10
1310 2b. King demonstrating to hill tribes how
to take medicine 20 10
1311 2b. King and Queen presenting gift bag
to wounded serviceman 20 10
1312 2b. King examining now system for small
farms 20 10
1305/1312 *Set of 9* . . . . 1·50 75
MS1313 190 × 144 mm. Nos. 1305/12 (sold at
40b.) . . . . 17·00 15·00

(b) Multicoloured. W **383** (sideways on Nos. 1314/18). *Litho Cartor*. P 13½.
1314 2b. Princess Mother Somdej Phra Sri
Nakarindra Boromrajjonnani . . . 55 15
1315 2b. Crown Prince Maha
Vajiralongkorn 55 15
1316 2b. Princess Maha Chakri Sirindhorn . . 55 15
1317 2b. Princess Chulabhorn . . . 55 15
1318 2b. King Bhumibol Adulyadej and Queen
Sirikit 55 15
1319 2b. King and family (48 × 33 mm) . . . 55 10
1314/1319 *Set of 6* . . . . 3·00 80

(c) W **383**. *Embossed and litho Cartor*. P 13½.
1320 100b. gold and deep bright blue (King
Bhumibol Adulyadej)
(48 × 33 mm) . . . . 34·00 34·00

(Litho Leigh-Mardon Ltd, Melbourne)

1988 (9 Jan). *Children's Day*. W **380**. P 14 × 14½.
1321 **444** 2b. multicoloured 15 10

445 Prince Kromamun Bridhyalongkorn (founder)

446 Society Building

(Des C. Yoowattana and Vachira Thongserm. Litho Leigh-Mardon Ltd, Melbourne)

1988 (26 Feb). *72nd Anniv of Thai Co-operatives*. W **380**. P 14 × 14½.
1322 **445** 2b. multicoloured 15 10

(Des C. Boonyasakdi. Litho Leigh-Mardon Ltd, Melbourne)

1988 (10 Mar). *84th Anniv of Siam Society (for promotion of arts and sciences)*. W **380**. P 14½ × 14.
1323 **446** 2b. multicoloured 15 10

447 Phra Phai Luang Monastery

(448) ("BAHT" 7¾ mm wide)

(Des T. Thongkambai (2b.), C. Boonyasakdi (3, 4b.), P. Chingchai (6b.). Litho Leigh-Mardon Ltd, Melbourne)

1988 (2 Apr). *Sukhothai Historical Park. T* **447** *and similar horiz designs. Multicoloured.* W **380**. P 14½ × 14.

1324	2b.	Type **447**	10	10
1325	3b.	Traphang Thonglang Monastery	20	10
1326	4b.	Maha That Monastery	30	20
1327	6b.	Thewalai Maha Kaset	45	25
1324/1327		*Set of 4*	95	60

1988 (3 Apr). *No. 1235a surch with T* **448**.

1328	**325**	1b.on 1b.25 yellow-green	15	10
		a. Surch inverted		

For similar surcharge on No. 1235a but with smaller letters, see No. 1557.

449 Syringe between Red Cross and Dog

450 King Rama V (founder)

(Des Veena Chantanatat. Litho Questa)

1988 (3 Apr). *Red Cross. Anti-rabies Campaign.* W **380**. P 13½ × 14.

1329	**449**	2b. multicoloured	15	10

(Des Dept of Fine Arts. Litho Leigh-Mardon Ltd, Melbourne)

1988 (26 Apr). *Centenary of Siriraj Hospital.* W **380**. P 14 × 14½.

1330	**450**	5b. multicoloured	1·30	45

451 Crested Fireback Pheasant (*Lophura ignita*)

452 Hand holding Coloured Ribbons

(Des N. Kaewsawang. Photo Govt Ptg Wks, Tokyo)

1988 (15 June). *Pheasants. T* **451** *and similar horiz designs. Multicoloured.* W **109**. P 13½.

1331	2b.	Type **451**	10	10
1332	3b.	Kalij pheasant (*Lophura leucomelana*)	20	10
1333	6b.	Silver pheasant (*Lophura nycthemera*)	45	20
1334	7b.	Mrs. Hume's pheasant (*Syrmaticus humiae*)	55	30
1331/1334		*Set of 4*	1·20	65

(Des Veena Chantanatat. Litho Cartor)

1988 (26 June). *Centenary of International Women's Council.* W **383**. P 13½.

1335	**452**	2b. multicoloured	15	10

453 King Rama IX in King's Own Bodyguard Uniform

454 King Rama IX in Full Robes

(Des P. Pipitpiyapakorn)

1988 (2 July)–93.

(a) Litho Leigh-Mardon Ltd, Melbourne. W **380**. P 14 × 14½.

1336	**453**	50s. yellow-olive (28.7.93)	10	10
1337		1b. bright new blue	10	10
1338		2b. rosine	10	10

(b) W **109**. *Recess Govt Ptg Wks, Tokyo.* P 13½ × 13.

1339	**453**	3b. slate-blue & lt brown (5.12.88)	10	10
1340		4b. Indian red & dp turq-bl (5.12.88)	15	10
1341		5b. chestnut & dp rose-lilac (1.7.89)	15	10
1342		6b. deep purple & dp green (1.7.89)	20	10
1343		7b. blackish brn & lake-brn (5.12.89)	20	10
1344		8b. dp yellow-grn & red-brn (1.7.89)	20	10
1345		9b. yellow-brn & dp vio-bl (1.7.89)	30	10
1346		10b. blackish ol & Indian red (5.12.88)	35	10
1348		20b. deep olive and orange (5.12.89)	65	20
1350		25b. dp turquoise-bl & dp ol (9.1.90)	75	30
1352		50b. dp blue-grn & slate-lilac (5.12.88)	1·50	30
1354		100b. indigo & yellow-orange (5.12.88)	3·00	65
1336/1354		*Set of 15*	7·00	2·30

Numbers have been left for additions to this series. See also Nos. 1455, 1631, **MS**1705 and 1752/3.

(Des P. Pipitpiyapakorn (1356), R. Thongdang (1357, 1360). Achara Livisidhi (1358), S. Chongthanapaithoon (1359, 1361), T. Thongkambai (others))

1988 (2 July). *42nd Anniv of Accession to Throne of King Rama IX. T* **454** *and similar multicoloured designs.*

(a) W **383**. *Litho Cartor.* P 13½.

1356   2b. Type **454** . . . . 1·10   10

(b) Royal Regalia. Size 33 × 48 *mm* (1357) *or* 48 × 33 *mm (others).* W **109** (*sideways on* 1358/61). *Photo Govt Ptg Wks, Tokyo.* P 13½.

1357   2b. Great Crown of Victory . . . 20   10
1358   2b. Sword of Victory and scabbard
        (*horiz*) 20   10
1359   2b. Sceptre (*horiz*) 20   10
1360   2b. Royal Fan and Fly Whisk (*horiz*)   20   10
1361   2b. Slippers (*horiz*) . . . 20   10

(c) Thrones. W **380**. *Litho Leigh-Mardon Ltd, Melbourne.* P 14 × 14½.

1362   2b. Atthathit Uthumphon Ratchaat throne
        (octagonal base) . . 20   10
1363   2b. Phatthrabit throne (rectangular
        base) 20   10
1364   2b. Phuttan Kanchanasinghat throne
        (gold throne on angular steps)   20   10
1365   2b. Butsabokmala Mahachakkraphat-
        phiman throne (ship shape)   20   10
1366   2b. Throne inlaid with mother-of pearl
        (blue throne on angular steps)   20   10
1367   2b. Peony design niello throne (circular
        steps) 20   10
1356/1367 *Set of 12* . . . 3·00   1·10
MS1368 130 × 172 mm. Nos. 1362/7 (sold at
   25b.) . . . . 26·00   21·00

455 Bridge, Building and Trees

(Des C. Pongsang. Litho Leigh-Mardon Ltd, Melbourne)

1988 (29 July). *National Tree Year.* W **380**. P 14½ × 14.
1369   **455**   2b. multicoloured . . . 15   10

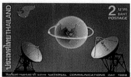

456 Globe and Dish Aerials

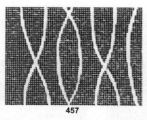

457

(Des S. Poonsawat. Litho Enschedé)

1988 (4 Aug). *National Communications Day.* W **457**. P 13½.
1370   **456**   2b. multicoloured . . . 20   10

458 Grasshopper

(Des N. Kaewsawang (1374). Napaporn Boonyasakdi (others). Litho Leigh-Mardon Ltd, Melbourne)

1988 (9 Oct). *International Correspondence Week. Woven Coconut-leaf Folk Toys. T* **458** *and similar horiz designs. Multicoloured.* W **380**. P 14½ × 14.
1371   2b. Type **458** 10   10
1372   2b. Carp 10   10
1373   6b. Bird 30   15
1374   6b. Takro 30   15
1371/1374 *Set of 4* . . . 90   45

459 Flats and Construction Workers   460 King Rama V in Full Uniform

(Des U. Niyomthum. Litho Harrison)

1988 (25 Oct). *Housing Development.* W **253** (*sideways*). P 14 × 15.
1375   **459**   2b. multicoloured . . . 15   10

(Des C. Moolpinit. Litho Cartor)

1988 (11 Nov). *120th Anniv of King's Own Bodyguard.* W **383**. P 13½.
1376   **460**   2b. multicoloured . . . 1·70   20

461 Road Signs   462 *Crotalaria sessiliflora*

(Des S. Sothonbun. Litho Govt Ptg Wks, Tokyo)

1988 (11 Nov). *Road Safety Campaign.* W **109**. P 13½.
1377   **461**   2b. multicoloured . . . 30   20

(Des Veena Chantanatat. Litho Cartor)

1988 (1 Dec). *New Year. T* **462** *and similar vert designs. Multicoloured.* W **380**. P 13½.
1378   1b. Type **462** . . . 15   10
1379   1b. *Uvaria grandiflora* . . 15   10

1380	1b. *Reinwardtia trigyna*		15	10
1381	1b. *Impatiens griffithii*		15	10
1378/1381	*Set of 4*		55	35

463 Buddha's Birthplace

464 Knight Grand Commander of Honourable Order of Rama

(Des T. Thongkambai. Litho Harrison)

1988 (5 Dec). *Buddha Monthon Celebrations.* T **463** *and similar multicoloured designs.* W 253 (*sideways on horiz designs*). P 15 × 14 (6b.) or 14 × 15 (*others*).

1382	2b. Type **463**		10	10
1383	3b. Buddha's place of enlightenment		15	10
1384	4b. Site of Buddha's first sermon		15	15
1385	5b. Buddha's Place of Nirvana		25	15
1386	6b. Statue of Buddha (*vert*)		40	15
1382/1386	*Set of 5*		95	60
MS1386*a*	82 × 110 mm. No. 1386 (Sold at 15b.)		7·50	6·50

(Des T. Thongkambai. Litho Cartor)

1988 (5 Dec). *Insignia of Orders.* T **464** *and similar vert designs. Multicoloured.* W 383. P 13½.

1387	2b. Type **464**		10	10
	a. Horiz pair. Nos. 1387/8		25	25
1388	2b. Close-up of badge		10	10
1389	3b. Knight Grand Cordon (Special Class) of Most Exalted Order of the White Elephant		20	10
	a. Horiz pair. Nos. 1389/90		45	25
1390	3b. Close-up of badge		20	10
1391	5b. Knight Grand Cordon of Most Noble Order of Crown of Thailand		30	15
	a. Horiz pair. Nos. 1391/2		65	35
1392	5b. Close-up of badge		30	15
1393	7b. Close-up of Rarana Varabhorn Order of Merit		45	15
	a. Horiz pair. Nos. 1393/4		95	35
1394	7b. Badge on chain of office		45	15
1387/1394	*Set of 8*		1·90	1·30

Stamps of the same value were issued together in *se-tenant* pairs within their sheets, each pair forming a composite design.

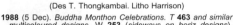

465 "Floating Market" (Thongbai Siyam)

(Litho Cartor)

1989 (14 Jan). *Children's Day.* T **465** *and similar horiz designs showing plasticine paintings by blind people. Multicoloured.* W 380. P 13½.

1395	2b. Type **465**		15	10
1396	2b. "Flying Birds" (Kwanchai Kerd-Daeng)		15	10

1397	2b. "Little Mermaid" (Chalermpol Jiengmai)		15	10
1398	2b. "Golden Fish" (Natetip Korsantirak)		15	10
1395/1398	*Set of 4*		55	35

466 Emblem and Symbols of Communication

(Des U. Niyomthum. Litho Leigh-Mardon Ltd, Melbourne)

1989 (25 Feb). *12th Anniv of Thai Communications Authority.* W 380. P 14½ × 14.

1399	**466**	2b. multicoloured	15	10

467 Statue of Kings Rama V and VI and Auditorium

468 Red Cross Worker

(Des Veena Chantanatat. Litho Leigh-Mardon Pty Ltd, Melbourne)

1989 (26 Mar). *72nd Anniv of Chulalongkorn University.* W 380. P 14½ × 14.

1400	**467**	2b. multicoloured	20	10

(Des S. Poonsawat. Litho Harrison (2b.) or Cartor (10b.))

1989 (31 Mar). *96th Anniv of Thai Red Cross (*1401*) and 125th Anniv of International Red Cross (*1402*). T **468** and similar vert design. Multicoloured.* W 253 (2b.) or 380 (10b.). P 15 × 14 (2b.) or 13½ (10b.).

1401	2b. Type **468**		15	10
1402	10b. Red Cross and pillar		55	20

469 Phra Kaeo Monastery

470 Lottery Office Building and Profit Recipients

(Des Achara Livisith (2, 3b.), C. Boonyasakdi (others). Litho
Leigh-Mardon Ltd. Melbourne)

1989 (2 Apr). *Phra Nakhon Khiri Historical Park*. *T* **469** *and similar
vert designs. Multicoloured.* W **380**. P 14 × 14½.
1403	2b.	Type **469**	10	10
1404	3b.	Chatchawan Wiangchai		
		Observatory	25	15
1405	5b.	Phra That Chom Phet stupa	45	30
1406	6b.	Wetchayan Wichian Phrasat Throne		
		Hall	45	30
1403/1406 *Set of 4*			1·10	75

(Des C. Boonyasakdi. Litho Cartor)

1989 (5 Apr). *50th Anniv of Government Lottery Office.* W **380**.
P 13½.
1407	**470**	2b. multicoloured	15	10

471 Campaign Emblem
and Figures

472 Gold Nielloware
Figures

(Des S. Sothonbun. Litho Cartor)

1989 (26 June). *International Anti-drugs Day.* W **380**. P 13½.
1408	**471**	2b. multicoloured	15	10

(Des N. Kaeosawang. Litho Cartor)

1989 (28 June). *National Arts and Crafts Year. T* **472** *and similar
multicoloured designs.* W **380**. P 13½.
1409	2b.	Type **472**	10	10
1410	2b.	Ceramics	10	10
1411	6b.	Ornament inlaid with gemstones		
		(*horiz*)	30	15
1412	6b.	Triangular cushion (*horiz*)	30	15
1409/1412 *Set of 4*			70	45

473 *Conus colubrinus thailandis* (*Conus
thailandis*)

(Des Napaporn Boonyasakdi. Photo Govt Ptg Wks, Tokyo)

1989 (28 June). *Shells. T* **473** *and similar horiz designs.
Multicoloured.* W **109**. P 13½.
1413	2b.	Type **473**	10	10
1414	3b.	*Spondylus* sp. (*Spondylus*		
		princeps)	20	10
1415	6b.	*Cypraea guttata* (*Cyprea*		
		guttata)	30	25
1416	10b.	*Nautilus pompilius* (Chambered,		
		Pearly nautilus)	1·10	65
1413/1416 *Set of 4*			1·50	1·00

474 Satellites, Submarine Cable
Network and Emblem

475 Phya Anuman
Rajadhon

(Des Veena Chantanatat. Litho Govt Ptg Wks, Tokyo)

1989 (1 July). *Tenth Anniv of Asia–Pacific Telecommunity.* W **109**
(*sideways*). P 13½.
1417	**474**	9b. multicoloured	40	20

(Des P. Pipitpiyapakorn. Litho Cartor)

1989 (1 July). *Birth Centenary (1988) of Phya Anuman Rajadhon
(writer).* W **380**. P 13½.
1418	**475**	2b. multicoloured	15	10

476 Emblem and School

477 Communications
Symbols

(Des U. Niyomthum. Litho Harrison)

1989 (4 Aug). *Centenary of Post and Telecommunications School.*
W **253** (*sideways*). P 14 × 15.
1419	**476**	2b. multicoloured	15	10

(Des U. Niyomthum. Litho Cartor)

1989 (4 Aug). *National Communications Day.* W **380**. P 13½.
1420	**477**	2b. multicoloured	15	10

478 Post Box

479 Dragonfly

(Des S. Poonsawat. Litho Harrison)

1989 (4 Aug). *"Thaipex '89" National Stamp Exhibition. Post Boxes. T **478** and similar vert designs. Multicoloured.* W **253**. P 15 × 14.

1421	2b. Type **478**	10	10
1422	3b. Provincial box	15	10
1423	4b. City box	15	15
1424	5b. Imported English box	25	15
1425	6b. West German box sent as gift on introduction of Thai Postal Service	40	15
1421/1425 *Set of 5*		95	60
MS1425*a* 127 × 130 mm. Nos. 1421/5 (sold at 30b.)		13·00	10·50

No. **MS**1425*a* exists imperforate from a limited printing.

(Des M. Sriwongkorakot (2b.), S. Suwanpak (5b.), W. Poonsawat (others). Photo Govt Ptg Wks, Tokyo)

1989 (8 Oct). *International Correspondence Week. T **479** and similar horiz designs. Multicoloured.* W **109**. P 13½.

1426	2b. Type **479**	10	10
1427	5b. Dragonfly (*different*)	15	10
1428	6b. Dragonfly (*different*)	15	15
1429	10b. Damselfly	25	15
1426/1429 *Set of 4*		60	45
MS1430 143 × 107 mm Nos. 1426/9 (sold at 40b.)		10·50	10·50

480 Means of Transport and Communications

481 Figure and "Thoughts"

(Des U. Niyomthum. Litho Leigh-Mardon Ltd, Melbourne)

1989 (24 Oct). *Asia–Pacific Transport and Communications Decade.* W **380**. P 14½ × 14.

1431	**480**	2b. multicoloured	15	10

(Des C. Boonyasakdi. Litho Harrison)

1989 (1 Nov). *Centenary of Mental Health Care.* W **253**. P 15 × 14.

1432	**481**	2b. multicoloured	15	10

482 Hypericum uralum

483 Catacanthus incarnatus

(Des Veena Chantanatat. Litho Leigh-Mardon Ltd, Melbourne)

1989 (15 Nov). *New Year. Flowers. T **482** and similar vert designs. Multicoloured.* W **380**. P 14 × 14½.

1433	1b. Type **482**	10	10
1434	1b. Uraria rufescens	10	10
1435	1b. Manglietia garrettii	10	10
1436	1b. Aeschynanthus macranthus	10	10
1433/1436 *Set of 4*		35	35
MS1437 85 × 100 mm. Nos. 1433/6 (sold at 14b.)		1·30	1·30

(Des S. Poonsawat. Photo Govt Ptg Wks, Tokyo)

1989 (15 Nov). *Beetles. T **483** and similar horiz designs. Multicoloured.* W **109**. P 13½.

1438	2b. Type **483**	10	15
1439	3b. Aristobia approximator	15	10
1440	6b. Chrysochroa chinensis	25	15
1441	10b. Enoplotrupes sharpi	45	35
1438/1441 *Set of 4*		85	70

484 Medalists on Rostrum

485 Official, Family and Graph

(Des C. Boonyasakdi. Litho Cartor)

1989 (16 Dec). *Sports Welfare Fund. T **484** and similar horiz designs. Multicoloured.* W **380**. P 13½.

1442	2b.+1b. Type **484**	10	10
1443	2b.+1b. Nurse attending fallen cyclist	10	10
1444	2b.+1b. Boxing	10	10
1445	2b.+1b. Football	10	10
1442/1445 *Set of 4*		35	35

(Des U. Niyomthum. Litho Cartor)

1990 (1 Jan). *Population and Housing Census.* W **380**. P 13½.

1446	**485**	2b. multicoloured	15	10

486 Skipping (Phethai Setharangsi)

487 Skull splitting Heart

(Litho Harrison)

1990 (13 Jan). *Children's Day. T **486** and similar multicoloured design.* W **253** (sideways on No. 1447). P 14 × 15 (1447) or 15 × 14 (1448).

1447	2b. Type **486**	15	10
1448	2b. Various sports activities (Chalermpol Wongpim) (*vert*)	15	10

(Des S. Sothonbun. Litho Cartor)

1990 (29 Mar). *Red Cross. Anti-AIDS Campaign.* W **380**. P 13½.

1449	**487**	2b. new blue, scarlet and black	15	10

488 Tiap

489 Dental Students and Old Chair

(Des C. Boonyasakdi (1451), T. Thongkambai (1452), Veena Chantanatat (others). Photo Govt Ptg Wks, Tokyo)

1990 (2 Apr). *Heritage Conservation Day. Mother-of-Pearl Inlaid Containers. T 488 and similar multicoloured designs.* W **109** (*sideways on* 8b.). P 13½.

1450	2b.	Type **488**	10	10
1451	2b.	Phan waenfa	10	10
1452	8b.	Lung (*horiz*)	30	25
1453	8b.	Chiat klom (*horiz*)	30	25
1450/1453		*Set of 4*	85	70

(Des S. Leedul. Litho Leigh-Mardon Ltd, Melbourne)

1990 (16 May). *50th Anniv of Chulalongkorn University Dentistry Faculty.* W **380**. P 14 × 14½.

1454	**489**	2b. multicoloured	15	10

(Photo Harrison)

1990 (16 May). W **253**. P 14 × 14½.

1455	**453**	1b. new blue	10	10

Nos. 1456/9 are vacant.

490 Tin	**491** Pigeon

(Des U. Niyomthum. Litho Leigh-Mardon Ltd, Melbourne)

1990 (29 June). *Minerals. T 490 and similar vert designs. Multicoloured.* W **380**. P 14 × 14½.

1460	2b.	Type **490**	10	10
1461	3b.	Zinc	15	10
1462	5b.	Lead	20	15
1463	6b.	Fluorite	25	20
1460/1463		*Set of 4*	65	50

MS1464 Two sheets, each 155 × 110 mm, each containing Nos. 1460/3. (a) Perf; (b) imperf (pair sold at 60b.) ... 3·00 ... 3·00

(Des S. Poonsawat. Litho Leigh-Mardon Ltd, Melbourne)

1990 (4 Aug). *National Communications Day.* W **380**. P 14½ × 14.

1465	**491**	2b. new blue, blue-violet & brt purple	15	10

492 Pigeons and Envelopes

(Des Veena Chantanatat. Litho Leigh-Mardon Ltd, Melbourne)

1990 (10 Sept). *20th Anniv of Asian–Pacific Postal Training Centre, Bangkok.* W **380**. P 14½ × 14.

1466	**492**	2b. blue green, ultramarine and black	15	10
1467		8b. ultramarine, blue-green and black	30	20

493 Jaipur Foot Project

(Des U. Niyomthum. Litho Cartor)

1990 (17 Sept). *60th Anniv of Rotary International in Thailand. T 493 and similar horiz designs. Multicoloured.* W **380**. P 13½.

1468	2b.	Type **493**	10	10
1469	3b.	Child anti-polio vaccination campaign	15	10
1470	6b.	Literacy campaign	20	15
1471	8b.	King Chulalongkorn and his engraved cipher (Thai Museum, Nordkapp, Norway)	40	25
1468/1471		*Set of 4*	75	55

494 Account and Staff at Computer Terminals

(Des C. Boonyasakdi. Litho Leigh-Mardon Ltd, Melbourne)

1990 (7 Oct). *Centenary of Comptroller-General's Department.* W **380**. P 14½ × 14.

1472	**494**	2b. multicoloured	15	10

495 Flowers in Dish (Cho Muang)	**496** Princess Mother with Flower

(Des S. Poonsawat (2, 3b.), C. Boonyasakdi (others). Litho)

1990 (7 Oct). *International Correspondence Week. T 495 and similar horiz designs. Multicoloured.* W **380**. P 14.

1473	2b.	Type **495**	10	10
1474	3b.	Flowers on tray (Cha Mongkut)	15	10
1475	5b.	Sweetmeats on tray with leaf design (Sane Chan)	20	15
1476	6b.	Fruit in bowl (Luk Chup)	40	15
1473/1476		*Set of 4*	75	45

MS1477 Two sheets, each 152 × 127 mm, each containing Nos. 1473/6. (a) Perf; (b) imperf (pair sold at 60b.) ... 3·00 ... 3·00

(Des S. Leedul. Litho Leigh-Mardon Ltd, Melbourne)

1990 (21 Oct). *90th Birthday of Princess Mother.* W **380**. P 14 × 14½.

1478	**496**	2b. multicoloured	45	10

497
Cytandromoea grandiflora

498 Wiman Mek Royal Hall

497a "Harrison and Sons Ltd"

(Des W. Niyomsmarn. Litho Harrison)

1990 (15 Nov). *New Year. Flowers. T* **497** *and similar vert designs. Multicoloured. W* **497a** (*sideways on Nos. 1479/82). P* 14½.
1479	1b. Type **497**		10	10
1480	1b. *Rhododendron arboreum* sp.			
	delavayi		10	10
1481	1b. *Merremia vitifolia*		10	10
1482	1b. *Afgekia mahidolae*		10	10
1479/1482 *Set of 4*			35	35

MS1483 Two sheets, each 85 × 100 mm, each containing Nos. 1479/82. (a) Perf; (b) imperf (pair sold at 20b.) . . . . . . 1·70 1·70

(Des T. Thongkambai. Photo Govt Ptg Wks, Tokyo)

1990 (5 Dec). *Dusit Palace. T* **498** *and similar horiz designs. Multicoloured. W* **109**. *P* 13½.
1484	2b. Type **498**		10	10
1485	3b. Ratcharit Rungrot Royal House		20	10
1486	4b. Aphisek Dusit Royal Hall		20	15
1487	5b. Amphon Sathan Palace		25	15
1488	6b. Udon Phak Royal Hall		30	15
1489	8b. Anantasamakhom Throne Hall		40	25
1484/1489 *Set of 6*			1·30	80

499 Phrachetuphon Wimolmangkalaram Temple and Supreme Patriarch

500 Judo

(Des U. Teekasab. Litho Cartor)

1990 (11 Dec). *Birth Bicentenary of Supreme Patriarch Somdet Phra Maha Samanachao Kromphra Paramanuchitchinorot (formerly Prince Wasukri). W* **380**. *P* 13½.
1490	**499**	2b. multicoloured	15	10

(Des S. Leedul. Litho Cartor)

1990 (16 Dec). *Sports Welfare Fund. T* **500** *and similar vert designs. Multicoloured. W* **380**. *P* 13½.
1491	2b.+1b. Type **500**		10	10
1492	2b.+1b. Archery		10	10
1493	2b.+1b. High jumping		10	10
1494	2b.+1b. Windsurfing		10	10
1491/1494 *Set of 4*			35	35

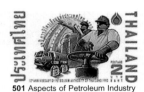

501 Aspects of Petroleum Industry

(Des Samnoh Co Ltd. Litho Leigh-Mardon Ltd, Melbourne)

1990 (29 Dec). *12th Anniv of Thai Petroleum Authority. W* **380**. *P* 14½ × 14.
1495	**501**	2b. multicoloured	15	10

502 Mae Klong Railway Locomotive No. 6

(Des U. Niyomthum. Litho Leigh-Mardon Ltd, Melbourne)

1990 (29 Dec). *Steam Locomotives. T* **502** *and similar horiz designs. Multicoloured. W* **380**. *P* 14½ × 14.
1496	2b. Type **502**		10	10
1497	3b. "Sung Noen" locomotive No. 32		20	10
1498	5b. Class C56 locomotive No. 715		30	30
1499	5b. Mikudo locomotive No. 953		45	30
1496/1499 *Set of 4*			95	70

MS1500 Two sheets, each 152 × 123 mm, each containing Nos. 1496/9. (a) Perf; (b) imperf (pair sold at 50b.) . . . . . . 4·25 4·25

503 Luk Khang (tops)

504 Map, Surveyor and Cartographer

(Des T. Thongkambai. Litho Leigh-Mardon Ltd, Melbourne)

1991 (12 Jan). *Children's Day. Games. T* **503** *and similar horiz designs. Multicoloured. W* **380**. *P* 14½ × 14.
1501	2b. Type **503**		10	10
1502	3b. Pid Ta Ti Mo (blindfolded child			
	smashing vase)		10	10
1503	5b. Doen Kala (walking on stones)		20	15
1504	6b. Phong Phang (blind man's buff)		30	15
1501/1504 *Set of 4*			65	45

(Des U. Niyomthum. Litho Leigh-Mardon Ltd, Melbourne)

1991 (17 Feb). *Land Deeds Project. W* **380**. *P* 14 × 14½.
1505	**504**	2b. multicoloured	15	10

505 Princess (patron) wearing Red Cross Uniform

506 "Indra's Heavenly Abode"

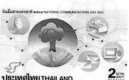

509 Pink Lotus (Sutthiporn Wiset)

510 World Map, Communication Systems and Healthy Tree

(Des J. Vimukmont. Litho Leigh-Mardon Ltd, Melbourne)

1991 (30 Mar). *Red Cross. Princess Maha Chakri Sirindhorn's "Third Cycle" (36th) Birthday.* W **380**. P 14 × 14½.
1506	**505**	2b. multicoloured	55	10

MS1507 Two sheets, each 80 × 105 mm, each containing No. 1506. (a) Perf; (b) imperf (pair sold at 16b.) . . . . . . 2·50 2·50

(Des C. Thongkaeo (2b.), V. Chantrsarn (3b.), A. Sutthinetre (4b.), T. Thongkambai (5b.). Photo Govt Ptg Wks, Tokyo)

1991 (2 Apr). *Heritage Conservation Day. Floral Hanging Decorations.* T **506** and similar vert designs. Multicoloured. W **109** (sideways on **MS**1512). P 13½.
1508	2b. Type **506**	10	10
1509	3b. "Celestial Couch"	15	10
1510	4b. "Crystal Ladder"	20	15
1511	5b. "Crocodile"	20	15
1508/1511 *Set of 4*	60	45

MS1512 Two sheets, each 116 × 154 mm, each containing Nos. 1508/11. (a) Perf; (b) imperf (pair sold at 60b.) . . . . . . 2·50 2·50

507 Goddess riding Goat

508 Prince Narisranuvattivongs

(Des N. Kaewsawang. Litho Leigh-Mardon Ltd, Melbourne)

1991 (13 Apr). *Songkran (New Year) Day. Year of the Goat.* W **380** P 14 × 14½.
1513	**507**	2b. multicoloured	75	30

MS1514 Two sheets, each 80 × 100 mm, each containing No. 1513. (a) Perf; (b) imperf (pair sold at 16b.) . . . . . . 9·50 9·50

(Des S. Leedul. Litho Leigh-Mardon Ltd, Melbourne)

1991 (28 Apr). *44th Death Anniv of Prince Narisranuvattivongs.* W **380**. P 14½ × 14.
1515	**508**	2b. dull orge-brn, reddish brn & lemon	15	10

(Litho Cartor)

1991 (28 May). *Runners-up in International Correspondence Week Competition.* T **509** and similar multicoloured designs. W **380**. P 13½.
1516	2b. Type **509**	10	10
1517	3b. Pink lotuses (Mathayom Suksa group, Khonkaenvityayon School)	15	10
1518	5b. White lotus (Rattanaporn Sukhasem) (*horiz*)	20	15
1519	6b. Red lotuses (Phanupongs Sayasombat and Kanokwan Cholaphum) (*horiz*)	20	15
1516/1519 *Set of 4*	60	45

(Des U. Niyomthum. Litho Cartor)

1991 (4 Aug). *National Communications Day. "Communications and Preservation of the Environment".* W **380**. P 13½.
1520	**510**	2b. multicoloured	20	10

511 Yok

512 Workers and Productivity Arrow

(Des Veena Chantanatat. Litho Leigh-Mardon Ltd, Melbourne)

1991 (4 Aug). *"Thaipex '91" National Stamp Exhibition.* T **511** and similar vert designs showing textile patterns. Multicoloured. W **380**. P 14 × 14½.
1521	2b. Type **511**	10	10
1522	4b. Mudmee	15	10
1523	6b. Khit	20	15
1524	8b. Chok	25	25
1521/1524 *Set of 4*	65	55

MS1525 110 × 145 mm. Nos. 1521/4 (sold at 30b.) . . . . . . 1·10 1·10

An imperforate version of No. **MS**1525 was sold with the Exhibition catalogue. No. **MS**1525 (perforate) with additional inscription in margin for "Phila Nippon '91" Stamp Exhibition was sold only at that exhibition.

(Des D. Toochinda. Litho Leigh-Mardon Ltd. Melbourne)

1991 (3 Sept). *International Productivity Congress.* W **380**. P 14½ × 14.
1526	**512**	2b. multicoloured	15	10

513 "Co-operation of Women around the World"

514 Black

(Des S. Sothonbun. Litho Cartor)

1991 (23 Sept). *26th International Council of Women Triennial.* W **380**. P 13½.
1527 **513** 2b. multicoloured 15 10

(Des C. Boonyasakdi (2, 8b.), N. Kaewsawang (3b.), V. Chantrsarn (6b.). Photo Govt Ptg Wks, Tokyo)

1991 (6 Oct). *International Correspondence Week. Japanese Bantams.* T **514** *and similar horiz designs. Multicoloured.* W **109**. P 13½.
1528 2b. Type **514** 10 10
1529 3b. Black-tailed buff 20 10
1530 6b. Buff 30 15
1531 8b. White 45 30
1528/1531 *Set of 4* 95 60
MS1532 Two sheets, each 145 × 110 mm, each containing Nos. 1528/31. (a) Perf; (b) imperf (pair sold at 70b.) . . . . 2·50 2·50

515 Silver Coin of King Rama IV and Wat Phra Sri Rattana Satsadaram

516 1908 1t. Stamp

(Des C. Boonyasakdi. Litho Leigh-Mardon Ltd, Melbourne)

1991 (15 Oct). *World Bank and International Monetary Fund Annual Meetings.* T **515** *and similar horiz designs. Multicoloured.* W **380**. P 14½ × 14.
1533 2b. Type **515** 10 10
1534 4b. Pod Duang money, Wat Mahathat Sukhothai and Wat Aroonrachawararam 15 10
1535 8b. Chieng and Hoi money and Wat Phrathat Doi Suthep 30 20
1536 10b. Funan, Dvaravati and Srivijaya money, Phra Pathom Chedi and Phra Borommathat Chaiya . . 40 25
1533/1536 *Set of 4* 85 60
MS1537 Two sheets, each 145 × 110 mm, each containing Nos. 1533/6. (a) Perf; (b) imperf (pair sold at 70b.) . . . . 2·50 2·50

(Des P. Pipitpiyapakorn. Litho Leigh-Mardon Ltd, Melbourne)

1991 (23 Oct). *"Bangkok 1993" International Stamp Exhibition (1st issue).* T **516** *and similar vert designs, each showing a stamp from the 1908 King Chulalongkorn issue. Multicoloured.* W **380**. P 14 × 14½.
1538 2b. Type **516** 10 10
1539 3b.2t. stamp 15 10
1540 4b.3t. stamp 15 10
1541 5b.5t. stamp 20 15
1542 6b.10t. stamp 25 15
1543 7b.20t. stamp 30 15
1544 8b.40t. stamp 35 25
1538/1544 *Set of 7* . . . . . . 1·40 90
MS1545 Two sheets, each 80 × 129 mm, each containing No. 1544. (a) Perf; (b) imperf (pair sold at 30b.) . . . . . . 2·10 2·10
See also Nos. 1618/**MS**1623, 1666/**MS**1670, 1700/**MS**1704 and **MS**1705.

517 Adult and Calves

518 *Dillenia obovata*

(Des S. Poonsawat. Photo Govt Ptg Wks, Tokyo)

1991 (5 Nov). *The Indian Elephant.* T **517** *and similar honz designs. Multicoloured.* W **109**. P 13½.
1546 2b. Type **517** 10 10
1547 4b. Elephants pulling logs 20 15
1548 6b. Adult male resting 25 20
1549 8b. Adults bathing 45 30
1546/1549 *Set of 4* 90 70
MS1550 Two sheets, each 96 × 78 mm, each containing No. 1549. (a) Perf; (b) imperf (pair sold at 44b.) . . . . . . 3·50 3·50

(Des Veena Chantanatat. Litho Cartor)

1991 (5 Nov). *New Year. Flowers.* T **518** *and similar vert designs, Multicoloured.* W **380**. P 13½.
1551 1b. Type **518** 10 10
1552 1b. *Melastoma sanguineum* 10 10
1553 1b. *Commelina diffusa* 10 10
1554 1b. *Plumbago indica* 10 10
1551/1554 *Set of 4* 35 35
MS1555 Two sheets, each 85 × 100 mm, each containing No. 1551/4. (a) Perf; (b) imperf (pair sold at 20b.) . . . . . . 1·30 1·30

(519) ("BAHT" 6 mm wide)

520 Jogging

1991 (5 Dec). *Surch with T* **519**.
1556 **325** 1b.on 1b.25 brt green (No. 1040a) 45 10
1557 1b.on 1b.25 yellow-grn (No. 1235a) 10 10
For similar surcharge on No. 1235a but with larger letters, see No. 1328.

(Des C. Boonyasakdi. Litho Cartor)

1991 (16 Dec). *Sports Welfare Fund.* T **520** *and similar horiz designs. Multicoloured.* W **380**. P 13½.
1558 2b.+1b. Type **520** 10 10
1559 2b.+1b. Cycling 10 10

1560	2b.+7b. Skipping	10	10
1561	2b.+1b. Swimming	10	10
1558/1561	Set of 4	35	35

521 Large Indian Civet (*Viverra zibetha*)
522 Prince Mahidol

(Des U. Niyomthum. Litho Leigh-Mardon Ltd, Melbourne)

1991 (26 Dec). *Mammals. T **521** and similar horiz designs. Multicoloured. W **380**. P $14\frac{1}{2} \times 14$.

1562	2b. Type **521**	10	10
1563	3b. Banded linsang (*Prionodon linsang*)	15	10
1564	6b. Asiatic golden cat (*Felis temmincki*)	20	15
1565	8b. Black giant squirrel (*Ratufa bicolor*)	30	25
1562/1565	Set of 4	70	55

MS1566 Two sheets, each 146×110 mm, containing Nos. 1562/5. (a) Perf; (b) imperf (pair sold for 60b.) ... 2·50 2·50

(Des S. Leedul. Litho Leigh-Mardon Ltd, Melbourne)

1992 (1 Jan). *Birth Centenary (1991) of Prince Mahidol of Songkla (pioneer of modern medicine in Thailand). W **380**. P $14 \times 14\frac{1}{2}$.*

1567	**522** 2b. dull orange-brown, gold and lemon	15	10

523 Archaeologists and Dinosaur Skeletons

(Des T. Ponchaiwong. Litho Leigh-Mardon Ltd, Melbourne)

1992 (1 Jan). *Centenary of Department of Mineral Resources. W **380**. P $14\frac{1}{2} \times 14$.*

1568	2b. Type **523**	15	10
1569	2b. Mining excavation	15	10
1570	2b. Extracting natural gas and oil	15	10
1571	2b. Digging artesian wells	15	10
1568/1571	Set of 4	55	35

524 Drawing by Nachadong Bunprasoet

(Litho Govt Ptg Wks, Tokyo)

1992 (11 Jan). *Children's Day. "World under the Sea". T **524** and similar multicoloured designs showing children's drawings. W **109** (sideways on 2, 3b.). P $13\frac{1}{2}$.*

1572	2b. Type **524**	10	10
1573	3b. Fishes and seaweed (Varaporn Phadkhan)	15	10
1574	5b. Mermaid (Phannipha Ngoenkon) (*vert*)	15	10

525 Battle Scene (mural, Chan Chittrakon)

(Litho Leigh-Mardon Ltd, Melbourne)

1992 (18 Jan). *400th Anniv of Duel between King Naresuan the Great of Thailand and Phra Maha Upparacha of Burma. W **380**. P $14\frac{1}{2} \times 14$.*

1575	**525** 2b. multicoloured	15	10

526 *Paphiopedilum bellatulum*
527 Sugar Cane

(Des P. Pipitpiyapakorn. Litho Leigh-Mardon Ltd, Melbourne)

1992 (20 Jan). *Fourth Asia–Pacific Orchid Conference. T **526** and similar horiz designs. Multicoloured. W **380**. P $14\frac{1}{2} \times 14$.*

1576	2b. Type **526**	10	10
1577	2b. Paphiopedilum exul	10	10
1578	3b. Paphiopedilum godefroyae	15	10
1579	3b. Paphiopedilum concolor	15	10
1580	6b. Paphiopedilum niveum	15	15
1581	6b. Paphiopedilum villosum	15	15
1582	10b. Paphiopedilum parishii	35	25
1583	10b. Paphiopedilum sukhakulii	35	25
1576/1583	Set of 8	1·40	1·10

MS1584 Four sheets, each 110×145 mm. (a) Nos. 1576, 1579/80 and 1582. Perf; (b) As a. but imperf; (c) Nos. 1577/8, 1581 and 1583. Perf; (d) As c. but imperf (4 sheets sold at 120b.) ... 5·25 5·25

(Des S. Sothonbun. Litho Leigh-Mardon Ltd, Melbourne)

1992 (5 Mar). *21st International Sugar Cane Technologists Society Congress. W **380**. P $14 \times 14\frac{1}{2}$.*

1585	**527** 2b. multicoloured	15	10

528 Prince Rabi Badhanasakdi (founder of School of Law)

529 "Innocent" (Kamolporn Tapsuang)

532 Royal Ceremony of First Ploughing

533 Ministry

(Des U. Niyomthum. Litho Leigh-Mardon Ltd, Melbourne)

1992 (1 Apr). *Centenary of Ministry of Agriculture and Co-operatives.* W **380**. P 14½ × 14.

1597	**532**	2b. multicoloured	10	10
1598		3b. multicoloured	15	10
1599		4b. multicoloured	20	15
1600		5b. multicoloured	25	15
1597/1600 *Set of 4*			65	45

(Des S. Sothonbun. Litho Leigh-Mardon Ltd, Melbourne)

1992 (1 Apr). *Centenary of Ministry of Education.* W **380**. P 14 × 14½.

1601	**533**	2b. multicoloured	15	10

(Des S. Leedul. Litho Cartor)

1992 (25 Mar). *Centenary of Ministry of Justice. Legal Reformers. T* **528** *and similar vert design. Multicoloured.* W **380**. P 13½.

1586	3b. Type **528**		15	10
1587	5b. King Rama V (reformer of Courts system)		45	15

(Litho Leigh-Mardon Ltd, Melbourne)

1992 (27 Mar). *Red Cross.* W **380**. P 14½ × 14.

1588	**529**	2b. multicoloured	15	10

534 Western Region

535 Demon riding Monkey

(Des Veena Chantanatat (2b.), S. Poonsawat (10b.), C. Boonyasakdi (others). Litho Leigh-Mardon Ltd, Melbourne)

1992 (2 Apr). *Thai Heritage Conservation Day. Traditional Carts. T* **534** *and similar horiz designs.* W **380**. P 14½ × 14.

1602	2b. Type **534**		10	10
1603	3b. Northern region		15	10
1604	5b. North-eastern region		20	15
1605	10b. Eastern region		35	25
1602/1605 *Set of 4*			70	55
MS1606 Two sheets, each 145 × 110 mm, each containing Nos. 1602/5. (a) Perf; (b) imperf (pair sold at 60b.)			2·50	2·50

530 Container Ships and Lorry

531 Prince Damrong Rajanubharb (first Minister)

(Des U. Niyomthum. Litho Leigh-Mardon Ltd, Melbourne)

1992 (1 Apr). *80th Anniv of Ministry of Transport and Communications. T* **530** *and similar vert designs. Multicoloured.* W **380**. P 14 × 14½.

1589	2b. Type **530**		10	10
1590	3b. Train and bus		15	10
1591	5b. Boeing 747-200 airliner and control tower		15	15
1592	6b. Lorry, satellites and aerials		20	15
1589/1592 *Set of 4*			55	45

(Des N. Kaewsawang. Litho Leigh-Mardon Ltd, Melbourne)

1992 (13 Apr). *Songkran (New Year) Day. Year of the Monkey.* W **380**. P 14 × 14½.

1607	**535**	2b. multicoloured	20	10
MS1608 Two sheets, each 80 × 100 mm, each containing No. 1607. (a) Perf; (b) imperf (pair sold at 16b.)			2·10	2·10

(Des C. Boonyasakdi. Litho Leigh-Mardon Ltd, Melbourne)

1992 (1 Apr). *Centenary of Ministry of the Interior. T* **531** *and similar vert designs. Multicoloured.* W **380**. P 14 × 14½.

1593	2b. Type **531**		15	10
1594	2b. Polling station		15	10
1595	2b. Emergency services and army		15	10
1596	2b. Child fetching water		15	10
1593/1596 *Set of 4*			55	35

536 American Brahman and Livestock

(Des Veena Chantanatat. Litho Leigh-Mardon Ltd, Melbourne)

1992 (5 May). *50th Anniv of Department of Livestock Development.* W **380**. P 14½ × 14.

1609	**536**	2b. multicoloured	15	10

537 "Birth of Buddha" (mural, Wat Angkaeo, Bangkok)

538 Weather Balloon, Dish Aerial, Satellite and Map

(Des T. Thongkhambai. Litho Leigh-Mardon Ltd, Melbourne)

1992 (16 May). *Wisakhabucha Day. T* **537** *and similar vert designs. Multicoloured.* W **380**. P 14½.

1610	2b. Type **537**	10	10
1611	3b. "Enlightenment of Buddha" (illustration by Phraya Thewaphinimmit from biography)	20	15
1612	5b. "Death of Buddha" (mural, Wat Kanmatuyaram, Bangkok)	30	25

(Des S. Sothonbun. Litho Leigh-Mardon Ltd, Melbourne)

1992 (23 June). *50th Anniv of Meteorological Department.* W **380**. P 14 × 14½.

1613	**538**	2b. multicoloured	15	10

539 Bua Tong Field, Mae Hong Son Province

540 1887 64a. stamp

(Des C. Boonyasakdi. Litho Leigh-Mardon Ltd, Melbourne)

1992 (1 July). *Association of South-East Asian Nations Tourism Year. T* **539** *and similar vert designs. Multicoloured.* W **380**. P 14 × 14½.

1614	2b. Type **539**	10	10
1615	3b. Klong Larn Waterfall, Kamphaeng Phet Province	15	10
1616	4b. Coral, Chumphon Province	15	10
1617	5b. Khao Ta-Poo, Phangnga Province	20	15
1614/1617	*Set of 4*	55	40

(Des P. Pipitpiyapakorn. Litho Leigh-Mardon Ltd, Melbourne)

1992 (1 July). *"Bangkok 1993" International Stamp Exhibition (2nd issue). T* **540** *and similar vert designs. Multicoloured.* W **380**. P 14 × 14½.

1618	2b. Type **540**	10	10
1619	3b. 1912 20b. stamp	15	10
1620	5b. 1928 40b. stamp	20	15

1621	7b. 1943 1b. stamp	25	15
1622	8b. 1947 20b. stamp	30	25
1618/1622	*Set of 5*	90	65

MS1623 Two sheets, each 123 × 185 mm, each containing Nos. 1618/22. (a) Perf; (b) imperf (pair sold at 70b.) . . . . 3·50 3·50

541 Prince Chudadhuj Dharadoli

542 "Communications"

(Des N. Kraisornrat. Litho Enschedé)

1992 (5 July). *Birth Centenary of Prince Chudadhuj Dharadolik of Bejraburna.* W **226**. P 13½.

1624	**541**	2b. multicoloured	15	10

(Des S. Poonsawat. Litho Leigh-Mardon Ltd, Melbourne)

1992 (4 Aug). *National Communications Day.* W **380**. P 14½ × 14.

1625	**542**	2b. multicoloured	15	10

543 Culture and Sports

544 Sirikit Medical Centre

(Des C. Boonyasakdi and U. Niyomthum. Litho Enschedé)

1992 (8 Aug). *25th Anniv of Association of South-East Asian Nations. T* **543** *and similar vert designs. Multicoloured.* W **226**. P 13½.

1626	2b. Type **543**	10	10
1627	3b. Tourist sites	15	10
1628	5b. Transport and communications	20	10
1629	7b. Agriculture	20	15
1626/1629	*Set of 4*	60	40

(Des S. Leedul. Litho Leigh-Mardon Ltd, Melbourne)

1992 (12 Aug). *Inauguration of Sirikit Medical Centre.* W **380**. P 14½ × 14.

1630	**544**	2b. multicoloured	15	10

(Des P. Pipitpiyapakorn. Litho Cartor)

1992 (12 Aug). W **380**. P 13½.

1631	**453**	25s. deep yellow-brown	10	10

Nos. 1632/4 are vacant.

545 Wedding Ceremony

546 Queen Sirikit and Cipher

(Des P. Pipitpiyapakorn (1635/**MS**1641, 1647), Achara Livisith (others). Embossed and litho Cartor (1647), photo Govt Ptg Wks, Tokyo (others))

1992 (12 Aug). *60th Birthday of Queen Sirikit.*

(a) T **545** *and similar horiz designs. Multicoloured.* W **109**. P 13½.

1635	2b. Type **545**	15	10
1636	2b. Royal couple seated at Coronation ceremony	15	10
1637	2b. Anointment as Queen	15	10
1638	2b. Seated on chair	15	10
1639	2b. Visiting hospital patient	15	10
1640	2b. Talking to subjects	15	10

MS1641 Two sheets, each 126 × 163 mm, each containing Nos. 1635/40. (a) Perf; (b) imperf (pair sold at 60b.) . . . . . 2·50 2·50

(b) Royal Regalia. Enamelled gold objects. Vert designs as T **546**. *Multicoloured.* W **109**. P 13½.

1642	2b. Bowls on footed tray (betel and areca nut set)	15	10
1643	2b. Kettle	15	10
1644	2b. Water holder within bowl	15	10
1645	2b. Box on footed tray (betel and areca nut set)	15	10
1646	2b. Vase	15	10
1635/1640, 1642/1646 *Set of 11*		1·50	1·00

(c) W **380**. P 13½.

1647 **546** 100b. deep bright blue and gold . . 4·25 4·25

547 Prince Wan Waithayakon

548 Bhirasri

(Des T. Thongkambai. Litho Cartor)

1992 (25 Aug). *Birth Centenary (1991) of Prince Wan Waithayakon, Krommun Naradhip Bongsprabandh (diplomat).* W **380**. P 13½.

1648 **547** 2b. multicoloured 15 10

(Des P. Inchin. Litho Leigh-Mardon Ltd, Melbourne)

1992 (15 Sept). *Birth Centenary of Silpa Bhirasri (sculptor).* W **380**. P 14 × 14½.

1649 **548** 2b. multicoloured 15 10

549 *Catalaphyllia jardinei*   **550** *Rhododendron simsii*

(Des S. Suwanpak (2b.), C. Boonyasakdi (others). Litho Leigh-Mardon Ltd, Melbourne)

1992 (4 Oct). *International Correspondence Week. Corals. T* **549** *and similar horiz designs. Multicoloured.* W **380**. P 14½ × 14.

1650	2b. Type **549**	10	10
1651	3b. *Porites lutea*	15	10
1652	6b. *Tubastraea coccinea*	20	15
1653	8b. *Favia pallida*	30	25
1650/1653 *Set of 4*		70	55

MS1654 145 × 110 mm. Nos. 1650/3 (sold at 30b.) . . . . . . 1·10 1·10

(Des Veena Chantanatat. Litho Enschedé)

1992 (15 Nov). *New Year. Flowers. T* **550** *and similar horiz designs. Multicoloured.* W **226**. P 14 × 13½.

1655	1b. Type **550**	10	10
1656	1b. *Cynoglossum lanceolatum*	10	10
1657	1b. *Tithonia diversifolia*	10	10
1658	1b. *Agapetes parishii*	10	10
1655/1658 *Set of 4*		35	35

MS1659 Two sheets, each 100 × 85 mm, each containing Nos. 1655/8. (a) Perf; (b) imperf (pair sold at 20b.) . . . . . 1·10 1·10

551 Figures of Man and Woman   **552** Anantasamakhom Throne Hall, National Assembly Building and King Prajadhipok's Monument

(Des T. Ponchaiwong. Litho Enschedé)

1992 (22 Nov). *First Asian–Pacific Allergy and Immunology Congress, Bangkok.* W **226**. P 13½.

1660 **551** 2b. multicoloured 15 10

(Des U. Niyomthum. Litho Cartor)

1992 (10 Dec). *60th Anniv of National Assembly.* W **380**. P 13½.

1661 **552** 2b. multicoloured 15 10

553 Bank's Emblem and Bang Khun
Phrom Palace (old headquarters)

(Des S. Poonsawat. Litho Leigh-Mardon Ltd, Melbourne)

1992 (10 Dec). *50th Anniv of Bank of Thailand.* W **380**. P 14½ × 14.
1662 **553** 2b. multicoloured 15 10

554 "River and Life" (Prathinthip Mensin)

(Litho Enschedé)

1993 (9 Jan). *Children's Day. T* **554** *and similar horiz designs
showing children's drawings. Multicoloured.* W **226** (*sideways*).
P 13½.
1663 2b. Type **554** 10 10
1664 2b. "Lovely Wild Animals and Beautiful
      Forest" (Pratsani Thammaprasert) 10 10
1665 2b. "Communications in the Next
      Decade" (Natchaliya Sutiprasit) . . . 10 10

555 Kendi, Water Dropper and
Bottle

556 Anniversary
Emblem

(Des P. Pipitpiyapakorn. Photo Govt Ptg Wks, Tokyo)

1993 (9 Jan). *"Bangkok 1993" International Stamp Exhibition (3rd
issue). Traditional Pottery. T* **555** *and similar horiz designs.
Multicoloured.* W **109**. P 13½.
1666 3b. Type **555** 10 10
1667 6b. Vase and bottles 25 15
1668 7b. Bowls 30 15
1669 8b. Jars 35 20
1666/1669 *Set of 4* 80 55
MS1670 145 × 110 mm. Nos. 1666/9 (sold at
  35b.) . . . . 1·40 1·40

(Des K. Timtet. Litho Enschedé)

1993 (16 Jan). *Centenary of Thai Teacher Training Institute.*
  W **226** (*sideways*). P 13½ × 14.
1671 **556** 2b. multicoloured 15 10

557 Agricultural Produce

(Des P. Pipitpiyapakorn. Litho Govt Ptg Wks, Tokyo)

1993 (2 Feb). *50th Anniv of Kasetsart University.* W **109**
  (*sideways*). P 13½.
1672 **557** 2b. multicoloured 15 10

558 Buddha preaching
(mural, Wat
Kanmatuyaram, Bangkok)

559 Queen Sri
Bajarindra (first royal
patron)

(Des T. Thongkambai. Litho Leigh-Mardon Ltd, Melbourne)

1993 (7 Mar). *Maghapuja Day.* W **380**. P 14½.
1673 **558** 2b. multicoloured 15 10

(Des N. Kraisornrat. Litho Leigh-Mardon Ltd, Melbourne)

1993 (27 Mar). *Centenary of Thai Red Cross.* W **380**. P 14 × 14½.
1674 **559** 2b. multicoloured 20 10

560 Clock, Emblem and Attorney General

(Des T. Ponchaiwong. Litho Enschedé)

1993 (1 Apr). *Centenary of Attorney General's Office.* W **226**
  (*sideways*). P 12½.
1675 **560** 2b. multicoloured 15 10

561 Wat Chedi Chet Thaeo

562 Demon
riding Cock

(Des Veena Chantanatat. Litho Enschedé)

1993 (2 Apr). *Thai Heritage Conservation Day. Si Satchanalai
Historical Park, Sukhothai Province. T* **561** *and similar horiz
designs. Multicoloured.* W **226** (*sideways*). P 13½.
1676 3b. Type **561** 15 10
1677 4b. Wat Chang Lom . . . 15 10
1678 6b. Wat Phra Si Rattanamahathat . . . 20 10
1679 7b. Wat Suan Kaeo Utthayan Noi . . . 25 15
1676/1679 *Set of 4* 70 40
MS1680 145 × 110 mm. Nos. 1676/9 (sold at
  25b.) 85 85

(Des N. Kaewsawang. Litho Leigh-Mardon Ltd, Melbourne)

1993 (13 Apr). *Songkran (New Year) Day. Year of the Cock.*
W **380**. P 14 × 14½.
1681   **562**   2b. multicoloured   10   10
MS1682 Two sheets, each 80 × 100 mm, each
containing No. 1681. (a) Perf; (b) imperf (pair
sold at 16b.)   65   65

563 *Marasmius* sp.

(Des R. Thongdang (2b.), C. Boonyasakdi (4k.), T. Khonakha
(6b.), N. Kaewsawang (8b.). Photo Enschedé))

1993 (1 July). *Fungi. T* **563** *and similar horiz designs.
Multicoloured.* W **226** (*sideways*). P 13½.
1683   2b. Type **563**   10   10
1684   4b. *Coprinus* sp.   15   10
1685   6b. *Mycena* sp.   20   15
1686   8b. *Cyathus* sp.   25   15
1683/1686 *Set of 4*   65   45
MS1687 145 × 110 mm. Nos. 1683/6 (sold at
30b.)   1·20   1·20

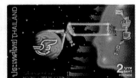

564 "Communications in the Next Decade"

(Des T. Chankham. Litho Cartor)

1993 (4 Aug). *National Communications Day.* W **380**. P 13½.
1688   **564**   2b. multicoloured   15   10

565 Emblem, Morse Key and Satellite

(Des U. Niyomthum. Litho Cartor)

1993 (4 Aug). *110th Anniv of Post and Telegraph Department.*
W **380**. P 13½.
1689   **565**   2b. multicoloured   30   10

566 Monument, Park and Reservoir

(Des S. Leedul. Litho Cartor)

1993 (12 Aug). *Unveiling of Queen Suriyothai's Monument.*
W **380**. P 13½.
1690   **566**   2b. multicoloured   15   10

567 Fawn Ridgeback   568 Tangerine
(*Citrus reticulata*)

(Des C. Boonyasakdi (2b.), V. Chantrsarn (3b.), C. Thongkaeo
(others). Photo Enschedé)

1993 (1 Oct). *International Correspondence Week. The Thai
Ridgeback. T* **567** *and similar horiz designs. Multicoloured.*
W **226** (*sideways*). P 13½.
1691   2b. Type **567**   10   10
1692   3b. Black   10   10
1693   5b. Tan   15   10
1694   10b. Grey   40   15
1691/1694 *Set of 4*   70   40
MS1695 145 × 110 mm. Nos. 1691/4 (sold at
30b.)   1·20   1·20

(Des C. Chaowatthana (2b.), P. Khamprapha
(6b.), C. Boonyasakdi (others). Photo Enschedé)

1993 (1 Oct). *Fruits. T* **568** *and similar vert designs. Multicoloured.*
W **226**. P 13½.
1696   2b. Type **568**   10   10
1697   3b. Bananas (*Musa* sp.)   10   10
1698   6b. Star gooseberry (*Phyllanthus
distichus*)   20   15
1699   8b. Marian plum (*Bouca burmanica*)   25   15
1696/1699 *Set of 4*   60   45

ประเทศไทย THAILAND

569 Bencharong   570 Emblem and Oil Rigs
Cosmetic Jar

(Des V. Chantrsarn (5b.), S. Plumthanom (6b.), Veena
Chantanatat (others). Photo Enschedé)

1993 (1 Oct). *"Bangkok 1993" International Stamp Exhibition (4th
issue). T* **569** *and similar vert designs. Multicoloured.* W **226**.
P 13½.
1700   3b. Type **569**   10   10
1701   5b. Bencharong round cosmetic jar   15   10
1702   6b. Lai Nam Thong tall cosmetic jar   15   10
1703   7b. Lai Nam Thong cosmetic jar   20   15
1700/1703 *Set of 4*   55   40
MS1704 110 × 145 mm. Nos. 1700/3 (sold at
30b.)   1·20   1·20
No. **MS**1704 exists imperforate from a limited printing.

(Recess Govt Ptg Wks, Tokyo)

1993 (1 Oct). *"Bangkok 1993" International Stamp Exhibition (5th issue). Sheet* 81 × 100 *mm containing No.* 1350. W **109**. P 13½ × 13.
MS1705 **453** 25b. dp turquoise-blue & dp
olive . . . . 4·00   4·00
No. **MS**1705 exists in ten versions, differing in the colour of the margin design. A different colour was sold on each day of the exhibition and sets from this source could only be obtained by attending on every day. A proportion of the print-run was supplied in complete sets to the Thai Philatelic Society for sale to their members.

The colours in order of sale were: blue-green, yellow-olive, deep magenta, salmon-pink, greenish blue, bright lilac, ultramarine, green, orange-red and dull yellow (*Price for set of* 10 *sheets:* £35).

(Des P. Pipitpiyapakorn. Litho Cartor)

1993 (2 Nov). *Fifth Association of South-East Asian Nations Council on Petroleum Conference and Exhibition.* W **380**. P 13½.
1706 **570** 2b. multicoloured   15   10

571 King Prajadhipok   **572** *Ipomea cairica*

(Des P. Pipitpiyapakorn. Litho Leigh-Mardon Ltd, Melbourne)

1993 (8 Nov). *Birth Centenary of King Prajadhipok (Rama VII).* W **380**. P 14 × 14½.
1707 **571** 2b. deep brown and gold   20   10

(Des S. Poonsawat. Litho Leigh-Mardon Ltd, Melbourne)

1993 (15 Nov). *New Year. Flowers. T* **572** *and similar horiz designs. Multicoloured.* W **380**. P 14½.
1708   1b. Type **572**   10   10
1709   1b. *Decaschistia parviflora*   10   10
1710   1b. *Hibiscus tiliaceus*   10   10
1711   1b. *Passiflora foetida*   10   10
1708/1711 *Set of 4*   35   35
MS1712 100 × 85 mm. Nos. 1708/11 (sold at
10b.)   55   55

= 1ᴮᴬᴴᵀ =
(573)

574 "Thaicom-1" Satellite, "Ariane 4" Rocket and Map of Thailand

1993 (25 Nov). *No.* 1031a *surch with T* **573**.
1713   **227** 1b.on 25s. brown-lake   10   10

(Des P. Pipitpiyapakorn. Litho Leigh-Mardon Ltd, Melbourne)

1993 (1 Dec). *Launch of "Thaicom-1" (first Thai communications satellite).* W **380**. P 14 × 14½.
1714   **574** 2b. multicoloured   15   10

575 "Play Land" (Piyathida Chapirom)

(Litho Leigh-Mardon Ltd, Melbourne)

1994 (8 Jan). *Children's Day.* W **380**. P 14½ × 14.
1715   **575** 2b. multicoloured   15   10

576 Hospital Administrative Building   **577** Emblem and Book

(Des T. Thongkambai. Litho Leigh-Mardon Ltd, Melbourne)

1994 (30 Mar). *Red Cross 80th Anniv of Chulalongkorn Hospital.* W **380**. P 14½ × 14.
1716   **576** 2b. multicoloured   10   10

(Des C. Boonyasakdi. Litho Leigh-Mardon Ltd, Melbourne)

1994 (31 Mar). *60th Anniv of Royal Institute.* W **380**. P 14 × 14½.
1717   **577** 2b. multicoloured   10   10

578 Wat Ratchaburana

(Des S. Leedul (2, 6b.), N. Kaewsawang (3b.), C. Boonyasakdi (9b.). Litho Leigh-Mardon Ltd, Melbourne)

1994 (2 Apr). *Thai Heritage Conservation Day. Phra Nakhon Si Ayutthaya Historical Park. T* **578** *and similar horiz designs. Multicoloured.* W **380**. P 14½ × 14.
1718   2b. Type **578**   10   10
1719   3b. Wat Maha That   10   10
1720   6b. Wat Maheyong   15   10
1721   9b. Wat Phra Si Sanphet   30   15
1718/1721 *Set of 4*   60   40
MS1722 145 × 110 mm. Nos. 1718/21 (sold at
25b.) . . . .   1·00   1·00

579 Friendship Bridge

580 Demon riding Dog

(Des T. Ponchaiwong. Litho Leigh-Mardon Ltd, Melbourne)

1994 (8 Apr). *Inauguration of Friendship Bridge (between Thailand and Laos).* W **380**. P 14½ × 14.
1723	**579**	9b. multicoloured	30	15

(Des N. Kaewsawang. Litho Leigh-Mardon Ltd, Melbourne)

1994 (13 Apr). *Songkran (New Year) Day. Year of the Dog.* W **380**. P 14½.
1724	**580**	2b. multicoloured	10	10

MS1725 Two sheets, each 80 × 100 mm, each containing No. 1724. (a) Perf; (b) imperf (pair sold at 16b.) 65 65

นิทรรศการตราไปรษณียากรไทย – จีน
泰國郵票展覽 · 北京
(581)

1994 (May). *Stamp Exhibition, Peking. As No.* **MS**1725 *but without sheet value and optd in bottom margin with T* **581** *in slate-lilac.*
MS1726 Two sheets, each 80 × 100 mm. **580**
2b. multicoloured. (a) Perf; (b) imperf .... 5·50 5·50

582 Football

(Des U. Niyomthum. Litho Leigh-Mardon Ltd, Melbourne)

1994 (23 June). *Centenary of International Olympic Committee. T* **582** *and similar horiz designs. Multicoloured.* W **380**. P 14½ × 14.
1727	2b. Type **582**		10	10
1728	3b. Running		10	10
1729	5b. Swimming		15	10
1730	6b. Weightlifting		15	10
1731	9b. Boxing		25	20
1727/1731	Set of 5		70	55

584 "Buddha giving First Sermon" (mural from Wat Thong Thammachat)

(Des T. Thongkambai. Litho Govt Ptg Wks, Tokyo)

1994 (22 July). *Asalhapuja Day.* W **109**. P 13½.
1733	**584**	2b. multicoloured	10	10

585 Communications orbiting Thailand

(Des T. Chankham. Litho Enschedé)

1994 (4 Aug). *National Communications Day.* W **226** (sideways). P 13½.
1734	**585**	2b. multicoloured	10	10

586 *Phricotelphusa limula*

(Des Veena Chantanatat. Photo Enschedé)

1994 (12 Aug). *Crabs. T* **586** *and similar horiz designs. Multicoloured.* W **457** (sideways). P 13½.
1735	3b. Type **586**		10	10
1736	5b. *Thaipotamon chulabhorn*		15	15
1737	6b. *Phricotelphusa sirindhorn*		15	15
1738	10b. *Thaiphusa sirikit*		30	20
1735/1738	Set of 4		55	55

MS1739 145 × 110 mm. Nos. 1735/8 (sold at 30b.) .... 1·20 1·20

No. **MS**1739 commemorates "Philakorea 1994" International Stamp Exhibition.

587 Gold Niello Betel Nut Set

583 Dome Building

(Des S. Leedul. Litho Leigh-Mardon Ltd, Melbourne)

1994 (27 June). 60th *Anniv of Thammsat University.* W **380**. P 14½ × 14.
1732	**583**	2b. multicoloured	10	10

(Des T. Ponchaiwong (2b.), Veena Chantanatat
(9b.), C. Boonyasakdi (others). Photo Enschedé)

1994 (9 Oct). *International Correspondence Week. Betel Nut
Sets. T* **587** *and similar horiz designs.* W **226** (*sideways*). P 13½.

1740	2b. Type **587**		10	10
1741	6b. Gold-plated silver niello set		20	10
1742	8b. Silver niello set		30	15
1743	9b. Gold niello set		35	20
1740/1743 *Set of 4*			85	50
MS1744 145 × 110 mm. Nos. 1740/3 (sold at 30b.)			1·20	1·20

588 Emblem and Workers

589 *Eriocaulon odoratum*

(Des T. Chankham. Litho Leigh-Mardon Ltd, Melbourne)

1994 (29 Oct). *75th Anniv of International Labour Organization.*
W **380**. P 14½ × 14.

1745	**588**	2b. multicoloured	10	10

(Des Veena Chantanatat. Litho Leigh-Mardon Ltd, Melbourne)

1994 (15 Nov). *New Year Flowers. T* **589** *and similar vert designs.
Multicoloured.* W **380**. P 14½.

1746	1b. Type **589**		10	10
1747	1b. *Utricularia bifida*		10	10
1748	1b. *Utricularia delphinioides*		10	10
1749	1b. *Utricularia minutissima*		10	10
1746/1749 *Set of 4*			35	35
MS1750 85 × 100 mm. Nos. 1746/9 (sold at 10b.)			45	45

590 Making Garland

(Des T. Ponchaiwong. Litho Leigh-Mardon Ltd, Melbourne)

1994 (4 Dec). *60th Anniv of Suan Dusit Teachers' College.* W **380**.
P 14½ × 14.

1751	**590**	2b. multicoloured	10	10

(Photo Enschedé)

1994 (5 Dec). W **457** (*sideways*). P 13½ × 14.

1752	**453**	1b. new blue	10	10
1753		2b. carmine-red	10	10

591 Chakri Mahaprasart Throne Hall and
Kings Chulalongkorn and Bhumibol

(Des T. Ponchaiwong. Litho Enschedé)

1994 (5 Dec). *120th Anniv of Council of State.* W **226** (*sideways*).
P 13½.

1754	**591**	2b. stone, dp turquoise-blue & ol-grn	20	10

592 Emblem and Airplane

(Des S. Poonsawat. Litho Leigh-Mardon Ltd, Melbourne)

1994 (7 Dec). *50th Anniv of International Civil Aviation
Organization.* W **380**. P 14½ × 14.

1755	**592**	2b. multicoloured	10	10

593 Dvaravati Grinding Stone
(7–11th century)

594 Water Polo

(Des T. Ponchaiwong. Litho Leigh-Mardon Ltd, Melbourne)

1994 (13 Dec). *80th Anniv of Pharmacy in Thailand. T* **593** *and
similar horiz designs.* W **380**. P 14½ × 14.

1756	2b. Type **593**		10	10
1757	6b. Lopburi grinding stone (11–13th century)		15	10
1758	9b. Bangkok period grinding stone (18–20th century)		25	20

(Des U. Niyomthum. Litho Enschedé)

1994 (16 Dec). *18th South-East Asian Games, Chiang Mai. T* **594**
and similar vert designs. Multicoloured. W **457**. P 13½.

1759	2b.+1b. Type **594**		10	10
1760	2b.+1b. Tennis		10	10
1761	2b.+1b. Hurdling		10	10
1762	2b.+1b. Gymnastics		10	10
1759/1762 *Set of 4*			35	35
MS1763 145 × 110 mm. Nos. 1759/62 (sold at 15b.)			55	55

595 First Bar Building and Kings
Vajiravudh and Bhumibol

596 "Kites decorate
the Summer Sky"
(Kontorn Taechoran)

(Des S. Poonsawat. Litho Enschedé)

1995 (1 Jan). *80th Anniv of the Bar.* W **226** (*sideways*). P 13½.
1764 **595** 2b. multicoloured 10 10

(Litho Questa)

1995 (14 Jan). *Children's Day.* T **596** *and similar multicoloured designs.* W **380**. P 14.
1765 2b. Type **596** 10 10
1766 2b. "Trees and Streams" (Yuvadee
Samutpong) (*horiz*) 10 10
1767 2b. "Youths and Religion" (Yutdanai
Polyium) (*horiz*) 10 10

597 Front Page of First Edition and Pen Nib in Camera Shutter

598 Breguet Biplane and General Dynamics Fighting Falcon Jet Fighter

(Des S. Poonsawat. Litho Questa)

1995 (4 Mar). *150th Anniv of Bangkok Recorder (newspaper).* W **380**. P 14.
1768 **597** 2b. multicoloured 10 10

(Des S. Poonsawat. Litho Enschedé)

1995 (27 Mar). *80th Anniv of Royal Thai Airforce.* W **226** (sideways). P 13½.
1769 **598** 2b. multicoloured 10 10

599 *Wetchapha*

(Des U. Niyomthum. Litho Enschedé)

1995 (30 Mar). *Red Cross. 40th Anniv of Wetchapha (hospital ship).* W **226** (sideways). P 13½.
1770 **599** 2b. multicoloured 10 10

600 Naga Bridge

(Des Veena Chantanatat (3b.), C. Boonyasakdi (9b.),
T. Thongkumbai (others). Litho Leigh-Mardon Ltd, Melbourne)

1995 (2 Apr). *Thai Heritage Conservation Day. Phimai Historical Park.* T **600** *and similar horiz designs. Multicoloured.* W **380**. P 14½ × 14.
1771 3b. Type **600** 10 10
1772 5b. Brahmin Hall 15 10

1773 6b. Gateway in inner wall 15 10
1774 9b. Main pagoda 25 15
1771/1774 *Set of 4* 60 40
MS1775 145 × 110 mm. Nos. 1771/4 (sold at
30b.) 85 85

601 Administration Hall   **602** Woman riding Boar

(Des T. Thongkambai. Litho Leigh-Mardon Ltd, Melbourne)

1995 (8 Apr). *108th Anniv of Ministry of Defence.* W **380**. P 14.
1776 **601** 2b. multicoloured 15 10

(Des N. Kaewsawang. Litho Questa)

1995 (13 Apr). *Songkran (New Year) Day.* W **380**. P 11 × 13.
1777 **602** 2b. multicoloured 10 10
MS1778 Two sheets, each 80 × 100 mm, each
containing No. 1777. (a) Perf; (b) imperf (pair
sold at 16b.) 50 50

603 King Rama V and Saranrom Palace   **604** Emerald Buddha

(Des S. Leedul. Litho Leigh-Mardon Ltd, Melbourne)

1995 (14 Apr). *120th Anniv of Ministry of Foreign Affairs.* W **380**. P 14.
1779 **603** 2b. multicoloured 20 10

(Des P. Pipitpiyapakorn. Photo Enschedé)

1995 (13 May). *Visakhapuja Day.* T **604** *and similar vert designs showing statues of Buddha. Multicoloured.* W **457**. P 13½.
1780 2b. Type **604** 10 10
1781 6b. Phra Phuttha Chinnarat 15 10
1782 8b. Phra Phuttha Sihing 25 20
1783 9b. Phra Sukhothai Traimit 30 20
1780/1783 *Set of 4* 70 55
MS1784 127 × 151 mm. Nos. 1780/3 (sold at
35b.) . . . . 1·10 1·10

605 Emblem forming
Flower and Globe

606 Emblem

(Des S. Poonsawat. Litho Enschedé)

1995 (5 June). *Association of South East Asian Nations Environment Year.* W **226**. P 13½.

1785	**605**	2b. multicoloured	10	10

(Des T. Chankam. Litho Enschedé)

1995 (9 June). *Thailand Information Technology Year.* W **457** (*sideways*). P 13½.

1786	**606**	2b. multicoloured	10	10

607 Asian Elephants and Young

(Des Veena Chantanatat. Photo Enschedé)

1995 (1 July). *20th Anniv of Thailand–China Diplomatic Relations. T* **607** *and similar horiz design. Multicoloured.* W **457**. P 13½.

1787	2b. Type **607**		10	10
	a. Horiz pair. Nos. 1787/8		25	25
1788	2b. Asian elephants at river (face value at left)		10	10
MS1789 145 × 110 mm. Nos. 1787/8 (sold at 8b.)			65	65

Nos. 1787/8 were issued together in horizontal *se-tenant* pairs within the sheet, each pair forming a composite design.

608 Optical Fibre Cables

(Des T. Chankam. Litho Thai British Security Ptg Co Ltd, Thailand)

1995 (4 Aug). *National Communications Day.* W **457** (*sideways*). P 14½ × 14.

1790	**608**	2b. multicoloured	10	10

609 Khoa Manee

610 Headquarters

(Des S. Suwanpak (3b.), N. Poon-ngern (6b.), C. Boonyasakdi (others). Photo Enschedé)

1995 (4 Aug). *"Thaipex '95" National Stamp Exhibition. Cats. T* **609** *and similar vert designs. Multicoloured.* W **457** (*sideways on* 1791/4). P 13½.

1791	3b. Type **609**		10	10
1792	6b. Korat		15	15
1793	7b. Sealpoint Siamese		20	15
1794	9b. Burmese		30	20
1791/1794	*Set of 4*		70	55
MS1795 110 × 145 mm. Nos. 1791/4 (sold at 35b.)			95	95

No. **MS**1795 was issued on 9 September overprinted on the margin for Singapore 95 Stamp Exhibition.

(Des S. Leedul. Litho Thai British Security Ptg Co Ltd)

1995 (2 Sept). *80th Anniv of Revenue Department.* W **457**. P 14 × 14½.

1796	**610**	2b. multicoloured	10	10

611 Money and Industry

612 Khong

(Des S. Leedul. Litho Thai British Security Ptg Co Ltd)

1995 (18 Sept). *120th Anniv of National Auditing.* W **457** (*sideways*). P 14½ × 14.

1797	**611**	2b. multicoloured	10	10

(Des V. Pimsuth (1799), Veena Chantanatat (1800), C. Boonyasakdi (others). Photo Enschedé)

1995 (8 Oct). *International Correspondence Week. T* **612** *and similar vert designs showing wicker aquatic animal baskets.* W **457**. P 13½.

1798	2b. Type **612**		10	10
1799	2b. Krachangklom (round basket)		10	10
1800	9b. Sum (open-ended basket)		25	15
1801	9b. Ichu (jar)		25	15
1798/1801	*Set of 4*		65	45
MS1802 110 × 145 mm. Nos. 1798/1801 (sold at 35b.)			95	95

613 Foodstuffs and Anniversary Emblem

(Des S. Sothonbun. Litho Thai British Security Ptg Co Ltd)

1995 (16 Oct). *50th Anniv of Food and Agriculture Organization.* W **457** (*sideways*). P 14½ × 14.

| 1803 | **613** | 2b. multicoloured | 10 | 10 |

The magenta used on No. 1803 is luminescent under U.V. light.

614 Telescope and Eclipse

(Des T. Chankam. Litho Enschedé)

1995 (24 Oct). *Total Solar Eclipse.* W **457** (*sideways*). P 13½.

| 1804 | **614** | 2b. multicoloured | 10 | 10 |

615 U.N. Building, Thailand

(Des T. Ponchaiwong. Litho Questa)

1995 (24 Oct). *50th Anniv of United Nations Organization.* W **380**. P 13½ × 14.

| 1805 | **615** | 2b. multicoloured | 10 | 10 |

616 Tower

617 *Adenium obesum*

(Des S. Leedul. Litho Thai British Security Ptg Co Ltd)

1995 (4 Nov). *"WORLDTECH '95" International Agricultural and Industrial Exhibition, Suranaree.* T **616** *and similar multicoloured designs.* W **457** (*sideways on* 1808/9). P 14 × 14½ (vert) or 14½ × 14 (horiz).

1806	2b. Type **616**	10	10
1807	5b. Agriculture	15	10
1808	6b. Modern technology (*horiz*)	15	10
1809	9b. Reservoirs and coastline (*horiz*)	25	15
1806/1809 *Set of 4*		60	40

(Des P. Khamprapha. Litho Enschedé)

1995 (15 Nov). *New Year. Flowers.* T **617** *and similar horiz designs. Multicoloured.* W **457**. P 14 × 13½.

1810	2b. Type **617**	10	10
1811	2b. *Bauhinia acuminata*	10	10
1812	2b. *Cananga odorata*	10	10
1813	2b. *Thunbergia erecta*	10	10
1810/1813 *Set of 4*		35	35
MS1814 100 × 85 mm. Nos. 1810/13 (sold at 15b.)		55	55

No. **MS**1814 was issued on 18 May 1996 overprinted on the margin for China 96 stamp exhibition.

618 Vaccinating Cattle

(Des S. Leedul. Litho Thai British Security Ptg Co Ltd)

1995 (9 Dec). *60th Anniv of Veterinary Science in Thailand.* W **457** (*sideways*). P 14½ × 14.

| 1815 | **618** | 2b. multicoloured | 10 | 10 |

619 Fencing

620 Queen Somdej Phra Sri Patcharin (founder)

(Des U. Niyomthum. Litho Enschedé)

1995 (9 Dec). *18th South-East Asian Games, Chiang Mai.* T **619** *and similar vert designs. Multicoloured.* W **380**. P 13½.

1816	2b. + 1b. Type **619**	10	10
	a. Horiz strip of 4.		
	Nos. 1815/18	45	
1817	2b. + 1b. Snooker	10	10
1818	2b. + 1b. Diving	10	10
1819	2b. + 1b. Pole vaulting	10	10
1816/1819 *Set of 4*		35	35
MS1820 145 × 110 mm. Nos. 1816/19 (sold at 15b.)		55	55

Nos. 1816/19 were issued together in horizontal *se-tenant* strips of four stamps within the sheet, each strip forming a composite design.

(Des C. Thongkaew. Litho Thai British Security Ptg Co Ltd)

1996 (12 Jan). *Centenary of Siriraj School of Nursing and Midwifery.* W **457**. P 14 × 14½.

| 1821 | **620** | 2b. multicoloured | 10 | 10 |

621 Breguet Biplane and Emblem

(Des U. Niyomthum. Litho Thai British Security Ptg Ltd)

1996 (13 Jan). *National Aviation Day.* W **457** *(sideways).*
P $14\frac{1}{2} \times 14$.

1822	**621**	2b. multicoloured		10	10

ประเทศไทยTHAILAND
625 Princess Mother and Golden
Crematorium

(Des Veena Chantanatat. Litho and die-stamped Thai British
Security Ptg Co Ltd)

1996 (10 Mar). *Princess Mother's Cremation.* W **457** *(sideways).*
P $14\frac{1}{2} \times 14$.

1832	**625**	2b. multicoloured		20	10

622 "Visakhapuja Day" (Malinee
Sanaewong)

(Litho Enschedé)

1996 (13 Jan). *Children's Day. Children's Drawings.* T **622** and
similar multicoloured designs. W **380**. P $13\frac{1}{2}$.

1823	2b. Type **622**		10	10
1824	2b. "Maghapuja Day" (Thirapon Deephlub) (tree in centre) *(vert)*		10	10
1825	2b. "Asalhapuja Day" (Voraphat Pankian) (tree at left) *(vert)*		10	10

626 Wat Phra Kaeo

(Des C. Boonyasakdi (2b.), P. Phukrongtung (3b.),
C. Thongkaew (6b.), V. Phimsuth (9b.). Litho Enschedé)

1996 (2 Apr). *Thai Heritage Conservation Day. Kamphaeng Phet
Historical Park.* T **626** and *similar horiz designs. Multicoloured.*
W **380**. P $13\frac{1}{2}$.

1833	2b. Type **626**		10	10
1834	3b. Wat Phra Non		10	10
1835	6b. Wat Chang Rop		15	10
1836	9b. Wat Pgra Si Iriyabot		30	20
1833/1836	*Set of 4*		60	45
MS1837	145 × 110 mm. Nos. 1833/6 (sold at 28b.)		85	85

623 Handshake and
Map of Asia and
Europe

624 Temiyajataka

(Des S. Poonsawat. Litho Thai British Security Ptg Co Ltd)

1996 (1 Mar). *Asia–Europe Summit Meeting, Thailand.* W **457**.
P $14 \times 14\frac{1}{2}$.

1826	**623**	2b. multicoloured		10	10

(Des T. Chinchusak. Photo Enschedé)

1996 (3 Mar). *Maghapuja Day.* T **624** and *similar horiz designs.
Multicoloured.* W **457** *(sideways).* P $13\frac{1}{2}$.

1827	2b. Type **624**		10	10
1828	6b. Mahajanakajataka		15	10
1829	8b. Suvannasamjataka		20	15
1830	9b. Nemijataka		30	20
1827/1830	*Set of 4*		70	50
MS1831	152 × 127 mm. Nos. 1827/30 (sold at 36b.)		1·10	1·10

627 Buddhist Pagoda, Wat Chiang Man

(Des T. Thongkhambai. Photo Enschedé)

1996 (12 Apr). *700th Anniv of Chiang Mai.* T **627** and *similar horiz
designs. Multicoloured.* W **457** *(sideways).* P $13\frac{1}{2}$.

1838	2b. Type **627**		10	10
1839	6b. Angel sculpture, Wat Chet Yot's Pagoda		15	10
1840	8b. Insignia of Wat Phan Tao monastery		20	15
1841	9b. Sattaphanta		30	20
1838/1841	*Set of 4*		70	50
MS1842	145 × 110 mm. Nos. 1838/41 (sold at 37b.)		1·10	1·10

628 Rufous-necked Hornbill   **629** Angel riding Rat

(Des V. Chantrasarn. Photo Enschedé)

1996 (12 Apr). *Second International Asian Hornbill Workshop. T* **628** *and similar vert designs. Multicoloured.* W **457**. P 13½.

1843	3b. Type **628**	10	10
1844	3b. Long-crested hornbill	10	10
1845	9b. Blyth's hornbill	25	20
1846	9b. Rhinoceros hornbill	25	20
1843/1846 *Set of 4*		65	55

MS1847 110 × 145 mm. Nos. 1843/6 (sold at 35b.) 95 95

No. **MS**1847 was issued on 8 June overprinted on the margin for Capex 96 stamp exhibition.

(Des N. Kaewsawang. Litho Enschedé)

1996 (13 Apr). *Songkran (New Year) Day. T* **629** *and previous designs. Multicoloured.* W **380**. P 13½ × 14.

1848   2b. Type **629** 10   10
MS1849 Two sheets, each 80 × 100 mm, containing No. 1848. (a) Perf; (b) imperf (pair sold at 16b.) 50   50
MS1850 Two sheets, each 135 × 160 mm. Nos. 1513, 1607, 1681, 1724, 1777 and 1848. (a) Perf; (b) imperf (pair sold at 40b.) . . . . 1·30   1·30

No. **MS**1849 was issued overprinted on the margin for China 96 stamp exhibition in Chinese and English.

630 Royal Ablutions Ceremony   **631** King Bhumibol

(Des T. Thongkhambai (1851/**MS**1856), Achara Livisith (1857/**MS**1860), T. Ponchaiwong (1861/**MS**1866), S. Poonsawat (1867).

1996 (9 June). *50th Anniv of King Bhumibol's Accession to Throne as Rama IX. Multicoloured.* (a) *Coronation Ceremony. T* **630** *and similar vert designs. Granite paper. Photo Courvoisier.* P 11½.

1851	3b. Type **630**	10	10
1852	3b. Pouring of the Libation	10	10
1853	3b. Grand Audience	10	10

1854	3b. Royal Progress by land	10	10
1855	3b. Making speech from balcony	10	10
1851/1855 *Set of 5*		45	45

MS1856 Five sheets, each 120 × 110 mm. (a) 3b. T **630**; (b) 3b. No. 1852; (c) 3b. No. 1853; (d) 3b. No. 1854; (e) 3b. No. 1855 (five sheets sold at 40b.) . . . . . . 1·30   1·30

The stamps from No. **MS**1856 have the design extending to the perforations whereas Nos. 1851/5 have white margins around the design.

(b) *Royal Regalia. Designs as T* **630**. W **109** *(sideways on Nos. 1859,* **MS**1860*). Photo Govt Ptg Wks, Tokyo.* P 13½

1857	3b. Betal and areca-nut set	10	10
1858	3b. Water urn	10	10
1859	3b. Gold-enamelled cuspidor and golden spittoon (*horiz*)	10	10

MS1860 110 × 145 mm. Nos. 1857/9 (sold at 17b.) 65   65

(c) *National Development. Horiz designs as T* **630**. W **457** *(sideways). Litho and holography (1863) or litho (others) Thai British Security Ptg Co Ltd.* P 13½

1861	3b. Cultivation of vetiver grass (prevention of soil erosion)	10	10
1862	3b. Chai Pattana aerator (improvement of water quality)	10	10
1863	3b. Airplane (rain-making project)	10	10
1864	3b. Dam (water resources development)	10	10
1865	3b. Sapling (Golden Jubilee Reforestation Campaign)	10	10
1861/1865 *Set of 5*		45	45

MS1866 185 × 122 mm. Nos. 1861/5 plus label (sold at 25b.) 75   75

(d) W **380**. *Litho and embossed Cartor.* P 13½

1867   **631**   100b. multicoloured . . . . . 3·75   3·75

632 Baron Pierre de Coubertin (founder) and Grave   **633** King Bhumibol using Short-wave Radio

(Des S. Poonsawat. Litho Thai British Security Ptg Co Ltd)

1996 (23 June). *Centenary of Modern Olympic Games. T* **632** *and similar vert designs. Multicoloured.* W **457**. P 14 × 14½.

1868	2b. Type **632**	10	10
1869	3b. Lighting Olympic flame at Olympia, Greece	10	10
1870	5b. First modern Games and Olympic flag	15	10
1871	9b. Athlete and medal from 1896 Games	30	20
1868/1871 *Set of 4*		60	45

(Des T. Ponchaiwong. Litho Thai British Security Ptg Co Ltd)

1996 (4 Aug). *National Communications Day.* W **457**. P 14 × 14½.

1872   **633**   2b. multicoloured 20   10

634 Tropical Rain Forest

(Des R. Saichumdee (3, 7b.), Veena Chantanatat (6b.),
S. Poonsawat (9b.). Litho Thai British Security Ptg Co Ltd)

1996 (18 Sept). *Centenary of Royal Forest Department.* T **634** *and
similar horiz designs. Multicoloured.* W **457** (*sideways*).
P 14½ × 14.

1873	3b. Type **634**	10	10
1874	6b. Evergreen mountain forest	15	10
1875	7b. Swamp forest	20	15
1876	9b. Mangrove forest	30	20
1873/1876	*Set of 4*	70	50
MS1877	144 × 108 mm. Nos. 1873/6. P 13½		
(sold at 35b.)		95	95

635 Ramayana

(Des T. Chinchusak. Photo Enschedé)

1996 (6 Oct). *International Correspondence Week. Thai
Novels.* T **635** *and similar horiz designs.* W **457** (*sideways*).
P 13½.

1878	3b. Type **635**	10	10
1879	3b. Inao and Budsaba in cave (*Inao*)	10	10
1880	9b. Lunhap being shown round forest (*Ngao Pa*)	25	20
1881	9b. The cursing of Nang Mathanal (*Mathanapatha*)	25	20
1878/1881	*Set of 4*	65	55
MS1882	145 × 110 mm. Nos. 1878/81 (sold at 36b.)	95	95

636 Youth Activities   **637** Huoy Kha Khang National Park

(Des V. Chantrasarn. Litho Thai British Security Ptg Co Ltd)

1996 (25 Oct). *Asia Regional Conference of Rotary International,
Thailand.* W **457**. P 14 × 14½.

1883	**636**	2b. multicoloured	10	10

(Des T. Ponchaiwong. Litho Thai British Security Ptg Co Ltd)

1996 (4 Nov). *50th Anniv of United Nations Educational, Scientific
and Cultural Organization.* W **457** (*sideways*). P 14½ × 14.

1884	**637**	2b. multicoloured	10	10

638 *Narai Song Suban H.M. King Rama IX*
(new royal barge) (⅓-*size illustration*)

(Des T. Thongkhambai. Photo Courvoisier)

1996 (7 Nov). *50th Anniv of King Bhumibol's Accession to Throne
as Rama IX (2nd issue). Multicoloured. Granite paper.* P 11½.

1885	**638**	9b. multicoloured	25	25
MS1886	170 × 110 mm. No. 1885 (sold at 16b.)	75	75

639 *Limnocharis flava*   **640** Indian Whistling
Duck (*Dendrocygna
javanica*)

(Des Veena Chantanatat. Litho)

1996 (15 Nov). *New Year. Flowers.* T **639** *and similar
multicoloured designs.* W **380**. P 14 × 14½ (*horiz*) or 14½ × 14
(*vert*).

1887	2b. Type **639**	10	10
1888	2b. *Crinum thaianum* (*vert*)	10	10
1889	2b. *Monochoria hastata* (*vert*)	10	10
1890	2b. *Nymphoides indicum*	10	10
1887/1890	*Set of 4*	35	35
MS1891	85 × 100 mm. Nos. 1887/90. P 14 (sold at 15b.)	55	55

No. **MS**1891 was issued on the 12th February 1997 overprinted
on the margin for Hong Kong 97 stamp exhibition.

(Des S. Poonsawat. Photo Harrison)

1996 (1 Dec). *Water Birds.* T **640** *and similar multicoloured
designs.* W **457** (*sideways on* 1893/4 *and* **MS**1896). P 13½.

1892	3b. Type **640**	10	10
1893	3b. Comb duck (*Sarkidiornis melanotos*) (*horiz*)	10	10
1894	7b. Cotton teal (*Nettapus coromandelianus*) (*horiz*)	20	15
1895	7b. White-winged wood duck (*Cairina scutulata*)	20	15
1892/1895	*Set of 4*	55	45
MS1896	153 × 120 mm. Nos. 1892/5 (sold at 33b.)	95	95

641 King
Rama IX in
Admiral's Uniform   **642** Children at Zoo (Ruangchai
Khot-Tha)

(Des S. Leedul and P. Taothong)

1996 (5 Dec)–**99**.

(a) Litho Thai British Security Ptg Co Ltd. W **457** *(sideways).* P 14 × 14½.

1897	**641**	2b. carmine-red	10	10
1899		4b. dull scarlet and deep turquoise-blue (19.7.97)	15	10
1900		5b. Indian red and slate-lilac (19.7.97)	15	10
1901		6b. deep lilac and yellowish green (19.7.97)	15	10
1902		7b. deep bluish green and rose (19.7.97)	20	10
1902a		9b. yellow-orange and deep violet-blue (19.7.97)	25	10

(b) Recess and litho Govt Ptg Wks, Tokyo. W **109**. P 13½ × 13.

1903	**641**	10b. brownish black and red-orange (19.7.97)	25	10
1903a		12b. deep blue and blue-green (1.7.99)	30	15
1903b		15b. deep green and ochre (1.7.99)	45	15
1904		20b. brown-lake and bluish violet (19.7.97)	55	15
1905		25b. brown-olive and blue-green (8.8.97)	65	30
1905a		30b. brown and rose (1.7.99)	85	30
1906		50b. myrtle green and dull violet (25.2.98)	1·30	45
1907		100b. slate-blue and olive-yellow (19.7.97)	2·50	45
1908		200b. blackish purple and bright magenta (8.8.97)	5·25	85
1909		500b. deep magenta and brigth orange (*p* 13 × 13½) (26 × 31 *mm*) (10.9.99)	13·00	2·10
1897/1909 *Set of 16*			23·00	5·00

(Litho Thai British Security Ptg Co Ltd)

1996 (11 Dec). *50th Anniv of United Nations Children's Fund.* W **457** *(sideways).* P 14½ × 14.

1910	**642**	2b. multicoloured	10	10

643 Medal, Flag and Boxers

644 School, King Rama V and Crown Prince Vajiravudh (Rama VI)

(Des U. Niyomthum. Litho and embossed Thai British Security Ptg Co Ltd)

1996 (16 Dec). *First Thai Olympic Gold Medal (won by Somluck Khamsingh for boxing at Atlanta, U.S.A.).* W **457** *(sideways).* P 14½ × 14.

1911	**643**	6b. multicoloured	20	10

(Des T. Thongkumbai. Litho Southern Colour Print, Dunedin, New Zealand)

1997 (1 Jan). *Centenary of Mahavajiravudh School, Songkhla.* W **380**. P 14 × 14½.

1912	**644**	2b. multicoloured	10	10

645 "Good Things in my Province" (Natamol Thongsai)

646 Old and New Buildings

(Litho Thai British Security Ptg Co Ltd)

1997 (11 Jan). *Children's Day. Children's Drawings.* T **645** *and similar vert design. Multicoloured.* W **457**. P 14 × 14½.

1913		2b. Type **645** (dried fish, Samut Prakan)	10	10
1914		2b. "Tourist Sites in my Province", Chanthaburi (Somkiat Thongchomphu)	10	10

(Des U. Niyomthum. Litho Thai British Security Ptg Co Ltd)

1997 (25 Feb). *20th Anniv of Communications Authority.* W **457** *(sideways).* P 14½ × 14.

1915	**646**	2b. multicoloured	10	10

647 Statue

648 Building

(Des Veena Chantanatat. Litho Thai British Security Ptg Co Ltd)

1997 (25 Feb). *Unveiling of Statue of Prince Bhanurangsi (founder of postal service) outside Communications Authority, Laksi (Bangkok).* W **457**. P 14 × 14½.

1916	**647**	2b. multicoloured	10	10

(Des T. Chankam. Litho Thai British Security Ptg Co Ltd)

1997 (25 Feb). *Laksi Mail Centre.* T **648** *and similar horiz design. Multicoloured.* W **457** *(sideways).* P 14½ × 14.

1917		2b. Type **648**	10	10
	a.	Horiz pair. Nos. 1917/18	25	25
1918		2b. Letter sorting equipment	10	10

Nos. 1917/18 were issued together in *se-tenant* pairs within the sheet, each pair forming a composite design.

649 Windsor Palace University building

(Des S. Srisuwan. Litho Thai British Security Ptg Co Ltd)

1997 (26 Mar). *80th Anniv of Chulalongkorn University. T* **649** *and similar horiz design. Multicoloured.* W **457** (*sideways*). P 14½ × 14.

1919	2b. Type **649**	10	10
1920	2b. Faculty of Arts building	10	10

650 Early Steam Locomotive

(Des U. Niyomthum. Litho Cartor)

1997 (26 Mar). *Centenary of Thai State Railway. T* **650** *and similar horiz designs. Multicoloured.* W **380**. P 13½.

1921	3b. Type **650**	10	10
1922	4b. Garratt steam locomotive	15	10
1923	6b. Sulzer diesel locomotive	15	15
1924	7b. Hitachi diesel-electric locomotive	20	15
1921/1925	*Set of 4*	55	45

MS1925 Two sheets. (a) 110 × 145 mm.
No. 1921; (b) 145 × 110 mm. Nos. 1921/4
(pair sold at 50b.)   1·50   1·50

651 Rajakarun Museum

(Des C. Thongkaew. Litho Thai British Security Ptg Co Ltd)

1997 (28 Mar). *Red Cross.* W **457** (*sideways*). P 14½ × 14.

1926	**651**	3b. multicoloured	10	10

652 First Headquarters

(Des S. Poonsawat. Litho Thai British Security Ptg Co Ltd)

1997 (1 Apr). *84th Anniv of Government Savings Bank.* W **457** (*sideways*). P 14½ × 14.

1927	**652**	2b. multicoloured	10	10

653 Outer Staircase   **654** Man riding Ox

(Des Veena Chantanatat (1928), R. Saichumdee (1929), C. Boonyasakdi (1930), V. Phimsuth (1931). Litho Thai British Security Ptg Co Ltd)

1997 (2 Apr). *Thai Heritage Conservation Day. Phanomrung Historical Park. T* **653** *and similar horiz designs. Multicoloured.* W **457** (*sideways*). P 14½ × 14.

1928	3b. Type **653**	10	10
1929	3b. Pavilion	10	10
1930	7b. Pathway and stairs to Sanctuary	20	15
1931	7b. Naga balustrade and Eastern Gallery central gate	20	15
1928/1931	*Set of 4*	55	45

MS1932 110 × 145 mm. Nos. 1928/31. P 13½
(sold at 30b.)   85   85

(Des N. Kaewsawang. Litho Thai British Security Ptg Co Ltd)

1997 (13 Apr). *Songkram (New Year) Day. Year of the Ox.* W **457** (*sideways*). P 14 × 14½.

1933	**654**	2b. multicoloured	10	10

MS1934 Two sheets, each 80 × 100 mm, each containing No. 1933. (a) Perf; (b) imperf (pair sold at 16b.)   50   50
No. **MS**1934 was issued overprinted with Thai and Chinese inscriptions for the China Stamp Exhibition, Bangkok on the sheet margin and was only available at the exhibition.

655 Pheasant-tailed Jacana

(Des U. Niyomthum (1935), M. Sriwongkorakot (1936), P. Khamprapha (1937), V. Chantrasarn (1938). Photo Courvoisier)

1997 (15 May). *Water Birds. T* **655** *and similar horiz designs. Multicoloured. Granite paper.* P 11½.

1935	3b. Type **655**	10	10
1936	3b. Bronze-winged jacana	10	10
1937	7b. Painted stork	20	15
1938	7b. Black-winged stilt	20	15
1935/1938	*Set of 4*	55	45

MS1939 145 × 110 mm. Nos. 1935/8 (sold at 30b.)   85   85
A miniature sheet as No. **MS**1939 but without the sheet price and bearing the "Pacific 97" International Stamp Exhibition, San Francisco, emblem in the margin was only sold at the exhibition.

656 Suthee Aerial and King Bhumibol using Radio

(Des Veena Chantanatat. Litho Thai British Security Ptg Co Ltd)

1997 (9 June). *Telecommunications. T* **656** *and similar horiz designs. Multicoloured.* W **457** (*sideways*). P 14½ × 14.

1940	2b. Type **656**	10	10
1941	3b. King using hand-held radio and various radios	10	10
1942	6b. King using computer	15	15
1943	9b. King, schoolchildren and "Thaicom" satellite (expanding secondary education to rural areas using satellite technology)	25	20
1940/1943	*Set of 4*	55	50

MS1944 145 × 110 mm. Nos. 1940/3. P 13½
(sold at 30b.)   85   85

657 First Thai Cinema Advertisement, Equipment and Prince Sanbassatra

(Des V. Chantrasarn. Litho Thai British Security Ptg Co Ltd)

1997 (10 June). *Centenary of Cinema in Thailand. T* **657** *and similar horiz designs. Multicoloured.* W **457** (*sideways*). P 14½ × 14.

1945	3b.	King Prajadhipok filming and King Chulalongkorn's state visit to Europe, 1897 (first film documenting Thai history)	10	10
1946	3b.	Type **657**	10	10
1947	7b.	Poster for *Double Luck* (first movie with Thai producer) and band outside cinema	20	15
1948	7b.	Open-air cinema and poster for *Going Astray* (first Thai sound film)	20	15
1945/1948 *Set of 4*			55	45

658 King Ananda Mahidol (Rama VIII) (founder), Building and Operation

(Des S. Poonsawat. Litho Thai British Security Ptg Co Ltd)

1997 (11 June). *50th Anniv of Faculty of Medicine, Chulalongkorn University.* W **457** (*sideways*). P 14½ × 14.

1949	**658**	2b. multicoloured	10	10

659 Peterhof Palace and King Chulalongkorn

(Des S. Poonsawat. Litho Thai Security Ptg Co Ltd)

1997 (3 July). *Centenary of Thailand–Russia Diplomatic Relations and State Visit of King Chulalongkorn (Rama V) to Russia.* W **457** (*sideways*). P 14½ × 14.

1950	**659**	2b. multicoloured	10	10

660 Mahosathajataka

(Des S. Chinawong (7b.), R. Chinchusak (others). Photo Courvoisier)

1997 (19 July). *Asalhapuja Day. T* **660** *and similar horiz designs illustrating ten Jataka stories. Multicoloured. Granite paper.* P 11½ × 12 (with one eliptical hole on each vert side).

1951	3b.	Type **660**	10	10
1952	4b.	Bhuridattajataka	15	10
1953	6b.	Candakumarajataka	15	15
1954	7b.	Naradajataka	20	15
1951/1954 *Set of 4*			55	45

MS1955 Five sheets. (a) 152 × 127 mm. Nos. 1951/4; (b) 100 × 80 mm. No. 1951; (c) 100 × 80 mm. No. 1952; (d) 100 × 80 mm. No. 1953; (e) 100 × 80 mm. No. 1954 (set of 5 sold at 66b.) .... 2·10 2·10

No. **MS**1955 was issued overprinted on the margin for Shanghai 1997 or for Bangkok 97 stamp exhibitions, they were only available at the exhibitions.

661 Northern Region

(Des N. Kaewsawang (2b.), C. Boonyasakdi (6b.), R. Saichumdee (others). Litho Govt Ptg Wks, Tokyo)

1997 (2 Aug). *"Thaipex 97" Stamp Exhibition. Traditional Houses. T* **661** *and similar horiz designs. Multicoloured.* W **109** (*sideways*). P 13½.

1956	2b.	Type **661**	10	10
1957	5b.	Central region	15	10
1958	6b.	North-eastern region	15	15
1959	9b.	Southern region	25	20
1956/1959 *Set of 4*			60	50

MS1960 125 × 165 mm. Nos. 1956/9 (sold at 32b.). Perf or imperf 85 85

662 Cape Blue Water Lily (*Nymphaea capensis*)

663 Means of Communications

1997 (4 Aug). *Greetings booklet stamps. No value indicated. T* **662** *and similar horiz design. Multicoloured.* W **380**. P 14 × 14½.

1961	(2b.)	Type **662**	10	10
		a. Booklet pane. Nos. 1961/2, each × 5, plus 4 labels	1·10	
1962	(2b.)	Indian lotus (*Nymphaea stellata*)	10	10

The booklet pane consists of ten stamps and four half-stamp sized labels each inscribed "Happy Birthday" or "Thinking of you" in English or Thai. The booklets were on sale in commercial stores only.

(Des T. Chankam. Litho Thai British Security Ptg Co Ltd)

1997 (4 Aug). *National Communications Day.* W **457**. P 14 × 14½.

1963	**663**	2b. multicoloured	10	10

664 Luang Chiang Dao Mountain, Chiang Mai

(Des P. Khamprapha. Litho Thai British Security Ptg Co Ltd)

1997 (8 Aug). *30th Anniv of Association of South-East Asian Nations. Tourist Sights. T* **664** *and similar horiz designs. Multicoloured.* W **457** (*sideways*). P 14½ × 14.

1964	2b. Type **664**		10	10
1965	2b. Thi Lo Su Falls, Tak		10	10
1966	9b. Thalu Island, Chumphon		25	20
1967	9b. Phromthep Cape, Phuket		25	20
1964/1967 *Set of 4*			65	55

665 *Phuwiangosaurus sirindhornae*

(Des T. Ponchaiwong. Photo)

1997 (28 Aug). *Dinosaurs. T* **665** *and similar horiz designs. Multicoloured.* P 13½ (with one elliptical hole on each horiz side).

1968	2b. Type **665**		10	10
1969	3b. *Siamotyrannus isanensis*		10	10
1970	6b. *Siamosaurus suteethorni*		15	15
1971	9b. *Psittacosaurus sattayaraki*		25	20
1968/1971 *Set of 4*			55	50
MS1972 145 × 110 mm. Nos. 1968/71 (sold at 30b.)			85	85

666 King Chulalongkorn

667 Rickshaw and Bicycle Hybrid

(Des S. Leedul. Litho Thai British Security Ptg Co Ltd)

1997 (12 Sept). *Centenary of Visit to Switzerland of King Chulalongkorn (Rama V).* W **457**. P 14 × 14½.

1973	**666** 2b. multicoloured	10	10

(Des N. Phul-Ngoen (1974), T. Thongkhambai (1975), C. Thongkaew (1976), U. Niyomthum (1977). Photo Courvoisier)

1997 (5 Oct). *International Correspondence Week. Tricycles. T* **667** *and similar horiz designs. Multicoloured. Granite paper.* P 11½.

1974	3b. Type **667**	10	10
1975	3b. Bicycle with attached side-seat and wheel	10	10

1976	9b. Motor tricycle No. 345		25	20
1977	9b. Tuk-tuk (open-sided three-wheel motor)		25	20
1974/1977 *Set of 4*			65	55
MS1978 144 × 110 mm. Nos. 1974/7 (sold at 30b.)			85	85

668 Purple Pacific Drupe (*Drupa morum*)

669 Chalerm Prakiat (energy efficient building), Khlong Har

(Des R. Saichumdee. Photo Courvoisier)

1997 (9 Oct). *World Post Day. Shells. T* **668** *and similar horiz designs. Multicoloured. Granite paper.* P 11½.

1979	2b. Type **668**		10	10
1980	2b. *Nerita chamaelon*		10	10
1981	9b. *Littoraria melanostoma*		25	20
1982	9b. *Cryptospira elegans*		25	20
1979/1982 *Set of 4*			65	55
MS1983 144 × 110 mm. Nos. 1979/82 (sold at 30b.)			85	85

Stamps of a similar design were issued by Singapore.

(Des U. Niyomthum. Litho Thai British Security Ptg Co Ltd)

1997 (10 Nov). *Energy Conservation.* W **457** (*sideways*). P 14½ × 14.

1984	**669** 2b. multicoloured	10	10

670 *Suphannahong* (Royal Barge, 1911) (⅓-*size illustration*)

(Des T. Thongkhambai. Photo Courvoisier)

1997 (13 Nov). *Granite paper.* P 11½.

1985	**670** 9b. multicoloured	25	20
MS1986 157 × 95 mm. No. 1985 (sold at 20b.)		65	65

No. **MS**1986 was issued on 7 July 2000 overprinted on the margin for "World Stamp Expo 2000" International Stamp Exhibition, Anaheim, California. It was sold for 20b. and was only available at the exhibition and to Post Office account members.

671 *Cassia alata*

672 Playing Saxophone and Score of his *Falling Rain*

(Des T. Ponchaiwong. Litho Cartor)

1997 (15 Nov). *New Year. Flowers. T* **671** *and similar vert designs. Multicoloured. Granite paper.* P 13½ × 13.

1987	2b. Type **671**		10	10
1988	2b. *Strophanthus caudatus*		10	10

1989	2b. *Clinacanthus nutans*	10	10
1990	2b. *Acanthus ilicifolius*	10	10
1987/1990	*Set of* 4	35	35

MS1991 85 × 100 mm. Nos. 1987/90 (sold at
15b.) 45 45

The filaments in the paper used for this issue are scattered so that some stamps appear to be on plain paper.

No. **MS**1991 was issued overprinted on the margin for Indepex 97 stamp exhibition, and was only available at the exhibition.

(Des T. Thongkhambai. Photo Courvoisier)

1997 (5 Dec). *70th Birthday of King Bhumibol. T* 672 *and similar horiz designs. Multicoloured. Granite paper.* P 11½.

1992	2b. Type **673**	10	10
1993	2b. At easel and one of his paintings	10	10
1994	2b. Model airplane, OK dinghy and bust and Bhumibol building boat	10	10
1995	2b. Sailing OK Class dinghy and wearing team blazer with gold medal from South-East Asian Games	10	10
1996	6b. With camera and his photograph of Royal Water Development Project	15	10
1997	7b. Writing and his books *Nai In, Tito* and *The Story of Mahajanaka*	20	10
1998	9b. Using computer, map from *The Story of Mahajanaka* and his New Year card	25	15
1992/1998	*Set of* 7	90	65

673 "Sport-minded in Maimed Bodies" (Sumonmarl Chaneiam)

674 Dental Tools and Emblem on Tooth

(Litho Thai British Security Ptg Co Ltd)

1998 (10 Jan). *Children's Day. Children's Drawings. T* 673 *and similar vert designs. Multicoloured.* W 457. P 14 × 14½.

1999	2b. Type **673**	10	10
	a. Block of 4. Nos. 1999/2002	45	
2000	2b. "Kite-flying Contest" (Pavinee Rodsawat)	10	10
2001	2b. "Gymnastics" (Kejsarin Nilwong)	10	10
2002	2b. "Windsurf Racing" (Voraphat Phankhian)	10	10
1999/2002	*Set of* 4	35	35

Nos. 1999/2002 were issued both in separate sheets and together in *se-tenant* blocks of four stamps within the sheet.

(Des T. Chankam. Litho Thai British Security Ptg Co Ltd)

1998 (17 Jan). *20th Asia Pacific Dental Congress, Bangkok. Granite paper.* P 14 × 14½.

| 2003 | **674** 2b. multicoloured | 10 | 10 |

675 Victory Monument and Military and Civilian Representatives

676 Queen Sirikit (Red Cross president)

(Des S. Poonsawat. Litho Thai British Security Ptg Co Ltd)

1998 (3 Feb). *50th Anniv of Veterans' Day.* W 457. P 14 × 14½.

| 2004 | **675** 2b. multicoloured | 10 | 10 |

(Des S. Leedul and P. Taothong. Photo Courvoisier)

1998 (25 Feb). *Granite paper.* P 11½ × 12.

2005	**641** 50s. olive-green	10	10
2006	2b. carmine-red (1998)	10	10
2007	9b. dull orange and slate-violet (1998)	25	15

Numbers have been left for possible additions to this series.

(Des C. Thongkaew. Litho Thai British Security Ptg Co Ltd)

1998 (27 Mar). *Red Cross.* W 457. P 14 × 14½.

| 2015 | **676** 2b. multicoloured | 10 | 10 |

677 Shooting

(Des U. Chai-klang. Litho Thai British Security Ptg Co Ltd)

1998 (27 Mar). *13th Asian Games, Bangkok. T* 677 *and similar horiz designs. Multicoloured.* W 457 (*sideways*). P 14½ × 14.

2016	2b. + 1b. Type **677**	10	10
2017	2b. + 1b. Gymnastics	15	15
2018	4b. + 1b. Swimming	15	15
2019	7b. + 1b. Windsurfing	20	20
2016/2019	*Set of* 4	55	55

678 Main Tower

(Des K. Moka-siri (3b.), N. Kaewsawang (4b.), V. Phimsuth (6b.), Veena (6b) Chantanatat (7b.).

Litho Thai British Security Ptg Co Ltd)

1998 (2 Apr). *Thai Heritage Conservation Day. Phanomrung Historical Park. T* 678 *and similar horiz designs.* W 457 (*sideways*). P 14½ × 14.

| 2020 | 3b. Type **678** | 10 | 10 |
| 2021 | 4b. Minor Tower | 15 | 10 |

2022	6b. Scripture repository		15	10
2023	7b. Lintel depicting Vishnu sleeping in ocean (eastern doorway, Main Tower)		20	15
2020/2023	*Set of 4*		55	40
MS2024	110 × 145 mm. Nos. 2020/3. P 13½		85	85

679 Woman riding Tiger

680 Fishing Cat (*Felis viverrina*)

(Des N. Kaewsawang. Litho Thai British Security Ptg Co Ltd)

1998 (13 Apr). *Songkram (New Year) Day. Year of the Tiger.* W **457** (*sideways*). P 14 × 14½.

| 2025 | **679** | 2b. multicoloured | | 10 | 10 |
| MS2026 | | Two sheets, each 80 × 100 mm, each containing No. 2025. (a) Perf; (b) Imperf (pair sold at 16b.) | | 50 | 50 |

No. **MS**2026 was issued on 16 October overprinted on the margin with the flags of Thailand and China and with Thai and Chinese inscriptions.

(Des T. Thongkhambai (4b.), U. Niyomthum (6b.), R. Saichumdee (others). Litho Thai British Security Ptg Co Ltd)

1998 (13 Apr). *Wild Cats. T* **680** *and similar horiz designs. Multicoloured.* W **457** (*sideways*). P 14½ × 14.

2027	2b. Type **680**		10	10
2028	4b. Tiger (*Panthera tigris*)		15	10
2029	6b. Leopard (*Panthera pardus*)		15	10
2030	8b. Jungle cat (*Felis chaus*)		20	15
2027/2030	*Set of 4*		55	40
MS2031	144 × 110 mm. Nos. 2027/30. P 13½		85	85

681 Airliner and Radar Grid

(Des Aeronautical Radio of Thailand Ltd. Litho Thai British Security Ptg Co Ltd)

1998 (15 Apr). *50th Anniv of Aerothai (air-traffic control).* W **457** (*sideways*). P 14½ × 14.

| 2032 | **681** | 2b. multicoloured | | 10 | 10 |

682 ''Vidhurajataka'' (Kritsana Moka-siri)

(Litho Thai British Security Ptg Co Ltd)

1998 (10 May). *Visakhapuja Day. Prize-winning Drawings of Ten Jataka Stories. T* **682** *and similar horiz designs. Multicoloured.* W **457** (*sideways on Nos. 2033/6*). P 13½.

2033	3b. Type **682**		10	10
2034	4b. ''Vessantarajataka: Dana Kanda'' (Chuttumrong Chalow-thornphises)		15	10
2035	6b. ''Vessantarajataka: Kumara Kanda'' (Surasin Chinna-wong)		15	10
2036	7b. ''Vessantarajataka: Sakkapabba Kanda'' (Chuttumrong Chalow-thornphises)		20	15
2033/2036	*Set of 4*		55	40
MS2037	162 × 120 mm. Nos. 2033/6 (sold at 30b.)		85	85

683 Kiartiwongse and *Phra Ruang* (destroyer)

(Des S. Leedul. Litho Thai British Security Ptg Co Ltd)

1998 (19 May). *75th Death Anniv of Admiral Prince Abhakara Kiartiwongse, Prince of Jumborn.* W **457** (*sideways*). P 14½ × 14.

| 2038 | **683** | 2b. multicoloured | | 10 | 10 |

684 Modern Technology (Porntiva Prasert)

(Litho Thai British Security Ptg Co Ltd)

1998 (15 June). *''Education Develops People and thus Nation''. Under-9 Years Prize-winning Drawings.* W **457** (*sideways*). P 14½ × 14.

| 2039 | **684** | 2b. multicoloured | | 10 | 10 |

685 Commemorative Coin and Map and Flags of Europe (½-*size illustration*)

(Des T. Ponchaiwong. Litho (6b.), embossed and litho (20b.) Thai British Security Ptg Co Ltd)

1998 (1 July). *Centenary (1997) of First State Visit to Europe of King Chulalongkorn (Rama V). Granite paper.* P 13½ × 13.

| 2040 | **685** | 6b. multicoloured | | 15 | 10 |
| 2041 | | 20b. multicoloured | | 55 | 30 |

686 Irrawaddy Dolphin (*Orcaella brevirostris*)

(Des C. Boonyasakdi (9b.), R. Saichumdee (others). Litho Thai British Security Ptg Co Ltd)

1998 (19 July). *International Year of the Ocean. Marine Mammals. T* **686** *and similar horiz designs. Multicoloured. Granite paper.* P 14½ × 14.
2042	2b. Type **686**	10	10
2043	3b. Bottle-nosed dolphin (*Tursiops truncatus*)	10	10
2044	6b. Sperm whale (*Physeter catodon*)	15	10
2045	9b. Dugong (*Dugong dugon*)	25	15
2042/2045 *Set of 4*		55	40
MS2046 164 × 110 mm. Nos. 2042/5 (sold at 30b.)		85	85

687 Dams

(Des C. Thongkaew. Litho Thai British Security Ptg Co Ltd)

1998 (1 Aug). *60th Anniv of Irrigation Engineering. Granite paper.* P 14½ × 14.
2047	**687** 2b. multicoloured	10	10

688 Model of Asynchronous Transfer Mode

(Des U. Niyomthum. Litho Thai British Security Ptg Co Ltd)

1998 (4 Aug). *National Communications Day. Granite paper.* P 14½ × 14.
2048	**688** 2b. multicoloured	10	10

689 Faculty Building and Emblems

(Des S. Leedul. Litho Thai British Security Ptg Co Ltd)

1998 (19 Aug). *50th Anniv of Faculty of Political Science, Chulalongkorn University. Granite paper.* P 14½ × 14.
2049	**689** 2b. multicoloured	10	10

690 Correspondence Students

(Des P. Ponatha. Litho Thai British Security Ptg Co Ltd)

1998 (5 Sept). *20th Anniv of Sukhothai Thammathirat Open University. Granite paper.* P 14½ × 14.
2050	**690** 2b. multicoloured	10	10

691 Warrior   **692** Archer

(Des K. Moka-Siri (2051), R. Saichumdee (2052, 2054), V. Thichuto (2053). Litho Thai British Security Ptg Co Ltd)

1998 (15 Sept). *Chinese Stone Statues. T* **691** *and similar vert designs. Multicoloured. Granite paper.* P 14 × 14½.
2051	2b. Type **691**	10	10
2052	2b. Warrior holding barbed spear	10	10
2053	10b. Warrior holding mace	25	15
2054	10b. Warrior holding spear with jagged blade	25	15
2051/2054 *Set of 4*		65	45
MS2055 110 × 145 mm. Nos. 2051/4. P 13½ (sold at 35b.)		95	95

No. **MS**2055 was issued on 21 August overprinted on the margin for China 1999 stamp exhibition.

(Des. P. Khamprapha (2058), P. Suwun (others). Litho Thai British Security Ptg Co Ltd)

1998 (15 Sept). *"Amazing Thailand" Year. Perforated Hides. T* **692** *and similar vert designs. Multicoloured. Granite paper.* P 13½.
2056	3b. Type **692**	10	10
2057	3b. Warriors on elephants	10	10
2058	7b. Warrior seizing opponent	20	15
2059	7b. Deity hovering in sky	20	15
2056/2059 *Set of 4*		55	45

693 Kraisara Rajasiha (king lion)

(Des A. Tularak. Photo Courvoisier)

1998 (3 Oct). *International Correspondence Week. Himavanta Mythical Animals of the Singha (lion) Family. T* **693** *and similar horiz designs. Multicoloured. Granite paper.* P 11½.
2060	2b. Type **693**	10	10
2061	2b. Gajasiha (tusked lions)	10	10

2062	12b. Kesara Singha (hoofed lions)	. . .	30	20
2063	12b. Singhas	. . . .	30	20
2060/2063 *Set of* 4	. . . .	70	55
MS2064 140 × 99 mm. Nos. 2060/3 (sold at				
	40b.)	. . . .	1·10	1·10

694 International Headquarters, Illinois

(Des S. Leedul. Litho Thai British Security Ptg Co Ltd)

1998 (8 Oct). *Thai Presidency of International Association of Lions Clubs. Granite paper.* P 14½ × 14.
2065 **694** 2b. multicoloured 10 10

ประเทศไทยTHAILAND

695 *Barleria luplina*   **696** Knight Grand Cross (First Class)

(Des Veena Chantanatat. Litho Thai British Security Ptg Co Ltd)

1998 (15 Nov). *New Year. Flowers.* T **695** *and similar horiz designs. Multicoloured. Granite paper.* P 14½ × 14.
2066	2b. Type **695**	. . . .	10	10
2067	2b. Glory lily (*Gloriosa superba*)	. .	10	10
2068	2b. *Asclepias curassavica*	. . . . .	10	10
2069	2b. *Sesamum indicum*	. . . . . .	10	10
2066/2069 *Set of* 4	. . . .	35	35
MS2070 99 × 85 mm. Nos. 2066/9 (sold at				
	15b.)	. . . .	45	45

(Des R. Saichumdee. Litho Thai British Security Ptg Co Ltd)

1998 (5 Dec). *Most Admirable Order of the Direkgunabhorn.* T **696** *and similar vert design. Multicoloured. Granite paper.* P 14 × 14½.
2071	15b. Type **696**	. . . .	40	25
	a. Pair. Nos. 2071/2	. . . .	85	55
2072	15b. Close-up of badge	. . . . .	40	25

Nos. 2071/2 were issued together in *se-tenant* pairs within the sheet.

697 Hockey

(Des S. Poonsawat. Litho Thai British Security Ptg Co Ltd)

1998 (6 Dec). *13th Asian Games, Bangkok.* T **697** *and similar horiz designs. Multicoloured. Granite paper.* P 14½ × 14.
2073	2b. + 1b. Type **697**	. . . . . .	10	10
2074	3b. + 1b. Wrestling	. . . .	15	15

2075	4b. + 1b. Rowing	. . . .	15	15
2076	7b. + 1b. Show jumping	. . . . .	20	20
2073/2076 *Set of* 4	. . . .	55	55

1998 (28 Dec)–**2000**. *Granite paper. Litho.* P 13½.
2077	**641**	2b. carmine-red (*p* 14 × 14½)		
		(1.9.00)	10	10
2078		4b. Venetian red and deep		
		turquoise-blue (1999)	10	10
		a. Perf 14 × 14½ (8.10.99)	10	10
2079		5b. chestnut and slate-violet . . .	15	15
		a. Perf 14 × 14½ (8.10.99)	15	15

The filaments (which are luminescent) in the paper used for this issue are scattered so that some stamps appear to be on plain paper.

Numbers have been left for additions to this series.

A set of eight gold stamps and two gold miniature sheets reproducing the designs of Nos. 2016/19 and 2073/6 have been issued for the 13th Asian Games, Bangkok.

698 "Gymkhana" (Khontorn Taechoran)

(Litho Thai British Security Ptg Co Ltd)

1999 (9 Jan). *Children's Day. Children's Paintings.* T **698** *and similar horiz designs. Multicoloured. Granite paper.* P 14½ × 14.
2081	2b. Type **698**	. . . .	10	10
2082	2b. "Swimming" (Sunhapong			
	Phitukburapa)	. . . .	10	10
2083	2b. "Volleyball" (Vipharat Sae Lim)	. .	10	10
2084	2b. "Sepak Takraw" (three-aside net			
	game) (Phanot Ratanawongkae)	. .	10	10
2081/2084 *Set of* 4	. . . .	35	35

Nos. 2081/4 were issued both in separate sheets and together in *se-tenant* blocks of four stamps within sheets of 20 stamps.

699 Wheel-chair Athletes

(Des S. Leedul. Litho Thai British Security Ptg Co Ltd)

1999 (10 Jan). *Asian and Pacific Decade of Disabled Persons. Granite paper.* P 14½ × 14.
2085 **699** 2b. multicoloured 10 10

700 Paddy Sprouts and Workers planting Rice

(Des S. Poonsawat. Litho Thai British Security Ptg Co Ltd)

1999 (25 Feb). *Rice Cultivation.* T **700** *and similar horiz designs. Multicoloured. Granite paper.* P 14½ × 14.
2086	6b. Type **700**	. . . .	15	10
2087	6b. Workers harvesting rice and ear of			
	paddy	. . . .	15	10

2088	12b. Paddy-threshing machine	30	20
2089	12b. Golden paddy field and bowl of cooked rice	30	20
2086/2089 *Set of 4*		80	55
MS2090 144 × 110 mm. Nos. 2086/90. P 13½ (sold at 45b.)		1·20	1·20

701 Birth of Mahajanaka

702 Queen Somdetch the Queen Grandmother

(Des K. Moka-Siri. Litho Thai British Security Ptg Co Ltd)

1999 (1 Mar). *Maghapuja Day.* T **701** *and similar horiz designs showing murals from Wat Tha Sutthawat illustrating the story of Mahajanaka. Granite paper.* P 13½.

2091	3b. Type **701**	10	10
2092	6b. Mani Mekkhala carrying Mahajanaka to Mithila City	15	10
2093	9b. Two mango trees	25	15
2094	15b. Mahajanaka founding educational institute	40	25
2091/2094 *Set of 4*		80	55
MS2095 151 × 127 mm. Nos. 2091/4 (sold at 45b.)		1·20	1·20

(Des C. Thongkaew. Litho Thai British Security Ptg Co Ltd)

1999 (30 Mar). *Red Cross.* W **457**. P 14 × 14½.

2096	**702** 2b. multicoloured	10	10

703 Kite Flying

704 "Hooks and Squids" Motif

(Des T. Lopaiboon. Litho Thai British Security Ptg Co Ltd)

1999 (30 Mar)–**2000**. *"BANGKOK 2000" World Youth Stamp Exhibition and 13th Asian International Stamp Exhibition, Bangkok. Children's Games.* T **703** *and similar horiz designs. Multicoloured. Granite paper.* P 14½ × 14.

2097	2b. Type **703**	10	10
	a. Booklet pane. Nos. 2097/2100 plus 2 labels (25.3.00)	1·10	
	b. Booklet pane. Nos. 2097/8, 2119/20 and 2195/6 (25.3.00)	65	
	c. Booklet pane. Nos. 2099/2100, 2121/2 and 2197/8 (25.3.00)	5·00	
2098	2b. Hoop rolling	10	10

2099	15b. Catching the last one in the line (children passing under arched arms)	40	25
2100	15b. Snatching a baby from Mother Snake	40	25
2097/2100 *Set of 4*		90	65
MS2101 145 × 110 mm. Nos. 2097/2100. P 13½ (sold at 45b.)		1·20	1·20

See also Nos. 2119/**MS**2123 and 2195/**MS**2199.

(Des Veena Chantanatat. Litho Thai British Security Ptg Co Ltd)

1999 (2 Apr). *Thai Heritage Conservation Day. Silk Mudmee Textiles.* T **704** *and similar vert designs. Multicoloured. Granite paper.* P 14 × 14½.

2102	2b. Type **704**	10	10
2103	4b. "Royal Umbrella" motif	15	10
2104	12b. "Naga upholding the Baisi" motif	30	20
2105	15b. "Naga upholding a flower pot" motif	40	25
2102/2105 *Set of 4*		85	60
MS2106 110 × 144 mm. Nos. 2102/5. P 13½ (sold at 45b.)		1·20	1·20

705 Woman riding Rabbit

706 Hands encircling Emblem

(Des N. Kaewsawang. Litho Thai British Security Ptg Co Ltd)

1999 (13 Apr). *Songkran (New Year) Day. Year of the Rabbit. Granite paper.* P 14 × 14½.

2107	**705** 2b. multicoloured	10	10
MS2108 Two sheets, each 80 × 100 mm, each containing No. 2107. (a) Perf; (b) Imperf (pair sold at 16b.)		50	50

No. **MS**2108 was issued on 21 August overprinted on the margin for China 99 stamp exhibition in Chinese and English.

(Des S. Poonsawat. Litho Thai British Security Ptg Co Ltd)

1999 (30 Apr). *Consumer Protection Years, 1998–1999. Granite paper.* P 14½ × 14.

2109	**706** 2b. multicoloured	10	10

707 Chitralada Villa, Dusit Palace, Bangkok

(Des S. Koshapasharin. Photo Courvoisier)

1999 (5 May). *Sixth Cycle (72nd Birthday) of King Bhumibol (1st issue). Royal Palaces.* T **707** *and similar horiz designs. Multicoloured. Granite paper.* P 11½.

2110	6b. Type **707**	25	15
2111	6b. Phu Phing Ratchaniwet Palace, Chieng Mai Province (red and green roofs)	25	15
2112	6b. Phu Phan Ratchaniwet Palace, Sakon Nakhon province (with large green lawn)	25	15
2113	6b. Thaksin Ratchaniwet Palace, Narathiwat Province (two-storey building with drive and ornamental trees)	25	15

2110/2113 *Set of 4* 90   55
MS2114 185 × 125 mm. Nos. 2110/13 (sold at
40b.) . . . . 1·10   1·10
See also Nos. 2130/**MS**2139, 2146/**MS**2155 and 2161/**MS**2164.

708 Administrative
Building and Faculty
Emblem

709 Float, Candle Festival, Ubon
Ratchathani

(Des S. Yadee. Litho)

1999 (14 June). *50th Anniv of Political Science Faculty,
Thammasat University.* P 14 × 14½.
2115 **708** 3b. multicoloured 10   10

(Des U. Niyomthum. Litho Thai British Security Ptg Co Ltd)

1999 (1 July). *125th Anniv of Universal Postal Union. T* **709** *and
similar horiz design. Multicoloured. Granite paper.* P 14½ × 14.
2116   2b. Floating vessel, Light Festival . . . 10   10
2117   15b. Type **709** 80   50

710 King Chulalongkorn and Customs
Building

(Des S. Poonsawat. Litho Chan Wanich Security Ptg Co Ltd)

1999 (3 July). *125th Anniv of the Customs Department. Granite
paper.* P 14½ × 14.
2118 **710** 6b. multicoloured 35   20

711 Sut Sakhon riding Dragon

(Des T. Lopaiboon. Litho Thai British Security Ptg Co Ltd)

1999 (4 Aug). *"BANGKOK 2000" World Youth Stamp Exhibition
and 13th Asian International Stamp Exhibition, Bangkok (2nd
issue). Folk Tales. T* **711** *and similar horiz designs.
Multicoloured. Granite paper.* P 14½ × 14.
2119   2b. Type **711** (Tale of Phra Aphai
Mani) 10   10
   a. Booklet pane. Nos. 2119/22 plus 2
labels (25.3.00) . . . . 1·30

2120   2b. Rishi transforming tiger cub and
cow calf into children (Tale of
Honwichai-Khawi) 10   10
2121   15b. Phra Sang climbing out of conch
shell (Tale of Sang Thong) 50   30
2122   15b. Khun Chang, Khun Phaen and
Nang Phim playing (Tale of Khun
Chang and Khun Phaen) 50   30
2119/2122 *Set of 4* . . . . 1·10   70
MS2123 144 × 110 mm. Nos. 2119/22. P 13½
(sold at 45b.) . . . . 2·50   2·50

712 Communication by Eye, Ear, Mouth
and Hand

(Des U. Niyomthum. Litho Thai British Security Ptg Co Ltd)

1999 (4 Aug). *National Communications Day. Granite paper.*
P 14½ × 14.
2124 **712** 4b. multicoloured 20   15

713 Rabbits

714 Prince Mahidol with
Bhumibol as Baby

(Des C. Boonyasakdi (2125, 2128), K. Kobsuntia (2126),
R. Saichumdee (2127). Litho Thai British Security Ptg Co Ltd)

1999 (4 Aug). *"THAIPEX '99" 13th Thailand Stamp Exhibition,
Bangkok. Domestic Rabbits. T* **713** *and similar horiz designs.
Multicoloured. Granite paper.* P 14½ × 14.
2125   6b. Type **713** 35   20
2126   6b. One golden and one brown
rabbit 35   20
2127   12b. One grey and one grey and white
rabbit 65   40
2128   12b. Two white rabbits 65   40
2125/2128 *Set of 4* . . . . 1·80   1·10
MS2129 144 × 110 mm. Nos. 2125/8. P 13½
(sold at 50b.) . . . . 3·50   3·25
No. **MS**2129 also exists imperforate with no selling price.

(Des T. Thongkhambai. Photo Courvoisier)

1999 (10 Sept). *Sixth Cycle (72nd Birthday) of King Bhumibol (2nd
issue). Portraits of the King. T* **714** *and similar vert designs.
Multicoloured. Granite paper.* P 12.
2130   3b. Type **714** 10   10
2131   3b. Princess Mother and her
children 10   10
2132   3b. With his brother King Ananda
Mahidol 10   10
2133   6b. Bhumibol and King Ananda Mahidol
in military uniform 30   20
2134   6b. On wedding day 30   20
2135   6b. Coronation ceremony 30   20
2136   12b. As a monk 65   40

2137	12b. King and Queen with their children	65	40
2138	12b. In royal robes	65	40
2130/2138	Set of 9	2·75	1·90

MS2139 134 × 214 mm. Nos. 2130/8 (sold at 90b.) . . . . 4·75 4·75

715 Older Person with Children

716 Orchid Tree (*Bauhinia variegata*)

(Des S. Leedul. Litho Thai British Security Ptg Co Ltd)

1999 (1 Oct). *International Year of the Elderly. Granite paper.* P 14½ × 14.

| 2140 | **715** | 2b. multicoloured | 10 | 10 |

(Des P. Khamprapha (2141, 2143), R. Kiewrueng (2142), C. Boonyasakdi (2144). Litho Thai British Security Ptg Co Ltd)

1999 (2 Oct). *International Correspondence Week. Flowers.* T **716** *and similar vert designs. Multicoloured. Granite paper.* P 14 × 14½.

2141	2b. Type **716**	10	10
2142	2b. *Bombax ceiba* (red flower)	10	10
2143	12b. *Radermachera ignea* (tubular yellow flowers)	65	40
2144	12b. *Bretschneidera sinensis* (pink bell flowers)	65	40
2141/2144	Set of 4	1·40	90

MS2145 110 × 145 mm. Nos. 2141/4. P 13½ (sold at 35b.) . . . . 1·90 1·90

717 In Open-top Car on Returning to School in Switzerland

(Des T. Ponchaiwong. Photo De La Rue)

1999 (21 Oct). *Sixth Cycle (72nd Birthday) of King Bhumibol (3rd issue). The King and his Subjects.* T **717** *and similar horiz designs. Multicoloured. Granite paper.* P 14½.

2146	3b. Type **717**	10	10
2147	3b. With Buddhist monks	10	10
2148	3b. King and Queen with students	10	10
2149	6b. With soldiers	30	20
2150	6b. With children prostrate at his feet	30	20
2151	6b. With boy on crutches	30	20
2152	12b. Visiting a hilltribe home	65	40
2153	12b. Drawing plan on ground	65	40
2154	12b. Talking to crowds	65	40
2146/2154	Set of 9	2·75	1·90

MS2155 215 × 135 mm. Nos. 2146/54 (sold at 90b.) . . . . 4·75 4·75

718 *Thunbergia laurifolia*

719 King Bhumibol

(Des R. Saichumdee. Litho Thai British Security Ptg Co Ltd)

1999 (15 Nov). *New Year. Flowers.* T **718** *and similar horiz designs. Granite paper.* P 14½ × 14.

2156	2b. Type **718**	10	10
2157	2b. *Gmelina arborea*	10	10
2158	2b. *Prunus cerasoides*	10	10
2159	2b. *Fagraea fragans*	10	10
2156/2159	Set of 4	35	35

MS2160 99 × 85 mm. Nos. 2156/9 (sold at 15b.) 90 90

Nos. 2156/8 were re-issued on 25 March 2000 in sheets of 15 stamps and ten plain labels intended for the addition of personalized photographs, either taken at the show by a private firm or submitted by the customer. The 15 values occur in vertical rows of five stamps of each value in vertical columns 1, 3 and 5.

The sheets were only available at the "Bangkok 2000" International Youth Stamp Exhibition at a cost of 60b.

(Des S. Poonsawat. Litho and embossed Cartor)

1999 (15 Nov). *Sixth Cycle (72nd Birthday) of King Bhumibol (4th issue).* W **380**. P 13½.

2161	**719**	100b. gold and deep ultramarine	6·00	6·00
2162		100b. silver and deep ultramarine	6·00	6·00
2163		100b. bronze and deep ultramarine	6·00	6·00

MS2164 175 × 140 mm. Nos. 2161/3 (sold at 350b.) . . . . 22·00 22·00

720 King Bhumibol and Prince Vajiralongkorn

721 Lilies, Thale Noi

(Des T. Ponchaiwong. Litho Thai British Security Ptg Co Ltd)

1999 (28 Dec). *Investiture of Crown Prince Maha Vajiralongkorn. Granite paper.* P 14 × 14½.

| 2165 | **720** | 3b. multicoloured | 20 | 20 |

(Des S. Poonsawat. Litho Thai British Security Ptg Co Ltd)

2000 (1 Jan). *Lake of Lilies, Phatthalung Province.* T **721** *and similar horiz designs. Multicoloured. Granite paper.* P 14½.

2166	3b. Type **721**	20	20
	a. Sheetlet of 12. Nos. 2166/77	2·10	
2167	3b. Forest and lilies	20	20
2168	3b. Forest, buildings and lilies	20	20

2169	3b. Birds flying over lilies		20	20
2170	3b. Fifteen lily flowers		20	20
2171	3b. Seven lily flowers		20	20
2172	3b. Six lily flowers		20	20
2173	3b. Eight lily flowers and three buds		20	20
2174	3b. Four lily flowers and two buds		20	20
2175	3b. Two lily flowers and eight lily pads		20	20
2176	3b. Two lily flowers		20	20
2177	3b. Three lily flowers		20	20
2166/2177 *Set of 12*			2·10	2·10

Nos. 2166/77 were issued together in *se-tenant* sheetlets of 12 stamps, each sheetlet forming a composite design of the lake. The stamps are identified by the number of complete flowers shown.

722 Flowers **723** Small Dwarf Honey Bee (*Apis andreniformis*)

(Des T. Thongkhambai. Litho Chan Wanich Security Ptg Co Ltd)

2000 (25 Feb). *Kulap Khao Meadow, Chiang Mai Province.* T **722** and similar horiz designs. Multicoloured. Granite paper. P 14½.

2178	3b. Type **722**		20	20
	a. Sheetlet of 12. Nos. 2178/89		2·10	
2179	3b. Flowers and two peaks		20	20
2180	3b. Flowers, four buds and mountains		20	20
2181	3b. Flowers, three buds and mountains		20	20
2182	3b. Three open flowers		20	20
2183	3b. Open flowers and seven buds		20	20
2184	3b. Open flowers and six buds		20	20
2185	3b. Open flowers and one bud		20	20
2186	3b. One open flower and five buds		20	20
2187	3b. Open flowers and four buds		20	20
2188	3b. Four open flowers		20	20
2189	3b. Four partially open flowers		20	20
2178/2189 *Set of 12*			2·10	2·10

Nos. 2178/89 were issued together in *se-tenant* sheetlets of 12 stamps, each sheetlet forming a composite design of the Kulap Khao meadow. The stamps are identified by the number of complete flowers and buds shown.

(Des R. Saichumdee. Photo Courvoisier)

2000 (19 Mar). *Bees.* T **723** and similar horiz designs. Multicoloured. Granite paper. P 12.

2190	3b. Type **723**		20	20
2191	3b. Dwarf bee (*Apis florea*)		20	20
2192	3b. Asian honey bee (*Apis cerana*)		20	20
2193	3b. Giant bee (*Apis dorsata*)		20	20
2190/2193 *Set of 4*			70	70

MS2194 Four sheets, each 83 × 54 mm. (a) As Type **723**; (b) As No. 2191; (c) As No. 2192; (d) As No. 2193 . . . . . 2·10 2·10

724 Child being Blessed

(Des Veena Chantanatat. Litho Thai British Security Ptg Co Ltd)

2000 (25 Mar). *"BANGKOK 2000" International Youth Stamp Exhibition and 13th Asian International Stamp Exhibition, Bangkok (3rd issue). Ceremonies.* T **724** and similar horiz designs. Multicoloured. Granite paper. P 14½ × 14.

2195	2b. Type **724**		10	10
	a. Booklet pane. Nos. 2195/8		2·10	
2196	2b. Woman cutting child's hair (Tonsure ceremony)		10	10
2197	15b. Pupils paying respects to teacher		95	60
2198	15b. Boy being carried aloft during ordination of novice		95	60
2195/2198 *Set of 4*			1·90	1·30

MS2199 110 × 144 mm. Nos. 2195/8. P 14 (sold at 45b.) . . . . 2·75 2·75

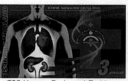

725 Human Body and Emblem

(Des U. Niyomthum. Litho Thai British Security Ptg Co Ltd)

2000 (30 Mar). *Thai Red Cross Organ Donation Campaign.* Granite paper. P 14½ × 14.

2200	**725**	3b. multicoloured	20	10

726 Sukhothai Province **727** Angel riding Dragon

(Des Veena Chantanatat. Litho Enschedé)

2000 (2 Apr). *Thai Heritage Conservation. Chok Cloth Designs.* T **726** and similar horiz designs. Multicoloured. W **380**. P 13½.

2201	3b. Type **726**		20	10
2202	6b. Chiang Mai Province		45	30
2203	8b. Uthai Thani Province		65	40
2204	12b. Ratchaburi Province		90	55
2201/2204 *Set of 4*			2·00	1·20

MS2205 110 × 145 mm. Nos. 2201/4 (sold at 40b.) . . . . 2·50 2·50

(Des N. Kaewsawang. Litho Thai British Security Ptg Co Ltd)

2000 (13 Apr). *Songkran (New Year) Day. Year of the Dragon.* Granite paper. P 14 × 14½.

2206	**727**	2b. multicoloured	10	10

MS2207 Two sheets, each 80 × 100 mm, each containing No. 2206. (a) Perf; (b) imperf (pair sold at 16b.) . . . . . 1·00 1·00

728 Engagement Photograph (⅓-size illustration)

(Ds T. Thongkhambai. Photo Courvoisier)

2000 (28 Apr). *Golden Wedding Anniversary of King Bhumibol and Queen Sirikit.* T **728** and similar horiz designs. Multicoloured. Granite paper. P 11½ × 12.

2208	10b. Type **728**		65	40
	a. Vert strip of 5. Nos. 2208/12		3·25	
2209	10b. Signing marriage register, 1950		65	40
2210	10b. Sitting on thrones during Coronation ceremony		65	40

2211	10b. With family	65	40
2212	10b. King Bhumibol and Queen Sirikit, 2000	65	40
2208/2212 *Set of 5*		3·00	1·80

729 Buddha   **730** Flowers and Trees, Krachieo

(Des T. Thongkhambai. Litho Thai British Security Ptg Co Ltd)

2000 (16 July). *Asalhapuja Day. Granite paper.* P 14 × 14½.

2213	**729**	3b. multicoloured	20	20

(Des Veena Chantanatat. Litho Thai British Security Ptg Co Ltd)

2000 (16 July). *Krachieo Meadow, Pa Hin Ngam, Chaiyaphum Province. T* **730** *and similar horiz designs. Multicoloured. Granite paper.* P 14½ × 14.

2214	3b. Type **730**		20	20
	a. Sheetlet of 12. Nos. 2214/25		2·20	
2215	3b. Flowers and sparse trees in distance		20	20
2216	3b. Flowers, two close trees and dense trees in distance		20	20
2217	3b. Flowers, four close trees and dense trees in distance		20	20
2218	3b. Six complete flowers		20	20
2219	3b. Eleven complete flowers		20	20
2220	3b. Seven complete flowers and half a flower at right-hand side		20	20
2221	3b. Six complete flowers and two incomplete flowers at bottom		20	20
2222	3b. Two flowers		20	20
2223	3b. Three flowers close together		20	20
2224	3b. One open and two partially open flowers		20	20
2225	3b. Two complete and three incomplete flowers		20	20
2214/2225 *Set of 12*			2·20	2·20

Nos. 2214/25 were issued together in *se-tenant* sheetlets of 12 stamps, each sheetlet forming a composite design of the meadow. The stamps are identified by the number of trees or flowers shown.

731 Crown Prince and Rice Seeds Sowing Ceremony

(Des T. Ponchaiwong. Litho Thai British Security Ptg Co Ltd)

2000 (28 July). *Fourth Cycle (48th Birthday) of Crown Prince Maha Vajiralongkorn. Granite paper.* P 14½ × 14.

2226	**731**	2b. multicoloured	10	10
MS2227 125 × 90 mm. No. 2226. P 13½ (sold at 8b.)			50	50

732 Sun, Emblem, Envelope and Moon

(Des T. Ponchaiwong. Litho Thai British Security Ptg Co Ltd)

2000 (4 Aug). *National Communications Day. Granite paper.* P 14½ × 14.

2228	**732**	3b. multicoloured	20	10

733 Cabbage Design Tea Set

(Des Veena Chantanatat (2229), K. Kobsuntia (2232), C. Boonyasakdi (others). Litho Thai British Security Ptg Co Ltd)

2000 (7 Oct). *International Correspondence Week. Rattanakosin Period Tea Sets. T* **733** *and similar horiz designs. Multicoloured. Granite paper.* P 14½ × 14.

2229	6b. Type **733**		35	20
2230	6b. Duck and animals in lotus pond design		35	20
2231	12b. Lotus bud design		75	45
2232	12b. Butterflies and bees design		75	45
2229/2232 *Set of 4*			2·00	1·20
MS2233 144 × 110 mm. Nos. 2229/32. P 13½ (sold at 45b.)			2·75	2·75

734 Princess Srinagarindra   **735** Glory Bower (*Clerodendrum philippinum*)

(Des C. Thongkaew. Litho Thai British Security Ptg Co Ltd)

2000 (21 Oct). *Birth Centenary of Princess Srinagarindra the Princess Mother. Granite paper.* P 14½ × 14.

2234	**734**	2b. multicoloured	10	10
MS2235 125 × 90 mm. **734** 2b. multicoloured. P 13½			50	50

(Des T. Ponchaiwong. Litho)

2000 (15 Nov). *New Year. Flowers. T* **735** *and similar horiz designs. Multicoloured. Granite paper.* P 14½ × 14.

2236	2b. Type **735**		10	10
2237	2b. *Capparis micracantha*		10	10
2238	2b. Leopard lily (*Belamcanda chinensis*)		10	10
2239	2b. *Memecylon caeruleum*		10	10
2236/2239 *Set of 4*			35	35
MS2240 85 × 100 mm. Nos. 2236/9 (sold at 15b.)			90	80

736 Flowers

737 *Anantanakkharat* (Royal Barge, 1914) (⅓-*size illustration*)

740 Manta Ray

741 Diamond and Ring

(Des R. Saichumdee. Litho Chan Wanich Security Ptg Co Ltd)

2000 (15 Nov). *Bua Tong Meadow, Mae Hong Son Province. T* **736** *and similar horiz designs. Multicoloured. Granite paper.* P 14½ × 14.

2241	3b. Type **736**	20	20
	a. Sheetlet of 12. Nos. 2241/52	2·20	
2242	3b. Meadow and trees (top left)	20	20
2243	3b. Meadow	20	20
2244	3b. Meadow and trees (top right)	20	20
2245	3b. Four flowers	20	20
2246	3b. Eleven flowers	20	20
2247	3b. Fifteen flowers	20	20
2248	3b. Twelve flowers	20	20
2249	3b. Three large flowers, two smaller flowers and one dead flower	20	20
2250	3b. Three large flowers	20	20
2251	3b. One large flower	20	20
2252	3b. Five flowers and one dead flower	20	20
2241/2252	*Set of 12*	2·20	2·20

Nos. 2241/52 were issued together in *se-tenant* sheetlets of 12 stamps, each sheetlet forming a composite design.

The stamps are identified by the number of complete flowers shown.

(Des T. Thongkhambai. Photo Enschedé)

2000 (15 Nov). W **457** (*sideways*). P 13½ × 14.

2253	**737**	9b. multicoloured	50	30
MS2254		157 × 95 mm. No. 2253 (sold at 15b.)	90	90

738 Moustached Parakeet (*Psittacula alexandri*)

739 King Rama V and First Title Deed

(Des T. Thongkhambai. Litho Thai British Security Ptg Co Ltd)

2001 (13 Jan). *Parrots. T* **738** *and similar vert designs. Multicoloured. Granite paper.* P 14 × 14½.

2255	2b. Type **738**	10	10
2256	5b. Alexandrine parakeet (*Psittacula eupatria*)	30	20
2257	8b. *Psittacula cyanurus*	45	30
2258	10b. Blossom-headed parakeet (*Psittacula roseate*)	60	35
2255/2258	*Set of 4*	1·30	85
MS2259	110 × 144 mm. Nos. 2255/8. P 13½ (sold at 35b.)	1·80	1·80

(Des U. Niyomthum. Litho Thai British Security Ptg Co Ltd)

2001 (17 Feb). *Centenary of Department of Lands. Granite paper.* P 14 × 14½.

2260	**739** 5b. multicoloured	30	20

(Des U. Niyomthum. Photo Questa)

2001 (15 Mar). *Marine Life. T* **740** *and similar multicoloured designs. Granite paper.* P 14.

2261	3b. Type **740**	20	20
	a. Sheetlet. Nos. 2261/9	1·90	
2262	3b. Fishes and jellyfish	20	20
2263	3b. Turtle	20	20
2264	3b. Coral and lionfish	20	20
2265	3b. Black and white fish and coral	20	20
2266	3b. Head of eel and yellow coral	20	20
2267	6b. Fishes and coral (28 × 47 *mm*)	30	30
2268	6b. Pufferfish and other fishes (28 × 47 *mm*)	30	30
2269	6b. Yellow and blue fish and coral (45 × 23 *mm*)	30	30
2261/2269	*Set of 9*	1·90	1·90

Nos. 2261/9 were issued together in *se-tenant* sheetlets of nine stamps, each sheetlet forming a composite design.

(Des K. Moka-siri (2270) or C. Boonyasakdi (others). Litho Thai British Security Ptg Co Ltd)

2001 (30 Mar). *Precious Stones. T* **741** *and similar horiz designs. Multicoloured. Granite paper.* P 14½ × 14.

2270	3b. Type **741**	20	10
2271	4b. Green sapphire and necklace	30	20
2272	6b. Pearl and necklace	35	20
2273	12b. Blue sapphire and necklace	65	40
2270/2273	*Set of 4*	1·30	80
MS2274	110 × 144 mm. Nos. 2270/3. P 13½–14 × 14½* (sold at 35b.)	2·10	2·10

The stamps in **MS**2274 are arranged in a staggered vertical strip of four. The bottom perforation of the 3b., both horizontal perforations of the 4b. and 6b. and the top perforation of the 12b. are a compound of 13½–14. The latter gauge occurs on the part of the perforation which is common to both stamps.

742 Women and Orphans

743 Gold and Red Brocade

(Des S. Leedul. Litho Chan Wanich Security Ptg Co Ltd)

2001 (1 Apr). *Red Cross. 20th Anniv of Thai Red Cross Children's Homes. Granite paper.* P 14½ × 14.

2275	**742** 4b. multicoloured	20	15

(Des Veena Chantanatat. Litho Chan Wanich Security Ptg Co Ltd)

2001 (2 Apr). *Thai Heritage Conservation Day. T* **743** *and similar vert designs showing different brocade designs. Multicoloured. Granite paper.* P 14 × 14½.

2276	2b. Type **743**	10	10
2277	3b. Green and gold design	20	15

2278	10b. Orange and gold design		60	25
2279	10b. Pink and gold design		60	25
2276/2279 *Set of 4*			1·30	85
MS2280 110 × 145 mm. Nos. 2276/9. P 13½				
(sold at 35b.)			2·10	2·10

744 Woman riding Snake   **745** Buddha

(Des N. Kaewsawang. Litho Enschedé)

2001 (13 Apr). *Songkran (New Year) Day. Year of the Snake. Granite paper.* W **380**. P 13½ × 14.

2281	**744**	2b. multicoloured	10	10

MS2282 Two sheets, each 80 × 100 mm, each containing No. 2281. (a) Perf; (b) imperf (pair sold at 16b.)   1·00   1·00

(Des T. Thongkhambai. Litho Chan Wanich Security Ptg Co Ltd)

2001 (7 May). *Visakhapuja Day. Granite paper.* P 14 × 14½.

2283	**745**	3b. multicoloured	20	15

746 Maiyarap, Emerald Buddha Temple   **747** Prince Purachatra Jayakara (first governor)

(Des Veena Chantanatat. Litho Thai British Security Ptg Co Ltd)

2001 (13 June). *Demon Statues. T* **746** *and similar vert designs. Multicoloured. Granite paper.* P 14 × 14½.

2284	2b. Type **746**		10	10
2285	5b. Wirunchambang, Emerald Buddha Temple		30	20
2286	10b. Thotsakan, Temple of Dawn		60	35
2287	12b. Sahatsadecha, Temple of Dawn		75	45
2284/2287 *Set of 4*			1·60	1·00
MS2288 145 × 110 mm. Nos. 2284/7. P 13½				
(sold at 33b.)			2·10	2·10

(Des S. Leedul. Litho Thai British Security Ptg Co Ltd)

2001 (1 July). *66th Anniv of Rotary International in Thailand. Granite paper.* P 14 × 14½.

2289	**747**	3b. multicoloured	20	15

748 Split Gill (*Schizophyllum commune*)

(Des C. Thongkaew. Photo Questa)

2001 (4 July). *Fungi. T* **748** *and similar horiz designs. Multicoloured. Granite paper.* P 14.

2290	2b. Type **748**		10	10
2291	3b. *Lentinus giganteus*		20	15
2292	5b. *Pleurotus citrinopileatus*		30	20
2293	10b. *Pleurotus flabellatus*		60	35
2290/2293 *Set of 4*			1·10	70
MS2294 110 × 145 mm. Nos. 2290/3. P 13½				
(sold at 26b.)			1·50	1·50

749 *Cheirotonus parryi*

(Des T. Ponchaiwong. Photo Govt Ptg Wks, Tokyo)

2001 (4 July). *Insects. T* **749** *and similar horiz designs. Multicoloured.* W **109**. P 13½.

2295	2b. Type **749**		10	10
2296	5b. *Mouhotia batsei*		30	20
2297	6b. *Cladognathus giraffa*		35	30
2298	12b. Violin beetle (*Mormolyce phyllodes*)		65	40
2295/2298 *Set of 4*			1·30	90
MS2299 145 × 110 mm. Nos. 2295/8 (sold at 34b.)			2·10	2·10

750 Lueng Hang Khoa (Aim-orn Saichumdee)

(Photo Questa)

2001 (4 Aug). *"THAIPEX '01" National Stamp Exhibition. Domestic Fowl. T* **750** *and similar horiz designs showing winning entries in the 1999 International Letter Writing Week painting competition. Multicoloured. Granite paper.* P 13½.

2300	3b. Type **750**		10	10
2301	4b. Lueng Hang Khoa (Rong Saichumdee)		20	15
2302	6b. Samae Dam (Rong Saichumdee)		35	20
2303	12b. Pradue Hang Dam (Chanthorn Niyomthum)		75	45
2300/2303 *Set of 4*			1·30	80
MS2304 145 × 110 mm. Nos. 2300/3. Perf or imperf (sold at 33b.)			1·90	1·90

751 "Thai Children in the I.T. Era"
(Sriarpha Kamlanglua)

752 Queen
Suriyodaya

(Litho Chan Wanich Security Ptg Co Ltd)

2001 (4 Aug). *National Communications Day. Winning Entry in the 2000 Children's International Letter Writing Week Painting Competition. Granite paper.* P 14½ × 14.

2305	**751**	4b. multicoloured	30	20

(Des Veena Chantanatat. Litho Thai British Security Ptg Co Ltd)

2001 (12 Aug). *Queen Suriyodaya Commemoration. Granite paper.* P 14½ × 14½.

2306	**752**	3b. multicoloured	30	20
MS2307	90 × 125 mm. No. 2306. P 13½ (sold at 10b.)		90	90

753 Queen meeting Pres. Jiang Ze Ming
and Great Wall of China

(Des S. Leedul. Litho Chan Wanich Security Ptg Co Ltd)

2001 (12 Aug). *Visit by Queen Sirikit to People's Republic of China. Granite paper.* P 14½ × 14.

2308	**753**	5b. multicoloured	30	20

754 *Pachliopta aristolochiae goniopeltis*

(Des R. Sichumdee. Photo Enschedé)

2001 (10 Sept). *Butterflies. T* **754** *and similar horiz designs. Multicoloured.* P 13½ (with one elliptical hole on each horiz edge).

2309	2b. Type **754**		15	10
2310	4b. *Rhinopalpa polynice*		30	20
2311	10b. *Poritia erycinoides*		65	40
2312	12b. *Spindasis iohita*		75	45
2309/2312	*Set of 4*		1·60	1·00
MS2313	145 × 110 mm. Nos. 2309/2312 (sold at 40b.)		2·75	2·75

755 *Piper nigrum*

756 King Chulalongkorn, Academy
Buildings and Logo

(Des V. Chantrasarn (2314), K. Moka (2315), Aim-Orn Saichumdee (2316), C. Boonyasakdi (2317). Litho Thai British Security Ptg Co Ltd)

2001 (6 Oct). *International Correspondence Week. Plants. T* **755** *and similar vert designs. Multicoloured. Granite paper.* P 14 × 14½.

2314	2b. Type **755**		10	10
2315	3b. *Solanum trilobatum*		20	10
2316	5b. *Boesenbergia rotunda*		30	20
2317	10b. *Ocimum tenuiflorum*		60	35
2314/2317	*Set of 4*		1·10	70
MS2318	110 × 144 mm. Nos. 2314/17. P 13½ (sold at 25b.)		1·60	1·60

(Des C. Thongkaew. Litho Thai British Security Ptg Co Ltd)

2001 (13 Oct). *Centenary of Police Cadet Academy. Granite paper.* P 14½ × 14.

2319	**756**	5b. multicoloured	35	20

757 *Pedicularis
siamensis*

758 *Anekkachat Puchong* (Royal Barge,
King Rama V) (⅓-size illustration)

(Des T. Ponchaiwong. Litho)

2001 (15 Nov). *New Year. Flowers. T* **757** *and similar vert designs. Multicoloured. Granite paper.* P 14 × 14½.

2320	2b. Type **757**		10	10
2321	2b. *Schouteina glomerata*		10	10
2322	2b. *Gentiana crassa*		10	10
2323	2b. *Colquhounia coccinea*		10	10
2320/2323	*Set of 4*		35	35
MS2324	85 × 100 mm. Nos. 2320/3 (sold at 11b.)		75	75

(Des T. Thongkhambai. Photo Questa)

2001 (15 Nov). *Granite paper.* P 14 × 14½.

2325	**758**	9b. multicoloured	60	35
MS2326	157 × 95 mm. No. 2325 (sold at 17b.)		1·10	1·10

759 Terminal Building

760 Rose

(Des T. Ponchaiwong. Litho Thai British Security Ptg Co Ltd)

2002 (19 Jan). *Foundation Stone Laying Ceremony, Suvarnabhumi Airport Passenger Terminal. Paper with fluorescent fibres. Litho.* P 14½ × 14.

| 2327 | **759** | 3b. multicoloured | 20 | 15 |

(Des R. Saichumdee. Litho Questa)

2002 (1 Feb). *Paper with fluorescent fibres.* P 14.

| 2328 | **760** | 4b. multicoloured | 30 | 20 |

761 Operating Theatre   **762** Globe, Satellite and Emblem

(Des C. Thongkaew. Litho Thai British Security Ptg Co Ltd)

2002 (24 Feb). *World Gastroenterology Congress. Paper with fluorescent fibres.* P 14 × 14½.

| 2329 | **761** | 3b. multicoloured | 20 | 15 |

(Des T. Ponchaiwong. Litho Thai British Security Ptg Co Ltd)

2002 (25 Feb). *25th Anniv of Communications Authority.* T **762** *and similar horiz design. Multicoloured. Paper with fluorescent fibres.* P 14½ × 14.

2330	3r. Type **762**	20	15
	a. Pair. Nos. 2330/1	45	35
2331	3r. Envelope and post box	20	15
MS2332	110 × 86 mm. Nos. 2330/1. P 13½	75	75

Nos. 2330/1 were issued in horizontal *se-tenant* pairs within the sheet, each pair forming a composite design.

763 Reclining Buddha

(Des T. Thongkhambai. Litho Thai British Security Ptg Co Ltd)

2002 (28 Feb). *Maghapuja Day. Paper with fluorescent fibres.* P 14½ × 14.

| 2333 | **763** | 3b. multicoloured | 20 | 15 |

764 Queen Sawang Wadhana Memorial Hospital

(Des C. Thongkaew. Litho Thai British Security Ptg Co Ltd)

2002 (30 Mar). *Red Cross. Paper with fluorescent fibres.* P 14½ × 14.

| 2334 | **764** | 4b. multicoloured | 30 | 20 |

765 Headquarters and Emblem   **766** Male Puppet

(Des C. Thongkaew. Litho Thai British Security Ptg Co Ltd)

2002 (1 Apr). *90th Anniv of Ministry of Transport and Communications. Paper with fluorescent fibres.* P 14½ × 14.

| 2335 | **765** | 3b. multicoloured | 20 | 15 |

(Litho Chan Wanich Security Ptg Co Ltd)

2002 (2 Apr). *Heritage Conservation Day. Puppets.* T **766** *and similar vert designs. Multicoloured. Paper with fluorescent fibres.* P 14 × 14½.

2336	3b. Type **766**	20	15
2337	3b. Female puppet	20	15
2338	4b. Demon	30	20
2339	15b. Monkey	95	60
2336/2339	*Set of 4*	1·50	1·00
MS2340	111 × 145 mm. Nos. 2336/9. P 13½		
	(sold at 30b.)	2·10	2·10

767 Female Angel riding Horse   **768** *Betta imbellis*

(Des N. Kaewsawang. Litho Thai British Security Ptg Co Ltd)

2002 (3 Apr). *Songkran (New Year) Day. Year of the Horse.* T **767** *and similar vert designs. Multicoloured. Paper with fluorescent fibres.* P 14 × 14½.

2341	2b. Type **767**	10	10
MS2342	Two sheets (a) 80 × 100 mm. No. 2341		
	Perf or imperf (sold at 8b.). (b) 137 × 161 mm.		
	2b. No. 1933; 2b. No. 2025; 2b. No. 2107;		
	2b. No. 2206; 2b. No. 2281; 2b. No. 2341.		
	Perf or imperf (sold at 14b.)	1·90	1·90

(Des U. Niyomthum. Litho Thai British Security Ptg Co Ltd)

2002 (15 May). *Fighting Fish.* T **768** *and similar horiz designs. Multicoloured. Paper with fluorescent fibres.* P 14½ × 14.

2343	3b. Type **768**	20	15
2344	3b. *Betta splendens* (blue)	20	15
2345	4b. *Betta splendens* (red)	30	20
2346	15b. *Betta splendens* (bi-colour)	90	55
2343/2346	*Set of 4*	1·40	95
MS2347	144 × 110 mm. Nos. 2343/6. P 13½		
	(sold at 30b.)	2·10	2·10

769 Wat Phra Si Rattanasatsadaram (Temple of the Emerald Buddha)

770 Crown Prince Maha Vajiralongkorn

(Des T. Thongkhambai. Litho)

2002 (17 June). *Tourism. T 769 and similar horiz designs. Multicoloured. Paper with fluorescent fibres.* P 14½ × 14.

2348	3b. Type **769**		10	10
2349	3b. Wat Phra Chetuphon Wimon Mangkhalaram (Wat Pho)		10	10
2350	4b. Wat Arun Ratchawararam (The Temple of Dawn)		15	10
2351	12b. Wat Bechamabophit Dusit Wanaram (The Marble Temple)		35	20
2348/2351 *Set of 4*			65	45
MS2352 144 × 110 mm. Nos. 2348/51. P 13½				
(sold at 27b.)			65	65

(Des C. Boonyasakdi. Chan Wanich Security Ptg Co Ltd)

2002 (28 July). *50th Birthday of Crown Prince Maha Vajiralongkorn. Paper with fluorescent fibres.* P 14 × 14½.

2353	**770**	3b. multicoloured	10	10

771 Figure and Communication Symbols

(Des U. Niyomthum. Litho Thai British Security Ptg Co Ltd)

2002 (4 Aug). *National Communications Day. Paper with fluorescent fibres.* P 14½ × 14.

2354	**771**	4b. multicoloured	15	10

772 *Nelumba nucifera*

(Des T. Ponchaiwong. Litho Thai British Security Ptg Co Ltd)

2002 (6 Aug). *Water Lilies. T 772 and similar horiz design. Paper with fluorescent paper.* P 14½ × 14.

2355	3b. Type **772**		10	10
2356	3b. *Nymphaea immutablis*		10	10
MS2357 110 × 65 mm. Nos. 2355/6. P 13½ (sold				
at 9b.)			25	25

Stamps of the same design were issued by Australia.

773 Queen Sirikit

(Des S. Poonsawat (No. 2358), C. Boonyasakdi (Nos. 2359, 2361), Aim-orn Saichumdee (No. 2360). Litho Thai British Security Ptg Co Ltd)

2002 (12 Aug). *70th Birthday of Queen Sirikit. T 773 and similar horiz designs. Multicoloured. Paper with fluorescent fibres.* P 14½ × 14.

2358	3b. Type **773**		10	10
2359	3b. "Queen Sirikit" rose		10	10
2360	4b. "Queen Sirikit" orchid		15	10
2361	15b. Dona "Queen Sirikit" (shrub)		45	25
2358/2361 *Set of 4*			70	50
MS2362 144 × 109 mm. Nos. 2358/61. P 13½				
(sold at 31b.)			90	90

774 Prince Damrong Rajanubhab and Script

(Des S. A. Osteras. Litho Thai British Security Ptg Co Ltd)

2002 (18 Aug). *50th Anniv of National Archives. Paper with fluorescent fibres.* P 14½ × 14.

2363	**774**	3b. multicoloured	10	10

775 Betel Nut Box

(Des Veena Chantanatat. Chan Wanich Security Ptg Co Ltd)

2002 (7 Sept). *Royal Artefacts from Vimanmek Mansion. T 775 and similar horiz designs. Multicoloured. Paper with fluorescent fibres.* P 14½ × 14.

2364	3b. Type **775**		10	10
2365	3b. Pedestal tray		10	10
2366	4b. Betel nut bowl		10	10
2367	12b. Oblong betel nut box		35	20
2364/2367 *Set of 4*			60	45
MS2368 110 × 145 mm. Nos. 2364/7. P 13½				
(sold at 26b.)			75	75

776 Portrait of Kings Rama V and Rama IX on Ancient Banknote

(Des C. Supharachatakarn. Recess)

2002 (7 Sept). *Centenary of First Thai Banknote. Granite paper.*
P 14½ × 13½.

2369	**776**	5b multicoloured	15	10
MS2370 162 × 120 mm. No. 2369 (sold at 11b.)			35	35

777 Animal-shaped Coconut Grater

(Des M. Sriwongkorakot (3b.), R. Saichumdee (4b.),
C. Boonyasakdi (15b.). Litho Thai British Security Ptg Co Ltd)

2002 (5 Oct). *International Letter Writing Week. Thai
Kitchenware. T 777 and similar horiz designs. Multicoloured.
Paper with fluorescent fibres.* P 14½ × 14.

2371	3b. Type **777**		10	10
2372	3b. Bamboo strainer		10	10
2373	4b. Coconut shell ladles		10	10
2374	15b. Earthenware cooking stove		40	25
2371/2374 *Set of 4*			65	50
MS2375 144 × 110 mm. Nos. 2371/4. P 13½ (sold at 31b.)			65	50

778 Khaochae (rice dish) (Central Region)

(Litho Thai British Security Ptg Co Ltd)

2002 (5 Oct). *Bangkok 2003 International Stamp Exhibition. Thai
Food. T 778 and similar horiz designs showing regional foods.
Multicoloured. Paper with fluorescent fibres.* P 14½ × 14.

2376	3b. Type **778**	10	10
2377	3b. Sato Phat Kung (prawn dish) and Kaenglueang (soup) (southern region)	10	10
2378	4b. Somtam (salad), Kaiyang (chicken dish) and Khaoniao Nueng (rice) (north-eastern region)	10	10
2379	15b. Khaepmu (pork), Namphrik Ong (chilli) and Sai-ua (sausage) (northern region)	40	25
2376/2379 *Set of 4*		65	50
MS2380 110 × 144 mm. Nos. 2376/9. P 13½ (sold at 30b.)		85	85

779 Dusit Maha Prasat Throne Hall   **780** *Guaiacum officinale*

(Des Veena Chantanatat. Recess and litho)

2002 (5 Oct). *Palaces. T 779 and similar horiz design.
Multicoloured.* P 13½ (with three conjoined holes on each vert
side).

2381	4b. Type **779**	10	10
2382	4b. The Royal Palace, Stockholm	10	10

Stamps of the same design were issued by Sweden.

(Des T. Thongkhambai. Litho Thai British Security Ptg Co Ltd)

2002 (15 Nov). *New Year. Flowers. Sheet* 99 × 85 *mm
containing T 780 and similar horiz designs. Multicoloured. Paper
with fluorescent fibres.* P 14½ × 14.

MS2383 3b. Type **780**; 3b. *Nyctanthes arbortristis*; 3b. *Barleria cristata*; 3b. *Thevetia peruviana* (sold at 16b.)	45	45

781 Young People

(Des U. Niyomthum. Litho Thai British Security Ptg Co Ltd)

2002 (28 Dec). *20th (2003) World Scout Jamboree. T 781 and
similar horiz design. Multicoloured. Paper with fluorescent
fibres.* P 14½ × 14.

2384	3b. Type **781**		10	10
2385	12b. Beach (Jamboree camp site), Sattahip district		35	20

STAMP BOOKLETS

The following checklist covers, in simplified form, booklets
issued by Thailand. It is intended that it should be used in
conjunction with the main listings and details of stamps listed there
are not repeated.

Prices are for complete booklets

Booklet No.	Date	Contents and Cover Price	Price
SB1	1926	King Prajadhipok (*T* 76) 1 pane, No. 252 × 6; 1 pane, No. 253 × 6; 2 panes, No. 254 × 13, 1 pane, No. 255 × 6 (1b.50)	—
SB2	2.5.79	King Bhumibol (*T* 227) 1 pane, No. 752 × 10 (7b.50)	2·00
SB3	3.5.80	Red Cross (*T* 317) 1 pane, No. 1021 × 10 (10b.)	3·50
SB4	12.8.80	Queen Sirikit's "Fourth Cycle" Anniv 1 pane, No. 1028 × 10 (7b.50)	2·00
SB5	5.10.80	Temples (*T* 322) 1 pane, No. 1033 × 10 (7b.50)	1·00
SB6	21.10.80	80th Birthday of Princess Mother (*T* 323) 1 pane, No. 1037 × 10 (7b.50)	11·00
SB7	24.10.80	United Nations Day (*T* 324) 1 pane, No. 1038 × 10 (7b.50)	2·00
SB8	1.1.81	King Vajiravudh (*T* 328) 1 pane, No. 1056 × 10 (7b.50)	4·50
SB9	16.1.81	Children's Day (*T* 329) 1 pane, No. 1057 × 10 (7b.50)	3·00
SB10	6.2.81	Handicraft Exhibition (*T* 331) 1 pane, No. 1059 × 10 (7b.50)	2·00
SB11	6.2.81	Handicraft Exhibition (Elephant) 1 pane, No. 1060 × 10 (7b.50)	2·00

SB12	28.2.81	International Year of Disabled Persons (T 332)	
		1 pane, No. 1063 × 10 (7b.50)	2·00
SB13	6.8.81	Luang Praditphairo (T 337)	
		1 pane, No. 1074 × 10 (12b.50)	3·00
SB14	24.10.81	United Nations Day (T 340)	
		1 pane, No. 1080 × 10 (12b.50)	2·50

Nos. SB15/43 each contain a strip of 4 × 1b.25 stamps, the booklet selling for 5b.

SB15	9.1.82	Children's Day (T 343)	
		No. 1087 × 4	1·00
SB16	22.2.82	Boy Scout Movement (T 344)	
		No. 1088 × 4	1·00
SB17	4.4.82	Raktanakosan Bicentenary (Bangkok)	
		No. 1090 × 4	80
SB18	7.4.82	Tubercle Bacillus (T 346)	
		No. 1100 × 4	80
SB19	30.6.82	Flowers (T 347)	
		No. 1101 × 4	60
SB20	4.8.82	"Bangkok 1983" Stamp Exhibition (T 348)	
		No. 1105 × 4	1·00
SB21	9.8.82	"Unispace '82" (T 349)	
		No. 1110 × 4	80
SB22	14.9.82	Prince Purachatra (T 350)	
		No. 1111 × 4	80
SB23	3.10.82	Sangaltok Pottery (T 351)	
		No. 1112 × 4	80
SB24	24.10.82	United Nations Day (T 352)	
		No. 1116 × 4	80
SB25	30.11.82	Musical Instruments	
		No. 1119 × 4	80
SB26	26.12.82	Pileated Gibbon (T 354)	
		No. 1125 × 4	80
SB27	8.1.83	Children's Day (T 356)	
		No. 1130 × 4	80
SB28	25.2.83	Postcodes (T 357)	
		No. 1131 × 4	1·00
SB29	25.2.83	Postcodes (Coded Envelope)	
		No. 1132 × 4	1·00
SB30	17.3.83	Int Maritime Organization (T 359)	
		No. 1136 × 4	80
SB31	1.4.83	Civil Servants' Day (T 360)	
		No. 1137 × 4	80
SB32	11.4.83	Prince Sithiporn Kridakara (T 362)	
		No. 1139 × 4	80
SB33	4.8.83	Prince Bhanurangsi (T 364)	
		No. 1141 × 4	1·20
SB34	4.8.83	"Bangkok 1983" Stamp Exhibition (T 365)	
		No. 1142 × 4	40
SB35	27.9.83	Submarine Cable (T 366)	
		No. 1147 × 4	40
SB36	24.10.83	United Nations Day (T 369)	
		No. 1155 × 4	80
SB37	14.1.84	Children's Day (T 372)	
		No. 1161 × 4	1·00
SB38	22.1.84	National Games (T 373)	
		No. 1162 × 4	1·20
SB39	22.1.84	Rheumatology Congress (T 374)	
		No. 1164 × 4	1·20
SB40	26.1.84	Armed Forces Day (T 375)	
		No. 1165 × 4	1·20
SB41	31.3.84	Royal Institute (T 376)	
		No. 1166 × 4	1·00
SB42	27.6.84	Thammasat University (T 379)	
		No. 1173 × 4	80

SB43	12.7.84	Buddha (T 382)	
		No. 1175 × 4	40

Except for No. SB90, all booklets from No. SB44 contained a strip of 5 × 2b. stamps, the booklet selling for 10b.

SB44	1.1.86	Express Mail Services T 410)	
		No. 1236 × 5	75
SB45	11.1.86	Children's Day (T 412)	
		No. 1241 × 5	1·00
SB46	26.6.86	Sunthon Phu (T 414)	
		No. 1243 × 5	1·00
SB47	26.6.86	Fruit (T 415)	
		No. 1244 × 5	2·75
SB48	26.6.86	Fruit (Malay apple)	
		No. 1245 × 5	2·75
SB49	21.7.86	National Tree Year (T 416)	
		No. 1248 × 5	75
SB50	4.8.86	National Communications Day (T 417)	
		No. 1249 × 5	75
SB51	5.10.86	Bamboo Baskets (T 418)	
		No. 1250 × 5	1·00
SB52	5.10.86	Bamboo Baskets (Krabung)	
		No. 1251 × 5	1·00
SB53	24.10.86	International Peace Year (T 420)	
		No. 1255 × 5	1·00
SB54	24.10.86	Productivity Year (T 421)	
		No. 1256 × 5	75
SB55	7.11.86	Orchid Congress (T 423)	
		No. 1261 × 5	1·00
SB56	26.11.86	Fungi (T 424)	
		No. 1266 × 5	1·00
SB57	26.11 86	Fungi (Pleurotus ostreatus)	
		No. 1267 × 5	1·00
SB58	19.12.86	Fisheries Department (T 425)	
		No. 1270 × 5	1·00
SB59	19.12.86	Fisheries Dept (Notopterus blanci)	
		No. 1271 × 5	1·00
SB60	27.3.87	Royal Thai Airforce (T 427)	
		No. 1276 × 5	1·50
SB61	31.3.87	King Rama III (T 428)	
		No. 1277 × 5	1·30
SB62	1.4.87	Ministry of Communications (T 429)	
		No. 1278 × 5	75
SB63	11.7.87	National Tree Year (T 431)	
		No. 1280 × 5	75
SB64	4.8.87	"Thaipex '87" Stamp Exhibition (T 432)	
		No. 1281 × 5	50
SB65	4.8.87	"Thaipex '87" Stamp Exhibition (Hand mirrors)	
		No. 1282 × 5	50
SB66	4.8.87	National Communications Day (T 433)	
		No. 1286 × 5	75
SB67	5.8.87	Chulachomklao Royal Military Academy (T 434)	
		No. 1287 × 5	75
SB68	8.8.87	ASEAN (T 435)	
		No. 1288 × 5	50
SB69	8.9.87	International Literacy Day (T 436)	
		No. 1292 × 5	75
SB70	18.9.87	Visit Thailand Year (T 437)	
		No. 1293 × 5	50
SB71	18.9.87	Auditor General's Office (T 438)	
		No. 1297 × 5	75
SB72	26.9.87	Thailand–Japan Friendship Treaty (T 439)	
		No. 1298 × 5	1·00
SB73	4.10.87	Floral Tassle	
		No. 1299 × 5	50
SB74	9.10.87	Thailand Cultural Centre (T 442)	
		No. 1304 × 5	75

SB75	5.12.87	King's 60th Birthday (T **443**) No. 1305 × 5	1·00	SB110	26.6.89	International Anti-drugs Day (T **471**) No. 1408 × 5	75
SB76	5.12.87	King's 60th Birthday No. 1306 × 5	1·00	SB111	28.6.89	National Arts and Crafts Year (T **472**) No. 1409 × 5	50
SB77	5.12.87	King's 60th Birthday No. 1307 × 5	1·00			
SB78	5.12.87	King's 60th Birthday No. 1308 × 5	1·00	SB112	28.6.89	National Arts and Crafts Year (Ceramics) No. 1410 × 5	50
SB79	5.12.87	King's 60th Birthday No. 1309 × 5	1·00	SB113	28.6.89	Shells (T **473**) No. 1413 × 5	50
SB80	5.12.87	King's 60th Birthday No. 1310 × 5	1·00	SB114	1.7.89	Phya Anuman Rajadhon (T **475**) No. 1418 × 5	75
SB81	5.12.87	King's 60th Birthday No. 1311 × 5	1·00	SB115	4.8.89	Post and Telecommunications School (T **476**) No. 1419 × 5	75
SB82	5.12.87	King's 60th Birthday No. 1312 × 5	1·00			
SB83	9.1.88	Children's Day (T **444**) No. 1321 × 5	75	SB116	4.8.89	National Communications Day (T **477**) No. 1420 × 5	75
SB84	26.2.88	Thai Co-operatives (T **445**) No. 1322 × 5	75	SB117	4.8.89	"Thaipex '89". Post Box (T **478**) No. 1421 × 5	50
SB85	10.3.88	Siam Society (T **446**) No. 1323 × 5	75			
SB86	2.4.88	Sukhotai Historical Park (T **447**) No. 1324 × 5	50	SB118	4.8.89	Dragonfly (T **479**) No. 1426 × 5	50
SB87	3.4.88	Red Cross (T **449**) No. 1329 × 5	75	SB119	24.10.89	Asia–Pacific Transport and Communications Decade (T **480**) No. 1431 × 5	75
SB88	15.6.88	Pheasant (T **451**) No. 1331 × 5	50			
SB89	26.6.88	International Women's Council (T **452**) No. 1335 × 5	75	SB120	1.11.89	Mental Health Care (T **481**) No. 1432 × 5	75
SB90	2.7.88	King Rama IX (T **453**) No. 1336 × 5 (5b.)	50	SB121	15.11.89	Beetle (T **483**) No. 1438 × 5	50
SB91	2.7.88	King Rama IX (T **453**) No. 1337 × 5	50	SB122	1.1.90	Population and Housing Census (T **485**) No. 1446 × 5	75
SB92	2.7.88	King Rama IX (T **454**) No. 1356 × 5	50	SB123	13.1.90	Children's Day (T **486**) No. 1447 × 5	75
SB93	29.7.88	National Tree Day (T **455**) No. 1369 × 5	75	SB124	13 1.90	Children's Day (Sports) No. 1448 × 5	75
SB94	4.8.88	National Communications Day (T **456**) No. 1370 × 5	1·00	SB125	29.3.90	Red Cross (T **487**) No. 1449 × 5	75
SB95	9.10.88	Coconut-leaf Folk Toys (T **458**) No. 1371 × 5	50	SB126	16.5.90	Dentistry Faculty (T **489**) No. 1454 × 5	75
SB96	9.10.88	Coconut-leaf Folk Toys (Carp) No. 1372 × 5	50	SB127	29.6.90	Minerals (T **490**) No. 1460 × 5	50
SB97	25.10.88	Housing Development (T **459**) No. 1375 × 5	75	SB128	4.8.90	National Communications Day (T **491**) No. 1465 × 5	75
SB98	11.11.88	King's Own Bodyguard (T **460**) No. 1376 × 5	8·50	SB129	10.9.90	Asian–Pacific Postal Training Centre (T **492**) No. 1466 × 5	75
SB99	11.11.88	Road Safety Campaign (T **461**) No. 1377 × 5	1·50	SB130	17.9.90	Rotary international (T **493**) No. 1468 × 5	50
SB100	5.12.88	Buddha Monthon Celebrations (T **463**) No. 1382 × 5	50	SB131	7.10.90	Comptroller-General's Department (T **494**) No. 1472 × 5	75
SB101	14.1.89	Children's Day (T **465**) No. 1395 × 5	75	SB132	21.10.90	90th Birthday of Princess Mother (T **496**) No. 1478 × 5	2·30
SB102	14.1.89	Children's Day (Birds) No. 1396 × 5	75	SB133	5.12.90	Wiman Mek Royal Hall T **498**) No. 1484 × 5	50
SB103	14.1.89	Children's Day (Mermaid) No. 1397 × 5	75	SB134	11.12.90	Supreme Patriarch (T **499**) No. 1490 × 5	75
SB104	14.1.89	Children's Day (Fish) No. 1398 × 5	75	SB135	29.12.90	Thai Petroleum Authority (T **501**) No. 1495 × 5	75
SB105	25.2.89	Thai Communications Authority (T **466**) No. 1399 × 5	50	SB136	29.12.90	Steam Locomotives (T **502**) No. 1496 × 5	50
SB106	26.3.89	Chulalongkorn University (T **467**) No. 1400 × 5	1·00	SB137	12.1.91	Children's Day (T **503**) No. 1501 × 5	50
SB107	31.3.89	Thai Red Cross (T **468**) No. 1401 × 5	75	SB138	17.2.91	Land Deeds Project (T **504**) No. 1505 × 5	65
SB108	2.4.89	Phra Nakhon Khiri Historical Park(T **469**) No. 1403 × 5	50	SB139	30.3.91	Red Cross (T **505**) No. 1506 × 5	2·75
SB109	5.4.89	Government Lottery Office (T **470**) No. 1407 × 5	75	SB140	13.4.91	Songkran Day (T **507**) No. 1513 × 5	4·50
				SB141	28.4.91	Prince Natisranuvattivongs No. 1515 × 5	75
				SB142	28.5.91	Lotus (T **509**) No. 1516 × 5	50

SB143	4.8.91	*National Communications Day (T 510)* No. 1520 × 5 ... 1·00
SB144	4.8.91	*"Thaipex '91" Stamp Exhibition (T 511)* No. 1521 × 5 ... 50
SB145	3.9.91	*Int Productivity Congress (T 512)* No. 1526 × 5 ... 75
SB146	23.9.91	*International Council of Women Triennial* No. 1527 × 5 ... 75
SB147	6.10.91	*Japanese Bantams (T 514)* No. 1528 × 5 ... 50
SB148	15.10.91	*World Bank and International Monetary Fund (T 515)* No. 1533 × 5 ... 50
SB149	23.10.91	*"Bangkok 1993" Stamp Exhibition (T 516)* No. 1538 × 5 ... 50
SB150	5.11.91	*Indian Elephant (T 517)* No. 1546 × 5 ... 50
SB151	26.12.91	*Mammals (T 521)* No. 1562 × 5 ... 50
SB152	1.1.92	*Prince Mahidol of Songkla (T 522)* No. 1567 × 5 ... 75
SB153	1.1.92	*Dept of Mineral Resources (T 523)* No. 1568 × 5 ... 75
SB154	1.1.92	*Dept of Mineral Resources (Mining)* No. 1569 × 5 ... 75
SB155	1.1.92	*Department of Mineral Resources (Gas and Oil)* No. 1570 × 5 ... 75
SB156	1.1.92	*Department of Mineral Resources (Artesian Wells)* No. 1571 × 5 ... 75
SB157	11.1.92	*Children's Day (T 524)* No. 1572 × 5 ... 50
SB158	18.1.92	*Elephant Duel (T 525)* No. 1575 × 5 ... 75
SB159	20.1.92	*Orchid Conference (T 526)* No. 1576 × 5 ... 50
SB160	20.1.92	*Orchid Conference (P. exul)* No. 1577 × 5 ... 50
SB161	5.3.92	*Sugar Cane Technologists Congress (T 527)* No. 1585 × 5 ... 75
SB162	27.3.92	*Red Cross (T 529)* No. 1588 × 5 ... 75
SB163	1.4.92	*Ministry of Transport (T 530)* No. 1589 × 5 ... 50
SB164	1.4.92	*Ministry of Interior (T 531)* No. 1593 × 5 ... 75
SB165	1.4.92	*Ministry of Interior (Polling Station)* No. 1594 × 5 ... 75
SB166	1.4.92	*Ministry of Interior (Emergency Services)* No. 1595 × 5 ... 75
SB167	1.4.92	*Ministry of Interior (Water)* No. 1596 × 5 ... 75
SB168	1.4.92	*Ministry of Agriculture (T 532)* No. 1597 × 5 ... 50
SB169	1.4.92	*Ministry of Education (T 533)* No. 1601 × 5 ... 75
SB170	2.4.92	*Traditional Carts (T 534)* No. 1602 × 5 ... 50
SB171	13.4.92	*Songkran Day (T 535)* No. 1607 × 5 ... 1·00
SB172	5.5.92	*Dept of Livestock Development (T 536)* No. 1609 × 5 ... 75
SB173	23.6.92	*Meteorological Department (T 538)* No. 1613 × 5 ... 75
SB174	1.7.92	*Visit ASEAN Year (T 539)* No. 1614 × 5 ... 50
SB175	1.7.92	*"Bangkok 1993" Stamp Exhibition (T 540)* No. 1618 × 5 ... 50
SB176	5.7.92	*Prince Chudadhuj Dharadolik (T 541)* No. 1624 × 5 ... 75
SB177	4.8.92	*National Communications Day (T 542)* No. 1625 × 5 ... 75
SB178	8.8.92	*ASEAN (T 543)* No. 1626 × 5 ... 50
SB179	12.8.92	*Sirikit Medical Centre (T 544)* No. 1630 × 5 ... 75
SB180	12.8.92	*Queen Sirikit's Birthday (T 546)* No. 1635 × 5 ... 75
SB181	12.8.92	*Queen Sirikit's Birthday (Coronation)* No. 1636 × 5 ... 75
SB182	12.8.92	*Queen Sirikit's Birthday (Anointment)* No. 1637 × 5 ... 75
SB183	12.8.92	*Queen Sirikit's Birthday (on Chair)* No. 1638 × 5 ... 75
SB184	12.8.92	*Queen Sirikit's Birthday (Hospital Visit)* No. 1639 × 5 ... 75
SB185	12.8.92	*Queen Sirikit's Birthday (Visit)* No. 1640 × 5 ... 75
SB186	25.8.92	*Prince Wan Waithayakon (T 547)* No. 1648 × 5 ... 75
SB187	15.9.92	*Silpa Bhirasri (T 548)* No. 1649 × 5 ... 75
SB188	4.10.92	*Corals (T 549)* No. 1650 × 5 ... 50
SB189	22.11.92	*Asian–Pacific Allergy Congress (T 551)* No. 1660 × 5 ... 75
SB190	10.12.92	*National Assembly (T 552)* No. 1661 × 5 ... 75
SB191	10.12.92	*Bank of Thailand (T 553)* No. 1662 × 5 ... 75
SB192	9.1.93	*Children's Day (T 554)* No. 1663 × 5 ... 50
SB193	9.1.93	*Children's Day (Forest)* No. 1664x5 ... 50
SB194	9.1.93	*Children's Day (Communications)* No. 1665 × 5 ... 50
SB195	16.1.93	*Teacher Training Institute (T 556)* No. 1671 × 5 ... 75
SB196	2.2.93	*Kasetsart University (T 557)* No. 1672 × 5 ... 75
SB197	27.3.93	*Red Cross (T 559)* No. 1674 × 5 ... 1·00
SB198	1.4.93	*Attorney General's Office (T 560)* No. 1675 × 5 ... 75
SB199	13.4.93	*Songkran Day (T 562)* No. 1681 × 5 ... 50
SB200	1.7.93	*Fungi (T 563)* No. 1683 × 5 ... 50
SB201	4.8.93	*National Communications Day (T 564)* No. 1688 × 5 ... 75
SB202	4.8.93	*Post and Telegraph Dept (T 565)* No. 1689 × 5 ... 1·00
SB203	12.8.93	*Queen Suriyothai's Monument (T 566)* No. 1690 × 5 ... 75
SB204	1.10.93	*Thai Ridgeback (T 567)* No. 1691 × 5 ... 50

SB205	1.10.93	Tangerines (T 568)	
		No. 1696 × 5	50
SB206	2.11.93	ASCOPE Conference (T 570)	
		No. 1706 × 5	75
SB207	8.11.93	King Rama VII (T 571)	
		No. 1707 × 5	1·00
SB208	1.12.93	"Thaicom" Satellite (T 574)	
		No. 1714 × 5	75
SB209	8.1.94	Children's Day (T 575)	
		No. 1715 × 5	75
SB210	30.3.94	Red Cross (T 576)	
		No. 1716 × 5	50
SB211	31.3.94	Royal Institute (T 577)	
		No. 1717 × 5	50
SB212	2.4.94	Phra Nakhon Si Ayutthaya Park (T 578)	
		No. 1718 × 5	50
SB213	13.4.94	Songkran Day (T 580)	
		No. 1724 × 5	50
SB214	23.6.94	Int Olympic Committee (T 581)	
		No. 1727 × 5	50
SB215	27.6.94	Thammasat University (T 582)	
		No. 1732 × 5	50
SB216	4.8.94	National Communications Day (T 585)	
		No. 1734 × 5	50
SB217	9.10.94	Betel Nut Sets (T 587)	
		No. 1740 × 5	50
SB218	29.10.94	Int Labour Organization (T 588)	
		No. 1745 × 5	50
SB219	4.12.94	Suan Dusit Teachers' College (T 590)	
		No. 1751 × 5	50
SB220	5.12.94	Council of State (T 591)	
		No. 1754 × 5	1·00
SB221	7.12.94	I.C.A.O. (T 592)	
		No. 1755 × 5	50
SB222	13.12.94	Pharmacy in Thailand (T 593)	
		No. 1756 × 5	50
SB223	1.1.95	The Bar (T 595)	
		No. 1764 × 5	50
SB224	14.1.95	Children's Day (T 596)	
		No. 1765 × 5	50
SB225	14.1.95	Children's Day (Trees)	
		No. 1766 × 5	50
SB226	14.1.95	Children's Day (Youths)	
		No. 1767 × 5	50
SB227	4.3.95	Bangkok Recorder (T 597)	
		No. 1768 × 5	50
SB228	27.3.95	Royal Thai Airforce (T 598)	
		No. 1769 × 5	50
SB229	30.3.95	Red Cross (T 599)	
		No. 1770 × 5	50
SB230	8.4.95	Ministry of Defence (T 601)	
		No. 1776 × 5	75
SB231	13.4.95	Songkran Day (T 602)	
		No. 1777 × 5	50
SB232	14.4.95	Ministry of Foreign Affairs (T 603)	
		No. 1779 × 5	1·00
SB233	5.6.95	ASEAN Environment Day (T 605)	
		No. 1785 × 5	50
SB234	9.6.95	Information Technology Year (T 606)	
		No. 1786 × 5	50
SB235	4.8.95	National Communications Day (T 608)	
		No. 1790 × 5	50
SB236	2.9.95	Revenue Department (T 610)	
		No. 1796 × 5	50
SB237	18.9.95	National Auditing (T 611)	
		No. 1797 × 5	50
SB238	8.10.95	Letter Writing Week (T 612)	
		No. 1798 × 5	50
SB239	8.10.95	Letter Writing Week	
		No. 1799 × 5	50
SB240	16.10.95	F.A.O. (T 613)	
		No. 1803 × 5	50

SB241	24.10.95	Total Solar Eclipse (T 614)	
		No. 1804 × 5	50
SB242	24.10.95	U.N.O. (T 615)	
		No. 1805 × 5	50
SB243	4.11.95	"WORLDTECH'95" (T 616)	
		No. 1806 × 5	50
SB244	9.12.95	Veterinary Science (T 618)	
		No. 1815 × 5	50
SB245	12.1.96	Siriraj School of Nursing and Midwifery (T 620)	
		No. 1821 × 5	50
SB246	13.1.96	National Aviation Day (T 621)	
		No. 1822 × 5	50
SB247	13.1.96	Children's Day (T 622)	
		No. 1823 × 5	50
SB248	13.1.96	Children's Day	
		No. 1824 × 5	50
SB249	13.1.96	Children's Day	
		No. 1825 × 5	50
SB250	1.3.96	Asia–Europe Summit Meeting (T 623)	
		No. 1826 × 5	50
SB251	10.3.96	Princess Mother's Cremation (T 625)	
		No. 1832 × 5	1·00
SB252	2.4.96	Thai Heritage Conservation (T 626)	
		No. 1833 × 5	50
SB253	12.4.96	700th Anniv of Chiang Mai (T 627)	
		No. 1838 × 5	50
SB254	13.4.96	Songkran Day (T 629)	
		No. 1848 × 5	50
SB255	23.6.96	Centenary of Modern Olympic Games (T 632)	
		No. 1868 × 5	50
SB256	4.8.96	National Communications Day (T 633)	
		No. 1872 × 5	1·00
SB257	25.10.96	Rotary International Conference (T 636)	
		No. 1883 × 5	50
SB258	4.11.96	U.N.E.S.C.O. (T 637)	
		No. 1884 × 5	50
SB259	5.12.96	King Rama IX (T 641)	
		No. 1897 × 5	50
SB260	11.12.96	U.N.I.C.E.F. (T 642)	
		No. 1910 × 5	50
SB261	1.1.97	Mahavajiravudh School (T 644)	
		No. 1912 × 5	50
SB262	11.1.97	Children's Day (T 645)	
		No. 1913 × 5	50
SB263	11.1.97	Children's Day	
		No. 1914 × 5	50
SB264	25.2.97	Communications Authority (T 646)	
		No. 1915 × 5	50
SB265	25.2.97	Prince Bhanurangsi (T 647)	
		No. 1916 × 5	50
SB266	26.3.97	Chulalongkorn University (T 649)	
		No. 1919 × 5	50
SB267	26.3.97	Chulalongkorn University	
		No. 1920 × 5	50
SB268	1.4.97	Government Savings Bank (T 652)	
		No. 1927 × 5	50
SB269	13.4.97	Songkran Day (T 654)	
		No. 1933 × 5	50
SB270	9.6.97	Telecommunications (T 656)	
		No. 1940 × 5	50
SB271	11.6.97	Faculty of Medicine, Chulalongkorn University (T 658)	
		No. 1949 × 5	50
SB272	3.7.97	Thailand–Russia Diplomatic Relations (T 659)	
		No. 1950 × 5	50
SB273	2.8.97	Traditional Houses (T 661)	
		No. 1956 × 5	50
SB274	4.8.97	Greetings Stamps	
		1 pane, No. 1961a	1·10

SB275	4.8.97	*National Communications Day (T **663**)*	
		No. 1963 × 5	50
SB276	8.8.97	*Association of South-East Asian Nations (T **664**)*	
		No. 1964 × 5	50
SB277	8.8.97	*Association of South-East Asian Nations*	
		No. 1965 × 5	50
SB278	28.8.97	*Dinosaurs (T **665**)*	
		No. 1968 × 5	50
SB279	12.9.97	*Centenary of Royal Visit to Switzerland (T **666**)*	
		No. 1973 × 5	50
SB280	9.10.97	*Shells (T **668**)*	
		No. 1979 × 5	50
SB281	9.10.97	*Shells*	
		No. 1980 × 5	50
SB282	10.11.97	*Energy Conservation (T **669**)*	
		No. 1984 × 5	50
SB283	10.1.98	*Children's Day (T **673**)*	
		No. 1999 × 5	50
SB284	10.1.98	*Children's Day*	
		No. 2000 × 5	50
SB285	10.1.98	*Children's Day*	
		No. 2001 × 5	50
SB286	10.1.98	*Children's Day*	
		No. 2002 × 5	50
SB287	17.1.98	*Dental Congress (T **674**)*	
		No. 2003 × 5	50
SB288	3.2.98	*Veterans' Day (T **675**)*	
		No. 2015 × 5	50
SB289	27.3.98	*Red Cross (T **676**)*	
		No. 2025 × 5	50
SB290	13.4.98	*Songkran Day (T **679**)*	
		No. 2027 × 5	50
SB291	13.4.98	*Wild Cats (T **680**)*	
		No. 2032 × 5	50
SB292	15.4.98	*Aerothai (T **681**)*	
		No. 2038 × 5	50
SB293	19.5.98	*Prince Abhakara Kiartiwongse (T**683**)*	
		No. 2039 × 5	50
SB294	15.6.98	*"Education Develops People…" (T **684**)*	
		No. 2042 × 5	50
SB295	19.7.98	*International Year of the Ocean (T **686**)*	
		No. 2047 × 5	50
SB296	1.8.98	*Irrigation Engineering (T **687**)*	
		No. 2048 × 5	50
SB297	4.8.98	*National Communications Day (T **688**)*	
		No. 2049 × 5	50
SB298	19.8.98	*Faculty of Political Science (T **689**)*	
		No. 2050 × 5	50
SB299	5.9.98	*Open University (T **690**)*	
		No. 2051 × 5	50
SB300	15.9.98	*Chinese Stone Statues (T **691**)*	
		No. 2052 × 5	50
SB301	15.9.98	*Chinese Stone Statues*	
		No. 2060 × 5	50
SB302	3.10.98	*Himavanta Mythical Animals (T **693**)*	
		No. 2061 × 5	50
SB303	3.10.98	*Himavanta Mythical Animals*	
		No. 2065 × 5	50
SB304	8.10.98	*Lions Clubs (T **694**)*	
		No. 2081 × 5	50
SB305	9.1.99	*Children's Day (T **698**)*	
		No. 2082 × 5	50
SB306	9.1.99	*Children's Day*	
		No. 2083 × 5	50
SB307	9.1.99	*Children's Day*	
		No. 2084 × 5	50
SB308	9.1.99	*Children's Day*	
		No. 2085 × 5	50
SB309	10.1.99	*Decade of Disabled Persons (T **699**)*	
		No. 2085 × 5	50

SB310	30.3.99	*Red Cross (T **702**)*	
		No. 2096 × 5	50
SB311	2.4.99	*Conservation Day (T **704**)*	
		No. 2102 × 5	50
SB312	13.4.99	*Songkran Day (T **705**)*	
		No. 2107 × 5	50
SB313	30.4.99	*Consumer Protection Years (T **706**)*	
		No. 2109 × 5	50
SB314	1.7.99	*Universal Postal Union*	
		No. 2116 × 5	50
SB315	1.10.99	*International Year of the Elderly (T **715**)*	
		No. 2140 × 5	50
SB316	2.10.99	*International Correspondence Week (T **716**)*	
		No. 2141 × 5	50
SB317	2.10.99	*International Correspondence Week*	
		No. 2142 × 5	50
SB318	25.3.00	*"Bangkok 2000" International World Youth Stamp Exhibition*	
		5 panes, Nos. 2097a/c, No. 2119a, No. 2195a	
		(204b.) (sold at 200b.)	10·50

No. SB318 contains three double-sided pages of interleaving, inscribed in Thai and English, giving details relating to the stamps contained in the following pane. The booklet also includes a double-sided page for the application of the handstamp available on each day of the show. Both sides of the page were divided into six squares, one containing an Exhibition emblem and the other five the date in Thai.

SB319	13.4.00	*Songkran Day (T **727**)*	
		No. 2206 × 5	50
SB320	28.7.00	*Fourth Cycle of Crown Prince Maha Vajiralongkorn (T **731**)*	
		No. 2226 × 5	50
SB321	21.10.00	*Princess Srinagarindra (T **734**)*	
		No. 2234 × 5	50
SB322	13.1.01	*Parrots (T **738**)*	
		No. 2255 × 5	50
SB323	2.4.01	*Thai Heritage Conservation Day (T **743**)*	
		No. 2276 × 5	50
SB324	13.4.01	*Songkran Day (T **744**)*	
		No. 2281 × 5	50
SB325	13.6.01	*Demon Statues (T **746**)*	
		No. 2284 × 5	50
SB326	4.7.01	*Fungi (T **748**)*	
		No. 2290 × 5	50
SB327	4.7.01	*Insects (T **749**)*	
		No. 2295 × 5	50
SB328	10.9.01	*Butterflies (T **754**)*	
		No. 2309 × 5	75
SB329	6.10.01	*International Correspondence Week (T **755**)*	
		No. 2314 × 5	50

This index provides in a condensed form a key to designs and subjects of portrait and pictorial stamps of Thailand. In order to save space, portrait stamps are listed under surname only, views under the name of the town or area and works of art under the name of the artist. In cases of difficulty part of the inscription has been used to identify the stamp. When the same design or subject appears on more than one stamp in a set, only the first appearance is indexed.

BRITISH POST OFFICE IN BANGKOK

An overseas postal service for foreign residents was operated by the British Consulate at Bangkok from 1858. Mail was despatched by steamer to Singapore and from 1876 onwards was increasingly franked with Straits Settlements stamps. These were initially cancelled on arrival at Singapore, but later an oval postmark inscribed "BRITISH CONSULATE BANGKOK" was used. In 1883 a circular "BANGKOK" datestamp was introduced for use with Nos. 1/23. Both cancellations can also be found used on Hong Kong stamps between 1881 and 1885.

(Currency. 100 cents = 1 Straits dollar)

Queen Victoria stamps of Straits Settlements cancelled with oval postmark inscribed "BRITISH CONSULATE BANGKOK" around Royal Arms.
1877to **82**. *Wmk Crown CC (Nos. 11/15, 33 and 35).*

Z1	2c. brown	£375
Z2	4c. rose	£375
Z3	6c. dull lilac	£425
Z4	8c. orange-yellow	£375
Z5	10c.on 30c. claret (thin "0") (No. 33)	£1000
Z6	10c.on 30c. claret (thick "10") (No. 34)	£1000
Z7	10c.on 30c. claret (thin "I", thick "0") (No. 35)	£1100
Z8	12c. blue	£475

Subsequent Straits Settlements values to 8c. watermarked Crown CA are known used at Bangkok in 1883 and 1884. During this period the stamps overprinted "B" were on sale at the British Post Office.

B
1

1882 (May)–**85**. *Queen Victoria stamps of Straits Settlements optd with T 1.*

(a) On 1867 issue (Indian stamp surch with crown and "32 CENTS").

1	32c.on 2a. yellow	£35000

(b) On issues of 1867–82. Wmk Crown over "CC".

2	2c. brown	£2750	£1400
3	4c. rose	£2250	£1200
	a. Opt double	—	£7500
4	5c. purple-brown	£275	£300
5	6c. lilac	£200	£100
6	8c. orange	£1900	£200
7	10c. slate	£350	£150
8	12c. blue	£900	£475
9	24c. green	£700	£150
10	30c. claret	£30000	£20000
11	96c. grey	£7500	£3500

(c) On issue of April 1883 (surch "TWO CENTS")

12	2c.on 32c. pale red (wide "S")	£2250	£2250
13	2c.on 32c. pale red (wide "E")	£2750	£2750

(d) On issues of 1882–84. Wmk Crown over "CA".

14	2c. brown	£475	£350
15	2c. pale rose (1883)	55·00	45·00
	a. Opt inverted	—	£9500
	b. Opt double	£2750	£2750
	c. Opt treble	£10000	
16	4c. rose (1883)	£500	£300
17	4c. pale brown (1883)	75·00	70·00
	a. Opt double	£3500	
	b. Broken oval	£1100	£1100
18	5c. blue (1884)	£225	£160
19	6c. lilac (1884)	£160	£110
20	8c. orange (1883)	£140	65·00
	a. Opt inverted	£17000	£10000
21	10c. slate (1883)	£150	85·00
22	12c. dull purple (1883)	£275	£150
23	24c. green (1884?)	£4500	£2500

The prices quoted for the overprint double errors, Nos. 3a, 15b and 17a, are for stamps showing two clear impressions of the overprint. Examples showing partial doubling, on these and other values, are worth a small premium over the price quoted for normal stamps.

No. 17b shows the edge of the central oval broken above the "O" of "POSTAGE". It occurs on R.10/5 of the lower right pane.

The use of these stamps ceased on 30 June 1885. Siam joined the Universal Postal Union on 1 July 1885.

Siamese Post Offices Abroad

A. NORTHERN MALAYA

The Thai monarchy exercised suzerainty over the northern states of the Malay Peninsula from the 16th century onwards. The extent of Thai involvement in the internal affairs of Kedah, Kelantan, Perlis and Trengganu was very variable, being dependent on the strength, or otherwise, of the Bangkok administration and the degree of co-operation of the local rulers.

The Thai public postal service, which had been inaugurated in 1883, gradually extended into the north of the Malay Peninsula from 1887 onwards and post offices were established in Kedah, Kelantan and Perlis. There is some evidence that Sultan Zainal Abidin III of Trengganu successfully blocked the use of Siamese stamps in his state.

The following types of postmark were used on Siamese stamps from the Malay tributary states:

Type A. Single ring with date at foot

Type B. Single ring with date in centre

Type C. Double ring. Bilingual

Type D. Double ring. English at top and ornament at foot

Type E. Double ring. English at top and bottom

PRICES are for stamps showing a large part of the postmark with the inscription clearly visible.

KEDAH

The Siamese post office at Alor Star was opened during 1887 with the first known postmark being dated 27 October. Further post offices at Kuala Muda, Kulim and Langkawi followed in 1907.

A straight-line obliteration showing "KEDAH" between short vertical dashes is not believed to be genuine.

Alor Star

Stamps of SIAM cancelled as Type A inscribed "KEDAH".

1883. *(Nos. 1/5).*

Z2	**1**	1 att. rose-carmine		£225
Z3		1 sio. red		£425
Z4	**2**	1 sik. yellow		£425

1887–91. *(Nos. 11/18).*

Z6	**9**	1a. green	80·00
Z7		2a. green and carmine	70·00
Z8		3a. green and blue	90·00
Z9		4a. green and yellow	80·00
Z10		8a. green and yellow	80·00
Z11		12a. purple and carmine	70·00
Z12		24a. purple and blue	80·00
Z13		64a. purple and brown	£130

1889–91. *Surch as T **12** (Nos. Z15, Z19), T **17** (No. Z21) or T **18** (No. Z22) (Nos. 20/30).*

Z15	**9**	1a. on 2a. green and carmine	90·00
Z19		1a. on 3a. green and blue	£100
Z21		2a. on 3a. green and blue	£130
Z22		2a. on 3a. green and blue	£160

1892. *Surch as T **24/5** (with or without stop) and Siamese handstamp (Nos. 33/6).*

Z28	**9**	4a. on 24a. purple and blue (Type **24**)	90·00
Z29		4a. on 24a. purple and blue (Type **25**)	£110
Z30		4a. on 24a. purple and blue (Type **24** with stop)	£110
Z31		4a. on 24a. purple and blue (Type **25** with stop)	£110

1894. *Surch as T **27** with variations of English figures as T **28** and **33** (Nos. 37/44).*

Z34	**9**	2a. on 64a. purple and brown (Type **28**)	90·00
Z39		2a. on 64a. purple and brown (Type **33**)	90·00

1894–95. *Surch as T **35** with variations of English figures as T **36/9** (Nos. 46/50).*

Z42	**9**	1a. on 64a. purple and brown (Type **35**)	90·00
Z43		1a. on 64a. purple and brown (Type **36**)	90·00
Z44		2a. on 64a. purple and brown (Type **37**)	90·00
Z45		2a. on 64a. purple and brown (Type **38**)	90·00
Z46		10a. on 24a. purple and blue (Type **39**)	90·00

1896. *Surch as T **39** (Siamese) and T **40** (English) (No. 51).*

Z47	**9**	4a. on 12a. purple and carmine	90·00

1897. *Surch as T* **39** *(Siamese) and T* **41** *(English) (No. 52).*
Z48   **9**   4a. on 12a. purple and carmine . . . . . .   90·00

1898–99.   *Surch*   *as*
   T **42** *with variations of English section as T* **44/6** *(Nos. 53/62).*
Z49   **9**   1a. on 12a. pur & carm (Type **42**–11½ mm
           long) £120
Z52   2a. on 64a. purple and brown (Type **44**) . . .   £110
Z53   3a. on 12a. pur & carm (Type **45**–13½ mm
           long) . . . .   90·00
Z54   3a. on 12a. purple and carmine (Type **45**–11½
           to 11¾ mm long) . . . . . .   90·00
Z55   4a. on 12a. purple & carm (Type **46**–8 mm
           long) . . . .   90·00
Z56   4a. on 12a. purple and carmine (Type **46**–8½
           to 9 mm long) . . . .   90·00

1899. *Surch in Siamese and English with T* **48a** *(Nos. 63/6).*
Z62   **9**   2a. on 64a. purple and brown £100

1899–1904. *(Nos. 67/81).*
Z63   **49**   1a. olive-green (wide Siamese characters in
            face value) . . . .   90·00
Z64   2a. grass-green . . . .   70·00
Z65   3a. red and blue . . . .   75·00
Z66   4a. carmine . . . .   70·00
Z67   8a. deep green and orange . . . .   70·00
Z70   24a. brown-purple and blue £160
Z71   64a. brown-purple and chestnut . . .   £130

1899. *(Nos. 82/6).*
Z72   **50**   1a. green £275
Z73   2a. green and red £425

Stamps of SIAM *cancelled as Type B inscr* "KEDAH".

1887–91. *(Nos. 11/18).*
Z74   **9**   12a. purple and carmine . . . . . .   70·00
Z75   24a. purple and brown . . . . . .   70·00

1898–99. *Surch with T* **42** *with variations of English section
as T* **45/6** *(Nos. 53/62).*
Z76   **9**   1a. on 12a. pur & carm (Type **42**–11½ mm
           long) . . . .   90·00
Z81   3a. on 12a. purple and carmine (Type **45**–11½
           to 11¾ mm long) . . . . . .   70·00
Z83   4a. on 12a. purple and carmine (Type **46**–8½
           to 9 mm long) . . . .   70·00
Z84   4a. on 24a. purple and blue (Type **46**) . . .   75·00

1899–1904. *(Nos. 67/81).*
Z86   **49**   1a. olive-green (wide Siamese characters in
            face value) . . . .   70·00
           a. Narrow Siamese characters in face
            value . . . .   65·00
Z87   2a. grass-green . . . .   55·00
Z88   2a. scarlet and pale blue . . . . .   55·00
Z89   3a. red and blue . . . .   65·00
Z90   3a. deep green . . . .   65·00
Z91   4a. carmine . . . .   55·00
Z92   4a. chocolate and pink . . . . . .   60·00
Z93   8a. deep green and orange . . . .   55·00
Z94   10a. ultramarine . . . .   55·00
Z95   12a. brown-purple and carmine . . .   65·00
Z96   24a. brown-purple and blue £130
Z97   64a. brown-purple and chestnut . . .   £120

1905–09. *(Nos. 92/105).*
Z102   **53**   1a. green and orange . . . . . .   55·00
Z103   2a. grey and deep violet . . . . .   55·00
Z104   3a. green . . . .   65·00
Z105   4a. pale red and sepia . . . . . .   55·00
Z106   5a. carmine . . . .   65·00
Z107   8a. olive-bistre and dull black . . . .   55·00
Z108   12a. blue . . . .   65·00
Z109   24a. red-brown £160
Z110   1t. bistre and deep blue £160

Stamps of SIAM *cancelled as Type C inscr* "Kedah" *at foot.*

1887–91. *(Nos. 11/18).*
Z111   **9**   12a. purple and carmine . . . . . .   80·00

1899–1904. *(Nos. 67/81).*
Z112   **49**   1a. olive-green (wide Siamese characters
            in face value) . . . .   65·00
           a. Narrow Siamese characters in face
            value . . . .   60·00
Z113   2a. scarlet and pale blue . . . . .   55·00
Z114   3a. red and blue . . . .   65·00
Z116   8a. deep green and orange . . . .   65·00
Z117   10a. ultramarine . . . .   60·00
Z118   12a. brown-purple and carmine . . .   60·00

1905–09. *(Nos. 95/105).*
Z128   **53**   1a. green and orange . . . . . .   55·00
Z129   2a. grey and deep violet . . . . .   55·00
Z130   3a. green . . . .   65·00
Z131   4a. pale red and sepia . . . . . .   55·00
Z132   4a. scarlet . . . .   55·00
Z133   5a. carmine . . . .   65·00
Z134   8a. olive-bistre and dull black . . . .   55·00
Z135   9a. blue . . . .   55·00
Z136   18a. red-brown . . . .   90·00
Z137   24a. red-brown £160
Z138   1t. bistre and deep blue £160

1907. *Surch with T* **56** *(No. 109).*
Z139   **9**   1a. on 24a. purple and blue . . . . .   65·00

Kuala Muda

Stamps of SIAM *cancelled as Type A inscr* "KUALA MUDA".

1887–91. *(Nos. 11/18).*
Z143   **9**   12a. purple and carmine £325

1899–1904. *(Nos. 67/81).*
Z144   **49**   2a. scarlet and pale blue £325
Z145   24a. brown-purple and blue £375

1905–09. *(Nos. 92/105).*
Z146   **53**   1a. green and orange £325
Z147   2a. grey and deep violet £325
Z148   3a. green £350
Z150   5a. carmine £350
Z151   8a. olive-bistre and dull black £325

Stamps of SIAM *cancelled as Type C inscr* "Kuala Muda" *at foot.*

1887–91. *(Nos. 11/18).*
Z155   **9**   12a. purple and carmine £150

1899–1904. *(Nos. 67/81).*
Z156   **49**   8a. deep green and orange £180
Z157   10a. ultramarine £180

1905–09. *(Nos. 92/105).*
Z158   **53**   1a. green and orange £180
Z159   2a. grey and deep violet £180
Z160   3a. green £190
Z161   4a. pale red and sepia £180
Z162   4a. scarlet £180
Z163   5a. carmine £200
Z164   8a. olive-bistre and dull black £180
Z165   9a. blue £150
Z166   24a. red-brown £375

1907. *Surch with T* **56** *(No. 109).*
Z167   **9**   1a. on 24a. purple and blue £150

1908–09. *(Nos. 105/9).*
Z170   **53**   4a. scarlet £150
Z171   9a. blue £120

Kulim

Stamps of SIAM cancelled as Type D inscr "KULIM".

1887–91. *(Nos. 11/18).*
Z173   **9**   12a. purple and carmine   £325

1899–1904. *(Nos. 67/81).*
Z174   **49**   8a. deep green and orange   £325

1905–09. *(Nos. 92/105).*
Z175   **53**   1a. green and orange   £350
Z176   2a. grey and deep violet   £350
Z178   4a. pale red and sepia   £325
Z179   4a. scarlet   £325
Z180   5a. carmine   £350
Z181   8a. olive-bistre and dull black   £325
Z182   9a. blue   £325

1907. *Surch with T 56 (No. 109).*
Z184   **9**   1a. on 24a. purple and blue   £325

Stamps of SIAM cancelled as Type C inscr "Kulim" at foot.

1887–91. *(Nos. 11/18).*
Z190   **9**   12a. purple and carmine   £130

1899–1904. *(Nos. 67/81).*
Z191   **49**   8a. deep green and orange   £130
Z192   10a. ultramarine   £140

1905–09. *(Nos. 92/105).*
Z196   **53**   4a. pale red and sepia   £130
Z197   4a. scarlet   £130
Z198   5a. carmine   £140
Z199   9a. blue   £140
Z200   24a. red-brown   £325
Z201   1t. bistre and deep blue   £325

1907. *Surch with T 56 (No. 109).*
Z202   **9**   1a. on 24a. purple and blue   £140

1908–09. *(Nos. 105/9).*
Z205   **53**   4a. scarlet   95·00
Z206   9a. blue   £110

Langkawi

Stamps of SIAM cancelled as Type D inscr "LANGKAWI".

1899–1904. *(Nos. 67/81).*
Z208   **49**   8a. deep green and orange   £325
Z209   10a. ultramarine   £325

1905–09. *(Nos. 92/105).*
Z212   **53**   3a. green   £350
Z213   4a. pale red and sepia   £325
Z215   8a. olive-bistre and dull black   £325

Stamps of SIAM cancelled as Type C inscr "Langkawi" at foot.

1887–91. *(Nos. 11/18).*
Z219   **9**   12a. purple and carmine   £140

1899–1904. *(Nos. 67/81).*
Z220   **49**   8a. deep green and orange   £150

1905–09. *(Nos. 92/105).*
Z222   **53**   2a. grey and deep violet   £140
Z223   3a. green   £190
Z224   4a. pale red and sepia   £140
Z225   4a. scarlet   £150
Z226   8a. olive-bistre and dull black   £140
Z228   24a. red-brown   £375
Z229   1t. bistre and deep blue   £375

1907. *Surch with T 56 (No. 109).*
Z230   **9**   1a. on 24a. purple and blue   £150

KELANTAN

The first Siamese post office in Kelantan opened at Kota Bharu in 1895. It appears that in the early years this office only accepted letters franked with stamps for delivery within Kelantan.

The operation of the Duff Development Company in Kelantan from 1903 led to a considerable expansion of the postal service based on the company's river steamers. A further post office opened at Batu Mengkebang in 1908 but may have been preceded by manuscript endorsements of "B.M." and date, known from early 1907 onwards.

Kota Bharu

Stamps of SIAM cancelled as Type B inscr "KALANTAN".

1887–91. *(Nos. 11/18).*
Z237   **9**   2a. green and carmine   90·00
Z238   3a. green and blue   95·00
Z239   4a. green and brown   95·00
Z240   8a. green and yellow   95·00
Z241   12a. purple and carmine   85·00
Z242   24a. purple and blue   90·00

1894. *Surch as T 27 with variation of English figures as T 33 (Nos. 37/44).*
Z251   **9**   2a. on 64a. purple and brown   £130

1894–95. *Surch as T 35 with variation of English figures as T 36 (Nos. 46/50).*
Z255   **9**   1a. on 64a. purple and brown   £110

1896. *Surch as T 39 (Siamese) and T 40 (English) (No. 51).*
Z259   **9**   4a. on 12a. purple and carmine   £110

1897. *Surch as T 39 (Siamese) and T 41 (English) (No. 52).*
Z260   **9**   4a. on 12a. purple and carmine   £110

1898–99. *Surch as T 42 with variation of English section as T 46 (Nos. 53/62).*
Z267   **9**   4a. on 12a. purple and carmine (8 mm long)   £110

1899–1904. *(Nos. 67/81).*
Z275   **49**   1a. olive-green (wide Siamese characters in face value)   90·00
Z276   2a. grass-green   85·00
Z277   2a. scarlet and pale blue   85·00
Z278   3a. red and blue   95·00
Z279   4a. carmine   85·00
Z280   4a. chocolate and pink   95·00
Z281   8a. deep green and orange   85·00
Z282   10a. ultramarine   90·00
Z283   12a. brown-purple and carmine   90·00
Z284   64a. brown-purple and chestnut   £190

1905–09. *(Nos. 92/105).*
Z293   **53**   1a. green and orange   85·00
Z294   2a. grey and deep violet   85·00
Z296   4a. pale red and sepia   85·00
Z297   4a. scarlet   85·00
Z298   5a. carmine   £100
Z299   8a. olive-bistre and dull black   85·00
Z300   12a. blue   £100
Z301   24a. red-brown   £275
Z302   1t. bistre and deep blue   £275

1907. *Surch with T 56 (No. 109).*
Z303   **9**   1a. on 24a. purple and blue   £110

1908–98. *(Nos. 105/9).*
Z305   **53**   4a. scarlet   66·00

Stamps of SIAM cancelled as Type E inscr "Kota Bahru/ Kelantan".

1887–91. *(Nos. 11/18).*
Z308   **9**   12a. purple and carmine   £110
Z309   24a. purple and blue   90·00

1899–1904. *(Nos. 67/81).*
Z310   49   8a. deep green and orange £130

1905–09. *(Nos. 92/105).*
Z311   53   1a. green and orange . . . . . . 90·00
Z312   2a. grey and deep violet . . . . . 90·00
Z313   2a. pale yellow-green . . . . . . 90·00
Z314   4a. pale red and sepia . . . . . 90·00
Z315   4a. scarlet . . . . 90·00
Z316   8a. olive-bistre and dull black . . . 85·00
Z317   9a. blue . . . . 95·00
Z318   18a. red-brown £150

1907. *Surch with T 56 (No. 109).*
Z320   9   1a. on 24a. purple and blue . . . . . 90·00

1908. *Surch as T 59 (Nos. 110/12).*
Z326   9   2a. on 24a. purple and blue £130
Z327   53   4a. on 5a. carmine £160
Z328   49   9a. on 10a. ultramarine £100

Batu Mengkebang

Stamps of SIAM *cancelled as Type E inscr* "Batu Menkebang/Kelantan".

1887–91. *(Nos. 11/18).*
Z329   9   12a. purple and carmine £150

1899–1904. *(Nos. 67/81).*
Z330   49   8a. deep green and orange £160

1905–09. *(Nos. 92/105).*
Z331   53   1a. green and orange £150
Z332   2a. grey and deep violet £150
Z333   2a. pale yellow-green £160
Z334   4a. pale red and sepia £160
Z335   4a. scarlet £150
Z336   8a. olive-bistre and dull black . . . £130
Z337   9a. blue £130
Z338   24a. red-brown £190
Z339   1t. bistre and deep blue £325

1907. *Surch with T 56 (No. 109).*
Z340   9   1a. on 24a. purple and blue £350

1908. *Surch as T 59 (Nos. 110/12).*
Z347   49   9a. on 10a. ultramarine £190

PERLIS

The Siamese post office at Kangar is recorded as opening during 1894. It is believed that the initial cancellation showed Thai characters only, but no complete example has so far been discovered.

Stamps of SIAM *cancelled as Type B inscr* "PERLIS".

1887–91. *(Nos. 11/18).*
Z349   9   12a. purple and carmine £150
Z350   24a. purple and blue £200

1897. *Surch as T 39 (Siamese) and T 41 (English) (No. 52).*
Z351   9   4a. on 12a. purple and carmine . . . £275

1899–1904. *(Nos. 67/81).*
Z352   49   1a. olive-green (wide Siamese characters
              in face value) £180
Z353   2a. grass-green £160
Z354   2a. scarlet and pale blue £160
Z355   3a. red and blue £250
Z356   4a. carmine £160
Z357   4a. chocolate and pink £160
Z358   8a. deep green and orange £160
Z359   10a. ultramarine £160
Z360   12a. brown-purple and carmine . . £150
Z361   24a. brown-purple and blue £300

1904. *(Nos. 83/9).*
Z362   49   2a. scarlet and pale blue £100
Z364   4a. chocolate and pink £100

1905–09. *(Nos. 97/105).*
Z370   53   1a. green and orange £150
Z371   2a. grey and deep violet £150
Z372   3a. green £160
Z373   4a. pale red and sepia £150
Z374   5a. carmine £160
Z375   8a. olive-bistre and dull black . . . £150
Z376   12a. blue £170
Z377   24a. red-brown £250

Stamps of SIAM *cancelled as Type C inscr* "Perlis" *at foot.*

1887–91. *(Nos. 11/18).*
Z379   9   12a. purple and carmine £170

1899–1904. *(Nos. 67/81).*
Z380   49   1a. olive-green (narrow Siamese
              characters in face value) £180
Z381   8a. deep green and orange £170
Z382   10a. ultramarine £180

1905–09. *(Nos. 92/105).*
Z383   53   1a. green and orange £180
Z384   2a. grey and deep violet £170
Z385   3a. green £180
Z386   4a. pale red and sepia £170
Z387   4a. scarlet £180
Z388   5a. carmine £180
Z389   8a. olive-bistre and dull black . . . £180
Z390   9a. blue £170
Z391   24a. red-brown £300

1907. *Surch with T 56 (No. 109).*
Z392   9   1a. on 24a. purple and blue £180

1908–09. *(Nos. 105/9).*
Z395   53   4a. scarlet £120
Z396   9a. blue £110

Siam transferred suzerainty over the four northern Malay states to Great Britain on 15 July 1909. Use of Siamese stamps in Kelantan and Perlis appears to have extended into early August 1909.

B. INDO-CHINA

In the 19th century the borders between Thailand and her eastern neighbours were imprecise and Thailand operated its postal service in these areas until they were ceded to France in 1904.

Although such usage of Thai stamps could be considered as "internal" use (and it should be noted that Nos. 87/8a of the Thailand listing were for use at Battambong), details of the post offices are given below.

CAMBODIA

For Types A to E see under section A.

Type F (Chantakirikate)

Pailin

Siemrap   Srisophon

Battembong. Types A, B and D.
Chantakirikate. Type F.
Pailin. Types F and C.
Siemrap. Types F and C (inscr "SIEMRAT").
Srisophon. Type F.

LAOS

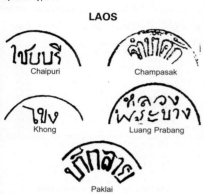

Chaipuri   Champasak

Khong   Luang Prabang

Paklai

Chaipuri. Type F.
Champasak. This was under the administration of the Battambong office. Type F.
Khong. Type F.
Luang Prabang. Type F.
Paklai. Type F.

   During the Japanese Occupation of Indo-China administration of former territories was restored to Thailand, from 1942 to 1946. Unoverprinted Thai stamps were used from the following post offices, using bilingual cancellations as Type G.

Type G.

CAMBODIA. Kriengsakpichit, Mongkolburi, Pailin, Pakphriak, Phratabong (formerly Battambong), Pibulasonggran (formerly Siemrap) and Srisophon.
LAOS. Champasak, Lanchang (formerly Paklai) and Sitandon.

Timor

1885. 1000 Reis = 1 Milreis
1894. 100 Avos = 1 Pataca
1960. 100 Centavos = 1 Escudo

The island of Timor is one of the Lesser Sunda islands in the south of the Indonesian archipelago. Portuguese merchants began trading there in about 1520 and took the island under their administration in 1586. The Dutch established themselves in Kupang in 1613 and the Portuguese moved to the north and east. Treaties ratified in 1860 and 1908 established boundaries whereby the eastern half of the island, the enclave of Ocussi Ambeno further west along the north coast, and the islands of Cambing and Jako were made part of the Dutch East Indies. Portuguese Timor was administered from Macao until 1896, when it became a separate colony, with Dili as capital. On 11 June 1951 it became an Overseas Province of Portugal and its inhabitants received Portuguese citizenship on 6 September 1961.

The Dutch retained the western part of Timor until 1949, when it became part of Indonesia.

PRINTERS. All the stamps of Portuguese Timor were printed at the Mint, Lisbon, Portugal *unless otherwise stated*.

REPRINTS. Reprints of the following issues were made in 1885 and 1905 as indicated in the footnotes. These can generally be distinguished as follows:—

1885 reprints are on stout very white paper, usually ungummed but sometimes with white gum having yellowish spots. They are perf 13½ with large clean-cut holes producing sharp pointed teeth.

1905 reprints are on creamy white paper of ordinary quality with shiny white gum, all perf 13½.

King Luis
11 November 1861–19 October 1889

TIMOR
(1)   2

1885. *Stamps of Macao optd with T 1.*

(a) P 12½.

1	5r. black (R.)		95	80
2	10r. deep green		1·80	1·50
	a. *Grey-green*		1·80	1·50
	b. On Mozambique stamp		6·00	6·00
	c. On Portuguese India stamp		35·00	35·00
3	20r. rosine		4·50	2·50
4	25r. dull lilac		80	60
5	40r. yellow		2·10	1·80
6	50r. deep blue		95	75
7	80r. grey		2·50	1·80
8	100r. dull purple		95	80
9	200r. orange		3·50	2·10
10	300r. yellow-brown		2·10	1·80
1/10	*Set of 10*		18·00	13·00

(b) P 13½.

11	5r. black (R.)		1·20	95
12	10r. deep green		2·40	2·10
	a. *Grey-green*		2·40	2·10
13	20r. rosine		4·00	2·75
14	25r. dull lilac		9·50	6·75
15	40r. yellow		6·75	6·00
16	50r. deep blue		6·75	6·00
	a. *Pale blue*		6·75	6·00
17	80r. grey		2·50	2·10
18	100r. lilac-grey		4·50	2·10
	a. *Dull purple*		4·50	2·10

19	200r. orange		2·10	1·80
20	300r. yellow-brown		2·10	1·80
11/20	*Set of 10*		38·00	29·00

Nos. 2b/c were of an experimental nature and were not intended for issue.

Varieties of the above with *double* and *inverted* overprints are only printer's waste.

The 20r. bistre, 25r. rose and 50r. green were prepared for use but were not issued.

All values were reprinted in 1885 and 1905.

(Des and eng F. A. de Campos. Head embossed, rest typo)

1887. *Chalk-surfaced paper.* P 12½.

21	**2**	5r. black	1·50	95
22		10r. green	1·60	1·30
		a. Double impression	24·00	24·00
		b. *Deep green*	1·60	1·30
23		20r. rosine	2·40	1·30
24		25r. bright mauve	3·00	1·50
25		40r. chocolate	5·25	2·20
26		50r. blue	5·25	2·40
27		80r. grey	6·25	2·50
28		100r. yellow-brown	6·75	3·25
29		200r. lavender	13·50	6·75
30		300r. red-orange	15·00	8·00
		a. *Orange*	15·00	8·00
21/30a		*Set of 10*	55·00	27·00

The 5, 25, 50 and 100r. were issued both with and without gum. The 5, 50, 100 and 200r. were reprinted in 1905.

King Carlos
19 October 1889–1 February 1908

JORNAES   **TIMOR**

TIMOR

2½   2½ **30**   **30** 
(N 3)   (4)   N 5

1892 (Aug). *NEWSPAPER. As T 2 but inscr "MACAU", surch with Type N 3. No gum.*

(a) P 12½.

N31	2½on 20r. rosine		1·10	75
	a. "TIMOR" inverted		6·25	6·25
N32	2½on 40r. chocolate		1·10	75
	a. "TIMOR" inverted		6·25	6·25
N33	2½on 80r. grey		1·10	75
	a. "TIMOR" inverted		6·25	6·25

(b) P 13½.

N34	2½on 40r. chocolate		2·75	2·20
	a. "TIMOR" inverted		9·25	9·25
N35	2½on 80r. grey		6·25	4·75

1892 (Sept). *As T 2 but inscr "MACAU", surch with T 4. No gum.*

31	30on 300r. orange (*p.* 12½)		3·75	1·90
32	30on 300r. orange (*p.* 13½)		3·00	1·80

(Des and eng E. C. Azedo Gneco. Typo)

1893 (25 Oct). *NEWSPAPER.* P 11½.

N36	N **5**	2½r. brown (*no gum*)	50	45
		a. Perf 12½	1·80	1·20
		b. Perf 13½	50	45

Stamps of this type could be, and often were, used for franking ordinary correspondence.

1 avo

(7) PROVISORIO 仙壹

5 avos

PROVISORIO 仙伍

6 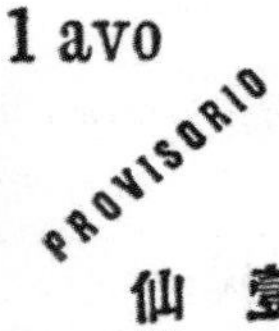 (7)  **(8)**

(Des and eng M. D. Neto. Typo)

1894 (15 Nov).

(a) Chalk-surfaced paper. With or without gum (5, 10, 15r.), no gum (others). P 11½.

33	**6**	5r. pale orange	90	50
34		10r. rosy mauve	90	60
35		15r. red-brown	1·30	60
36		20r. lilac	1·30	60
37		25r. green	1·50	90
38		50r. pale blue	2·20	1·60
39		75r. rose	3·00	2·20
40		80r. pale green	3·00	2·20
41		100r. brown/*buff*	2·20	1·90
42		150r. carmine/*rose*	9·50	4·75
43		200r. blue/*blue*	9·50	5·25
44		300r. blue/*pale brown*	12·00	6·00
33/44	*Set of 12*		43·00	24·00

(b) Enamel-surfaced paper. P 13½.

45	**6**	50r. pale blue	65·00	65·00

1894. New Currency. No gum.

(a) Surch as T 7. P 12½.

46	**2**	1a.on 5r. black (R.)	90	55
47		2a.on 10r. green	90	50
48		3a.on 20r. rosine (G.)	1·10	90
49		4a.on 25r. bright purple	1·50	90
50		6a.on 40r. chocolate	1·50	90
51		8a.on 50r. blue (R.)	2·20	1·20
52		13a.on 80r. grey	3·00	1·80
53		16a.on 100r. yellow-brown	5·25	5·25
54		31a.on 200r. lavender	5·25	5·25
55		47a.on 300r. orange (G.)	15·00	12·00
46/55	*Set of 10*		33·00	26·00

Nos. 46/9 and 51 exist with broken "y" for "v" in "avo" or "avos".

(b) Nos. 31/2 further surch with T 8.

56		5a.on 30 on 300r. (*p.* 12½)	16·00	12·50
57		5a.on 30 on 300r. (*p.* 13½)	3·75	2·20
		a. "avos" omitted	11·00	11·00

½ avo

PROVISORIO 仙半

(N 9) **10**

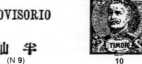

1894. NEWSPAPER. Surch with Type N 9.

N58	**N 5**	½a.on 2½r. brown (*p.* 11½)	1·20	1·20
N59		½a.on 2½r. brown (*p.* 12½)	2·10	1·50

1898 (1 Apr). *400th Anniv of Vasco da Gama's Discovery of Route to India. As Nos. 1/8 of Portuguese Colonies and Overseas Territories. P 14 to 15.*

58	1a. blue-green	1·20	80
59	1a. vermilion	1·20	80
60	2a. dull purple	1·20	80
61	4a. yellow-green	1·20	80
62	8a. deep blue	1·60	1·20
63	12a. chocolate	2·20	1·50
64	16a. bistre-brown	2·20	1·80
65	24a. ochre	3·50	2·40
58/65	*Set of 8*	13·00	9·00

(Des and eng E. Mouchon. Typo)

1898 (1 July)–**1900**. *Name and value in black, on the 78a. in carmine. With or without gum (Nos. 68, 78), no gum (66/7, 70/4, 79, 83).*

(a) P 12½.

66	**10**	½a. pale grey	65	30
67		1a. orange-red	30	30

(b) P 11½.

68	**10**	½a. pale grey	1·60	1·50
69		1a. orange-red	1·60	1·50
70		2a. green	30	30
71		2½a. chocolate	80	65
72		3a. deep lilac	80	65
73		4a. blue-green	80	65
74		8a. blue	80	65
75		10a. blue (1899)	80	65
76		12a. rose	2·40	2·20
77		13a. mauve	2·40	2·20
78		16a. deep blue/*blue*	2·40	2·20
79		20a. brown/*straw* (1899)	2·40	2·20
80		24a. brown/*buff*	2·40	2·20
81		31a. purple/*flesh*	2·40	2·20
82		47a. blue/*pink*	4·50	3·50
83		78a. black/*azure* (1900)	6·00	4·50
68/83	*Set of 16*		29·00	25·00

See also Nos. 112/23.

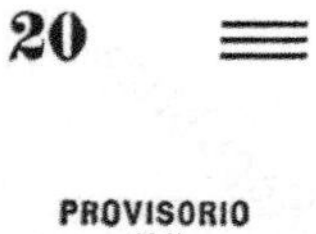

20 **=** **AVOS** PROVISORIO **(11)**  **(12)**

D 13

1899. *Surch as T 11.*

84	**10**	10on 16a. blue/*blue*	1·60	1·50
85		20on 31a. purple/*flesh*	1·60	1·50

1902. *Surch as T 12.*

86	**2**	5a.on 25r. (12½)	1·50	80
87		5a.on 200r. (12½)	2·20	1·50
88	**6**	5a.on 5r. (11½)	80	65
		a. Surch inverted	8·50	8·50
89		5a.on 25r. (11½)	80	65
90		5a.on 50r. (11½)	95	80
91		5a.on 50r. (E) (13½)	1·70	1·60
92	**2**	6a.on 10r. (12½)	95·00	75·00
93		6a.on 300r. (12½)	2·20	2·20
94	**6**	6a.on 5r. (11½)	95	80
95	**N 5**	6a.on 2½r. (11½)	60	50
		a. Surch inverted	6·75	6·75
96		6a.on 2½r. (12½)		
97		6a.on 2½r. (13½)	1·10	95
98	**2**	9a.on 40r. (12½)	2·50	2·20
99		9a.on 100r. (12½)	2·50	2·20
100	**6**	9a.on 15r. (11½)	95	80
101		9a.on 75r. (11½)	95	80
102	**2**	15a.on 20r. (12½)	2·50	2·20
103		15a.on 50r. (12½)	75·00	65·00
104	**6**	15a.on 10r. (11½)	1·50	1·30
105		15a.on 100r. (11½)	1·50	1·30
106		15a.on 300r. (11½)	1·50	1·30
107	**2**	22a.on 80r. (12½)	5·25	4·50
108	**6**	22a.on 80r. (11½)	2·50	2·40
109		22a.on 200r. (11½)	2·50	2·40

The 5/25, 5/200, 6/10, 6/300, 9/40, 9/100, 15/50 and 22/200 values, all T **2**, were reprinted in 1905.

PROVISORIO **(13a)**

1902. *Optd with T 13a.*

110	**10**	3a. deep lilac	1·20	80
111		12a. rose	3·00	2·20

The 12a. was reprinted in 1905.

1903 (1 Jan). *Colours changed. Name and value in black. No gum.*
P 11½.

112	**10**	3a. deep green		1·40	80
113		5a. carmine		1·20	80
114		6a. pale yellow-brown		1·20	80
115		9a. red-brown		1·20	80
116		10a. grey-brown		1·20	80
117		12a. dull blue		6·00	5·25
118		13a. dull purple		1·50	95
119		15a. grey-lilac		2·50	1·80
120		22a. orange-brown/*pink*		2·50	2·20
121		31a. sepia/*cream*		2·50	2·20
122		47a. purple/*pink*		2·75	2·20
123		78a. dull blue/*straw*		6·25	4·50
112/123		*Set of 12*		27·00	21·00

(Des and eng J. S. de Carvalho e Silva. Typo)

1904. *POSTAGE DUE. Name and value in black. With or without gum* (1, 2a). *no gum (others).* P 11½.

D124	D **13**	1a. yellow-green		35	35
D125		2a. slate		35	35
D126		5a. brown		95	80
D127		6a. orange		95	80
D128		10a. deep brown		95	80
D129		15a. pale red-brown		1·60	1·30
D130		24a. blue		4·00	2·75
D131		40a. carmine		4·00	2·75
D132		50a. orange		5·50	3·25
D133		1p. deep lilac		12·00	7·00
D124/133		*Set of 10*		27·00	18·00

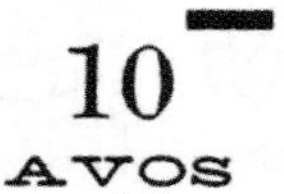

(14)

(15)

1905. *Surch with T* **14**.

124	**10**	10a.on 12a. dull blue		1·60	1·50

King Manool II
1 February 1908–5 October 1910

PORTUGUESE REPUBLIC
5 October 1910

(15a)

1911. *Optd with T* **15a**, *in red or green* (G.). P 11½.

125	**10**	½a. grey		30	30
126		1a. orange-red		30	30
		a. Perf 12½		1·60	1·60
127		2a. green		30	30
128		3a. deep green		60	30
129		5a. carmine (G.)		60	30
130		6a. pale yellow-brown		60	30
131		9a. red-brown		80	75
132		10a. grey-brown		80	75
133		13a. dull purple		80	75
134		15a. grey-lilac		80	75
135		22a. orange-brown/*pink*		80	75
136		31a. sepia/*cream*		80	75
137		47a. purple/*pink*		1·80	1·50
138		78a. dull blue/*straw*		2·40	1·90
125/138		*Set of 14 (cheapest)*		10·00	6·50

1911. *POSTAGE DUE. Optd with T* **15a**, *in red or green* (G.).

D139	D **13**	1a. yellow-green		30	35
D140		2a. slate		30	35
D141		5a. brown		30	80
D142		6a. orange		35	80
D143		10a. deep brown		60	80
D144		15a. pale red-brown		90	1·30
D145		24a. blue		1·30	2·75
D146		40a. carmine (G.)		1·60	2·75
D147		50a. orange		2·20	3·25
D148		1p. deep lilac		5·50	7·00
D139/148		*Set of 10*		12·00	18·00

1913. *Various stamps of 1902–5 optd locally.*

(a) With T **15**, *in red.*

139	**10**	3a. deep green		1·00	90
		a. Opt inverted		16·00	
140	**6**	5a.on 5r. (11½)		75	75
141		5a.on 25r. (11½)		75	75
142		5a.on 50r. (11½)		1·80	1·50
143		5a.on 50r. (E) (13½)		1·80	1·50
144	N **5**	6a.on 2½r. (11½)		1·50	95
145		6a.on 2½r. (13½)		1·50	95
146	**6**	6a.on 20r. (11½)		90	75
147		9a.on 15r. (11½)		90	75
148	**10**	10a.on 12a. (14)		90	75
149	**6**	15a.on 100r. (11½)		1·00	1·00
150		22a.on 80r. (11½)		1·90	1·50
151		22a.on 200r. (11½)		1·90	1·50

(16)

(17)

(18)

(b) With T **16**.

152	**10**	5a. carmine (G.)		1·10	1·00
153	**6**	9a.on 75r. (11½) (G.)		1·10	1·00
154		15a.on 10r. (11½) (G.)		1·10	1·00
155		15a.on 300r. (11½) (R.)		1·50	1·50
		a. "REPBLICAU" (pos. 11)		7·25	7·25
		b. "REUBPLICA" (pos. 12)		7·25	7·25

(c) With T **17**, *in red.*

156	**10**	6a. pale yellow-brown		80	75
157		9a. red-brown		80	75
158		10a. grey-brown		80	75
159		13a. mauve		80	75
160		13a. dull purple		80	75
161		15a. grey-lilac		1·20	1·00
162		22a. orange-brown/*pink*		1·50	1·20
163		31a. purple/*flesh*		1·50	1·20
164		31a. sepia/*cream*		1·50	1·20
165		47a. blue/*pink*		2·40	1·90
166		47a. purple/*pink*		2·40	1·90
167		78a. dull blue/*straw*		3·00	2·20

(d) With T **18**, *in red.*

168	**10**	78a. black/*azure*		3·00	3·00

1913. *POSTAGE DUE. Optd locally with T* **17**, *in red or green* (G.).

D169	D **13**	1a. yellow-green		5·25	4·00
D170		2a. slate		5·25	4·00
D171		5a. brown		2·20	1·50
D172		6a. orange		2·20	1·60
D173		10a. deep brown		2·40	1·90
D174		15a. pale red-brown		2·40	1·90
D175		24a. blue		2·75	1·90
D176		40a. carmine (G.)		2·75	1·90
D177		50a. orange		5·50	3·75
D178		1p. deep lilac		5·50	3·75
D169/178		*Set of 10*		32·00	23·00

REPUBLICA

REPUBLICA　10　A.
(19)　　　　　(20)

21 Ceres

1913. *Stamps of Vasco da Gama Issue optd or surch in Lisbon with T* **19** *or* **20.**

169	½a. blue-green		45	35
170	1a. vermilion		45	35
171	2a. dull purple		45	35
172	4a. yellow-green		45	35
173	8a. deep blue		80	80
174	10a.on 12a. chocolate		1·50	1·20
175	16a. bistre-brown		1·20	80
176	24a. ochre		1·50	1·30
169/176 *Set of 8*			6·00	4·75

(Des C. Fernandes. Eng J. S. de Carvalho a Silva. Typo)

1914. *Name and value in black. Chalk-surfaced paper.* P 15 × 14.

177	**21**	½a. brown-olive	35	35
178		1a. black	35	35
179		2a. deep green	35	35
180		3a. chocolate	60	45
181		4a. carmine	60	45
182		6a. violet	65	45
183		10a. deep blue	65	45
184		12a. yellow-brown	95	75
185		16a. slate	95	75
186		20a. brown-red	9·50	3·00
187		40a. claret	5·25	3·00
188		58a. chocolate/*green*	5·25	2·50
189		76a. brown/*rose*	5·25	4·50
190		1p. orange/*salmon*	8·00	6·75
191		3p. deep green/*azure*	22·00	13·50
177/191 *Set of 15*			55·00	34·00

See also Nos. 209/27.

1915. *Provisionais of 1902–5 optd with T* **15a,** *in red (reading down on* 2½r.*).*

192	**10**	3a. deep lilac (110)	45	35
193		10a.on 12a. (124)	45	35
194	**6**	5a.on 5r. (11½)	45	30
195		5a.on 25r. (11½)	45	30
196		5a.on 50r. (11½)	45	65
197		5a.on 50r. (E) (13½)	45	65
198	N **5**	6a.on 2½r. (11½)	45	30
199		6a.on 2½r. (12½)	45	30
200		6a.on 2½r. (13½)	45	30
201	**6**	6a.on 20r. (11½)	45	30
202		9a.on 15r. (11½)	45	30
203		9a.on 75r. (11½)	50	30
204		15a.on 10r. (11½)	50	30
205		15a.on 100r. (11½)	60	30
206		15a.on 300r. (11½)	60	30
207		22a.on 80r. (11½)	1·50	95
208		22a.on 200r. (11½)	2·20	1·60

1919–23. *Name and value in black.*

(a) Unsurfaced paper. P 15 × 14 (1919).

209	**21**	1a. black	75	60
210		2a. deep green	75	60

(b) Unsurfaced paper. P 12 × 11½ (1922–23).

211	**21**	½a. brown-olive	60	60
212		1a. black	60	60
213		1½a. yellow-green (1923)	60	60
214		2a. deep green	60	60
215		4a. carmine	1·50	1·20
216		7a. yellow-green (1923)	95	90
217		7½a. pale blue (1923)	95	90
218		9a. pale dull blue (1923)	1·10	90
219		11a. drab (1923)	1·50	1·20
220		12a. yellow-brown	1·50	1·20
221		15a. mauve (1923)	4·50	2·75
222		18a. deep blue (1923)	4·50	2·75
223		19a. deep grey-green (1923)	4·50	2·75
224		36a. turquoise (1923)	4·50	2·75
225		54a. chocolate (1923)	4·50	2·75
226		72a. bright rosine (1923)	8·75	5·50

(c) Glazed paper. P 12 × 11½ (1923).

227	**21**	5p. bright carmine	37·00	16·00
211/227 *Set of 17*			78·00	40·00

CHARITY TAX STAMPS. Stamps bearing C numbers were for compulsory use on internal letters on certain days of the year as an additional postal tax for public charities. Other values in some of the designs were for use on telegrams or for fiscal purposes.

2 AVOS

TAXA DE GUERRA
(C **22**)

2

TAXA DE GUERRA
(C **23**)

½ Avo

P. P. n.º 68

19·3·1920
(24)

1919 (1 July). *CHARITY TAX. No. 177 surch locally with Type* C **22.** *With or without gum.*

C228　**21**　2a.on ½a. brown-olive (R.)　3·50　1·60
　　a. Surch inverted
A similar 9a. surcharge was only for fiscal use.

1919. *CHARITY TAX. Nos. 196/7 surch locally with Type* C **23** *in red, with bars obliterating "5" of previous surcharge in black.*

C229　**6**　2 on 5a. on 50r. (11½)
C230　　　2 on 5a. on 50r. (E) (13½)　30·00　18·00
A similar 9a. value was only for fiscal use.

1920 (Mar). *Nos. 196/7 surch locally with T* **24.**

228	**6**	½a.on 5a. on 50r. (11½)	5·25	4·50
229		½a.on 5a. on 50r. (E) (13½)	8·00	7·50

1925 (8 May). *Marquis de Pombal Commemoration.* P 12½.

(a) CHARITY TAX.

C231	2a. carmine-lake	30	20
C232	2a. carmine-lake	30	20
C233	2a. carmine-lake	30	20

Designs:—C231; Pombal Monument; C232; Planning the reconstruction of Lisbon; C233 Marquis de Pombal.

(b) POSTAGE DUE. Optd with "MULTA" Islands.

D231	4a. carmine-lake	30	20
D232	4a. carmine-lake	30	20
D233	4a. carmine-lake	30	20
C231/D233 *Set of 6*		1·60	1·10

Nos. C231/3 were in use from 8 to 13 May 1925 and from 5 to 15 May in 1926 and 1929. Nos. D231/3 were used in default.

50 C.
(24a)

1931. *Nos. 226 and 221 surch as T* **24a.**

230	**21**	6a.on 72a. rosine	90	75
231		12a.on 15a. mauve	90	75

7 avos

Instrução

D. L. n.º 7 de 3-2-1934
(C **25**)

Assistência

D. L. n.º 72
(C **26**)

1934–35. *CHARITY TAX for Education. Fiscal stamps with values in black, optd or surch locally as Type* C **25.** *With or without gum.* P 12 × 11½.

C234	2a. green (R.)	1·90	1·50
	a. Inverted "5" for " "	5·25	4·50
C235	5a. green (R.)	3·00	1·60
	a. Inverted "5" for " "	5·25	4·50
C236	7a.on ½a. rose ('35)	3·50	2·20
	a. Inverted "5" for " "	5·25	4·50

The above were in use in Nov and Dec 1934, Jan, Nov and Dec 1935, and Jan 1936.

1935 (8 July). *As T* **50** *of Macao.* W **51** *of Macao.*

232	½a. brown	20	15
233	1a. sepia	20	15
234	2a. blue-green	20	15
235	3a. mauve	35	15
236	4a. black	35	20
237	5a. grey	35	30
238	6a. cinnamon	35	30
239	7a. carmine	35	30
240	8a. turquoise	60	30
241	10a. vermilion	60	30
242	12a. blue	60	30
243	14a. olive-green	60	30
244	15a. claret	60	30
245	20a. orange	75	30
246	30a. yellow-green	75	45
247	40a. violet	2·40	1·20
248	50a. bistre-brown	2·40	1·20
249	1p. grey-blue	5·50	3·50
250	2p. red-brown	14·00	5·50
251	3p. emerald	19·00	7·50
252	5p. mauve	31·00	15·00
232/252	*Set of 21*	75·00	34·00

1936 (1 Nov)**–37.** *CHARITY TAX. Fiscal stamps with values in black, optd locally with Type* C **26.** *With or without gum.* P 12 × 11½.

C253	10a. rose	2·20	1·60
C254	10a. grey-green (1.11.37)	1·60	1·50

1938 (1 Oct). *Name and value in black.* P 13½ × 13.

(a) POSTAGE.

253	1a. grey-olive	20	20
254	2a. orange-brown	20	20
255	3a. slate-violet	20	20
256	4a. emerald-green	20	20
257	5a. carmine	20	20
258	6a. slate	20	20
259	8a. bright purple	20	20
260	10a. magenta	20	20
261	12a. scarlet	30	30
262	15a. orange	60	45
263	20a. blue	60	45
264	40a. grey-black	90	60
265	50a. brown	1·30	90
266	1p. lake	4·50	2·75
267	2p. olive-green	12·00	3·00
268	3p. ultramarine	13·50	6·75
269	5p. red-brown	30·00	13·50
253/269	*Set of 17*	60·00	27·00

Designs:—1a. to 4a. Vasco da Gama; 5a. to 8a. Mousinho de Albuquerque; 10 to 15a. Prince Henry the Navigator; 20 to 50a. Dam; 1 to 5p. Afonso de Albuquerque.

(b) AIR.

270	1a. scarlet	45	45
271	2a. bright violet	50	45
272	3a. orange	50	45
273	5a. bright blue	60	60
274	10a. brown-lake	75	75
275	20a. blue-green	1·60	95
276	50a. red-brown	3·25	2·75
277	70a. carmine	4·00	3·50
278	1p. magenta	8·75	4·00
270/278	*Set of 9*	18·00	12·50

Designs:—1a. to 1p. Airplane over Globe.

The whole of Timor was occupied by the Japanese in the Second World War, though Japan was not at war with Portugal. From November 1942 to December 1945 there were no postal facilities for the civilian population. A shortage of stamps after liberation was met by overprinting stamps of Mozambique.

TIMOR
8
AVOS

≋ ≋≋≋ ≋
27

REPÚBLICA
PORTUGUESA

10 avos
TIMOR
——
Assistência

* LIBERTAÇÃO *
(28)

C 29

1946 (7 Sept). *1938 issue of Mozambique surch as T* **27.**

(a) POSTAGE. Nos. 354/64 surcharged.

279	1a.on 15c. brown-purple	3·25	2·75
280	4a.on 35c. emerald-green	3·25	2·75
281	8a.on 50c. magenta	3·25	2·75
282	10a.on 70c. slate-violet	3·25	2·75
283	12a.on 1E. scarlet	3·25	2·75
284	20a.on 1E.75, blue	3·25	2·75

(b) AIR. Nos. 371/7 surcharged.

285	8a.on 50c. orange	3·25	2·75
286	12a.on 1E. bright blue	3·25	2·75
287	40a.on 3E. blue-green	3·25	2·75
288	50a.on 5E. red-brown	3·25	2·75
289	1p.on 10E. magenta	3·75	2·75
279/289	*Set of 11*	32·00	27·00

1947 (15 Mar). *Liberation. Nos. 253, etc., optd with T* **28.**

(a) POSTAGE.

290	1a. grey-olive	9·50	6·25
291	2a. orange-brown	22·00	12·00
292	3a. slate-violet	8·75	3·75
293	4a. emerald-green	8·75	3·75
294	5a. carmine	3·75	1·50
295	8a. bright purple	95	45
296	10a. magenta	3·75	1·60
297	12a. scarlet	3·75	1·60
298	15a. orange	3·75	1·60
299	20a. blue	48·00	27·00
	a. Opt inverted	60·00	60·00
300	40a. grey-black	9·50	7·50
290/300	*Set of 11*	£110	60·00

(b) AIR.

301	1a. scarlet	15·00	4·00
302	2a. bright violet	15·00	4·00
303	3a. orange	15·00	4·00
304	5a. bright blue	15·00	4·00
305	10a. brown-lake	3·75	1·30
306	20a. blue-green	3·75	1·30
307	50a. red-brown	3·75	1·30
308	70a. carmine	15·00	3·75
309	1p. magenta	6·25	1·50
301/309	*Set of 9*	85·00	22·00

1948. *CHARITY TAX. Typo locally. No gum.* P 11½.

C310	C **29**	10a. deep blue	1·60	1·30
C311		20a. green	2·20	1·50

The 20a. has a different emblem.

30 Girl with Gong   **31** Pottery-making   **32**

(Des A. de Sousa. Litho Litografia Maia, Oporto)

1948 (Sept). *As T* **30**. P 14.

310	1a. red-brown and turquoise	60	30
311	3a. red-brown and grey	1·30	65
312	4a. myrtle green and magenta	1·60	1·30
313	8a. greenish slate and vermilion	95	35
314	10a. blue-green and orange-brown	95	35
315	20a. ultramarine and light blue	95	60
316	1p. ultramarine and orange	19·00	4·50
317	3p. red-brown and violet	19·00	8·00
310/317	*Set of 8*	40·00	14·50

MS317*a* 130 × 99 mm. Nos. 310/17 (sold at 5p.) ..... 55·00

Designs:—1a. Native woman; 4a. Girl with baskets; 8a. Chief of Aleixo de Ainaro; 10a. Timor chief; 20a. Warrior and horse; 1, 3p. Tribal chieftains.

1948 (Oct). *Honouring the Statue of Our Lady of Fatima.* P 14.
318	8a. grey (Statue of Our Lady of Fatima)	5·50	5·50

For No. 318 in miniature sheet see No. **MS**1 of Portuguese Colonies and Overseas Territories (Part 9, *Portugal and Spain*).

1949 (Oct). *75th Anniv of Universal Postal Union.* P 14.
319	16a. yellow-brown (Globe)	13·50	8·00

(Litho Litografia Nacional, Oporto)

1950 (Apr). *T* **31** *and similar type.* P 14.
320	20a. blue	60	60
321	50a. brown (Young girl)	1·80	80

1950 (May). *Holy Year.* P 13½.
322	40a. green (Bells and dove)	1·30	90
323	70a. sepia (Angel)	1·90	1·30

For No. 322 in miniature sheet see No. **MS**2 of Portuguese Colonies and Overseas Territories (Part 9, *Portugal and Spain*).

(Des V. P. da C. Sequeira. Litho Litografia Nacional, Oporto)

1950 (Oct). *T* **32** *and similar floral designs.* P 14.
324	1a. carmine, green and grey	45	30
325	3a. yellow, green and olive-brown	1·90	1·50
326	10a. rose, green and blue	2·20	1·60
327	16a. red, orange, green and brown	4·50	2·20
328	20a. yellow, green and blue-green	1·90	1·60
329	30a. yellow, green and deep blue	2·20	1·60
330	70a. red, yellow, green and purple	3·00	1·80
331	1p. carmine, yellow and green	5·25	3·75
332	2p. yellow, green and crimson	7·50	6·00
333	5p. pink, green and black	12·50	9·50
324/333	*Set of 10*	37·00	27·00

Flowers:—1a. *Belamcanda chinensis*; 3a. *Caesalpinia pulcherrima*; 10a. *Calotropis gigantea*; 16a. *Delonix regia*; 20a. *Plumeria rubra*; 30a. *Allamanda cathartica*; 70a. *Haemanthus multiflorus*, 1p. *Bauhinia*; 2p. *Eurycles amboiniensis*; 5p. *Crinum longiflorum*.

1951 (Oct). *Termination of Holy Year.* P 14.
334	86a. greenish blue and turquoise (Our Lady of Fatima)	1·50	1·30

No. 334 was issued se-tenant with a stamp-size label bearing a papal declaration.

1952 (June). *First Tropical Medicine Congress, Lisbon.* P 13½.
335	10a. brown and blackish green	80	65

Design:—Nurse weighing baby.

1952. *POSTAGE DUE.* P 14.
D336	1a. multicoloured	15	15
D337	3a. multicoloured	15	15
D338	5a. multicoloured	15	15
D339	10a. multicoloured	15	15
D340	30a. multicoloured	20	15
D341	1p. multicoloured	60	35
D336/341	*Set of 6*	1·30	1·00

33 St Francis Xavier Statue   **34** Statue of The Virgin

(Litho Litografia Nacional, Oporto, Portugal)

1952 (25 Oct). *400th Death Anniv of St. Francis Xavier. T* **33** *and similar vert designs.* P 14.
336	1a. black and grey	15	15
337	16a. sepia and buff	65	50
338	1p. lake and bluish grey	3·00	1·60

Designs:—16a. Miraculous arm of St. Francis; 1p. Tomb of St. Francis.

1953 (Jan). *Missionary Art Exhibition. Litho.* P 13½.
339	**34**	3a. reddish brown and grey-brown	15	10
340		16a. red-brown and stone	45	35
341		50a. deep ultramarine and grey-brown	1·30	1·20

1954. *Portuguese Stamp Centenary. Multicoloured.* P 13.
342	10a. Arms of Portuguese Overseas Provinces	90	80

1954. *Fourth Centenary of So Paulo. Multicoloured.* P 13½.
343	16a. Father M. de Nabrega	75	45

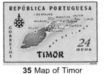

35 Map of Timor   **(36)**

(Des J. Moura. Litho Enschedé)

1956 (21 May). P 14 × 13.
344	**35**	1a. multicoloured	10	10
345		3a. multicoloured	10	10
346		8a. multicoloured	30	20
347		24a. multicoloured	35	20
348		32a. multicoloured	45	20
349		40a. multicoloured	65	35
350		1p. multicoloured	1·90	45
351		3p. multicoloured	5·50	2·75
344/351	*Set of 8*	8·50	4·00

1958 (5 Sept). *Sixth International Congress of Tropical Medicine. Diamond-shaped design. Multicoloured.* P 13½.
352	32a. *Calophyllum inophyllum*	2·75	1·90

1958 (Sept). *Brussels International Exhibition. Multicoloured.* P 12 × 11½.
353	40a. Exhibition emblem	45	35

1960 (1 Jan). *New Currency. Nos. 344/51 surch as T* **36**.
354	**35**	5c.on 1a. multicoloured	15	10
355		10c.on 3a. multicoloured	15	10

356	20c.on 8a. multicoloured		15	10
357	30c.on 24a. multicoloured		15	10
358	50c.on 32a. multicoloured		15	10
359	1E.on 40a. multicoloured		15	15
360	2E.on 40a. multicoloured		30	20
361	5E.on 1p. multicoloured		65	45
362	10E.on 3p. multicoloured		2·20	1·10
363	15E.on 3p. multicoloured		2·20	1·30
354/363	Set of 10		5·50	3·25

C 37

38 Elephant Jar

1960–66. *CHARITY TAX. New Currency. Sans-serif lettering. Typo locally. No gum.*

(a) P 11½ (1960).

C364	**37**	70c. indigo		65	65
C365		1E.30 green		1·30	1·30

(b) P 10½ (1966).

C366	**37**	70c. deep blue		1·30	1·30
C367		1E.30 emerald		1·30	1·30

In No. C364 "PORTUGUESA" is 17 mm wide and in No. C366 it is 18 mm; No. C365 has "1$30" 8 mm wide and in No. C367 it is 7 mm. There are other differences also.
See also Nos. C398/400.

1960 (25 June). *Fifth Death Centenary of Prince Henry the Navigator. Multicoloured.* P 13½ × 13.

364	4E.50 Prince Henry's motto (*horiz*)		40	25

1961 (28 Apr). *Timor Art. T* **38** *and similar multicoloured designs. Litho.* P 11½ × 12 (vert) or 12 × 11½ (horiz).

365	5c. Type **38**		10	10
366	10c. House on stilts		10	10
	a. Blue (inscription) inverted		14·50	
367	20c. Idol		20	20
368	30c. Rosary		20	20
369	50c. Model of outrigger canoe (*horiz*)		45	35
370	1E. Casket		35	35
371	2E.50 Archer		60	35
372	4E.50 Elephant		75	35
373	5E. Native climbing palm tree		95	35
374	10E. Statuette of woman		3·00	95
375	20E. Model of cockfight (*horiz*)		7·50	2·40
376	50E. House, bird and cat		7·25	2·40
365/376	Set of 12		19·00	7·25

1962 (22 Mar). *Sports. Multicoloured.* P 13.

377	50c. Game shooting		10	10
378	1E. Horse-riding		65	20
379	1E.50 Swimming		50	30
380	2E. Athletes		35	35
381	2E.50 Football		65	50
382	15E. Big-game hunting		1·90	1·30
377/382	Set of 6		3·75	2·50

1962. *Malaria Eradication. Multicoloured.* P 13½.

383	2E.50 Anopheles sundaicus		50	45

1964 (16 May). *Centenary of National Overseas Bank. Multicoloured.* P 13½.

384	2E.50 M. P. Chagas		60	45

1965 (17 May). *I.T.U. Centenary.* P 14½.

385	1E.50 multicoloured		90	60

1966 (28 May). *40th Anniv of Portuguese National Revolution. Multicoloured.* P 12½ × 11½.

386	4E.50 Dr. V. Machado's College and Health Centre, Dili		80	50

1967 (31 Jan). *Centenary of Military Naval Association.* P 13.

387	10c. Gago Coutinho and gunboat *Patria*		20	20
388	4E.50 Sacadura Cabral and Fairey IIID seaplane *Lusitania*		1·50	80

39 Sepoy Officer, 1792

40 Pictorial Map of 1834, and Arms

(Des A. Cutileiro. Litho)

1967 (12 Feb). *Portuguese Military Uniforms. T* **39** *and similar vert designs. Multicoloured.* P 13 × 13½.

389	35c. Type **39**		15	15
390	1E. Infantry Officer, 1815		1·30	30
391	1E.50 Infantryman, 1879		20	15
392	2E. Infantryman, 1890		20	15
393	2E.50 Infantry officer, 1903		30	15
394	3E. Sapper, 1918		50	30
395	4E.50 Commando, 1964		90	30
396	10E. Parachutist, 1964		1·30	65
389/396	Set of 8		4·25	1·90

1967 (13 May). *50th Anniv of the Fatima Apparitions. Multicoloured.*

397	3E. Virgin of the Pilgrims		35	15

1967. *CHARITY TAX. Designs similar to Type C* **37.** *No gum.* P 10½.

(a) Serifed lettering.

C398	70c. deep blue		10·50	7·25

(b) Sans-serif lettering. Whole design smaller ("PORTUGUESA" 12 mm long)

C399	70c. violet-blue		60	60
C400	1E.30 emerald		1·20	1·20

1968 (22 Apr). *500th Birth Anniv of Pedro Cabral (explorer). Multicoloured.* P 14.

398	4E.50 Lopo Homen-Reineis' map, 1519 (*horiz*)		80	35

1969 (17 Feb). *Birth Centenary of Admiral Gago Coutinho. Multicoloured.* P 14.

399	4E.50 Frigate *Almirante Gago Coutinho* (*horiz*)		95	65

(Des J. de Moura. Litho Litografia Nacional, Oporto)

1969 (25 July). *Bicentenary of Dili (Capital of Timor).* P 14.

400	**40**	1E. multicoloured		35	20

1969 (29 Aug). *500th Birth Anniv of Vasco da Gama (explorer). Multicoloured.* P 14.

401	5E. Convert Medallion		35	20

1969 (25 Sept). *Centenary of Overseas Administrative Reforms.* P 14.

402	5E. multicoloured		35	15

1969 (1 Dec). *500th Birth Anniv of King Manoel I. Multicoloured.* P 14.

403	4E. Emblem of Manoel I, Jeronimos Monastery		35	15

41 Map, Sir Ross Smith and Arms of Britain, Timor and Australia

C 42 Woman and Star

(Des J. de Moura. Litho Litografia Nacional, Oporto)

1969 (9 Dec). *50th Anniv of First England–Australia Flight.* P 14.
404 **41** 2E. multicoloured 45 30

1969–70. *CHARITY TAX. Litho.* P 13.
C405 **C 42** 30c. deep blue & light blue
(1970) 20 20
C406   50c. reddish purple & lt yell-
orge 20 20
C407   1E. yellow-brown and pale
yellow 20 20

D. L. n.° 776

$30
(C **43**)

1970. *CHARITY TAX. Nos.* C399/400 *such as Type* C **43**, *in red.*
C408   30c.on 70c. violet-blue . . . . 7·00 7·00
C409   30c.on 1E.30 emerald . . . . 7·00 7·00
C410   50c.on 70c. violet-blue . . . . 12·00 12·00
C411   50c.on 1E.30 emerald . . . . 7·00 7·00
C412   1E.on 70c. violet-blue . . . . 7·00 7·00
C413   1E.on 1c.30 emerald . . . . 7·00 7·00

1970 (15 Nov). *Birth Centenary of Marshal Carmona. Multicoloured.* P 14.
414   1E.50 Portrait in civilian dress 15 15

1972 (25 May). *400th Anniv of Camoens' "The Lusiads" (epic poem). Multicoloured.* P 13.
415   1E. Missionaries, natives and galleon . . 20 15

1972 (20 June). *Olympic Games. Munich. Multicoloured.* P 14 × 13½.
416   4E.50 Football 45 20

1972 (20 Sept). *50th Anniv of 1st Flight from Lisbon to Rio de Janeiro. Multicoloured.* P 13½.
417   1E. Aviators Gago Coutinho and
Sacadura Cabral in Fairey IIID
seaplane 35 30

1973 (15 Dec). *Centenary of World Meterological Organization.* P 13.
418   20E. multicoloured . . . . 1·50 1·10

In August 1975 a coup d'etat was staged by the right-wing UDT (Democratic Union of Timor). In the ensuing civil war Fretilin (the Front for the Independence of East Timor) soon gained the upper hand and occupied the capital, Dili. By 8 September they claimed total control of the colony and on 27 November 1975 declared the independence of the People's Democratic Republic of East Timor.

Following disputes over border clashes, Indonesian troops, backed by local pro-Indonesian factions, invaded East Timor on 7 December 1975 and quickly gained complete control, despite a U.N. resolution of 11 December calling on them to withdraw. On 17 July 1976 East Timor was declared a province of Indonesia.

EAST TIMOR

UNITED NATIONS TRANSITIONAL ADMINISTRATION IN EAST TIMOR

100 cents = 1 dollar

Following negotiations between Portugal and Indonesia a referendum was conducted on 30 August 1999 with the majority voting for independence for East Timor. On the 20 September 1999 the first United Nations peace keeping troops arrived in East Timor and the Indonesian troops began to withdraw. By October the United Nations had established the International Force for East Timor (I.N.T.E.R.F.E.T.). On the 19 October 1999 the Indonesian Consultative Assembly confirmed the establishment and on the 25 October 1999 the United Nations voted to replace I.N.T.E.R.F.E.T. with a force to help with the establishment of a United Nations Transitional Administration of East Timor (U.N.T.A.E.T.). The East Timor National Council (E.T.N.C.), which was formed to help with policy recommendations, held its first meeting on 11 December 1999.

1 Man with Arms Raised

(Des J. Machado. Litho The Mint, Lisbon, Portugal)

2000 (29 Apr). P 12. *(a) Inscr "Dom.".*
1   **1**   (21c.) multicoloured 30 30
         (b) Inscr "Int.".
2   **1**   ($1.05.) multicoloured . . . . 1·40 1·40
No. 1 was for use on Domestic mail and No. 2 was for use on International mail.

Vietnam

In 111 B.C. the Chinese Emperor Wu Ti annexed the kingdom of Canton, together with Tongking and Annam, which were then known as Namviet. A rebellion by the Trung sisters in 40 to 43 A.D. was quelled and the sisters drowned themselves. Other revolts also failed and itwas not until 939 that Ngo Quyen founded the first of a series of independent Annamite dynasties under nominal Chinese suzerainty. In the 16th and 17th centuries ambitious families usurped authority from weak monarchs and from 1620 to 1674 there was an indecisive civil war between the Trinh, who controlled Tongking, and the Nguyen, who held Annam. During the 18th century there were constant wars between Annam and Tongking. Then, French help, secured by Bishop Pigneau de Behaine of Adran, enabled Nguyen Anh from Annam to conquer Cochin China in 1789; in 1802 his forces overran Tongking and he proclaimed himself Emperor Gia-Long of Vietnam. In the mid-19th century, French desires to acquire territory in the area were aroused and eastern Cochin China was ceded to France in 1862 and the remainder in 1874. A French protectorate over Annam and Tongking was established in 1883. Together with Cambodia, which became a French protectorate in 1863, the Vietnamese territories were formed into the Indochinese Union in 1887; Laos was added in 1893 (see Part 6 (*France*) of this catalogue).

After the fall of France in 1940, Indo-China was occupied by the Japanese army and on 9 March 1945 the Japanese declared that rule by the French authorities was ended. They appointed the Emperor Bao Dai of Annam as head of an autonomous state of Vietnam. On 14 August 1945 Japan surrendered, and on 23 August Bao Dai abdicated.

The Viet Minh nationalist resistance movement had been founded in 1941 by a Comintern agent, Nguyen Ai Quoc, who had changed his name to Ho Chi Minh ("He who enlightens"). By August 1945 the Viet Minh had become the National Liberation Army and were in control of large areas in Tongking. On 2 September 1945 Ho Chi Minh proclaimed in Hanoi the independence of the Democratic Republic of Vietnam. On 6 March 1946 the republic was recognised by France as a free state within the Indo-Chinese Federation.

A. VIETNAM DEMOCRATIC REPUBLIC

100 Cents = 1 Piastre
100 Xu = 10 Hao = 1 Dong

Nos. 1/55 are all stamps of Indo-China overprinted or surcharged

Translations

"VIET-NAM DAN-CHU CONG-HOA" = Vietnam Democratic Republic
"DOC-LAP, TU-DO, HANH-PHUC" = Independence, Freedom, Happiness
"BUU-CHINH" = Postal Service

VIET-NAM
DAN-CHU CONG-HOA
DOC-LAP
TU-DO HANH-PHUC
BUU-CHINH   III
(1)

1945. *Independence. Variously optd as T 1 (all with "DOC-LAP TU-DO HANH-PHUC" in opt).*

1	53	1c. brown	1·50	1·50
2	68	2c. mauve	1·50	1·50
		a. "HANH PHUC" inverted	15·00	
3	—	3c. brown (Courbet)	1·50	1·50
		a. "VIET-NAM" omitted		
4	68	4c. brown	1·50	1·50
		a. "HANH PHUC" inverted	15·00	

5	—	5c. sepia (De Genouilly)	1·50	1·50
6	—	6c. rose (304)	1·50	1·50
7	—	6c. rose (305)	2·50	2·50
8	—	10c. grey-green (307)	2·20	2·20
9	68	10c. grey-green	3·75	11·00
		a. "HANH PHUC" inverted	15·00	
10	—	20c. brown-red (309)	3·75	11·00
11	64	40c. deep blue	3·75	11·00
12	—	$1 yellow-green (311)	7·50	18·00
1/12		*Set of 12*	29·00	60·00

Nos. 3 and 5 were not issued without overprint.

1945–46. *Variously optd as follows:*

(a) "VIET-NAM DAN-CHU CONG-HOA".

13	69	10c. purple and yellow (1946)	6·00	7·50
14	61	15c. brown-purple	2·20	3·00
		a. Optd in green	7·50	7·50
15		30c. orange-brown (p 11½)	2·20	2·20
		a. Opt inverted		
		b. Perf 13½	3·75	4·50
		ba. Opt inverted (Perf 13½)		
16	69	50c. brown-red	15·00	18·00
17	60	$1 green	2·20	3·75
13/17		*Set of 5*	25·00	31·00

(b) "VIET-NAM DAN-CHU CONG-HOA BUU-CHINH".

18	53	3c. bistre- brown (perf 11½)	2·20	2·20
		a. Perf 14		
		b. Perf 11½ × 14	7·50	
19	—	4c. yellow-orange (316)	2·20	2·20
20	53	6c. carmine	2·20	2·20
21	—	10c. green (R.)	3·75	3·75
22	—	10c. grey-green (319)	3·75	4·50
23	—	20c. red (Pavie)	2·20	2·20
24	53	40c. blue (R.)	35	35
25		40c. slate (R.)	7·50	7·50
18/25		*Set of 8*	22·00	22·00

No. 23 was not issued without overprint.

VIET-NAM
DAN-CHU
3$00   CONG-HOA

CUU-DOI
(2) ("CUU-DOI" = Famine Relief)

1945. *Famine Relief. Nos. 326/7 surch with new premium as T 2.*

26	70	"2$00" on 15c.+60c. brown-purple	18·00	18·00
27		"3$00" on 40c.+$1.10 blue (R.)	18·00	18·00

1945. *War Wounded. No. 326 surch with new premium as T 2 inscr "Binh-si Bi-nan" (= Fund for War Wounded).*

28	70	"5$00" on 15c.+60c. brown-purple	30·00	30·00

1945–46. *Surch in new currency, and variously optd as before (except Nos. 43/7).*

(a) "VIET-NAM DAN-CHU CONG-HOA BUU-CHINH"

29	64	30x. on 1c. grey-brown (R.)	2·20	2·50
30	—	30x. on 15c. purple-brown (Garnier) (R.) (1945)	1·50	2·20
31	67	50x. on 1c. grey-brown	3·00	3·75
32	—	60x. on 1c. olive-brown (313)	3·75	3·75
33	65	1d. on 5c. brown (B.)	6·00	6·00
		a. Surch inverted		
34	—	1d.60x. on 10c. grey-green (322)	2·20	3·00
35	64	3d. on 15c. purple	3·00	4·50
36	67	3d. on 15c. purple (B.)	4·50	5·25
37	65	4d. on 1c. olive-bistre	3·00	4·50
38		5d. on 1c. olive-bistre (301)	4·50	5·25
29/38		*Set of 10*	30·00	36·00

(b) "VIET-NAM DAN-CHU CONG-HOA"

39	—	1d. on 5c. brown-purple (318)	2·20	3·00
40	49	2d. on 3c. brown (G.)	33·00	33·00
41	—	2d. on 10c. grey-green (321)	3·00	3·75
42	49	4d. on 6c. carmine (G.)	33·00	33·00

(c) New value only.

43	56	50x. on 1c. purple-brown	3·75	4·50
44		2d. on 6c. carmine	22·00	22·00

45	**48**	5d. on 1c. orange-red (B.)	. . . .	33·00	33·00
46		10d. on 6c. violet (R.)	. . . . . .	37·00	37·00
47		15d. on 25c. blue (R.)	. . . . . .	37·00	37·00
43/47 *Set of 5*			. . . .	£120	£120

No. 30 was not issued without overprint.

Nos. 48 to 55 are all overprinted "VIET-NAM DAN-CHU CONG-HOA" with varying inscriptions as noted in the headings.

1946. *National Defence ("Quoc-Phong").*

48	**49**	"+5d." on 3c. brown (B.)	. . . . .	6·00	7·50
49		"+10d." on 6c. carmine (B.)	. . . . .	6·00	8·75

1946. *People's Livelihood ("DAN SINH").*

50	**57**	"30xu.+3d." on 6c. rose	. . . . . .	1·50	2·20
51	**55**	"30xu.+3d." on 6c. rose	. . . . . .	1·80	2·20

1946. *Campaign against Illiteracy ("Chng nan mu chu").*

52	**59**	"+4dng" on 6c. carmine	. . . . . .	7·50	7·50

1946. *New Life Movement ("Doi sng moi").*

53	**66**	"+4dng" on 6c. rose	. . . . . .	3·75	4·50

1946. *Child Welfare ("Bao-Anh").*

54	**60**	"+2 dng" on 6c. rose	. . . . . .	3·75	5·25

1946. *War Wounded ("Binh si bi nan").*

55	—	"+3 dng" on 20c. brown-red (293)	. . .	6·75	6·75

3 Ho Chi Minh

(Des Nguyen Sang. Litho State Ptg Wks, Hanoi)

1946 (19 May). *No gum.* P 11½.

56	**3**	1h. yellow-green	. . . . .	75	75
57		3h. rose	. . . . . .	75	75
58		9h. yellow-bistre	. . . . .	75	75

1946 (19 May). *National Defence. No gum.* P 11½.

59	**3**	4h. + 6h. blue	. . . . . .	1·80	3·75
60		6h. + 9h. brown	. . . . . .	1·80	3·75

Relations between French and Vietnamese worsened in 1946, after the failure of a conference at Fontainebleau. When a French demand that Viet Minh forces should evacuate the port of Haiphong was rejected, French troops took the town and over 6,000 Vietnamese civilians were killed by gunfire from the French cruiser *Suffren* on 23 November 1946. An unsuccessful attack on 19 December by the Viet Minh on French troops in Hanoi was followed by the withdrawal of Ho Chi Minh's government to northern Tongking. From there and from areas in central Annam they made war against the French until July, 1954.

The stamps issued by the Democratic Republic in this period are listed under North Vietnam Nos. N1/ND16.

B. INDEPENDENT STATE

(WITHIN THE FRENCH UNION)

After the break with Ho Chi Minh the French opened negotiations with Bao Dai, ex-emperor of Annam. On 14 June 1949, agreement was reached that Vietnam, comprising Tongking, Annam and Cochin China, should become an independent state within the French Union, and on 29 January 1950 the agreement was ratified.

100 Cents = 1 Piastre

4 Bongour Falls, Dalat

(Photo Vaugirard, Paris)

1951 (6 June–Nov). *T* **4** *and similar designs.* P 13½.

61	10c. bronze-green (16.8)	. . . .		35	15
62	20c. purple (16.8)	. . . . .		1·10	15
63	30c. light blue (16.8)	. . . . .		1·10	30
64	50c. red (16.8)	. . . . .		2·10	15
65	60c. sepia (16.8)	. . . . .		1·10	15
66	1p. red-brown (16.8)	. . . . .		1·10	15
67	1p.20 yellow-brown (23.10)	. . .		7·50	1·80
68	2p. violet (16.8)	. . . . .		2·10	15
69	3p. blue	. . . . .		7·50	15
70	5p. green (16.8)	. . . . .		5·50	30
71	10p. carmine (16.8)	. . . . .		13·50	35
72	15p. lake-brown (16.8)	. . .		44·00	2·20
73	30p. blue-green (23.10)	. . .		£100	2·50
61/73 *Set of 13*		. . . .		£170	7·75

Designs: *Horiz*—10c., 60c., 5p. Type **4**; 20c., 2p., 10p. Imperial Palace, Hue; 30c., 15p. The Small Lake, Hanoi; 50c., 1p. Temple of Remembrance, Saigon. *Vert*—1p.20, 3p., 30p. Emperor Bao Dai.

1952. *Anniversary of First Issue of Independent Vietnam Stamps. Souvenir booklet containing five sheets, each 122 × 97 mm.* P 13½.

MS73a	Five sheets. (a) No. 61; (b) No. 62; (c) No. 66; (d) No. 69; (e) No. 72	. . . . . .	£110

9   D **10** Dragon

(Des L. D. Khai (T **9**); C.A.M.P. (6p.30). Photo Vaugirard, Paris)

1952 (8 Mar)–**53**. *AIR. T* **9** *and similar horiz design.* P 13½ × 12½.

74	**9**	3p.30 apple green and brown-lake	. .	80	60
75		4p. bright lemon and brown			
		(24.11.53)	. . .	1·10	35
76		5p.10 salmon-pink and royal blue	. .	1·10	80
77	—	6p.30 scarlet and greenish yellow	. .	1·20	95
74/77 *Set of 4*			. . . .	3·75	2·40

Design:—6p.30, Symbolic of airlines.

1952 (16 June). *POSTAGE DUE. Typo.* P13½.

D78	D **10**	10c. green and scarlet	. . . .	75	75
D79		20c. yellow and emerald	. . . .	75	75
D80		30c. red-orange and violet	. . . .	75	75
D81		40c. rose and deep green	. . . .	75	75
D82		50c. grey-brown and lake	. . . .	75	75
D83		1p. silver and blue	. . . .	1·50	1·50
D78/83 *Set of 6*			. . . . .	6·25	6·25

10 Empress Nam Phuong

11 Globe and Lightning

(Photo Vaugirard, Paris)

1952 (15 Aug). P 12½.
78	**10**	30c. brown, yellow and slate-purple		1·10	30
79		50c. brown, yellow and blue		1·50	45
80		1p.50 brown, yellow and olive		3·25	30

(Recess De La Rue)

1952 (24 Aug). *First Anniv of Admission of Vietnam to International Telecommunications Union.* P 13.
81	**11**	1p. deep greenish blue		6·00	1·00

12 Dragon

13 U.P.U. Monument, Berne and Coastline

(Recess De La Rue)

1952 (3 Sept). *AIR. Day of Wandering Souls. T* **12** *and similar design.* P 13.
82	**12**	40c. scarlet		1·50	30
83		70c. green		1·80	35
84		80c. blue		1·80	35
85		90c. brown		1·80	35
86	–	3p.70 purple (Fish) (*vert*)		4·00	60
82/86	*Set of 5*			8·75	1·75

See also No. **MS**90a.

(Recess De La Rue)

1952 (12 Sept). *First Anniv of Admission of Vietnam to U.P.U.* P 13.
87	**13**	5p. red-brown		3·25	1·50

(14)

15 Emperor Bao Dai and Gateway

1952 (10 Nov). *Red Cross Fund. As No. 80, but colour changed. Surch with T* **14**.
88	**10**	1p.50+50c. brown, yellow & blue (R.)		7·50	2·50

(Recess De La Rue)

1952 (10 Nov). *40th Birthday of Emperor Bao Dai.* P 12.
89	**15**	1p.50 purple		3·75	1·10

No. 89 exists imperf.

16 Sabres and Flag

17 Crown Prince Bao Long

(Recess De La Rue)

1952 (21 Dec). *Wounded Soldiers' Relief Fund.* P 13.
90	**16**	3p.30+1p.70 brown-purple		2·50	2·20

1952 (21 Dec). *Wounded Soldiers' Relief Fund. Souvenir booklet containing five sheets, each* 150 × 100 *mm. No gum.* Imperf.
MS90a	Five sheets. (a) No. 82; (b) No. 83; (c) No. 84; (d) No. 85; (e) No. 86		£130

(Recess Govt Ptg Wks, Paris)

1954 (15 June). *T* **17** *and similar vert portrait.* P 13.
91	**17**	40c. turquoise-blue		35	35
92		70c. lake		35	35
93		80c. sepia		35	35
94	–	90c. deep green		1·10	1·10
95	–	20p. bright carmine		1·50	1·50
96	–	50p. reddish violet		5·25	5·25
97	**17**	100p. bluish violet		15·00	15·00
91/97	*Set of 7*			29·00	29·00

Portrait:—90c., 20p., 50p. Crown Prince Bao Long in uniform.

These stamps were current only in areas under French control. Large areas in Tongking and Annam were controlled by Viet Minh forces under General Vo Nguyen Giap, supplied with arms through China. On 7 May 1954 these forces compelled the surrender, after a two months siege, of a French army holding the entrenched camp of Dien Bien Phu. An international conference sat at Geneva from 26 April and by the Geneva Declaration of 21 July 1954 Vietnam was partitioned near the 17th Parallel and all authority of Bao Dai's government north of that line ended. Later issues are therefore those of SOUTH VIETNAM and NORTH VIETNAM.

INTERNATIONAL COMMISSION. Overprinted Indian stamps were used from field post offices in Vietnam from 1954 to 1968. For details see under INTERNATIONAL COMMISSION IN INDO-CHINA.

C. SOUTH VIETNAM

100 Cents = 1 Piastre

INDEPENDENT STATE

(Within the French Union)

D 1 Dragon

1 Turtle

(Typo Vaugirard, Paris)

1955 (6 June). *POSTAGE DUE.* P 13½.
SD1	D **1**	2p. yellow and bright purple		1·10	1·10
SD2		3p. turquoise-green and violet		1·50	1·50
SD3		5p. yellow and violet		2·20	2·20
SD4		10p. scarlet and myrtle-green		2·50	2·50
SD1/4	*Set of 4*			6·50	6·50

See also Nos. SD14/17.

(Des Nguyen Tanh De. Recess Govt Ptg Wks, Paris)

1955 (20 July). *First Anniv of Govt of Ngo Dinh Diem.* P 13.
S1	**1**	30c. purple-brown		1·20	80
S2		50c. deep emerald		5·50	3·25
S3		1p.50 ultramarine		3·25	1·20

2 Phoenix

(Des Nguyen Van Thu. Recess Govt Ptg Wks, Paris)

1955 (7 Sept). *AIR.* P 13.
S4	**2**	4p. bright purple and violet		2·20	2·20

3 Refugees

(Des Tran Kim Hung. Recess Govt Ptg Wks, Paris)

1955 (11 Oct). *First Anniv of Arrival of Refugees from North Vietnam.* P 13.
S5	**3**	70c. scarlet		2·00	1·20
S6		80c. brown-purple		4·75	2·75
S7		10p. indigo		8·75	5·25
S8		20p. orange-brown, orange and violet		18·00	6·75
S9		35p. brown-black, yellow and blue		35·00	28·00
S10		100p. plum, orange & deep blue-green		80·00	44·00
S5/10 *Set of 6*				£130	80·00

No. S9 is inscribed "CHIÊN-DICH-HUYNH-DE" in margin at foot. See also No. S26.

REPUBLIC

After a referendum, a Republic was proclaimed on 26 October 1955, with Ngo Dinh Diem as President. South Vietnam left the French Union.

4 G.P.O. Saigon

5 Pres. Ngo Dinh Diem

(Recess American Bank Note Co)

1956 (10 Jan). *Fifth Anniv of Entry of Vietnam into Universal Postal Union.* P 12.
S11	**4**	60c. deep myrtle-green		2·75	1·20
S12		90c. violet		5·25	2·00
S13		3p. red-brown		9·50	2·75

1956 (4 June). *POSTAGE DUE. As Type D* **1** *but inscr* "BUU-CHINH" *instead of* 'TIMBRE-TAXE". P 13½.
SD14		20p. green and vermilion		7·50	1·10
SD15		30p. yellow and emerald		11·00	1·50
SD16		50p. yellow and brown		24·00	2·20
SD17		100p. yellow and reddish violet		37·00	2·50
SD14/17 *Set of 4*				70·00	6·50

(Des F. Watabe. Recess Govt Ptg Wks, Tokyo)

1956 (7 July–Nov). P 13.
S14	**5**	20c. Venetian red (9.11)		40	40
S15		30c. reddish purple (9.11)		80	40
S16		50c. carmine		40	40
S17		1p. violet (9.11)		80	40
S18		1p.60 deep lilac		1·60	40
S19		3p. sepia		1·60	40
S20		4p. indigo		2·20	80
S21		5p. reddish brown (9.11)		3·25	80
S22		10p. blue (9.11)		4·00	1·20
S23		20p. black (9.11)		9·50	2·00
S24		35p. green		27·00	4·75
S25		100p. brown (9.11)		55·00	20
S14/25 *Set of 12*				95·00	11·00

1956 (6 Aug). *No. S9 with bottom marginal inscription obliterated by a single bar, in brown-black.*
S26	**3**	35p. brown-black, yellow and blue		20·00	14·00
		a. Two-bar obliteration		37·00	

Công-thự Bưu-điện
(6 "Government Postal Building")

1956 (6 Aug). *Nos.* S11/13 *optd with T* **6.**
S27	**4**	60c. deep myrtle-green		3·25	1·60
S28		90c. violet		4·75	1·60
S29		3p. red-brown		7·00	2·40

7 Bamboo   **8** Refugee Children   **9** Hunters on Elephants

(Des Ngo Long Ho. Photo Govt Ptg Wks, Tokyo)

1956 (26 Oct). *First Anniv of Republic.* P 13.
S30	**7**	50c. bright scarlet		75	75
S31		1p.50 deep reddish purple		75	75
S32		2p. emerald		1·50	1·50
S33		4p. deep ultramarine		3·00	3·00
S30/33 *Set of 4*				5·50	5·50

(Des K. Hirano. Eng K. Kato. Recess Govt Ptg Wks, Tokyo)

1956 (7 Nov). *United Nations "Operation Brotherhood".* P 13.
S34	**8**	1p. magenta		80	40
S35		2p. turquoise-green		1·60	80
S36		6p. reddish violet		2·40	80
S37		35p. violet-blue		17·00	7·00
S34/37 *Set of 4*				19·00	8·00

(Des T. Yamanouchi (T **9**). K. Maeno (others). Photo Govt Ptg Wks, Tokyo)

1957 (7 July). *Third Anniv of Govt of Ngo Dinh Diem.* T **9** *and similar vert design.* P 13.
S38	**9**	20c. purple and yellow-green		80	40
S39		30c. reddish purple and bistre		1·20	40
S40	—	90c. sepia and green		1·60	80
S41	—	2p. blue and bluish green		2·75	80
S42	—	3p. bistre-brown & bright bluish violet		3·50	1·60
S38/42 *Set of 5*				8·50	3·50

Design:—90c., 2p., 3p. Mountain hut.

10 Ship's Cargo being off-loaded at Saigon	11 Torch and Constitution	12 Youth felling Tree

15 U.N.E.S.C.O. Emblem and Building	16 U.N. Emblem and "Torch of Freedom"

(Photo Govt Ptg Wks, Tokyo)

1957 (21 Oct). *Ninth Colombo Plan Conference, Saigon.* P 13½.

S43	10	20c. purple	75	75
S44		40c. olive-green	75	75
S45		50c. carmine	75	75
S46		2p. deep bright blue	75	75
S47		3p. emerald	1·50	1·50
S43/47	*Set of 5*		4·00	4·00

(Litho Giesecke & Devrient, Munich)

1957 (26 Oct). *Inauguration of National Assembly.* P 13 × 13½.

S48	11	50c. salmon, green and black	40	40
S49		80c. bright reddish purple, blue & black	80	40
S50		1p. brt rose, dp bluish green & black	80	40
S51		4p. orange-brown, deep olive & black	1·60	80
S52		5p. yellow-olive, turquoise-blue & blk	2·00	80
S53		10p. brown-red, bright blue and black	3·25	2·00
S48/53	*Set of 6*		8·00	4·25

(Des Nguyen Minh Hoang. Recess De La Rue)

1958 (7 July). *Better Living Standards.* P 13½.

S54	12	50c. yellowish green	80	40
S55		1p. deep lilac	1·20	80
S56		2p. deep ultramarine	1·60	80
S57		10p. vermilion	3·50	1·60
S54/57	*Set of 4*		6·25	3·25

13 Young Girl with Chinese Lantern	14

(Des Miss Vu Thi Nga. Recess De La Rue)

1958 (27 Sept). *Children's Festival.* P 13½.

S58	13	30c. lemon	40	40
S59		50c. lake-purple	40	40
S60		2p. carmine-red	80	80
S61		3p. bluish green	1·60	80
S62		4p. yellow-olive	2·00	80
S58/62	*Set of 5*		4·50	2·75

(Des Vinh Phoi. Recess De La Rue)

1958 (26 Oct). *United Nations Day.* P 13½.

S63	14	1p. Venetian red	80	40
S64		2p. turquoise-blue	1·20	80
S65		4p. carmine-rose	1·60	80
S66		5p. brown-purple	2·40	1·20
S63/66	*Set of 4*		5·25	2·75

(Des Nguyen Chi Hung. Recess Govt Ptg Wks, Paris)

1958 (3 Nov). *Inauguration of United Nations Educational, Cultural and Scientific Organization Building, Paris.* P 12½ × 13.

S67	15	50c. dull ultramarine	75	40
S68		2p. bright scarlet	75	80
S69		3p. bright purple	1·50	80
S70		6p. reddish violet	2·20	1·20
S67/70	*Set of 4*		4·50	2·75

(Des Nguyen Van Trien. Recess De La Rue)

1958 (10 Dec). *Tenth Anniv of Declaration of Human Rights.* P 13½.

S71	16	50c. deep blue	80	40
S72		1p. brown-red	1·20	80
S73		2p. yellow-green	1·60	80
S74		6p. purple	2·40	1·20
S71/74	*Set of 4*		5·50	2·75

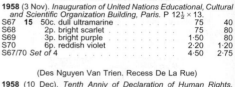

17 Phu Cam Cathedral	18 Saigon Museum

(Recess De La Rue)

1958 (25 Dec)–**59**. *Various designs as T 17/8.* P 13½.

S75	17	10c. deep slate	80	40
S76	—	30c. deep green (15.5.59)	1·20	80
S77	18	40c. deep green (16.2.59)	80	40
S78	—	50c. emerald-green (7.9.59)	80	40
S79	—	2p. deep turquoise-blue (7.9.59)	1·20	80
S80	—	4p. deep lilac (15.5.59)	1·60	80
S81	18	5p. carmine (16.2.59)	2·00	80
S82	17	6p. brown	2·00	80
S75/82	*Set of 8*		9·25	4·50

Designs: *Horiz*—30c., 4p. Thien Mu Pagoda; 50c., 2p. Palace of Independence, Saigon.

19 Trung Sisters (national heroines) on Elephants	20

(Des Nguyen Gia Tri. Photo De La Rue)

1959 (14 Mar). *Trung Sisters Commemoration. Multicoloured, colour of inscriptions given.* P 13 × 12½.

S83	19	50c. blue	2·75	2·00
S84		2p. yellow-brown	4·75	2·40
S85		3p. light green	7·00	3·50
S86		6p. carmine-red	11·00	5·25
S83/86	*Set of 4*		23·00	12·00

(Des Lam Van Be. Recess Govt Ptg Wks, Paris)

1959 (7 July). *Agricultural Reform.* P 13.

S87	**20**	70c. bright purple	40	40
S88		2p. deep green and turquoise-blue	80	40
S89		3p. olive-green	1·20	40
S90		6p. carmine-red and vermilion	2·40	1·20
S87/90 *Set of 4*			4·25	2·10

PRINTERS AND PROCESS. All the following stamps of South Vietnam to No. S290 were recess-printed at the Government Printing Works, Paris, *except where otherwise stated.*

21 Diesel Train   22 Tilling the Land

(Des Huynh Van Phung. Eng J. Combet)

1959 (7 Aug). *Re-opening of Trans-Vietnam Railway.* P 12½ × 13.

S91	**21**	1p. green and reddish violet	1·30	40
S92		2p. green and grey	2·50	80
S93		3p. green and turquoise-blue	2·50	1·20
S94		4p. green and lake	4·75	1·20
S91/94 *Set of 4*			10·00	3·25

(Des Nguyen Minh Hoang. Eng C. Durrens)

1959 (26 Oct). *Fourth Anniv of Republic.* P 13.

S95	**22**	1p. chestnut, deep green & ultramarine	1·20	40
S96		2p. reddish violet, blue-green & orange	1·20	80
S97		4p. deep blue, blue and bistre	2·40	1·20
S98		5p. chocolate, olive and yellow-brown	3·25	1·60
S95/98 *Set of 4*			7·25	3·50

25 Scout climbing Mountain   26 "Family Code"

(Des Thai Van Ngon. Eng J. Combet)

1959 (25 Dec). *First National Scout Jamboree, Trang Bom.* P 12½ × 13.

S99	**25**	3p. yellow-green	1·50	30
S100		4p. magenta	1·80	45
S101		8p. magenta and maroon	3·25	1·00
S102		20p. blue-green and turquoise-blue	9·50	2·40
S99/102 *Set of 4*			14·50	3·75

(Des Thai Nguyen Ba. Eng P. Gandon)

1960 (2 Jan). *First Anniv of Family Code.* P 13.

S103	**26**	20c. emerald	75	75
S104		30c. turquoise-blue	75	75
S105		2p. brown-red and orange	1·50	1·50
S106		6p. bluish violet and scarlet	1·50	1·50
S103/106 *Set of 4*			4·00	4·10

27 Refugee Family in Flight   28 Henri Dunant

(Des Nguyen Minh Hoang)

1960 (7 Apr). *World Refugee Year.* P 13.

S107	**27**	50c. magenta	1·20	40
S108		3p. emerald	1·20	80
S109		4p. vermilion	2·40	1·20
S110		5p. deep violet-blue	3·25	1·60
S107/110 *Set of 4*			7·25	3·50

(Des Miss Vu Thi Nga. Eng J. Piel)

1960 (8 May). *Red Cross Day. Cross in red.* P 13.

S111	**28**	1p. blue	1·60	80
S112		2p. green	2·00	80
S113		4p. red	2·75	1·20
S114		6p. magenta	3·50	2·00
S111/114 *Set of 4*			8·75	4·25

MF 29 Soldier and Village   29 Co-operative Farm

(Printed locally)

1960 (1 July)–**61**. *MILITARY FRANK.* No value indicated. Rouletted.

(a) Litho.

SMF115	MF29 (–)	Orge-yell, brn, dp grn & blk	48·00	37·00

(b) Typo (1.10.61).

SMF116	MF29 (–)	Orange-yell, brn & dp grn	48·00	37·00

The bottom inscription is in black on No. SMF115 and in brown on No. SMF116.

(Des Tran Xuan Vinh. Eng G. Aufschneider)

1960 (7 July). *Establishment of Co-operative Rice Farming.* P 13.

S115	**29**	50c. ultramarine	80	40
S116		1p. deep green	80	40
S117		3p. yellow-orange	1·60	80
S118		7p. bright magenta	2·75	1·20
S115/118 *Set of 4*			5·25	2·50

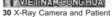

30 X-Ray Camera and Patient   31 Flag and Map

(Eng G. Bétemps)

1960 (1 Aug). *National Tuberculosis Relief Campaign Day.* P 13.
S119   **30**   3p.+50c. blue-green and red   .   .   2·00   2·00

(Des Shen Yung Ling. Eng G. Aufschneider)

1960 (26 Oct). *Fifth Anniv of Republic.* P 13.
S120   **31**   50c. red, yellow and turquoise-
blue   75   75
S121   1p. red, yellow and bright blue   .   .   75   75
S122   3p. red, yellow and violet   .   .   .   1·50   1·50
S123   7p. red, yellow and yellow-
green   .   .   .   2·20   2·20
S120/123 *Set of 4*   .   .   .   .   4·75   4·75

32 Woman with Rice   **33** Crane carrying Letter

(Des Nguyen Minh Hoang. Eng R. Fenneteaux)

1960 (21 Nov). *Food and Agriculture Organization Regional Conference, Saigon.* P13.
S124   **32**   2p. turquoise-green and emerald   1·50   1·50
S125   4p. dull ultramarine and light
blue   .   .   .   .   2·20   2·20

(Des Do Hoang Ke. Eng J. Pheulpin)

1960 (20 Dec). *AIR.* P 13.
S126   **33**   1p. olive-green   .   .   .   3·75   1·50
S127   4p. deep blue and blue-green   .   5·25   2·20
S128   5p. reddish violet and yellow-
brown   .   .   .   6·75   3·00
S129   10p. bright crimson   .   .   .   10·50   4·50
S126/129 *Set of 4*   .   .   .   .   23·00   10·00

34 Farm Tractor   **35** Child and Plant

(Des Le Van Giai)

1961 (3 Jan). *Agricultural Development and Pres. Diem's 60th Birthday.* P 13.
S130   **34**   50c. lake-brown   80   40
S131   70c. bright purple   80   40
S132   80c. bright rose-red   .   .   .   80   80
S133   10p. magenta   .   .   .   .   2·75   1·20
S130/133 *Set of 4*   .   .   .   .   .   4·50   2·50

(Des Nguyen Tan An)

1961 (22 Mar). *Child Welfare.* P 13.
S134   **35**   70c. light blue   .   .   .   80   40
S135   80c. ultramarine   .   .   .   80   40
S136   4p. olive-bistre   .   .   .   1·20   80
S137   7p. yellow-green and turquoise   .   2·40   1·20
S134/137 *Set of 4*   .   .   .   .   4·50   2·50

36 Pres. Ngo Dinh   **37** Young People and Torch
Diem

(Eng J. Piel)

1961 (29 Apr). *Second Term of President.* P 13.
S138   **36**   50c. ultramarine   .   .   .   80   40
S139   1p. red   .   .   .   .   1·20   80
S140   2p. bright purple   .   .   .   1·60   80
S141   4p. bright violet   .   .   .   2·40   80
S138/141 *Set of 4*   .   .   .   .   5·50   2·50

(Des Truong Van Phat)

1961 (7 July). *Sports and Youth.* P 13.
S142   **37**   50c. red   40   40
S143   70c. magenta   80   40
S144   80c. crimson and red   .   .   .   1·20   80
S145   8p. bright purple and crimson   .   2·75   1·20
S142/145 *Set of 4*   .   .   .   .   4·50   2·50

38 Bridge over Mekong   **39** Alexander of Rhodes

(Des U.S. Operation Mission)

1961 (28 July). *Inauguration of Saigon–Bien Hoa Highway.* P 13.
S146   **38**   50c. yellow-green   .   .   .   80   40
S147   1p. orange-brown   .   .   .   80   40
S148   2p. blue   .   .   .   .   1·20   80
S149   5p. bright purple   .   .   .   2·00   80
S146/149 *Set of 4*   .   .   .   .   4·25   2·10

(Des Do Ba Yen. Eng R. Fenneteaux)

1961 (5 Sept). *300th Death Anniv of Alexander of Rhodes.* P 13.
S150   **39**   50c. carmine   40   40
S151   1p. brown-purple   .   .   .   80   40
S152   3p. bistre-brown   .   .   .   1·20   80
S153   6p. emerald-green   .   .   .   2·00   80
S150/153 *Set of 4*   .   .   .   .   4·00   2·10

40 Vietnamese   **41** Gateway of   **42** Tractor and
with Torch   Van Mieu Temple,   Cottages
Hanoi

(Des Luu Tan Phuoc)

1961 (26 Oct). *Youth Moral Rearmament.* P 13.
S154   **40**   50c. red   80   40
S155   1p. bluish green   .   .   .   80   40

S156		3p. carmine-red	1·20	80
S157		8p. chocolate and bright purple	2·00	80
S154/157		Set of 4	4·25	2·10

(Des Nguyen Ai Linh. Eng J. Miermont)

1961 (4 Nov). *15th Anniv of U.N.E.S.C.O.* P 13.

S158	**41**	1p. blue-green	75	75
S159		2p. deep rose-red	75	75
S160		5p. yellow-olive	1·50	1·50

(Des Hoang Nhat Tan. Eng P. Munier)

1961 (11 Dec). *Rural Reform.* P 13.

S161	**42**	50c. deep green	75	75
S162		1p. lake and greenish blue	75	75
S163		2p. bistre-brown and deep green	75	75
S164		10p. turquoise-blue	3·00	3·00
S161/164		Set of 4	4·75	4·75

43 Attack on Mosquito   **44** Postal Cheque Building, Saigon   **45** St. Mary of La Vang

(Des Nguyen Minh Hoang. Eng J. Piel)

1962 (7 Apr). *Malaria Eradication.* P 13.

S165	**43**	50c. magenta	80	40
S166		1p. orange	80	40
S167		2p. emerald	1·20	80
S168		6p. deep ultramarine	2·40	80
S165/168		Set of 4	4·75	2·10

(Des and eng J. Combet)

1962 (15 May). *Inauguration of Postal Cheques Service.* P 13.

S169	**44**	70c. deep bluish green	75	75
S170		80c. red-brown	75	75
S171		4p. bright purple	75	75
S172		7p. bright rose-red	2·20	2·20
S169/172		Set of 4	4·00	4·00

(Eng G. Bétemps)

1962 (7 July). *St. Mary of La Vang Commemoration.* P 13.

S173	**45**	50c. carmine-red and violet	80	40
S174		1p. indigo and red-brown	80	40
S175		2p. lake and chocolate	1·20	40
S176		8p. deep blue and bluish green	3·25	1·20
S173/176		Set of 4	5·50	2·10

46 Armed Guards and Fortified Village   **47** Gougah Waterfalls, Dalat

(Des Nguyen Minh Hoang. Eng J. Pheulpin)

1962 (26 Oct). *Strategic Villages.* P 13.

S177	**46**	50c. vermilion	40	40
S178		1p. deep olive	80	40
S179		1p.50 bright purple	1·20	40
S180		7p. ultramarine	2·00	1·20
S177/180		Set of 4	4·00	2·10

(Recess De La Rue)

1963 (3 Jan). *Pres. Ngo Dinh Diem's 62nd Birthday and Spring Festival.* P 13½.

S181	**47**	60c. orange-red	80	45
S182		1p. indigo	1·20	45

48 Trung Sisters Monument   **49** Harvester

(Des Nguyen Minh Hoang. Eng C. Hertenberger)

1963 (1 Mar). *Women's Day.* P 13.

S183	**48**	50c. green	80	40
S184		1p. claret	80	40
S185		3p. bright purple	1·20	80
S186		8p. violet-blue	2·00	1·20
S183/186		Set of 4	4·25	2·50

(Des Nguyen Minh Hoang. Eng C. Hertenberger)

1963 (21 Mar). *Freedom from Hunger.* P 13.

S187	**49**	50c. vermilion	80	40
S188		1p. lake	80	40
S189		3p. deep magenta	1·20	80
S190		5p. violet	2·00	1·20
S187/190		Set of 4	4·25	2·50

50 Sword and Fortress   **51** Soldier and Emblem

(Des Pham Van Tru)

1963 (7 July). *Communal Defence and 9th Anniv of Inauguration.* P 13.

S191	**50**	30c. brown-ochre	40	40
S192		50c. magenta	80	40
S193		3p. emerald	1·60	80
S194		8p. red	2·40	1·20
S191/194		Set of 4	4·75	2·50

(Des Pham Van Tru. Eng P. Béquet)

1963 (26 Oct). *Republican Combatants.* P 13.

S195	**51**	50c. rosine	75	75
S196		1p. emerald	75	75
S197		4p. violet	75	75
S198		5p. orange	2·20	2·20
S195/198		Set of 4	4·00	4·00

52 Centenary Emblem and Globe

53 Scales of Justice and Constitution

(Des Nguyen Huu Phuoc. Eng J. Gauthier)

1963 (17 Nov). *Red Cross Centenary. Cross in red.* P 13.
S199	**52**	50c. Prussian blue	75	35
S200		1p. carmine-red	1·10	75
S201		3p. yellow-orange	1·50	75
S202		6p. orange-brown	2·50	1·50
S199/202 *Set of 4*			5·25	3·00

(Des Nguyen Minh Hoang)

1963 (10 Dec). *15th Anniv of Declaration of Human Rights.* P 13.
S203	**53**	70c. bright orange	75	75
S204		1p. cerise	75	75
S205		3p. deep blue-green	75	75
S206		8p. brown-ochre	2·20	2·20
S203/206 *Set of 4*			4·00	4·00

54 Danhim Hydro-Electric Station

55 Dalat Atomic Reactor

(Des Nguyen Minh Hoang. Eng J. Miermont)

1964 (15 Jan). *Inauguration of Danhim Hydro-electric Station.* P 13.
S207	**54**	40c. deep rose-red	75	75
S208		1p. orange-brown	75	75
S209		3p. deep violet	75	75
S210		8p. yellow-green	2·20	2·20
S207/210 *Set of 4*			4·00	4·00

(Des Nguyen Minh Hoang. Eng C. Haley)

1964 (3 Feb). *Peaceful Uses of Atomic Energy.* P 13.
S211	**55**	80c. brown-olive	75	35
S212		1p.50 orange-brown	75	35
S213		3p. chocolate	1·50	75
S214		7p. new blue	2·10	1·10
S211/214 *Set of 4*			4·50	2·25

56 "Meteorology"

57 "Unification"

(Des Nguyen Minh Hoang. Eng R. Fenneteaux)

1964 (23 Mar). *World Meteorological Day.* P 13.
S215	**56**	50c. brown-ochre	75	75
S216		1p. vermilion	75	75

S217	1p.50 carmine-lake	75	75
S218	10p. light green	2·20	2·20
S215/218 *Set of 4*		4·00	4·00

(Des Nguyen Minh Hoang. Eng A. Frères)

1964 (20 July). *10th Anniv of Partition of Vietnam.* P. 13.
S219	**57**	30c. blue, brown-pur & dp bluish grn	75	75
S220		50c. indigo, lake and yellow	75	75
S221		1p.50 indigo, ultram & red-orge	75	75

58 Hatien Beach

59 "Support of the People"

(Recess De La Rue)

1964 (7 Sept). P 13½.
S222	**58**	20c. ultramarine	75	35
S223		3p. bright green	1·10	35

In 1966 1p.50 (flag and three soldiers looking through "porthole") and 3p. (three soldiers planting flag in map) stamps were prepared but not issued. (*Price* £16 *pair un.*)

(Des Nguyen Minh Hoang (50c.), Vo Van Tai (80c.), Nguyen Van Ri (3p.))

1964 (1 Nov). *1st Anniv of Revolution of 1 November 1963.* T **59** *and similar designs.* P. 13.
S224		50c. deep blue and bright purple	75	75
S225		80c. orange-brown and reddish violet	75	75
S226		3p. chestnut and blue	2·20	2·20

Designs: *Horiz*—80c. Soldier breaking chain. *Vert*—3p. Allegory of Revolution.

In a military *coup d'etat* on 1-2 November 1963 Pres. Ngo Dinh Diem's government was overthrown and he was killed.

60 Temple and Monument, Botanic Gardens, Saigon

61 Face of bronze Drum

(Des Lao Van Mui (50c.), Lai Hai Loc (1p.), Truong Hung Nghia (1p.50), Nguyen Ai Linh (3p.))

1964 (2 Dec). *Monuments and views.* T **60** *and similar horiz designs.* P 13 × 12½.
S227		50c. red-brown, light green and blue	1·10	55
S228		1p. slate-blue and bistre	1·10	55
S229		1p.50 black-green and greenish drab	1·70	1·10
S230		3p. carmine, black-green and violet	3·50	1·10
S227/230 *Set of 4*			6·75	3·00

Designs:—1p. Tomb of Minh Mang, Hué; 1p.50, Phan Thiet waterfront; 3p. General Le Van Duyet Temple, Gia Dinh.
For 1p. in smaller size see No. S352.

(Des Nguyen Minh Hoang. Eng P. Forget)

1965 (11 Apr). *Hung Vuong (legendary founder of Vietnam, 2000 B.C.).* P 13 × 12½.
S231	**61**	3p. orange-red and lake	5·50	2·20
S232		100p. violet and maroon	48·00	22·00

62 Dharmachakra and "Fire of Clemency"

63 I.T.U. Emblem and Symbols

(Des Nguyen Thuong An, Vu Thanh Lang and Lam Van Be, respectively)

1965 (15 May). *Buddhism. T 62 and similar designs.* P 13 × 12½ (1p.50) or 12½ × 13 (others).

S233	50c. carmine-red		75	35
S234	1p.50 orange, dp ultramarine & blue		75	35
S235	3p. chocolate, brown & orange-brown		1·10	75

Designs: *Horiz*—1p.50, Dharmachakra, lotus and Globe. *Vert*—3p. Dharmachakra and flag.

(Des Lai Hai Loc)

1965 (17 May). *Centenary of International Telecommunications Union.* P 12½ × 13.

S236	**63**	1p. deep rose-red and bistre	75	75
S237		3p. scarlet, Indian red and deep claret	1·10	75

64 "World Solidarity"   **65** Ixora

(Des Nguyen Minh Hoang)

1965 (26 June). *International Co-operation Year.* P 12½ × 13.

S238	**64**	50c. indigo and olive-brown	75	35
S239		1p. purple-brown and yellow-brown	75	35
S240		1p.50 deep red and olive-grey	1·10	35

(Des Pham Bac Phi, Luu My Tam, Nguyen Minh Hoang, Mai Dong Hai and Do Duy Hien, respectively)

1965 (10 Sept). *Mid-Autumn Festival. T 65 and similar floral designs.* P 13 × 12½ (1p.50) or 12½ × 13 (others).

S241	70c. vermilion, blackish green & emerald	1·10	35
S242	80c. brt purple, dp bluish green & mar	1·10	75
S243	1p. yellow, indigo and deep blue	2·10	75
S244	1p.50 lt olive-green and blackish olive	2·50	75
S245	3p. yellow-orange and slate-green	4·00	1·10
S241/245	Set of 5	9·75	3·25

Flowers: *Vert*—80c. Orchid; 1p. Chrysanthemum; 3p. *Ochna harmandii. Horiz*—1p.50, Nenuphar.

66 Student and University Building

67 Young Farmers

(Des Tran Van Duoc. Recess Govt Ptg Wks, Tokyo)

1965 (15 Oct). *Re-opening of Vietnam University.* P 13½.

S246	**66**	50c. deep red-brown	75	75
S247		1p. deep emerald	75	75
S248		3p. rosine	75	75
S249		7p. deep bluish violet	1·50	1·50
S246/249	*Set of* 4		3·50	3·50

(Des Nguyen Uyen (3p.), Miss Dao Kim Ngan (4p.))

1965 (25 Nov). *Tenth Anniv of "4-T" Rural Youth Clubs. T 67 and similar horiz design.* P 13 × 12½.

S250	3p. brown-red and bright green	1·50	75
S251	4p. reddish violet, dp vio-bl & brn-pur	1·50	75

Design:—4p. Young farmer and Club banner.

68 Basketball   **69** Aerial Mast and Equipment

(Des Nguyen Minh Hoang, Ngo Nhat Khanh, Lam Van Be and Pham Van Thang, respectively)

1965 (14 Dec). *Third South-East Asia Peninsular Games, Kuala Lumpur (Malaysia). T 68 and similar horiz designs.* P 13 × 12½.

S252	50c. cinnamon, brown-red and carmine	1·10	35
S253	1p. lake-brown and orange-brown	1·50	75
S254	1p.50 blue-green	2·10	75
S255	10p. lake-brown and bright purple	6·25	1·80
S252/255	*Set of* 4	9·75	3·25

Designs:—1p. Throwing the javelin; 1p.50, "Physical Culture" (gymnasts and Olympic Games' symbols); 10p. Pole vaulting.

(Des Nguyen Minh Hoang (3p.), Lai Hai Loc (4p.))

1966 (24 Apr). *First Anniv of Saigon Microwave Station. T 69 and similar vert design.* P 12½ × 13.

S256	3p. purple-brown, new blue & yell-brn	75	35
S257	4p. plum, red and deep green	1·10	75

Design:—4p. Aerial mast, telephone dial and map.

In 1966 1p.50 and 10p. stamps, depicting clasped hands and two men holding a torch against background of a wheel, to commemorate Buddhist Youth Conference, were prepared but not issued. (*Price £16 pair un.*)

70 Hook and Hemispheres   **71** Help for Refugees

(Des Pham Van Thang)

1966 (22 June). *"Free World's Aid to Vietnam".* P 12½ × 13.
S258	**70**	3p. brown-lake and slate	75	35
S259		4p. reddish violet and olive-brown	75	35
S260		6p. blue and emerald	1·10	75

(Des Nguyen Minh Hoang)

1966 (20 July). *Refugee Aid.* P 13 × 12½.
S261	**71**	3p. olive-brown, purple-brn & lt brn	75	35
S262		7p. reddish violet, chocolate & brn-pur	1·10	75

72 Paper "Soldiers"   **73** "Violinist"

(Des Nguyen Thi Hien, Tran Ngoc Tang, Nguyen Huu Chau and Nguyen Uyen, respectively)

1966 (30 Aug). *Wandering Souls' Festival.* T **72** *and similar horiz designs.* P 13 × 12½.
S263	50c. bistre-brown, orge-brn & carm-red	75	35
S264	1p.50 red, emerald and brown	1·10	35
S265	3p. orange-red, crimson and red	1·50	75
S266	5p. brown, ochre and orange-brown	2·10	75
S263/266	*Set of 4*	4·75	2·00

Designs:—1p.50, Obeisance; 3p. Pool of candles; 5p. Votive offering.

(Des Tran Van Chau, Nguyen Van Trong, Nguyen Van Thanh and Miss Nguyen Thi Le, respectively)

1966 (28 Sept). *Ancient Musical Instruments.* T **73** *and similar horiz designs.* P 13 × 12½.
S267	1p. chocolate, reddish pur & lake-brown	75	35
S268	3p. reddish violet and light purple	75	35
S269	4p. brown and claret	1·10	75
S270	7p. ultramarine and blue	2·50	1·10
S267/270	*Set of 4*	4·50	2·25

Designs:—3p. "Harpist"; 4p. Small band; 7p. "Flautists". For 3p. in smaller size, see No. S302.

74 W.H.O. Building

(Des Lai Hai Loc, Lam Van Be and Tran Hue Dung, respectively. Recess De La Rue)

1966 (12 Oct). *Inauguration of World Health Organization Headquarters, Geneva.* T **74** *and similar designs.* P 13.
S271	50c. plum, reddish violet and red	75	35
S272	1p.50 black, violet-blue and red-brn	75	35
S273	8p. dp blue, blackish brown & turq-bl	1·10	75

Designs: *Vert*—1p.50, W.H.O. Building and flag; 8p. U.N. flag and W.H.O. Building.

75 Spade in Hand, and Soldiers   **76** U.N.E.S.C.O. Emblem and Tree

(Des Le Thanh Lam, Nguyen Uyen, Lam Van Be and Nguyen Ai Linh, respectively. Recess De La Rue)

1966 (1 Nov). *Third Anniv of Overthrow of Diem Government.* T **75** *and similar designs.* P 13.
S274	80c. orange-brown and bistre-brown	35	35
S275	1p.50 dp pur-brn, carm-red & yell	75	35
	a. Yellow (flag) omitted		
S276	3p. bronze-green, brown & yellow-brn	75	75
S277	4p. red-brown, black and plum	2·10	1·10
S274/277	*Set of 4*	3·50	2·25

Designs: *Horiz*—1p.50, Agricultural workers, soldier and flag. *Vert*—3p. Soldier, tractor and labourers; 4p. Soldier and horseman.

(Des Nguyen Thiet Nhi (1p.), Nguyen Van Ri (3p.) and Tran Thi Hieu Hanh (7p.). Recess Staderini Carte Valori (De La Rue), Rome)

1966 (15 Dec). *20th Anniv of United Nations Educational, Scientific and Cultural Organization.* T **76** *and similar designs.* P 13.
S278	1p. deep lake-brown and brown-lake	75	35
S279	3p. orange-brown, turquoise and blue	75	75
S280	7p. dp blue, turquoise-blue & carm-red	1·80	75

Designs: *Vert*—3p. Globe and laurel sprigs. *Horiz*—7p. Pagoda.

77 Cashew Apples   **78** Phan Boi Chau

(Des Bui Huu Dong, Ho Van Vang, Le Minh Ngu and Nguyen Minh Hoang, respectively)

1967 (12 Jan). *Exotic Fruits.* T **77** *and similar designs.* P 13.
S281	50c. red, myrtle-green and new blue	1·10	35
S282	1p.50 yell-orge, yell-grn & lake-brn	1·50	35
S283	3p. orange-brown, yellow-grn & choc	1·80	75
S284	20p. yell-ochre, dp bluish grn & brn-lake	4·75	2·10
S281/284	*Set of 4*	8·25	3·25

Designs: *Horiz*—1p.50, Bitter "cucumbers"; 3p. Cinnamon apples; 20p. Areca-nuts.

(Des Nguyen Van Ri (1p.), Lam Van Be (20p.). Recess Staderini
Carte Valori (De La Rue), Rome)

1967 (24 Mar). *Vietnamese Patriots. T **78** and similar horiz design.*
P 13.
S285   1p. dp purple-brn, chestnut &
crimson 75   75
S286   20p. black, violet and myrtle-green   3·00   3·00
Design:—20p. Phan Chau-Trinh (portrait and making speech).

83 "Freedom and Justice"   84 Lions Emblem and
Pagoda

79 Horse-cab   80 Pottery-making

(Des Nguyen Van Ri (5p.), Vo Hung Kiet (others). Photo Govt
Ptg Wks, Tokyo)

(Des Nguyen Van Thanh, Lam Van Be, Dong Cong Huan and
Nguyen Minh Hoang, respectively)

1967 (1 Nov). *Democratic Elections. T **83** and similar horiz
designs. Multicoloured.* P 13½.
S297   4p. Type **83** . . . . 1·10   75
S298   5p. Vietnamese and hands casting
votes . . . . 1·50   75
S299   30p. Two Vietnamese with Constitution
and flaming torch . . . . . . 1·80   1·80

1967 (1 May). *Life of the People. T **79** and similar horiz designs.*
P 13 × 12½.
S287   50c. ultramarine, dp vio-bl & bluish
grn 75   75
S288   1p. reddish violet, dp grn & myrtle-
grn 75   75
S289   3p. brown-red and carmine . . 75   75
S290   8p. reddish violet and deep carmine . . 1·50   1·50
S287/290 *Set of 4* . . . . 3·25   3·25
Designs:—50c. Itinerant merchant; 1p. Market-place; 8p.
Pastoral activities.

(Des Lai Hai Loc. Photo Govt Ptg Wks, Tokyo)

1967 (5 Dec). *50th Anniv of Lions International.* P 13½.
S300   **84**   3p. multicoloured . . . . . . 3·00   1·10

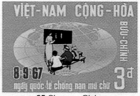

85 Class on Globe

(Des Tran Tu Hai, Pham Van Thang, Nguyen Ai Linh and
Nguyen Minh Hoang, respectively. Recess (35p. litho) Staderini
Carte Valori (De La Rue), Rome)

1967 (22 July). *Arts and Crafts. T **80** and similar designs.
Multicoloured.* P 13
S291   50c. Type **80** 35   35
S292   1p.50 Wicker-basket and vase . . 75   75
S293   3p. Weavers and potters (*horiz*) . . 1·80   1·10
S294   35p. Baskets and pottery . . . . 5·25   2·50
S291/294 *Set of 4* . . . . 7·25   4·00

(Des Nguyen Hung Bang. Photo Govt Ptg Wks, Tokyo)
1967 (10 Dec). *World Literacy Day (on 8 Sept).* P 13½.
S301   **85**   3p. multicoloured . . . . . . 1·10   35

81 Wedding Procession   82 "Culture"

86 "Harpist"   87 Tractor

(Des Nguyen Minh Hoang. Recess Staderini Carte Valori (De La
Rue), Rome)

(Des Do Huy Hien. Recess Govt Ptg Wks, Paris)

1967 (18 Sept). *Vietnamese Wedding.* P 13.
S295   **81**   3p. red, deep violet and reddish
purple . . . . 1·50   75
a. red (inscription) omitted . . . .

1967 (15 Dec). *Inauguration of Mobile Post Office. As No. S268
but smaller, size 23 × 17 mm.* P 13.
S302   **86**   3p. reddish violet and light
purple . . . . 44·00 37·00
The above was only issued in coils and in booklets.

(Des Bui Huu Hanh, Nguyen Duc Tuan, Nguyen Cong Tam and
Nguyen Van Ri, respectively. Photo Govt Ptg Wks, Tokyo)

(Des Nguyen Minh Hoang. Recess Staderini Carte Valori (De La
Rue), Rome)

1967 (27 Oct). *Foundation of Vietnamese Cultural Institute.* P 13.
S296   **82**   10p. black, red, dp blue & lt grey-
blue . . . . 1·80   75

1968 (26 Jan). *Rural Development. T **87** and similar horiz designs.
Multicoloured.* P 13½.
S303   1p. Type **87** 75   35
S304   9p. Bulldozer . . . . 1·10   75
S305   10p. Workers with wheelbarrow and
tractor . . . . 1·50   75
S306   20p. Building construction . . . . 3·25   1·10
S303/306 *Set of 4* . . . . 6·00   2·75

88 W.H.O. Emblem

(Des Health Dept. Photo Govt Ptg Wks, Tokyo)

1968 (7 Apr). *20th Anniv of World Health Organisation.* P 13½.
S307 **88** 10p. greenish yellow, black & dull
grn . . . . 1·50 75

89 Flags of Allied Nations

(Des Lam Van Be (1p.), Nguyen Van Ri (1p.50, 3p.). Mrs.
Nguyen Thi Tuyet (50p.). Photo Govt Ptg Wks, Tokyo)

1968 (22 June). *Thanks for International Aid.* T **89** *and similar
horiz designs. Multicoloured.* P 13½.
S308 1p. Handclasp, flags and soldiers . . . 35 35
S309 1p.50 South-East Asian Treaty
Organization emblem and flags . . 75 75
S310 3p. Handclasp and flags . . . 1·50 1·10
S311 50p. Type **89** . . . . 4·75 2·50
S308/311 *Set of 4* . . . . 6·50 4·25

D **90** *Attacus atlas*

D **91** *Limenitis populi*

(Des Lai Hai Loc (D **90**), Ha Trung Tri (D **91**). Photo Govt Ptg
Wks, Tokyo)

1968 (20 Aug). *POSTAGE DUE.* P 13½ × 13.
SD312 D **90** 50c. multicoloured . . . . . 1·50 1·50
SD313 1p. multicoloured . . . . . 1·50 1·50
SD314 2p. multicoloured . . . . . 1·80 1·80
SD315 D **91** 3p. multicoloured . . . . . 6·00 6·00
SD316 5p. multicoloured . . . . . 12·00 12·00
SD317 10p. multicoloured . . . . . 15·00 15·00
SD312/317 *Set of 6* . . . . 34·00 34·00

92 Farmers, Farm, Factory
and Transport

93 Human Rights
Emblem

(Des Lam Kieu My, Le Van Nhon, Ha Van Duc and Nguyen Viet
Van, respectively. Photo Govt Ptg Wks, Tokyo)

1968 (1 Nov). *Development of Private Ownership.* T **92** *and similar
horiz designs. Multicoloured.* P 13½.
S318 80c. Type **92** 75 75
S319 2p. Motor vehicles and labourers . . . 75 75

S320 10p. Tractor and tri-car 75 75
S321 30p. Motor vehicles and land
cultivation . . . . 4·50 4·50
S318/321 *Set of 4* . . . . 6·00 6·00

(Des Vietnamese U.N.E.S.C O. Commission (10p.), Nguyen
Minh Hoang (16p.). Photo Govt Ptg Wks, Tokyo)

1968 (10 Dec). *Human Rights Year.* T **93** *and similar vert design.
Multicoloured.* P 13½.
S322 10p. Type **93** . . . . 1·10 35
S323 16p. Men of all races acclaiming Human
Rights Emblem . . . . 1·80 75

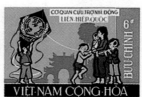

94 Children with U.N.I.C.E.F. "Kite"

(Des Vo Hung Kiet (6p.), Mrs. Nguyen Thi Tuyet (16p.). Photo
Govt Ptg Wks, Tokyo)

1968 (11 Dec). *United Nations Children's Fund Day.* T **92** *and
similar horiz design. Multicoloured.* P 13½.
S324 6p. Type **94** . . . . 1·50 75
S325 16p. Mother and child . . . . 2·50 75

95 Diesel Train, Map and
Mechanical Loader

MF **96** Refugees

(Des Nguyen Van Ri. Photo Govt Ptg Wks, Tokyo)

1968 (15 Dec). *Re-opening of Trans-Vietnam Railway.* T **95** *and
similar horiz design. Multicoloured.* P13½.
S326 1p.50 Type **95** 75 35
S327 3p. Type **95** . . . . 1·10 75
S328 9p. Train and permanent-way
workers . . . . 2·20 1·10
S329 20p. As 9p. . . . . 5·25 2·50
S326/329 *Set of 4* . . . . 8·25 4·25

1969 (22 Feb). *MILITARY FRANK. Defeat of Communist Tet
Offensive. No value indicated. Litho locally. No gum.* Imperf.
SMF330 MF **96** (–) Red and green . . . . . 55·00

97 Peasant Woman

98 Soldier and Militiaman

(Des Bui Van Ky (50c.), Pham Van Thang (1p.), Nguyen Minh Hoang (others). Recess Staderini Carte Valori, Rome)

1969 (23 Mar). *Vietnamese Women. T* **97** *and similar designs.* P 13.

S331	50c. reddish violet, ochre and deep blue		75	75
S332	1p. red-brn, bronze-grn & lt orge-brn		75	75
S333	3p. black, blue and sepia		75	75
S334	20p. black, lake, purple and myrtle-green		2·20	2·20
S331/334 *Set of 4*			4·00	4·00

Designs: *Vert*—1p. Tradeswoman; 20p. "Ladies of fashion". *Horiz*—3p. Nurse.

(Des Nguyen Van Ri (2p.), Nguyen Minh Hoang (50p.). Photo Govt Ptg Wks, Tokyo)

1969 (1 June). *"Open-arms" National Unity Campaign. T* **98** *and similar horiz design. Multicoloured.* P 13.

S335	2p. Type **98**		75	75
S336	50p. Family welcoming soldier		3·75	3·75

99 Vietnamese and Scales of Justice   **100** Mobile Post Office Van in Street

(Des Ho Vu Nam (1p.), Nguyen Van Ri (20p.). Photo Govt Ptg Wks, Tokyo)

1969 (9 June). *First Anniv of New Constitution. T* **99** *and similar home design. Multicoloured.* P13.

S337	1p. Type **99**		75	75
S338	20p. Voters at polling station		2·20	2·20

(Des Nguyen Minh Hoang (3p.), Nguyen Van Ri (20p.), Mrs. Nguyen Thi Tuyet (others). Photo Govt Ptg Wks, Tokyo)

1969 (10 July). *Vietnamese Mobile Post Offices System. T* **100** *and similar horiz designs. Multicoloured.* P 13.

S339	1p. Type **100**		75	75
S340	3p. Clerk serving customers		75	75
S341	4p. Child with letter, and mobile post office		75	75
S342	20p. Queue at mobile post office, and postmark		2·20	2·20
S339/342 *Set of 4*			4·00	4·00

101 Djarai Woman   **102** "Civilians to Soldiers"

(Des Nguyen Minh Hoang. Photo Govt Ptg Wks, Tokyo)

1969 (29 Aug). *2nd Anniv of Ethnic Minorities Statute. T* **101** *and similar vert designs. Multicoloured.* P 13.

S343	1p. Type **101**		1·50	75
S344	6p. Mnong-gar woman		3·75	1·10
S345	50p. Bahnar man		15·00	5·50

(Des Nguyen Van Ri (1p.50), Nguyen Minh Hoang (3p.), Nguyen Van Que (5p.), Ho Vu Nam (10p.). Photo Govt Ptg Wks, Tokyo)

1969 (20 Sept). *General Mobilisation. T* **102** *and similar horiz designs.* P. 13.

S346	1p.50 multicoloured		35	35
S347	3p. multicoloured		75	35
S348	5p. blackish brown, carm-red & orge-yell		1·10	75
S349	10p. multicoloured		1·50	75
S346/349 *Set of 4*			3·25	2·00

Designs:—3p. Bayonet practice; 5p. Recruits arriving at depot; 10p. Happy conscripts.

103 I.L.O. Emblem and Globe   **104** Tomb of Minh Mang, Hué

(Des Mrs. Nguyen Thi Tuyet. Photo Govt Ptg Wks, Tokyo)

1969 (29 Oct). *50th Anniv of International Labour Organization.* P13.

S350	**103**	6p. black, grey & turquoise-green	75	35
S351		20p. black, grey and red	1·80	75

1970 (2 Jan). *Reconstruction of Hué. Recess.* P. 13.

S352	**104**	1p. grey-blue and ochre	31·00	31·00

No. S352 is a smaller version of No. S228. It was issued in coils.

105 Asian Golden Weaver and Baya Weaver

(Des Nguyen Van Ri (2p.), Nguyen Van Minh Chau (7p.), Nguyen Minh Hoang (others). Photo Govt Ptg Wks, Tokyo)

1970 (15 Jan). *Birds of Vietnam. T* **105** *and similar triangular designs. Multicoloured.* P 13½ × 12.

S353	2p. Type **105**		3·25	1·50
S354	6p. Chestnut mannikin		3·25	1·50
S355	7p. Great Indian hornbill		5·25	2·20
S356	30p. Tree sparrow		14·00	4·50
S353/356 *Set of 4*			23·00	8·75

106 Ruined House and Family

(Des Nguyen Minh Hoang. Photo Govt Ptg Wks, Tokyo)

1970 (31 Jan). *Aid for Victims of Communist Tet Offensive. T* **106** *and similar horiz design. Multicoloured.* P. 13.

S357	10p. Type **106**		75	75
S358	20p. Refugee family, and First Aid		2·20	2·20

107 Man, Woman and Priest in Traditional Costume

108 Builders and Pagoda

(Des Nguyen Van Que (1p.), Nguyen Uyen (2p.), Vo Hung Kiet (3p.), Le Minh Duc (100p.). Photo Govt Ptg Wks, Tokyo)

1970 (13 Mar). *Vietnamese Traditional Costumes. T* **107** *and similar multicoloured designs.* P 13.

S359	1p. Type **107**		75	35
S360	2p. Seated woman (*horiz*)		75	35
S361	3p. Three women with carved lion (*horiz*)		1·50	75
S362	100p. Man and woman (*horiz*)		9·50	5·25
S359/362 *Set of 4*			11·00	6·00

(Des Nguyen Van Ri (6p.), Nguyen Minh Hoang (20p.). Recess and litho Nakano Co, Japan)

1970 (10 June). *Reconstruction of Hué. T* **108** *and similar horiz design. Multicoloured.* P 13.

S363	6p. Type **108**		1·50	75
S364	20p. Mixing cement		2·50	1·10

109 Ploughing Paddyfield

110 Scaffolding and New Building

(Des Agriculture Ministry. Recess and litho Nakano Co, Japan)

1970 (29 Aug). *"Land to the Tiller" Agrarian Reform Law.* P 13.

S365	**109**	6p. black, light emerald and buff	1·50	75

(Des Nguyen Ngoc Bi (8p.), Nguyen Van Ri (16p.). Recess and litho Nakano Co, Japan)

1970 (15 Sept). *Reconstruction after Tet Offensive. T* **110** *and similar horiz design. Multicoloured.* P 13.

S366	8p. Type **110**		75	75
S367	16p. Construction workers		2·20	2·20

111 A.P.Y. Symbol

112 Nguyen Dinh Chieu and Poems

(Des Ho Van Na. Recess and litho Nakano Co, Japan)

1970 (3 Oct). *Asian Productivity Year.* P 13.

S368	**111**	10p. multicoloured	1·50	75

(Des Le Minh Duc. Recess and litho Nakano Co, Japan)

1970 (16 Nov). *Nguyen Dinh Chieu (poet) Commemoration.* P 13.

S369	**112**	6p. dp yellow-brn, scar & slate-vio	75	75
S370		10p. brown, scarlet and emerald	1·80	75

113 I.E.Y. Emblem

114 Senate House

(Recess and litho Nakano Co, Japan)

1970 (30 Nov). *International Education Year.* P 13.

S371	**113**	10p. black, greenish yell & yell-brn	1·50	75

(Recess and litho Nakano Co, Japan)

1970 (8 Dec). *9th Council Meeting and 6th General Assembly of Asian Interparliamentary Union, Saigon. T* **114** *and similar horiz design. Multicoloured.* P 13.

S372	6p. Type **114** (8.12)		75	75
S373	10p. House of Representatives (9.12)		1·10	75

115 Two Dancers

116 Paddyfield, Peasants and Agrarian Law

(Des Nguyen Van Que (2p.), Nguyen Minh Hoang (10p.), Nguyen Ai Linh (others). Recess and litho Nakano Co, Japan)

1971 (12 Jan). *Vietnamese Traditional Dances. T* **115** *and similar designs.* P 13.

S374	2p. multicoloured		1·10	35
S375	6p. purple-brown, indigo & turq-green		1·50	75
S376	7p. multicoloured		2·20	75
S377	10p. multicoloured		2·50	1·10
S374/377 *Set of 4*			6·50	2·50

Designs: *Horiz*—6p. Drum dance; 7p. Drum dancers in various positions. *Vert*—10p. Flower dance.

(Des Nguyen Minh Hoang (16p.), Nguyen Van Ri (others). Recess and litho Nakano Co, Japan)

1971 (26 Mar). *First Anniv of "Land to the Tiller" Agrarian Reform Law. T* **116** *and similar horiz designs. Multicoloured.* P 13.

S378	2p. Type **116**		1·10	75
	a. Dated "26.3.1970"			
S379	3p. Tractor and Law		1·10	75
S380	16p. Peasants ringing Law		1·50	75

First printings of No. S378 were wrongly dated. The error was corrected in later printings.

117 Postal Courier

(Des Nguyen Tri Tue (2p.), Le Minh Duc (6p.). Recess and litho Nakano Co, Japan)

1971 (6 June). *History of Vietnamese Postal Service. T* **117** *and similar horiz design. Multicoloured.* P.13.
S381	2p. Type **117**		1·10	75
S382	6p. Mounted courier with banner		2·50	1·10

118 Armed Forces on Map of   **119** Hog-deer
Vietnam

(Des Defence Ministry. Recess and litho Nakano Co, Japan)

1971 (19 June). *Armed Forces Day.* P. 13.
S383	**118**	3p. multicoloured		1·10	1·10
S384		40p. multicoloured		1·80	75

Nos. S383/4 were each issued with a *se-tenant* vertical label inscribed "MUNG NGAY QUAN LUC 19.6.1971" in red on a yellow background.

(Des Ly Hon (9p.), Nguyen Van Hiep (30p.). Recess and litho Nakano Co, Japan)

1971 (20 Aug). *Vietnamese Fauna. T* **119** *and similar vert design. Multicoloured.* P. 13.
S385	9p. Type **119**		1·80	75
S386	30p. Tiger		4·50	2·20

120 Rice Harvesters   **121** New Headquarters
Building

(Des Nguyen Van Ri (1p.), Nguyen Minh Hoang (30p.), Mrs. Nguyen Thi Tuyet (40p.). Recess and litho Nakano Co, Japan)

1971 (28 Sept). *"The Rice Harvest". T* **120** *and similar horiz designs.* P. 13.
S387	1p. multicoloured		75	75
S388	30p. slate-lilac, black and carmine		3·00	3·00
S389	40p. sepia, greenish yellow & turq-bl		3·00	3·00

Designs:—30p. Threshing and winnowing rice; 40p. Harvesters in paddyfield.

(Des Nguyen Minh Hoang. Recess and litho Nakano Co, Japan)

1971 (9 Oct). *Inauguration of New Universal Postal Union Headquarters Building, Berne (1970).* P. 13.
S390	**121**	20p. multicoloured		2·50	1·10

122 Percoid Fish   **123** "Local Delivery"
(Ca Bong)

(Des Nguyen Hoang Hoanh (2p.), Nguyen Van Ri (10p.), Nguyen Minh Hoang (100p.). Recess and litho Nakano Co. Japan)

1971 (16 Nov). *Vietnamese Fishes. T* **122** *and similar multicoloured designs.* P 13.
S391	2p. Type **122**		75	35
S392	10p. Striped Scat (Ca Nau) *(horiz)*		3·00	75
S393	100p. Freshwater angelfish (Ca Ong Tien) *(horiz)*		20·00	10·50

(Des Huynh Van Muoi (5p.), Mrs. Nguyen Thi Tuyet (10p.), Nguyen Van Ri (20p.). Recess and litho Nakano Co, Japan)

1971 (20 Dec). *Development of Rural Post System. T* **123** *and similar horiz designs. Multicoloured.* P. 13.
S394	5p. Type **123**		1·10	75
S395	10p. Symbolic crane		3·00	3·00
S396	20p. Cycle postman delivering letter		2·20	75

124 Fishermen in Boat, and   **125** Emperor Quang
Modern Trawler   Trung

(Des Nguyen Van Ri (4p.), Le Minh Duc (7p.), Nguyen Minh Hoang (50p.). Recess and litho Nakano Co, Japan)

1972 (10 Jan). *Vietnamese Fishing Industry. T* **124** *and similar horiz designs. Multicoloured.* P.13.
S397	4p. Type **124**		1·10	75
S398	7p. Fishermen hauling net		1·10	75
S399	50p. Trawl net		6·00	3·00

1972 (28 Jan). *Emperor Quang Trung (victor of Dong Da) Commemoration.*

(a) P 13.
S400	**125**	6p. multicoloured		75	75
S401		20p. multicoloured		2·20	2·20

(b) Imperf × p 13 *(from booklets)*
S402	**126**	6p. multicoloured		21·00	21·00

126 Community Workers   **127** Harvesting Rice

(Des Nguyen Minh Hoang. Recess and litho Nakano Co, Japan)

1972 (4 Feb). *Community Development Projects.* P. 13.
S403	**126**	3p. multicoloured		75	35
S404		8p. multicoloured		1·10	35

(Des Agriculture Ministry. Recess and litho Nakano Co, Japan)

1972 (26 Mar). *Farmers' Day. T* **127** *and similar horiz design. Multicoloured.* P 13.

S405	1p. Type **127**	75	35
S406	10p. Sowing rice	1·10	75

128 Boeing 727 over Dalat   **129** Vietnamese Scholar

(Des Nguyen Minh Hoang. Recess and litho Nakano Co. Japan)

1972 (18 Apr). *20th Anniv of Vietnam Airlines. T* **128** *and similar horiz designs, each including Boeing 727 airliner. Multicoloured.* P 13.

S407	10p. Type **128**	1·10	75
	a. Block of 4. Nos. S407/10	4·50	
S408	10p. Ha Tien	1·10	75
S409	10p. Hué	1·10	75
S410	10p. Saigon	1·10	75
S411	25p. Type **128**	2·20	2·20
	a. Block of 4. Nos. S411/14	8·75	
S412	25p. As No. S408	2·20	2·20
S413	25p. As No. S409	2·20	2·20
S414	25p. As No. S410	2·20	2·20
S407/414 Set of 8		12·00	10·50

Nos. S407/10 and S411/14 respectively were issued together in *se-tenant* blocks of four within their sheets.

(Des Vo Hung Kiet (5p.), Nguyen Van Sien (others). Recess and litho Nakano Co, Japan)

1972 (5 May). *Vietnamese Scholars. T* **129** *and similar horiz designs. Multicoloured.* P 13.

S415	5p. Type **129**	75	75
S416	20p. Scholar with pupils	1·50	1·50
S417	50p. Scholar with scroll	4·50	4·50

130 Sentry   **131** Hands supporting Savings Bank

(Des Nguyen Huu Tri (2p.), Nguyen Huu Qui (6p.), NguyenThanh Truc (20p.). Recess and litho Nakano Co, Japan)

1972 (15 June). *Civilian Self-defence Force. T* **130** *and similar multicoloured designs.* P 13.

S418	2p. Type **130**	75	35
S419	6p. Young volunteer and badge (*horiz*)	1·10	1·10
S420	20p. Volunteers at rifle practice	1·50	1·10

(Des Finance Ministry. Recess and litho Nakano Co, Japan)

1972 (10 July). *Treasury Bonds Savings Scheme.* P 13.

S421	**131**	10p. multicoloured	75	75
S422		25p. multicoloured	1·50	1·50

132 Three Guards with Horse   **133** Wounded Soldier

(Des Vo Hung Kiet (10p.), Le Minh Duc (30p.), Phan Chanh Nguyen (40p.). Recess and litho Nakano Co, Japan)

1972 (14 Aug). *Traditional Vietnamese Frontier Guards. T* **132** *and similar multicoloured designs.* P 13.

S423	10p. Type **132**	75	75
S424	30p. Pikeman (*vert*)	2·20	2·20
S425	40p. Guards on parade	3·75	3·75

(Des Nguyen Huu Phuoc (9p.), Le Minh Duc (16p.), Vo Hung Kiet (100p.). Recess and litho Nakano Co, Japan)

1972 (1 Sept). *Vietnamese War Veterans. T* **133** *and similar vert designs. Multicoloured.* P 13.

S426	9p. Type **133**	75	75
S427	16p. Soldier on crutches	75	75
S428	100p. Veterans' Memorial	8·75	8·75

134 Soldiers on Tank, and Memorial   **135** "Books for Everyone"

(Des Nguyen Minh Hoang. Litho Nakano Co, Japan)

1972 (25 Nov). *Victory at Binh Long. T* **134** *and similar multicoloured design.* P 13.

S429	5p. Type **134**	75	35
S430	10p. Soldiers on map of An Loc (*vert*)	1·10	35

(Des Education Ministry. Litho Nakano Co, Japan)

1972 (30 Nov). *International Book Year. T* **135** *and similar horiz designs. Multicoloured.* P 13.

S431	2p. Type **135**	75	75
S432	4p. Book Year emblems encircling Globe	75	75
S433	5p. Emblem, books and Globe	75	75

136 "200,000 Returnees"   **137** Soldiers raising Flag

(Des "Open Arms" Ministry. Litho Nakano Co, Japan)

1973 (18 Feb). *200,000th Returnee under "Open Arms" National Unity Campaign.* P 13.

S434	**136**	10p. multicoloured	1·50	75

(Des General Office of Political War. Litho Nakano Co, Japan)

1973 (24 Feb). *Victory at Quang Tri. T* **137** *and similar multicoloured design.* P 13.
S435	3p. Type **137**	75	35
S436	10p. Map and defenders (*horiz*)	1·10	75

138 Satellite and Globe

139 Programme Emblem and Farm-workers

(Des Nguyen Minh Hoang. Litho De La Rue)

1973 (23 Mar). *World Meteorological Day.* P 12½ × 12.
S437	**138** 1p. multicoloured	1·10	75

(Des Vo Hung Kiet (2p.), Nguyen Van Hiep (5p.), Nguyen Minh Hoang (10p.))

1973 (26 Mar). *Five-Year Agricultural Development Programme.*

(a) *T* **139** *and similar horiz design. Multicoloured. Litho De La Rue.* P 12½ × 12.
S438	2p. Type **139**	35	35
S439	5p. Ploughing in paddyfield	75	35

(b) *Vert design as T* **149** *but larger (34 × 54 mm) and dated "26–03–1973". Litho.* P.11.
S439a	10p. multicoloured	£130	

140 Emblem and Headquarters, Paris

141 I.T.U. Emblem

(Des Nguyen Van Ri (25p.), Vo Hung Kiet (others). Litho De La Rue)

1973 (8 Apr). *50th Anniv of International Criminal Police Organization (Interpol). T* **140** *and similar horiz designs. Multicoloured.* P 12½ × 12.
S440	1p. Type **140**	75	75
S441	2p. "INTERPOL 1923 1973"	75	75
S442	25p. Emblem and view of Headquarters (*different*)	2·20	2·20

(Des Truong Tuan Khanh (1p.), Vo Hung Kiet (others). Litho De La Rue)

1973 (17 May). *World Telecommunications Day. T* **141** *and similar horiz designs.* P 12½ × 12.
S443	1p. multicoloured	75	35
S444	2p. black, ultramarine and greenish blue	75	35
S445	3p. multicoloured	1·10	35
Designs:—2p. Globe; 3p. I.T.U. emblem in frame.

142 Lamp in Hand

143 Water Buffaloes and Calf

(Des Truong Tuan Khanh (8p.), Nguyen Uyen (10p.), Nguyen Van Hiep (15p.). Litho De La Rue)

1973 (6 Nov). *National Development T* **142** *and similar vert designs.* P 12 × 12½.
S446	8p. multicoloured	75	75
S447	10p. chalky blue, black and drab	1·10	75
S448	15p. multicoloured	1·50	75
Designs:—10p. "Agriculture, Industry and Fisheries"; 15p. Workers on power pylon.

(Des Vo Hung Kiet (5p.), Nguyen Van Hiep (10p.). Litho De La Rue)

1973 (20 Dec). *Year of the Buffalo. T* **143** *and similar horiz design. Multicoloured.* P 12½ × 12.
S449	5p. Type **143**	1·80	75
S450	10p. Water buffalo	2·50	75

144 Flame Emblem and "Races of the World"

145 Emblem within "25"

(Des Le Minh Duc (15p.), Nguyen Uyen (100p.). Litho De La Rue)

1973 (29 Dec). *25th Anniv of Declaration of Human Rights. T* **144** *and similar multicoloured design.* P 12½ × 12 (15p.) or 12 × 12½ (100p.).
S451	15p. Type **144**	1·50	75
S452	100p. Flame emblem and Scales of Justice (*vert*)	3·00	1·10

(Des Nguyen Van Ri (8p.), Nguyen Van Hiep (15p.). Litho De La Rue)

1973 (31 Dec). *25th Anniv of World Health Organization. T* **145** *and similar horiz design.* P 12½ × 12.
S453	8p. multicoloured	1·10	75
S454	15p. new blue, magenta & reddish brn	2·50	1·10
Design:—15p. W.H.O. emblem and inscription.

146 Sampan crossing River

147 Flags and Soldiers of Allies

(Des Nguyen Minh Hoang (5p.), Vo Hung Kiet (10p.). Litho De La Rue)

1974 (13 Jan). *Vietnamese Sampan Women. T* **146** *and similar horiz design. Multicoloured.* P 14 × 13½.
S455	5p. Type **146**	1·50	1·10
S456	10p. Sampan and passengers	2·20	1·10

(Des Nguyen Minh Hoang (8p.), Le Minh Duc (15p. No. 458), Vo Hung Kiet (15p. No. 459), Nguyen Thanh Truc (60p.). Litho De La Rue)

1974 (28 Jan). *Allies Day. T* **147** *and similar multicoloured designs.* P 12 × 12½ (60p.) or 12½ × 12 (others).
S457	8p. Type **147**	75	75
S458	15p. Soldiers and flags	1·50	75
S459	15p. Allied Nations Monument	1·50	75
S460	60p. Raising South Vietnamese flag, and map (*vert*)	3·00	1·50
S457/460 *Set of 4*		6·00	3·25

148 Trung Sisters on Elephant   **149** Pres. Thieu holding Agrarian Reform Law

(Des Vo Hung Kiet. Litho De La Rue)

1974 (27 Feb). *Trung Sisters' Festival.* P 12½ × 12.
S461	**148**	8p. turquoise-grn, pale ol-yell & blk	1·10	75
S462		15p. orange-red, greenish yell & blk	1·50	75
S463		80p. blue, rose and black	3·00	1·10

(Des Nguyen Minh Hoang (10p.), Nguyen Van Ri (20p.), Nguyen Thanh Truc (70p.). Litho De La Rue)

1974 (26 Mar). *Farmers' Day.* T **149** *and similar multicoloured designs.* P 14 (10p.), 12½ × 12 (20p.) or 12 × 12½ (70p.)
S464	10p. Type **149**	75	75
S465	20p. Farm-workers (32 × 22 mm)	75	75
S466	70p. Girl harvesting rice (22 × 32 mm)	90·00	£110
For similar design to T **149** dated "26-03-1973" see No. S439a.

150 King Hung Vuong

(Des Vo Hung Kiet (20p.), Le Minh Duc (100p.). Litho De La Rue)

1974 (2 Apr). *King Hung Vuong (first Vietnamese monarch) Commemoration.* T **150** *and similar horiz design. Multicoloured.* P14 × 13½.
| S467 | 20p. Type **150** | 1·10 | 75 |
| S468 | 100p. Banner inscribed "Hung Vuong, National Founder" | 4·50 | 1·80 |

151 National Library   **(151a)**

(Des Nguyen Hiep (10p.), Vo Hung Kiet (15p.). Litho De La Rue)

1974 (14 Apr). *New National Library Building.* T **151** *and similar horiz design. Multicoloured.* P 14 × 13½.
| S469 | 10p. Type **151** | 75 | 75 |
| S470 | 15p. Library and Phoenix bas-relief | 1·10 | 75 |
A 5p. stamp was also prepared but not issued (*Price* £10.50 *un*).

1974 (1 June)–**75**. *Various issues surch as T* **151a**, *in red.*

(a) POSTAGE
S470a	142	10p. on 8p. multicoloured (R.) (4.75)	
S470b	145	10p. on 8p. multicoloured (R.) (4.75)	
S470c	120	25p. on 1p. multicoloured (1.1.75)	
S470d	140	25p. on 1p. multicoloured (1.1.75)	
S470e	138	25p. on 1p. multicoloured (18.11.74)	
S470f	141	25p. on 1p. multicoloured (18.11.74)	
S470g	–	25p. on 7p. lake, indigo and orange-brown (No. S376) (18.11.74)	
S470h	147	25p. on 8p. multicoloured (1.4.75)	
S470i		25p. on 16p. multicoloured (No. S427) (1.6.74)	
S470j		25p. on 16p. multicoloured (No. S380) (2.7.74)	

(b) POSTAGE DUE (1.10.74).
SD470k	D 91	5p. on 3p. multicoloured	15·00	
SD470l	D 90	10p. on 50c. multicoloured	15·00	
SD470m		40p. on 1p. multicoloured	15·00	
SD470n		60p. on 2p. multicoloured	15·00	
SD470k/n	Set of 4		55·00	
The figures of value in the surcharge on No. S470h are more squat, and on No. S470j more elongated, than T **151a**.

152 Allied Nations Memorial, Saigon   **153** "Tourist Attractions"

(Des Le Minh Ngu (10p.), Nguyen Van Ri (20p.), Le Minh Duc (60p.). Litho De La Rue)

1974 (22 June). *International Aid Day.* T **152** *and similar multicoloured designs.* P 12½ × 12 (20p.) or 12 × 12½ (others).
S471	10p. Type **152**	75	75
S472	20p. Flags on crane (*horiz*)	75	75
S473	60p. Crate on hoist	2·20	2·20

(Des Vo Hung Kiet (5p.), Nguyen Hiep (10p.), Nguyen Minh Hoang (15p.). Litho De La Rue)

1974 (12 July). *Tourism.* T **153** *and similar multicoloured designs.* P 13½ × 14 (15p.) or 14 × 13½ (others).
S474	5p. Type **153**	1·10	75
S475	10p. Xom Bong Bridge, Nhatrang	1·10	75
S476	15p. Thien Mu Pagoda, Hué (*vert*)	1·50	75

154 *Rynchostylis gigantea*   **155** "International Exchange of Mail"

(Des Nguyen Hiep (10p.), Nguyen Huu Qui (20p.), Nguyen Minh Hoang (200p.). Litho De La Rue)

1974 (18 Aug). *Orchids.* T **154** *and similar multicoloured designs.* P 13½ × 14 (20p.) or 14 × 13½ (others).
S477	10p. Type **154**	1·80	1·50
S478	20p. *Cypripedium callosum* (*vert*)	1·80	1·50
S479	200p. *Dendrobium nobile*	17·00	12·00

(Des Nguyen Van Ri (20p.), Le Minh Ngu (30p.), Le Minh Duc (300p.). Litho De La Rue)

1974 (9 Oct). *Centenary of Universal Postal Union. T* **155** *and similar multicoloured designs.* P 12 × 12½ (300p.) or 12½ × 12 (others).

S480	20p. Type **155**	1·80	75
S481	30p. "U.P.U. letter" and		
	Hemispheres	3·00	75
S482	300p. U.P.U. emblem and girl (*vert*)	9·25	4·00

156 Hien Lam Pavilion, Hué

157 Conference Emblem

(Des Nguyen Sien (25p.), Nguyen Huu Qui (30p.), Vo Hung Kiet (60p.). Litho De La Rue)

1975 (5 Jan). *Historical Sites. T* **156** *and similar horiz designs. Multicoloured.* P 14 × 13½.

S483	25p. Type **156**	1·10	1·10
S484	30p. Throne Room, Imperial Palace,		
	Hué	1·50	1·50
S485	60p. Tu Duc's Pavilion, Hué	1·80	1·80

A 100p. stamp, depicting Klong Garai Tower, Phan Rang, was prepared but not issued (*Price* £3.75 *un*).

(Des Social Welfare Ministry. Litho Saigon An Quan (20p.). Des Vo Hung Kiet. Litho De La Rue (70p.))

1975 (14 Jan). *International Conference on Children and National Development, Saigon. T* **157** *and similar multicoloured design.* P 11 × 11½ (20p.) or 12½ × 12 (70p.).

S486	20p. Type **157**	1·10	1·10
S487	70p. Vietnamese family (32 × 22 mm)	1·50	1·50

158 Unicorn Dance

(Des Nguyen Uyen (30p.), Vo Hung Kiet (others). Litho De La Rue)

1975 (26 Jan). *Vietnamese New Year Festival. T* **158** *and similar multicoloured designs.* P 14 × 13½ (20p.) or 13½ × 14 (others).

S488	20p. Type **158**	1·50	1·10
S489	30p. Letting off fire-crackers (*vert*)	1·80	1·10
S490	100p. New Year greeting custom		
	(*vert*)	4·00	3·00

159 Military Mandarin ("San Hau" play)

160 Produce for Export and Map

(Des Nguyen Hiep (25p.), Nguyen Sien (40p.), Nguyen Thanh Truc (100p.). Litho De La Rue)

1975 (23 Feb). *"Hat Bo" Vietnamese Traditional Theatre. T* **159** *and similar multicoloured designs.* P 14 × 13½ (25p.) or 13½ × 14 (others).

S491	25p. Type **159**	1·50	75
S492	40p. Two characters from "Tam Ha		
	Nam Duong" (*vert*)	2·20	2·20
S493	100p. Heroine, "Luu Kim Dinh Giai Gia		
	Tho Chau" (*vert*)	7·50	3·75

(Des Vo Hung Kiet (10p.), Nguyen Van Ri (50p.). Litho De La Rue)

1975 (26 Mar). *Farmers' Day. T* **160** *and similar horiz design. Multicoloured.* P 12½ × 12.

S494	10p. Type **160**	75	75
S495	50p. Ancient and modern irrigation	2·20	2·20

In the 1980s the following South Vietnamese stamps appeared on the market. These were apparently prepared for issue but, with the collapse of the Republic, saw no postal use.
10p. on 8p. (No. S461) (£6)
10, 25, 50, 80p. Economic Development (£16 *set*)
10, 25, 200p. Transport (£16 *set*)
10, 500p. Dragons (£12 *set*)
20, 25p. Western Vietnam Electrification (£7 *set*)
25, 80p. Rural Electrification (£11.50 *set*)

Later issues used in South Vietnam are listed under NATIONAL FRONT FOR THE LIBERATION OF SOUTH VIETNAM.

D. NATIONAL FRONT FOR THE LIBERATION OF SOUTH VIETNAM

1963. 100 Xu = 1 Dong

The value of the N.L.F. dong fluctuated considerably and was not on parity with the currency used in North Vietnam.

On 20 December 1960, Communists in South Vietnam, commonly known as the Vietcong, formed a "National Front for the Liberation of South Vietnam". Supported by troops from North Vietnam, they increased their hold over large areas of South Vietnam, in spite of opposition from government troops, supported from 7 February 1965 by large forces from the United States and contingents from countries in the Pacific area.

On 6 June 1969 the Vietcong set up a Provisional Government to administer the areas under their control. On 27 January 1973 an agreement was signed in Paris under which non-Vietnamese forces withdrew from Vietnam. The war continued, till on 1 May 1975 the last South Vietnamese Republican forces surrendered and the country came under the control of a military government until the Provisional Revolutionary Government took over on 6 June 1975.

In 1963 the first National Liberation Front stamps were issued and as they have been used for international postage we list them. They can be distinguished from other Vietnamese stamps in that they are inscribed "MAT TRAN DAN TOC GIAI PHONG (or M.T.D.T.G.P.) MIEN NAM VIET-NAM" or "CONG HOA MIEN NAM VIET NAM".

PRINTERS. All issues of the National Front for the Liberation of South Vietnam were printed by lithography by the State Printing Works, Hanoi, and are without gum.

1 Vietcong Flag

1963 (5 Oct). *3rd Anniv of National Liberation Front.* P. 11.

NLF1	**1**	20x. multicoloured (English inscr)	3·75	3·75
NLF2		20x. multicoloured (French inscr)	3·75	3·75
NLF3		20x. multicoloured (Spanish inscr)	3·75	3·75

No. NLF3 exists imperforate.

2 Attack on Village

1963 (5 Oct). *3rd Anniv of Revolutionary Struggle in South Vietnam. T **2** and similar horiz design. Multicoloured.* P 11.
NLF4   10x. Type **2**   7·50   7·50
NLF5   10x. Attack on U.S. helicopter   7·50   7·50
    No. NLF5 exists imperforate.

6 "Guerrilla"   7 Casting Votes

1968. *"The Struggle for Freedom". Paintings. T **6** and similar multicoloured designs.* P 12.
NLF15   10x. Type **6**   3·75   3·75
NLF16   20x. "Jungle Patrol" (*horiz*)   3·75   3·75
NLF17   30x. "Woman Soldier"   3·75   3·75
NLF18   40x. "Towards the Future" (*horiz*)   3·75   3·75
NLF15/18 *Set of 4*   13·50   13·50

3 Demonstrators with Banner

1964 (20 Dec). *4th Anniv of National Liberation Front. T **3** and similar horiz designs.* P 11.
NLF6   10x. multicoloured   3·75   3·75
    a. Horiz strip of 3. Nos. NLF6/8   11·50
NLF7   20x. multicoloured   3·75   3·75
NLF8   30x. blackish green and cobalt   3·75   3·75
    Designs:—20x. Harvesting rice; 30x. Sinking of U.S.S. *Card* (destroyer).
    Nos. NLF6/8 were issued together in *se-tenant* strips of three within the sheet.

1968 (20 Dec). *Eighth Anniv of National Liberation Front. T **7** and similar horiz designs. Multicoloured.* P 11.
NLF19   20x. Type **7**   3·75   3·75
NLF20   20x. Bazooka crew and burning airplane   3·75   3·75
NLF21   30x. Vietcong flag and crowd (French inscr)   3·75   3·75
    a. Pair. Nos. NLF21/2   7·75   7·75
NLF22   30x. Vietcong flag and crowd (English inscr)   3·75   3·75
NLF19/22 *Set of 4*   13·50   13·50
    Nos. NLF21/2 were issued together in *se-tenant* pairs within the sheet.

4 Attack on Bien Hoa Airfield   5 Vietcong Soldiers on U.S Tanks

1965 (15 Oct–20 Dec). *5th Anniv of National Liberation Front. T **4** and similar horiz designs.* P 11.
NLF9   10x. multicoloured   3·75   3·75
NLF10   20x. black, grey and scarlet   3·75   3·75
NLF11   40x. multicoloured (20.12)   4·50   4·50
    Designs:—20x. Nguyen Van Troi facing firing squad; 40x. Vietcong flags.

8 Lenin and Vietcong Flag   9 Ho Chi Minh watering Kainito Plant

1970 (22 Apr). *Birth Centenary of Lenin.* P 11.
NLF23   **8**   20x. multicoloured   3·75   3·75
NLF24   30x. multicoloured   3·75   3·75
NLF25   50x. multicoloured   4·50   4·50
NLF26   2d. multicoloured   5·50   5·50
NLF23/26 *Set of 4*   16·00   16·00

1970 (19 May). *80th Birth Anniv of Ho Chi Minh. Multicoloured, background colour given.* P 11.
NLF27   **9**   20x. light blue   3·75   3·75
NLF28   30x. pale Venetian red   3·75   3·75
        a. Value omitted
NLF29   50x. brown-ochre   4·50   4·50
NLF30   2d. dull green   5·50   5·50
NLF27/30 *Set of 4*   16·00   16·00
    Nos. NLF27/30 exist imperforate.

1967 (20 Dec). *7th Anniv of National Liberation Front. T **5** and similar multicoloured designs.* P 11.
NLF12   20x. Type **5**   3·75   3·75
NLF13   20x. Vietcong guerrillas (*horiz*)   3·75   3·75
NLF14   30x. Crowd with banners   3·75   3·75

10 Vietcong "Lightning Flash"

12 Children in School

20ᵈ
(16)

15 Ho Chi Minh watering Kainito Plant

11 Home Guards defending Village

1970 (20 Dec). *10th Anniv of National Liberation Front.* P 11.

NLF31	**10**	20x. multicoloured	35	35
NLF32		30x. multicoloured	75	75
NLF33		50x. multicoloured	1·10	1·10
NLF34		3d. multicoloured	3·75	3·75
NLF31/34	*Set of 4*		5·25	5·25

Nos. NLF31/4 exist imperforate (*Price £11.50 un or used*).

1971 (15 Feb). *10th Anniv of People's Liberation Armed Forces. T* **11** *and similar horiz designs. Multicoloured.* P 11.

NLF35	20x.	Type **11**	3·75	3·75
NLF36	30x.	Surrender of U.S. tank	3·75	3·75
NLF37	50x.	Agricultural workers	4·50	4·50
NLF38	1d.	Vietcong ambush	5·50	5·50
NLF35/38	*Set of 4*		16·00	16·00

1971 (6 June). *2nd Anniv of Provisional Government. Life in Liberated Areas. T* **12** *and similar square designs. Multicoloured.* P 11.

NLF39	20x.	Type **12**	75	75
NLF40	30x.	Women sewing Vietcong flag	1·50	1·50
NLF41	40x.	Fortifying village	2·20	2·20
NLF42	50x.	Medical clinic	3·00	3·00
NLF43	1d.	Harvesting	4·50	4·50
NLF39/43	*Set of 5*		10·75	10·75

13 Harvesting Rice

14 Ho Chi Minh with Vietcong Soldiers

1974 (6 June). *Fifth Anniv of Provisional Government. Vert designs as T* **13** *and T* **14**. *Multicoloured.* P 11.

NLF44	10d.	Type **13**	1·80	1·80
	a.	Horiz strip of 5. Nos. 44/8	9·25	
NLF45	10d.	Demonstrators with banner	1·80	1·80
NLF46	10d.	Schoolchildren	1·80	1·80
NLF47	10d.	Women home guards	1·80	1·80
NLF48	10d.	Vietcong conference delegate	1·80	1·80
NLF49	10d.	Soldiers and tanks	1·80	1·80
NLF50	10d.	Type **14**	75	75
NLF51	20d.	Type **14**	1·10	1·10
NLF44/51	*Set of 8*		11·50	11·50

Nos. NLF44/8 were issued together in horizontal *se-tenant* strips of five stamps within the sheet.

Nos. NLF44/8 exist imperforate.

For stamps as Type **14** but 35½ × 26 mm, see Nos. NLF57/60.

1975 (8 May–July). *85th Birth Anniv of Ho Chi Minh (1st issue).* P 11.

NLF52	**15**	5d. multicoloured	35	35
NLF53		10d. multicoloured	75	75
NLF54		30d. multicoloured (*magenta frame*) (4.6.75)	3·75	3·75
NLF54*a*		30d. multicoloured (*olive frame*) (16.7.75)	3·75	3·75
NLF52/54*a*	*Set of 4*		7·25	7·25

No. NLF52 exists imperforate.

1975 (2 Sept)–**76**. *15th Anniv of National Front for the Liberation of South Vietnam. As T* **14**, *but smaller* 35½ × 26 *mm*. P 11.

NLF55	**14**	15d. black and bright green (15.1.76)	75	75
NLF56		30d. black and orange-red	1·50	1·50
NLF57		60d. black and royal blue (15.1.76)	2·20	2·20
NLF58		300d. black and yellow (18.12.75)	7·50	7·50
NLF55/58	*Set of 4*		11·00	11·00

1975 (2 Oct). *85th Birth Anniv of Ho Chi Minh (2nd issue). As T* **284** *of North Vietnam, but inscr* "MIEN NAM VIET-NAM". P 11.

NLF59	30d. multicoloured	1·10	1·10
NLF60	60d. multicoloured	2·20	2·20

1976 (Feb–onwards). *Various stamps surch as T* **16**.

NLF61	–	10p. on 1d. multicoloured (NLF38)	
NLF62	–	20p. on 6x. bright yellow and carmine-red (NLF75)	
NLF63	**9**	20p. on 20x. multicoloured (NLF27)	
NLF64	–	20p. on 40x. multicoloured (NLF11)	
NLF65	**9**	20p. on 2d. multicoloured (NLF30)	
NLF66	**15**	20p. on 5d. multicoloured (NLF52) (R.)	
NLF67	**14**	20p. on 10d. multicoloured (NLF50)	
NLF68	**15**	20p. on 10d. multicoloured (NLF53) (R.)	
		a. Black opt	
NLF69		20p. on 30d. multicoloured (NLF54)	
NLF70		20p. on 30d. multicoloured (NLF54a)	

The stamps issued by the National Liberation Front were denominated in North Vietnamese currency while in the area of their use South Vietnamese currency was still in circulation. Postmasters were therefore authorised to surcharge the stamps in the latter currency. As they made their own handstamps many varieties of surcharge exist on a wide range of issues, some of which are listed above. All such surcharges are scarce and, because of the circumstances of their issue, are best collected used, preferably on cover.

17 *Cocos nucifera*

18 Flag of the Provisional Revolutionary Government

1976 (Mar). *Fruits. T* **17** *and similar horiz designs. Multicoloured.*
P 11.
NLF71	20d. Type **17**		2·20	2·20
NLF72	30d. *Garcinia mangostana*		3·75	3·75
NLF73	60d. *Nargifera indica*		7·00	7·00
	Nos. NLF61/3 exist imperforate.			

1976 (15–25 Apr). *First Elections to Unified National Assembly.
As Nos. N858/60 of North Vietnam, but inscr "MIEN NAM VIET-
NAM". P 11*
NLF74	6x. scarlet and ultramarine (*as N858*)	35	35
NLF75	6x. bright yellow and carmine-red (*as N859*) (25.4)	35	35
NLF76	12x. scarlet and bright emerald (*as N860*)	1·10	75
	Nos. NLF64 and NLF66 exist imperforate.		

1976 (18 May). *First Anniv of Liberation of South Vietnam.* P 11.
NLF77	**18**	30d. multicoloured	1·30	1·10

1976 (24 June). *First Session of Unified National Assembly. As
Nos. N861/2 of North Vietnam, but inscr "MIEN NAM VIET-
NAM". P 11.*
NLF78	6x. brown-purple, rose and pale yellow	35	35
NLF79	12x. greenish blue, rose and pale yellow	1·10	75

The Unified National Assembly proclaimed the reunification of
the two Vietnams on 2 July 1976 and the united country was then
known as the Socialist Republic of Vietnam. The issues of the
Socialist Republic are listed after those of North Vietnam.

E. NORTH VIETNAM

VIETNAM DEMOCRATIC REPUBLIC

**1946. 100 Cents = 1 Dong
1959. 100 Xu = 1 Dong**

The following issues up to April 1954 were in use in the areas
under Viet Minh control during the war against the French.

GUM. All the following stamps were issued without gum, *except
where otherwise stated.*

OFFICIAL STAMPS. The values on the Official stamps issued
from 1952 to January 1955 are expressed in *kilograms* of rice, the
basis of the State's economy.

I. TONGKING

V *VIET-NAM* N
DAN-CHU
CONG-HOA
BUU CHINH

(1)

2 Ho Chi Minh

1946. *No. 190 of Indo-China optd with T* **1**, *in red.*
N1	**35**	25c. blue	75·00	90·00
		a. Top line of opt 20 mm instead of 18mm long	65·00	90·00

The sheet of 50 (5 × 10) had the two overprint widths distributed
as follows:
1st and 3rd vertical rows, 20 mm; 2nd and 4th vertical rows,
18 mm; 5th vertical row, 5 of each (18 mm in positions 5, 10,
15, 25 and 45; 20 mm, positions 30, 35, 40 and 50).
This stamp was prepared for use in the whole of Vietnam but
was only issued in the northern part.

(Des Nguyen Sang. Die eng Manh Quynh. Typo)

1948. *Rough hand-made brownish paper. P 7.*
N2	**2**	2d. brown	15·00	£150
		a. Light brown (later ptgs)	15·00	£150
N3		5d. red	15·00	£150
		a. Vermilion (later ptgs)	15·00	£150

There are two types of value tablet in each stamp, which occur
in alternate vertical rows in the sheet, as follows:—

2d. A. "O" of "DONG" above centre of "N" of "CHINH".
     B. "O" above left vertical stroke of "N".

5d. A. Thin "5" as in illustration.
     B. Thicker "5".

No. N2 exists imperforate.

3 Ho Chi Minh and Vietnam Map

(D 4)

(Des Bui Trang Chuoc. Litho)

1951–55. *Imperf or P 11 (200d.).*
N4	**3**	100d. green	22·00	22·00
		a. Perf 11 (1955)	22·00	22·00
N5		100d. brown	22·00	22·00
		a. Perf 11 (1955)	22·00	22·00
N6		200d. red	22·00	22·00
		a. Imperf (1955)	22·00	22·00

("T T" = Timbre Taxe or THIEU TEM)

1952. *POSTAGE DUE. Nos. N4/6 handstamped with Type D* **4**.
ND11	**3**	100d. green (Br.–R.)	—	37·00
ND12		100d. brown (Br.–R.)	—	37·00
ND13		200d. red (Bk.)	—	37·00
		a. Handstamped in red	—	50·00

See also Nos. ND14, NAD18/19 and ND33/39.

5 Blacksmith

O **6** Rice-harvester

(Des Le Pha. Litho)

1953 (June)–**55.** *Production Campaign.* P 11.

N11	**5**	100d. violet		6·00	3·00
N12		500d. brown (2.55)		8·75	4·50

(Des Bui Trang Chuoc. Litho)

1953 (July). *OFFICIAL. Production and Economy Campaign.* P 11.

NO17	O **6**	0.600k. carmine-red		9·25	1·80
NO18		1.000k. brown		9·25	3·75
NO19		2.000k. orange		7·50	11·00
NO20		5.000k. slate		11·00	15·00
NO17/20 *Set of 4*				33·00	28·00

1954. *POSTAGE DUE. No. N11 handstamped with Type* D **4.**

ND14	**5**	100d. violet (Br.–R,)	44·00	41·00

See also No. ND35.

7 Malenkov, Ho Chi Minh, Mao Tse-tung and Flags

(Des Tran Dinh Tho. Litho)

1954 (18 Jan). *Friendship Month.* P 11.

N13	**7**	100d. red (*shades*)		15·00	15·00

II. CENTRAL ANNAM

NA **1** Ho Chi Minh

$30d$
(NA **2**)

1950–51. *Figures of value in white.* Typo. Imperf.

NA1	NA **1**	1d. slate-violet	
NA2		1d. grey-green	
NA3		5d. dull green	
NA4		15d. brown	

1952 (Mar). *Nos. NA3 and NA1 surch as Type* NA **2,** *in red.*

NA5	NA **1**	30d. on 5d. dull green	£250	£200
NA6		60d. on 1d. slate-violet	£275	£250

See also Nos. NA8*a/c.*

1952–53. *Figures of value coloured.* Typo. Imperf.

NA7	NA **1**	300d. blue	£350	£350
NA8		500d. red	£750	£750

1952–54. *Surch as Type* NA **2** *in black.*

(a) On stamp with white figures.

NA8*a*	NA **1**	90d. on 3d. deep rose-red	

(b) On stamps with coloured figures.

NA8*b*	NA **1**	5d. on 10d. rose-magenta	
NA8*c*		100d. on 300d. dp turquoise-blue	

NAO **3** "Family left Behind"

1952–54. *OFFICIAL. Typo on rough hand-made brownish paper.* Imperf.

NAO9	NAO **3**	0.050k. red		—	£180
NAO10		0.300k. red		—	£180
NAO11		0.300k. dull violet		—	£180
NAO12		0.600k. grey-green		—	£180
NAO13		0.600k. violet-blue		—	£375
NAO14		1.000k. olive		—	£375

The plates were made by hand and each cliché differs slightly. There are two types of No. NAO10, with large or small letters in "BUU-DIEN" (same value).

TEM SỰ VỤ
0.^k300 THÓC
(NAO **4**)

$0.^{kg}05$
(NAO **5**)

1954. *OFFICIAL. No. NA5 surch with Type* NAO **4,** *in black.*

NAO15	NA **1**	0.300k.on 30d. on 5d. dull grn		£375	£250

1954. *OFFICIAL. Nos. 56/7 of Vietnam Democratic Republic surch as Type* NAO **5,** *No. NAO17 also optd "LKV" at top and "THOC" below value.*

NAO16	**3**	0kg.05 on 1h. yellow-green		£180
NAO17		0kg.050 on 3h. rose		£180

1954. *POSTAGE DUE. Nos. N4/5 handstamped as Type* D **4** *but with single-lined frame and smaller letters.*

NAD18	**3**	100d. green	60·00
NAD19		100d. brown	60·00

These were in use in No. 4 Administrative District in the town of Ha Tinh.

1954. *OFFICIAL. Type* NA **1** *surch as Type* NAO **4,** *in black.*

(a) On unsurcharged stamps with coloured (No. NAO20) or white (others) figures.

NAO20		0.750k. on 10d. rose-magenta	
NAO21		0.800k. on 1d. reddish violet	
NAO22		0.900k. on 5d. dull green	

(b) On stamps with coloured figures, previously surcharged in red as Type NA **2.**

NAO23		0.030k. on 3d. on 35d. deep claret	
NAO24		0.050k. on 35d. on 300d. deep blue	
NAO25		0.350k. on 70d. on 100d. slate	

III. GENERAL ISSUES

Following the partition of the country after the victory at Dien Bien Phu the stamps listed from here on were current throughout North Vietnam.

PRINTERS AND PROCESS. All stamps were lithographed at the State Printing Works, Hanoi and issued without gum, *unless otherwise stated.*

8 Malenkov, Ho Chi Minh and Mao Tse-tung

(Des Tran Dinh Tho)

1954 (18 Oct)–**55**. P11.
N14	**8**	50d. brown and red (*shades*)	21·00	21·00
N15		100d. red and yellow (*shades*)		
		(4.55)	22·00	22·00

9 Battlefield 10 dNHP **10ᵈ**
(10) (11)

12 Lake of the Returned Sword, Hanoi (O **13**)

(Des Bui Trang Chuoc)

1954 (4 Nov). *Proclamation of Hanoi as Capital.* P 11½.
N30	**12**	10d. blue and pale blue	4·50	90
N31		50d. green and pale green	4·50	75
N32		150d. carmine and pink	7·50	75

1955 (Jan). OFFICIAL. Nos. N2/3 *surch with Type* O **13**.
NO33	**2**	0.100k. on 2d. brown	£160	£130
		a. Surch double		
NO34		0.100k. on 5d. red (*shades*)	£160	£130
		a. Top line of surcharge inverted		

There are two types of this surcharge, with large and small "k". Although issued at the G.P.O. in Hanoi, these stamps were only in use in the provinces of Ha Nam, Hadong and Hoa Binh.

(Des Bui Trang Chuoc)

1954 (Oct)–**56**. *Victory at Dien Bien Phu.* Imperf.
N16	**9**	10d. bistre and brown-red	75·00	75·00
		a. Perf 11 (1956)	15·00	15·00
N17		50d. ochre and scarlet (*shades*)	15·00	11·00
		a. Perf 11 (1956)	15·00	5·50
N18		150d. blue and brown	15·00	11·00
		a. "1951" for "1954"	30·00	
		b. "4" of "1954" omitted		
		c. No flag on tent		
		d. Perf 11 (1956)	15·00	7·50

The imperforate stamps have coloured dotted lines between the rows.

1955 (Apr). POSTAGE DUE Nos. N4/6 *and* N11 *handstamped as Type* D **4** *(double-lined frame), measuring* 21 *mm wide.*
ND33	**3**	100d. green (R.)	55·00	44·00
ND34		100d. brown (R.)	55·00	44·00
ND35	**5**	100d. violet (R.)	55·00	48·00
ND36		200d. red (R.)	55·00	48·00

1954 (Oct)–**55**. OFFICIAL. *Victory at Dien Bien Phu. As T* **9** *but value expressed in* "KILO". Imperf.
NO24	**9**	0.600k. ochre and sepia	13·50	7·50
		a. Perf 6 (12.54)	13·50	7·50
		b. Perf 11 (1955)	44·00	44·00

No. NO24a was an experimental perforation, made at Nam Dinh. The note after No. N18d also applies here.

1955 (Apr–Aug). POSTAGE DUE. Nos. N4/6 *handstamped as Type* D **4** *(double-lined frame), measuring* 19 *mm.*
ND37	**3**	100d. green (R.)	55·00	44·00
ND38		100d. brown (R.)	55·00	44·00
ND39		200d. red (R.)	55·00	44·00
		a. Handstamped in violet	55·00	44·00

In both issues the inner frame-line is usually broken.
On Nos. ND37/9 the colour of the handstamp ranges from red to brown-red. This handstamp normally occurs in the bottom-right of the stamp or across two stamps, about half on each.

1954 (Oct). Nos. N4/6 *with handstamped surcharges.*

(a) As T **10**
N19	**3**	10d. on 100d. green (R.)	18·00	18·00
		a. Perf 11		
N20		10d. on 100d. brown (R.)	18·00	18·00
N21		20d. on 200d. red (B.)	18·00	18·00

(b) As T **11**.
N22	**3**	10d. on 100d. green (R.)	19·00	19·00
		a. Perf 11		
N23		10d. on 100d. green (R.)	19·00	19·00
N24		10d. on 100d. green (B.)	19·00	19·00
N25		10d. on 100d. brown (R.)	19·00	19·00
N26		10d. on 100d. brown	19·00	19·00
N27		10d. on 100d. brown (B.)	19·00	19·00
N28		20d. on 200d. red	44·00	55·00
		a. Pair, one with surch omitted		
N29		20d. on 200d. red (B.)	55·00	55·00
		a. Error. 10d. on 200d	90·00	90·00

Type **10** normally appears in top-right corner and Type **11** in bottom-right but both have been found elsewhere on some values.
There are two types of the "20d" handstamp, differing in the figures and there are other varieties.
No. N22 exists with surch inverted, and No. N23 pin-perf with double surch, one inverted.

D **13** Letter Scales **13** Distribution of Title Deeds

1955 (July). POSTAGE DUE. Typo. P 12½.
ND40	D **13**	50d. brown and lemon	12·00	8·75

1954 (Oct). No. N29a *further handstamped* "20d".
N29b	**3**	20d. on 10d. on 200d. red	£250	£250

(Des Bui Trang Chuoc)

1955 (Dec)–**56**. *Land Reform.* P 11½.
N33	**13**	5d. sage-green (6.56)	7·00	3·75
N34		10d. grey (6.56)	7·00	3·75
N35		20d. orange (2.56)	11·00	3·75
N36		50d. magenta (2.56)	24·00	3·75
N37		100d. pale brown	37·00	3·75
N33/37 Set of 5			75·00	17·00

1955 (Dec)–**56**. OFFICIAL. *Land Reform. As T* **13** *but inscr* "SU VU" *(Service) above value. Thin greyish paper.* P 11.
NO38	**13**	40d. blue	10·50	5·50
		a. Thick white paper (1956)	10·50	5·50
NO39		80d. rose	15·00	6·25
		a. Thick white paper (1956)	15·00	6·25

14 Crowd Welcoming Steam Train

1956 (1 Mar). *Hanoi–China Railway Re-Opening.* P 11½.
N38	**14**	100d. blue	18·00	3·75
		a. Imperf between and at left (horiz pair)		
N39		200d. turquoise-green	18·00	3·75
N40		300d. violet	37·00	3·75
N41		500d. red-brown	44·00	3·75
N38/41		*Set of 4*	£100	13·50

15 Parade, Ba Dinh Square, Hanoi   **(16)**

(Des Bui Trang Chuoc)

1956 (1 Mar). *Return of Government to Hanoi.* P 11½.
N42	**15**	1000d. violet	44·00	7·50
N43		1500d. blue	60·00	7·50
N44		2000d. greenish blue	60·00	7·50
N45		3000d. turquoise-green	75·00	7·50
N42/45		*Set of 4*	£220	27·00

1956 (May). *Nos. N4/6 with surch handstamped as T* **16**.
N46	**3**	10d.on 100d. green	22·00	22·00
N47		10d.on 100d. green (R.)	£180	£180
N48		10d.on 100d. brown	22·00	22·00
N49		20d.on 200d. red	15·00	15·00
N46/49		*Set of 4*	£210	£210

Type **16** normally appears in bottom left-hand corner, but exists also at bottom right.

O **17** Cu Chinh Lan ("Tank Destroyer")   **17** Tran Dang Ninh

(Des Bui Trang Chuoc)

1956 (June)–**57**. *OFFICIAL. Cu Chinh Lan Commemoration.* P 11–11½.
NO50	**17**	20d. deep green and turquoise	3·25	3·25
NO51		80d. maroon and rose (1956)	3·75	3·75
		a. *Brown-red & rose-orange* (4.57)	18·00	18·00
NO52		100d. sepia and drab	4·50	4·50
NO53		500d. blue and pale blue	12·50	12·50
NO54		1000d. brown and salmon (7.57)	30·00	30·00
NO55		2000d. purple & pale green (7.57)	44·00	44·00
NO56		3000d. lake and lilac (7.57)	80·00	80·00
NO50/56		*Set of 7*	£160	£160

(Des Bui Trang Chuoc)

1956 (July). *First Death Anniv of Tran Dang Ninh (patriot).* P 11–11½.
N50	**17**	5d. green and pale green	4·00	1·80
N51		10d. lake and rose	4·00	1·80
N52		20d. grey-brown and brown	5·25	2·50
N53		100d. ultramarine and pale blue	6·00	3·25
N50/53		*Set of 4*	17·00	8·50

18 Mac Thi Buoi   **19** Bai Thuong Dam

(T **18/19**. Des Bui Trang Chuoc)

1956 (3 Nov). *Fifth Death Anniv of Mac Thi Buoi (guerrilla heroine).* P 11½.
N54	**18**	1000d. carmine and rose	41·00	15·00
N55		2000d. brown and pale brown	80·00	22·00
N56		4000d. blue-green and light green	£160	33·00
N57		5000d. blue and grey-blue	£200	55·00
N54/57		*Set of 4*	£425	£110

Nos. N54 and N57 exist imperforate.

1956 (15 Dec)–**58**. *Reconstruction of Bai Thuong Dam.* P 11.
N58	**19**	100d. violet and brown	7·50	6·00
		a. Perf 12½ (1958)	8·75	8·75
N59		200d. claret and black	9·50	6·00
		a. Perf 12½ (1958)	10·50	10·50
N60		300d. carmine and lake	12·50	11·00
		a. Perf 12½ (1958)	10·50	10·50

50 ĐỒNG
(20) (15 mm)

21 Cotton Mill

1956 (Dec). *No. N3 handstamped with T* **20**.
| N61 | **2** | 50d.on 5d. red | 60·00 | 75·00 |
| | | a. Surch 12 mm long | 60·00 | 75·00 |

(Des Bui Trang Chuoc)

1957 (9 Mar). *First Anniv of Opening of Nam Dinh Mill.* P 12½.
N62	**21**	100d. brown and lake	5·50	5·50
		a. Perf 11½	5·50	5·50
		b. Perf 11½ × 12½	18·00	18·00
N63		200d. slate and blue	6·25	6·25
N64		300d. pale green and green	8·00	8·00

No. N62 is also known imperforate and imperf × perf 11½.

22 Pres. Ho Chi Minh   **23** Arms of Republic

(T **22/23**. Des Ngo Ton De)

1957 (19 May–Dec). *President's 67th Birthday.* P 12½.
| N65 | **22** | 20d. deep green and pale green (Dec) | 3·00 | 1·10 |
| N66 | | 60d. bistre and yellow (Dec) | 3·00 | 1·10 |

N67	100d. blue and pale blue	4·50	1·80
	a. Small figures "100"	3·75	3·00
N68	300d. brown and light brown	7·50	3·25
	a. Perf 10	37·00	
N65/68 Set of 4		16·00	6·50

1957 (12 Aug). *OFFICIAL. Fourth World Trade Union Congress, Leipzig. As T **24** but inscr "SU VU" above value.* P 12½.

NO69	**24**	20d. blue-green	2·20	2·20
NO70		40d. blue	3·00	3·00
NO71		80d. carmine	3·75	3·75
NO72		100d. brown	7·50	7·50
NO69/72 Set of 4			15·00	15·00

1957 (2 Sept). *Twelfth Anniv of Democratic Republic.* P 12½.

| N69 | **23** | 20d. dull green | 2·20 | 1·50 |
| N70 | | 100d. rose-red | 5·25 | 3·75 |

24 Congress Emblem   **25** Presidents Voroshilov and Ho Chi Minh

1957 (25 Sept). *Fourth World Trade Union Congress, Leipzig.* P 12½.

| N71 | **24** | 300d. reddish purple | 7·50 | 5·25 |
| | | a. Value tablet inverted in mirror print | £375 | |

(Des Ta Luu)

1957 (7 Nov). *40th Anniv of Russian Revolution.* P 12½.

N72	**25**	100d. carmine-red	7·50	6·00
N73		500d. chocolate	11·00	8·75
N74		1000d. orange-red	18·00	15·00

O **26** Mot Cot Pagoda, Hanoi   **26** Open-air Class

(Des Bui Trang Chuoc)

1957 (22 Dec)–**58**. *OFFICIAL.* P 12½.

NO75	O **26**	150d. brown and pale green	7·50	3·25
		a. Without imprint and designer's name	8·00	3·25
NO76		150d. black and yellow (4.58)	12·00	6·00
		a. Without imprint and designer's name	12·00	6·00

(Des Le Pha. Typo)

1958 (6 Jan). *Education Campaign.* P 12½.

N75	**26**	50d. blue and pale blue	4·50	60
N76		150d. lake and rose	7·50	60
N77		1000d. sepia and ochre	18·00	60

27 Girl Gymnast   **28**   F **29**

(Des Le Pha)

1958 (8 Mar). *Physical Education.* P 12½.

| N78 | **27** | 150d. brown and pale blue | 11·00 | 1·10 |
| N79 | | 500d. brown and pale rose | 18·00 | 1·10 |

(Des Nguyen Van Khanh. Typo)

1958 (1 May). *Labour Day.* P 12½.

N80	**28**	50d. yellow and carmine	3·75	50
N81		150d. carmine and orange-yellow	6·00	50
		a. Error. In colours of 50d	37·00	37·00

(Des Bui Trang Chuoc. Typo)

1958 (1 May). *FRANK. No value indicated.* P 12½.

| NF82 | F **29** | (–) Red, yellow and green | 11·00 | 4·50 |

Small quantities of this stamp were issued each quarter to war-disabled persons for private correspondence.

29 Congress Emblem   O **30** Lathe

(Des Bui Trang Chuoc. Typo)

1958 (20 May). *Fourth International Congress of Democratic Women, Vienna.* P 12½.

| N82 | **29** | 150d. blue | 7·50 | 75 |

(Des Bui Trang Chuoc)

1958 (30 May). *OFFICIAL. Arts and Crafts Fair, Hanoi.* P 12½.

| NO83 | O **30** | 150d. black and pink | 2·50 | 1·90 |
| NO84 | | 200d. grey-blue and orange | 3·25 | 2·50 |

30 Cup, Basket and Lace   O **31** Congress Symbol

(Des Nguyen Van Khanh)

1958 (26 June). *Arts and Crafts Fair, Hanoi.* P 12½.

| N83 | **30** | 150d. sepia and turquoise-green | 3·00 | 35 |
| N84 | | 2000d. black and lilac | 18·00 | 1·50 |

(Des Bui Trang Chuoc)

1958 (26 June). *OFFICIAL. First World Congress of Young Workers, Prague.* P 12½.

| NO85 | O **31** | 150d. red and pale green | 2·50 | 1·30 |

31 Hanoi-Saigon Railway
Reconstruction

32 Revolution in Hanoi

(Des Le Pha)

1958 (20 July). *Propaganda for Re-unification of Vietnam.* P 12½.
N85   **31**   50d. blue .... 1·80   35
N86   150d. orange-brown .... 2·50   35

(Des Bui Trang Chuoc)

1958 (19 Aug). *Thirteenth Anniv of August Revolution.* P 12½.
N87   **32**   150d. carmine-red .... 2·20   50
N88   500d. blue .... 3·75   50

33 Woman Potter

O 34 Soldier, Factory and
Crops

(Des Nguyen Van Khanh)

1958 (19 Aug). *Handicrafts Exhibition.* P 12½.
N89   **33**   150d. lake and rose .... 2·20   75
N90   1000d. chocolate and ochre .... 5·25   75

(Des Le Pha)

1958 (19 Aug). *OFFICIAL. Military Service.* P 12½.
NO91   O **34**   50d. slate-blue and magenta   1·90   65
NO92   150d. chestnut and green .. 2·50   90
NO93   200d. carmine and yellow ... 4·00   1·00

34 Vo Thi Sau and Crowd

35 Tran Hung Dao

(T **34/35**. Des Nguyen Van Khanh)

1958 (23 Sept). *Thirteenth Anniv of South Vietnam Resistance
Movement.* P 12½.
N91   **34**   50d. green and buff .... 3·00   35
N92   150d. lake and orange ...... 4·50   35

1958 (2 Oct). *658th Death Anniv of Tran Hung Dao.* P 12½.
N93   **35**   150d. grey and light blue ..... 2·20   35

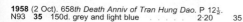

36 Hanoi Factories

37 Harvesting Rice

(Des Bui Trang Chuoc. Recess State Ptg Wks, Prague)

1958 (7 Nov). *Hanoi Mechanical Engineering Plant.* P 11½.
N94   **36**   150d. sepia .... 2·50   35

(Des Le Pha. Recess State Ptg Wks, Prague)

1958 (7 Nov). *Mutual Aid Teams.* P 11½.
N95   **37**   150d. lake .... 2·20   1·30
N96   500d. yellow-brown ...... 5·25   1·30

38 Temple of Jade, Hanoi   D 39

(Des Nguyen Van Khanh (T **38**), Le Pha (others). Photo State
Ptg Wks, Prague)

1958 (1 Dec)–**59**. *T 38 and similar horiz design.* P 12.
N97   **38**   150d. green .... 2·20   1·80
N98   —   150d. deep blue (2.59) ... 2·20   60
N99   —   350d. red-brown (2.59) ... 3·75   1·20
N100   **38**   2000d. deep green ..... 16·00   1·80
N97/100 *Set of 4* .... 22·00   5·00
   Design:—150, 350d. Bay of Halong.
   Nos. N97 and N100 exist imperforate.

(Des Bui Trang Chuoc)

1958 (1 Dec). *POSTAGE DUE.* P 12½.
ND101   D **39**   10d. red and violet 80   75
ND102   20d. blue-grn & brown-
         orange ...... 1·60   1·10
ND103   100d. red and slate .... 3·50   3·00
ND104   300d. red and yellow-olive   5·25   3·75
ND101/104 *Set of 4* .... 7·25   7·75

39 Furniture-makers

O 40 Footballer and Hanoi
Stadium

(Des Nguyen Van Khanh. Photo State Ptg Wks, Prague)

1958 (31 Dec). *Furniture Co-operatives.* P 12.
N101   **39**   150d. turquoise-blue ...... 2·50   60

(Des Nguyen Van Khanh)

1958 (31 Dec). *OFFICIAL. Opening of new Hanoi Stadium..*
   P 12½.
NO102   O **40**   10d. blue and grey-blue .. 75   30
NO103   20d. olive and salmon ... 1·20   50
NO104   80d. brown and ochre ... 1·90   50
NO105   150d. brown and turquoise .. 3·25   1·00
NO102/105 *Set of 4* .... 6·25   2·00

40 Cam Pha Coal Mines

(Des Bui Trang Chuoc. Recess State Ptg Wks, Prague)

1959 (Feb). P 11½.
N102   **40**   150d. deep blue .... 5·50   35

Currency Revaluation

41 The Trung Sisters   **F 42** Invalids in Rice-field

(T **41** and F **42**. Des Nguyen Van Khanh)

1959 (14 Mar). *Trung Sisters Commemoration. Toned paper.* P 11.
N103 **41** 5x. carmine-red and yellow . . . . 2·20 60
N104 8x. chocolate and bistre-brown . . 4·50 60

1959 (14 Mar)–**60**. *FRANK. No value indicated.* P 11.
NF105 F **42** (–) Light brown . . . . . . 3·75 1·10
NF106 (–) Olive & lt grey-blue
(7.7.60) . . . . . 5·50 1·60
These stamps were issued to invalids in agriculture for private correspondence.

42 Mother and Child

(Des Le Pha)

1959 (15 Apr). *Tenth Anniv of World Peace Movement. Toned paper.* P 11.
N105 **42** 12x. reddish violet . . . . 1·10 60

43 Xuan Quan Dam   **44** Victims in Phu Loi Concentration Camp

(T **43/44**. Des Bui Trang Chuoc)

1959 (1 May). *Bac Hung Hai Irrigation Project.* P 11.
N106 **43** 6x. yellow, green and violet . . . 1·50 35
N107 12x. ochre, blue and grey . . . . . 4·50 35

1959 (15 May). *Massacre at Phu Loi on* 1 *December* 1958. P 11.
N108 **44** 12x. salmon, olive and black . . . 1·50 35
N109 20x. ochre, grey and black . . . . 3·75 35

45 Radio Mast   **MF 46** Soldier and Train

(Des Bui Trang Chuoc)

1959 (June). *Erection of Me Tri Radio Station.* P 11.
N110 **45** 3x. green and yellow-orange . . . 1·50 35
N111 12x. sepia and light blue . . . . . 2·20 65

(Des Le Pha)

1959 (15 July). *MILITARY FRANK. No value indicated.* P 11.
NMF112 MF **46** (–) Black and bluish
green . . . . 3·75 1·50

46 Hien Luong Railway Bridge   **47** Rifle-shooting

(Des Bui Trang Chuoc)

1959 (20 July). *Vietnam Day.*
N112 **46** 12x. red and black . . . . 2·20 75

(Des Le Pha, Bui Trang Chuoc and Nguyen Van Khanh, respectively)

1959 (2 Sept). *Sports.* T **47** *and similar horiz designs.* P 11.
N113 1x. ultramarine and light blue (T **47**) 1·10 35
N114 6x. olive and red (Swimming) . . 1·80 35
N115 12x. brown-red and rose (Wrestling) . . 3·00 35

48 Balloons   **49** Coconuts

(Des Trinh Quoc Thu and Nguyen The Vinh)

1959 (1 Oct). *Tenth Anniv of Chinese People's Republic.* P 11.
N116 **48** 12x. red, yellow and green . . . . 3·75 75

(Des Bui Trang Chuoc, Nguyen Van Khanh and Le Pha, respectively)

1959 (20 Nov). *Fruits.* T **49** *and similar designs. Multicoloured.* P 11.
N117 3x. Type **49** 75 35
N118 12x. Bananas . . . . 1·80 35
N119 30x. Pineapple . . . . 3·25 35

50 Convair CV 340   **51** Soldiers

(Des Bui Trang Chuoc)

1959 (20 Nov). *AIR.* P 11.
N120 **50** 20x. black and blue . . . . . 7·50   1·80

(Des Nguyen Van Khanh)

1959 (22 Dec). *Fifteenth Anniv of North Vietnam People's Army.*
P 11.
N121 **51** 12x. yellow, olive-brown & light
blue . . . . 2·20   35

52 Sailing Ship   **53** Girl in "E-De"
Costume

(Des Nguyen The Vinh and Trinh Quoc Thu)

1960 (6 Jan). *30th Anniv of North Vietnam Workers' Party.* P 11.
N122 **52** 2x. red, yellow, blue-green &
drab . . . . 1·10   35
N123   12x. red, yellow, blue and drab . . 3·00   35

(Des Nguyen Van Khanh (N124, N126), Le Pha (N125), Bui
Trang Chuoc (N127))

1960 (6 Jan). *Ethnic Costumes.* T **53** *and similar vert designs.*
P 11.
N124   2x. red, deep blue & light purple
(T **53**) . . . . 1·10   50
N125   10x. blue, orange & sage-grn
("Meo") . . . . 1·50   50
N126   12x. blue and orange-brown ("Thai") . . 2·20   50
N127   12x. indigo and buff ("Tav") . . . . . 2·20   50
N124/127 *Set of 4* . . . . 6·25   1·80

54 Women of Vietnam   **55** Emblem and Women

(Des Le Pha)

1960 (20 Feb). *National Census.* T **54** *and similar horiz design
inscr "1960".* P 11.
N128   1x. bluish green 20   35
N129   12x. deep brown and red . . . . . 2·50   75
Design:—12x. Workers and factories.

(Des Trinh Quoc Thu)

1960 (8 Mar). *50th Anniv of International Women's Day.* P 11.
N130 **55** 12x. ultramarine, bistre, buff and
grey-blue (*shades*) . . . . . 1·50   75

56 Hung Vuong   **57** Lenin   **58** Ballot Box
Temple

(Des Bui Trang Chuoc)

1960 (5 Apr). *Hung Vuong Anniversary Day.* P 11.
N131 **56** 12x. dull green and buff . . . . 3·75   1·50
N132   4d. brown and light blue . . . . 37·00   21·00

(Des Nguyen The Vinh)

1960 (22 Apr). *90th Birth Anniv of Lenin.* P 11.
N133 **57** 5x. brown-purple and light
blue . . . . 1·10   35
N134   12x. deep blue and buff . . . 3·25   75
MSN134a   50 × 77 mm. **57** 5x. blue
and deep brown.
Imperf . . . . 60·00   60·00

(Des Nguyen Van Khanh)

1960 (8 May). *Second Election of Parliamentary Deputies. Toned
paper.* P 11.
N135 **58** 12x. multicoloured . . . . . . 1·50   45

59 Red Cross Nurse   **60** Pres. Ho Chi
Minh

(Des Nguyen Van Khanh)

1960 (8 May). *International Red Cross Commemoration.* P 11.
N136 **59** 8x. deep blue, red and bistre . . . 1·50   35
N137   12x. bluish green, red & grey-
green . . . . 2·20   35

(Des Nguyen The Vinh)

1960 (19 May). *President Ho Chi Minh's 70th Birthday.* T **60** *and
similar vert designs.* P 11.
N138 **60** 4x. lilac and light green . . . 1·50   35
N139   12x. dull purple and rose . . . 2·20   35
N140   —   12x. mult (Ho Chi Minh and
children) . . . . . . 2·20   35
MSN140a   Two sheets, 60 × 85 mm
and 58 × 78 mm. 10x.
brown and ochre (as
N139) and 10x. mult (as
N140). Toned paper.
Imperf . . . . 18·00   18·00
    b. Pink (flowers) omitted (on
sheet as N140) . . . . .

61 "New Constitution"

62 Pres. Ho Chi Minh at Microphone

(Des Bui Trang Chuoc)

1960 (7 July). *Opening of Second National Assembly.* P 11.
N141   **61**   12x. sepia and ochre (*shades*)   2·20   1·10

(Des Le Pha (Nos. N144/5), Bui Trang Chuoc (others))

1960 (2 Sept). *15th Anniv of Vietnam Democratic Republic.* T **62** and similar horiz designs. P 11.
N142	**62**	4x. black, red, ochre & yell (*shades*)	2·20	35
N143		12x. black, red, light green and ochre	3·25	35
N144	–	12x. deep and pale blue (Ploughing)	3·25	35
N145	–	12x. grey-green and yellow (Electricity Works, Vietri)	3·25	35
N146	–	12x. ind & Venetian red (Classroom)	3·25	35
N142/146 *Set of 5*			12·00	1·60

63 Workers and Flags

(Des Nguyen The Vinh)

1960 (4 Sept). *Third Vietnam Workers' Party Congress.* P 11.
N147	**63**	1x. brown, red, yellow & grey-green	2·20	35
N148		12x. choc, red, yellow & grey-brown	2·50	35

64 Handclasp of Three Races   **65** Dragon

(Des Do Viet Tuan)

1960 (3 Oct). *15th Anniv of World Federation of Trades Unions.* P 11.
N149   **64**   12x. black and red   4·50   35
No. N149 exists imperforate.

(Des Nguyen The Vinh)

1960 (10 Oct). *950th Anniv of Founding of Hanoi.* P 11.
N150	**65**	8x. yellow, brown and turquoise	2·20	35
N151		12x. yellow, brown and blue	3·75	35
MSN151a		98 × 67 mm. No. N151. Imperf	11·00	11·00

66 Exhibition Entrance   **67** Badge, Dove and Flag

(Des Nguyen The Vinh)

1960 (20 Oct). *"Fifteen Years of Republic" Exhibition.* P 11.
N152	**66**	2x. grey-brown and red	1·00	35
N153		12x. slate-green and red	1·80	35

(Des Do Viet Tuan)

1960 (10 Nov). *Fifteenth Anniv of World Federation of Democratic Youth.* P 11.
N154   **67**   12x. multicoloured   2·50   35

MF **68** Mounted Frontier Guard   **68** Emblem of Vietnamese Trade Unions

(Des Nguyen Van Khanh)

1961 (3 Jan). *MILITARY FRANK. No value indicated.* P 11.
NMF154   MF **68** (–) Multicoloured   12·50   7·50

(Des Nguyen Van Khanh)

1961 (10 Feb). *Second National Congress of Trade Unions. Toned paper.* P 11.
N155   **68**   12x. red, ultramarine and yellow   1·80   35

69 Women, Globe and Dove   **70** Sambar   **71** Ly Tu Trong (revolutionary)

(Des Trinh Quoc Thu)

1961 (8 Mar). *Third National Congress of Women. Toned paper.* P 11.
N156	**69**	6x. olive-green and light blue	2·50	60
N157		12x. olive-green and salmon	2·50	90

(Des Nguyen The Vinh and Trinh Quoc Thu)

1961 (8 Mar). *Vietnamese Fauna.* T **70** and similar vert designs. P 11.
N158		12x. yellow-buff, black and deep olive	3·00	90
N159		20x. indigo, bistre, black & orange-brn	4·50	90

N160 50x. grey-green, black & dp grey-
    green . . . . 6·75   90
N161 1d. black, grey and green . . . . . 8·75   90
N158/161 *Set of 4* . . . . 21·00   3·50
    Designs:—20x. Sun bear; 50x. Indian elephant; 1d. Crested
gibbon.
    Nos. N158/61 exist imperforate (*Price £47 set un or used*).

(Des Do Viet Tuan and Nguyen The Vinh)

1961 (18 Mar). *Third Vietnam Labour Youth Union Congress.
Toned paper.* P 11.
N162 **71** 2x. olive and blue 90   45
N163 12x. olive and salmon . . . . . . 1·80   45

72 Bugler and Drummer   **73** Disabled Soldier
                    learning to use
                    Crutches

(Des Do Viet Tuan)

1961 (2 May). *20th Anniv of Vietnam Youth Pioneers. Toned
paper.* P 11.
N164 **72** 1x. red, ultramarine, grey &
    yellow . . . . 1·10   45
N165 12x. red, ultramarine, black & pale
    bl . . . . 2·50   45

(Des Bui Trang Chuoc)

1961 (8 May). *101st Anniv of Proposal for International Red Cross.
Toned paper.* P 11.
N166 **73** 6x. brown-red, yell-olive, yell &
    red . . . . 2·20   45
N167 12x. blue-green, yell-olive, grey &
    red . . . . 3·75   45

74 Nurse weighing Baby   **75** Major Yuri Gagarin

(Des Nguyen The Hung)

1961 (1 June). *International Children's Day.* P 11.
N168 **74** 4x. light green, black and red . . 1·50   35
N169 12x. orange-yellow, black and
    red . . . . 3·00   35

(Des Trinh Quc Thu and Nguyen The Vinh)

1961 (15 June). *World's First Manned Space Flight.* P 11.
N170 **75** 6x. red and bright violet . . . . 8·75   1·10
N171 12x. red and bluish green . . . . 8·75   1·10
    Nos. N170/1 exist imperforate (*Price £22 pair un or used*).

76   **77** Women

(Des Huy Toan)

1961 (20 July). *Vietnam Reunification Campaign.* P 11.
N172 **76** 12x. multicoloured 75   50
N173 2d. multicoloured . . . . 6·75   60
    No. N173 exists imperforate.

(Des Nguyen The Hung)

1961 (20 July). *Tripling of Hanoi, Hué and Saigon.* P 11.
N174 **77** 12x. multicoloured (*shades*) . . . . 3·00   50
N175 3d. multicoloured . . . . 12·00   8·00

78 Mother and Child   **79** Prospecting
                    Team

(T **78/9**. Des Nguyen Van Khanh)

1961 (21 Aug). *National Savings Campaign.* P 11.
N176 **78** 3x. multicoloured . . . . 1·10   35
N177 12x. multicoloured . . . . 1·80   35

1961 (21 Aug). *Geological Research.* P 11.
N178 **79** 2x. green, blue and slate-
    purple . . . . 1·10   35
N179 12x. brown, black and turquoise . . 1·80   35

80 Thien Mu   **81** Workers and   **82** Major Titov and
Tower, Hué   Rocket   Rocket

(Des Nguyen The Vinh and Trinh Quoc Thu)

1961 (12 Sept). *Ancient Towers. T* **80** *and similar vert designs.*
P 11.
N180 6x. chocolate and orange-brown . . . 1·10   60
N181 10x. deep olive and buff . . . . . . 1·80   80
N182 12x. olive-green and emerald . . . . 2·20   95
N183 12x. yellow-brown and light blue . . . 2·20   95
N180/183 *Set of 4* . . . . 6·75   3·00
    Towers:—No. N181, Pen Brush, Bac Ninh; N182, Binh Son,
Vinh Phuc; N183, Cham, Phan Rang.
    Nos. N180/3 exist imperforate (*Price £8.75 set un or used*).

(Des Trinh Quoc Thu)

1961 (17 Oct). *22nd Communist Party Congress, Moscow.* P 11.
N184 **81** 12x. red and black . . . . 2·50   35

(Des Trinh Quoc Thu)

1961 (17 Oct). *Second Manned Space Flight.* P 11.
N185 **82** 6x. multicoloured . . . . 2·20   35
N186   12x. multicoloured . . . . 3·75   35
Nos. N185/6 exist imperforate (*Price £8.75 pair un or used*).

83 *Hanoi* (freighter) at Haiphong   **84** Cymbalist

(Des Trinh Quoc Thu)

1961 (7 Nov). *Haiphong Port Commemoration.* P 11.
N187 **83** 5x. grey-blue, grey-green & dp
         grn . . . . 2·20   35
N188   12x. brown, light brown and
         sepia . . . . 5·25   35

(Litho State Ptg Wks, Budapest)

1961 (18 Nov). *Third Writers and Artists Congress.* T **84** and similar vert designs. Multicoloured. P 13½.
N189   12x. Type **84** . . . . 1·50   45
N190   12x. Flautist . . . . 1·50   45
N191   30x. Fan dancer . . . . 3·75   45
N192   50x. Guitarist . . . . 5·25   45
MSN192*a*   136 × 102 mm. Nos. N189/92
         in strip of four perf on outer
         edges only . . . . . 44·00   44·00
N189/192 *Set of 4* . . . . . . 11·00   1·70
Nos. N189/92 exist imperforate (*Price £15 set un or used*).

85 Congress Emblem   **86** Resistance Fighters

1961 (4 Dec). *Fifth World Federation of Trade Union Congress, Moscow.* P 11.
N193 **85** 12x. bright purple and drab . . . . 1·10   45

(Des Huy Toan)

1961 (19 Dec). *15th Anniv of National Resistance. Toned paper.* P 11.
N194 **86** 4x. multicoloured 50   20
N195   12x. multicoloured 95   35

87 "Pigs"   **88** Watering Tree

1962 (16 Jan). *New Year.* T **87** and similar folk-engraving. Multicoloured. P 11.
N196   6x. Type **87** . . . . 3·00   60
N197   12x. "Poultry" . . . . 3·00   90

(Des Nguyen The Hung)

1962 (16 Jan). *Tree-planting Festival.* P 11.
N198 **88** 12x. multicoloured . . . . 1·80   35
N199   40x. multicoloured . . . . 3·25   35

89 Tea Plant   **90** Gong Dance   **91** Hibiscus

(Des Bui Trang Chuoc)

1962 (1 Mar). T **89** and similar horiz designs. Multicoloured. P 11.
N200   2x. Type **89** . . . . 1·10   60
N201   6x. Aniseed . . . . 1·10   60
N202   12x. Coffee . . . . 4·00   60
N203   12x. Castor-oil . . . . 4·00   60
N204   30x. Lacquer-tree . . . . 7·50   60
N200/204 *Set of 5* . . . . . . 16·00   2·75

(Photo State Ptg Wks, Budapest)

1962 (20 Mar). *Folk-dancing.* T **90** and similar vert designs. Multicoloured. P 11½ × 12.
N205   12x. Type **90** . . . . 2·20   50
N206   12x. Bamboo dance . . . . 2·20   50
N207   30x. Hat dance . . . . 3·75   50
N208   50x. Parasol dance . . . . 6·75   50
MSN208*a*   67 × 91 mm. **90** 30x. . . . . 15·00   15·00
N205/208 *Set of 4* . . . . . . 14·00   1·80
Nos. N205/8 exist imperforate (*Price £15.00 set un or used*).

(Photo State Ptg Wks, Budapest)

1962 (10 Apr). T **91** and similar vert designs showing flowers. Multicoloured. P 12½ × 11½.
N209   12x. Type **91** . . . . 2·20   75
N210   12x. Frangipani . . . . 2·20   75
N211   20x. Chrysanthemum . . . . 3·00   75
N212   30x. Lotus . . . . 4·50   75
N213   50x. Ipomoea . . . . 7·50   75
MSN213*a*   64 × 87 mm. No. N212 . . . . 11·00   11·00
N209/213 *Set of 5* . . . . 18·00   3·50
Nos. N209/13 exist imperforate (*Price £22.00 set un or used*).

92 Kim Lien Flats, Hanoi

93 Workers and Rose

(Des Trinh Quoc Thu)

1962 (10 Apr). *First Five-Year Plan (1st issue).* T **92** *and similar horiz designs.* P 11.
N214   1x. light blue, black and grey-brown   35   20
N215   3x. ochre, orange-brn, sepia & grey-
        brn   90   35
N216   8x. bluish violet, black and stone   1·30   60
    Designs:—3x. State agricultural farm; 8x. Institute of Hydraulic and Electro-Dynamic Studies.
    See also Nos. N245/8, N251/2, N270/1, N294/6, N391/3 and N417/9.

(Des Trinh Quoc Thu)

1962 (4 May). *Third National "Heroes of Labour" Congress. Toned paper.* P.11.
N217 **93**   12x. red-orange, dp olive &
               carmine   2·20   50

94 Dai Lai Lake

(Des Nguyen Van Khanh)

1962 (25 May). P 11.
N218 **94**   12x. turquoise and bistre-brown   1·80   35

95 "Plough of Perfection"

(Des Nguyen Van Khanh)

1962 (25 May). P 11.
N219 **95**   6x. black and turquoise-blue   1·10   45

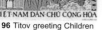

96 Titov greeting Children

O **97** Armed Forces on Boat

(Des Tran Luong, Do Viet Tuan and Trinh Quoc Thu, respectively)

1962 (12 June). *Visit of Major Titov.* T **96** *and similar horiz designs.* P 11.
N220   12x. sepia and light blue   35   20
N221   20x. sepia and salmon   90   35
N222   30x. sepia and dull green   1·30   60
    Designs:—20x. Pres. Ho Chi Minh pinning medal on Titov; 30x. Titov in space-suit.
    Nos. N220/2 exist imperforate (*Price* £8.75 *set un or used*).

(Des Huy Toan)

1962 (15 June). OFFICIAL. *Military Service.* P 11.
NO223   O **97**   12x. multicoloured   4·75   1·80

97 Mosquito and Red Cross

98 Factory (North) and Soldiers (South)

(Des Le Pha)

1962 (9 July). *Malaria Eradication.* P 11.
N223 **97**   8x. carm-red, black & turquoise-
                bl   1·30   50
N224   12x. carmine-red, black & violet-
                blue   1·60   50
N225   20x. carmine-red, black & reddish
                pur   2·75   50

(Des Trinh Quoc Thu)

1962 (20 July). *Eighth Anniv of Geneva Vietnamese Agreements.* P 11.
N226 **98**   12x. multicoloured   2·20   35

99 Ban Gioc Falls

O **100** Woman with Rice-planter

(Des Bui Trang Chuoc)

1962 (14 Aug). T **99** *and another view.* P 11.
N227   —   12x. reddish purple and blue   1·50   45
N228 **99**   12x. sepia and turquoise   1·50   45
    Design: (32½ × 23 mm)—No. N227, Ba Be Lake.

(Des Anh Tuan)

1962 (1 Sept). OFFICIAL. *Rural Service.* P.11.
NO229   O **100**   3x. red   50   50
NO230   6x. blue-green   75   75
NO231   12x. olive   95   95

99a Weightlifting

(Des Bui Trang Chuoc)

1962 (2 Sept). *International Military Sports Festival of Socialist States, Prague. Toned paper.* P 11.
N228a **99a** 12x. multicoloured . . . . . 75·00 £110
This event did not take place and the stamps were to be withdrawn before issue. However, copies were sold at some post offices before withdrawal instructions were received.

100 Quang Trung   **101** Groundnuts

(Des Trinh Quoc Thu (T **100**), Nguyen The Vinh (others))

1962 (16–19 Sept). *National Heroes. T **100** and another vert portrait.* P 11.
N229 **100** 3x. yellow, red-brown and
     grey 75 30
N230 – 3x. orge, blk & ochre/*toned*
     (19.9) 75 30
N231 **100** 12x. yellow, blue-green and
     grey . . . . . 1·80 35
N232 – 12x. orge, blk & grey/*toned*
     (19.9) . . . . . . 1·80 35
N229/232 *Set of 4* . . . . . 4·50 1·20
     Portrait:—N230, 232, Nguyen Trai.

1962 (10 Oct). *T **101** and similar horiz designs. Multicoloured.* P.11.
N233 1x. Type **101** 35 30
N234 4x. Haricot beans 65 35
N235 6x. Sweet potatoes 90 45
N236 12x. Maize . . . . . 2·10 95
N237 30x. Manioc . . . . . 4·75 2·40
N233/237 *Set of 5* . . . . . 8·00 4·00
     No. N234 exists imperforate.

102 Girl feeding Poultry   **103** Popovich in "Vostok 4"

(Des Do Viet Tuan)

1962 (28 Nov). *Farm Stock-breeding. T **102** and similar horiz designs.* P 11.
N238 2x. red, grey and blue 45 35
N239 12x. ochre, turquoise and black . . . 1·50 45
N240 12x. brown, pale and deep green . . 1·50 45
N241 12x. buff, mauve and sepia . . . . 1·50 45
N238/241 *Set of 4* . . . . . 4·50 1·50
     Designs:—No. N239, Woman tending pigs; N240, Herd-girl with oxen; N241, Boy feeding buffalo.

1962 (28 Dec). *First "Team" Manned Space Flights. T **103** and similar designs.* P 11.
N242 12x. reddish purple, purple, turq &
     blk . . . . . . 1·10 35
N243 20x. ochre, blue and black . . . . 1·50 35
N244 30x. red, blue and black . . . . 2·20 35
     a. Blue ptg inverted
     Designs: *Horiz*—20x. Nikolaev in "Vostok 3". *Vert*—30x. "Vostoks 3 and 4".
     Nos. N242/4 exist imperforate (*Price £8.75 set un or used*).

104 Teacher and Students   **105** Guerrilla Fighter

1962 (28 Dec). *First Five-Year Plan (2nd issue). Higher Education and Land Cultivation. T **104** and similar horiz design.* P. 11.
N245 12x. black and yellow 90 35
N246 12x. black, brown & buff (Tree-
     felling) . . . . . 2·20 35

1963 (15 Jan). *First Five-Year Plan (3rd issue). National Defence.* P. 11.
N247 **105** 5x. slate-green and grey . . . 90 20
N248 12x. red-brown and buff . . 1·30 20

106 Hoang Hoa Tham   **107** Workers in Field

(Des Trinh Quoc Thu)

1963 (10 Feb). *50th Death Anniv of Hoang Hoa Tham (freedom fighter).* P.11.
N249 **106** 6x. deep green and light blue . . 90 35
N250 12x. black and pale chocolate . . 1·30 50

1963 (25 Feb). *First Five-Year Plan (4th issue). Agriculture and Chemical Manufacture. T **107** and similar horiz design.* P.11.
N251 **107** 12x. multicoloured . . . . . 1·10 35
N252 – 12x. carmine-red, mauve and
     black 75 35
     Design:—No. N252, Lam Thao Fertiliser Factory.

108 Karl Marx   **109** Castro and Vietnamese Soldiers

(Des Trinh Quoc Thu)

1963 (14 Mar). *80th Death Anniv of Karl Marx. Toned paper.* P11.
N253 **108** 3x. olive-black and grey-green   60   30
N254   12x. olive-black and drab   . . . .   1·60   35

(Des Tran Luong)

1963 (17 Apr). *Vietnamese-Cuban Friendship.* P. 11.
N255 **109** 12x. multicoloured   . . . . . .   1·50   50

110 Doves and Labour Emblem

111 Nurse tending Child

(Des Trinh Quoc Thu and Tran Luong)

1963 (1 May). *Labour Day.* P 11.
N256 **110** 12x. orange, black and blue   . .   1·50   45

1963 (8 May). *Red Cross Centenary.* T **111** *and similar vert designs.* P 11.
N257 12x. red, black and light blue   . . . . .   1·50   35
N258 12x. red, black and turquoise-green   . .   1·50   35
N259 20x. red, grey, deep green and
     yellow   . . . .   2·20   35
     Designs:—Nos. N257, T **111**; N258, Child and syringe inscr "BCG". (25 × 42 mm)—N259, Centenary emblem.

112 "Mars 1" Interplanetary Station

(Des Tran Luong)

1963 (21 May). *Launching of Soviet Rocket "Mars 1".* T **112** *and similar multicoloured design.* P. 11.
N260 6x. Type **112**   75   35
N261 12x. Type **112**   . . . .   1·10   35
N262 12x. "Mars 1" in space (*vert*)   . . . .   1·50   35
N263 20x. As No. N262   . . . .   2·20   35
N260/263 *Set of 4*   . . . .   5·00   1·30
     Nos. 260/3 exist imperforate (*Price £11 set un or used*).

113 Common Carp

114 Pres. Ho Chi Minh embracing Prof. Nguyen Van Hien of South Vietnam

(Des Quang Lac and Thanh Huu)

1963 (3 July). *Fishing Industry.* T **113** *and similar horiz design. Multicoloured.* P 11.
N264 12x. Type **113**   . . . .   3·75   35
N265 12x. Korean mackerel and trawler   . .   3·75   35

(Des Trinh Quoc Thu)

1963 (20 July). *Campaign for Reunification of Vietnam.* P 11.
N266 **114** 12x. black, blue and pale blue   .   1·50   35

115 Globe and "Vostoks 3 and 4"

116 Viet Tri Insecticide Factory

(Des Tran Luong and Do Viet Tuan)

1963 (11 Aug). *First Anniv of "Team" Manned Space Flights.* T **115** *and similar horiz designs.* P11.
N267 12x. black, brown and olive-yellow   . .   75   35
N268 20x. black, light blue and green   . .   1·50   35
N269 30x. black, bluish violet and light
     blue   . . . .   3·00   35
     Designs:—20x. Nikolaev and "eagle" motif; 30x. Popovich and "phoenix" motif.
     Nos. N267/9 exist imperforate (*Price £11 set un or used*).

(Des Do Viet Tuan)

1963 (11 Aug). *First Five-Year Plan (5th issue).* T **116** *and similar horiz design.* P 11.
N270 3x. orange-buff, red-brown & grey-bl   60   20
N271 12x. pink, chocolate and deep bistre   .   1·60   35
     Design:—12x. Viet Tri Chemical Factory.

117 Black Carp (*Myloharyngodon piceus*)

MF **118** Military Medal and Invalids' Badge

(Des Trinh Quoc Thu. Litho State Ptg Wks, Budapest)

1963 (10 Sept). *Freshwater Fish Culture.* T **117** *and similar horiz designs. Multicoloured.* P 11.
N272 12x. Type **117**   . . . . .   1·50   60
N273 12x. Common carp (*Cyprinus carpio*)   . .   1·50   60
N274 12x. Silver carp (*Hypophthalmichthys*
     molitrix)   . . . .   1·50   60
N275 20x. Asiatic snakehead
     (*Ophiocephalus*)   . . . . .   3·75   60
N276 30x. Mozambique mouthbrooder (*Tilapia*
     mossambica)   . . . . . .   4·50   60
N272/276 *Set of 5*   . . . . . .   24·00   3·75
     No. N275 exists in a miniature sheet. There is no evidence this was issued.
     Nos. N272/6 exist imperforate (*Price £15 set un or used*).

(Des Tran Luong)

1963 (10 Sept). *MILITARY FRANK. For use on disabled soldiers' mail.* P 11.
NMF277 MF **118** 12 (x.) multicoloured   . .   3·75   3·75

118 Chinese Francolin

119 Broken Chain and Map

(Des Le Vinh (Nos. N278/9, N281), Bui Trang Chuoc (others).Photo State Ptg Wks, Budapest)

1963 (15 Oct). *Birds. T* **118** *and similar multicoloured designs.* P 12 × 11½ (20x.) or 11½ × 12 (others).

N277	12x. Type **118**		2·20	60
N278	12x. Chinese jungle mynah		2·20	60
N279	12x. White-throated kingfisher		2·20	60
N280	20x. Siamese fireback pheasant (horiz)		4·50	60
N281	30x. Reef heron		6·75	60
N282	40x. Slaty-headed parakeet		8·75	60
MSN282a	64 × 93mm. 50x. (as 30x.)		65·00	65·00
N277/282	Set of 6		24·00	3·25

Nos. N277/282 exist imperforate (*Price £33 set un or used*).

(Des Trinh Quoc Thu)

1963 (20 Oct). *World Trade Unions Federation Assembly, Hanoi.* P 11.

N283	**119**	12x. multicoloured	1·50	35

120 Football

121 *Rauwolfia verticillata*

122 "Solidarity"

(Des Tran Luong)

1963 (10 Nov). *"GANEFO" Athletic Games, Jakarta. T* **120** *and similar designs.* P 11.

N284	12x. black, grey and ochre		75	35
N285	12x. black, grey and orange		75	35
N286	12x. black, grey and light blue		75	35
N287	30x. black, grey and deep magenta		1·50	35
N284/287	Set of 4		3·50	1·20

Sports: *Vert*—Nos. N284, Type **120**; N285, Volleyball. *Horiz*—No. N286, Swimming; N287, High jumping.
Nos. N284/7 exist imperforate (*Price £4.50 set un or used*).

1963 (3 Dec). *Medicinal Plants. T* **121** *and similar vert designs. Multicoloured.* P 11.

N288	6x. Type **121**		75	35
N289	12x. Chenopodium ambrosioides		90	35
N290	12x. Sophora japonica		90	35
N291	12x. Fibraurea tinctoria		90	35
N292	20x. Momordica cochinchinensis		2·20	35
N288/292	Set of 5		5·00	1·60

Nos. N288/92 exist imperforate (*Price £8.75 set un or used*).

(Des Tran Luong)

1963 (20 Dec). *Third Anniv of South Vietnam National Liberation Front.* P 11.

N293	**122**	12x. black, yellow-brown & ochre	60	35

123 Pylon

124 Sun, Globe and Dragon

(Des Tran Luong (T **123**), Quang Lac (others))

1964 (25 Jan). *First Five-Year Plan (6th issue). T* **123** *and similar designs.* P 11.

N294	6x. black, red and purple		45	35
N295	12x. multicoloured		1·10	60
N296	12x. black, grey and orange		1·10	60

Designs: *Horiz* (40 × 22½ mm)—No. N294, Tapping cast-iron; N295, Thai Nguyen Iron and Steel Works. N296, T **123**.

(Des Ngoc Uyen)

1964 (25 Jan). *International Quiet Sun Years.* P 11.

N297	**124**	12x. orange, black & emerald-green	1·10	35
N298		50x. drab, black and reddish purple	85	35

Nos. N297/8 exist imperforate (*Price £12.50 pair un or used*).

125 Twin Space Flights

126 *Hibiscus mutabilis*

(Des Le Thanh Duc)

1964 (25 Mar). *Space Flights of Bykovsky and Tereshkova. T* **125** *and similar horiz designs. Multicoloured.* P.11.

N299	12x. Type **125**		1·10	35
N300	12x. Bykovsky and "Vostok 5"		1·10	35
N301	30x. Tereshkova and "Vostok 6"		3·00	35

Nos. N299/301 exist imperforate (*Price £8.75 set un or used*).

(Des Tran Luong and Trinh Quoc Thu. Photo State Ptg Wks, Budapest)

1964 (10 Apr). *Flowers. T* **126** *and similar vert designs. Multicoloured.* P 11½ × 12.

N302	12x. Type **126**		90	35
N303	12x. Persica vulgaris		90	35
N304	12x. Saraca dives		90	35
N305	12x. Passiflora hispida		90	35
N306	20x. Michelia champaca		2·50	35
N307	30x. Camellia amplexicaulis		4·50	35
N302/307	Set of 6		9·50	1·90

Nos. N302/7 exist imperforate (*Price £11 set un or used*).

127 Rural Costume

128 Artillery

(Des Uyen Lac Thanh)

1964 (27 Apr). *National Costumes.* T **127** *and similar vert designs. Multicoloured.* P 11.

N308	6x. Type **127**	75	35
N309	12x. "Ceremonial"	1·50	35
N310	12x. "Everyday"	1·50	35

No. N308 exists imperforate.

(Des Tran Luong)

1964 (7 May). *Tenth Anniv of Battle of Dien Bien Phu.* T **128** *and similar horiz designs.* P 11.

N311	3x. black and red	75	35
N312	6x. black and light blue	90	35
N313	12x. black and yellow	1·50	35
N314	12x. black and purple	1·80	35
MSN314a	106 × 74 mm. Nos. N311/14 in new colours. Imperf	9·50	9·50
N311/314 *Set of 4*		4·50	1·30

Designs:—No. N312, Machine-gun post; N313, Bomb disposal; N314, Dien Bien Phu and tractor.

Nos. N311/14 exist imperforate (*Price* £8.75 *set un or used*).

129 Ham Rong Railway Bridge

130 Spotted Deer

(Des Quoc Tuan)

1964 (17 May). *Inauguration of reconstructed Ham Rong Bridge.* P 11.

N315	**129**	12x. multicoloured	1·80	35

(Des Le Thanh Duc. Litho State Ptg Wks, Budapest)

1964 (2 June). *Wild Animals.* T **130** *and similar multicoloured designs.* P 10½.

N316	12x. Type **130**	90	35
N317	12x. Malayan tapir (*horiz*)	90	35
N318	12x. Tiger	90	35
N319	20x. Water buffalo (*horiz*)	2·20	35
N320	30x. Sumatran rhinoceros (*horiz*)	3·25	35
N321	40x. Banteng (*horiz*)	4·50	35
N316/321 *Set of 6*		11·50	1·90

Nos. N316/21 exist imperforate (*Price* £11 *set un or used*).

131 Women Fighters, Map, Industrial Scene and Watch-Towers

132 Nhu Quynh Pumping Station

(Des Tran Luong (T **131**))

1964 (20 July). *Tenth Anniv of Geneva Agreements on Vietnam.* T **131** *and another design inscr* "NHÂN DAN MIEN NAM", *etc on map. Multicoloured.* P 11.

N322	12x. Type **131**	1·10	35
N323	12x. Map of Vietnam, T.U. emblem and flag (23 × 45 *mm*)	1·10	35

(Des Ngoc Uyen)

1964 (25 Aug). *Irrigation for Agriculture.* P 11.

N324	**132**	12x. slate-blue and black	1·50	35

MF **133** Soldier and Army Badge

133 Populace Greeting Soldiers

(Des Quang Lac)

1964 (20 Sept). *MILITARY FRANK. No value indicated.* P 11.

NMF325	MF **133**	(–) Green, black & red-orge	3·75	3·75

(Des Do Viet Tuan (6x.), Quang Lac (12x.))

1964 (10 Oct). *Tenth Anniv of Liberation of Hanoi.* T **133** *and similar horiz design. Multicoloured.* P 11.

N325	6x. Type **133**	1·10	35
N326	12x. Building construction	1·80	35

134 Rowing

135 *Guarcinia mangostana*

(Des Tran Luong)

1964 (10 Oct). *"National Defence" Games.* T **134** *and similar designs.* P 11.

N327	5x. black, grey and light blue	75	45
N328	12x. black, grey and yellow	1·50	60
N329	12x. black, light brown and light blue	1·50	60
N330	12x. black, pink, grey and green	1·50	60
N327/330 *Set of 4*		4·75	2·00

Designs: *Horiz*—No. N328, Pistol-shooting. *Vert*—N329, Gliding; N330, Parachuting.

(Des Luu Van Sin. Photo State Ptg Wks, Budapest)

1964 (31 Oct). *Tropical Fruits. T* **135** *and similar vert designs. Multicoloured.* P 11½ × 12.

N331	12x. Type **135**		90	35
N332	12x. *Mangifera indica*		90	35
N333	12x. *Nephelium litchi*		90	35
N334	20x. *Anona squamosa*		2·20	35
N335	50x. *Citrus medica*		4·75	35
N331/335 *Set of 5*			8·75	1·60

Nos. N331/5 exist imperforate (*Price £11 set un or used*).

139 Le Hong Phong

140 Party Flag

(Des Nghiep Toan)

1965 (3 Feb). *35th Anniv of Vietnamese Workers' Party.* P 11 or imperf.

(a) Portraits of politicians as T **139**.

N344	**139**	6x. deep purple-brown and grey	35	35
		a. Strip of 5. Nos. N344/8	2·75	
N345	–	6x. dp purple-brown & yellow-brn	35	35
N346	–	6x. deep purple-brown and drab	35	35
N347	–	6x. deep purple-brown and brown	35	35
N348	–	6x. deep purple-brown and dull lilac	35	35

(b) As T **140**.

N349	**140**	12x. greenish yell, red-orge & mag	1·10	75
		a. Pair. Nos. N349/50	2·30	60
N350	–	12x. mag, greenish yell & red-orge	1·10	75
N344/350 *Set of 7*			3·50	3·00

Designs:—No. N345, Tran Phu; N346, Hoang Van Thu; N347, Ngo Gia Tu; N348, Nguyen Van Cu; N350, Foundryman and guerrilla fighter

Nos. N344/8 and N349/50 were issued together in *se-tenant* strips of 5 or pairs respectively within their sheets.

136 Conference Building

(Des Toan Tri Luong)

1964 (25 Nov). *World Solidarity Conference, Hanoi. T* **136** *and similar horiz designs. Multicoloured.* P.11.

N336	12x. Type **136**		1·10	35
	a. Vert strip of 3. Nos. N336/8		3·75	
N337	12x. Soldier greeting workers		1·10	35
N338	12x. Clenched fist, ships and Boeing B-52 Stratofortress		1·10	35

Nos. N336/8 were issued together in vertical *se-tenant* strips of three within the sheet.

137 Soldiers with Standard

138 Cuban Revolutionaries

(Des Luong Khanh)

1964 (22 Dec). *20th Anniv of Vietnamese People's Army. T* **137** *and similar multicoloured designs.* P. 11.

N339	12x. Type **137**		1·00	35
N340	12x. Coastguards		1·00	35
	a. Pair. Nos. N340/1		2·20	80
N341	12x. Frontier guards (*vert*)		1·00	35

Nos. N340/1 were issued together in *se-tenant* pairs within the sheet.

141 Women tending Maize

142 Steam Locomotive and Nguyen Van Troi (patriot)

(Des Ngoc Uyen)

1965 (28 Feb). *Populating Mountain Settlements. T* **141** *and similar vert design.* P. 11.

N351	**141**	2x. multicoloured	20	35
N352		3x. multicoloured	75	35
N353	–	12x. blue, orange and light blue	90	35

Design:—No. N352, Young girls going to school.
Nos. N352/3 exist imperforate.

(Des Tran Luong)

1965 (1 Jan). *Sixth Anniv of Cuban Republic. T* **138** *and similar vert design.* P. 11.

N342	**138**	12x. black, red and ultramarine	1·50	35
		a. Pair. Nos. N342/3	3·25	3·25
N343	–	12x. ultramarine, red, yellow & black	1·50	1·50

Design:—No. N343, Flags of Cuba and North Vietnam.
Nos. N342/3 were issued together in *se-tenant* pairs within the sheet.

(Des Tran Luong)

1965 (23 Mar). *Transport Ministers' Congress, Hanoi. T* **142** *and similar horiz design.* P. 11.

N354	12x. deep violet-blue and red		1·80	35
N355	30x. black and green		3·25	35

Design:—30x. As T **142** but position of locomotive, portrait and value transposed.
Nos. N354/5 exist imperforate.

143 Cosmonauts, Komarov, Feoktistov,
Yegorov and "Voskhod 1"

(Des Tran Nghiep)

1965 (30 Mar). *Three-manned Space Flight. T* **143** *and similar
horiz design.* P 11.

N356	20x.	violet, yellow-green and new blue	1·50	35
N357	1d.	dp violet, lt violet, orge-red & mag	5·25	35

Design:—1d. "Voskhod 1" and cosmonauts.
Nos. N356/7 exist imperforate (*Price £8.75 pair un or used*).

144 Lenin with Red Guards   145 Pres. Ho Chi Minh

(T **144/5**. Des Tran Khanh)

1965 (22 Apr). *Lenin's 95th Birth Anniv.* P 11.

N358	**144**	8x. dp maroon & lt yellow-orange	1·10	35
N359		12x. deep maroon and grey	1·10	35

1965 (19 May). *President Ho Chi Minh's 75th Birthday.* P 11.

N360	**145**	6x. bluish violet, pale yellow and light grey-green	75	35
N361		12x. bluish vio, pale yell & yell-orge	1·10	35

Nos. N360/1 exist imperforate.

146 Hands clasping   147 Two Soldiers
Serpent   advancing

(Des Quang Lac)

1965 (19 May). *Tenth Anniv of Afro-Asian Conference, Bandung.*
P11 or imperf.

N362	**146**	12x. multicoloured	1·50	35

(Des Toan Nghiep)

1965 (2 June). *Trade Union Conference, Hanoi. T* **147** *and similar
designs.* P 11 or imperf.

N363	**147**	12x. grey-blue and reddish purple	1·10	35
N364	–	12x. blk, red, yell-ol & reddish vio	1·10	35
N365	–	12x. red, black and grey-green	1·10	35

Designs: Horiz—No. N364, Sea battle; N365, "Peoples of the
world" on Globe, and soldiers.

148 Yellow-throated Marten (*Martes flavigula*)

(Des Tuan Uyen Lac. Photo State Ptg Wks, Budapest)

1965 (24 June). *Fauna Protection. T* **148** *and similar multicoloured
designs.* P 12.

N366	12x.	Type **148**	1·10	35
N367	12x.	Owston's palm civet (*Chrotogale ovvstoni*)	1·10	35
N368	12x.	Chinese pangolin (*Manis pentadactyla*)	1·10	35
N369	12x.	Francois' monkey (*Presbytis delacouri*) (*vert*)	1·10	35
N370	20x.	Red giant flying squirrel (*Petaurista lylei*) (*vert*)	3·00	35
N371	50x.	Lesser slow loris (*Nycticebus pygmaeus*) (*vert*)	5·25	35
N366/371		Set of 6	12·00	1·90

Nos. N366/71 exist imperforate (*Price £18 set un or used*).

149 Marx and Lenin   MF **150** Soldier   150 Nguyen Van
in Action   Troi (patriot)

(Des Li Fu. Photo Govt Ptg Wks, Peking)

1965 (1 July). *Postal Ministers Congress, Peking.* P 11½ × 11.

N372	**149**	12x. multicoloured	2·50	35

(Des Quang Lac)

1965. *MILITARY FRANK. No value indicated.* P 11.

NMF373	MF **150**	(–) Black and red (1 July)	3·75	3·75
NMF374		(–) Black & yell-grn (1965)	3·75	3·75

Nos. NMF373/4 exist imperforate.

(Des Do Viet Tuan)

1965 (20 July). *Nguyen Van Troi Commemoration.* P 11 or imperf.

N373	**150**	12x. dp brown, orge-brn & turq-grn	75	35
N374		50x. dp brn, orge-brn & yell-ochre	1·50	35
N375		4d. deep brown and red	4·50	35

151 *Rhynchocoris humeralis*   **152** Revolutionaries

(Des Nguyen Toan. Photo)

1965 (24 July). *Noxious Insects.* T **151** *and similar multicoloured designs.* P. 11.

N376	12x.	Type **151**	1·10	35
N377	12x.	*Tessaratoma papillosa*	1·10	35
N378	12x.	*Poeciliocoris latus*	1·10	35
N379	12x.	*Tosena melanoptera*	1·10	35
N380	20x.	*Cicada* sp	2·50	35
N381	30x.	*Fulgora candelaria*	3·25	35
N376/381		*Set of 6*	6·25	1·90

Nos. N377/8 are square, as T **151**; Nos. N379/81 are vertical (20½ × 38 *mm*).
Nos. N376/81 exist imperforate (*Price* £15 *set un or used*).

1965 (19 Aug). *20th Anniv of August Revolution.* P.11.

N382	**152**	6x. sepia, black and blue	75	35
N383		12x. black and rose-red	1·50	35

153 Prawn   **154** Air Battle

(Des Nguyen Toan. Photo)

1965 (19 Aug). *Marine Life.* T **153** *and similar multicoloured designs.* P. 11.

N384	12x.	Type **153**	1·50	35
N385	12x.	Shrimp	1·50	35
N386	12x.	Swimming Crab	1·50	35
N387	12x.	Serrate Swimming Crab	1·50	35
N388	20x.	Spiny Lobster	3·00	35
N389	50x.	Fiddler Crab	6·00	35
N384/389		*Set of 6*	14·00	2·75

Nos. N384/9 exist imperforate (*Price* £15 *set un or used*).

(Des Tran Luong)

1965 (29 Aug). *500th U.S. Aircraft Brought Down over North Vietnam.* P 11 or imperf.

N390	**154**	12x. deep bluish green and lilac	4·00	2·75

155 Foundryman ("Heavy Industries")   **156** Drummer and Peasants

1965 (2 Sept). *20th Anniv of Democratic Republic and Completion of First Five Year Plan.* T **155** *and similar horiz designs.* P. 11.

N391	**155**	12x. black and orange	90	50
N392	–	12x. black and green	90	50
N393	–	12x. black and light purple	90	50

Designs:—No. N392, Irrigation, pylon and power station ("Hydro-electric Power"); N393, Nurse examining child ("Social Medicine").
Nos. N391/3 exist imperforate.
For second issue, see Nos. N417/9.

(Des Nguyen Khanh)

1965 (12 Sept). *35th Anniv of Movement of Nghe An and Ha Tinh Soviet Peasants.* P. 11.

N394	**156**	10x. multicoloured	1·00	35
N395		12x. multicoloured	1·20	35

No. N395 exists imperforate.

157 Flag, Friendship Gate and Girls

(Des Nguyen Van Ty)

1965 (1 Oct). *16th Anniv of Friendship between China and Vietnam.* T **157** *and similar multicoloured design.* P.11.

N396	12x.	Type **157**	3·75	75
N397	12x.	Vietnamese and Chinese girls with flags (*vert*)	3·75	75

158 Tsiolkovsky and "Sputnik 1"   **159** *Cethosia biblis*

(Des Phan Chi)

1965 (5 Oct). *Space Flight of "Voskhod 2".* T **158** *and similar horiz designs.* P. 11.

N398	**158**	12x. violet-blue and reddish purple	75	35
N399	–	12x. yellow-ochre and bright blue	75	35
N400	–	50x. violet-blue and bright green	2·20	1·10
N401	–	50x. violet-blue and turquoise-blue	2·20	1·10
N398/401		*Set of 4*	5·50	2·75

Designs:—No. N399, A. Leonov, P. Belyaev and "Voskhod 2"; N400, Yuri Gagarin; N401, Leonov in space.
Nos. N398/401 exist imperforate.

(Des Uyen Diep)

1965 (18 Nov). *Butterflies.* T **159** *and similar multicoloured designs.* P. 11.

N402	12x.	Type **159**	1·80	35
N403	12x.	*Cethosia cyane*	1·80	35
N404	12x.	*Graphium sarpedon*	1·80	35
N405	12x.	*Apatura ambica*	1·80	35
N406	20x.	*Papilio paris*	3·75	35
N407	30x.	*Atrophaneura aristolochiae*	5·25	35
N402/407		*Set of 6*	15·00	1·90

Nos. N402/7 exist imperforate (*Price* £41 *set un or used*).

160
Norman R. Morrison
and Demonstrators

161 Birthplace of
Nguyen Du (poet)

1965 (22 Nov). *Homage to Norman R. Morrison (American Quaker who immolated himself)*. P 11 or imperf.

N408	**160**	12x. black and vermilion	2·20	35

1965 (25 Nov). *Nguyen Du Commemoration. T* **161** *and similar vert designs. Multicoloured*. P 11 or imperf.

N409	12x. Type **161**		75	35
N410	12x. Nguyen Du Museum		75	35
N411	20x. *Kieu* (volume of poems)		1·10	35
N412	1d. Scene from *Kieu*		1·80	35
N409/412 *Set of 4*			4·00	1·30

162 Pres. Ho Chi Minh

163 Rice-field and
Insecticide-sprayer
("Agriculture")

(Des Huy Khanh. No. N413 recess and litho, others litho)

1965 (28 Nov). *Engels' 145th Birth Anniv. T* **162** *and similar vert designs. Multicoloured.* P 11½.

N413	12x. Type **162**		75	35
N414	12x. Marx		75	35
N415	12x. Lenin		75	35
N416	50x. Engels		2·20	35
N413/416 *Set of 4*			4·00	1·30

1965 (Dec). *Completion of First Five-Year Plan (2nd issue). T* **163** *and similar vert designs inscr "1961 1965"*. P.11.

N417	**163**	12x. red-orange and green	90	30
N418	–	12x. ultramarine and red	90	30
N419	–	12x. red-orange and ultramarine	90	30

Designs:—No. N418, Factory worker ("Light Industries"); N419, Children at play and students ("Social Education").
Nos. N418/19 exist imperforate.

164 Soldier and Demonstrators

(Des Huy Khanh)

1965 (20 Dec). *Fifth Anniv of South Vietnam National Liberation Front.* P 11.

N420	**164**	12x. dp reddish violet & reddish lilac	1·80	35

No. N420 exists imperforate.

165 Casting Votes

166 *Dendrobium moschatum*

(Des Anh Tuan)

1966 (6 Jan). *20th Anniv of First Vietnamese General Elections.* P 11.

N421	**165**	12x. black and red	1·80	50

(Des Uyen Diep)

1966 (10 Jan). *Orchids. T* **166** *and similar vert designs. Multicoloured.* P 12.

N422	12x. Type **166**		1·10	35
N423	12x. *Vanda teres*		1·10	35
N424	12x. *Dendrobium crystallinum*		1·10	35
N425	12x. *Dendrobium nobile*		1·10	35
N426	20x. *Vandopsis gigantea*		1·80	35
N427	30x. *Dendrobium*		2·50	35
N422/427 *Set of 6*			8·00	1·90

Nos. N422/7 exist imperforate (*Price £15 set un or used*).

167 Child on Rocking-
horse

168 *Physignathus cocincinus*

(Des Kim Diep)

1966 (18 Jan). *New Year.* P 11.

N428	**167**	12x. multicoloured	1·80	35

No. N428 exists imperforate.

(Des Le Toan)

1966 (25 Feb). *Protection of Nature—Reptiles. T* **168** *and similar vert designs. Multicoloured.* P 12½ × 12.

N429	12x. Type **168**		1·10	35
N430	12x. *Trionyx sinensis*		1·10	35
N431	12x. Gecko (inscr "GEKKO GECKO")		1·10	35
N432	12x. *Testudo elongata*		1·10	35
N433	20x. *Varanus salvator*		1·50	35
N434	40x. *Eretmochelys imbricata*		3·00	35
N429/434 *Set of 6*			8·00	1·90

Nos. N429/34 exist imperforate (*Price £15 set un or used*).

169 Wrestling

170 Ly Tu Trong
(revolutionary), Badge
and Banner

(Des Tran Luong)

1966 (25 Mar). *National Games. T* **169** *and similar horiz designs.
Multicoloured.* P 11.
N435   12x. Type **169** . . . . 1·30   35
N436   12x. Archery (with crossbow) . . . . 1·30   35
N437   12x. "Fencing" . . . . 1·30   35
Nos. N435/6 exist imperforate.

(Des Luong Diep)

1966 (26 Mar). *35th Anniv of Labour Youth Union.* P 11.
N438   **170**   12x. multicoloured . . . . . 1·50   50

171 Republic F-105D Thunderchief
in Flames

172 Worker with Rifle

1966 (29 Apr). *1000th U.S. Aircraft Brought Down over North
Vietnam.* P 11.
N439   **171**   12x. multicoloured . . . . . 5·25   3·75
No. N439 exists imperforate.

1966 (1 May). *Labour Day.* P 11.
N440   **172**   6x. black, vermilion and salmon   1·50   35
No. N440 exists imperforate.

173 Battle Scene on Co Island

174 Children and
Banners

(Des Tran Khanh)

1966 (1 June). *Defence of Con Co ("Steel Island").* P 11 or imperf.
N441   **173**   12x. multicoloured . . . . . 1·50   35

(Des Kim Diep)

1966 (1 June). *25th Anniv of Vietnam Youth Pioneers.* P 11.
N442   **174**   12x. black and red . . . . . 1·50   35
No. N442 exists imperforate.

175 View of Dien An
(Yenan)

O 176 Postman delivering
Letter

(Des Huy Khanh)

1966 (1 July). *45th Anniv of Chinese Communist Party. T* **175** *and
similar vert design inscr "1921–1966". Multicoloured.* P 11.
N443   3x. Type **175** . . . . 1·50   35
N444   12x. Ho Chi Minh and Mao Tse-tung . . 1·50   35
Nos. N443/4 exist imperforate.

1966 (1 July). OFFICIAL. *Rural Service. Type O* **176** *and similar
horiz design.* P 11.
NO445   3x. dull purple, bistre and lilac . . . 45   45
NO446   6x. dull purple, bistre & turquoise-
        grn 60   60
Design:—6x. As Type O **176**, but design reversed.
Nos. NO445/6 exist imperforate.
Nos. NO445/6 exist handstamped "TEM NI B" (= Internal
Service Stamp) in a box, for use in the Hanoi area.

176 "Luna 9" in Space

MF 177 Soldiers and
Weapons

(Des Tran Luong)

1966 (5 Aug). *Space Flight of "Luna 9". T* **176** *and similar vert
design inscr "MAT TRĂNG 9". Multicoloured.* P 11.
N445   12x. Type **176** . . . . 1·50   75
N446   50x. "Luna 9" on Moon . . . . . 3·75   75
Nos. N445/6 exist imperforate (*Price £7.50 pair un or used*).

1966 (25 Sept). MILITARY FRANK. *No value indicated.* P 11.
NMF447   MF **177**   (–) Violet and light blue . . 7·50   7·50
See also Nos. NMF519 and NMF579.

177 Airplane in Flames   **178** Liberation Fighter

(Des Huy Khanh)

1966 (14 Oct). *1500th U.S. Aircraft Brought Down over North Vietnam*. P 11.
N447 **177** 12x. multicoloured . . . . 7·50   2·50
    Additionally optd "NGAY 14.10.1966"
N448 **177** 12x. multicoloured . . . . . 11·00   2·50
Nos. N447/8 exist imperforate.

(Des Tran Nghiep)

1966 (15 Oct). *Victories of Liberation Army*. T **178** *and similar horiz design inscr* "1965–1966". P 11.
N449 **178** 1x. brown-purple . . . . . . 1·30   50
N450   12x. multicoloured . . . . . . 1·30   50
N451 –   12x. multicoloured (Soldier
    escorting prisoners-of-war)   1·30   50
Nos. N449/51 exist imperforate.
See also No. N646.

179 Women from different Regions and Child   **180** Moluccan Pittas

(Des Uyen Diep)

1966 (20 Oct). *20th Anniv of Vietnamese Women's Union*. P 11.
N452 **179** 12x. black and salmon-red 75   35
No. N452 exists imperforate.

1966 (31 Oct). *Birds*. T **180** *and similar multicoloured designs*.
P12 × 12½ (horiz) or 12½ × 12 (vert).
N453 **180** 12x. Type **180** 90   35
N454   12x. Black-naped orioles (*vert*) . . . 90   35
N455   12x. River kingfisher (*vert*) 90   35
N456   12x. Long-tailed broadbill 90   35
N457   20x. Hoopoe (*vert*) . . . . . . 1·60   35
N458   30x. Maroon orioles . . . . . 2·20   45
N453/458 *Set of 6* . . . . 6·75   1·90
Nos. 453/8 exist imperforate (*Price £18 set un or used*).

181 Football   **182** Harvesting Rice

(Des Khanh and Uyen)

1966 (Nov). *Ganefo Games*. T **181** *and similar square designs*.
Multicoloured. P 11.
N459   12x. Type **181** . . . . 1·10   35
N460   12x. Rifle-shooting . . . . . . 1·10   35
N461   30x. Swimming . . . . . . 1·50   35
N462   30x. Running . . . . . . 1·50   35
N459/462 *Set of 4* . . . . 4·75   1·30
Nos. N459/62 exist imperforate (*Price £7.50 set un or used*).

(Des Huy Khanh)

1967 (30 Jan). *Agricultural Production*. P 11.
N463 **182** 12x. multicoloured . . . . . 1·10   35
No. N463 exists imperforate.

183 Ho Chi Minh Text and Fighters   **184** Bamboo

(Des Huy Khanh)

1967 (30 Jan). *Ho Chi Minh's Appeal*. T **183** *and similar horiz design. Both dull purple and red*. P 11.
N464   12x. Type **183** 90   35
N465   12x. Ho Chi Minh text and marchers
    with banners . . . . . . 1·10   35
Nos. N464/5 exist imperforate.
See also Nos. N519/22.

1967 (5 Feb). *Bamboo*. T **184** *and similar vert designs. Multicoloured*. Photo. P 12 × 11½.
N466   12x. Type **184** (*Arundinaria rolleana*) . . 90   35
N467   12x. *Arundinaria racemosa* 90   35
N468   12x. *Bambusa bingami* 90   35
N469   12x. *Bambusa arundinaceu* . . . 90   35
N470   30x. *Bambusa nutans* . . . . 1·60   35
N471   50x. *Dendrocalamus patellaris* . . 2·20   35
N466/471 *Set of 6* . . . . 6·75   1·90
Nos. N466/71 exist imperforate (*Price £8.75 set un or used*).

185 Dhole (*Cuon rutilans*)

(Des Tran Nghiep)

1967 (20 Mar). *Wild Animals*. T **185** *and similar horiz designs. Multicoloured*. P 12.
N472 **185** 12x. Type **185** 75   35
N473   12x. Binturong (*Arctictis binturong*) . . 75   35
N474   12x. Hog-badger (*Arctonix collaris*) . . . 75   35
N475   20x. Large Indian civet (*Viverra
    zibetha*) . . . . 1·50   35

N476 40x. Bear macaque (*Macaca*
     speciosa) . . . . 2·20   35
N477 50x. Clouded leopard (*Neofelis*
     nebulosa) . . . . 3·00   35
N472/477 *Set of 6* . . . . 8·25 1·90
Nos. N472/7 exist imperforate (*Price £9.50 set un or used*).

186 Captured Pilot

187 Rocket
Launching and
Agricultural Scene

1967 (5 June). *2000th U.S. Aircraft Brought Down over North Vietnam*. P 11.
N478 **186** 6x. black and red/pale flesh . . . 2·50 1·50
N479   12x. black and red/pale green . . 2·50 1·50
No. N479 is additionally inscribed with the dates "5-8-1964" and "5-6-1967" in red, representing the dates of the first and 2000th shooting down.

1967 (25 July). *Launching of First Chinese Rocket*. T **187** *and similar vert design*. P 11.
N480 12x. multicoloured . . . . 1·80 90
N481 30x. multicoloured . . . . 3·00 1·50
Design:—30x. Rocket launching, and Gate of Heavenly Peace, Peking.
Nos. N480/1 exist imperforate.

188 Betted Bearded Grunt
(*Haplogenys mucronatus*)

MF **189** "Star" Badge
of People's Army

1967 (25 July). *Vietnamese Fishes*. T **188** *and similar horiz designs*. Multicoloured. P 12.
N482 12x. Type **188** 75 35
N483 12x. Japanese Mackerel
     (*Scomberomorus niphonius*) 75 35
N484 12x. Thread-finned Lizardfish (*saurida*
     filamentosa) 75 35
N485 20x. Adjutant Emperor (*Lethrinus*
     haematopterus) . . . . 1·50 35
N486 30x. Black ponfret (*Formio niger*) . . 2·20 35
N487 50x. Blood snapper (*Lutianus*
     erythropterus) . . . . 3·00 35
N482/487 *Set of 6* . . . . 8·25 1·90
Nos. N482/7 exist imperforate (*Price £11 set un or used*).

(Des Huy Khanh)

1967 (10 Oct). *MILITARY FRANK. No value indicated*. P 11.
NMF488 MF **189** (–) Multicoloured . . . . 1·10 1·10

189 Lenin and
Revolutionary
Soldiers

190 Air Battle

(Des Huy Khanh)

1967 (15 Oct). *50th Anniv of October Revolution*. T **189** *and similar vert designs inscr* "1917–1967". Multicoloured. P11.
N488 6x. Type **189** 45 35
N489 12x. Lenin and revolutionaries 80 35
    a. Pair. Nos. N489/90 . . . . . . 1·70 75
N490 12x. Lenin, Marx and Vietnamese
     soldiers 80 35
N491 20x. *Aurora* (Russian cruiser) . . . . 1·20 35
N488/491 *Set of 4* . . . . 3·00 1·30
Nos. 489/90 were issued together in *se-tenant* pairs within the sheet.

(Des Tran Luong)

1967 (6 Nov). *2500th U.S. Aircraft Brought Down over North Vietnam*. T **190** *and similar design inscr* "2.500". P 11.
N492 **190** 12x. black, red and light green . . 3·25 90
N493   12x. black, red and light blue . . 3·25 90
Design: *Vert*—No. N493, Aircraft falling in flames.

191 Atomic Symbol and Gate of
Heavenly Peace, Peking

1967 (20 Nov). *First Chinese "H"-Bomb Test*. T **191** *and similar multicoloured design*. P 11.
N494 12x. Type **191** . . . . 1·50 75
N495 20x. Chinese lantern, atomic symbol and
     dove (30 × 35 mm) . . . . 2·20 75
Nos. N494/5 exist imperforate.

192 Machine Gun Crew and Airplane on
Fire

(Des Le Toan and Nghiep)

1967 (19 Dec). *Anti-aircraft Defences*. T **192** *and similar horiz designs*. Multicoloured. P 12½.
N496 12x. Type **192** 45 35
N497 12x. Rifle-fire from trenches 45 35
N498 12x. Seaborne gun-crew 45 35
N499 12x. Militiawoman with captured U.S.
     pilot 45 35
N500 20x. Air Battle 90 35
N501 30x. Military anti-aircraft post . . . 1·80 35
N496/501 *Set of 6* . . . . 4·00 1·90

193 Chickens

(Des Uyen)

1968 (29 Feb). *Domestic Fowl. T* **193** *and similar horiz designs showing cocks and hens. Multicoloured.* P 12.

N502	12x. Type **193**		60	35
N503	12x. Inscr "Ga ri"		60	35
N504	12x. Inscr "Ga trong thien ri"		60	35
N505	12x. Inscr "Ga den chanchi"		60	35
N506	20x. Junglefowl		1·10	35
N507	30x. Hen		1·50	35
N508	40x. Hen and chicks		2·20	35
N509	50x. Two hens		2·50	35
N502/509 *Set of* 8			8·75	2·50

Nos. N502/9 exist imperforate (*Price* £15 *set un or used*).

194 Gorky   **195** Burning Village

(Des Huy Khanh)

1968 (5 Mar). *Birth Centenary of Maxim Gorky.* P 11.

N510	**194**	12x. black and light bistre-brown	1·10	35

No. N510 exists imperforate.

1968 (5 Mar). *Victories of 1966–67, T* **195** *and similar horiz designs.* P 11.

N511	12x. chocolate and brown-lake		60	60
	a. Block of 4. Nos. N511/14		2·50	
N512	12x. chocolate and brown-lake		60	60
N513	12x. chocolate and brown-lake		60	60
N514	12x. chocolate and brown-lake		60	60
N515	12x. black and violet		60	60
	a. Block of 4. Nos. N515/18		2·50	
N516	12x. black and violet		60	60
N517	12x. black and violet		60	60
N518	12x. black and violet		60	60
N511/518 *Set of* 8			4·25	4·25

Designs:—Nos. N511, Type **195**; N512, Firing mortars; N513, Attacking tanks with rocket-gun; N514, Sniping; N515, Attacking gun-site; N516, Escorting prisoners; N517, Interrogating refugees; N518, Civilians demonstrating.

Nos. N511/14 and N515/18 respectively were issued together in *se-tenant* blocks of four within their sheets.

Nos. 511/18 exist imperforate.

MF **196** Soldiers and Weapons   **197** Ho Chi Minh Text and Fighters

1968. *MILITARY FRANK. No value indicated.* P 11.

NMF519	MF **196**	(–) Brown and yellow-olive	11·00	11·00

No. NMF519 is similar in design to No. NMF447, but shows more modern equipment and is dated "1967".

(Des Huy Khanh)

1968 (25 Apr). *Intensification of Production.* P 11.

N519	**197**	6x. turquoise-blue/*yellow*	75	20
N520		12x. bright blue	1·10	20
N521		12x. brown-purple	1·10	20
N522		12x. rose-red	1·10	20
N519/522 *Set of* 4			3·75	70

Type **197** is a redrawn version, in a smaller size, of Type **183**.

No. N519 exists imperforate.

No. N519 exists handstamped "TEM NÔI BÔ" (= Internal Service Stamp) in a box.

198 Rose   **199** Ho Chi Minh and Flag

(Des Kim Diep. Photo)

1968 (25 Apr). *Roses. T* **198** *and similar vert designs, showing different species. Multicoloured.* P 11½ × 12.

N523	12x. Type **198** (Hong boch.)	75	35
N524	12x. Hong canh sap	75	35
N525	12x. Hong leo	75	35
N526	20x. Hong varg	1·50	35
N527	30x. Hong nhung	2·20	35
N528	40x. Hong canh tim	3·00	35
N523/528 *Set of* 6		8·00	1·90

Nos. N523/8 exist imperforate (*Price* £12 *set un or used*).

1968 (19 May). *Ho Chi Minh's New Year Message.* P 11.

N529	**199**	12x. red-brown and vermilion	1·50	45

No. N529 exists imperforate.

200 Karl Marx   **201** Anti-aircraft Machine-gun Crew

(Des Viet Tuan)

1968 (19 May). *150th Birth Anniv of Karl Marx.* P 11.

N530	**200**	12x. black and olive	1·50	35

1968 (25 June). *3000th U.S. Aircraft Brought Down over North Vietnam. T* **201** *and similar horiz designs. Multicoloured.* P 11.

N531	12x. Type **201**		1·50	1·10
	a. Vert pair. Nos. N531/2		2·25	2·30
N532	12x. Women manning anti-aircraft gun		1·50	1·10
N533	40x. Aerial dogfight		3·75	1·10
	a. Vert pair. Nos. N533/4		8·00	2·30
N534	40x. Surface-to-air missile		3·75	1·10
N531/534 *Set of* 4			9·50	4·00

Nos. N531/2 and N533/4 respectively were issued together in vertical *se-tenant* pairs within their sheets.

Nos. N531/4 exist imperforate.

202 Rattan-cane Work

1968 (5 July). *Arts and Crafts. T* **202** *and similar diamond shaped designs. Multicoloured.* P 12.
N535	6x. Type **202**	35	35
N536	12x. Bamboo work	45	35
N537	12x. Pottery	45	35
N538	20x. Ivory carving	75	35
N539	30x. Lacquer work	1·10	35
N540	40x. Silverware	1·50	35
N535/540 *Set of 6*		4·25	1·90

Nos. N535/40 exist imperforate (*Price* £11 *set un or used*).

203 Quarter-staff Contest

MF **204** Soldiers attacking

(Des Huy Khanh)

1968 (25 Oct). *Traditional Sports. T* **203** *and similar horiz designs. Multicoloured.* P 12.
N541	12x. Type **203**	60	35
N542	12x. Dagger fighting	60	35
N543	12x. Duel with sabres	60	35
N544	30x. Unarmed combat	1·50	35
N545	40x. Scimitar fighting	1·90	35
N546	50x. Sword and buckler duel	2·20	35
N541/546 *Set of 6*		6·50	1·90

Nos. N541/6 exist imperforate (*Price* £12 *set un or used*).

(Des Huy Khanh)

1968 (10 Nov). *MILITARY FRANK. No value indicated.* P 11.
NMF547	MF **204** (–) Lilac	1·20	1·20

No. NMF547 exists imperforate.

205 Temple, Khue

1968 (15 Nov). *Vietnamese Architecture. T* **205** *and similar multicoloured designs.* P 12.
N548	12x. Type **205**	45	35
N549	12x. Bell tower, Keo Pagoda	45	35
N550	20x. Bridge, Bonze Pagoda (*horiz*)	60	35
N551	30x. Mot Cot Pagoda, Hanoi	75	35
N552	40x. Gateway, Ninh Phuc Pagoda (*horiz*)	1·20	35
N553	50x. Tay Phuong Pagoda (*horiz*)	1·50	35
N548/553 *Set of 6*		4·50	1·90

Nos. N548/53 exist imperforate (*Price* £8.75 *set un or used*).

206 Vietnamese Militia

207 "Ploughman with Rifle"

(Des Huy Khanh. Litho State Ptg Wks, Havana)

1968 (15 Dec). *Cuban-North Vietnamese Friendship. T* **206** *and similar multicoloured designs. W* **324** *of Cuba ("R de C"). With gum.* P 12½.
N554	12x. Type **206**	75	60
N555	12x. Cuban revolutionary (*vert*)	75	60
N556	20x. "Revolutionary Solidarity" (*vert*)	1·10	75

(Litho State Ptg Wks, Havana)

1968 (15 Dec). *"The War Effort". T* **207** *and similar designs, showing paintings. W* **324** *of Cuba ("R de C"). With gum.* P 12½.
N557	12x. multicoloured	35	30
N558	12x. multicoloured	35	30
N559	30x. light brown, turquoise-blue & lt blue	90	75
N560	40x. multicoloured	1·30	1·10
N557/560 *Set of 4*		2·75	2·20

Designs: *Vert*—No. N557, Type **207**. *Horiz*—No. N558, "Defending the Mines"; N559, "Repairing Railway Track"; N560, "Crashed Aircraft".

208 Nam Ngai shooting down Aircraft

1969 (16 Feb). *Lunar New Year. Victories of the National Liberation Front. T* **208** *and similar horiz designs. Multicoloured.* P 11½.
N561	12x. Type **208**	35	35
N562	12x. Tay Nguyen throwing grenade	35	35
N563	12x. Gun crews, Tri Thien	35	35
N564	40x. Insurgents, Tay Ninh	1·10	35
N565	50x. Home guards	4·50	35
N561/565 *Set of 5*		6·00	1·90

209 Loading Timber Lorries

(Des Tran Nghiep)

1969 (10 Apr). *North Vietnamese Timber Industry. T* **209** *and similar horiz designs. Multicoloured.* P 11½.

N566	6x. Type **209**	45	35
N567	12x. Log raft on river	80	35
N568	12x. Tug towing "log train"	80	35
N569	12x. Elephant hauling logs	80	35
N570	12x. Insecticide spraying	80	35
N571	20x. Buffalo hauling log	1·10	35
N572	30x. Logs on overhead cable	1·80	35
N566/572	*Set of 7*	5·00	2·20

Nos. N566/72 exist imperforate (*Price £11 set un or used*).

210 "Young Guerrilla" (Co Tan Long Chau)

1969 (20 June). *"South Vietnam—Land and People". T* **210** *and similar multicoloured designs, showing paintings.* P 11½ × 12½ (20x.) or 12½ × 11½ (others).

N573	12x. Type **210**	45	35
N574	12x. "Scout on Patrol" (Co Tan Long Chau)	45	35
N575	20x. "Woman Guerrilla" (Le Van Chuong) (*vert*)	75	35
N576	30x. "Halt at a Relay Station" (Co Tan Long Chau)	95	35
N577	40x. "After a Skirmish" (Co Tan Long Chau)	1·50	35
N578	50x. "Liberated Hamlet" (Huynh Phuong Dong)	2·20	35
N573/578	*Set of 6*	5·75	1·90

Nos. N573/8 exist imperforate (*Price £11 set un or used*).

1969. MILITARY FRANK. *Type MF* **177** *but undated. No value indicated.* P 11.

NMF579	MF **177**	(–) Dp brown & dull yell-grn	15·00

211 Woman Soldier, Ben Tre

1969 (20 Sept). *Victories in Tet Offensive (1968). T* **211** *and similar designs.* P 11.

N579	8x. black, dull green and pale flesh	60	45
N580	12x. black, emerald and apple-green	60	45
N581	12x. multicoloured	60	45
N582	12x. multicoloured	60	45
N583	12x. multicoloured	60	45
N579/583	*Set of 5*	2·75	2·10

Designs: Horiz—Nos. N579/80, Type **211**. Vert—No. N581, Urban guerrilla and attack on US Embassy, Saigon; N582, Two soldiers with flag, Hué; N583, Mortar crew, Khe Sanh.
Nos. N579/80 exist imperforate.

212 Soldier with Flame-thrower   **213** Grapefruit

1969 (10 Oct). *15th Anniv of Liberation of Hanoi. T* **212** *and similar horiz design.* P 11.

N584	12x. black and scarlet	1·50	35
N585	12x. multicoloured	1·50	35

Design:—No. N585, Children with construction toy.
No. N585 exists imperforate.

(Des Tran Nghiep)

1969 (20 Nov). *Fruits (1st series). T* **213** *and similar vert designs. Multicoloured.* P 12.

N586	12x. Type **213**	30	10
N587	12x. Pawpaw	30	10
N588	20x. Tangerines	35	20
N589	30x. Oranges	60	35
N590	40x. Lychees	1·10	60
N591	50x. Persimmons	1·80	1·10
N586/591	*Set of 6*	4·00	2·20

Nos. N586/91 exist imperforate (*Price £6.75 set un or used*).
See also Nos. N617/21 and N633/6.

214 Tribunal Emblem and Falling Aircraft   **215** Ho Chi Minh in 1924

1969 (20 Nov). *International War Crimes Tribunal, Stockholm and Roskilde.* P 11.

N592	**214** 12x. black, red & light bistre-brown	1·80	35

No. N592 exists imperforate.

1970 (3 Feb). *40th Anniv of Vietnamese Workers' Party. T* **215** *and similar horiz designs, showing portraits. Multicoloured.* P 11.

N593	12x. Type **215**	75	60
	a. Horiz pair. Nos. N593/4	1·60	1·30
N594	12x. Ho Chi Minh in 1969	75	60
N595	12x. Le Hong Phong	75	60
	a. Vert strip of 3. Nos. N595/7	2·40	
N596	12x. Tran Phu	75	60
N597	12x. Nguyen Van Cu	75	60
N593/597	*Set of 5*	3·25	2·75

Nos. N593/4 were issued together in horizontal se-tenant pairs within the sheet.
Nos. N595/7 were issued in vertical se-tenant strips of three within the sheet.
Nos. N593/7 exist imperforate.

216 Playtime in Nursery School

217 Lenin and Red Flag

220 Vietcong Flag

221 Water-melon

1970 (8 Mar). *Children's Activities. T* **216** *and similar square designs. Multicoloured.* P 12.

N598	12x. Type **216**	30	35
N599	12x. Playing with toys	30	35
N600	20x. Watering plants	50	35
N601	20x. Pasturing buffalo	50	35
N602	30x. Feeding chickens	60	35
N603	40x. Making music	75	35
N604	50x. Flying model aircraft	1·10	35
N605	60x. Going to school	1·50	35
N598/605 *Set of 8*		5·00	2·50

(Des Huy Khanh)

1970 (22 Apr). *Birth Centenary of Lenin. T* **217** *and similar horiz design.* P 11.

N606	12x. multicoloured	35	35
N607	1d. blackish purple, red and yellow	3·00	35

Design:—1d. Portrait of Lenin.

No. N607 exists imperforate.

(Des Viet Tuan)

1970 (6 June). *1st Anniv of National Liberation Front Provisional Government in South Vietnam.* P 11.

N616	**220**	12x. multicoloured	1·10	35

(Des Toan Hiep)

1970 (15 July). *Fruits (2nd series). T* **221** *and similar vert designs. Multicoloured.* P 12.

N617	12x. Type **221**	35	35
N618	12x. Pumpkin	35	35
N619	20x. Cucumber	35	35
N620	50x. Courgette	1·10	35
N621	1d. Charantais melon	2·20	35
N617/621 *Set of 5*		4·25	1·60

Nos. N617/21 exist imperforate (*Price £9.50 set un or used*).

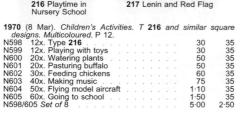

218 *Turbo marmoratus* (Great Green Turban)

219 Ho Chi Minh in 1930

(Des Le Toan)

1970 (26 Apr). *Sea-shells. T* **218** *and similar horiz designs. Multicoloured.* P 12½ × 12.

N608	12x. Type **218**	75	35
N609	12x. *Melo melo* (Indian volute)	75	35
N610	20x. *Cypraea tigris* (Tiger cowrie)	1·10	35
N611	1d. *Charonia tritonis* (Trumpet triton)	2·50	35
N608/611 *Set of 4*		4·50	1·30

Nos. N608/11 exist imperforate (*Price £7.50 set un or used*).

(Des Quoc Thu)

1970 (19 May). *80th Birth Anniv of Pres. Ho Chi Minh. T* **219** *and similar vert portraits.* P 11.

N612	12x. black, red-brown and pale flesh	35	35
N613	12x. agate, blue and pale yellow	35	35
N614	2d. black, ochre and pale yellow	3·00	35
MSN615	Two sheets 134 × 93 mm, each containing Nos. N612/14 (a) Background in pale orange; (b) Background in mauve. Imperf	5·25	5·25

Portraits:—No. N612, Type **219**; N613, In 1945 with microphone: N614, In 1969.

Nos. N612/14 exist imperforate.

222 Power Linesman

223 Peasant Girl with Pigs

(Des Le Toan (Nos. N622, N624), Tran Luong (N623), Quoc Thu (N625). Eng E. Tirdiszek (N622), J. Miller (N623), B. Kowalska (N624), Z. Kowalski (N625). Recess and litho State Ptg Wks, Warsaw)

1970 (25 Aug). *North Vietnamese Industries. T* **222** *and similar designs.* P 11½.

N622	12x. deep blue and light salmon-red	50	35
N623	12x. rose, greenish yellow and blue	50	35
N624	12x. black, red-orange and light blue	50	35
N625	12x. yellow-ochre, brn-pur & grey-grn	50	35
N622/625 *Set of 4*		1·80	1·30

Designs: *Vert*—No. N622, Type **222**; N623, Hands winding thread on bobbin ("Textiles"); N624, Stoker and power station ("Electric Power"). *Horiz*—No. N625, Coal miners and lorry ("More Coal for the Fatherland").

(Des Toan Hiep)

1970 (25 Aug). *North Vietnamese Agriculture.* P 10½.

N626	**223**	12x. multicoloured	1·50	35

No. N626 exists imperforate.

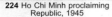

224 Ho Chi Minh proclaiming Republic, 1945

225 Chuoi Tieu

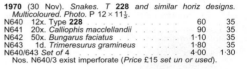

228 Akistrodon ciatus

229 Mother and Child with Flag

1970 (2 Sept)–**71**. *25th Anniv of Democratic Republic of Vietnam. T* **224** *and similar horiz designs.* P 11.

N627	12x. black, cinnamon and scarlet	30	35
N628	12x. blackish brn, cinnamon & turq-grn	30	35
N629	12x. blackish brown, olive-grey and light red-brown (3.71)	30	35
N630	12x. blackish brown, cinnamon and green (3.71)	30	35
N631	20x. blackish brn, Venetian red & bistre	50	35
N632	1d. blackish brown, drab and chestnut (3.71)	1·80	35
N627/632	*Set of 6*	3·25	1·90

Designs:—No. N627, Type **224**; N628, Vo Thi Sau facing firing-squad; N629, Nguyen Van Troi and captors; N630, Phan Dinh Giot attacking pillbox; N631, Nguyen Viet Xuan encouraging troops; N632, Nguyen Van Be attacking tank.
Nos. N627 and N629/32 exist imperforate.

(Des Huy Khanh)

1970 (25 Oct). *Fruits (3rd series). Bananas. T* **225** *and similar vert designs. Multicoloured.* P 12.

N633	12x. Type **225**	35	35
N634	12x. Chuoi Tay	35	35
N635	50x. Chuoi Ngu	90	35
N636	1d. Chuoi Mat	1·30	35
N633/636	*Set of 4*	2·75	1·30

Nos. N633/6 exist imperforate (*Price £8.75 set un or used*).

226 Flags, and Bayonets in Helmet

(Des Huy Khanh)

1970 (25 Oct). *Indo-Chinese People's Summit Conference.* P 11.

N637	**226** 12x. multicoloured	1·50	35

Nos. N637 exists imperforate.

227 Engels and Signature

(Des Viet Tuan)

1970 (28 Nov). *150th Birth Anniv of Friedrich Engels.* P 11.

N638	**227** 12x. black, bistre and red	75	35
N639	1d. black, bistre & light blue-green	1·50	35

No. N639 exists imperforate.

1970 (30 Nov). *Snakes. T* **228** *and similar horiz designs. Multicoloured. Photo.* P 12 × 11½.

N640	12x. Type **228**	60	35
N641	20x. *Calliophis macclellandii*	90	35
N642	50x. *Bungarus faciatus*	1·10	35
N643	1d. *Trimeresurus gramineus*	1·80	35
N640/643	*Set of 4*	4·00	1·30

Nos. N640/3 exist imperforate (*Price £15 set un or used*).

(Des Huy Khanh)

1970 (20 Dec). *10th Anniv of National Front for Liberation of South Vietnam. T* **229** *and similar multicoloured design.* P 11.

N644	6x. Type **229**	75	35
N645	12x. Vietcong flag and torch (*horiz*)	1·50	35

Nos. N644/5 exist imperforate.

1971 (Feb). *Victories of Liberation Army. As T* **178** *but new value.*

N646	**178** 2x. black and orange	1·50	35

F 230 Invalid's Badge

MF 231 Nguyen Van Be attacking Tank

(Des Huy Khanh)

1971 (Feb). *FRANK. For use by disabled veterans. No value indicated.* P 11.

NF647	F **230** (–) Deep purple-brown and rose	1·10	1·10

1971 (15 Feb). *MILITARY FRANK. No value indicated.* P 11.

NMF648	MF **231** (–) Black, red and drab	1·10	1·10

232 Satellite in Earth Orbit

1971 (10 Apr). *1st Anniv of Launching of Chinese Satellite.* P 11.

N649	**232** 12x. multicoloured	75	35
N650	50x. multicoloured	1·10	35

No. N649 exists imperforate.

F **233** Disabled Soldier with Baby

(Des Huy Khanh)

1971 (30 Apr). *FRANK. For use by disabled veterans. No value indicated.* P 11.
NF651 F **233** (–) Sepia, red and yellow . . . 1·10 1·10

234 Ho Chi Minh Medal

236 Karl Marx and Music of the *Internationale*

235 Emperor Quang Trung liberating Thang Long

(Des B. T. Chuoc)

1971 (19 May). *81st Birth Anniv of Ho Chi Minh.* P 11.
N652 **234** 1x. multicoloured 30 20
N653 3x. multicoloured 35 30
N654 10x. multicoloured 50 45
N655 12x. multicoloured 60 50
MSN656 90 × 130 mm. **234** 12x. multicoloured
(53 × 52 mm). Imperf . 4·50 4·50
N652/655 *Set of 4* . . . . 1·60 1·30
Nos. N652/4 exist imperforate.

(Des Le Toan)

1971 (25 May). *200th Anniv of Tay Son Rising.* P 11.
N657 **235** 6x. multicoloured 75 35
N658 12x. multicoloured . . . . 1·50 35
Nos. N657/8 exist imperforate.

(Des Le Toan)

1971 (20 June). *Centenary of Paris Commune.* P 12½.
N659 **236** 12x. black, rosine and pale
salmon 90 35
No. N659 exists imperforate.

237 Hai Thuong Lan Ong   **238** "Kapimala"

(Des Xuoc Thu)

1971 (1 July). *250th Birth Anniv of Hai Thuong Lan Ong (physician).* P 12½.
N660 **237** 12x. black, grey-green and buff 75 35
N661 50x. multicoloured . . . . . . 1·10 35
Nos. N660/1 exist imperforate.

(Des Le Toan. Photo)

1971 (30 July). *Folk Sculptures from Tay Phuong Pagoda.* T **238** and similar vert designs. Multicoloured. P 12.
N662 12x. Type **238** 45 35
N663 12x. "Sangkayasheta" 45 35
N664 12x. "Vasumitri" 45 35
N665 12x. "Dhikaca" 45 35
N666 30x. "Bouddha Nandi" . . . 1·10 35
N667 40x. "Rahulata" . . . . . 1·10 35
N668 50x. "Sangha Nandi" . . . 1·80 35
N669 1d. "Cakyamuni" . . . . 2·40 35
N662/669 *Set of 8* . . . . . . 7·50 2·50
Nos. N662/9 exist imperforate (*Price £12.50 set un or used*).

239 Ho Chi Minh, Banner and Young Workers   **240** "Luna 16" on Moon

(Des H. K. Gam)

1971 (7 Sept). *40th Anniv of Ho Chi Minh Working Youth Union.* P 11.
N670 **239** 12x. multicoloured 90 35
No. N670 exists imperforate.

1971 (17 Sept). *Moon Flight of "Luna 16".* T **240** and similar vert designs. P 11.
N671 12x. multicoloured 75 35
a. Horiz pair. Nos. N671/2 . . . 1·60 80
N672 12x. multicoloured 75 35
N673 1d. brownish blk, greenish bl & turq-
bl . . . . 2·20 35
Designs:—No. N671, "Luna 16" in flight to Moon; N672, Return to Earth.
Nos. N671/2 were issued together in horizontal *se-tenant* pairs within the sheet, each pair forming a composite design.
Nos. N671/3 exist imperforate (*Price £8.75 set un or used*).

241 "Luna 17" landing on Moon

MF 242 Nguyen Viet Xuan and Anti-aircraft Gun

1971 (15 Oct). *Moon Flight of "Luna 17".* **T 241** *and similar designs.* P 11.
N674 12x. orange-red, royal blue & pale
grn 75   35
N675 12x. salmon, pale green & myrtle-
green 75   35
N676   1d. salmon, sepia and pale green . . . 2·20   35
Designs: *Vert*—No. N674, Type **241**. *Horiz*—No. N675, "Luna 17" on Moon; N676, "Lunokhod 1" crossing Moon crevasse.
Nos. N674/6 exist imperforate (*Price* £12 *set un or used*).

1971 (30 Oct)–**72**. *MILITARY FRANK. No value indicated.* P 12½.
NMF677 MF **242** (–) Black, pink and buff . . 75   75
NMF678   (–) Bistre-brn & emer
(8.72) 75   75
No. NMF677 exists imperforate.

243 "White Tiger"

244 Flags and Gate of Heavenly Peace, Peking

1971 (25 Nov). *"The Five Tigers" (folk-art paintings).* **T 243** *and similar vert designs. Multicoloured.* P 12.
N679 12x. Type **243** 35   35
N680 12x. "Yellow Tiger" 35   35
N681 12x. "Red Tiger" 35   35
N682 40x. "Green Tiger" . . . . . 1·50   35
N683 50x. "Grey Tiger" . . . . . 1·80   35
N684   1d. "The Five Tigers" . . . . 2·50   35
MSN685 90 × 120 mm. 1d. As No. N684,
but size 47 × 63 mm. Imperf . 8·75 8·75
N679/684 *Set of 6* . . . . . 6·25 1·90
Nos. N679/84 exist imperforate (*Price* £13.50 *set un or used*).

1971 (1 Dec). *50th Anniv of Chinese Communist Party.* P 11.
N686 **244** 12x. multicoloured 75   35

245 Mongolian Arms

246 "Drum Procession"

(Des Huy Khanh)

1971 (25 Dec). *50th Anniv of Mongolian People's Republic.* P 11.
N687 **245** 12x. multicoloured 75   35
No. N687 exists imperforate.

1972 (30 Jan). *Folk Engravings from Dong Ho.* **T 246** *and similar designs.* P 11.
N688 12x. brownish blk, flesh & pale
cinnamon 75   75
     a. *Tête-bêche* pair. Nos. N688/9 . . 1·60 1·60
N689 12x. brownish blk, flesh & pale
cinnamon 75   75
N690 12x. multicoloured 75   75
     a. Pair. Nos. N690/1 . . . 1·60 1·60
N691 12x. multicoloured 75   75
N692 40x. multicoloured . . . . . 1·80   75
N693 50x. multicoloured . . . . . 2·50   75
N688/693 *Set of 6* . . . . 6·50 4·00
Designs: *Horiz*—No. N688, Type **246**; N689, "Traditional Wrestling"; N692, "Wedding of Mice"; N693, "The Toads' School". *Vert*—No. N690, "Jealous Attack"; N691, "Gathering Coconuts".
Nos. N688/9 and N690/1 respectively were issued together in *se-tenant* pairs within their sheets, Nos. N688/9 being arranged *tête-bêche*.
Nos. N688/93 exist imperforate (*Price* £8.75 *set un or used*).
No. N690 exists with value 30x. instead of 12x., overprinted "HUY BO" ("invalid").

247 Workers

248 Planting Rice

(Des Viet Tuan)

1972 (1 May). *3rd Vietnamese Trade Unions Congress.* **T 247** *and similar horiz design, showing workers facing left.* P 11.
N694   1x. black and light blue 75   35
N695 12x. black and orange 75   35
Nos. 694/5 exist imperforate.

1972 (5 May). *25th Anniv of National Resistance.* **T 248** *and similar vert designs.* P 11.
N696 12x. multicoloured 50   35
N697 12x. multicoloured 50   35
N698 12x. multicoloured 50   35
N699 12x. turq-grn, carm-red & Venetian
red 50   35
N696/699 *Set of 4* . . . . 1·80 1·40
Designs:—No. N696, Type **248**; N697, Munitions worker; N698, Soldier with flame-thrower; N699, Text of Ho Chi Minh's Appeal.
Nos. N696/9 exist imperforate.

249 Ho Chi Minh's Birthplace

250 Captured Pilot and Falling Aircraft

1972 (19 May). *82nd Birth Anniv of Ho Chi Minh. T 249 and similar horiz design.* P 11.

N700	12x. black, drab and yellow-ochre	1·10	35
N701	12x. black, turquoise-green and pink	1·10	35

Designs: No. N700, Type **249**; N701, Ho Chi Minh's house, Hanoi.

No. N700/1 exists imperforate.

1972 (20 June). *3500th U.S. Aircraft Brought Down over North Vietnam.* P 11.

N702	**250**	12x. bluish green and red	1·80	1·10
N703		12x. black and red	1·80	1·10

No. N703 has the inscription amended to record the actual date on which the 3500th aircraft was brought down.

No. N702 exists imperforate.

251 Georgi Dimitrov

252 Falcated Teal (*Anas falcata*)

1972 (15 Aug). *90th Birth Anniv of Georgi Dimitrov (Bulgarian statesman). T 251 and similar vert design.* P 11.

N704	12x. blackish brown & light grey-green	95	35
N705	12x. black and salmon (Dimitrov at Leipzig Court, 1933)	95	35

Nos. N704/5 exist imperforate.

1972 (12 Oct). *Vietnamese Birds. T 252 and similar vert designs. Multicoloured.* P 12.

N706	12x. Type **252**	50	35
N707	12x. Red-wattled lapwing (*Lobivanellus indicus*)	50	35
N708	30x. Cattle egret (*Bubulcus ibis*)	90	35
N709	40x. Water cock (*Gallicrex cinerea*)	1·30	35
N710	50x. Purple swamphen (*Porphyrio porphyrio*)	1·80	35
N711	1d. Greater adjutant stork (*Leptoptilos dubius*)	4·00	35
N706/711	*Set of 6*	8·00	1·90

Nos. N706/11 exist imperforate (*Price* £18 *set un or used*).

253 Anti-aircraft Gunner

254 Umbrella Dance

(Des Tuan Nghiep (N712), Huy Khanh (N713))

1972 (17 Oct). *4000th U.S. Aircraft Brought Down over North Vietnam. T 253 and similar vert design.* P 11.

N712	12x. black, bright purple & cinnamon	2·20	75
N713	12x. black, emerald and brown-red	2·20	75

Design:—No. N713, Anti-aircraft gunner with shell.

No. N712 exists imperforate.

1972 (20 Dec). *Tay Nguyen Folk Dances. T 254 and similar vert designs. Multicoloured.* P 12.

N714	12x. Type **254**	35	30
N715	12x. Drum dance	35	30
N716	12x. Shield dance	35	30
N717	20x. Horse dance	60	35
N718	30x. Ka Dong dance	75	35
N719	40x. Grinding-rice dance	90	35
N720	50x. Gong dance	1·50	35
N721	1d. Cham Rong dance	2·50	35
N714/721	*Set of 8*	6·50	2·40

Nos. N714/21 exist imperforate (*Price* £7.50 *set un or used*).

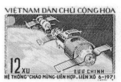

255 "Soyuz 11" Spacecraft and "Salyut" Space Laboratory

1972 (30 Dec). *Space Flight of "Soyuz 11". T 255 and similar horiz design.* P 11.

N722	12x. blue and pale lilac	75	35
N723	1d. blackish brown and flesh	1·80	35

Design:—1d. "Soyuz 11" cosmonauts.

Nos. N722/3 exist imperforate (*Price* £5.25 *pair un or used*).

256 Dhole

(Des Duong Ngoc Canh)

1973 (15 Feb). *Wild Animals (1st series). T 256 and similar horiz designs. Multicoloured.* P 12.

N724	12x. Type **256**	50	35
N725	30x. Leopard	90	35
N726	50x. Leopard cat	1·80	35

N727   1d. European otter   . . . . 2·50   35
N724/727 *Set of 4* . . . . 5·25   1·30
   Nos. N724/7 exist imperforate (*Price* £12.50 *set un or used*).
   See also Nos. N736/9.

257 Copernicus and Globe

260 Striated Canegrass Warblers

F 261 "Returning Home"

1973 (19 Feb). *500th Birth Anniv of Nicholas Copernicus (astronomer). T **257** and similar designs.* P 11.
N728   12x. black, rose-vermilion & orange-
      brn   75   60
   a. Pair. Nos. N728/9   1·60   1·30
N729   12x. black, rose-vermilion & orange-
      brn   75   60
N730   30x. black and orange-brown   1·10   75
   Designs: *Horiz*—No. N728, Type **257**; N729, Copernicus and sun. *Vert*—No. N730, Copernicus and facsimile signature.
   Nos. N728/9 were issued together in *se-tenant* pairs within the sheet.
   Nos. N728/30 exist imperforate.

(Des Tran Nghiep)

1973 (15 July). *Birds Useful to Agriculture. T **260** and similar horiz designs. Multicoloured.* P 12.
N740   12x. Type **260**   35   35
N741   12x. Red-whiskered bulbuls   . .   35   35
N742   20x. Magpie robin   75   35
N743   40x. White-browed fantails   . . 1·10   35
N744   50x. Great tits   . . . . 1·50   35
N745   1d. Japanese white eyes   . . 1·80   35
N740/745 *Set of 6* . . . . 5·25   1·90
   Nos. N740/5 exist imperforate (*Price* £11 *set un or used*).

(Des Viet Tuan)

1973 (27 July). *FRANK. For use by disabled veterans. Type F **261** and similar vert design.* P 11.
NF746   12x. black and rose-red   35   35
NF747   12x. black and turquoise   35   35
   Design: (22 × 33 mm)—No. NF747, Disabled soldier with drill.
   Nos. NF746/7 exist imperforate.

258 "Drummers"

259 Lesser Malay Chevrotain

262 "Ready to Learn"

263 Flags of North Vietnam and North Korea

1973 (12 Apr). *Engravings from Ngoc Lu Bronze Drums. T **258** and similar horiz designs.* P 12½.
N731   12x. pale yellow and slate-green   60   35
N732   12x. pale yellow and slate-green   60   35
N733   12x. pale yellow and slate-green   60   35
N734   12x. pale yellow and grey-green   60   35
N735   12x. pale-yellow and slate-green   60   35
N731/735 *Set of 5* . . . . 2·75   1·60
   Designs:—No. N731, Type **258**; N732, "Pounding Rice"; N733, "Dancers"; N734, "War Canoe"; N735, "Birds and Beasts".
   Nos. N731/3 were issued together in the same sheet, which consists of pairs of vertical rows of each stamp. Thus each stamp may be found *se-tenant* with the next-listed stamp (*Price per se-tenant pair* £1.20 *un*).
   Nos. N731/5 exist imperforate.

1973 (2 Sept). *"Three Readies" Youth Movement. T **262** and similar horiz designs.* P 11.
N748   12x. purple-brown & light yellow-
      green   50   35
N749   12x. slate-violet and pale blue   50   35
N750   12x. deep bluish green and light
      mauve   50   35
   Designs:—No. N748, Type **262**; N749, Soldiers on the march ("Ready to Fight"); N750, Road construction ("Ready to Work").
   Nos. N748/50 exist imperforate.

(Des Viet Tuan)

1973 (9 Sept). *25th Anniv of People's Republic of Korea.* P 11.
N751 **263** 12x. multicoloured   75   35
   No. N751 exists imperforate.

(Des Le Vinh)

1973 (25 May). *Wild Animals (2nd series). T **259** and similar vert designs. Multicoloured.* P 12.
N736   12x. Type **259**   35   35
N737   30x. Mainland serow   75   35
N738   50x. Wild boar   . . . . 1·10   35
N739   1d. Siberian musk deer   . . . . 1·50   35
N736/739 *Set of 4* . . . . 3·50   1·30
   Nos. N736/9 exist imperforate (*Price* £8.75 *set un or used*).

264 Dogfight over Hanoi

MF 265 Soldier with Bayonet advancing

(Des Tuan Luong)

1973 (10 Oct). *Victory over U.S. Air Force. T* **264** *and similar horiz designs.* P 11.

N752	12x. multicoloured	75	45
N753	12x. multicoloured	75	45
N754	12x. multicoloured	75	45
N755	1d. dull rose and black	3·00	45
N752/755 *Set of 4*		4·75	1·60

Designs:—No. N752, Type **264**; N753, Boeing B-52 Stratofortress bomber exploding over Haiphong; N754, Anti-aircraft gun; N755, Aircraft wreckage in China Sea.
No. N755 exists imperforate.

1974 (Jan)–**75**. *MILITARY FRANK. No value indicated.* P 11.

NMF756	MF **265** (–) black, lt yellow & blue	35	35
NMF757	– (–) black, red and light bistre	35	35
NMF758	MF **265** (–) black, flesh & orge-red (19.5.75)	75	75

Design: (40 × 24 mm)—No. NMF757, Soldier with sub-machine gun, and tanks.
No. NMF758 is smaller, 31 × 21 mm, and inscribed "BUU CHINH".
No. NMF758 exists imperforate.

266 Elephant hauling Logs   **267** Dahlia

1974 (10 Feb). *Vietnamese Elephants. T* **266** *and similar square designs. Multicoloured.* P 11.

N758	12x. Type **266**	35	35
N759	12x. War elephant	35	35
N760	40x. Elephant rolling logs	1·10	35
N761	50x. Circus elephant	1·10	35
N762	1d. Elephant carrying war supplies	2·20	35
N758/762 *Set of 5*		4·50	1·60

Nos. N758/62 exist imperforate (*Price £8.75 set un or used*).

1974 (1 May–Sept). *Flowers. T* **267** *and similar vert designs.* P 11.

N763	12x. carmine, lake and blue-green	60	35
N764	12x. carmine, lake and emerald	60	35
N765	12x. orge-yell, bronze-grn & greenish bl	60	35
N766	12x. multicoloured (Sept)	90	35
N767	12x. multicoloured (Sept)	90	35
N763/767 *Set of 5*		3·25	1·90

Flowers:—No. N763, Type **267**; N764, Rose; N765, Chrysanthemum; N766, Bach Mi; N767, Dai Doa.
Nos. N763/7 exist imperforate.

268 Soldier planting Flag   **269** Armed Worker and Peasant

(Des Huy Khanh)

1974 (7 May). *20th Anniv of Victory at Dien Bien Phu. T* **268** *and similar vert design. Multicoloured.* P 11.

N768	12x. Type **268**	90	35
	a. Pair. Nos. N768/9	2·50	80
N769	12x. Victory badge	90	35

Nos. N768/9 were issued together in *se-tenant* pairs within the sheet.
Nos. N768/9 exist imperforate.

1974 (1 June). *"Three Responsibilities" Women's Movement. T* **269** *and similar vert design.* P 11.

N770	**269** 12x. salmon and blue	90	35
	a. Pair. Nos. N770/1	2·00	80
N771	– 12x. salmon and blue	90	35

Design:—No. N771, Woman operating loom.
Nos. N770/1 were issued together in *se-tenant* pairs within the sheet.
Nos. N770/1 exist imperforate.

270 Cuc Nau Chrysanthemum   **271** *Corchorus capsularis*

1974 (20 June). *Vietnamese Chrysanthemums. T* **270** *and similar vert designs. Multicoloured.* P 12.

N772	12x. Type **270**	35	20
N773	12x. Cuc Vang	35	20
N774	20x. Cuc Ngoc Khong Tuoc	45	20
N775	30x. Cuc Trang	60	30
N776	40x. Kim Cuc	75	45
N777	50x. Cuc Hong Mi	90	50
N778	60x. Cuc Gam	1·10	60
N779	1d. Cuc Tim	1·50	1·00
N772/779 *Set of 8*		5·50	3·00

Nos. N772/9 exist imperforate (*Price £7.50 set un or used*).

(Des Viet Tuan)

1974 (15 Aug). *Textile Plants. T* **271** *and similar vert designs.* P 11.

N780	12x. blackish brown, emerald & ol-brn	35	10
N781	12x. sepia, emerald and rose	35	10
N782	30x. sepia, emerald and pale yellow	75	25

Designs:—No. N780, Type **271**; N781, *Cyperus tojet jormis*; N782, *Morus alba*.
Nos. N780/1 exist imperforate.

272 Nike Statue, Warsaw

(Des Tuan Luong)

1974. 30th Anniv of People's Republic of Poland. P 11.

N783	**272**	1x. bright purple, flesh & vermilion	35	30
N784		2x. brown-red, flesh and vermilion	35	30
N785		3x. lake, flesh and red	35	30
N786		12x. carmine, flesh and vermilion	75	60
N783/786 Set of 4			1·60	1·40

Nos. N783/6 exist imperforate.

273 Flags of China and Vietnam

274 Handclasp with Vietnamese and East German Flags

(Des Viet Tuan)

1974 (Oct). 25th Anniv of People's Republic of China. P 11.

N787	**273**	12x. multicoloured	75	35

No. N787 exists imperforate.

(Des Viet Tuan)

1974 (Oct). 25th Anniv of German Democratic Republic. P 11.

N788	**274**	12x. multicoloured	75	35

No. N788 exists imperforate.

275 Woman Bricklayer

276 Pres. Allende and Chilean Flag

(Des Huy Khanh)

1974 (10 Oct). 20th Anniv of Liberation of Hanoi. T **275** and similar vert design. Multicoloured. P 11.

N789		12x. Type **275**	75	35
		a. Pair. Nos. N789/90	1·60	80
N790		12x. Soldier with child	75	35

Nos. N789/90 were issued together in se-tenant pairs within the sheet.

1974 (15 Oct). 1st Death Anniv of Salvador Allende (President of Chile) and Pablo Neruda (Chilean poet). T **276** and similar horiz design. P 11.

N791	**276**	12x. ultramarine and vermilion	75	35
N792	—	12x. ultramarine (Pablo Neruda)	75	35

No. N792 exists imperforate.

277 Rhizostoma

1974 (25 Oct). Marine Life. T **277** and similar horiz designs. Multicoloured. P 12½.

N793		12x. Type **277**	35	10
N794		12x. Loligo	35	10
N795		30x. Haleotis diversicolor	75	20
N796		40x. Pteria martensii	90	20
N797		50x. Sepia officinalis	1·30	45
N798		1d. Palinurus japonicus	1·80	95
N793/798 Set of 6			5·00	1·80

Nos. N793/8 exist imperforate (Price £8.75 un or used).

278 Flags of Algeria and Vietnam

279 Albanian Arms

1974 (Nov). 20th Anniv of Algerian War of Liberation. P 11.

N799	**278**	12x. multicoloured	75	35

No. N799 exists imperforate.

(Des Huy Khanh)

1974 (29 Nov). 30th Anniv of People's Republic of Albania. T **279** and similar vert design. Multicoloured. P 11.

N800		12x. Type **279**	75	35
		a. Pair. Nos. N800/1	1·60	80
N801		12x. Girls from Albania and North Vietnam	75	35

Nos. N800/1 were issued together in se-tenant pairs within the sheet.

Nos. N800/1 exist imperforate.

280 Signing of Paris Agreement

1975 (27 Jan). 2nd Anniv of Paris Agreement on Vietnam. T **280** and similar horiz design. P 11.

N802	**280**	12x. black, yellow-green & emerald	20	10
N803	—	12x. black, light blue and grey-blue	20	10

Design:—No. N803, International Conference in session.

Nos. N802/3 exist imperforate.

281 Tran Phu

282 Costus speciosus

1975 (3 Feb). *45th Anniv of Vietnamese Workers' Party. T* **282** *and similar portraits.* P 11.

N804	12x. blackish brown, vermilion & flesh	20	20
N805	12x. blackish brown, vermilion & flesh	20	20
N806	12x. blackish brown, vermilion & flesh	20	20
N807	12x. blackish brown, vermilion & flesh	20	20
N808	60x. blackish brown, chestnut & flesh	90	45
N804/808	*Set of 5*	1·60	1·10

Portraits: *Horiz*—No. N804, Type **281**; N805, Nguyen Van Cu; N806, L Hong Phong; N807, Ngo Gia Tu. *Vert*—No. 808, Ho Chi Minh in 1924.

Nos. N804/8 exist imperforate.

1975 (8 Feb). *Medicinal Plants. T* **282** *and similar vert designs. Multicoloured.* P 12 × 11½.

N809	12x. Type **282**	35	35
N810	12x. *Rosa laevigata*	35	35
N811	12x. *Curcuma zedoaria*	35	35
N812	30x. *Erythrina indica*	60	35
N813	40x. *Lilium brownii*	75	35
N814	50x. *Hibiscus sagittifolius*	90	35
N815	60x. *Papaver somniferum*	90	35
N816	1d. *Belamcanda chinensis*	2·20	35
N809/816	*Set of 8*	5·75	2·50

Nos. N809/16 exist imperforate (*Price* £9.50 *set un or used*).

283 *Achras sapota*

284 Ho Chi Minh

1975 (25 Apr). *Fruits. T* **283** *and similar vert designs. Multicoloured.* P 12 × 12½.

N817	12x. Type **283**	35	35
N818	12x. *Persica vulgaris*	35	35
N819	20x. *Eugenia jambos*	35	35
N820	30x. *Chrysophyllum cainito*	35	35
N821	40x. *Lucuma mamosa*	75	35
N822	50x. *Prunica granitum*	75	35
N823	60x. *Durio ziberthinus*	1·10	35
N824	1n. *Prunus salicina*	1·80	35
N817/824	*Set of 8*	5·25	2·50

Nos. N817/24 exist imperforate (*Price* £9.50 *set un or used*).

1975 (19 May). *85th Birth Anniv of Ho Chi Minh.* P 11.

N825	**284** 12x. multicoloured	75	35
N826	60x. multicoloured	1·50	75

See also Nos. NLF55/6 of National Front for the Liberation of South Vietnam.

Nos. N825/6 exist imperforate.

285 Ho Chi Minh proclaiming Independence, 1945

286 *Dermochelys coriacea*

(Des Huy Khanh Type **285**, Viet Tuan (others))

1975 (2 Sept). *30th Anniv of Democratic Republic of Vietnam. T* **285** *and similar horiz designs. Multicoloured.* P 11.

N827	12x. Type **285**	50	35
N828	12x. Democratic Republic emblem	50	35
N829	12x. Democratic Republic flag	50	35
MSN830	130 × 100 mm. 20x. Type **285** (45 × 30 mm). Imperf	11·00	11·00

1975 (25 Nov). *Reptiles. T* **286** *and similar vert designs. Multicoloured.* P 12.

N831	12x. Type **286**	35	35
N832	12x. *Physignathus cocincinus*	35	35
N833	20x. *Hydrophis brookii*	60	35
N834	30x. *Platysternum megacephalum*	75	35
N835	40x. *Leiolepis belliana*	90	35
N836	50x. *Python molurus*	1·00	35
N837	60x. *Naja hannah*	1·20	35
N838	1d. *Draco maculatus*	1·50	35
N831/838	*Set of 8*	6·00	2·50

Nos. N831/8 exist imperforate (*Price* £12 *set un or used*).

287 Arms of Hungary

288 *Graphium antiphates* (*Pathysa antiphates*)

(Des Huy Khanh)

1975. *30th Anniv of Liberation of Hungary.* P 11.

N839	**287** 12x. multicoloured	75	35

(Des N. Uyen)

1976 (6 Jan). *Butterflies. T* **288** *and similar horiz designs. Multicoloured.* P 12.

N840	12x. Type **288**	35	35
N841	12x. *Danus genutia* (wrongly inscr "Danais plexippus")	35	35
N842	20x. *Gynautocera papilionaria*	75	35
N843	30x. *Eudocima salaminia* (*Maenas salaminia*)	80	35
N844	40x. *Papilio machaon*	90	35
N845	50x. *Ixias pyrene*	1·00	35
N846	60x. *Episteme vetula* (*Eusemia vetula*)	1·20	35
N847	1d. *Polyura eudamippus* (*Eribaea* sp.)	1·50	35
N840/847	*Set of 8*	6·25	2·50

Nos. N840/7 exist imperforate (*Price* £19 *set un or used*).

289 Hoang Thao Orchid

290 Masked Palm Civet (*Paguma larvata*)

1976 (25 Jan). *Lunar New Year.* P 11.

N848	**289** 6x. lemon, brt green & violet-blue	1·50	75
N849	12x. lemon, bright green & carmine	1·50	75

See also Nos. 126a/b.

1976 (20 Mar). *Wild Animals. T* **290** *and similar vert designs. Multicoloured.* P 12.

N850	12x. Type **290**		50	10
N851	12x. Belly-banded squirrel (*Callosciurus erythraeus*)		50	10
N852	20x. Rhesus macaque (*Macaca mulatta*)		50	10
N853	30x. Chinese porcupine (*Hystrix hodgsoni*)		75	10
N854	40x. Racoon-dog (*Nyctereutes procyonoides*)		75	20
N855	50x. Asiatic black bear (*Selenarctos thibetanus*)		75	30
N856	60x. Leopard (*Panthera pardus*)		90	45
N857	1d. Malayan flying lemur (*Cynocephalus variegatus*)		1·30	60
N850/857 *Set of 8*			5·50	1·80

Nos. N805/7 exist imperforate (*Price* £11 *set un or used*).

291 Voters and Map

292 Map and Saying of Ho Chi Minh

(Des Huy Khanh)

1976 (25 Apr). *First Elections to Unified National Assembly. T* **291** *and similar horiz design.* P 11.

N858	**291**	6x. scarlet and sepia	60	35
N859	–	6x. bright yellow and carmine-red	60	35
N860	**291**	12x. scarlet and new blue	1·50	35

Design: 35 × 24 mm—No. N859, map and ballot box.

Nos. N858 and N860 exist imperforate.

See also Nos. NLF64/6 of National Front for the Liberation of South Vietnam.

1976 (24 June). *First Session of Unified National Assembly. T* **292** *and similar design.* P 12½ (No. N863) or 11 (others).

N861	**292**	6x. brn-purple, rose & pl yellow	35	35
N862		12x. grnish blue, rose & pl yellow	75	35
N863	–	12x. bistre-brown, rosine and yellow	75	35

Design: *Vert* (27 × 42 mm)—No. N863, Vietnam map and design from Ngoc Lu Drum.

No. N862 shows a different text from that on Type **292**.

See also Nos. NLF68/9 of National Front for the Liberation of South Vietnam.

293 Dendrobium devonianum

(Des N. Uyen)

1976 (24 June). *Orchids. T* **293** *and similar vert designs. Multicoloured.* P 12.

N864	12x. Type **293**		45	10
N865	12x. *Habenaria rhodocheila*		45	10
N866	20x. *Dendrobium tortile*		60	10

N867	30x. *Doritis pulcherrima*		60	10
N868	40x. *Dendrobium farmeri*		75	10
N869	50x. *Dendrobium aggregatum*		90	20
N870	60x. *Eria pannea*		1·10	35
N871	1d. *Paphiopedilum concolor*		1·80	50
N864/871 *Set of 8*			6·00	1·40

Nos. N864/71 exist imperforate (*Price* £8 *set un or used*).

F. SOCIALIST REPUBLIC OF VIETNAM

Following elections held in April 1976 a National Assembly representing the whole of Vietnam met in Hanoi on 24 June 1976 and on 2 July proclaimed the reunification of the country as the Socialist Republic of Vietnam, with Hanoi as capital. Saigon was renamed Ho Chi Minh City.

100 xu = 1 dong

PRINTERS, PROCESS AND GUM. All stamps from No. 99 to 1068 were lithographed at the State Printing Works, Hanoi, and issued without gum, *unless otherwise stated.*

18 Red Cross and Vietnam Map on Globe

F **19** Invalid's Badge

1976 (27 July). *30th Anniv of Vietnamese Red Cross.* P 11.

99	**18**	12x. vermilion, ultram & apple-grn	1·80	35

No. 99 exists imperforate.

1976 (27 July). *FRANK. For use by disabled veterans. Type* F **19** *and similar design, dated "27.7.75". No value indicated.* P 11.

F100	(–) carmine-red and blue		75	75
F101	(–) myrtle-green, apple-grn & olive-brn		75	75

Design: *Horiz*—No. F101, Disabled veteran in factory.

20 Emperor Snapper (*Lutjanus sebae*)

MF **21** Soldier and Map of Vietnam

(Des Lê Ton)

1976 (15 Aug). *Marine Fishes. T* **20** *and similar horiz designs. Multicoloured.* P 12.

102	12x. Type **20**		35	35
103	12x. Black-striped dottyback (*Dampieria melanotaenia*)		35	35
104	20x. Tigerperch (*Therapon theraps*)		45	35
105	30x. Two-striped anemonefish (*Amphiprion bifasciatus*)		50	35
106	40x. Stripe-tailed damselfish (*Abudefduf sexfasciatus*)		60	35
107	50x. Pennant coralfish (*Heniochus acuminatus*)		65	35
108	60x. Large-mouthed anemonefish (*Amphiprion macrostoma*)		75	35
109	1d. Sail-finned snapper (*Symphorus spilurus*)		90	35
102/109 *Set of 8*			4·00	2·50

Nos. 102/9 exist imperforate (*Price* £7.50 *set un or used*).

(Des Nguyên Hiêp)

1976 (21 Oct). *MILITARY FRANK. No value indicated.* P 11.
MF110 MF **21** (–) brownish black & verm . . 75 75

22 Party Flag and Map   **23** Workers and Flag

1976 (12 Nov). *4th Congress of Vietnam Workers' Party. (1st issue). Flag in yellow and vermilion, background colours given below.* P 11.
111	**22**	2x. greenish blue	. . . .	45	35
112		3x. reddish purple	. . . .	45	35
113		5x. turquoise-green	. . . . .	45	35
114		10x. bright green	. . . . . .	45	35
115		12x. myrtle-green	. . . . .	45	35
116		20x. emerald	. . . .	45	35
111/116		*Set of 6*	. . . .	2·40	1·90

1976 (10 Dec). *4th Congress of Vietnam Workers' Party (2nd issue). T* **23** *and similar vert design.* P 11.
117	12x. black, bright crimson and lemon	. .	75	35
	a. Pair. Nos. 117/18	. . . . .	1·60	80
118	12x. bright crimson, orange and black	. .	75	35

Design:—No. 118, Industry and agriculture.
Nos. 117/18 were isued together in *se-tenant* pairs within the sheet.
Nos. 117/18 exist imperforate.

24 Ho Chi Minh and Map of Vietnam   **25** Soldiers seizing Buon Me Thuot

(Des Viet Tuan)

1976 (14 Dec). *Unification of Vietnam.* P 11.
119	**24**	6x. multicoloured	. . . .	90	35
120		12x. multicoloured	. . . . . .	90	35

Nos. 119/20 exist imperforate.

1976 (14 Dec). *Liberation of South Vietnam. T* **25** *and similar horiz designs. Multicoloured.* P 11.
121	2x. Type **25**	. . . .	35	35
122	3x. Soldiers landing on Son Tra peninsula, Da Nang	. . . .	35	35
123	6x. Soldiers attacking Presidential Palace, Saigon	. . . .	35	35
124	50x. Type **25**	. . . .	35	35
125	1d. As No. 122	. . . .	75	35
126	2d. As No. 123	. . . .	1·80	35
121/126	*Set of 6*	. . . .	3·50	1·90

1976. *As Nos. N848/9 but inscr "VIET NAM 1976" at foot and background colours changed.* P 11.
126a	**289**	6x. lemon, brt green & pale orange	. . . . .	1·80	1·10
126b		12x. lemon, brt green & blue-green	. . . . .	1·80	1·10

Imperf stamps with the above colours and inscription but with values 5 and 10x. exist; their status is unknown.

26 *Crocothemis servilia* (Ho)   **27** Great Indian Hornbill and Emblem of Protection

(Des Viet Tuan)

1977 (28 Jan). *Dragonflies. T* **26** *and similar horiz designs. Multicoloured.* P 12.
127	12x. Type **26**	. .	35	10
128	12x. *Ictinogomphus clavatus* (Bao)	. .	35	10
129	20x. *Rhinocypha fenestrella* (Canh dom)	. .	35	10
130	30x. *Neurothemis tullia* (Nuong)	. .	35	10
131	40x. *Neurobavis chinensis* (Suoi)	. .	75	10
132	50x. *Neurothemis fulvia* (Canh vang)	. .	90	10
133	60x. *Rhyothemis variegata* (Canh khoang)	. .	90	20
134	1d. *Rhyothemis fuliginosa* (Canh den)	. .	1·20	35
127/134	*Set of 8*	. . .	4·75	1·00

Nos. 127/34 exist imperforate (*Price £11 set un or used*).

1977 (15 Apr). *Rare Birds. T* **27** *and similar vert designs. Multicoloured.* P 12.
135	12x. Type **27**	. .	35	10
136	12x. Tickell's hornbill (*Ptilolaemus tickelli*)	. .	35	10
137	20x. Long-crested hornbill (*Berenicornis comatus*)	. .	45	10
138	30x. Wreathed hornbill (*Aceros undulatus*)	. .	50	10
139	40x. Indian pied hornbill (*Anthracoceros malabaricus*)	. .	75	20
140	50x. Black hornbill (*Anthracoceros malayanus*)	. .	90	20
141	60x. Great Indian hornbill (*Bucerus bicornis*)	. .	1·20	35
142	1d. Rufous-necked hornbill (*Aceros nipalensis*)	. .	1·40	50
135/142	*Set of 8*	. . .	5·25	1·50

Nos. 135/42 exist imperforate (*Price £7.50 set un or used*).

28 Thang Long Tower and Bronze Drum   **29** *Anoplophora bowringii* (Dom Den)

(Des Quóc Thái (12x.))

1977 (25 Apr). *First Anniv of National Assembly General Election. T* **28** *and similar vert designs.* P 11.
143	4x. multicoloured	. . . .	35	35
144	5x. multicoloured	. . . .	45	35
145	12x. bistre, black and light green	. .	75	35
146	50x. multicoloured	. . . . . .	1·50	75
143/146	*Set of 4*	. . . .	2·75	1·60

Designs:—5x. Map of Vietnam and drum; 12x. Lotus flower and drum; 50x. Vietnamese flag and drum.
No. 145 exists imperforate.

1977 (15 June). *Beetles. T* **29** *and similar horiz designs. Multicoloured.* P 12½ × 12.

147	12x. Type **29**	35	10
148	12x. *Anoplophora horsfieldi* (Lang vang)	35	10
149	20x. *Aphrodisium griffithi* (Van gach)	45	10
150	30x. *Alomia meschata* (Nhung xanh)	50	10
151	40x. *Calloplophora tonkinea* (Hoa xanh)	60	15
152	50x. *Thysia wallacei* (Van den)	75	15
153	60x. *Aristobia approximator* (Da bao)	80	20
154	1d. *Batocera rubus* (Chin cham)	1·30	50
147/154	*Set of 8*	4·75	1·20

Nos. 147/54 exist imperforate (*Price* £8.75 *set un or used*).

30 *Thevetia peruviana*   **31** Pink Dahlias (Hoa Dong Tien)

1977 (19 Aug). *Wild Flowers. T* **30** *and similar vert designs. Multicoloured.* P 12 × 12½.

155	12x. Type **30**	20	10
156	12x. *Broussonetia papyrifera*	20	10
157	20x. *Aleurites montana*	35	10
158	30x. *Cerbera manghes*	35	10
159	40x. *Cassia multijuga*	45	15
160	50x. *Cassia nodosa*	60	15
161	60x. *Hibiscus schizopetalus*	75	20
162	1d. *Lagerstroesnia speciosa*	1·10	50
155/162	*Set of 8*	3·50	1·30

Nos. 155/62 exist imperforate (*Price* £7.50 *set un or used*).

1977 (10 Sept). *Cultivated Flowers (1st series). T* **31** *and similar vert design. Multicoloured.* P 11.

163	6x. Type **31**	75	15
164	6x. Orange cactus dahlias (Bong tien kep)	75	15
165	12x. Type **31**	75	15
166	12x. As No. 164	75	15
163/166	*Set of 4*	2·75	55

See also Nos. 192/5.

32 Children drawing Map of Vietnam   **33** Goldfish (Dong Nai Hoa)

1977 (10 Sept). *Unification of Vietnam.* P 11.

167	**32**	4x. multicoloured	35	35
168		5x. multicoloured	35	15
169		10x. multicoloured	75	15
170		12x. multicoloured	75	15
171		30x. multicoloured	1·10	35
167/171		*Set of 5*	3·00	1·60

1977 (20 Oct). *Goldfishes. T* **33** *and similar horiz designs. Multicoloured.* P 12.

172	12x. Type **33**	20	10
173	12x. Hoa nhung	20	10
174	20x. Tau xanh	35	10
175	30x. Mat rong	35	10
176	40x. Cam trang	50	15
177	50x. Ngu sac	60	20
178	60x. Dong nai	75	20
179	1d. Thap cam	1·50	45
172/179	*Set of 8*	4·00	1·30

Nos. 172/9 exist imperforate (*Price* £13 *set un or used*).

34 Ho Chi Minh and Lenin Banner   **35** Southern Grackle (*Gracula religiosa*)

(Des Ngoc Uyên (1d.), Huy Khánh (others))

1977 (7 Nov). 60*th Anniv of Russian Revolution. T* **34** *and similar vert designs. Multicoloured.* P 12.

180	12x. Type **34** (new blue background)	35	35
181	12x. Type **34** (olive-bistre background)	35	35
182	50x. Mother holding child with flag	35	35
183	1d. Workers, banner, Moscow Kremlin and *Aurora* (Russian cruiser)	1·10	35
180/183	*Set of 4*	1·90	1·30

(Des Lê Toan)

1978 (25 Jan). *Songbirds. T* **35** *and similar vert designs. Multicoloured.* P 12.

184	12x. Type **35**	15	10
185	20x. Spotted-necked dove (*Streptopelia chinensis*)	20	10
186	20x. Melodious laughing thrush (*Garrulax canorus*)	20	10
187	30x. Black-headed shrike (*Linius schach*)	35	10
188	40x. Crimson-winged laughing thrush (*Garrulax formosus*)	60	15
189	50x. Black-throated laughing thrush (*Garrulax chinensis*)	75	15
190	60x. Chinese jungle mynah (*Acridotheres cristatellus*)	1·10	20
191	1d. Yersin's laughing thrush (*Garrulax yersini*)	1·80	1·50
184/191	*Set of 8*	4·75	1·30

Nos. 184/91 exist imperforate (*Price* £12 *set un or used*).

(Des Ngoc Uyên (6, 12x.))

1978 (20 Mar). *Cultivated Flowers (2nd series). Vert designs as T* **31**. *Multicoloured.* P 11.

192	5x. Sunflower	90	15
193	6x. Marguerites	90	15
194	10x. As No. 192	90	15
195	12x. As No. 193	90	15
192/195	*Set of 4*	3·25	55

36 Vietnamese Children   **37** Throwing the Discus

(Des Viet Tuan)

1978 (20 Mar). *International Children's Day (June 1977)*. P 11.
196   **36**   12x. multicoloured   1·10   35

1978 (10 Apr). *Athletics. T* **37** *and similar vert designs. Multicoloured.* P 11½ × 11.

197	12x. Type **37**	20	10
198	12x. Long jumping	20	10
199	20x. Hurdling	30	10
200	30x. Throwing the hammer	35	10
201	40x. Putting the shot	45	15
202	50x. Throwing the javelin	50	15
203	60x. Sprinting	75	20
204	1d. High jumping	90	50
197/204	*Set of* 8	3·25	1·30

Nos. 197/204 exist imperforate (*Price* £7.50 *set un or used*).

38 Ho Chi Minh and Workers   **39** Ho Chi Minh

1978 (1 May). *Fourth Vietnamese Trade Union Congress. T* **38** *and similar vert design. Multicoloured.* P 11.

205	10x. Trade Union Emblem	15	10
206	10x. Type **38**	20	10

1978 (15 May). *88th Birth Anniv of President Ho Chi Minh. T* **39** *and similar horiz design. Multicoloured.* P 11.

207	10x. Type **39**	75	35
208	12x. Ho Chi Minh Monument (38 × 22 mm)	75	35

40 Young Pioneers' Cultural House, Hanoi   **41** Sanakavasa

(Des Viet Tuan)

1978 (29 May). *International Children's Day.* P 11.
209   **40**   10x. black, flesh and Venetian red   90   35

1978 (1 July). *Sculptures from Tay Phuong Pagoda. T* **41** *and similar vert designs. Multicoloured.* P 12.

210	12x. Type **41**	35	10
211	12x. Parsva	35	10
212	12x. Punyasas	35	10
213	20x. Kumarata	35	10
214	20x. Nagarjuna	35	10
215	30x. Yayata	35	10
216	40x. Cadiep	75	15
217	50x. Ananda	75	20
218	60x. Buddhamitra	1·10	20
219	1d. Asvaghosa	1·80	45
210/219	*Set of* 10	6·00	1·40

Nos. 210/19 exist imperforate (*Price* £15 *set un or used*).

42 Cuban Flag   **43** Worker, Peasant, Soldier and Intellectual

1978 (20 July). *25th Anniv of Cuban Revolution.* P 11.

220	**42**	6x. orange-vermilion, black & dp vio-bl	90	35
221		12x. orange-vermilion, black & dp vio-bl	95	35

1978 (15 Aug). *33rd Anniv of Proclamation of Vietnam Democratic Republic. T* **43** *and similar vert design.* P 11.

222	6x. vermilion, greenish yellow & magenta	60	35
223	6x. dp turquoise-green, pale green & blue	60	35
224	12x. vermilion, greenish yellow & magenta	90	35
225	12x. rose-carmine and pink	90	75
222/225	*Set of* 4	2·75	1·60

Designs:—Nos. 222 and 224, Type **43**; 223 and 225, Industrial complex and tractor on field.
No. 225 exists imperforate.

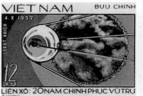

44 "Sputnik"   **45** Printed Circuit

(Des Trân Luong)

1978 (28 Aug). *20 Years of Russian Space Exploration. T* **44** *and similar horiz designs. Multicoloured.* P 12½ × 12.

226	12x. Type **44**	30	10
227	12x. "Venus 1"	30	10
228	30x. Space capsules docking	35	10
229	40x. "Molniya 1" satellite	60	15
230	60x. "Soyuz"	75	20
231	2d. A. Gubarev and G. Grechko	1·50	65
226/231	*Set of* 6	3·50	1·20

Nos. 225/31 exist imperforate (*Price* £7.50 *set un or used*).

1978 (25 Sept). *World Telecommunications Day.* T **45** *and similar vert design.* P 11.
232   12x. orange and sepia 90   35
      a. Horiz pair. Nos. 232/3 . . . . 1·90   80
233   12x. sepia and orange 90   35
Design:—No. 233, International Telecommunications Union emblem.
Nos. 232/3 were issued together in horizontal *se-tenant* pairs within the sheet.
Nos. N232/3 exist imperforate.

46 Telephone Dial and Letter   **47** Chrysanthemum "Cuc Tim"

1978 (25 Sept). *20th Congress of Socialist Countries' Postal Ministers.* P 11.
234   **46**   12x. multicoloured . . . . 1·10   35

(Des Ngoc Uyên)

1978 (1 Oct). *Chrysanthemums.* T **47** *and similar vert designs. Multicoloured.* P 12.
235   12x. Type **47** 35   10
236   12x. "Cuc kim tien" 35   10
237   20x. "Cuc hong" 45   10
238   30x. "Cuc van tho" 50   10
239   40x. "Cuc vang" 60   10
240   50x. "Cuc thuy tim" 65   20
241   60x. "Cuc vang mo" 75   20
242   1d. "Cuc nau do" . . . . 1·30   45
235/242 *Set of 8* . . . . 4·50   1·20
Nos. 235/42 exist imperforate (*Price £8.75 set un or used*).

48 Plesiosaurus   **49** Cuban and Vietnamese Flags and Militiawomen

1979 (1 Jan). *Prehistoric Animals.* T **48** *and similar square designs. Multicoloured.* P 11½.
243   12x. Type **48** 45   10
244   12x. Brontosaurus 45   10
245   20x. Iguanodon 60   10
246   30x. Tyrannosaurus 75   10
247   40x. Stegosaurus 90   10
248   50x. Mozasaurus . . . . 1·10   15
249   60x. Triceratops . . . . 1·30   20
250   1d. Pteranodon . . . . 1·80   35
243/250 *Set of 8* . . . . 6·75   1·10
Nos. 243/50 exist imperforate (*Price £12.50 set un or used*).

(Des Huy Khánh)

1979 (1 Jan). *20th Anniv of Socialist Republic of Cuba.* P 11.
251   **49**   12x. multicoloured . . . . 1·10   35
No. 251 exists imperforate.

50 Battle Plan   **51** Einstein

(Des Huy Khánh)

1979 (1 Feb). *190th Anniv of Quang Trung's Victory over the Thanh.* T **50** *and similar vert design.* P 11.
252   12x. light green, rose-red and new blue 90   35
253   12x. multicoloured 90   35
Design:—No. 253, Quang Trung.

(Des Nguyên Sâm)

1979 (14 Mar). *Birth Centenary of Albert Einstein (physicist).* T **51** *and similar vert design.* P 11.
254   12x. black, ochre and turquoise-blue . . . 75   15
255   60x. multicoloured . . . . 1·50   35
Design:—60x. Equation, sun and planets.

52 Ram   **53** Emblem

(Des Huy Khánh)

1979 (20 Mar). *Domestic Animals.* T **52** *and similar multicoloured designs.* P 12½.
256   10x. Type **52** 30   10
257   12x. Ox 30   10
258   20x. Ewe and lamb 35   10
259   30x. White buffalo (*vert*) 35   10
260   40x. Cow 35   10
261   50x. Goat 75   15
262   60x. Buffalo and calf 75   20
263   1d. Young goat (*vert*) 90   35
256/263 *Set of 8* . . . . 3·75   1·10
Nos. 256/63 exist imperforate (*Price £6 set un or used*).

(Des Huy Khánh)

1979 (1 May). *Five Year Plan.* T **53** *and similar vert designs.* P 11.
264   6x. deep magenta and pale magenta . . 75   35
265   6x. dull yellow-green and buff . . . 75   35
266   6x. emerald and dull claret 75   35
267   6x. orange and turquoise-green . . 75   35
268   6x. dull blue and bistre-yellow . . 75   35
269   12x. carmine and rose-pink 75   35
270   12x. deep brown and rose 75   35
271   12x. deep green and bistre-yellow . . 75   35
272   12x. deep violet-blue and orange-brown 75   35
273   12x. maroon and dull blue 75   35
264/273 *Set of 10* . . . . 6·75   3·00
Designs:—Nos. 264 and 269, Type **53**; 265 and 270, Worker; 266 and 271, Peasant and tractor; 267 and 272, Soldier; 268 and 273, Intellectual.
Nos. 265 and 267 exist imperforate.

54 "Philaserdica '79"
Emblem

55 Ho Chi Minh and
Children

(Des Trinh Kuoć Thu)

1979 (27 May). *"Philaserdica '79" International Stamp Exhibition, Sofia.* P 12.

274	**54**	12x. turq-bl, reddish brn & pale orge	90	35
275		30x. turq-bl, reddish brn & rose-pk	90	35

1979 (1 June). *International Children's Day. T **55** and similar vert designs. Multicoloured.* P 11.

276	12x. Type **55**	35	35
277	20x. Nurse, mother and child	60	35
278	50x. Children with painting materials and model glider	90	35
279	1d. Children of different races	1·50	35
276/279	*Set of 4*	3·00	1·30

56 Silver Pheasant
(*Lophura nycthemera*)

57 *Dendrobium heterocacpum*

(Des Ton and Viet Tuan)

1979 (15 June). *Ornamental Birds. T **56** and similar multicoloured designs.* P 12½ × 12.

280	12x. Siamese fireback pheasant (*Lophura diardi*) (*horiz*)	35	15
281	12x. Temminck's tragopan (*Tragopan temminickii*) (*horiz*)	35	15
282	20x. Common pheasant (*Phasianus colchicus*) (*horiz*)	35	15
283	30x. Edwards's pheasant (*Lophura edwardsi*) (*horiz*)	35	15
284	40x. Type **56**	35	15
285	50x. Germain's peacock-pheasant (*Polyplectron germaini*)	75	20
286	60x. Crested argus (*Rheinartia ocellata*)	75	20
287	1d. Green peafowl (*Pavo muticus*)	1·50	45
280/287	*Set of 8*	4·25	1·40

Nos. 280/7 exist imperforate (*Price £8.75 set un or used*).

(Des Ngoc Uyên)

1979 (10 Aug). *Orchids. T **57** and similar horiz designs. Multicoloured.* P 12.

288	12x. Type **57**	35	15
289	12x. *Cymbidium hybridum*	35	15
290	20x. *Rhynchostylis gigantea*	35	15
291	30x. *Dendrobium mobile*	35	15
292	40x. *Aerides falcatum*	35	15
293	50x. *Paphiopedilum callosum*	75	20
294	60x. *Vanda teres*	75	20
295	1d. *Dendrobium phalaenopsis*	1·50	45
288/295	*Set of 8*	4·25	1·40

Nos. 288/95 exist imperforate (*Price £8.75 set un or used*).

58 Cat (Meo muop)

MF **59** Pilot

(Des Ngoc Uyên)

1979 (10 Nov). *Cats. T **58** and similar multicoloured designs.* P 12.

296	12x. Type **58**	30	35
297	12x. Meo tam the (*horiz*)	30	35
298	20x. Meo khoang	30	35
299	30x. Meo dom van (*horiz*)	30	35
300	40x. Meo muop dom	30	35
301	50x. Meo vang	60	35
302	60x. Meo xiem (*horiz*)	90	35
303	1d. Meo nau am (*horiz*)	1·30	35
296/303	*Set of 8*	3·75	2·50

Nos. 296/303 exist imperforate (*Price £8.75 set un or used*).

(Des Huy Ton (MF304), Trinh Quc Thu (MF305))

1979 (22 Dec). *MILITARY FRANK. 35th Anniv of Vietnam People's Army. No value indicated. Type MF **59** and similar horiz design. Each maroon and rose-pink.* P 11.

MF304	(–) Type MF **59**	1·10	1·10
	a. Vert pair. Nos. MF304/5	2·40	2·40
MF305	(–) Badge of People's Army	1·10	1·10

Nos. MF304/5 were issued together in vertical *se-tenant* pairs within the sheet.

60 Citizens greeting Soldiers

MF **61** Tank Driver
and Tanks

(Des Huy Ton (306), Trinh Quc Thu (307))

1979 (22 Dec). *35th Anniv of Vietnam People's Army. T **60** and similar horiz design. Each sepia and bright green.* P 11.

306	12x. Type **60**	35	35
	a. Vert pair. Nos. 306/7	80	80
307	12x. Soldiers in action	35	35

Nos. 306/7 were issued together in vertical *se-tenant* pairs within the sheet.

(Des Nguyên Hiêp)

1979. *MILITARY FRANK. Type MF **61** and similar vert designs. No value indicated.* P 11.

MF308	(–) black and dull mauve	1·10	35
MF309	(–) bluish violet and turquoise-green	1·10	35
MF310	(–) black and orange-red	1·10	35

Designs:—MF309, Sailor and ship; MF310, Pilot and aircraft.

62 Red and Pink Roses

63 *Nelumbium nuciferum*

(Des Huy Khánh)

1980 (1 Jan). *Roses. T* **62** *and similar vert design. Multicoloured.* P 11.

311	1x. Type **62**	75	35
312	2x. Single pink rose	75	35
313	12x. Type **62**	75	35
314	12x. As No. 312	75	35
311/314 *Set of* 4		2·75	1·30

(Des Toan Thu)

1980 (15 Jan). *Water Flowers. T* **63** *and similar vert designs. Multicoloured.* P 12½.

315	12x. Type **63**	35	10
316	12x. *Nymphala stellata*	35	10
317	20x. *Ipomola reptans*	45	10
318	30x. *Nymphoides indicum*	45	10
319	40x. *Jussiala repens*	45	10
320	50x. *Eichhornia crassipes*	80	20
321	60x. *Monochoria voginalis*	90	20
322	1d. *Nelumbo nucifera*	1·50	30
315/322 *Set of* 8		4·75	1·10

Nos. 315/22 exist imperforate (*Price* £7.50 *set un or used*).

64 Peasants with Banner and Implements as Weapons

1980 (3 Feb). *50th Anniv of Vietnamese Communist Party. T* **64** *and similar horiz designs. Multicoloured.* P 11.

323	12x. Type **64**	35	35
	a. Vert pair. Nos. 323/4	80	80
324	12x. Ho Chi Minh proclaiming independence in 1945	35	35
325	20x. Soldiers with flag at Dien Bien Phu	35	35
	a. Vert pair. Nos. 325/6	80	80
326	20x. Map of Vietnam and soldiers and tanks storming Palace (Unification of Vietnam)	35	35
327	2d. Ho Chi Minh, soldier and workers and industrial and agricultural scene	1·80	35
323/327 *Set of* 5		2·75	1·40

Nos. 323/4 and 325/6 respectively were issued together in vertical *se-tenant* pairs within their sheets.

65 Lenin

66 Running

1980 (22 Apr). *110th Birth Anniv of Lenin.* P 11½ × 12.

328	**65**	6x. flesh and deep green	35	35
329		12x. flesh and dull claret	35	35
330		1d. flesh and blue	1·10	1·10

(Des Trân Luong)

1980 (1 May). *Olympic Games, Moscow. T* **66** *and similar multicoloured designs.* P 12 × 12½.

331	12x. Type **66**	35	10
332	12x. Hurdling	35	10
333	20x. Basketball	35	10
334	30x. Football	35	10
335	40x. Wrestling	35	10
336	50x. Gymnastics (*horiz*)	75	15
337	60x. Swimming (*horiz*)	75	20
338	1d. Sailing (*horiz*)	1·50	35
331/338 *Set of* 8		4·25	1·10

Nos. 331/8 exist imperforate (*Price* £7.50 *set un or used*).

67 Ho Chi Minh in 1924

68 Children dancing round Globe

1980 (19 May). *90th Birth Anniv of Ho Chi Minh. T* **67** *and similar vert design. Multicoloured.* P 11.

339	12x. Type **67**	45	35
340	40x. Ho Chi Minh as President	1·00	75

(Des Viet Tuan)

1980 (15 June). *International Children's Day.* P 11.

341	**68**	5x. multicoloured	75	35

69 Soviet and Vietnamese Cosmonauts

70 Whale Shark (*Rhincodon typus*)

(Des Trân Luong)

1980 (24–31 July). *Soviet–Vietnamese Space Flight.* T **69** *and similar vert designs. Multicoloured.* P 12 × 12½.

342	12x. Type **69**	35	10
343	12x. Launch of rocket	35	10
344	20x. "Soyuz 37"	35	10
345	40x. "Soyuz–Salyut" space complex (31.7)	75	10
346	1d. "Soyuz" re-entering Earth's atmosphere (31.7)	1·50	20
347	2d. Parachute landing (31.7)	3·00	50
342/347	*Set of 6*	5·50	1·00
MS348	111 × 91 mm. 3d. Cosmonauts and "Soyuz–Salyut". P 11 × 12	4·50	4·50

Nos. 342/8 exist imperforate (*Price £8 set un or used*).

(Des Lê Ton (12, 20x.), Ng Hiêp (60x., 1d.), Huy Khánh (others))

1980 (1 Aug). *Fishes.* T **70** *and similar horiz designs. Multicoloured.* P 12½.

349	12x. Type **70**	30	15
350	12x. Tiger shark (*Galeocerdo cuvier*)	30	15
351	20x. Bearded shark (*Orectolobus japonicus*)	35	15
352	30x. Zebra horn shark (*Heterodontus zebra*)	35	15
353	40x. Coachwhip stingray (*Dasyatis uarnak*)	50	20
354	50x. Wide shawfish (*Pristis microdon*)	50	20
355	60x. Scalloped hammerhead (*Sphyrna lewini*)	75	20
356	1d. Tobij-ei eagle ray (*Myliobatis tobijei*)	1·50	35
349/356	*Set of 8*	4·00	1·40

Nos. 349/56 exist imperforate (*Price £7.50 set un or used*).

71 Ho Chi Minh telephoning	**72** Pink Rose (Hong Bach)	**73** Telephone Switchboard Operator

(Des Huy Khánh)

1980 (15 Aug). *Posts and Telecommunications Day.* T **71** *and similar vert designs. Multicoloured.* P 11.

357	12x. Ho Chi Minh reading newspaper *Nhan Dan*	45	35
358	20x. Type **71**	50	35
359	50x. Kim Dong, "the heroic postman", carrying magpie robin in cage	75	35
360	1d. Dish aerial	1·50	35
357/360	*Set of 4*	2·75	1·30

(Des Huy Khánh (Nos. 361/2))

1980 (25 Aug). *Flowers.* T **72** *and similar vert designs.* P 11.

361	12x. rose and dull green	75	35
362	12x. bright crimson and bright green	75	35
363	12x. magenta and yellowish green	75	35

Designs: As T **71**—No. 362, Red roses (Hong nhung). 15 × 20 mm—363, Camellia.

(Des Viet Tuan)

1980 (25 Aug). *National Telecommunications Day.* T **73** *and similar vert design. Multicoloured.* P 11.

364	12x. Type **73**	90	35
365	12x. Diesel train and railway route map	90	35

74 Ho Chi Minh	**75** Vietnamese Arms

1980 (2 Sept). *35th Anniv of Democratic Republic of Vietnam.* T **74** *and similar multicoloured designs.* P 12½.

366	12x. Type **74**	35	35
367	12x. Arms of Vietnam (29 × 40 mm)	35	35
368	40x. Pac Bo cave (29 × 40 mm)	75	35
369	1d. Source of Lenine (40 × 29 mm)	1·80	35
366/369	*Set of 4*	3·00	1·30

1980 (20 Sept). *National Emblems.* T **75** *and similar designs.* P 12.

370	6x. multicoloured	1·10	35
371	12x. greenish yellow, orange-verm & blk	1·10	35
372	12x. black, pale orange and pale yellow	1·10	35

Designs: *Horiz*—371, Vietnamese Flag. *Vert*—372, National Anthem.

76 Nguyên Trai	**77** Ho Chi Minh with Women

1980 (6 Oct). *600th Anniv of Nguyên Trai (national hero).* T **76** *and similar designs.* P 11.

373	12x. bistre-yellow and black	35	35
374	50x. black and dull blue	1·50	35
375	1d. black and orange-brown	2·20	35

Designs: *Horiz*—50x. Three books by Nguyên Trai. *Vert*—1d. Ho Chi Minh reading commemorative stele in Con Son Pagoda.

(Des Huy Khánh)

1980 (20 Oct). *50th Anniv of Vietnamese Women's Union.* T **77** *and similar vert design.* P 11.

376	12x. bright yellow-green, blue and lilac	60	35
377	12x. blue and reddish lilac	60	35

Design:—No. 377, Group of women.

78 *Biguoniaceae venusta*	**79** Blue Discus (*Symphysodon aequifasciata*)

(Des Nguyên Sâm)

1980 (20 Nov). *Creeping Flowers. T 78 and similar vert designs.*
Multicoloured. P 12½.

378	12x.	Type **78**	35	10
379	12x.	Ipomoea pulchella	35	10
380	20x.	Petunia hybrida	45	10
381	30x.	Trapaeolum majus	45	10
382	40x.	Thunbergia grandiflora	50	10
383	50x.	Anlamanda cathartica	75	15
384	60x.	Campsis radicans	80	20
385	1d.	Bougainvillaea spectabilis	1·50	35
378/385	Set of 8		4·50	1·10

Nos. 378/85 exist imperforate (*Price £8 set un or used*).

(Des Ngoc Uyên)

1981 (15 Jan). *Ornamental Fishes. T 79 and similar horiz designs.*
Multicoloured. P 12.

386	12x.	Type **79**	35	35
387	12x.	Siamese fighting fish (Betta splendens)	35	35
388	20x.	Platy (Poecilobrycon eques)	45	35
389	30x.	Guppy (Gyrinocheilus aymonieri)	45	35
390	40x.	Tiger barb (Barbus tetrazona)	50	35
391	50x.	Freshwater angelfish (Pterophyllum eimekei)	75	35
392	60x.	Swordtail (Xiphophorus helleri)	80	35
393	1d.	Pearl gourami (Trichopterus sumatranus)	1·50	35
386/393	Set of 8		4·50	2·50

Nos. 386/93 exist imperforate (*Price £8 set un or used*).

80 Rocket, Flowers and Flag

81 Bear Macaque (*Macaca speciosa*)

(Des Trân Luong)

1981 (23 Feb). *26th U.S.S.R. Communist Party Congress. T 80 and similar vert design. Multicoloured.* P 11.

394	20x.	Type **80**	35	35
395	50x.	Young citizens with flag	1·50	35

1981 (10 Apr). *Animals of Cuc Phuong Forest. T 81 and similar horiz designs. Multicoloured.* P 12½ × 12.

396	12x.	Type **81**	35	15
397	12x.	Crested gibbons (Hylobates concolor)	35	15
398	20x.	Asiatic black bears (Selenarctos thibetanus)	45	15
399	30x.	Dhole (Cuon alpinus)	50	15
400	40x.	Wild boar (Sus scrofa)	75	15
401	50x.	Sambars (Cervus unicolor)	80	20
402	60x.	Leopard (Panthera pardus)	90	20
403	1d.	Tiger (Panthera tigris)	1·50	35
396/403	Set of 8		5·00	1·40

Nos. 396/403 exist imperforate (*Price £8 set un or used*).

82 Green Imperial Pigeon (*Ducula aenea*)

83 Yellow-backed Sunbird (*Aethopyga siparaja*)

(Des Nguyên Hiêp (404, 408), Huy Khánh (406/7), Lê Toãn (others))

1981 (5 June). *Turtle Doves. T 82 and similar multicoloured designs.* P 12.

404	12x.	Type **82**	30	35
405	12x.	Japanese green pigeons (Treron sieboldi) (horiz)	30	35
406	20x.	Red-collared dove (Streptopelia tranquebarica)	30	35
407	30x.	Bar-tailed cuckoo dove (Macropygia unchall)	30	35
408	40x.	Mountain imperial pigeon (Ducula badia)	45	35
409	50x.	Pin-tailed green pigeon (Treron apicauda) (horiz)	50	35
410	60x.	Emerald dove (Chalcophaps indica) (horiz)	80	35
411	1d.	Yellow-vented pin-tailed green pigeon (Seimun treron seimundi) (horiz)	1·50	35
404/411	Set of 8		4·00	2·50

Nos. 404/11 exist imperforate (*Price £7.50 set un or used*).

(Des Huy Khánh)

1981 (5 Aug). *Nectar-sucking Birds. T 83 and similar horiz designs. Multicoloured.* P 12½ × 12.

412	20x.	Type **83**	30	15
413	20x.	Ruby-cheeked sunbird (Anthreptes singalensis)	30	15
414	30x.	Black-throated sunbird (Aethopyga saturata)	30	15
415	40x.	Mrs. Gould's sunbird (Aethopyga gouldiae)	30	15
416	50x.	Macklot's sunbird (Nectarinia chalcostetha)	60	20
417	50x.	Blue-naped sunbird (Nectarinia hypogrammica)	60	20
418	60x.	Van Hasselt's sunbird (Nectarinia sperata)	80	20
419	1d.	Green-tailed sunbird (Aethopyga nipalensis)	1·30	35
412/419	Set of 8		4·00	1·40

Nos. 412/19 exist imperforate (*Price £6.75 set un or used*).

MF **84** Ho Chi Minh in Naval Uniform

85 *Elaeagnus latifolia*

1981 (5 Aug). *MILITARY FRANK. Type MF 84 and similar vert design. No value indicated.* P 11 (MF420) or 12 (MF421).

MF420	(—)	flesh and new blue	75	75
MF421	(—)	multicoloured	75	75

Design: 13 × 17 mm—No. MF421, Factory militiawoman.

(Des Hiệp Sâm)

1981 (12 Oct). *Fruits. T 85 and similar vert designs. Multicoloured.*
P 12.

422	20x.	Type **85**	30	10
423	20x.	*Fortunella japonica*	30	10
424	30x.	*Nephelium lappaceum*	35	10
425	40x.	*Averrhoa bilimbi*	35	10
426	50x.	*Ziziphus mauritiana*	50	15
427	50x.	Strawberries (*Fragaria vesca*)	50	15
428	60x.	*Bouea oppositifolia*	60	20
429	1d.	*Syzygium aqueum*	1·10	35
422/429	*Set of 8*		3·50	1·10

Nos. 422/9 exist imperforate (*Price £6 set un or used*).

86 Girl with Rice Sheaf

87 Ho Chi Minh planting Tree

(Des Ngoc Uyên)

1981 (16 Oct). *World Food Day. T 86 and similar horiz design.*
P 11.

430	**86**	30x. apple green	45	35
431		50x. emerald	60	35
432	—	2d. dull orange	1·90	35

Design: *Horiz*—2d. Food and Agriculture Organization emblem and rice.

(Des Huy Khánh)

1981 (15 Nov). *Tree Planting Festival. T 87 and similar vert design.* P 11.

433	30x. dull orange and new blue		65	20
434	30x. brown-rose and new blue		65	20

Design:—No. 434, Family planting tree.

88 European Bison (*Bison bonasus*)

89 Congress Emblem

(Des Nguyên Hiệp)

1981 (1 Dec). *Animals. T 88 and similar horiz designs.*
Multicoloured. P 12½ × 12.

435	30x.	Type **88**	35	10
436	30x.	Orang-utan (*Pongo pymaeus*)	35	10
437	40x.	Hippopotamus (*Hippopotamus amphibius*)	45	15
438	40x.	Red kangaroo (*Macropus rubra*)	45	15
439	50x.	Giraffe (*Giraffa camelopardis*)	60	15
440	50x.	Javan rhinoceros (*Rhinoceros sondaicus*)	60	15
441	60x.	Common zebra (*Equus burchelli*)	75	20
442	1d.	Lion (*Panthera leo*)	90	45
435/442	*Set of 8*		4·00	1·30

Nos. 435/42 exist imperforate (*Price £6.75 set un or used*).

(Des Trinh Quốc Thu)

1982 (10 Feb). *Tenth World Trade Unions Congress, Havana, Cuba.* P 11.

443	**89**	50x. multicoloured	75	35
444		5d. multicoloured	3·00	35

90 Ho Chi Minh and Party Flag

1982 (15 Feb). *Fifth Vietnamese Communist Party Congress (1st issue). T 90 and similar horiz design. Multicoloured.* P 11.

445	30x.	Type **90**	75	35
446	30x.	Hammer, sickle and rose	75	35

See also Nos. 455/6.

91 *Thyreus decorus* (Ong Van Xanh)

1982 (20 Feb). *Bees and Wasps. T 91 and similar horiz designs.*
Multicoloured. P 12.

447	20x.	Type **91**	35	10
448	20x.	*Vespa affinis* (Ong bò vẽ)	35	10
449	30x.	*Eumenes esuriens* (Tò vò nâu)	35	10
450	40x.	*Polistes* sp. (Ong vàng)	45	15
451	50x.	*Sphex* sp. (Tò vò xanh)	60	20
452	50x.	*Chlorion lobatum* (Ong dã nâu)	60	20
453	60x.	*Xylocopa* sp. (Ong bầu)	80	20
454	1d.	*Apis mellifera* (Ong mật)	90	45
447/454	*Set of 8*		4·00	1·40

Nos. 447/54 exist imperforate (*Price £6.75 set un or used*).

92 Electricity Worker and Pylon

1982 (27 Mar). *Fifth Vietnamese Communist Party Congress (2nd issue). T 92 and similar horiz design.* P 11.

455	30x.	yellow-ochre, black and cerise	75	35
456	50x.	multicoloured	1·10	35

Design:—50x. Women harvesting rice.

93 Football

94 Militiawoman

(Des Trân Luong)

1982 (15 Apr). *Football Training Movement. T* **93** *and similar horiz designs showing football scenes.* P 12.

457	30x. multicoloured (Type **93**)		30	10
458	30x. multicoloured (Two players)		30	10
459	40x. multicoloured		35	10
460	40x. multicoloured (*diag striped background*)		35	15
461	50x. multicoloured (*vert striped background*)		50	15
462	50x. multicoloured (*horiz striped background*)		50	15
463	60x. multicoloured		60	20
464	1d. multicoloured		1·10	35
457/464 *Set of 8*			3·50	1·20

Nos. 457/64 exist imperforate (*Price £6 set un or used*).

1982 (22 Apr). P 11.

465	**94**	30x. multicoloured	1·10	75

1982 (22 Apr). *MILITARY FRANK. Vert designs as T* **94** *but smaller (13 × 16 mm). Multicoloured.* P 11.

MF466	(–) Soldier and militiawoman		75	75
MF467	(–) As Type **94**		75	75

95 Bulgarian Arms

96 Map of Vietnam and Red Cross

(Des Trịnh Quốc Thu)

1982 (7 May). *1300th Anniv of Bulgarian State.* P 11.

468	**95**	30x. salmon-pink and crimson	45	35
469		50x. yellow-ochre and crimson	90	35
470		2d. orange and crimson	2·40	35

(Des Trịnh Quốc Thu)

1982 (15 May). *35th Anniv of Vietnamese Red Cross. T* **96** *and similar vert design.* P 11.

471	30x. rose-red, pale blue and black		50	35
472	1d. rose-red, pale green and black		1·80	35

Design:—1d. Red cross.

97 Georgi Dimitrov

98 Rejoicing Women

(Des Trịnh Quốc Thu)

1982 (16 May). *Birth Centenary of Georgi Dimitrov (Bulgarian statesman).* P 11.

473	**97**	30x. salmon and black	35	35
474		3d. yellow-brown and black	3·25	35

(Des Huy Khánh)

1982 (19 May). *Fifth National Women's Congress. T* **98** *and similar vert design. Multicoloured.* P 12.

475	12x. Type **98**		75	35
476	12x. Congress emblem and three women		75	35

99 Common Kestrel (*Falco tinnunculus*)

100 Red Dahlia

(Des Huy Khánh)

1982 (10 June). *Birds of Prey. T* **99** *and similar multicoloured designs.* P 12.

477	30x. Type **99**		35	10
478	30x. Pied falconet (*Microhierax melanoleucos*)		35	10
479	40x. Black baza (*Aviceda leuphotes*)		45	10
480	50x. Black kite (*Milvus korscun*)		60	15
481	50x. Lesser fishing eagle (*Icthyophaga nana*)		60	15
482	60x. White-rumped pygmy falcon (*Neohierax harmandi*) (*horiz*)		75	15
483	1d. Black-shouldered kite (*Elanus caeruleus*) (*horiz*)		1·50	50
484	1d. Short-toed eagle (*Circaetus gallicus*)		1·50	50
477/484 *Set of 8*			5·50	1·60

Nos. 477/84 exist imperforate (*Price £6 set un or used*).

(Des Hiệp Sâm)

1982 (15 July). *Dahlias. T* **100** *and similar vert designs. Multicoloured.* P 12 × 12½.

485	30x. Type **100**		35	10
486	30x. Orange dahlia		35	10
487	40x. Rose dahlia		45	10
488	50x. Red decorative dahlia		60	15
489	50x. Yellow dahlia		60	15
490	60x. Red single dahlia		75	20
491	1d. White dahlia		1·10	50
492	1d. Pink dahlia		1·10	50
485/492 *Set of 8*			4·75	1·60

Nos. 485/92 exist imperforate (*Price £7.75 set un or used*).

101 Dribble

102 Cuban Flag

(Des Nguyên Hiệp)

1982 (25 July). *World Cup Football Championship, Spain. T* **101** *and similar vert designs. Multicoloured.* P 12 × 12½.

493	50x. Type **101**		60	35
494	50x. Tackle		60	35

495	50x. Passing ball	60	35
496	1d. Heading ball	90	35
497	1d. Goalkeeper saving ball	90	35
498	2d. Shooting	2·40	35
493/498	*Set of 6*	5·50	1·90

Nos. 493/8 exist imperforate (*Price* £8.75 *set un or used*).

1982 (15 Aug). *20th Anniv of Cuban Victory at Girón.* P 11.

| 499 | **102** | 30x. multicoloured | 1·10 | 35 |

103 Ho Chi Minh and Children planting Tree

104 Rabindranath Tagore

(Des Trinh Quôc Thu (500), Nguyên Sâm (501))

1982 (15 Aug). *World Environment Day.* T **103** *and similar horiz design.* P 11.

| 500 | 30x. emerald and black | 75 | 35 |
| 501 | 30x. emerald and black | 75 | 35 |

Design:—No. 501, U.N. Environment emblem and plants.

1982 (20 Sept). *120th Birth Anniv of Rabindranath Tagore (Indian poet).* P 11.

| 502 | **104** | 30x. salmon, brown and black | 1·10 | 35 |

105 *Sycanus falleni*

106 Lenin and *Aurora* (Russian cruiser)

(Des Nguyên Hiêp (503/6), Viet Tuan (507/10))

1982 (25 Sept). *Harmful Insects.* T **105** *and similar vert designs. Multicoloured.* P 12 × 12½.

503	30x. Type **105**	30	10
504	30x. *Catacanthus incarnatus*	30	10
505	40x. *Nezara viridula*	30	10
506	50x. *Helcomeria spinosa*	45	15
507	50x. *Lohita grandis*	45	15
508	60x. *Chrysocoris stollii*	50	20
509	1d. *Tiarodes ostentans*	1·10	50
510	1d. *Pterygamia srayi*	1·10	50
503/510	*Set of 8*	4·10	1·60

Nos. 503/10 exist imperforate (*Price* £6.75 *set un or used*).

(Des Nguyên Sâm)

1982 (7 Nov). *65th Anniv of Russian Revolution.* T **106** *and similar vert design.* P 11.

| 511 | 30x. vermilion and black | 75 | 35 |
| 512 | 30x. vermilion and black | 75 | 35 |

Design:—No. 512, Man and woman, Lenin and space station.

MF 107 Disabled Soldier **108** Swimming

1982 (9 Nov). *MILITARY FRANK. 35th Anniv of Disabled Soldiers' Day. No value expressed.* P 11.

| MF513 | MF **107** | (–) pale magenta and blue-green | 50 | 35 |

(Des Nguyên Hiêp)

1982 (19 Nov). *Ninth South-East Asian Games, New Delhi.* T **108** *and similar horiz designs.* P 11.

514	30x. light blue and brown-lilac	75	35
515	30x. new blue and bright mauve	75	35
516	1d. orange and blue	1·10	35
517	2d. bright green and purple-brown	1·50	35
514/517	*Set of 4*	3·75	1·30

Designs:—30x. (No. 515), Table tennis; 1d. Wrestling; 2d. Rifle shooting.

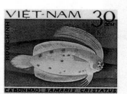
109 Gray's crested flounder (*Samaris cristatus*)

110 Foundry and Textile Workers

(Des Ngoc Uyên)

1982 (15 Dec). *Fishes. Soles.* T **109** *and similar horiz designs. Multicoloured.* P 12.

518	30x. Type **109**	35	10
519	30x. Chinese flounder (*Tephrinectes sinensis*)	35	10
520	40x. Queensland halibut (*Psettodes erumei*)	45	10
521	40x. Zebra sole (*Zebrias zebra*)	45	10
522	50x. Peacock sole (*Pardachirus pavoninus*)	60	15
523	50x. Spotted tonguesole (*Cynoglossus puncticeps*)	60	15
524	60x. Oriental sole (*Brachirus orientalis*)	75	30
525	1d. Iijima lefteye flounder (*Psettina iijimae*)	90	45
518/525	*Set of 8*	4·00	1·30

Nos. 518/25 exist imperforate (*Price* £6.75 *un or used*).

(Des Ngoc Uyên)

1982 (25 Dec). *"All for the Socialist Fatherland, All for Happiness of the People".* T **110** *and similar vert designs.* P 11.

526	30x. light dull blue and steel blue	60	35
527	30x. chestnut and bistre-yellow	60	35
528	1d. yellow-brown and emerald	1·10	35
529	2d. flesh and deep reddish purple	2·20	35
526/529	*Set of 4*	4·00	1·30

Designs:—30x. Women holding sheaf of wheat and basket of grain; 1d. Soldiers; 2d. Nurse with children holding books.

111 Lenin on Map   **112** Sampan

1982 (30 Dec). *60th Anniv of U.S.S.R.* P 11.
530 **111** 30x. multicoloured . . . . 1·80 35

IMPERFORATE STAMPS. From No. 531 most Havana printed
stamps exist imperforate (*Price per set, un or used: approx.*
1½ × *quoted mint set price*).

(Litho National Ptg Wks, Havana)

1983 (10 Jan). *Boats. T* **112** *and similar multicoloured designs.*
P 12½ × 13 (10d.) or 13 × 12½ (others).
531 30x. Type **112** 35 10
532 50x. Junk with striped sails 45 10
533 1d. Houseboats 50 15
534 3d. Junk 90 20
535 5d. Sampan with patched sails . . . 1·50 35
536 10d. Sampan (*horiz*) . . . . 2·20 95
531/536 *Set of 6* . . . . 5·25 1·60

113 Type 30 Steam Locomotive

(Des Nguyên Hiêp and Hiêp Sâm. Litho National Ptg Wks,
Havana)

1983 (20 Feb). *Railway Steam Locomotives. T* **113** *and similar
horiz designs.* Multicoloured. P 13.
537 30x. Type **113** 20 10
538 50x. Type 000 . . . . 35 10
539 1d. Type 601 . . . . 45 15
540 2d. Type 000 . . . . 75 30
541 3d. Type 500 . . . . 1·10 30
542 5d. Type 000 . . . . 1·50 50
543 8d. Type 300 . . . . 1·90 80
537/543 *Set of 7* . . . . 5·75 2·00

114 Montgolfier Balloon, 1783   **115** Flags and Dove

(Litho National Ptg Wks, Havana)

1983 (7 Mar). *Bicentenary of Manned Flight. T* **114** *and similar
vert designs.* Multicoloured. P 12½ × 13.
544 30x. Type **114** 20 10
545 50x. Charles's hydrogen balloon, 1783 . . 35 10
546 1d. Parseval Sigsfeld kite-type
observation balloon, 1898 . . . . 45 15
547 2d. Eugène Godard's balloon *L'Aigle*,
1864 . . . . 90 20
548 3d. Blanchard and Jeffries' balloon,
1785 . . . . 1·10 20
549 5d. Nadar's balloon *Le Géant*, 1863 . . 1·50 35
550 8d. Balloon . . . . 2·20 60
544/550 *Set of 7* . . . . 7·00 1·90
MS551 70 × 80 mm. 10d. Montgolfier balloon
(*different*) (31 × 39 *mm*). P 13 . . . . . 6·00 1·50

(Des Trân Luong)

1983 (25 Mar). *Laos–Kampuchea–Vietnam Summit Conference.*
P 11.
552 **115** 50x. dull scarlet, pale yellow &
ultram 35 35
553 5d. dull scarlet, ultram & orge-
yell . . . . 2·20 35

116 Robert Koch   **117** *Teratolepis fasciata*

1983 (25 Mar). *Centenary of Discovery of Tubercle Bacillus.* P 11.
554 **116** 5d. black, pale greenish blue and
red . . . . 2·20 75

(Des Hiêp Sâm. Litho National Ptg Wks, Havana)

1983 (5 Apr). *Reptiles. T* **117** *and similar horiz designs.*
Multicoloured. P 12½ × 12.
555 30x. Type **117** 20 35
556 30x. Jackson's chameleon (*Chamaeleo
jacksoni*) 20 35
557 50x. Spiny-tailed agamid (*Uromastyx
acanthinurus*) 35 35
558 80x. *Heloderma suspectum* 45 35
559 1d. *Chamaeleo meileri* 50 35
560 2d. *Amphibolurus barbatus* . . . . 1·10 35
561 5d. *Chlamydosaurus kingi* . . . . . 1·50 35
562 10d. *Phrynosoma coronatum* . . . . 2·50 35
555/562 *Set of 8* . . . . 6·00 2·50

118 A. Gubarev and V. Remek   **119** "Madonna of the
Chair"

(Des Trân Luong. Litho National Ptg Wks, Havana)

1983 (12 Apr). *Cosmonauts. T* **118** *and similar horiz designs.*
Multicoloured. P 12½.
563 30x. Type **118** 35 10
564 50x. P. Klimuk and Miroslaw
Hermaszewski 35 10
565 50x. V. Bykovsky and Sigmund Jahn . . 35 10

566	1d. Nikolai Rukavishnikov and Georgi Ivanov	35	10
567	1d. Bertalan Farkas and V. Kubasov	35	10
568	2d. Gorbatko and Pham Tuân	75	20
569	2d. Arnaldo Tamayo Mendez and I. Romanenko	75	20
570	5d. V. Dzhanibekov and Gurragcha	1·50	35
571	8d. L. Popov and D. Prunariu	1·80	60
563/571	Set of 9	6·00	1·60

MS572 80 × 80 mm. 10d. Yuri Gagarin (first man in space) (36 × 28 mm). P 13 ... 3·75 1·50

The date of issue given is that quoted officially. Postmarked examples dated 5 April exist.

(Litho National Ptg Wks, Havana)

1983 (30 Apr). *500th Birth Anniv of Raphael (artist). T **119** and similar vert designs. Multicoloured.* P 12½.

573	30x. Type **119**	20	10
574	50x. "Madonna of the Grand Duke"	35	10
575	1d. "Sistine Madonna"	50	10
576	2d. "The Marriage of Mary"	90	20
577	3d. "The Beautiful Gardener"	1·10	30
578	5d. "Woman with Veil"	1·50	45
579	8d. "Self-portrait"	1·80	65
573/579	Set of 7	5·75	1·70

MS580 93 × 71 mm. 10d. Close-up of "Self-portrait". P 13 ... 4·75 1·50

MF **120** Militia

121 Burmese King and Rook

1983 (30 Apr). *MILITARY FRANK. No value indicated.* P 11.
MF581 MF **120** (–) multicoloured ... 75 75

(Litho National Ptg Wks, Havana)

1983 (9 May). *Chess Pieces. T **121** and similar vert designs. Multicoloured.* P 13.

582	30x. Type **121**	20	10
583	50x. 18th-century Delhi king (elephant)	30	10
584	1d. Lewis knight and bishop	45	10
585	2d. 8th–9th-century Arabian king (elephant)	75	20
586	3d. 12th-century European knight	1·10	30
587	5d. 16th-century Russian rook (sailing boat)	1·50	45
588	8d. European Chinese-puzzle bishop and rook (fool and elephant)	1·80	65
582/588	Set of 7	5·50	1·70

MS589 77 × 79 mm. 10d. Abstract king and queen (28 × 36 mm) ... 6·00 1·50

122 Coach and Horses

123 Long Jumping

(Litho National Ptg Wks, Havana)

1983 (21 May). *"Tembal '83" International Stamp Exhibition, Basel. Sheet 90 × 70 mm.* P 13.
MS590 **122** 10d. multicoloured ... 4·50 1·50

(Litho National Ptg Wks, Havana)

1983 (13 June). *Olympic Games, Los Angeles (1984). T **123** and similar multicoloured designs.* P 13.

591	30x. Type **123**	35	10
592	50x. Running	35	15
593	1d. Javelin throwing	35	10
594	2d. High jumping (*horiz*)	75	20
595	3d. Hurdling (*horiz*)	1·10	30
596	5d. Putting the shot	1·50	45
597	8d. Pole vaulting	1·80	65
591/597	Set of 7	5·50	1·75

MS598 82 × 71 mm. 10d. Throwing the discus (31 × 39 mm). P 13 ... 5·25 1·50

124 Toco Toucan (*Rhamphastos toco*)

125 Terias hecabe

(Litho National Ptg Wks, Havana)

1983 (20 July). *"Brasiliana '83" International Stamp Exhibition, Rio de Janeiro. Sheet 69 × 95 mm.* P 13.
MS599 **124** 10d. multicoloured ... 4·50 1·50

(Des Trinh Quc Thu. Litho National Ptg Wks, Havana)

1983 (30 July). *Butterflies. T **125** and similar vert designs. Multicoloured.* P 12.

600	30x. Type **125**	35	35
601	30x. Lamproptera meges (*Leptocircus meges*)	35	35
602	40x. Lyssa patroclus (*Nyctalemon patroclus*)	45	35
603	40x. Graphium agamemnon (*Zetides agamemnon*)	45	35
604	50x. Precis almana	75	35
605	50x. Papilio nephelus	75	35
606	60x. Thauria aliris (*Thauria lathyi*)	90	35
607	1d. Kallima inachus	1·30	35
600/607	Set of 8	4·75	2·50

Nos. 608/15 are vacant.

127 Steam Car

128 Karl Marx

(Des Ngoc Uyên. Litho National Ptg Wks, Havana)

1983 (4 Aug). *"Bangkok 1983" International Stamp Exhibition. Sheet 102 × 67 mm.* P 13.
MS616 **127** 10d. multicoloured ... 7·50 1·50

(Des T. Lieu)

1983 (4 Aug). *Death Centenary of Karl Marx.* P 11.
617 **128** 50x. black and dull vermilion . . . 75 35
618 10d. black and bright claret . . . 3·00 75

129 Postman

(Litho National Ptg Wks, Havana)

1983 (30 Sept). *World Communications Year.* T **129** and similar horiz designs. Multicoloured. P 12½.
619 50x. Type **129** 20 20
620 2d. Mail sorting office 75 35
621 8d. Telephonists . . . . 1·60 35
622 10d. Wireless operator and dish aerial . 2·20 50
619/622 Set of 4 . . . . 4·25 1·30
MS623 77 × 64 mm. 10d. Telephone, air mail envelope, dish aerial, truck and boat. P 13 3·00 1·50

130 Running, Stadium and Sports Pictograms   **131** *Pleurotus ostreatus*

(Des Viet Tuan)

1983 (10 Oct). *National Youth Sports Festival.* P 11.
624 **130** 30x. chalky blue and turquoise-
blue 35 35
625 1d. deep brown and dull orange 1·50 35

(Litho National Ptg Wks, Havana)

1983 (10 Oct). *Fungi.* T **131** and similar vert designs. Multicoloured. P 12 × 12½.
626 50x. Type **131** 35 35
627 50x. *Coprinus atramentarius* 35 35
628 50x. *Flammulina velutipes* 35 35
629 50x. *Cantharellus cibarius* 35 35
630 1d. *Volvariella volvacea* 75 35
631 2d. *Agaricus silvaticus* . . . . . . 1·10 35
632 5d. *Morchella esculenta* . . . . . 2·20 35
633 10d. *Amanita caesarea* . . . . . . 3·75 35
626/633 Set of 8 . . . . 8·25 2·50

132 Child with Fish

(Litho National Ptg Wks, Havana)

1983 (16 Oct). *World Food Day.* T **132** and similar horiz design. Multicoloured. P 12½.
634 50x. Type **132** 35 35
635 4d. Family . . . . 1·50 35

133 Envelope with I.T.U. Emblem

(Des Trinh Quôc Thu)

1983 (1 Nov). *World Telecommunications Year.* T **133** and similar horiz design. P 11.
636 50x.+10x. dp new blue, lt green &
verm . . . . 1·10 35
637 50x.+10x. lake, buff and reddish brown 1·10 35
Design:—No. 637, W.C.Y. emblem and dish aerial.

134 Building Dam

(Des Ngoc Uyên)

1983 (7 Nov). *Fifth Anniv of Vietnam–U.S.S.R. Co-operation Treaty.* P 11.
638 **134** 20x. deep grey-green and greenish
yellow . . . . 1·50 1·50
639 50x. chestnut and reddish brown . . 2·20 1·50
640 4d. bluish grey and grey-black . . 7·50 1·50
641 20d. carmine-rose and agate . . . 26·00 1·50
638/641 Set of 4 . . . . 33·00 5·50
Designs:—20x. Building Cultural Palace; 50x. Building road-rail bridge; 20d. Type **134**.

135 Girl with Flowers   **136** Grey Herons (*Ardea cinerea*)

(Des T. Lieu (50x.))

1983 (16 Nov). *Fifth Trade Unions Congress.* T **135** and similar design. P 11.
642 50x. new blue, light orange and black . . 35 35
643 2d. black, greenish blue and
cinnamon 75 35
644 30d. black, new blue and carmine-rose 4·50 75
Design:—2, 30d. Worker and industrial complex.

(Litho National Ptg Wks, Havana)

1983 (20 Nov). *Birds.* T **136** and similar vert designs. Multicoloured. P 12 × 12½.
645 50x. Type **136** 35 35
646 50x. Painted storks (*Ibis
leucocephalus*) 35 35
647 50x. Black storks (*Ciconia nigra*) . . . 35 35
648 50x. Purple herons (*Ardea purpurea*) . . 35 35

649	1d.	Common cranes (*Grus grus*) (inscr "Grus grue")	50	35
650	2d.	Black-faced spoonbills (*Platalea minor*)	75	35
651	5d.	Black-crowned night herons (*Nycticorax nycticorax*)	1·80	35
652	10d.	Asian open-bill storks (*Anastomus oscitans*)	2·50	35
645/652 *Set of 8*			6·25	2·50

137 Conference Emblem and Hands

138 Biathlon

(Des Nguyên Hiêp)

1983 (19 Dec)–**84**. *World Peace Conference, Prague. T* **137** *and similar vert design.* P 11.

653	–	50x. pale blue, Venetian red and greenish yellow	15	15
654	**137**	3d. yellowish green, Venetian red and bistre-yellow (25.6.84)	1·10	35
655		5d. slate-lilac, Venetian red and bistre-yellow (25.6.84)	2·20	60
656		20d. turq-bl, Venetian red & bistre-yell	4·50	75
653/656 *Set of 4*			7·25	1·60

Design:—50x. Conference Emblem and women.

(Litho National Ptg Wks, Havana)

1984 (30 Jan). *Winter Olympic Games, Sarajevo. T* **138** *and similar multicoloured designs.* P 12½.

657	50x.	Type **138**	35	10
658	50x.	Cross-country skiing	35	10
659	1d.	Speed skating	45	10
660	2d.	Bobsleighing	75	20
661	3d.	Ice hockey (*horiz*)	1·10	30
662	5d.	Ski jumping (*horiz*)	1·50	45
663	6d.	Slalom (*horiz*)	1·80	65
657/663 *Set of 7*			5·75	1·75
MS664 72 × 88 mm. 20d. Ice skating (39 × 31 mm). P 13			3·75	1·50

139 Marbled Cat (*Felix marmorata*)

140 Orchid Tree (*Bauhinia variegata*)

(Litho National Ptg Wks, Havana)

1984 (26 Feb). *Protected Animals. T* **139** *and similar horiz designs. Multicoloured.* P 12½.

665	50x.	Type **139**	20	10
666	50x.	Leopard (*Panthera pardus*)	20	10
667	50x.	Tiger (*Panthera tigris*)	20	10
668	1d.	Common gibbon (*Hylobates lar*)	45	15
669	1d.	Slow loris (*Nycticebus coucang*)	45	15
670	2d.	Indian elephant (*Elephas indidus*)	1·30	20
671	2d.	Gaur (*Bos gaurus*)	1·30	20
665/671 *Set of 7*			3·75	90

(Des Nguyên Thi Sâm. Litho National Ptg Wks, Havana)

1984 (15 Mar). *Flowers. T* **140** *and similar vert designs. Multicoloured.* P 12 × 12½.

672	50x.	Type **140**	35	10
673	50x.	*Caesalpinia pulcherrima*	35	10
674	1d.	Golden shower (*Cassia fistula*)	35	10
675	2d.	Flamboyant (*Delonix regia*)	75	15
676	3d.	*Artabotrys uncinatus*	1·10	45
677	5d.	*Corchorus olitorius*	1·50	65
678	8d.	*Bauhinia grandiflora*	1·80	90
672/678 *Set of 7*			5·50	2·20
MS679 70 × 106 mm. 10d. As No. 675 but with inscriptions rearranged			3·75	1·50

Nos. 672 and 678 are wrongly inscribed "Banhinia".

141 *Brasse cattleya*

(142)

(Des Ngoc Uyên. Litho National Ptg Wks, Havana)

1984 (28 Mar). *Orchids. T* **141** *and similar vert designs. Multicoloured.* P 12½.

680	50x.	Type **141**	20	10
681	50x.	*Cymbidium* sp.	20	10
682	1d.	*Cattleya dianx* var. *alba*	35	10
683	2d.	*Cymbidium* sp. (*different*)	75	20
684	3d.	*Cymbidium hybridum*	1·00	30
685	5d.	Phoenix winged orchids	1·50	45
686	8d.	Yellow Queen orchids	1·80	65
680/686 *Set of 7*			5·25	1·70

1984 (25 Apr). *Nos. 362 and 373 surch as T* **142**.

687	–	50x. on 12x. brt crimson & brt green	1·50	35
688	**76**	50x. on 12x. bistre-yellow and black	1·50	35

The surcharge on No. 687 has no cancelling bars.

143 Flyingfish (*Cypselurus spilopterus*)

144 White Storks (*Ciconia ciconia*)

(Des Ngoc Uyên. Litho National Ptg Wks, Havana)

1984 (25 Apr). *Deep Sea Fishes. T* **143** *and similar horiz designs. Multicoloured.* P 12.

688a	30x.	Type **143**	15	15
688b	30x.	Long-horned cowfish (*Ostracion cornutus*)	15	15
688c	50x.	Porcupinefish (*Diodon hystrix*)	35	35
688d	80x.	Copper-banded butterflyfish (*Chelmon rostratus*)	45	35

688e	1d. Bearded anglerfish (*Antennarius bidens*)		45	35
688f	2d. Plane-tailed lionfish (*Pterois russelli*)		75	35
688g	5d. Oceanic sunfish (*Mola mola*)		1·50	45
688h	10d. Lionfish (*Minous monodactylus*)		2·20	75
688a/688h	Set of 8		5·50	2·50

(Litho National Ptg Wks, Havana)

1984 (27 Apr). *"España 84" International Stamp Exhibition, Madrid. Sheet* 81 × 80 *mm.* P 12½.

MS689 **144** 10d. multicoloured . . . . 4·50 1·50

148 Three-spotted Gourami
(*Trichogaster trichopterus*)

149 Nguyên Dúc Cánh

(Litho National Ptg Wks, Havana)

1984 (29 June). *Fishes. T* **148** *and similar horiz designs. Multicoloured.* P 13.

700	50x. Type **148**		15	10
701	50x. Zebra danio (*Brachydanio rerio*)		15	10
702	1d. Paradise fish (*Macropodus opercularis*)		35	15
703	2d. Black widow tetra (*Gymnocorymbus ternetzi*)		60	30
704	3d. Serpa tetra (*Hyphessobrycon serpae*)		75	45
705	5d. Red-tailed black shark (*Labeo bicolor*)		1·10	75
706	8d. Siamese fightingfish (*Betta splendens*)		1·80	1·30
700/706	Set of 7		4·50	2·75

MF 145 Star and Soldiers on Bunker

146 Ho Chi Minh discussing Battle Plan

1984 (5 May). *MILITARY FRANK. 30th Anniv of Battle of Dien Bien Phu. No value indicated.* P 11.

MF690	MF **145**	(–) greenish yellow, bright orange and lake-brown	60	45

1984 (20 July). *55th Anniv of Vietnamese Trade Union Movement. T* **149** *and similar designs.* P 11.

707	50x. Venetian red and black		15	15
	a. Horiz pair. Nos. 707/8		35	35
708	50x. Venetian red and black		15	15
709	1d. multicoloured		45	15
710	2d. multicoloured		75	30
711	3d. multicoloured		1·10	45
712	5d. multicoloured		1·50	90
707/712	Set of 6		3·75	1·75

MS713 99 × 98 mm. 2d. multicoloured.
Imperf . . . . 7·50 7·50

Designs: *Vert*—No. 708, Founder's house. *Horiz*—No. 709, Workers presenting demands to employer; 710, **MS**713; Ho Chi Minh with workers; 711, Factory; 712, Workers, procession and doves.

Nos. 707/8 were issued together in horizontal *se-tenant* pairs within the sheet. Nos. 709/10 and 711/12 respectively were issued in sheets containing 50 of each value, giving horizontal *se-tenant* pairs from the middle rows.

(Des Huy Ton. Litho National Ptg Wks, Havana)

1984 (7 May). *30th Anniv of Battle of Dien Bien Phu. T* **146** *and similar horiz designs. Multicoloured.* P 12½ × 13.

691	50x. Type **146**		30	10
692	50x. Vietnamese soldiers and truck		30	10
693	1d. Students carrying provisions		45	10
694	2d. Pulling field gun up hill		60	20
695	3d. Anti-aircraft gun and crashed airplane		75	30
696	5d. Fighting against tanks		1·20	45
697	8d. Vietnamese soldiers with flag on bunker		1·60	65
691/697	Set of 7		4·75	1·70

MS698 99 × 110 mm. 10d. Type **146** (36 × 26 *mm*). P 12½ . . . . 3·75 1·50

147 Junkers Ju 52/3m

(Litho National Ptg Wks, Havana)

1984 (19 June). *Universal Postal Union Congress, Hamburg, and 50th Anniv of First South Atlantic Air Service. Sheet* 68 × 60 *mm.* P 13.

MS699 **147** 10d. multicoloured . . . . 4·00 1·50

A set of stamps for the Olympic Games, Los Angeles, which exist with cancelled-to-order datestamps of 5 June 1984, were not issued in Vietnam until 1992 (see Nos. 1640/**MS**1647).

150 Hòn Dua

(Litho National Ptg Wks, Havana)

1984 (30 July). *Coastal Scenes. T* **150** *and similar horiz designs. Multicoloured.* P 12 × 12½.

714	50x. Type **150**		30	10
715	50x. Hang con gai		30	10
716	50x. Hang B Nâu		30	10
717	50x. Núi Yên Ngua		30	10
718	1d. Hòn Ga Choi		45	15
719	1d. Hòn Cóc		45	15
720	2d. Hòn Dinh Huong		60	20
721	3d. Hòn Su Tu		75	30

722	5d. Hôn Am		1·20	50
723	8d. Núi Bài The		1·50	80
714/723	*Set of* 10		5·50	2·30

151 Styracosaurus

(Litho National Ptg Wks, Havana)

1984 (15 Aug). *Prehistoric Animals. T* **151** *and similar horiz designs. Multicoloured.* P 12½ × 12.

724	50x. Type **151**	50	35
725	50x. Diplodocus	50	35
726	1d. Rhamphorhynchus	80	35
727	1d. Corythosaurus	80	35
728	2d. Seymouria	1·10	35
729	3d. Allosaurus	1·50	35
730	5d. Dimetrodon	2·20	35
731	8d. Brachiosaurus	3·75	35
724/731	*Set of* 8	10·00	2·50

MF **152** Coastal Militia **153** Dove and Flags

(Des Khich)

1984 (30 Aug). *MILITARY FRANK. No value indicated.* P 11.

MF732	MF **152**	(–) dp brn, reddish orge & lemon	75	45

(Des Ngoc)

1984 (30 Aug). *Laos–Kampuchea–Vietnam Co-operation.* P 11.

733	**153**	50x. vermilion, greenish blue and greenish yellow	15	15
734		10d. dull vermilion, greenish blue and bistre-yellow	3·50	60

154 Koala **155** Students and Cultural and Industrial Motifs

(Litho National Ptg Wks, Havana)

1984 (21 Sept). *"Ausipex 84" International Stamp Exhibition, Melbourne.* P 13.

MS735 **154**	10d. multicoloured	7·50	1·50

1984 (30 Sept). *Fifth Anniv of Kampuchea–Vietnam Friendship Treaty. T* **155** *and similar vert design. Multicoloured.* P 11.

736	50x. Type **155**	15	15
737	3d. Type **155**	1·10	60
738	50d. Kampuchean and Vietnamese dancers	6·25	75

156 Bridge

(Des Viet Tuan (50x.). Ngoc Uyên (others))

1984 (5 Oct). *30th Anniv of Liberation of Hanoi. T* **156** *and similar horiz designs.* P 11.

739	50x. myrtle green and olive-yellow	60	35
740	1d. purple-brown and Venetian red	1·10	35
741	2d. red-brown and pale cerise	1·60	35

Designs:—1d. Gateway; 2d. Ho Chi Minh mausoleum.

No. 742 is vacant.

157 Vis-à-vis F **158** Children and Disabled Teacher

(Litho National Ptg Wks, Havana)

1984 (30 Oct). *Motor Cars. T* **157** *and similar horiz designs. Multicoloured.* P 12½ × 13.

743	50x. Type **157**	20	15
744	50x. Two-seater	20	15
745	1d. Tonneau	35	15
746	2d. Double phaeton	60	30
747	3d. Landaulet	75	45
748	5d. Torpedo	90	60
749	6d. Town coupé	1·40	65
743/749	*Set of* 7	4·00	2·20

1984 (10 Nov). *FRANK. Disabled and Invalids. No value indicated.* P 11.

F750	F **158**	(–) black and olive-bistre	60	45

159 "Lenin" (V. A. Serov)

160 "Madonna and Child with St. John"

(Litho National Ptg Wks, Havana)

1984 (15 Nov). *60th Death Anniv of Lenin. T* **159** *and similar vert designs. Multicoloured.* P 12 × 12½.
751	50x. Type **159**		30	15
752	1d. Painting by A. Plotnov of Lenin at meeting		45	15
753	3d. Painting by K. V. Filatov of Lenin at factory		90	45
754	5d. Painting by V. A. Serov of Lenin with three comrades		1·30	65
751/754 *Set of 4*			2·75	1·30

(Litho National Ptg Wks, Havana)

1984 (30 Nov). *450th Death Anniv of Correggio (artist). T* **160** *and similar vert designs showing different "Madonna and Child" paintings. Multicoloured. With gum.* P 13 × 12½.
755	50x. Type **160**		15	15
756	50x. Bolognini Madonna		15	15
757	1d. Campori Madonna		30	15
758	2d. "Virgin adoring the Child"		60	30
759	3d. "Madonna della Cesta"		75	45
760	5d. "Madonna della Scodella"		1·10	60
761	6d. "Madonna and Child with Angels"		1·50	65
755/761 *Set of 7*			4·00	2·20
MS762 59 × 73 mm. 10d. "Madonna and Child with St. Catherine" (31 × 39 *mm*). P 12½			4·50	1·80

161 "Keep the Peace" (Le Quốc Lộc)

162 Mounted Frontier Guards

(Litho National Ptg Wks, Havana)

1984 (7 Dec). *United Nations Children's Fund. Paintings. T* **161** *and similar multicoloured designs.* P 12.
763	30x. Type **161**		15	15
764	50x. "Sunday" (Nguyên Tiên Chung)		15	15
765	1d. "Baby of the Mining Region" (Trân Van Cân)		30	15
766	3d. "Little Thúy" (Trân Van Cân) (*vert*)		75	30
767	5d. "Children at Play" (Nguyên Phan Chánh)		1·10	65
768	10d. "After Guard Duty" (Nguyên Phan Chánh) (*vert*)		2·20	1·20
763/768 *Set of 6*			4·00	2·30

(Des Dung)

1984 (15 Dec). *25th Anniv of Frontier Forces. Litho.* P 11.
769	**162**	50x. black, pale blue and drab	15	15
770		30d. black, yellowish green & blue-grn	8·00	1·60

163 Water Buffalo (*Bubalus bubalis*)

MF **164** Soldiers and Emblem

(Litho National Ptg Wks, Havana)

1984. *T* **163** *and similar vert designs.* P 12½.
771	20x. light brown		10	10
772	30x. brown-red		10	10
773	50x. apple green		15	10
774	50x. rose-red		15	10
775	50x. bright magenta		15	10
776	50x. orange-brown		15	10
777	1d. reddish violet		35	15
778	1d. yellow-orange		35	15
779	1d. blue		35	15
780	1d. new blue		35	15
781	2d. yellow-brown		80	35
782	2d. yellow-orange		80	35
783	2d. Indian red		80	35
784	5d. mauve		2·20	60
785	10d. emerald		3·75	1·10
771/785 *Set of 15*			9·45	3·50

Designs:—No. 772, Marbled cat (*Felis marmorata*); 773, Siamese fightingfish (*Betta splendens*); 774, Cabbage rose (*Rosa centifolia*); 775, Hibiscus (*Hybiscus rosa-sinensis*); 776, Lesser panda (*Ailurus fulgens*); 777, Chrysanthemum sinense; 778, Tiger (*Panthera tigris*); 779, Water lily (*Nymphaea ampla*); 780, Eastern white pelican (*Pelecanus onocrotalus*); 781, Slow loris (*Nycticebus coucang*); 782, Dahlia (*Dahlia coccinea*); 783, Crab-eating macaque (*Macaca fascicularis*); 784, Tokay gecko (*Gekko gecko*); 785, Great Indian hornbill (*Rhytidoceros bicornis*).
Nos. 776 and 782 have errors in the Latin inscriptions.

1984 (22 Dec). *MILITARY FRANK. No value indicated.* P 11.
MF786	MF **164** (–) pale orange, brown-red & blk		50	45

165 Ho Chi Minh and Troops

166 Boy on Buffalo

(Litho National Ptg Wks, Havana)

1984 (22 Dec). *40th Anniv of Vietnamese People's Army. T* **165** *and similar horiz designs. Multicoloured.* P 13.
787	50x. Type **165**		20	15
788	50x. Oath-taking ceremony		20	15
789	1d. Soldier with flag and Boeing B-52 Stratofortress bomber on fire		35	15
790	2d. Civilians building gun emplacement		60	20
791	3d. Soldiers and tank breaking through gates		80	35
792	5d. Soldier instructing civilians		1·00	80
793	8d. Map and soldiers		1·50	1·10
787/793 *Set of 7*			4·25	2·50
MS794 78 × 58 mm. 10d. Flag and Vietnamese soldiers, sailor and airman			3·00	1·50

1985 (21 Jan–Mar). *New Year. Year of the Buffalo.* P 11.

795	**166**	3d. deep dull purple and brown-rose	90	35
796		5d. red-brown and orange (30 Mar)	1·30	35

167 *Echinocereus knippelianus*

168 Nguyên Ai Quoc (Ho Chi Minh)

(Des P. Quang. Litho National Ptg Wks, Havana)

1985 (30 Mar). *Flowering Cacti.* T **167** *and similar square designs. Multicoloured.* P 11½.

797	50x. Type **167**		20	20
798	50x. *Lemaireocereus thurberi*		20	20
799	1d. *Notocactus haselbergii*		45	35
800	2d. *Parodia chrysacanthion*		75	35
801	3d. *Pelecyphora pseudopectinata*		1·00	35
802	5d. *Rebutia frebrighii*		1·50	35
803	8d. *Lobivia aurea*		1·80	50
797/803 *Set of 7*			5·25	2·10

1985 (26 Apr). *55th Anniv of Vietnam Communist Party.* P 11.

804	**168**	2d. olive-grey and dull vermilion	75	35

169 Soldiers with Weapons

170 Long Chau Lighthouse

(Litho National Ptg Wks, Havana)

1985 (30 Apr). *Tenth Anniv of Reunification of Vietnam.* T **169** *and similar horiz designs. Multicoloured.* P 12½.

805	1d. Type **169**		35	35
806	2d. Soldiers and tank		75	35
807	4d. Soldier and oil rig		1·10	35
808	5d. Map, flag and girls		1·50	35
805/808 *Set of 4*			3·25	1·30
MS809 65 × 90 mm. 10d. As No. 806. P 13			3·00	1·60

1985 (13 May). *30th Anniv of Liberation of Haiphong.* T **170** *and similar designs.* P 11.

810	2d. multicoloured		60	35
811	5d. multicoloured		1·30	35
MS812 110 × 75 mm. 10d. red-brown and turquoise-green. Imperf			2·50	1·50

Designs: *Horiz*—5d. An Duong bridge. *Vert*—10d. To Hieu (Communist Party official in Haiphong).

171 Ho Chi Minh and Soldiers

(Litho National Ptg Wks, Havana)

1985 (19 May). *95th Birth Anniv of Ho Chi Minh (President).* T **171** *and similar multicoloured designs.* P 12½ × 13 (4d.) or 13 × 12½ (others).

813	1d. Type **171**		35	15
814	2d. Ho Chi Minh reading in cave at Viêt Bac		60	30
815	4d. Portrait (*vert*)		90	60
816	5d. Ho Chi Minh writing in garden of Presidential Palace		1·10	80
813/816 *Set of 4*			2·75	1·60
MS817 74 × 99 mm. 10d. As No. 815 but smaller (28 × 35 mm). P 13			3·00	1·30

172 Soviet Memorial, Berlin-Treptow

173 Globe and People carrying Flags

(Litho National Ptg Wks, Havana)

1985 (5 June). *40th Anniv of Victory in Europe Day.* T **172** *and similar vert designs. Multicoloured.* P 12 × 12½.

818	1d. Type **172**		35	15
819	2d. Soldier and fist breaking swastika		60	20
820	4d. Hand releasing dove and eagle falling		1·30	50
821	5d. Girl releasing doves		1·50	65
818/821 *Set of 4*			3·25	1·40
MS822 115 × 78 mm. 10d. Type **172**			3·00	1·50

(Litho National Ptg Wks, Havana)

1985 (20 June). *12th World Youth and Students' Festival, Moscow.* T **173** *and similar horiz designs. Multicoloured.* P 12½.

823	2d. Type **173**		75	35
824	2d. Workers, pylons and dish aerial		75	35
825	4d. Coastguards and lighthouse		1·10	35
826	5d. Youths and balloons		1·50	35
823/826 *Set of 4*			3·75	1·30
MS827 82 × 100 mm. 10d. Main motif of Type **173** and plan of Moscow Kremlin (39 × 32 mm). P 13			2·50	1·30

174 Daimler, 1885

175 King Penguin
(*Aptenodytes pennati*)

(Litho National Ptg Wks, Havana)

1985 (28 June). *Centenary of Motor Cycle.* T **174** *and similar horiz designs. Multicoloured.* P 13.

828	1d. Type **174** (wrongly inscr "1895")	30	15
829	1d. Three-wheeled vehicle, France, 1898	30	15
830	2d. Harley Davidson, U.S.A., 1913	45	35
831	2d. Cleveland, U.S.A., 1918	45	35
832	3d. Simplex, U.S.A., 1935	75	35
833	4d. Minarelli, Italy, 1984	90	35
834	6d. Honda, Japan, 1984	1·30	75
828/834	*Set of 7*	4·00	2·20
MS835	82 × 48 mm. 10d. Honda, Japan, 1984 (31 × 39 mm)	3·00	1·30

(Litho National Ptg Wks, Havana)

1985 (5 July). *"Argentina '85" International Stamp Exhibition, Buenos Aires.* T **175** *and similar multicoloured designs.* P 12½.

836	1d. Type **175**	45	15
837	1d. Patagonian cavy (*Dolichotis patagonum*)	45	15
838	2d. Capybara (*Hydrochoerus capibara*) (*horiz*)	60	20
839	2d. Leopard (*Panthera onca*) (*horiz*)	60	20
840	3d. Lesser rhea (*Peterocnemia pennata*)	1·10	35
841	4d. Giant armadillo (*Priodontes giganteus*) (*horiz*)	1·50	45
842	6d. Andean condor (*Vultur gryphus*) (wrongly inscr "Voltur") (*horiz*)	2·20	90
836/842	*Set of 7*	6·25	2·20
MS843	97 × 80 mm. 10d. Llama (*Lama glama*) (39 × 31 mm). P 13	3·75	1·50

176 *Holothuria monacaria*

177 Flag and Sickle "40"

(Litho National Ptg Wks, Havana)

1985 (30 July). *Marine Life.* T **176** *and similar horiz designs. Multicoloured.* P 12.

844	3d. Type **176**	10	35
845	3d. *Stichopus chloronotus*	10	35
846	3d. *Luidia maculata*	10	35
847	3d. *Nadoa tuberculata*	10	35
848	4d. *Astropyga radiata*	1·10	35
849	4d. *Linckia laevigata*	1·10	35
850	4d. *Astropecten scoparius*	1·10	35
844/850	*Set of 7*	3·25	2·20

(Litho National Ptg Wks, Havana)

1985 (10 Aug). *40th Anniv of Socialist Republic.* T **177** *and similar vert designs. Multicoloured.* P 13.

851	2d. Type **177**	45	45
852	3d. Doves around globe as heart above handclasp	60	45
853	5d. Banner	1·00	45
854	10d. Ho Chi Minh, flag and laurel branch	1·60	45
851/854	*Set of 4*	3·25	1·60
MS855	70 × 100 mm. 10d. Similar to Type **177** (25 × 35 mm)	3·00	1·30

178 Globe, Transport and People around Postman

(Litho National Ptg Wks, Havana)

1985 (15 Aug). *40th Anniv of Postal and Telecommunications Service.* T **178** *and similar vert designs. Multicoloured.* P 13.

856	2d. Type **178**	50	20
857	2d. Telephonist and telegraph operator	50	20
858	4d. Wartime deliveries and postwoman Nguyên Thi Nghiá	75	45
859	5d. Dish aerial	90	45
856/859	*Set of 4*	2·40	1·20

179 Profile of Ho Chi Minh and Policeman

180 Gymnasts

(Des Trân Luong and T. Mai)

1985 (30 Aug). *40th Anniv of People's Police.* T **179** *and similar horiz design, each dull vermilion and black.* P 11.

(a) POSTAGE.

860	10d. Type **179**	3·25	35

(b) FRANK. No value indicated.

F861	(–) Policeman and militia members	50	50

1985 (30 Aug). *First National Sports and Gymnastics Games.* T **180** *and similar horiz design. Multicoloured.* P 11.

862	5d. Type **180**	1·10	35
863	10d. Badminton player, gymnast, athlete and swimmer	2·50	35

181 Locomotive *Reuth*, 1843

(Litho National Ptg Wks, Havana)

1985 (13 Sept). *150th Anniv of German Railways. T* **181** *and similar multicoloured designs.* P 12½.

864	1d. Type **181**	35	15
865	1d. German tank locomotive, 1900	35	15
866	2d. Andreas Schubert's *Saxonia*, 1836	60	20
867	2d. German passenger locomotive	60	20
868	3d. Prussian steam locomotive No. 2024, 1910	80	45
869	4d. Prussian tank locomotive, 1920	1·20	45
870	6d. Bavarian State steam locomotive No. 659, 1890	1·50	80
864/870 *Set of 7*		4·75	2·20
MS871 80 × 53 mm. 10d. Stephenson locomotive *Adler*, 1835 (31 × 39 *mm*). P 13		3·75	1·50

182 Off-shore Rig, Derrick and Helicopter

(Des Trân Luong)

1985 (5 Oct). *30th Anniv of Geological Service. T* **182** *and similar horiz design.* P 11.

872	1d. new blue and plum	80	35
873	1d. light green and chestnut	80	35

Design:—Airplane over coastline.

183 Alfa Romeo, 1922

(Litho National Ptg Wks, Havana)

1985 (25 Oct). *"Italia '85" International Stamp Exhibition, Rome. Motor Cars. T* **183** *and similar horiz designs. Multicoloured.* P 13.

874	1d. Type **183**	30	15
875	1d. Bianchi "Berlina", 1932	30	15
876	2d. Isotta Fraschini, 1928	45	20
877	2d. Bugatti, 1930	45	20
878	3d. Itala, 1912	75	30
879	4d. Lancia "Augusta", 1934	90	45
880	6d. Fiat, 1927	1·50	80
874/880 *Set of 7*		4·25	2·00
MS881 76 × 60 mm. 10d. Fiat, 1927 (*different*) (39 × 31 *mm*). P 12½		3·00	1·30

184 Sei Whale (*Balaenoptera borealis*)

(Litho National Ptg Wks, Havana)

1985 (15 Nov). *Marine Mammals. T* **184** *and similar horiz designs. Multicoloured.* P 13.

882	1d. Type **184** (wrongly inscr "Balaena")	30	15
883	1d. Blue whale (*Balaenoptera musculus*)	30	15
884	2d. Killer whale (*Orcinus orca*)	45	20
885	2d. Common dolphin (*Delphinus*)	45	20
886	3d. Humpback whale (*Megaptera boops*)	75	30
887	4d. Fin whale (*Balaenoptera physalis*)	90	45
888	6d. Black right whale (*Eubalaena glacialis*)	1·50	80
882/888 *Set of 7*		4·25	2·00

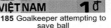

185 Goalkeeper attempting to save ball

186 Laotian Girl and Dove

(Litho National Ptg Wks, Havana)

1985 (30 Nov). *World Cup Football Championship, Mexico (1986) (1st issue). T* **185** *and similar multicoloured designs.* P 13.

889	1d. Type **185**	20	15
890	1d. Scoring goal	20	15
891	2d. Goalkeeper diving for ball	45	20
892	2d. Goalkeeper holding ball (*vert*)	45	20
893	3d. Goalkeeper preparing to catch ball (*vert*)	75	30
894	4d. Punching ball away (*vert*)	90	35
895	6d. Goalkeeper catching ball (*vert*)	1·50	35
889/895 *Set of 7*		4·00	1·50
MS896 92 × 67 mm. 10d. Goal mouth scene (39 × 31 *mm*)		3·00	1·30

See also Nos. 920/**MS**927.

1985 (2 Dec). *Tenth Anniv of Laos People's Democratic Republic. T* **186** *and similar vert design. Multicoloured.* P 11.

897	1d. Type **186**	60	60
	a. Vert pair. Nos. 897/8	1·30	1·30
898	1d. Laotian girl and arms	60	60

Nos. 897/8 were issued together in sheets containing blocks of 50 of each design, giving vertical *se-tenant* pairs from the middle horizontal rows.

187 Decorated Drum

188 Agriculture

1985 (5 Dec). *Traditional Musical Instruments. T* **187** *and similar horiz designs. Multicoloured.* P 12½ × 12.

899	1d. Type **187**	30	35
900	1d. Xylophone	30	35
901	2d. Double-ended drum	45	35
902	2d. Flutes	45	35
903	3d. Single-stringed intrument	75	35
904	4d. Four-stringed instrument	90	35
905	6d. Double-stringed bowed instrument	1·50	35
899/905 *Set of 7*		4·25	2·20

1985 (6 Dec). *40th Anniv of Independence. T* **188** *and similar vert designs. Multicoloured.* P 11.

906	10d.	Type **188**	3·75	1·50
907	10d.	Industry	3·75	1·50
908	20d.	Health care	7·50	3·75
909	30d.	Education	11·00	4·50
906/909		*Set of 4*	23·00	10·00

193 Plan of Battle of Chi Lang

194 Footballer

1986 (1 Mar). *600th Birth Anniv (1985) of Le Loi (founder of Le Dynasty).* P 11.

919	**193**	1d. multicoloured	75	35

189 Hands, Emblem and Dove

190 Ho Chi Minh, Map, Line of Voters and Ballot Box

1986 (6 Jan). *40th Anniv of United Nations Organization.* P 11.

910	**189**	1d. multicoloured	65	45

(Des Viet Tuan)

1986 (6 Jan). *40th Anniv of First Assembly Elections.* P 11.

911	**190**	50x. mauve and black	35	35
912		1d. reddish orange and black	75	75

(Litho National Ptg Wks, Havana)

1986 (3 Mar). *World Cup Football Championship, Mexico (2nd issue). T* **194** *and similar multicoloured designs.* P 13.

920	1d.	Type **194**	20	15
921	1d.	Two players	20	15
922	2d.	Player heading ball	45	15
923	3d.	Player tackling	75	35
924	3d.	Two players chasing ball	75	35
925	5d.	Footballer (*different*)	1·10	60
926	5d.	Two players (*different*)	1·10	60
920/926		*Set of 7*	4·00	2·10
MS927		113 × 52 mm. 10d. Goalkeeper (39 × 31 mm)	3·00	1·30

191 Isaac Newton

192 Map of U.S.S.R. and Kremlin Buildings

(Litho National Ptg Wks, Havana)

1986 (24 Feb). *Appearance of Halley's Comet. T* **191** *and similar vert designs. Multicoloured.* P 13 × 12½.

913	**191**	2d. Type **191**	35	35
914		2d. Edmond Halley	35	35
915		3d. Launch of "Vega" space probe and flags	75	35
916		5d. Comet and planet	1·50	35
913/916		*Set of 4*	2·75	1·25

195 Konstantin Tsiolkovski and "Sputnik I"

(Litho National Ptg Wks, Havana)

1986 (12 Apr). *25th Anniv of First Man in Space. T* **195** *and similar multicoloured designs.* P 13.

928	1d.	Type **195**	20	15
929	1d.	Rocket on launch vehicle, Baikanur cosmodrome	20	15
930	2d.	Yuri Gagarin and "Vostok I"	45	15
931	3d.	Valentina Tereshkova and "Vostok VI" on launch vehicle (*vert*)	75	35
932	3d.	Cosmonaut Leonov and cosmonaut on space walk	75	35
933	5d.	"Soyuz"–"Apollo" link and crews	1·10	60
934	5d.	"Salyut"–"Soyuz" link and two cosmonauts	1·10	60
928/934		*Set of 7*	4·00	2·10
MS935		60 × 81 mm. 10d. Cosmonauts (31 × 39 mm)	3·00	1·30

1986 (25 Feb). *27th Russian Communist Party Congress, Moscow. T* **192** *and similar vert design. Multicoloured.* P 11.

917		50x. Type **192**	35	35
918		1d. Lenin on flag and transport, industrial and scientific motifs	75	35

196 Thälmann and Flag

197 Flag, Hammer and Globe in Sickle

(Des Viet Tuan)

1986 (16 Apr). *Birth Centenary of Ernst Thälmann (German Communist leader).* P. 11.

936	**196**	2d. vermilion and black	90	35

(Des Trân Luong)

1986 (1 May). *Centenary of May Day.* P 11.

937	**197**	1d. dull vermilion and light blue	30	15
938		5d. dull vermilion and brown	1·20	20

198 Hawker Hart

(Litho National Ptg Wks, Havana)

1986 (12 May). *"Expo '86" World's Fair, Vancouver. Historic Aircraft.* T **198** *and similar horiz designs. Multicoloured.* P. 13.

939	1d. Type **198**	20	10
940	1d. Curtiss JN-4 "Jenny"	20	10
941	2d. PZL P-23 Karas	45	15
942	3d. Yakovlev Yak-11	75	30
943	3d. Fokker Dr-1 triplane	75	30
944	5d. Boeing P12, 1920	1·10	50
945	5d. Nieuport-Delage 29C1, 1929	1·10	50
939/945	*Set of 7*	4·00	1·75

199 Ho Chi Minh and People working on Barriers

(Des Trân Luong)

1986 (22 May). *40th Anniv of Committee for Protection of Flood Barriers.* P. 11.

946	**199**	1d. dull rose and blackish brown	60	45

200 Black and White Cat

(Litho National Ptg Wks, Havana)

1986 (16 June). *Cats.* T **200** *and similar multicoloured designs.* P 12½ × 13 (952) or 13 × 12½ (others).

947	1d. Type **200**	20	15
948	1d. Grey and white cat	20	15
949	2d. White cat	45	15
950	3d. Brown-faced cat	75	35
951	3d. Beige cat	75	35
952	5d. Black-faced cat (*vert*)	1·10	60
953	5d. Beige and cream cat	1·10	60
947/953	*Set of 7*	4·00	2·10

201 Thái Den House

202 European Bee Eater (*Merops apiaster*)

(Litho National Ptg Wks, Havana)

1986 (20 June). *Traditional Architecture of Ethnic Minorities.* T **201** *and similar multicoloured designs.* P 12½ × 12 (horiz) or 12 × 12½ (vert).

954	1d. Type **201**	20	15
955	1d. Nung house	20	15
956	2d. Thái Tráng house	45	20
957	3d. Tày house	75	35
958	3d. H'mng house	75	35
959	5d. Dao house	1·10	65
960	5d. Tày Nguyên house (*vert*)	1·10	65
954/960	*Set of 7*	4·00	2·30

MS961 100 × 70 mm. 10d. As No. 960

(Litho National Ptg Wks, Havana)

1986 (28 Aug). *"Stockholmia 86" International Stamp Exhibition. Birds.* T **202** *and similar multicoloured designs.* P. 13.

962	1d. Type **202**	20	15
963	1d. Green magpie (*Cissa chinensis*)	20	15
964	2d. Red-winged shrike babbler (*Pteruthius erythropterus*)	45	15
965	3d. White-crested laughing thrush (*Garrulax leucolophus*)	75	35
966	3d. Long-tailed broadbill (*Psarisomus dalhousiae*) (*horiz*)	75	35
967	5d. Pied wagtail (*Motacilla alba*)	1·10	60
968	5d. Azure-winged magpie (*Cyanopica cyanus*) (*horiz*)	1·10	60
962/968	*Set of 7*	4·00	2·10

MS969 95 × 65 mm. 10d. White-rumped shamas (*Copsychus malabaricus*) (31 × 39 *mm*).

P 12½	3·75	1·30

203 Plymouth Rock Cock   **204** Emblem

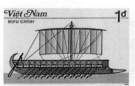 

207 Greek Bireme   **208** Hands cupping Red Cross in Flower

(Litho National Ptg Wks, Havana)

1986 (15 Sept). *Domestic Fowl. T* **203** *and similar vert designs. Multicoloured.* P 12 × 12½.

970	1d. Type **203**	20	35
971	1d. Common turkey (*Meleagris gallopavo*)	20	35
972	2d. Rhode Island Red cock	45	35
973	2d. White Plymouth Rock cock	45	35
974	3d. Rhode Island (inscr "Islan") Red hen	75	35
975	3d. White Leghorn cock	75	35
976	3d. Rhode Island Red cock (*different*)	75	35
977	5d. Barred Plymouth Rock cock	1·10	35
970/977	*Set of 8*	4·00	2·50

(Litho National Ptg Wks, Havana)

1986 (20 Oct). *Sailing Ships. T* **207** *and similar multicoloured designs.* P 12½ × 13 (2d.) or 12½ (others).

988	1d. Type **207**	20	10
989	1d. Viking longship	20	10
990	2d. Medieval kogge (36 × 46 *mm*)	45	15
991	3d. Greek cargo galley	75	30
992	3d. Phoenician war galley with ram	75	30
993	5d. Ancient Mediterranean cargo ship	1·10	50
994	5d. Roman trireme	1·10	50
988/994	*Set of 7*	4·00	1·75

1986 (20 Oct). *40th Anniv of Vietnamese Red Cross.* P 11.

995	**208**	3d. magenta and greenish blue	75	35

(Des T. Liêu)

1986 (16 Sept). *11th World Federation of Trades Unions Congress, Berlin.* P 12½.

978	**204**	1d. blue and vermilion	65	35

209 *Catopsilia scylla*

(Des Sâm Uyên. Litho National Ptg Wks, Havana)

1986 (11 Nov). *Butterflies. T* **209** *and similar square designs. Multicoloured.* P 12½.

996	1d. Type **209**	20	10
997	1d. *Euploea midamus*	20	10
998	2d. *Appias nero*	45	15
999	3d. *Papilio polytes*	75	30
1000	3d. *Danais chrysippus*	75	30
1001	5d. *Charaxes polyxena*	1·10	50
1002	5d. *Euploea diocletiana*	1·10	50
996/1002	*Set of 7*	4·00	1·75

MF 205 Soldier and Woman holding Sheaf of Rice   **206** Woman-shaped Sword Handle

(Des L. Tuấn)

1986 (1 Oct). *MILITARY FRANK.* P 11.

MF979	MF **205**	1d. olive-sepia and black	65	65

(Des Nguyên Hiêp. Litho National Ptg Wks, Havana)

1986 (15 Oct). *Historic Bronzes Excavated at Mt. Do. T* **206** *and similar multicoloured designs.* P 12 × 12½ (vert) or 12½ × 12 (horiz).

980	1d. Type **206**	20	35
981	1d. Seated figure with man on back	20	35
982	2d. Saddle pommel (*horiz*)	45	35
983	3d. Shoe-shaped hoe (*horiz*)	75	35
984	3d. Bowl (*horiz*)	75	35
985	5d. Vase (*horiz*)	1·10	35
986	5d. Pot with lid (*horiz*)	1·10	35
980/986	*Set of 7*	4·00	2·20
MS987	107 × 88 mm. 10d. As No. 981	3·00	1·30

210 Red Flag and Symbols of Industry and Agriculture

1986 (20 Nov). *Sixth Vietnamese Communist Party Congress. T* **210** *and similar horiz designs. Multicoloured.* P 11 × 12½ (4d.) or 11 (others).

1003	1d. Type **210**	45	35
1004	2d. Red flag and weapons	90	35
1005	4d. Red flag and Ho Chi Minh	1·50	35
1006	5d. Red flag and symbols of peace	1·60	35
1003/1006	*Set of 4*	4·00	1·25
MS1007	73 × 110 mm. 10d. Type **210**. Imperf	3·00	1·30

211 *Poecilocoris nepalensis*   **212** Dove and Emblem

(Litho National Ptq Wks, Havana)

1986 (30 Nov). *Insects. T* **211** *and similar multicoloured designs.*
P 13.

1008	1d.	Type **211**	20	20
1009	1d.	*Bombus americanorum*	20	20
1010	2d.	*Romalea microptera*	45	35
1011	3d.	*Chalcocoris rutilans*	75	35
1012	3d.	*Chrysocoris sellatus*	75	35
1013	5d.	*Crocisa crucifera*	1·10	35
1014	5d.	*Paranthrene palmi*	1·10	50
1008/1014 *Set of 7*			4·00	2·10
MS1015 78 × 78 mm. 10d. *Anabrus simplex*				
(31 × 39 *mm*). P 12½			3·00	1·30

(Des Trân Luong)

1986 (7 Dec). *International Peace Year.* P 11.

1016	**212**	1d. turquoise-green and black	45	35
1017		3d. brown-rose and black	1·00	35

213 *Ficus glomerata*   **214** Basket

(Dos Viet Tuan and Uyên. Litho National Ptg Wks, Havana)

1986 (10 Dec). *Bonsai. T* **213** *and similar multicoloured designs.*
P 12 × 12½.

1018	1d.	Type **213**	20	35
1019	1d.	*Ficus benjamina*	20	35
1020	2d.	*Ulmus tonkinensis*	45	35
1021	3d.	*Persica vulgaris*	75	35
1022	3d.	*Streblus asper*	75	35
1023	5d.	*Podocarpus macrophyllus*	1·10	35
1024	5d.	*Pinus khasya*	1·10	35
1018/1024 *Set of 7*			4·00	2·20
MS1025 86 × 66 mm. 10d. *Serissa foetida*				
(41 × 29 *mm*). P 12½ × 12			3·00	1·30

(Des Trân Luong. Litho National Ptg Wks, Havana)

1986 (10 Dec). *Basketry and Wickerwork. T* **214** *and similar diamond-shaped designs. Multicoloured.* P 11½.

1026	1d.	Type **214**	20	35
1027	1d.	Tall basket with lid and handles	20	35
1028	2d.	Stool	45	35
1029	3d.	Handbag	75	35
1030	3d.	Dish	75	35
1031	5d.	Tall basket for carrying on back	1·10	35
1032	5d.	Square basket with star-shaped foot	1·10	35
1026/1032 *Set of 7*			4·00	2·20
MS1033 107 × 90 mm. 10d. Tall basket			3·00	1·30

215 Soldiers and Women   **216** *Fokienia hodginsii*

1986 (18 Dec). *40th Anniv of National Resistance.* P 11.

1034	**215**	2d. orange-brown & dp turquoise grn	90	35

(Des P. Quang. Litho National Ptg Wks, Havana)

1986 (26 Dec). *Fruits of Conifers. T* **216** *and similar vert designs. Multicoloured.* P 12 × 12½.

1035	1d.	Type **216**	20	35
1036	1d.	*Amentotaxus yunnanensis*	20	35
1037	2d.	*Pinus kwangtungensis*	45	35
1038	3d.	*Cupressus torulosa*	75	35
1039	3d.	*Taxus chinensis*	75	35
1040	5d.	*Tsuga yunnanensis*	1·10	35
1041	5d.	*Ducampopinus krempfii*	1·10	35
1035/1041 *Set of 7*			4·00	2·20
MS1042 67 × 85 mm. 10d. *Abies nukiangensis*				
			3·00	1·30

217 Mother and Calf

(Litho National Ptg Wks, Havana)

1986 (30 Dec). *Elephants. T* **217** *and similar multicoloured designs.* P 12½ (1048) or 13 (others).

1043	1d.	Type **217**	20	10
1044	1d.	Two elephants	20	10
1045	3d.	Elephant (*vert*)	75	20
1046	3d.	Elephant feeding	75	20
1047	5d.	Working elephant (*vert*)	1·10	45
1048	5d.	Elephants by water (68 × 27 *mm*)	1·10	45
1043/1048 *Set of 6*			3·75	1·40

218 Girl watering Tree   **219** My Chân

(Des T. Liêu)

1987 (6 Jan). *New Year. Year of the Cat.* P 11.
1049 **218** 3d. chocolate and magenta . . . 65 45

(Litho National Ptg Wks, Havana)

1987 (20 Jan). *"Son Tinh-Thuy Tinh" (folk tale).* **T 219** *and similar square designs. Multicoloured.* P 12.
1050	3d.	Type **219**	75	35
	a.	Strip of 8. Nos. 1050/7	6·25	
1051	3d.	Mountain Genius bearing gift and leading horse	75	35
1052	3d.	Elephants carrying materials for flood barrier	75	35
1053	3d.	Men working through the night against flood sent by Water Genius	75	35
1054	3d.	Men felling trees	75	35
1055	3d.	Pounding rice in preparation for festival after storms	75	35
1056	3d.	Canoes bringing fruit and grain	75	35
1057	3d.	Canoe	75	35
1050/1057		*Set of 8*	5·50	2·50

Nos. 1050/7 were issued together in *se-tenant* strips of eight stamps, each strip forming a composite design.

220 *Nymphaea lotus*

221 Crowd attacking Building (August 1945 Revolution)

(Des L. Tuân. Litho National Ptg Wks, Havana)

1987 (19 Feb). *Water Lilies.* **T 220** *and similar vert designs. Multicoloured.* P 12 × 12½.
1058	5d.	Type **220**	15	15
1059	10d.	*Nymphaea nouchali*	30	15
1060	10d.	*Nymphaea pubescens*	45	15
1061	20d.	*Nymphaea rubra*	60	20
1062	20d.	*Nymphaea gigantea*	75	30
1063	30d.	*Nymphaea laydekeri*	80	35
1064	50d.	*Nymphaea capensis*	1·00	50
1058/1064		*Set of 7*	3·75	1·60

1987 (10 Apr). *Eighth National Assembly.* **T 221** *and similar horiz designs. Multicoloured.* P 11.
1065	10d.	Type **221**	75	35
1066	20d.	Proclamation of Democratic Republic (Sept 1945)	1·10	35
1067	30d.	Fall of Dien Bien Phu (May 1954)	1·50	35
1068	50d.	Tank entering Saigon (April 1975)	1·80	35
1065/1068		*Set of 4*	4·75	1·25

222 Temple, Da Nang

223 Hanoi

(Des T. T. Vinh. Litho National Ptg Wks, Havana)

1987 (30 June). *Cham Culture.* **T 222** *and similar vert designs. Multicoloured.* P 12 × 12½.
1069	3d.	Type **222**	20	15
1070	10d.	Temple, Phú Khánh	45	20
1071	15d.	Temple, Da Nang (*different*)	75	20
1072	20d.	Figure of dancer, Nghia Binh	90	35
1073	25d.	Bust, Da Nang	1·00	35
1074	30d.	Woman playing flute (statuette), Nghia Binh	1·20	50
1075	40d.	Figure of dancer on capital, Da Nang	1·50	65
1069/1075		*Set of 7*	5·50	2·10
MS1076		80 × 100 mm. 50d. As No. 1074	3·00	1·30

(Des Viet Tuan and Ngoc Uyên. Litho National Ptg Wks, Havana)

1987 (July). *Tourism.* **T 223** *and similar horiz designs. Multicoloured.* P 12½ × 12.
1077	5d.	Type **223**	15	20
1078	10d.	Hai Phong	30	35
1079	15d.	Thiên Mu Pagoda, Hué	45	35
1080	20d.	Da Nang	60	35
1081	25d.	Nha Trang	75	35
1082	30d.	Waterfall, Da Lat	80	35
1083	40d.	Ho Chi Minh City	1·00	45
1077/1083		*Set of 7*	3·75	2·10
MS1084		87 × 105 mm. 50d. Quang Ninh	3·00	1·20

224 Cactus

225 People on Globe

(Litho National Ptg Wks, Havana)

1987 (10 July). *Cacti.* **T 224** *and similar vert designs showing various flowering cacti. Multicoloured.* P 12½.
1085	5d.	multicoloured	15	15
1086	10d.	multicoloured	30	15
1087	15d.	multicoloured	45	15
1088	20d.	multicoloured	60	20
1089	25d.	multicoloured	75	30
1090	30d.	multicoloured	80	35
1091	40d.	multicoloured	1·00	50
1085/1091		*Set of 7*	3·75	1·60
MS1092		60 × 72 mm. 50d. multicoloured (31 × 39 *mm*). P 13	3·00	1·20

PRINTERS. From No. 1093 all stamps were lithographed at Post Office Ptg Wks, Ho Chi Minh City, *unless otherwise stated.* The locally printed stamps were issued without gum while those printed abroad usually exist both with and without gum.

1987 (11 July). *Day of Five Billion Inhabitants of Earth.* P 13.
1093 **225** 5d. magenta and new blue 65 45

226 Man from Bana

227 Silhouettes of Soldiers and Disabled Soldier

(Des Ngoc Uyên. Litho National Ptg Wks, Havana)

1987 (25 July). *Costumes. T* **226** *and similar vert designs. Multicoloured.* P 12 × 12½.

1094	5d. Type **226**	20	15
1095	20d. Woman from Bana	75	35
1096	20d. Woman from Gia Rai	75	35
1097	30d. Man from Gia Rai	1·10	35
1098	30d. Man from Ede	1·10	35
1099	40d. Woman from Ede	1·50	65
1094/1099 *Set of 6*		4·75	2·00

1987 (27 July). *40th Anniv of Association of Disabled Soldiers.* P 13.

1100	**227**	5d. rose-carmine and dull violet	60	35

228 Rose

229 Postwoman and Mail Transport

(Litho National Ptg Wks, Havana)

1987 (28 Aug). *Roses. T* **228** *and similar vert designs. Multicoloured.* P 13 × 12½.

1101	5d. Type **228**	15	20
1102	10d. Red hybrid tea	30	35
1103	15d. Pink hybrid tea	45	35
1104	20d. Species rose	60	35
1105	25d. Species rose (*different*)	75	35
1106	30d. Floribunda	80	35
1107	40d. *Rosa odorata*	1·00	45
1101/1107 *Set of 7*		3·50	2·10
MS1108 65 × 85 mm. 50d. Roses (28 × 36 *mm*).			
P 13		3·00	1·20

1987 (30 Aug). *40th Anniv of Postal Trade Union. T* **229** *and similar horiz design.* P 13.

1109	5d. black and dull rose	60	35
1110	30d. black and green	90	75
Design:—30d. Linesman, dish aerial and telephonist.			

230 Siamese Fighting Fish (*Betta splendens*)

(Litho National Ptg Wks, Havana)

1987 (15 Sept). *Fishes. T* **230** *and similar horiz designs. Multicoloured.* P 13.

1111	5d. Type **230**	15	15
1112	10d. Red-tailed black shark (*Labeo bicolor*)	30	15
1113	15d. Tiger barb (*Puntis tetrazona*)	45	15
1114	20d. Pearl danio (*Brachydanio albolineatus*)	60	20
1115	25d. Rosy barb (*Puntis conchonius*)	75	30
1116	30d. Rasbora sp.	80	45
1117	40d. Silver loach (*Botia lecontei*)	1·00	50
1111/1117 *Set of 7*		3·75	1·75

231 I.Y.S.H. Emblem

MF **232** Armed Forces Personnel and Flag

1987 (23 Sept). *International Year of Shelter for the Homeless.* P 13.

1118	**231**	5d. black and turquoise-blue	60	35

1987 (23 Sept). *MILITARY FRANK.* P 11.

MF1119	MF **232**	5d. brt crimson & cinnamon	90	90

233 Crested gibbons (*Hylobates concolor*)

234 "Three Musicians"

(Litho National Ptg Wks, Havana)

1987 (23 Sept). *Monkeys. T* **233** *and similar vert designs. Multicoloured.* P 13.

1120	5d. Type **233**	75	35
1121	5d. Variegated langurs (*Pygathrix nemaeus*)	75	35
1122	15d. Crested gibbon (*different*)	1·50	35
1123	40d. Variegated langur (*different*)	3·00	35
1120/1123 *Set of 4*		5·25	1·25

(Litho National Ptg Wks, Havana)

1987 (1 Oct). *Paintings by Picasso. T* **234** *and similar multicoloured designs.* P 13.

1124	3d. Type **234**	15	15
1125	20d. Horse-drawn wagon	60	20

1126	20d. Winged horse on shore	60	20
1127	30d. "Child with Dove" (vert)	90	30
1128	30d. "Gertrude Stein" (vert)	90	30
1129	40d. "Guernica" (44 × 27 mm)	1·50	50
1124/1129 Set of 6		4·25	1·40

MS1130 75 × 100 mm. 50d. "Artist's Son as
Harlequin" (39 × 31 mm). P 12½ . . . . . . 3·75 1·50

235 Industrial and
Agricultural Symbols

236 Consolidated PBY-5 Catalina
Flying Boat

(Litho National Ptg Wks, Havana)

1987 (6 Oct). 70th Anniv of Russian Revolution. T **235** and similar
vert designs. Multicoloured. P 13.

1131	5d. Type **235**	20	35
1132	20d. Soviet Memorial, Berlin-Treptow, *Aurora* (Russian cruiser) and Lenin	45	35
1133	30d. "70" and symbols of progress	80	35
1134	50d. Ho Chi Minh and scenes of Vietnamese history	1·50	35
1131/1134 Set of 4		2·75	1·25

MS1135 90 × 90 mm. 65d. As No. 1133 . . . . 3·00 1·20

(Litho National Ptg Wks, Havana)

1987 (12 Oct). "Hafnia 87" International Stamp Exhibition,
Copenhagen. Flying Boats. T **236** and similar horiz designs.
Multicoloured. P 13.

1136	5d. Type **236**	15	15
1137	10d. Liore et Olivier LeO 246	30	15
1138	15d. Dornier Do-18	45	15
1139	20d. Short S.25 Sunderland	60	20
1140	25d. Flying boat, 1923	75	30
1141	30d. Chetverikov ARK-3	80	35
1142	40d. Cant Z.509	1·00	50
1136/1142 Set of 7		3·75	1·60

MS1143 87 × 54 mm. 50d. Flying boat . . . . 2·50 1·20

237 Epanouis

238 Doves as Clasped Hands
Forming Heart

(Des L. Tuân. Litho National Ptg Wks, Havana)

1987 (30 Oct). Corals. T **237** and similar vert designs.
Multicoloured. P 12 × 12½.

1144	5d. Type **237**	20	20
1145	10d. Acropora	45	35
1146	15d. Rhizopsammia	65	35
1147	20d. Acropora (different)	90	35
1148	25d. Alcyone	1·10	35
1149	30d. Corollum	1·30	35
1150	40d. Cristatella	1·80	45
1144/1150 Set of 7		5·75	2·10

1987 (31 Oct). Fifth Anniv of Vietnam–Czechoslovak Friendship
Treaty. T **238** and similar horiz design, each blue, yellow and
rosine. P 13.

1151	10d. Type **238**	75	35
1152	50d. Pagoda on One Pillar (Hanoi), flags and buildings of Prague	1·80	35

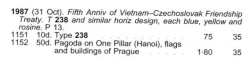

239 Symbols of Industry and
Agriculture

1987 (3 Nov). Soviet–Vietnam Friendship Treaty. T **239** and
similar horiz design. P 13.

1153	5d. rose, black and yellow-orange	35	35
1154	50d. rose, deep brown and yellow-orange	1·80	35

Design:—50d. Buildings of Moscow Kremlin and Hanoi.

240 Coloured Circles

241 Polyporellus
squamosus

1987 (10 Nov). Peace. P 13.

1155	**240**	10d. multicoloured	90	35

(Litho National Ptg Wks, Havana)

1987 (10 Nov). Fungi. T **241** and similar vert designs.
Multicoloured. P 13.

1156	5d. Type **241**	15	15
1157	10d. Clitocybe geotropa	30	20
1158	15d. Tricholoma terreum	45	20
1159	20d. Russula aurata	60	20
1160	25d. Collybia fusipes	75	20
1161	30d. Cortinarius violaceus	80	35
1162	40d. Boletus aereus	1·00	50
1156/1162 Set of 7		3·75	1·60

242 Dove on Open Hands

243 Wrecked Boeing
B-52 Stratofortress
Bomber and Girl
watering Flowers

1987 (30 Nov). 30th Anniv of Africa–Asia Co-operation
Committee. T **242** and similar design. P 13.

1163	10d. turquoise-blue, black and yellow	35	35
1164	30d. black, lake brown and yellow	1·10	35

Design: Vert—30d. Hands and map.

1987 (26 Dec). *15th Anniv of U.S. Air Bombardment of Vietnam.* T **243** *and similar vert design.* P 13.
1165	10d. black and yellow		35	35
1166	30d. black and reddish orange		1·10	35

Design:—30d. Young Pioneers and weapons.

244 Woman carrying Bales of Cloth

245 Junk, Man blowing Horn and Map

1987 (30 Dec). *Sixth Party Congress Decisions.* T **244** *and similar vert designs.* P 13.
1167	5d. dull yellowish green and chocolate		35	35
1168	20d. dull orange and chocolate		60	35
1169	30d. deep violet and light blue		90	35

Designs:—20d. Tractor driver; 30d. Loading crate on freighter.

1988 (18 Jan). *Paracel and Spratley Islands.* T **245** *and similar horiz design.* P 13.
1170	10d. black, carmine-rose & rose-carmine		35	15
1171	100d. light brown, black & reddish brown		2·50	75

Design:—100d. Maps showing Paracel Islands.

246 Anniversary Emblem and Dove

247 Fleet

1988 (17 Feb). *125th Anniv of International Red Cross.* P 13.
1172	**246**	10d. brt carmine, black & dull violet-bl	95	35

1988 (9 Apr). *700th Anniv of Battle of Bach Dang River.* T **247** *and similar horiz design.* P 13.
1173	80d. black, bright rose-red and rose-pink		75	20
1174	200d. multicoloured		2·50	50

Design:—200d. Battle scene.

248 Oil Rig

249 Blue and Yellow Macaw (*Ara ararauna*)

(Des T. T. Vinh)

1988 (28 Apr). *Oil Industry.* P 13.
1175	**248**	1000d. black, deep cobalt & brt scarlet	7·50	1·80

(Des Dinh Luć. Litho National Ptg Wks, Havana)

1988 (5 May). *Parrots.* T **249** *and similar vert designs. Multicoloured.* P 12 × 12½.
1176	10d. Type **249**		30	35
1177	10d. Slaty-headed parakeet (*Psittacula himalayana*)		30	35
1178	20d. Red-winged parrot (*Aprosmictus eryrhropterus*)		60	35
1179	20d. Green-winged macaw (*Ara chloroptera*)		60	60
1180	30d. Moustached parakeet (*Psittacula alexandri*)		80	35
1181	30d. Military macaw (*Ara militaris*)		80	35
1182	50d. Vernal hanging parrot (*Loriculus vernalis*)		1·00	35
1176/1182 *Set of 7*			4·00	2·40
MS1183 65 × 85 mm. 80d. Scarlet macaw (wrongly inscr "Ara chloroptera") (*different*)			3·25	1·30

250 Map

251 Child and Syringe

(Des Nghiêp)

1988 (29 May). *33rd Council for Mutual Economic Aid Meeting and Tenth Anniv of Vietnam's Membership.* T **250** *and similar vert design.* P 13.
1184	200d. multicoloured		1·50	50
1185	300d. dull ultramarine and olive-bistre		2·20	75

Design:—300d. COMECON headquarters building, Moscow.

1988 (1 June). *Child Vaccination Campaign.* P 13½ × 13.
1186	**251**	60d. red-orange, black and new blue	90	75

252 Emblem and Building   **253** Tôn Dúc Tháng

1988 (20 July). *30th Anniv of Peace and Socialism (magazine).* P 13.
1187   **252**   20d. multicoloured   75   35

1988 (20 Aug). *Birth Centenary of President Tôn Dúc Tháng.* P 13.
1188   **253**   150d. multicoloured   1·10   35

254 Emblem   **255** Pointed-scaled Pit Viper
(*Trimeresurus mucrosquamatus*)

1988 (28 Aug). *Sixth Trade Unions Congress.* T **254** *and similar vert design. Multicoloured.* P 13.
1189   50d. Type **254**   60   35
1190   100d. "VI" and couple   90   35

(Litho National Ptg Wks, Havana)

1988 (5 Sept). *Snakes.* T **255** *and similar multicoloured designs.* P 13.
1191   10d. Type **255**   35   15
1192   10d. Pope's pit viper (*Trimeresurus popeorum*)   35   15
1193   20d. Banded krait (*Bungarus fasciatus*)   60   20
1194   20d. Malayan krait (*Bungarus candidus*)   60   20
1195   30d. Coral snake (*Calliophis maclellandi*)   65   30
1196   30d. Striped beaked snake (*Ancistridon acutus*)   65   30
1197   50d. King cobra (*Ophiophagus hannah*) (*vert*)   90   45
1191/1197 *Set of 7*   3·75   1·60

256 Family (Triêu Khắc Tiến)

(Litho National Ptg Wks, Havana)

1988 (25 Sept). *Children's Drawings.* T **256** *and similar multicoloured designs.* P 12½ × 12 (horiz) or 12 × 12½ (vert).
1198   10d. Type **256**   30   20
1199   10d. Couple and house (Phuong Ti)   30   20
1200   20d. Fishermen (Lâm Hoàng Thắng)   60   35

1201   20d. Children Flying kite (Nguyêñ Xuân Anh)   60   35
1202   30d. Couple (Hông Hanh) (*vert*)   80   35
1203   30d. Animals and girl playing guitar (Quynh Mây)   80   35
1204   50d. Woman holding dove (Ta Phuong Trà) (*vert*)   1·00   50
1198/1204 *Set of 7*   4·00   2·10
MS1205 100 × 80 mm. 80d. Couple with child (Hông Hanh) (*vert*)   3·00   1·30

257 Tri An

(Des T. T. Vinh)

1988 (27 Sept). *U.S.S.R.–Vietnam Co-operation. Hydro-electric Power Stations.* T **257** *and similar horiz designs.* P 13.
1206   2000d. black, bright orange and vermilion   3·75   2·20
1207   3000d. black, yellow-bistre & brt scarlet   5·25   3·00
Design:—3000d. Hoa Binh.

258 Kamov Ka-26

(Litho National Ptg Wks, Havana)

1988 (9 Oct). *Helicopters.* T **258** *and similar horiz designs Multicoloured.* P 13.
1208   10d. Type **258**   30   15
1209   10d. Boeing-Vertol 234 Commercial Chinook   30   15
1210   20d. MBB-Bolkow Bo 105   50   20
1211   20d. Mil Mi-10K   50   20
1212   30d. Kawasaki-Hughes 369HS   60   30
1213   30d. Bell 206 JetRanger   60   30
1214   50d. Mil Mi-8   75   45
1208/1214 *Set of 7*   3·25   1·60
MS1215 87 × 86 mm. 80d. Sud Aviation SA 330 Puma (39 × 31 *mm*). P 12½   2·50   1·30

259 Gaur (*Bos gaurus*)   **260** Flower and Banners

(Litho National Ptg Wks, Havana)

1988 (20 Oct). *Mammals. T* **259** *and similar horiz designs. Multicoloured.* P 12½.

1216	10d. Type **259**	20	15
1217	10d. Banteng (*Bos banteng*)	20	15
1218	20d. Malayan tapir (*Tapirus indicus*)	60	20
1219	20d. Hog deer (*Axis porcinus*)	60	20
1220	30d. Mainland serow (*Capricornis sumatraensis*)	75	35
1221	30d. Wild boar (*Sus scrofa*)	75	35
1222	50d. Water buffalo (*Bubalus bubalis*)	1·00	50
1216/1222 *Set of 7*		3·75	1·75

MS1223 82 × 62 mm. 80d. Javan rhinoceros (*Rhinoceros sondaicus*) (wrongly inscr "sodaicus") . . . . 3·00 1·30

(Des T. T. Vinh)

1988 (3 Nov). *Tenth Anniv of U.S.S.R.–Vietnam Friendship.* P 13½ × 13.

1224	**260** 50d. multicoloured	60	45

261 Indian Star Tortoise (*Testudo elegans*)　　**262** Skaters

(Litho National Ptg Wks, Havana)

1988 (6 Nov). *Turtles and Tortoises. T* **261** *and similar vert designs. Multicoloured.* P 12½.

1225	10d. Type **261**	35	20
1226	10d. Three-banded box turtle (*Cuora trifasciata*)	35	20
1227	20d. Big-headed turtle (*Platysternon megacephalum*)	50	30
1228	20d. Hawksbill turtle (*Eretmochelys imbricata*)	50	30
1229	30d. Indian Ocean green turtle (*Chelonia mydas*)	60	35
1230	30d. Leatherback turtle (*Dermochelys coriacea*)	60	35
1231	50d. Loggerhead turtle (*Caretta caretta*)	75	45
1225/1231 *Set of 7*		3·25	1·90

MS1232 80 × 98 mm. 80d. Loggerhead turtle (*different*) . . . . 2·50 1·20
No. **MS**1232 commemorates "Finland 88" International Stamp Exhibition, Helsinki.

(Litho National Ptg Wks, Havana)

1988 (10 Dec). *Ice Skating. T* **262** *and similar multicoloured designs showing different skating scenes.* P 13.

1233	10d. multicoloured	20	10
1234	10d. multicoloured	20	10
1235	20d. multicoloured	45	15
1236	20d. multicoloured (*horiz*)	45	15
1237	30d. multicoloured	60	30
1238	30d. multicoloured (*horiz*)	60	30
1239	50d. multicoloured (*horiz*)	75	45
1233/1239 *Set of 7*		3·00	1·40

MS1240 100 × 65 mm. 80d. multicoloured (39 × 31 *mm*) . . . . 3·00 1·20

263 Bowden "Spacelander"　　**264** Fidel Castro

(Litho National Ptg Wks, Havana)

1988 (20 Dec). *Bicycles. T* **263** *and similar horiz designs. Multicoloured.* P 13.

1241	10d. Type **263**	30	15
1242	10d. Rabasa Derbi with red tyres	30	15
1243	20d. Huffy	50	20
1244	20d. Rabasa Derbi with black tyres	50	20
1245	30d. VMX-PL	60	30
1246	30d. Premier	60	30
1247	50d. Columbia RX5	75	45
1241/1247 *Set of 7*		3·25	1·60

1988 (27 Dec). *30th Anniv of Cuban Revolution. T* **264** *and similar vert designs. Multicoloured.* P 13½ × 13.

1248	100d. Type **264**	30	10
1249	300d. National flags and Cuban and Vietnamese workers	80	35

265 Cosmonauts on Spacecraft Wing　　**266** *Conus miles* (Soldier Cone)

(Litho National Ptg Wks, Havana)

1988 (29 Dec). *Cosmonauts Day. T* **265** *and similar vert designs showing various space scenes. Multicoloured.* P 13.

1250	10d. Type **265**	15	10
1251	10d. Spacecraft moving across surface of planet	15	10
1252	20d. Space rocket heading for planet	45	15
1253	20d. Spacecraft and cosmonauts on planet with Earth in sky	45	15
1254	30d. Spacecraft hovering over surface	75	30
1255	30d. "Soyuz"–"Salyut" complex	75	30
1256	50d. Space "bubble" and rocket	1·00	45
1250/1256 *Set of 7*		3·25	1·40

MS1257 65 × 75 mm. 80d. Spacecraft (31 × 39 *mm*) . . . . 3·00 1·20

(Litho National Ptg Wks, Havana)

1988 (30 Dec). *Sea Shells. T* **266** *and similar horiz designs. Multicoloured.* P 12½ × 12.

1258	10d. Type **266**	20	20
1259	10d. *Strombus lentiginosus* (Silver conch)	20	20
1260	20d. *Bursa rana* (Common frogshell)	45	35
1261	20d. *Turbo petholatus* (Tapestry turban)	45	35
1262	30d. *Oliva minacea* (Red-mouth olive)	75	35

```
1263   30d. Nautilus pompilius           75     35
1264   50d. Mitra mitra (Episcopal mitre)
           (wrongly inscr "eriscopalis")   1·00   50
1258/1264 Set of 7                        3·50   2·10
MS1265 90 × 65 mm. 80d. Tonna tessellata   3·00   1·30
   The inscriptions on Nos. 1261 and 1263 have been transposed.
```

270 Junk from Quang Nam

(Des Dinh Luc. Litho National Ptg Wks, Havana)

267 Class VL85 Diesel
Locomotive, Russia

268 Gourd
(*Lagenaria siceraria*)

(Litho National Ptg Wks, Havana)

1988 (30 Dec). *Locomotives.* T **267** *and similar horiz designs.*
Multicoloured. P 13.

```
1266   20d. Type 267                      45     20
1267   20d. LRC high speed diesel train,
           Canada                         45     20
1268   20d. Monorail, Japan               45     20
1269   20d. Kitta 80 diesel railcar, Japan 45    20
1270   30d. Class DR 1A diesel-electric,
           U.S.S.R.                        75     30
1271   30d. Class RC 1 electric locomotive 75    30
1272   50d. Class TE-136 diesel-electric
           locomotive, Russia            1·00    75
1266/1272 Set of 7                       4·00   1·40
MS1273 102 × 71 mm. 80d. "Z6400", France
   (36 × 26 mm)                          3·00   1·20
```

1989 (8 Jan). *Regional Fishing Junks.* T **270** *and similar horiz
designs. Multicoloured.* P 12½ × 12.

```
1283   10d. Type 270                      35     30
1284   10d. Quang Tri                     35     30
1285   20d. Tha Thiên                     50     30
1286   20d. Dà Nang                       50     30
1287   30d. Quang Tri (different)         60     30
1288   30d. Dà Nang (different)           60     30
1289   50d. Huê                           75     30
1283/1289 Set of 7                       3·25   1·90
```

271 Juniona evarete

(Litho National Ptg Wks, Havana)

1989 (17 Jan). *"India-89" International Stamp Exhibition, New
Delhi (1st issue). Butterflies.* T **271** *and similar horiz designs.*
Multicoloured. P 12½.

```
1290   50d. Type 271                      30     35
1291   50d. Anaea echemus                 30     35
1292   50d. Ascia monuste                 30     35
1293  100d. Phoebis avellaneda            45     35
1294  100d. Eurema proterpia              45     35
1295  200d. Papilio palamedes             90     35
1296  300d. Danaus plexippus            1·00     35
1290/1296 Set of 7                      3·25   2·20
MS1297 87 × 77 mm. 400d. Parides
   gundlachiamus (39 × 31 mm)            2·50   1·20
```

Nos. 1290/6 were each issued with *se-tenant* half stamp-size
label illustrating the chrysalis stage of the featured butterfly.

(Litho National Ptg Wks, Havana)

1988 (30 Dec). *Fruits.* T **268** *and similar vert designs.*
Multicoloured. P 12 × 12½.

```
1274   10d. Type 268                      20     35
1275   10d. Momordica charantia           20     35
1276   20d. Pumpkin (Cucurbita moschata)  60     35
1277   20d. Eggplant (Solanum melongena)  60     35
1278   30d. Benincasa hispida             75     35
1279   30d. Luffa gourd (Luffa cylindrica)
           (wrongly inscr "Cylidrica")    75     35
1280   50d. Tomatoes (Lycopercicon
           esculentum)                  1·00     35
1274/1280 Set of 7                      3·75   2·20
```

272 Indian Flag
and
T-
elecommunicati-
ons

273 Festival

269 Soldiers and Field Workers

(Des Viet Tuan)

1989 (7 Jan). *Tenth Anniv of People's Republic of
Kampuchea.* T **269** *and similar horiz design. Multicoloured.*
P 13 × 13½.

```
1281  100d. Type 269                      45     35
1282  500d. Crowd greeting soldier and mother
           with child                    1·80    75
```

1989 (20 Jan). *"India-89" International Stamp Exhibition, New
Delhi (2nd issue).* T **272** *and similar vert designs.* P 13½ × 13.

```
1298  100d. multicoloured                 35     30
1299  100d. multicoloured                 35     30
1300  300d. multicoloured                 80     30
1301  600d. chocolate, bright orange &
           emerald                       1·80    60
1298/1301 Set of 4                       3·00   1·40
```

Designs:—No. 1299, Oil and electricity industries; 1300, Government Secretariat and Asokan capital; 1301, Jawaharlal Nehru (Indian statesman, birth centenary).

1989 (10 Feb). *Bicentenary of Battle of Dongda. T* **273** *and similar horiz design.* P 13½ × 13.
1302	100d. reddish violet and emerald	35	20
1303	1000d. deep mauve and bright rose	2·20	1·30

Design:—1000d. Battle scene.

274 Emblems on Banner

(Des T. T. Vinh)

1989 (1 Mar). *Centenary of Interparliamentary Union. T* **274** *and similar horiz design.* P 13 × 13½.
1304	100d. multicoloured	45	30
1305	200d. gold, dull ultram & lt greenish bl	1·00	30

Design:—200d. "100" on banner.

275 Dachshunds

(Litho National Ptg Wks, Havana)

1989 (20 Apr). *Dogs. T* **275** *and similar multicoloured designs.* P 12½.
1306	50d. Type **275**	30	10
1307	50d. Basset hounds	30	10
1308	50d. Setters (*vert*)	30	10
1309	100d. Hunting dogs (*vert*)	45	20
1310	100d. Basset hounds (66 × 25 *mm*)	45	20
1311	200d. Hound (*vert*)	90	35
1312	300d. Basset hound puppy	90	60
1306/1312 *Set of 7*		3·25	1·50

276 Footballers   **277** Jug

(Litho National Ptg Wks, Havana)

1989 (22 Apr). *World Cup Football Championship, Italy* (*1st issue*). *T* **276** *and similar multicoloured designs.* P 13.
1313	50d. Type **276**	30	10
1314	50d. Striker and goalkeeper	30	10
1315	50d. Goalkeeper	30	10
1316	100d. Player No. 5 tackling	45	20
1317	100d. Tackling (*vert*)	45	20
1318	200d. Player No. 3 (*vert*)	90	35
1319	300d. Players heading ball (*vert*)	1·00	60
1313/1319 *Set of 7*		3·25	1·50
MS1320 62 × 92 mm. 400d. Player (31 × 38 *mm*)		3·00	1·20

See also Nos. 1382/**MS**1389 and 1482/9.

(Des Nghiêp. Litho National Ptg Wks, Havana)

1989 (1 May). *Pottery T* **277** *and similar vert designs. Multicoloured.* P 12½ × 12.
1321	50d. Type **277**	30	15
1322	100d. Bowl with geometric pattern	45	20
1323	100d. Round pot with flower decoration	45	20
1324	200d. Tall pot with animal decoration	90	35
1325	300d. Vase	1·00	50
1321/1325 *Set of 5*		2·75	1·25

278 Baby Thanh Giong with Mother

(Des T. T. Vinh. Litho National Ptg Wks, Havana)

1989 (1 May). *Legend of Thanh Giong. T* **278** *and similar horiz designs. Multicoloured.* P 12½ × 12.
1326	50d. Type **278**	30	15
1327	100d. Thanh Giong with King's messenger	45	20
1328	100d. Thanh Giong at head of army	45	20
1329	200d. Thanh Giong beating out flames	90	35
1330	300d. Thanh Giong riding to heaven	1·00	50
1326/1330 *Set of 5*		2·75	1·25

279 Fuchsia fulgens   **280** Bird carrying Envelope above Dish Aerial

(Des L. Tuân. Litho National Ptg Wks, Havana)

1989 (10 May). *Flowers. T* **279** *and similar vert designs. Multicoloured.* P 12½.
1331	50d. Type **279**	30	10
1332	50d. Bird-of-paradise flower (*Strelitzia reginae*)	30	10
1333	100d. Glory lily (*Gloriosa superba*)	45	20
1334	100d. Orange day lily (*Hemerocallis fulva*)	45	20
1335	200d. Paphiopedilum siamense	90	35
1336	300d. Iris sp.	1·00	60
1331/1336 *Set of 6*		3·00	1·40

On Nos. 1332 and 1335 the inscriptions have been transposed.

1989 (5 June). *Communications.* P 13.
1337	**280** 100d. yellow-brown	60	20

281 Birds   **282** "Return from Varennes"

(Des T. T. Vinh (1338/9))

1989 (14 July). *Bicentenary of French Revolution and "Philexfrance 89" International Stamp Exhibition, Paris.*

(a) T **281** *and similar vert design. Multicoloured.* P 13½ × 13.

1338	100d. Type **281**	30	20
1339	500d. "Liberty guiding the People" (detail, Eugene Delacroix)	1·20	50

(b) T **282** *and similar multicoloured designs.* P 13½ × 13 (horiz) or 13 × 13½ (vert). *Litho National Ptg Wks, Havana.*

1340	50d. Type **282**	30	15
1341	50d. "Revolutionary Court"	30	15
1342	50d. "Oath of the Tennis Court" (Jacques-Louis David) (*vert*)	30	15
1343	100d. "Assassination of Marat" (David) (*vert*)	45	20
1344	100d. "Storming the Bastille" (*vert*)	45	20
1345	200d. Two children (Pierre-Paul Prud'hon) (*vert*)	90	35
1346	300d. "Slave Trade" (Jean-Léon Gérme)	1·40	80
1338/1346	*Set of 9*	5·00	2·40

MS1347 105 × 105 mm. 400d. "Liberty guiding the People" (Eugene Delacroix) (32 × 43 *mm*). P 13 .... 2·50   1·30

283 Man and Ox   **284** Appaloosa

(Des Mrs. Nguyên Thi Sâm)

1989 (14 Sept). *Rice Cultivation.* T **283** *and similar vert designs. Multicoloured.* P 12 × 12½.

1348	50d. Type **283**	30	15
1349	100d. Ploughing with ox	45	20
1350	100d. Flooding fields	45	20
1351	200d. Fertilizing	90	35
1352	300d. Harvesting crop	1·00	50
1348/1352	*Set of 5*	2·75	1·25

(Litho National Ptg Works, Havana)

1989 (15 Sept). *Horses.* T **284** *and similar horiz designs. Multicoloured.* P 12½ (300d.) or 13 (others).

1353	50d. Type **284**	30	10
1354	50d. Tennesse walking horse	30	10
1355	50d. Tersky	30	10
1356	100d. Kladruber	45	20
1357	100d. Welsh cob	45	20
1358	200d. Pinto	90	35
1359	300d. Pony and bridle (68 × 27 *mm*)	1·00	60
1353/1359	*Set of 7*	3·25	1·50

285 Brandenburg Gate, Flag and Emblem

(Des Mrs. Nguyên Thi Sâm)

1989 (7 Oct). *40th Anniv of German Democratic Republic.* P 13.

1360	**285**	200d. greenish yellow, black & mag	75	35

286 Polio Oral Vaccination   **287** Horse

1989 (20 Oct). *Immunization Campaign.* T **286** *and similar horiz designs.* P 13.

1361	100d. chestnut, black and red	35	30
1362	100d. carmine-rose, black and blue-green	35	30
1363	100d. yellow-olive, black and red	35	30

Designs:—No. 1362, Vaccinating pregnant woman; 1363, Health clinic.

(Des T. T. Vinh. Litho National Ptg Wks, Havana)

1989 (1 Dec). *Paintings of Horses by Hsu Pei-Hung.* T **287** *and similar multicoloured designs.* P 13.

1364	100d. Type **287**	15	15
1365	200d. Two horses galloping	20	15
1366	300d. Three horses grazing	35	15
1367	500d. Horse galloping (*horiz*)	50	15
1368	800d. Galloping horse	90	20
1369	1000d. Two horses under tree	1·20	30
1370	1500d. Galloping horse (*different*)	1·50	35
1364/1370	*Set of 7*	4·25	1·30

MS1371 117 × 72 mm. 2000d. Horses (43 × 32 *mm*) .... 4·50   1·30

288 Niña, Pinta and Santa Maria and Mochica Ceramic Figure

(Litho National Ptg Wks, Havana)

1989 (31 Dec). *500th Anniv (1992) of Discovery of America by Columbus (1st issue).* T **288** *and similar horiz designs. Multicoloured.* P 12½.

1372	50d. Type **288**	20	20
1373	100d. Columbus and King Ferdinand the Catholic and Peruvian ceramic bottle	50	50
1374	100d. Columbus's arrival at Rabida and Mexican decorated vessel	50	50

1375 100d. Columbus offering gifts
(18th-century engraving) and
human shaped jug 50 50
1376 200d. Early map and Peruvian
ceramic 95 95
1377 200d. Portrait and arms of Columbus
and Nazca ceramic 95 95
1378 300d. Chart by Toscanelli and Chimu
vessel . . . . . . 1·10 1·10
1372/1378 Set of 7 . . . . . 4·25 4·25
MS1379 85 × 69 mm. 500d. Teotihuacana
lidded vessel (36 × 30 mm) . . 2·50 2·50
See also Nos. 1545/**MS**1552 and 1664/**MS**1669.

289 Storming of Presidential Palace,
Saigon, and Ho Chi Minh

1990 (3 Feb). 60th Anniv of Vietnamese Communist Party. T **289**
and similar horiz design. Multicoloured. P 13.
1380 100d. Type **289** 45 35
1381 500d. Industry, workers, hammer and
sickle and flag . . . . 1·80 75

290 Players

(Litho National Ptg Wks, Havana)

1990 (15 Feb). World Cup Football Championship, Italy (2nd
issue). T **290** and similar designs showing footballers. P 13.
1382 100d. Type **290** 10 10
1383 200d. Argentina player with
possession 10 10
1384 300d. Netherlands and Scotland
players 15 15
1385 500d. Soviet Union player tackling 30 15
1386 1000d. Scotland and West Germany
player 60 20
1387 2000d. Soviet Union player losing
possession 90 35
1388 3000d. Goalkeeper . . . . 1·30 45
1382/1388 Set of 7 . . . . 3·00 1·30
MS1389 90 × 67 mm. 3500d. Boy with ball
behind goal net (30 × 37 mm) . . 2·20 1·20

291 Hybrids of Mallard and Local
Species

1990 (15 Feb). Ducks. T **291** and similar horiz designs.
Multicoloured. P 13.
1390 100d. Type **291** 10 15
a. Block of 6. Nos. 1390/5 . . 4·00
1391 300d. European mallard (Anas
penelope) 15 15
1392 500d. Mallards (Anas platyrhynchos) 30 15

1393 1000d. Red-billed pintails (Anas
erythrorhyncha) 60 20
1394 2000d. White duck preening . . 1·10 35
1395 3000d. African yellow-bills (Anas
undulata) . . . . 1·50 45
1390/1395 Set of 6 . . . . 3·40 1·30
Nos. 1390/5 were issued together in se-tenant blocks of six
stamps within the sheet.

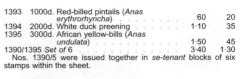

292 Mack Truck and Trailer

(Des Viet Tuàn and L. Nhi)

1990 (20 Feb). Trucks. T **292** and similar horiz designs.
Multicoloured. P 13.
1396 100d. Type **292** 15 15
1397 200d. Volvo "F89" tipper . . 15 15
1398 300d. Tatra "915 S1" tipper . . 20 15
1399 500d. Hino "KZ30000" lorry . . 20 15
1400 1000d. Italia Iveco 45 20
1401 2000d. Leyland-Daf "Super Comet"
tipper 90 35
1402 3000d. Kamas "53212" lorry . . 1·30 35
1396/1402 Set of 7 . . . . 3·00 1·30

293 8th/9th-century Viking Longship

(Des T. T. Vinh)

1990 (10 Mar). Sailing Ships. T **293** and similar multicoloured
designs. P 13.
1403 100d. Type **293** 10 10
1404 500d. 15th-century caravel . . 30 30
1405 1000d. 15th-century carrack (vert) 60 60
1406 1000d. 14th/15th-century carrack . 60 60
1407 1000d. 17th-century frigate . . 60 60
1408 2000d. 16th-century galleons and
pinnace (vert) . . . 1·20 1·20
1409 3000d. 16th-century galleon . . 1·50 1·50
1403/1409 Set of 7 . . . . 4·50 4·50
MS1410 60 × 53 mm. 4200d. Ancient Egyptian
Nile galley (43 × 32 mm) . . 2·50 2·50

294 Red-bodied Goldfish

(Des T. Liêu)

1990 (20 Mar). Goldfish (Carassius auratus auratus). T **294** and
similar designs depicting goldfish. P 13.
1411 100d. multicoloured 15 15
1412 300d. multicoloured 15 15
1413 500d. multicoloured 30 15
1414 1000d. multicoloured (vert) . . 50 20

1415	2000d. multicoloured (*vert*)	1·10	35
1416	3000d. multicoloured (*vert*)	1·50	45
1411/1416	Set of 6	3·25	1·30

295 Gate of Noble Mankind

(Des Dinh Lu)

1990 (2 Apr). *Hué Temples. T* **295** *and similar horiz designs. Multicoloured.* P 12½ × 12.

1417	100d. Type **295**	35	15
1418	100d. Lotus pool at tomb of Emperor Tu Dúc	35	15
1419	200d. Southern Gate	55	20
1420	300d. Thiên Pagoda	80	85
1417/1420	Set of 4	1·90	1·30
MS1421	97 × 68 mm. 400d. Great Stairway, Khai-Dinh burial place	1·70	1·00

296 "Antonia Zarate" (Francisco de Goya)

297 Henry Giffard's Steam-powered Dirigible Airship

(Des Sâm Hiêp)

1990 (10 Apr). *"Stamp World London 90" International Stamp Exhibition. T* **296** *and similar vert designs. Multicoloured.* P 13.

1422	100d. Type **296**	10	10
1423	200d. "Girl with Paper Fan" (Auguste Renoir)	10	10
1424	300d. "Janet Grizel" (John Russell)	15	15
1425	500d. "Love unfasten's Beauty's Girdle" (Joshua Reynolds)	25	15
1426	1000d. "Portrait of a Lady" (George Romney) (wrongly inscr "Omney")	55	20
1427	2000d. "Mme. Ginoux" (Vincent van Gogh)	1·00	35
1428	3000d. "Lady in Green" (Thomas Gainsborough)	1·30	40
1422/1428	Set of 7	3·25	1·30
MS1429	90 × 70 mm. 3500d. "Girl sitting in a Wheat Field" (Vincent van Gogh) (26 × 38 mm)	2·75	1·10

(Des Nhi Sâm (**MS**1437). Litho National Ptg Wks, Havana)

1990 (3 May). *"Helvetia 90" International Stamp Exhibition, Geneva. Airships, T* **297** *and similar horiz designs. Multicoloured.* P 13.

1430	100d. Type **297**	10	10
1431	200d. Lebaudy-Juillot airship No. 1 *La Jaune*	10	10
1432	300d. LZ-127 *Graf Zeppelin*	15	15
1433	500d. R-101	25	25
1434	1000d. *Osoaviachim*	55	55
1435	2000d. Tissandier Brothers' airship	1·10	1·10
1436	3000d. U.S. Navy "N" Class airship ZPN-1	1·60	1·60
1430/1436	Set of 7	3·50	3·50
MS1437	77 × 104 mm. 3500d. *Zodiac* (35 × 28 mm). P 12½	1·90	1·90

No. 1431 is wrongly inscribed "Lebandy".

298 Silver Tabby and White Cat

299 Ho Chi Minh, 1923

(Des Luong Nhi)

1990 (5 May). *Cats. T* **298** *and similar multicoloured designs.* P 13.

1438	100d. Type **298**	10	10
1439	200d. Black cat (*vert*)	10	10
1440	300d. Black and white cat	20	15
1441	500d. Brown tabby and white (*vert*)	35	15
1442	1000d. Silver tabby	60	20
1443	2000d. Tortoiseshell and white (*vert*)	80	35
1444	3000d. Tortoiseshell tabby and white (*vert*)	95	40
1438/1444	Set of 7	2·75	1·30
MS1445	67 × 95 mm. 3500d. Silver tabby (43 × 32 mm)	2·30	1·00

The miniature sheet commemorates "Belgica 90" Stamp Exhibition, Brussels.

(Des T. T. Vinh (**MS**1452))

1990 (13 May). *Birth Centenary of Ho Chi Minh. T* **299** *and similar vert designs. Multicoloured.* P 13.

1446	100d. Type **299**	10	10
1447	300d. Ho Chi Minh, 1945	15	15
1448	500d. Dove, hand holding rifle, and Ho Chi Minh	25	25
1449	1000d. Ho Chi Minh conducting	55	55
1450	2000d. Ho Chi Minh embracing child	80	80
1451	3000d. Globe and Ho Chi Minh	95	95
1446/1451	Set of 6	2·50	2·50
MS1452	86 × 94 mm. 3500d. Ho Chi Minh and star (29 × 42 mm)	1·90	1·90

300 King Charles Spaniel

301 Gorgosaurus

(Des Sâm)

1990 (15 May). *"New Zealand 90" International Stamp Exhibition, Auckland. Dogs. T* **300** *and similar vert designs. Multicoloured.* P 13.

1453	100d. Type **300**	10	10
1454	200d. Spaniel	10	10
1455	300d. Saluki	20	15
1456	500d. Dachshund	35	15

1457	1000d. Dalmatian	60	20
1458	2000d. Highland terrier	80	35
1459	3000d. Boxer	95	40
1453/1459	Set of 7	2·75	1·30
MS1460	85 × 85 mm. 3500d. Rough collie and pups (32 × 43 mm)	2·30	1·00

1990 (1 June). *Prehistoric Animals.* T **301** *and similar horiz designs. Multicoloured.* P 13.

1461	100d. Type **301**	10	10
1462	500d. Ceratosaurus	35	15
1463	1000d. Ankylosaurus	65	65
1464	2000d. Ankylosaurus (*different*)	1·50	1·50
1465	3000d. Edaphosaurus	1·70	1·70
1461/1465	Set of 5	3·75	3·75

302 High Jumping　　(**303**)　　(**304**)

(Des T. T. Vinh)

1990 (20 June). *11th Asian Games, Peking.* T **302** *and similar vert designs. Multicoloured.* P 13.

1466	100d. Type **302**	10	10
1467	200d. Basketball	10	10
1468	300d. Table tennis	15	15
1469	500d. Volleyball	25	25
1470	1000d. Gymnastics	60	60
1471	2000d. Tennis	1·10	1·10
1472	3000d. Judo	1·60	1·60
1466/1472	Set of 7	3·50	3·50
MS1473	73 × 93 mm. 3500d. Steeplechase (32 × 43 mm)	1·90	1·90

1990 (22 June). *Tourism. Nos.* 626/33 *optd with* T **303** *in brown-red and black.*

1474	50x. multicoloured (No. 626)	15	15
1475	50x. multicoloured (No. 627)	15	15
1476	50x. multicoloured (No. 628)	15	15
1477	50x. multicoloured (No. 629)	15	15
1478	1d. multicoloured	30	30
1479	2d. multicoloured	90	90
1480	5d. multicoloured	1·50	1·50
1481	10d. multicoloured	3·00	3·00
1474/1481	Set of 8	5·50	5·50

1990 (22 June). *World Cup Football Championship, Italy* (3rd issue). *Nos.* 457/64 *optd with* T **304** *in black, green and red.*

1482	30x. multicoloured (No. 457)	30	30
1483	30x. multicoloured (No. 458)	30	30
1484	40x. multicoloured (No. 459)	35	35
1485	40x. multicoloured (No. 460)	35	35
1486	50x. multicoloured (No. 461)	50	50
1487	50x. multicoloured (No. 462)	50	50
1488	60x. multicoloured	60	60
1489	1d. multicoloured	1·10	1·10
1482/1489	Set of 8	3·50	3·50

305 *Pyotr Yemtsov* (container ship)

1990 (20 July). *Ships.* T **305** *and similar horiz designs. Multicoloured.* P 13.

1490	100d. Type **305**	10	10
1491	300d. *Colima* (container ship)	15	15
1492	500d. *Crown Odyssey* (liner)	25	25
1493	1000d. *Ben Nevis* (tanker)	55	55
1494	2000d. *Saga Star* (Roll-on Roll-off ferry)	1·10	1·10
1495	3000d. Sealink train ferry	1·60	1·60
1490/1495	Set of 6	3·25	3·25

306 Emblem, Globe and Dove　　**307** Red Flags and Symbols of Construction and Agriculture

(Des T. T. Vinh)

1990 (15 Aug). *45th Anniv of Postal Service.* T **306** *and similar horiz design. Multicoloured.* P 13 × 13½.

1496	100d. Type **306**	10	10
1497	1000d. Emblem, dish aerial and globe	55	55

1990 (2 Sept). *45th Anniv of Independence.* T **307** *and similar vert designs. Multicoloured.* P 13½ × 13.

1498	100d. Type **307**	10	10
1499	500d. Map, storming of Government Palace (1945), siege of Dien Bien Phu and tank entering Presidential Palace, Saigon (1975)	25	25
1500	1000d. Satellite communications ship, dish aerial and "VI"	40	55
1501	3000d. Hammer and sickle, industrial symbols and couple	1·60	1·60
1498/1501	Set of 4	2·10	2·10
MS1502	69 × 105 mm. 3500d. State arms and Ho Chi Minh proclaiming independence (32 × 43 mm). P 13	1·90	1·90

308 Thach Sanh collecting Wood　　(**309**)

1. GERMANY
2. ARGENTINA
3. ITALY

(Des T. T. Vinh and V. Huyen)

1990 (5 Sept). *Legend of Thach Sanh.* T **308** *and similar vert designs. Multicoloured.* P 13.

1503	100d. Type **308**	10	10
	a. Block of 6. Nos. 1503/8	4·00	
1504	300d. L Thng	15	15
1505	500d. Thach Sanh fighting fire-breathing snake	25	25
1506	1000d. Thach Sanh shooting down bird	55	55

1507 2000d. Thach Sanh in prison . . . . . 1·10 1·10
1508 3000d. Thach Sanh and wife . . . . . 1·60 1·60
1503/1508 *Set of 6* . . . . 3·25 3·25
Nos. 1503/8 were issued together in *se-tenant* blocks of six within the sheet.

1990 (15 Sept). *World Cup Football Championship Results. Nos. 1382/MS1389 optd with T 309.*
1509 100d. multicoloured 10 10
1510 200d. multicoloured 10 10
1511 300d. multicoloured 15 15
1512 500d. multicoloured 25 25
1513 1000d. multicoloured 55 55
1514 2000d. multicoloured . . . . 1·10 1·10
1515 3000d. multicoloured . . . . 1·60 1·60
1509/1515 *Set of 7* . . . . 3·50 3·50
MS1516 90 × 67 mm. 3500d. multicoloured . . 2·40 2·40
The miniature sheet is overprinted in the margin.

BẢO VỆ RỪNG - RỪNG LÀ MÔI TRƯỜNG SỐNG

200ᵈ *Việt Nam*

313 Hands holding Forest and City

314 *Amanita pantherina*

(Des Vinh Dung)

1990 (15 Nov). *Preservation of Forests. T 313 and similar horiz design. Multicoloured. P 13½ × 13.*
1528 200d. Type **313** 20 10
1529 1000d. Forest fire, "S.O.S." and river . . 75 20

Việt Nam 100ᵈ

(**310**)   **311** Soldier

1990 (25 Sept). *Red Cross. "For the Future Generation". Nos. N598/605 optd with red cross and as T 310 in black, the inscription in various languages (given in brackets).*
1517 12x. multicoloured (Italian) 20 20
1518 12x. multicoloured (Chinese) 20 20
1519 20x. multicoloured (German) 35 35
1520 20x. multicoloured (Vietnamese) . . . 35 35
1521 30x. multicoloured (English) 55 55
1522 40x. multicoloured (Russian) 65 65
1523 50x. multicoloured (French) 80 80
1524 60x. multicoloured (Spanish) 95 95
1517/1524 *Set of 8* . . . . 3·50 3·50
On Nos. 1518, 1520 and 1522/4 the overprint is horizontal.

(Des Mrs. Vo Luong Nhi)

1991 (21 Jan). *Poisonous Fungi. T 314 and similar vert designs. Multicoloured. P 13.*
1530 200d. Type **314** 10 10
1531 300d. *Amanita phalloides* 20 10
1532 1000d. *Amanita virosa* 45 35
1533 1500d. *Amanita muscaria* 75 35
1534 2000d. *Russula emetica* . . . . . 1·10 35
1535 3000d. *Boletus satanas* . . . . . 1·50 60
1530/1535 *Set of 6* . . . . 3·50 2·00

Thuyền buồm

Việt Nam

315 High-Performance Dinghies

316 Nguyên Binh Khiêm

(Des Quốc Dung)

1991 (31 Jan). *Olympic Games, Barcelona (1992) (1st issue). T 315 and similar multicoloured designs. P 13.*
1536 200d. Type **315** 10 10
1537 300d. Boxing 20 10
1538 400d. Cycling 20 15
1539 1000d. High jumping 60 20
1540 2000d. Show jumping 95 20
1541 3000d. Judo . . . . 1·30 45
1542 3000d. Wrestling (*horiz*) . . . . . 1·30 45
1536/1542 *Set of 7* . . . . 4·25 1·50
MS1543 80 × 92 mm. 5000d. Football (43 × 32 mm). P 13 × 12½ . . . . 2·40 1·10
See also Nos. 1679/MS1686.

(Des Mrs. Nguyên Thi Sâm)

1990 (20 Oct). *60th Anniv of Vietnamese Women's Union. T 311 and similar horiz design. Multicoloured. P 13.*
1525 100d. Type **311** 10 10
1526 500d. Women in various occupations . . 25 25

VIỆT NAM

312 Emblems

1990 (20 Oct). *20th Anniv of Asian–Pacific Postal Training Centre, Bangkok. P 13.*
1527 **312** 150d. multicoloured 35 35

(Des Mrs. Vu Liên)

1991 (15 Feb). *500th Birth Anniv of Nguyên Binh Khiêm (poet). P 13.*
1544 **316** 200d. black, red-brown and ochre 35 20

317 *Marisiliana* **318** Woman in
Blue Tunic

(Des Mrs. Hoang Thuy Lieu)

1991 (22 Feb). *500th Anniv (1992) of Discovery of America by Columbus (2nd issue). T* **317** *and similar multicoloured designs.* P 13.

1545	200d. Type **317**		10	10
1546	400d. Venitien		20	15
1547	400d. Cromster (vert)		20	15
1548	2000d. Pinta		85	20
1549	2000d. Niña		85	20
1550	3000d. Howker (vert)		1·20	35
1551	5000d. Santa Maria		2·00	60
1545/1551 Set of 7			4·75	1·60
MS1552 98 × 74 mm. 6500d. Columbus (39 × 27 mm)			2·40	1·10

(Des Mrs. Vo Luong Nhi)

1991 (26 Feb). *Golden Heart Charity. T* **318** *and similar vert designs showing traditional women's costumes.* P 13½ × 13.

1553	200d. multicoloured		10	10
1554	500d. multicoloured		15	15
1555	1000d. multicoloured		45	15
1556	5000d. multicoloured		2·10	60
1553/1556 Set of 4			2·50	90

319 Japanese White-naped Crane (*Grus vipio*)

(Des Mrs. Vu Liên)

1991 (14 Mar). *Birds. T* **319** *and similar multicoloured designs.* P 13.

1557	200d. Type **319**		15	15
1558	300d. Sarus crane chick (Grus antigone) (vert)		15	15
1559	400d. Manchurian crane (Grus japonensis) (vert)		25	15
1560	1000d. Sarus cranes (adults) (vert)		40	15
1561	2000d. Black-necked crane (Grus nigricollis) (vert)		85	40
1562	3000d. South African crowned cranes (Balearica regulorum) (vert)		1·50	55
1563	3000d. Great white crane (Bugeranus leucogerranus)		1·50	55
1557/1563 Set of 7			4·25	1·90

320 Black-finned Reef Shark
(*Carcharhinus melanopterus*)

(Des T. T. Vinh)

1991 (6 Apr). *Sharks. T* **320** *and similar horiz designs. Multicoloured.* P 13.

1564	200d. Type **320**		10	10
1565	300d. Grey reef shark (Carcharhinus amblyrhynchos)		10	10
1566	400d. Leopard shark (Triakis semifasciata)		20	15
1567	1000d. Great hammerhead (Sphyrna mokarran)		35	15
1568	2000d. Whitetip reef shark (Triaenodon obesus)		75	35
1569	3000d. Sand tiger (Carcharias laurus)		1·30	45
1570	3000d. Bull shark (Carcharhinus leucas)		1·30	45
1564/1570 Set of 7			3·75	1·60

321 Lobster (*Palinurus* sp.) **322** *Fusée*, 1829

(Des Mrs. Nguyên Thi Sâm)

1991 (20 Apr). *Shellfish. T* **321** *and similar horiz designs. Multicoloured.* P 13.

1571	200d. Type **321**		10	10
1572	300d. Alpheus bellulus		10	10
1573	400d. Periclemenes brevicarpalis		20	15
1574	1000d. Lobster (different)		35	15
1575	2000d. Lobster (different)		75	35
1576	3000d. Lobster (different)		1·30	45
1577	3000d. Astacus sp.		1·30	45
1571/1577 Set of 7			3·75	1·60

(Des Mrs. Hoang Thuy Lieu)

1991 (10 May). *Early Locomotives. T* **322** *and similar multicoloured designs.* P 13.

1578	400d. Type **322**		15	15
1579	400d. Blenkinsop's rack locomotive (inscr "Puffing Billy")		15	15
1580	500d. John Stevens rack locomotive, 1825 (horiz)		20	15
1581	1000d. Crampton No. 80 locomotive, 1852 (horiz)		35	20
1582	2000d. Locomotion, 1825 (horiz)		75	35
1583	3000d. Saint-L, 1843 (horiz)		1·30	45
1584	3000d. Coutances, 1855 (horiz)		1·30	45
1578/1584 Set of 7			3·75	1·70
MS1585 83 × 62 mm. 5000d. Atlantic, 1843 (32 × 43 mm)			2·40	1·10

323 Ho Chi Minh, "VII" and Buildings

324 Pioneers

1991 (19 May). *Seventh Vietnamese Communist Party Congress. T* **323** *and similar vert designs. Multicoloured.* P 13.

1586	200d. Type **323**	20	15
1587	300d. Workers	35	20
1588	400d. Mother and children	45	20

(Des Mrs. Nguyên Thi Sâm)

1991 (19 May). *50th Anniv of Vietnam Youth Pioneers (200d.) and United Nations Convention on Children's Rights (400d.). T* **324** *and similar vert design. Multicoloured.* P 13.

1589	200d. Type **324**	35	20
1590	400d. Child's face and U.N. emblem	60	35

325 Lada

(Des T. T. Vinh)

1991 (24 May). *Rally Cars. T* **325** *and similar horiz designs. Multicoloured.* P 13.

1591	400d. Type **325**	15	15
1592	400d. Nissan	15	15
1593	500d. Ford Sierra RS Cosworth	20	15
1594	1000d. Suzuki	35	15
1595	2000d. Mazda "323"	75	35
1596	3000d. Peugeot	1·30	45
1597	3000d. Lancia	1·30	45
1591/1597 *Set of 7*		3·75	1·70
MS1598 85 × 75 mm. 5000d. Peugeot "405" (43 × 29 *mm*)		3·00	1·10

326 Yellow-banded Poison-arrow Frog (*Dendrobates leucomelas*)

327 Ho Chi Minh and Party Emblem

(Des Mrs. Vo Luong Nhl)

1991 (12 June). *Frogs. T* **326** *and similar vert designs. Multicoloured.* P13 × 13½.

1599	200d. Type **326**	15	15
1600	400d. Edible frog (*Rana esculenta*)	15	15
1601	500d. Golden mantella (*Mantella aurantiaca*)	25	15
1602	1000d. Dyeing poison-arrow frog (*Dendrobates tinctorius*)	40	15
1603	2000d. Tree frog (*Hyla hallowelli*)	85	40
1604	3000d. Red-eyed tree frog (*Agalychnis calidryas*)	1·50	55
1605	3000d. Golden tree frog (*Hyla aurea*)	1·50	55
1599/1605 *Set of 7*		4·25	1·90

(Des T. T. Vinh)

1991 (24 June). *60th Anniv (1990) of Vietnamese Communist Party.* P 13 × 13½.

1606	**327** 100d. rose-red	45	15

328 Speed Skating

(Des T. T. Vinh)

1991 (15 July). *Winter Olympic Games, Albertville (1992). (1st issue). T* **328** *and similar multicoloured designs.* P 13.

1607	200d. Type **328**	15	15
1608	300d. Freestyle skiing	15	15
1609	400d. Four-man bobsleighing (*horiz*)	20	15
1610	1000d. Biathlon (rifle shooting) (*horiz*)	35	15
1611	2000d. Skiing (*horiz*)	75	35
1612	3000d. Cross-country skiing	1·30	45
1613	3000d. Ice skating	1·30	45
1607/1613 *Set of 7*		3·75	1·70
MS1614 93 × 106 mm. 5000d. Ice hockey (32 × 43 *mm*). P 12½ × 13		2·30	1·10

See also Nos. 1659/63.

329 Arsinoitherium zitteli

330 Pawn

(Des Mrs. Nguyên Thi Sâm and Mrs. Vu Liên)

1991 (26 July). *Prehistoric Animals. T* **329** *and similar horiz designs. Multicoloured.* P 13.

1615	200d. Type **329**	15	15
	a. Block of 6. Nos. 1615/20	5·00	
1616	500d. *Elephas primigenius*	20	15
1617	1000d. *Baluchitherium*	35	20
1618	2000d. *Deinotherium giganteum*	1·10	35
1619	3000d. *Brontops*	1·50	45
1620	3000d. *Uintatherium*	1·50	45
1615/1620 *Set of 6*		4·25	1·60

Nos. 1615/20 were issued together in *se-tenant* blocks of six stamps within the sheet.

(Des Mrs. Nguyên Thi Sâm)

1991 (20 Aug). *Chess. T* **330** *and similar vert designs showing Staunton pieces. Multicoloured.* P 13.

1621	200d. Type **330**	15	15
1622	300d. Knight	20	15
1623	1000d. Rook	35	20
1624	2000d. Queen	85	45
1625	3000d. Bishop	1·30	45
1626	3000d. King	1·30	45
1621/1626 *Set of 6*		3·75	1·70

MS1627 92 × 70 mm. 5000d. Knight, pawn and king. P 12½ × 13 . . . . 2·30 1·10

331 Atlas Moth (*Attacus atlas*)

(Des Quôć Dung and Mrs. Vu Lién)

1991 (29 Aug). *"Phila Nippon '91" International Stamp Exhibition, Tokyo. Moths and Butterflies. T* **331** *and similar multicoloured designs.* P 13.

1628	200d. Type **331**	15	15
1629	400d. Blue morpho (*Morpho cypris*)	20	15
1630	500d. Birdwing (*Troides rotschildi*)	20	15
1631	1000d. Red admiral (*Vanessa atalanta*)	45	20
1632	1000d. *Papilio demetrius*	45	20
1633	3000d. *Papilio weiskei*	1·20	45
1634	5000d. Lesser purple emperor (*Apatura ilia substituta*)	1·70	60
1628/1634 *Set of 7*		4·00	1·70

MS1635 85 × 87 mm. 5500d. *Heliconius melpomene-aglaope* (43 × 32 mm). P 13 × 12½ . . . . 2·30 1·10

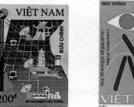

332 Means of Communication

333 Eye and Clasped Hands

(Des Mrs. Vu Lién)

1991 (17 Sept). *25th Anniv of Posts and Telecommunications Research Institute. T* **332** *and similar horiz design. Multicoloured.* P 13.

1636 200d. Type **332** 35 20
MS1637 90 × 73 mm. 3500d. Means of communication (*different*) (43 × 32 *mm*) . . . 1·70 1·00

(Des Mrs. Hoang Thuy Lieu)

1991 (19 Dec). *Golden Heart Charity for Disabled People. T* **333** *and similar vert design.* P 13.

1638	200d. royal blue, bright lilac & brt orange	15	15
1639	3000d. bluish violet, new bl & greenish bl	1·20	45

Design:—3000d. Tennis player in wheelchair.

334 Gymnastics

(335)

(Litho National Ptg Wks, Havana)

1992 (9 Jan). *Olympic Games, Los Angeles* (1984). *T* **334** *and similar multicoloured designs.* P 12½.

1640	50x. Type **334**	15	10
1641	50x. Football (*vert*)	15	10
1642	1d. Wrestling	25	15
1643	2d. Volleyball (*vert*)	55	15
1644	3d. Hurdling	65	25
1645	5d. Basketball (*vert*)	80	45
1646	8d. Weightlifting	1·70	75
1640/1646 *Set of 7*		3·75	1·75

MS1647 80 × 100 mm, 10d. Running (31 × 39 mm) . . . . 3·25 1·70

1992 (15 Jan). *"Expo '92" World's Fair, Seville. Nos.* 1372/ **MS**1379 *optd with T* **335** *in carmine.*

1648	50d. multicoloured	20	15
1649	100d. multicoloured (No. 1373)	45	20
1650	100d. multicoloured (No. 1374)	45	20
1651	100d. multicoloured (No. 1375)	45	20
1652	200d. multicoloured (No. 1376)	85	35
1653	200d. multicoloured (No. 1377)	85	35
1654	300d. multicoloured	1·50	85
1648/1654 *Set of 7*		4·25	2·10

MS1655 85 × 69 mm. 500d. multicoloured . . . 3·00 1·20
The miniature sheet is overprinted in the margin.

336 Chu Van An teaching

337 Atomic Symbol, Communications, Industry and Agriculture

(Des Mrs. Vo Luong Nhi)

1992 (18 Jan). *700th Death Anniv of Chu Van An.* P 13.
1656 **336** 200d. multicoloured . . . . . 2·00 2·00

(Des Mrs. Vu Liên and T. T. Vinh)

1992 (3 Feb). *Resolutions of Seventh Communist Party Congress. T 337 and similar vert design. Multicoloured.* P 13.
1657	200d. Type **337**	15	15
1658	2000d. Hands clasped and map of Asia	1·60	1·30

340 Tupolev Tu-154M

341 Weather System and Forecasting Equipment

(Des Mrs. Nguyên Thi Sâm)

1992 (6 Mar). *Aircraft. T 340 and similar horiz designs. Multicoloured.* P 13.
1670	400d. Type **340**	15	15
1671	500d. Concorde	15	15
1672	1000d. Airbus Industrie A320	20	15
1673	3000d. Airbus Industrie A340-300	25	20
1674	4000d. De Havilland D.H.C.8 Dash Eight-400	80	20
1675	5000d. Boeing 747-200	1·10	45
1676	6000d. McDonnell Douglas MD-11CF	1·30	45
1670/1676 *Set of 7*		3·50	1·60

338 Biathlon

(Des T. T. Vinh)

1992 (5 Feb). *Winter Olympic Games, Albertville (2nd issue). T 338 and similar diamond-shaped designs. Multicoloured.* P 13.
1659	200d. Type **338**	15	15
1660	2000d. Ice hockey	45	15
1661	4000d. Skiing (slalom)	85	20
1662	5000d. Ice skating	1·10	45
1663	6000d. Skiing (downhill)	1·50	60
1659/1663 *Set of 5*		3·50	1·40

(Des T. T. Vinh)

1992 (23 Mar). *International Decade for Natural Disaster Reduction. T 341 and similar vert design. Multicoloured.* P 13.
1677	400d. Type **341**	15	15
1678	4000d. Man taking flood depth readings	85	35

342 Archery   343 Suzuki "500 F"

(Des Mrs. Vu Liên)

1992 (28 Mar). *Olympic Games, Barcelona (2nd issue). T 342 and similar vert designs. Multicoloured.* P 13.
1679	400d. Type **342**	15	15
1680	600d. Volleyball	15	15
1681	1000d. Wrestling	20	15
1682	3000d. Fencing	45	20
1683	4000d. Running	80	20
1684	5000d. Weightlifting	95	35
1685	6000d. Hockey	1·30	60
1679/1685 *Set of 7*		3·50	1·60
MS1686 94 × 74 mm. 10000d. Basketball (27 × 39 *mm*). P 14 × 13½		2·75	1·10

339 Columbus's Fleet

(Des Mrs. Hoang Thuy Lieu)

1992 (12 Feb). *500th Anniv of Discovery of America by Columbus (3rd issue). T 339 and similar multicoloured designs.* P 13.
1664	400d. Type **339**	15	15
	a. Sheetlet. Nos. 1664/8 plus label	4·75	
1665	3000d. *Santa Maria*	60	20
1666	4000d. Columbus and flag on land	1·00	20
1667	6000d. Columbus offering gifts to Amerindians	1·30	45
1668	8000d. Ship returning home	1·60	60
1664/1668 *Set of 5*		4·25	1·40
MS1669 102 × 70 mm. 11000d. Columbus before King Ferdinand and Queen Isabella (*vert*). P 14 × 13½		3·00	1·10

Nos. 1664/8 were issued in *se-tenant* sheetlets of five stamps and one label, the frames and label forming a composite design of the route map of the first voyage.

(Des Mrs. Vo Luong Nhi)

1992 (8 Apr). *Racing Motor Cycles. T 343 and similar multicoloured designs.* P 13.
1687	400d. Type **343**	15	15
1688	500d. Honda "CBR 600F"	15	15
1689	1000d. Honda "HRC 500F"	20	15
1690	3000d. Kawasaki "250F" (*vert*)	45	20
1691	4000d. Suzuki "RM 250 F" (*vert*)	80	20

1692	5000d. Suzuki "500F"	1·00	35
1693	6000d. BMW "1000F"	1·30	60
1687/1693 Set of 7		3·75	1·60
MS1694 103 × 78 mm. 10000d. Suzuki "RM 250 F" (different) (32 × 42 mm)		2·75	1·10

344 Shuttle Launch

345 Main Entrance

(Des T. T. Vinh)

1992 (12 Apr). *International Space Year. T* **344** *and similar multicoloured designs.* P 13.

1695	400d. Type **344**	15	15
1696	500d. Launch of space shuttle *Columbia*	15	15
1697	3000d. *Columbia* in space (horiz)	60	20
1698	4000d. Projected shuttle *Hermes* docked at space station (horiz)	80	35
1699	5000d. *Hermes* in space with solar panel (horiz)	1·00	35
1700	6000d. Astronauts repairing Hubble space telescope	1·30	60
1695/1700 Set of 6		3·50	1·60

(Des Mrs. Hoang Thuy Lieu)

1992 (30 Apr). *Centenary of Saigon Post Office. T* **345** *and similar horiz design. Multicoloured.* P 13.

1701	200d. Type **345**	65	20
MS1702 84 × 69 mm. 10000d. Post Office. P 13½ × 14		2·00	1·10

346 Footballer

347 "Portrait of a Girl" (Francisco de Zurbarán)

(Des T. T.Vinh)

1992 (14 May). *European Cup Football Championship. T* **346** *and similar vert designs. Multicoloured.* P 13.

1703	200d. Type **346**	15	15
1704	2000d. Goalkeeper	35	15
1705	4000d. Two players with ball on ground	75	35
1706	5000d. Two players with ball in air	1·00	45
1707	6000d. Three players	1·50	60
1703/1707 Set of 5		3·25	1·50
MS1708 70 × 93 mm. 9000d. Players (42 × 30 mm)		3·00	1·10

(Des T. T. Vinh)

1992 (30 May). *"Expo '92" World's Fair, Seville. Paintings by Spanish Artists. T* **347** *and similar multicoloured designs.* P 13.

1709	400d. Type **347**	15	15
1710	500d. "Woman with a Jug" (Bartolomé Esteban Murillo)	15	15
1711	1000d. "Maria Aptrickaia" (Diego Velázquez)	20	15
1712	3000d. "Holy Family with St. Katharine" (José de Ribera)	55	20
1713	4000d. "Madonna and Child with Sts. Agnes and Thekla" (El Greco)	80	35
1714	5000d. "Woman with Jug" (Francisco Goya)	1·30	35
1715	6000d. "The Naked Maja" (Goya) (horiz)	1·30	45
1709/1715 Set of 7		4·00	1·60
MS1716 82 × 85 mm. 10000d. "Three Women" (Pablo Picasso) (43 × 32 mm)		2·75	1·10

348 Clean Water sustaining Life and Polluted Water

349 Cù Lao Xanh Lighthouse

(Des Mrs. Nguyên Thi Sâm)

1992 (1 June). *20th Anniv of United Nations Conference on Environmental Protection. T* **348** *and similar horiz design. Multicoloured.* P 13.

1717	200d. Type **348**	15	15
1718	4000d. Graph comparing current world development and environmentally sound development	85	35

(Des Mrs. Nguyên Thi Sâm)

1992 (14 June). *"Genova '92" International Thematic Stamp Exhibition. Lighthouses. T* **349** *and similar vert designs. Multicoloured.* P 13½ × 13.

1719	200d. Type **349**	15	15
1720	3000d. Cần Gió	45	20
1721	5000d. Vùng Tàu	95	35
1722	6000d. Long Châu	1·50	45
1719/1722 Set of 4		2·75	1·00

350 Citrus maxima

351 Australian Pied Imperial Pigeons (*Ducula spilorrhoa*)

(Des Mrs. Vo Luong Nhi)

1992 (28 June). *Flowers. T* **350** *and similar vert designs. Multicoloured.* P 13.

1723	200d. Type **350**	15	15
1724	2000d. *Nerium indicum*	40	15

1725	4000d. *Ixora coccinea*		65	20
1726	5000d. *Cananga oborata*		85	20
1727	6000d. *Cassia surattensis*		1·30	45
1723/1727 *Set of 5*			3·00	1·00

(Des Mrs. Vu Liên)

1992 (3 July). *Pigeons and Doves. T* **351** *and similar vert designs. Multicoloured.* P 13.

1728	200d. Type **351**		15	15
1729	2000d. Red-plumed pigeon (*Petrophassa ferruginea*)		40	15
1730	4000d. Feral rock dove (*Columba livia*)		65	20
1731	5000d. Top-knot pigeon (*Lopholaimus antarcticus*) (wrongly inscr "Antareticus")		1·00	20
1732	6000d. Laughing doves (*Streptopelia senegalensis*) (*horiz*)		1·20	45
1728/1732 *Set of 5*			3·00	1·00

352 Guinea Pig

(Des Mrs. Hoang Thuy Lieu)

1992 (26 July). *Rodents. T* **352** *and similar multicoloured designs.* P 13.

1733	200d. Type **352**		15	15
1734	500d. Guinea pigs (*Cavia porcellus*)		15	15
1735	3000d. Indian crested porcupine (*Hystrix indica*)		55	20
1736	4000d. Lesser Egyptian gerbil (*Gerbillus gerbillus*) (*vert*)		80	20
1737	5000d. Red giant flying squirrel (*Petaurista petaurista*) (*vert*)		1·00	45
1738	6000d. Common rabbit (*Oryctolagus cuniculus*) (*vert*)		1·50	60
1733/1738 *Set of 6*			3·75	1·60

353 Memorials and "45"

(Des Mrs. Nguyên Thi Sâm)

1992 (27 July). *45th Anniv of Disabled Soldiers' Day.* P 13 × 13½.

| 1739 | **353** | 200d. multicoloured | | 35 | 20 |

354 Stylized Sportsmen

(Des Mrs. Hoang Thuy Lieu)

1992 (1 Aug). *Third Phu Dong Games.* P 13.

| 1740 | **354** | 200d. lt new blue, dp ultram & pale bl | | 35 | 20 |

355 Siamese Fighting Fish   **356** Members' Locations on Map

(Des Mrs. Nguyên Thi Sâm)

1992 (15 Aug). *Siamese Fighting Fishes* (*Betta splendens*). *T* **355** *and similar horiz designs.* P 13.

1741	200d. multicoloured		15	15
1742	500d. multicoloured		15	15
1743	3000d. multicoloured		65	20
1744	4000d. multicoloured		80	20
1745	5000d. multicoloured		1·00	45
1746	6000d. multicoloured		1·30	60
1741/1746 *Set of 6*			3·75	1·60

1992 (1 Oct). *40th Anniv of International Planned Parenthood Federation. T* **356** *and similar multicoloured design.* P 13.

| 1747 | 200d. Type **356** | | 15 | 15 |
| 1748 | 4000d. Emblem on world map (*horiz*) | | 85 | 35 |

357 Trainee Doctors   **358** Adult protecting Child

(Des Mrs. Nguyên Thi Sâm)

1992 (20 Nov). *90th Anniv of Hanoi Medical School. T* **357** *and similar horiz design. Multicoloured.* P 13.

| 1749 | 200d. Type **357** | | 15 | 15 |
| 1750 | 5000d. Alexandre Yersin (bacteriologist) and school | | 1·00 | 35 |

(Des Mrs. Hoang Thuy Lieu)

1992 (22 Dec). *SOS Children's Villages. T* **358** *and similar vert design. Multicoloured.* P 13.

| 1751 | 200d. Type **358** | | 15 | 15 |
| 1752 | 5000d. Houses and woman with children | | 1·00 | 35 |

359 Kick Boxing

(Des T. T. Vinh)

1993 (1 Jan). *17th South-East Asian Games, Singapore.* P 13.

| 1753 | **359** | 200d. multicoloured | | 35 | 20 |

360 Giant Bee (*Apis dorsata*)

361 Tam-Cam returning from the River

364 Communications Equipment

365 Giant Panda (*Ailuropoda melanoleuca*)

(Des Mrs. Vo Luong Nhi)

1993 (15 Jan). *Bees. T* **360** *and similar multicoloured designs.* P 13.

1754	200d. Type **360**	15	15
1755	800d. *Apis koschevnikovi*	20	15
1756	1000d. *Apis laboriosa*	35	15
1757	2000d. *Apis cerana japonica*	45	20
1758	5000d. *Apis cerana cerana*	1·00	45
1759	10000d. Honey bee (*Apis mellifera*) (*vert*)	1·90	75
1754/1759 *Set of 6*		3·75	1·70

(Des Trinh Quôc Thu)

1993 (18 Jan). *Legend of Tam-Cam. T* **361** *and similar vert design. Multicoloured.* P 13.

1760	200d. Type **361**	15	15
1761	800d. Apparition of old man by goldfish basin	20	15
1762	1000d. Tam-Cam with unsold rice at the market	35	15
1763	3000d. Tam-Cam trying on slipper for Prince	55	20
1764	4000d. Tam-Cam rising from lotus	95	45
1765	10000d. The royal couple	1·90	75
1760/1765 *Set of 6*		3·75	1·70

(Des T. T. Vinh)

1993 (1 Mar). *"Communication in Service of Life". T* **364** *and similar vert design. Multicoloured.* P 13.

1773	200d. Type **364**	10	10
1774	2500d. Fibre-optic cable and map of Hong Kong–Sri Racha submarine cable route	45	20

(Des T. T. Vinh)

1993 (10 Mar). *Mammals. T* **365** *and similar horiz designs. Multicoloured.* P 13.

1775	200d. Type **365**	10	10
1776	800d. Tiger (*Panthera tigris*)	20	15
1777	1000d. Indian elephant (*Elephas maximus*)	20	15
1778	3000d. Indian rhinoceros (*Rhinoceros unicornis*)	65	20
1779	4000d. Family of gibbons (*Hylobates leucogenys*)	95	35
1780	10000d. Clouded leopard (*Neofelis nebulosa*)	1·60	80
1775/1780 *Set of 6*		3·25	1·60
MS1781 79 × 85 mm. 10000d. Kouprey (*Bos sauveli*). P 13½ × 13		2·30	1·10

366 Players, Statue of Liberty and Emblem

(Des Lenh Tuân)

1993 (30 Mar). *World Cup Football Championship, U.S.A. (1994) (1st issue). T* **366** *and similar horiz designs.* P 13.

1782	200d. multicoloured	10	10
1783	1500d. multicoloured	35	15
1784	7000d. multicoloured	1·30	35

Designs:—1500, 7000d. Different match scenes.
See also Nos. 1865/**MS**1871.

362 Rooster with Family

363 *Atractylodes macrocephala*

(Des Mrs. Vu Liên)

1993 (20 Jan). *New Year. Year of the Cock. T* **362** *and similar square design. Multicoloured.* P 13.

1766	200d. Type **362**	15	15
1767	5000d. Rooster with family (*different*)	1·00	35

(Des T. T. Vinh)

1993 (27 Feb). *Medicinal Plants. T* **363** *and similar square designs. Multicoloured.* P 13.

1768	200d. Type **363**	15	15
1769	1000d. Rangoon creeper (*Quisqualis indica*)	20	15
1770	1000d. Japanese honeysuckle (*Lonicera japonica*)	20	15
1771	3000d. *Rehmannia glutinosa*	80	20
1772	12000d. *Gardenia jasminoides*	2·75	75
1768/1772 *Set of 5*		3·75	1·30

367 Wheelbarrow

368 Pylon and Lightbulb

(Des Mrs. Nguyên Thi Sâm)

1993 (6 Apr). *Traditional Transport. T* **367** *and similar horiz designs. Multicoloured.* P 13.

1785	200d. Type **367**	10	10
1786	800d. Buffalo cart	20	15
1787	1000d. Rickshaw	20	15
1788	2000d. Rickshaw with passenger	55	15
1789	5000d. Rickshaw (*different*)	1·10	35
1790	10000d. Horse-drawn carriage	1·60	95
1785/1790 *Set of 6*		3·25	1·70

(Des T. T. Vinh)

1993 (1 May). 500*kv Electricity Lines.* P 13.

1791	**368** 300d. black, brt orange & carm-verm	20	15
1792	400d. black, bright blue & brt orange	35	15

369 "Sunflowers" (Vincent van Gogh)

(Des Mrs. Nguyên Thi Sâm and Mrs. Vu Liên)

1993 (7 May). *"Polska '93" International Stamp Exhibition, Poznań Paintings. T* **369** *and similar multicoloured designs.* P 13.

1793	200d. Type **369**	10	10
1794	1000d. "Young Woman" (Amedeo Modigliani)	20	15
1795	1000d. "Couple in Forest" (Henri Rousseau)	20	15
1796	5000d. "Harlequin with Family" (Pablo Picasso)	1·10	20
1797	10000d. "Female Model" (Henri Matisse) (*horiz*)	2·10	55
1793/1797 *Set of 5*		3·25	1·00

MS1798 85 × 85 mm. 10000d. "Dr. Gachet" (Vincent van Gogh) (27 × 37 *mm*). P 14 × 13½ . . . . 2·30 1·10

370 *Paphiopedilum hirsutissimum*

(Des Mrs. Vu Liên)

1993 (21 June). *Centenary of Da Lat. Orchids. T* **370** *and similar horiz designs. Multicoloured.* P 13.

1799	400d. Type **370**	10	10
1800	1000d. *Paphiopedilum gratrixianum*	20	15
1801	1000d. *Paphiopedilum malipoense*	20	15
1802	12000d. *Paphiopedilum hennisianum*	2·75	1·10
1799/1802 *Set of 4*		2·75	1·40

Việt Nam 400d

371 Wat Phra Sri Rattana Satsadaram, Thailand

(Des Mrs. Vo Luong Nhi and L. Tuân)

1993 (10 July). *Historic Asian Architecture. T* **371** *and similar multicoloured designs.* P 13 × 13½ (vert) or 13½ × 13 (horiz).

1803	400d. Type **371**	10	10
1804	800d. Prambanan Temple, Indonesia	15	15
1805	1000d. City Hall, Singapore	20	15
1806	2000d. Angkor Vat, Cambodia (*horiz*)	40	15
1807	2000d. Ubudiah Mosque, Kuala Kangsar, Malaysia (*horiz*)	40	15
1808	6000d. That Luang, Laos (*horiz*)	1·00	35
1809	8000d. Omar Ali Saifuddin Mosque, Brunei (*horiz*)	1·50	40
1803/1809 *Set of 7*		3·25	1·30

MS1810 86 × 116 mm. 10000d. Chùa Keo, Thái Biình, Vietnam (31 × 42 *mm*). P 14 × 13 . . . 2·30 1·30

VIỆT NAM 400d

372 Industry and Communications

(Des T. T. Vinh)

1993 (28 July). *Seventh Trade Union Congress. T* **372** *and similar horiz design. Multicoloured.* P 13.

1811	400d. Type **372**	10	10
1812	5000d. Doves, atomic symbol, hammer in hand and flowers	1·00	25

373 *Scylla serrata*   374 Stamps and Globe

(Des L. Tuân)

1993 (30 July). *Salt-water Crabs. T* **373** *and similar square designs. Multicoloured.* P 13.

1813	400d. Type **373**	10	10
1814	800d. *Portunus sanguinolentus*	15	15
1815	1000d. *Charybdis bimaculata*	20	15
1816	2000d. *Paralithodes brevipes*	35	15
1817	5000d. *Portunus pelagicus*	1·00	35
1818	10000d. *Lithodes turritus*	1·70	55
1813/1818 *Set of 6*		3·25	1·30

(Des Mrs. Vo Luong Nhi)

1993 (15 Aug). *Stamp Day.* T **374** *and similar horiz design.*
Multicoloured. P 13.

1819	400d. Type **374**		10	10
1820	5000d. Airmail letter		1·00	25

375 Player

376 Lô Lô Costume

(Des Mrs. Vo Luong Nhi and Mrs. Nguyên Thi Sâm)

1993 (20 Sept). *Tennis.* T **375** *and similar vert designs showing players.* P 13.

1821	400d. multicoloured		10	10
	a. Block. Nos. 1821/4 plus			
	labels		2·75	
1822	1000d. multicoloured (male player)		25	15
1823	1000d. multicoloured (female player)		25	15
1824	12000d. multicoloured		2·10	80
1821/1824 *Set of 4*			2·40	1·10

Nos. 1821/4 were issued together in *se-tenant* sheetlets of four stamps and two labels (showing a ball and net) within the sheet.

(Des Mrs. Nguyên Thi Sâm (MS1831), Mrs. Vu Liên (others))

1993 (1 Oct). *"Bangkok 1993" International Stamp Exhibition.* T **376** *and similar multicoloured designs.* P 13½ × 13.

1825	400d. Type **376**		10	10
1826	800d. Thái costume		15	15
1827	1000d. Dao Do costume		20	15
1828	2000d. H'mông costume		35	15
1829	5000d. Kho Mú costume		1·00	35
1830	10000d. Kinh costume		1·30	65
1825/1830 *Set of 6*			2·75	1·40
MS1831 78 × 108 mm. 10000d. Precious stones				
(42 × 31 *mm*). P 13½ × 14			2·30	1·10

377 Dog with Puppies

378 Peach (*Prunus persica*)

(Des Q. Thu)

1994 (1 Jan). *New Year. Year of the Dog.* T **377** *and similar square design. Multicoloured.* P 13.

1832	400d. Type **377**		10	10
1833	6000d. Dog		1·30	35

(Des T. T. Vinh)

1994 (4 Jan–Oct). *Flowers of the Four Seasons.* T **378** *and similar horiz designs. Multicoloured.* P 13 × 13½.

1834	400d. Type **378** (spring)		35	15
1835	400d. Chrysanthemum morifolium			
	(autumn) (30 July)		35	15
1836	400d. Rosa chinensis (winter)			
	(10 Oct)		35	15
1837	15000d. Delonix regia (summer)			
	(30 Apr)		3·00	1·00
1834/1837 *Set of 4*			3·50	1·30

379 Anatoly Karpov

380 Hôi Lim

(Des L. Tuân)

1994 (20 Jan). *Chess.* T **379** *and similar multicoloured designs.* P 13.

1838	400d. Type **379**		10	10
1839	1000d. Gary Kasparov		20	15
1840	2000d. Robert Fischer		45	20
1841	4000d. Emanuel Lasker		95	20
1842	10000d. José Raúl Capablanca		1·70	65
1838/1842 *Set of 5*			3·00	1·20
MS1843 85 × 90 mm. 10000d. Chess piece				
(*vert*) P 14 × 13½			2·30	1·10

No. 1840 is wrongly inscribed "Robers".

(Des Mrs. Hoang Thuy Lien)

1994 (18 Feb). *"Hong Kong '94" Stamp Exhibition. Traditional Festivals.* T **380** *and similar vert designs. Multicoloured.* P 13.

1844	400d. Type **380**		10	10
1845	800d. Chăm		20	10
1846	1000d. Tây Nguyên		35	10
1847	12000d. Nam Bô		2·40	80
1844/1847 *Set of 4*			2·75	1·00

381 Lôi Nhuoc

382 Red Gladioli

(Des Mrs. Nguyên Thi Sâm)

1994 (15 Mar). *Operatic Masks.* T **381** *and similar square designs. Multicoloured.* P 13.

1848	400d. Type **381**		10	10
1849	500d. Dào Tax Xuân		10	10
1850	2000d. Ta Ngoc Lân		35	15
1851	3000d. Lý Khắc Minh		60	20
1852	4000d. Ta On Dinh		80	20
1853	7000d. Khuong Linh Tá		1·50	65
1848/1853 *Set of 6*			3·00	1·25

(Des Mrs. Vu Liên)

1994 (30 Mar). *Gladioli.* T **382** *and similar vert designs. Multicoloured.* P 13½ × 13.

1854	400d. Type **382**		10	10
1855	2000d. Salmon gladioli		35	15
1856	5000d. White gladioli		95	20
1857	8000d. Magenta gladioli		1·50	60
1854/1857 *Set of 4*			2·50	95

383 Painting by Utamaro Kitagawa **384** Footballers

(Des Mrs. Vu Liên)

1994 (9 Apr). *Paintings by Japanese Artists. T* **383** *and similar square designs. Multicoloured.* P 13.
1858	400d. Type **383** (wrongly inscr "Kigatawa")	10	10
1859	500d. Harunobu Suzuki	10	10
1860	1000d. Hokusai Katsushika	20	15
1861	2000d. Hiroshige	40	15
1862	3000d. Hokusai Katsushika (*different*)	55	20
1863	4000d. Utamaro Kitagawa (*different*)	65	20
1864	9000d. Choki Eishosai	1·70	65
1858/1864 *Set of 7*		3·25	1·40

(Des T. T. Vinh)

1994 (20 Apr). *World Cup Football Championship, U.S.A. (2nd issue). T* **384** *and similar vert designs. Multicoloured.* P 13.
1865	400d. Type **384**	10	10
1866	600d. Running with ball	10	10
1867	1000d. Heading ball	20	15
1868	2000d. Goalkeeper	35	15
1869	3000d. Two players chasing ball	65	25
1870	11000d. Tackling	2·30	80
1865/1870 *Set of 6*		3·25	1·40
MS1871 102 × 77 mm. 10000d. Play at goalmouth (31 × 42 *mm*). P 14 × 13½		2·30	1·10

385 Hauling Piece of Equipment **386** Pioneers reading Newspaper

(Des Q. Thu)

1994 (7 May). *40th Anniv of Victory at Dien Bien Phu. T* **385** *and similar horiz design.* P 13 × 13½.
1872	400d. reddish brown, cinnamon & black	15	10
1873	3000d. ultramarine, lt new blue & black	65	35

Design:—3000d. Entertaining the troops.

(Des Mrs. Nguyên Thi Sâm)

1994 (15 May). *40th Anniv of Young Pioneer (newspaper).* P 13 × 13½.
1874	**386** 400d. bright scarlet and black	35	15

387 Estuarine Crocodile (*Crocodylus porosus*) **388** Alexandre Yersin

1994 (1 June). *Reptiles. T* **387** *and similar horiz designs. Multicoloured.* P 13 × 13½.
1875	400d. Type **387**	10	10
1876	600d. Mississippi alligator (*Alligator mississippiensis*)	10	10
1877	2000d. Nile crocodile (*Crocodylus niloticus*)	35	15
1878	3000d. Chinese alligator (*Alligator sinensis*)	45	20
1879	4000d. Paraguay caiman (*Caiman yacare*)	80	35
1880	9000d. Australian crocodile (*Crocodylus johnsoni*)	1·70	65
1875/1880 *Set of 6*		3·00	1·40
MS1881 100 × 67 mm. 10000d. Spectacled caiman (*Caiman crocodilus*) (42 × 31 *mm*). P 13½ × 14		2·30	1·10

(Des L. Tuân)

1994 (15 June). *Centenary of Discovery of Plague Bacillus.* P 13 × 13½.
1882	**388** 400d. multicoloured	45	15

389 Pierre de Coubertin (founder) **390** Cicindela aurulenta

(Des T. T. Vinh)

1994 (15 June). *Centenary of International Olympic Committee. T* **389** *and similar vert design. Mutticoloured.* P 13½ × 13.
1883	400d. Anniversary and National Committee emblems and sports pictograms	65	35
1884	6000d. Type **389**	1·30	45

(Des L. Tuân)

1994 (15 June). *Beetles. T* **390** *and similar vert designs. Multicoloured.* P 13.
1885	400d. Type **390**	15	15
1886	1000d. *Harmonia octomaculata*	20	15
1887	6000d. *Cicindela tennipes*	1·00	35
1888	7000d. *Collyris* sp.	1·30	45
1885/1888 *Set of 4*		2·40	1·00

391 Anniversary Emblem **392** Curlew (*Numenius arquata*)

(Des T. T. Vinh and L. Tuân)

1994 (1 Aug). *120th Anniv of Universal Postal Union. T* **391** *and similar multicoloured designs.* P 13.
1889	400d. Type **391**	10	35
1890	5000d. Envelopes forming world map	1·00	40
MS1891 100 × 80 mm. 10000d. U.P.U. emblem (29 × 41 *mm*). P 14 × 13½		2·30	55

(Des Mrs. Hoang Thuy Lieu)

1994 (16 Aug). *"Philkorea 1994" International Stamp Exhibition, Seoul. Sea Birds. T* **392** *and similar horiz designs. Multicoloured.* P 13 × 13½.

1892	400d. Type **392**	10	10
1893	600d. Wilson's storm petrel (*Oceanites oceanicus*)	10	10
1894	1000d. Great frigate bird (*Fregata minor*)	20	15
1895	2000d. Cape gannet (*Morus capensis*)	35	15
1896	3000d. Tufted puffins (*Lunda cirrhata*)	65	25
1897	11000d. Band-tailed gulls (*Larus belcheri*)	2·30	65
1892/1897 *Set of 6*		3·25	1·25

MS1898 78 × 65 mm. 10000d. Grey-rumped swiftlet (*Collocalia fuciphaga*) (38 × 31 *mm*). P 13½ × 14 . . . . 2·30 1·10

393 *Bambusa blumeana*

394 Log Bridge with Handrail

(Des Mrs. Nguyên Thi Sâm)

1994 (17 Aug). *"Singpex '94" Stamp Exhibition, Singapore. Bamboos. T* **393** *and similar vert designs. Multicoloured.* P 13½ × 13.

1899	400d. Type **393**	10	10
1900	1000d. *Phyllostachys aurea*	20	15
1901	2000d. *Bambusa vulgaris*	40	15
1902	4000d. *Tetragonocalamus quadrangularis*	65	20
1903	10000d. *Bambusa venticosa*	2·30	80
1899/1903 *Set of 5*		3·25	1·25

(Des Mrs. Nguyên Thi Sâm)

1994 (20 Sept). *Rudimentary Bridges. T* **394** *and similar horiz designs. Multicoloured.* P 13 × 13½.

1904	400d. Type **394**	10	10
1905	900d. Interwoven bridge	25	25
1906	8000d. Log bridge on stilts	1·30	45

395 Girl in Wheelchair and Boy playing

396 Electric Tramcar No. 1 with Overhead Conductor

(Des Mrs. Nguyên Thi Sâm and Mrs. Vu Liên)

1994 (20 Sept). *"For Our Children's Future". T* **395** *and similar multicoloured design.* P 13 × 13½.

| 1907 | 400d.+100d. Type **395** | 10 | 10 |
| 1908 | 2000d. Children dancing around emblem (*vert*) | 45 | 25 |

(Des Mrs. Vu Liên)

1994 (10 Oct). *Trams. T* **396** *and similar horiz designs. Multicoloured.* P 13 × 13½.

1909	400d. Type **396**	10	10
1910	900d. Paris double-deck battery-powered tram	10	10
1911	8000d. Philadelphia U.S. Mail electric tram	75	25

397 Civilians greeting Soldiers

398 Airplane in Air

(Des Mrs. Vu Liên)

1994 (10 Oct). *40th Anniv of Liberation of Hanoi. T* **397** *and similar horiz design. Multicoloured.* P 13 × 13½.

| 1912 | 400d. Type **397** | 10 | 10 |
| 1913 | 2000d. Workers and students and symbols of development | 45 | 25 |

(Des L. Tuân)

1994 (7 Dec). *50th Anniv of International Civil Aviation Organization. T* **398** *and similar horiz design. Multicoloured.* P 13.

| 1914 | 400d. Type **398** | 15 | 10 |
| 1915 | 3000d. Airplane on ground | 65 | 25 |

399 Parade

400 Sow with Piglets

(Des Mrs. Hoang Thuy Lieu)

1994 (22 Dec). *50th Anniv of Vietnamese People's Army. T* **399** *and similar horiz designs. Multicoloured.* P 13 × 13½.

1916	400d. Type **399**	10	10
1917	1000d. Plan of attacks on Saigon	20	15
1918	2000d. Veteran recounting the past to young girl	35	20
1919	4000d. Naval anti-aircraft gun crew	80	25
1916/1919 *Set of 4*		1·30	65

(Des L. Tuân)

1995 (2 Jan). *New Year. Year of the Pig. T* **400** *and similar square design's. Multicoloured.* P 13.

| 1920 | 400d. Type **400** | 15 | 10 |
| 1921 | 8000d. Pig | 1·50 | 45 |

401 Osprey
(*Pandion haliaetus*)

402 Girls with Bicycle

(Des Mrs. Hoang Thuy Lieu)

1995 (20 Jan). *Birds. T* **401** *and similar designs.* P 13½ × 13.

1922	400d. deep blue		10	10
1923	400d. emerald		10	10
1924	400d. deep reddish purple		10	10
1925	400d. dull orange		10	10
1926	5000d. carmine-lake		85	40
1922/1926 *Set of 5*			1·10	75

Designs: Horiz—No. 1923, Sociable weaver (*Philetarius socius*); 1924, Sharpbill (*Oxyruncus cristatus*); 1925, Golden plover (*Pluvialis apricaria*). Vert—No. 1926, Red-legged seriema (*Cariama cristata*).

(Des T. T. Vinh)

1995 (1 Feb). *Women's Costumes. T* **402** *and similar vert designs. Multicoloured.* P 13.

1927	400d. Type **402**		10	10
1928	3000d. Girl with sheaf of flowers		45	20
1929	5000d. Girl with traditional hat		95	40

403 Statue and Building

404 Brown Fish Owl
(*Ketupa zeylonensis*)

(Des T. T. Vinh)

1995 (18 Feb). *"Vietstampex '95" Stamp Exhibition. F.I.A.P. Executive Committee Meeting.* P 13.

1930	**403**	5500d. multicoloured	1·10	45

(Des Mrs. Hoang Thuy Lieu)

1995 (1 Mar). *Owls. T* **404** *and similar vert designs. Multicoloured.* P 13½ × 13.

1931	400d. Type **404**		10	10
1932	1000d. Tawny owl (*Strix aluco*)		20	15
1933	2000d. Great grey owl (*Strix nebulosa*)		35	15
1934	5000d. Spotted wood owl (*Strix seloputo*)		80	35
1935	10000d. White-faced scops owl (*Otus leucotis*)		1·50	65
1931/1935 *Set of 5*			2·75	1·25
MS1936 64 × 81 mm. 12500d. Barn owl (*Tyto alba*) (31 × 42 mm). P 14 × 13½			2·30	1·00

405 Grey Angel Fish
(*Pomacanthus arcuatus*)

406 Throwing the Hammer

(Des Mrs. Nguyên Thi Sâm)

1995 (20 Mar). *Fishes. T* **405** *and similar horiz designs. Multicoloured.* P 13.

1937	400d. Type **405**		10	10
1938	1000d. Rectangle trigger fish (*Rhinecanthus rectangulus*)		20	15
1939	2000d. Regal angel fish (*Pygoplites diacanthus*)		35	15
1940	4000d. Queen angel fish (*Pomacanthus ciliaris*)		55	20
1941	5000d. Queen trigger fish (*Balistes vetula*)		85	25
1942	9000d. Clown trigger fish (*Balistes conspicillum*)		1·30	55
1937/1942 *Set of 6*			3·00	1·25

(Des L. Tuân)

1995 (5 Apr). *Olympic Games, Atlanta (1996) (1st issue). T* **406** *and similar vert designs. Multicoloured.* P 13.

1943	400d. Type **406**		10	10
1944	3000d. Cycling		45	20
1945	4000d. Running		55	25
1946	10000d. Pole vaulting		1·70	65
1943/1946 *Set of 4*			2·50	1·10
MS1947 59 × 100 mm. 12500d. Handball. P 14 × 13½			2·30	1·00

See also Nos. 2063/5.

407 Lenin

408 Adult and Young

(Des Mrs. Vo Luong Nhi)

1995 (22 Apr). *125th Birth Anniv of Lenin.* P 13.

1948	**407**	400d. black and bright scarlet	20	15

(Des Mrs. Vo Luong Nhi (1949/52); Mrs. Vu Liên, Mrs. Nguyên Thi Sâm, Mrs. Hoang Thuy Lieu and T. T. Vinh (others))

1995 (25 Apr). *The Malayan Tapir (Tapirus indicus). T* **408** *and similar horiz designs. Multicoloured.* P 13.

(a) With World Wildlife Fund emblem

1949	400d. Type **408**		25	35
	a. Sheetlet of 4. Nos. 1949/52		1·70	
1950	1000d. Standing		35	35
1951	2000d. Walking		40	35
1952	4000d. Calling		65	35
1949/1952 *Set of 4*			1·50	1·25

(b) Without W.W.F. emblem

1953	4000d. Standing by trees		55	35
	a. Sheetlet of 4. Nos. 1953/6		2·50	
1954	4000d. Eating		55	35

1955	5000d. Swimming		60	35
1956	6000d. In water		75	35
1953/1956	Set of 4		2·20	1·25

Nos. 1949/52 and 1953/6 respectively were issued together in *se-tenant* sheetlets of four stamps, forming a composite design.

409 Dove and "50"

410 Montgolfier's Hot Air Balloon, 1783

(Des T. T. Vinh)

1995 (2 May). *50th Anniv of End of Second World War in Europe.* P 13.

1957	**409** 400d. multicoloured		20	15

(Des T. T. Vinh)

1995 (5 May). *"Finlandia 95" International Stamp Exhibition, Helsinki. Balloons. T 410 and similar vert designs. Multicoloured.* P 13.

1958	500d. Type **410**		10	10
1959	1000d. Jacques Charles and Marie-Noel Robert's balloon (first untethered flight by manned hydrogen balloon)		15	15
1960	2000d. Jean-Pierre Blanchard's oared balloon		35	15
1961	3000d. Jean-François Pilatre de Rozier and Jules Romain's balloon over English Channel, 1785		45	15
1962	4000d. Free balloon		55	20
1963	5000d. Captive balloon over Red Square, Moscow, 1890		65	20
1964	7000d. Auguste Piccard's balloon F.N.R.S., 1931		1·10	45
1958/1964	Set of 7		3·00	1·40

411 Parachutist

412 *Rhododendron fleuryi*

(Des Mrs. Hoang Thuy Lieu)

1995 (24 May). *Parachuting. T 411 and similar vert designs. Multicoloured.* P 13½ × 13.

1965	400d. Type **411**		15	10
	a. Sheetlet of 4. Nos. 1965/8		2·40	
1966	2000d. Two parachutists		35	15
1967	3000d. Landing		55	20
1968	4000d. Gathering in the parachute		1·30	60
1965/1968	Set of 4		2·10	95

Nos. 1965/8 were issued together in *se-tenant* sheetlets of four stamps, forming a composite design.

(Des L. Tuân)

1995 (30 June). *Rhododendrons. T 412 and similar horiz designs. Multicoloured.* P 13.

1969	400d. Type **412**		10	10
1970	1000d. *Rhododendron sulphoreum*		20	15
1971	2000d. *Rhododendron sinofalconeri*		35	15
1972	3000d. *Rhododendron lyi*		45	20
1973	5000d. *Rhododendron ovatum*		80	25
1974	9000d. *Rhododendron tanastylum*		1·50	55
1969/1974	Set of 6		3·00	1·25

413 Tan and Lang pay Court to Lu's Daughter

414 Statue of Mother and Child

(Des T. T. Vinh)

1995 (20 July). *"Betel and Areca Nut" (fable). T 413 and similar horiz designs. Multicoloured.* P 13.

1975	400d. Type **413**		10	10
	a. Sheetlet of 4. Nos. 1975/8		2·30	
1976	1000d. Girl chooses Tan		20	15
1977	3000d. Lang changes into rock		45	20
1978	10000d. Girl changes into betel pepper plant and Tan into areca nut palm		1·50	45
1975/1978	Set of 4		2·00	80

Nos. 1975/8 were issued together in *se-tenant* sheetlets of four stamps, forming a composite design.

(Des Mrs. Nguyên Thi Sâm)

1995 (26 July). *65th Anniv of Women's Union (400d.) and World Conference on Women, Peking (3000d.). T 414 and similar multicoloured design.* P 13½ × 13 (400d.) or 13 × 13½ (3000d.).

1979	400d. Type **414**		15	10
1980	3000d. Globe and women of different races (*horiz*)		45	25

415 Flags around Emblem

416 Ho Chi Minh, Dove and Crowd

(Des L. Tuân)

1995 (5 Aug). *Admission of Vietnam to Association of South East Asian Nations.* P 13.

1981	**415** 400d. multicoloured		25	15

(Des L. Tuân)

1995 (14 Aug). *Anniversaries. T 416 and similar vert designs. Multicoloured.* P 13.

1982	400d. Type **416** (65th Anniv of Communist Party of Indo-China)		10	10
1983	400d. Ho Chi Minh embracing child (105th birth anniv)		10	10

1984 1000d. Civic building, road bridge, power
      lines and oil derrick (40th anniv
      of evacuation of French troops
      from North Vietnam)   15   15
1985 1000d. Ho Chi Minh saluting and
      building flying flags (20th anniv of
      end of Vietnam war)   15   15
1986 2000d. Soldiers and flag (50th anniv of
      National Liberation Army) 35   20
1987 2000d. Radio mast, dish aerial, motor
      cycle couriers and mail van (50th
      anniv of postal and
      telecommunications services) . . 35   20
1982/1987 *Set of 6* . . . . 1·10   80

417 Bust of Hill and Penny   **418** Torch Carriers and
       Black   Sports Pictograms

(Des Mrs. Nguyên Thi Sâm)

1995 (15 Aug). *Birth Bicentenary of Sir Rowland Hill (instigator of
postage stamp).* P 13 × 13½.
1988 **417** 4000d. multicoloured 65   20

(Des K. Liên)

1995 (30 Aug). *National Sports Festival.* P 13.
1989 **418** 400d. ultramarine, vermilion and
      reddish lilac 20   15

419 *Paphiopedilum druryi*   **420** Palace, Hué

(Des K. Liên)

1995 (1 Sept). *"Singapore '95" International Stamp Exhibition.
Orchids. T* **419** *and similar multicoloured designs.* P 13.
1990   400d. Type **419** 10   10
1991   2000d. Dendrobium ochraceum 35   15
1992   3000d. Vanda sp. 45   15
1993   4000d. Cattleya sp. 55   20
1994   5000d. Paphiopedilum hirsutissimum . . 80   20
1995   6000d. Christenosia vietnamica . . . 1·10   45
1990/1995 *Set of 6* . . . . 3·00 1·10
MS1996 65 × 90 mm. 12500d. *Angraecum
sesquipedale (31 × 42 mm).* P 14 × 13½ . . . 2·30 1·00

(Des Mrs. Nguyên Thi Sâm and K. Liên)

1995 (6 Sept). *Asian Cityscapes. T* **420** *and similar vert designs.
Multicoloured.* P 13.
1997   400d. Type **420** 10   10
1998   3000d. Park, Doanh Châu 45   20
1999   4000d. Temple, Macao 55   20
2000   5000d. Kowloon, Hong Kong 80   20
2001   6000d. Pagoda, Dài Loan 85   35
1997/2001 *Set of 5* . . . . 2·50   95

421 Dove and Anniversary Emblem

(Des T. T. Vinh)

1995 (10 Oct). *50th Anniv of United Nations Organization.* P 13.
2002 **421** 2000d. multicoloured 35   15

422 Woman with Vase of   **423** Map and Eclipse
      Flowers (T Ngoc Vân)

(Des Mrs. Nguyên Thi Sâm)

1995 (15 Nov). *Paintings. T* **422** *and similar vert designs.
Multicoloured.* P 13 × 13½.
2003   400d. Type **422** 15   15
2004   2000d. Woman washing hair (Trân Văn
      Cân) 35   35
2005   6000d. Woman and vase of flowers
      (Tô Ngoc Vân) 85   85
2006   8000d. Two women resting (Trân Văn
      Cân) . . . . 1·20 1·20
2003/2006 *Set of 4* . . . . 2·30 2·30

(Des T. T. Vinh)

1995 (23 Dec). *Total Eclipse of the Sun.* P 13.
2007 **423** 400d. multicoloured 25   25

424 Rats carrying Canopy   **425** Apricot
      and on Horseback

(Des T. T. Vinh)

1996 (2 Jan). *New Year. Year of the Rat. T* **424** *and similar
multicoloured design.* P 13.
2008   400d. Type **424** 15   15
2009   8000d. Rats in and carrying sedan
      chair . . . . 1·10 1·10
MS2010 110 × 75 mm. 13000d. Rat carrying
placard *(31 × 42 mm).* P 14 × 13½ . . . 1·70 1·70
No. **MS**2010 is also known imperf.

(Des Mrs. Hoang Thuy Lieu)

1996 (10 Jan). *Flowers. T **425** and similar designs.* P 13½ × 13 (5000d.) or 13 × 13½ (others).

2011	400d. deep yellow-brown		10	10
2012	400d. dull claret		10	10
2013	400d. emerald		10	10
2014	400d. dull ultramarine		10	10
2015	5000d. bright carmine		65	65
2011/2015 *Set of 5*			95	95

Designs: *Horiz*—No. 2012, Chrysanthemums; 2013, Orchid; 2014, Orchids (*different*). *Vert*—No. 2015, Asters.

426 Communist Symbols and Ho Chi Minh

427 Thanh Trừ Tai

(Des T. T. Vinh)

1996 (3 Feb). *Eighth Vietnamese Communist Party Congress. T **426** and similar horiz design. Multicoloured.* P 13.

2016	400d. Type **426**	10	10
2017	3000d. Symbols of communications, industry, Communism and agriculture within outline of dove	45	45

1996 (10 Feb). *Statues in Tay Phuong Pagoda, Thach That. T **427** and similar vert designs. Multicoloured.* P 13½ × 13.

2018	400d. Type **427**	10	10
2019	600d. Tich Dôc Thân	10	10
2020	1000d. Hoàng Tùy Câu	15	15
2021	2000d. Bach Tinh Thúy	25	25
2022	3000d. Xich Thanh Hóa	40	40
2023	5000d. Dinh Trừ Tai	60	60
2024	6000d. Tú Hiên Thân	75	75
2025	8000d. Dai Thân Luc	1·10	1·10
2018/2025 *Set of 8*		3·00	3·00

428 Tsintaosaurus

429 White-throated Kingfisher (*Halcyon smyrnensis*)

(Des Mrs. Nguyên Thi Sâm)

1996 (6 Mar). *Prehistoric Animals. T **428** and similar horiz designs. Multicoloured.* P 13.

2026	400d. Type **428**	10	10
2027	1000d. Archaeopteryx	15	15
2028	2000d. Psittacosaurus	25	25
2029	3000d. Hypsilophodon	45	45
2030	13000d. Parasaurolophus	1·70	1·70
2026/2030 *Set of 5*		2·40	2·40

(Des Mrs. Nguyên Thi Sâm)

1996 (11 Mar). *Kingfishers. T **429** and similar square designs. Multicoloured.* P 13.

2031	400d. Type **429**	10	10
2032	1000d. Belted kingfisher (*Megaceryle alcyon*)	15	15
2033	2000d. River kingfisher (*Alcedo atthis*)	25	25
2034	4000d. Ruddy kingfisher (*Halcyon coromanda*)	55	55
2035	12000d. Lesser pied kingfisher (*Ceryle rudis*)	1·70	1·70
2031/2035 *Set of 5*		2·50	2·50

430 Temple of Literature, Hanoi

431 Dàn Tỳ Bà

(Des Mrs. Vo Luong Nhi)

1996 (10 Apr). *Asian Temples. T **430** and similar square designs. Multicoloured.* P 13.

2036	400d. Type **430**	10	10
2037	2000d. Wat Mahathat, Sukhothai, Thailand	25	25
2038	3000d. Lingaraja Temple, Bhubaeshwar, India	40	40
2039	4000d. Kinkakuju Temple, Kyoto, Japan	60	60
2040	10000d. Borobudur Temple, Java, Indonesia	1·30	1·30
2036/2040 *Set of 5*		2·40	2·40

(Des Mrs. Hoang Thuy Lieu)

1996 (24 Apr). *"China '96" Ninth Asian International Stamp Exhibition, Peking. Stringed Musical Instruments. T **431** and similar vert designs. Multicoloured.* P 13½ × 13.

2041	400d. Type **431**	10	10
	a. Sheetlet of 4. Nos. 2041/4		
2042	3000d. Dàn nhi	40	40
2043	4000d. Dàn déy	55	55
2044	9000d. Dàn tranh	1·10	1·10
2041/2044 *Set of 4*		2·00	2·00

Nos. 2041/4 were issued together in *se-tenant* sheetlets of four stamps.

432 Ho Chi Minh

433 Children of Different Races

(Des Mrs. Nguyên Thi Sâm)

1996 (8 May). *50th Anniv of Vietnamese Red Cross.* P 13½.

2045	**432**	3000d. multicoloured	55	55

(Des Mrs. Hoang Thuy Lieu)

1996 (15 May). *50th Anniv of United Nations' Children's Fund. T* **433** *and similar vert design. Multicoloured.* P 13.
2046   400d. Type **433** 15   15
2047   7000d. Water droplets containing
          symbols and globe "plant" . . . 1·10   1·10

434 Tiger Beetle
(*Cicindela japonica*)

435 Emblem in Hand

(Des L. Tuân)

1996 (20 May). *Beetles. T* **434** *and similar vert designs. Multicoloured.* P 13.
2048   400d. Type **434** 10   10
2049   500d. *Calodema wallacei* 10   10
2050   1000d. Blister beetle (*Mylabris
              oculata*) 15   15
2051   4000d. *Chrysochroa buqueti* . . . 55   55
2052   5000d. *Ophioniea nigrofasciata* . . 75   75
2053   12000d. Ground beetle (*Carabus
              tauricus*) . . . . 1·50   1·50
2048/2053 Set of 6 . . . . 2·75   2·75

(Des T. T. Vinh)

1996 (22 May). *50th Natural Disaster Reduction Day.* P 13.
2054   **435**   400d. multicoloured 20   20

436 Goalkeeper

437 Airbus Industrie A320

(Des T. T. Vinh)

1996 (1 June). *European Football Championship, England. T* **436** *and similar vert design. Multicoloured.* P 13.
2055   400d. Type **436** 15   15
          a. Horiz pair. Nos. 2055/6 . . . 1·40   1·40
2056   8000d. Player . . . . 1·20   1·20
          Nos. 2055/6 were issued together in horizontal *se-tenant* pairs within the sheet, each pair forming a composite design.

(Des L. Tuân)

1996 (1 June). *Aircraft. T* **437** *and similar horiz designs. Multicoloured.* P 13.
2057   400d. Type **437** 10   10
2058   1000d. Antonov An-72 15   15
2059   2000d. McDonnell Douglas MD-11F . 25   25
2060   6000d. RJ-85 85   85
2061   10000d. Boeing 747-400F . . . 1·30   1·30
2057/2061 Set of 5 . . . . 2·40   2·40
MS2062 86 × 50 mm. 13000d. Space shuttle
          riding on Boeing 747 (42 × 31 *mm*).
          P 13½ × 14. . . . . 1·70   1·70

438 Women's Football

439 1946 1h. Stamp

(Des T. T. Vinh)

1996 (8 July). *Olympic Games, Atlanta, U.S.A. (2nd issue). T* **438** *and similar horiz designs. Multicoloured.* P 13.
2063   2000d. Type **438** 35   25
2064   4000d. Sailing 65   55
2065   5000d. Hockey 85   85

(Des Mrs. Hoang Thuy Lieu)

1996 (15 Aug). *Stamp Day. 50th Anniv of First Unoverprinted Vietnamese Stamp.* P 13.
2066   **439**   400d. multicoloured 20   20

440 Orange Peel Fungus
(*Aleuria aurantia*)

441 Pupils at Main
Gate

(Des Mrs. Vo Luong Nhi)

1996 (26 Aug). *Fungi. T* **440** *and similar square designs. Multicoloured.* P 13.
2067   400d. Type **440** 10   10
2068   500d. *Morchella conica* 15   15
2069   1000d. *Anthurus archeri* 25   25
2070   4000d. Chicken mushroom (*Laetiporus
              sulphureus*) (wrongly inscr
              "serlphureus") 55   55
2071   5000d. *Filoboletus manipularis* . . 65   65
2072   12000d. *Tremiscus helvelloides* . . 1·70   1·70
2067/2072 Set of 6 . . . . 3·00   3·00

(Des Mrs. Nguyên Thi Sâm)

1996 (5 Sept). *Centenary of Hue School. T* **441** *and similar vert designs. Multicoloured.* P 13.
2073   400d. Type **441** 15   15
2074   3000d. Main building 40   40

442 Woman and Vase of Lotus
Flowers

(Des Mrs. Nguyên Thi Sâm)

1996 (10 Sept). *Paintings by Nguyên Sáng. T* **442** *and similar horiz design. Multicoloured.* P 13.
2075   400d. Type **442** 15   15
2076   8000d. Soldiers at Dien Bien Phu . . 1·10   1·10

443 Variegated Langurs (*Pygathrix nemacus*) **444** Tree of Children's Heads

(Des K. Liên)

1996 (10 Oct). *"Taipeh '96" International Stamp Exhibition, Taiwan. Endangered Animals.* T **443** *and similar horiz designs. Multicoloured.* P 13.

2077	400d. Type **443**	15	15
	a. Sheetlet of 4. Nos. 2077/80	2·40	
2078	2000d. Tigers (*Panthera tigris*)	35	35
2079	4000d. Javan rhinoceroses (*Rhinoceros sondaicus*)	55	55
2080	10000d. South African crowned cranes (*Balearica regulorum*)	1·30	1·30
2077/2080 *Set of 4*		2·10	2·10

Nos. 2077/80 were issued together in *se-tenant* sheetlets of four stamps.

(Des T. T. Vinh)

1996 (2 Nov). *Campaign for Use of Iodized Salt.* P 13.

2081	**444** 400d. multicoloured	25	25

445 Armed Combatants, National Flag and Quote from Ho Chi Minh **446** Rambutan (*Nephelium lappaceum*)

(Des T. T. Vinh and Mrs. Nguyên Thi Sâm)

1996 (19 Dec). *50th Anniv of Formation of National Front for the Liberation of South Vietnam.* P 13.

2082	**445** 400d. multicoloured	25	25

(Des Mrs. Nguyên Thi Sâm)

1997 (2 Jan). *Fruits.* T **446** *and similar horiz designs.* P 13 × 13½.

2083	400d. rose-red and black	15	15
2084	400d. bistre and black	15	15
2085	400d. light green and black	15	15
2086	400d. bright violet and black	15	15
2087	400d. cerise and black	15	15
2083/2087 *Set of 5*		70	70

Designs:—No. 2084, Durian (*Durio zibethinus*); 2085, Avocado (*Persea americana*); 2086, Mangostela (*Garcinia mangostana*); 2087, Queen-of-the-night (*Hylocereus undatus*)

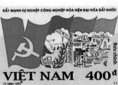

447 Ox and Calf **448** Flags and Symbols of Development

(Des Mrs. Vo Luong Nhi. Photo)

1997 (8 Jan). *New Year. Year of the Ox.* T **447** *and similar square design. Multicoloured.* P 13.

2088	400d. Type **447**	15	15
2089	8000d. Ox	1·20	1·20

(Des T. T. Vinh)

1997 (3 Feb). *Eighth Vietnamese Communist Party Congress.* P 13.

2090	**448** 400d. multicoloured	25	25

449 Red-capped Goldfish **450** Snake Design

(Des L. Tuân)

1997 (5 Feb). *The Goldfish (Carassius auratus). T **449** and similar multicoloured designs.* P 13.

2091	400d. Type **449**	10	10
2092	1000d. Black and red and long-tailed red goldfishes	15	15
2093	5000d. Goldfish with gaping mouth	65	65
2094	7000d. Black and yellow goldfishes	1·00	1·00
2095	8000d. Red goldfish with black tail and fins	1·10	1·10
2091/2095 *Set of 5*		2·75	2·75
MS2096	110 × 80 mm. 14000d. Two red-capped goldfishes (42 × 31 *mm*). P 13½ × 14.	2·00	2·00

No. **MS**2096 also commemorates "Hong Kong '97" stamp exhibition.

(Des K. Liên)

1997 (5 Mar). *Ly Dynasty Sculptures.* T **450** *and similar multicoloured designs.* P 13.

2097	400d. Type **450**	10	10
2098	1000d. Terracotta dragon's head	15	15
2099	3000d. Musicians in rectangular panel (*horiz*)	45	45
2100	5000d. Lion base (*horiz*)	85	85
2101	10000d. Vessel with dragon design (*horiz*)	1·50	1·50
2097/2101 *Set of 5*		2·75	2·75

Việt Nam Bưu chính 400ᵈ

451 Pagoda in Lake, Hà Tây

(Des T. T. Vinh)

1997 (20 Mar). *Landscapes. T **451** and similar horiz designs. Multicoloured.* P 13.

2102	400d. Type **451**		10	10
2103	5000d. Bamboo suspension bridge, Lai Châu		75	75
2104	7000d. Mist-wreathed trees behind village, Lào Cai		1·00	1·00

452 Red Lily   **453** Huỳnh Thúc Kháng

(Des Mrs. Nguyên Thi Sâm)

1997 (15 Apr). *The Lily (Lilium longiflorum). T **452** and similar vert designs. Multicoloured.* P 13.

2105	400d. Type **452**		10	10
2106	1000d. White lily		15	15
2107	5000d. Pink and white lily		75	75
2108	10000d. Red and cream lily		1·50	1·50
2105/2108 *Set of 4*			2·25	2·25

(Des Mrs. Nguyên Thi Sâm)

1997 (21 Apr). *50th Death Anniv of Huỳnh Thúc Kháng.* P 13½ × 13.

2109	**453** 400d. multicoloured		25	25

454 Tennis   **455** Owton's Palm Civet (*Chrotogale owstoni*)

(Des Mrs. Hoang Thuy Lieu)

1997 (27 Apr). *Sports for Disabled People. T **454** and similar vert design. Multicoloured.* P 13.

2110	1000d. Type **454**		15	15
2111	6000d. Rifle shooting		85	85

(Des L. Tuân)

1997 (2 May). *Cat Ba National Park. T **455** and similar horiz designs. Multicoloured.* P 13.

2112	400d. Type **455**		10	10
2113	3000d. European otter (*Lutra lutra*)		40	40
2114	4000d. Palla's squirrel (*Callosciurus erythraeus*)		60	60
2115	10000d. Leopard cat (*Felis bengalensis*) (wrongly inscr "bangalensis")		1·50	1·50
2112/2115 *Set of 4*			2·30	2·30

456 Golden Gate Bridge, San Francisco

(Des K. Liên)

1997 (12 May). *"Pacific '97" International Stamp Exhibition, San Francisco. Suspension Bridges. T **456** and similar horiz designs. Multicoloured.* P 13.

2116	400d. Type **456**		10	10
2117	5000d. Raippaluoto Bridge, Finland		75	75
2118	10000d. Seto Great road and rail bridge, Japan		1·50	1·50

457 Women and Girl   **458** Umbrella protecting Children

(Des N. M. Lân)

1997 (19 May). *Eighth Vietnamese Women's Union Congress.* P 13.

2119	**457** 400d. multicoloured		25	25

(Des Mrs. Nguyên Thi Sâm)

1997 (1 June). *Children's Rights. T **458** and similar vert design. Multicoloured.* P 13.

2120	400d. Type **458** (United Nations Convention on Rights of the Child)		10	10
2121	5000d. Mother breastfeeding ("Breastmilk is Best")		75	75

459 Cha Láng, Hanoi, Vietnam

460 San Chay

(Des Mrs. Vo Luong Nhi)

1997 (20 June). *Asian Temples. T 459 and similar square designs. Multicoloured.* P 13.

2122	400d. Type **459**		10	10
2123	1000d. Persepolis, Iran		15	15
2124	3000d. Statue, Denion, Iraq		40	40
2125	5000d. Kyaiktiyo Pagoda, Myanmar		75	75
2126	10000d. Sleeping Buddha, Polonnaruwa, Sri Lanka		1·50	1·50
2122/2126 *Set of 5*			2·60	2·60

(Des T. T. Vinh)

1997 (8 July). *Women's Costumes. T 460 and similar vert designs. Multicoloured.* P 13.

2127	400d. Type **460**		10	10
2128	2000d. Daco		25	25
2129	5000d. Phù Lá		75	75
2130	10000d. Kho Me		1·50	1·50
2127/2130 *Set of 4*			2·30	2·30

461 Ringing Bell

462 War Memorial, Cu Chi

(Des Mrs. Hoang Thuy Lieu)

1997 (11 July). *AIDS Awareness Campaign.* P 13.

2131	**461**	400d. multicoloured	25	25

(Des Mrs. Nguyên Thi Sâm)

1997 (25 July). *50th Anniv of War Disabled Day.* P 13.

2132	**462**	400d. multicoloured	25	25

463 Hibiscus rosa-sinensis

464 Flags of Member Nations

(Des Mrs. Vo Luong Nhi, Mrs Hoang Thuy Lieu, Mrs. Nguyên Thi Sâm and L. Tuân)

1997 (1 Aug). *Flowers. T 463 and similar vert designs. Multicoloured.* P 13.

2133	1000d. Type **463**		15	15
	a. Sheetlet of 4. Nos. 2133/6		2·75	
2134	3000d. Hibiscus schizopetalus		40	40
2135	5000d. Hibiscus syriacus (pink)		80	80
2136	9000d. Hibiscus syriacus (yellow)		1·30	1·30
2133/2136 *Set of 4*			2·40	2·40

Nos. 2133/6 were issued together in *se-tenant* sheetlets of four stamps.

(Des N. Thanh)

1997 (8 Aug). *30th Anniv of Association of South East Asian Nations.* P 13.

2137	**464**	400d. multicoloured	25	25

465 Statue and Women using Modern Technology

466 Seahorses

(Des L. Tuân)

1997 (26 Aug). *50th Anniv of Vietnamese Post and Telecommunications Union.* P 13.

2138	**465**	400d. multicoloured	25	25

(Des Mrs. Hoang Thuy Lieu)

1997 (4 Sept). *Seahorses. T 466 and similar vert. designs. Multicoloured.* P 13.

2139	400d. Type **466**		10	10
2140	1000d. Seahorses		15	15
2141	3000d. Common seahorse (Hippocampus guttulatus)		40	40
2142	5000d. Hippocampus kelloggi		75	75
2143	6000d. Hippocampus japonicus		95	95
2144	7000d. Short-snouted seahorse (Hippocampus hippocampus)		1·10	1·10
2139/2144 *Set of 6*			3·00	3·00

467 Globe and Emblem

468 Table Tennis Player

(Des T. T. Vinh)

1997 (24 Sept). *Seventh Francophone Summit, Hanoi.* P 13.

2145	**467**	5000d. multicoloured	1·50	1·50
	a. Tête-bêche (pair)			

(Des N. N. Than)

1997 (11 Oct). *19th South East Asian Games, Djakarta.* P. 13.
2146 **468** 5000d. multicoloured 80 80

469 Elliot's Pheasant
(*Syrmaticus ellioti*)

470 Lamp

(Des T. T. Vinh)

1997 (15 Oct). *Pheasants. T 469 and similar horiz designs. Multicoloured.* P 13.
2147 400d. Type **469** 10 10
2148 3000d. Siamese fireback pheasant
(*Lophura diardi*) 40 40
2149 5000d. Common pheasant (*Phasianus colchicus*) 75 75
2150 6000d. Lady Amherst's pheasant
(*Chrysolophus amherstiae*) . . 95 95
2151 8000d. Germain's peacock-pheasant
(*Polyplectron germaini*) . . . 1·20 1·20
2147/2151 *Set of 5* . . . . . 3·00 3·00
MS2152 80 × 87 mm. 14000d. Imperial
pheasants (*Lophura imperialis*) (42 × 30 mm).
P 13½ × 14. . . . . 2·00 2·00
No. 2149 is wrongly inscribed "cholchicus".

(Des Mrs. Nguyên Thi Sâm)

1998 (1 Jan). *Wickerwork. T 470 and similar horiz designs.*
P 13 × 13½.
2153 400d. ochre, black and pale green . . 10 10
2154 400d. black, orange-red and blue . . 10 10
2155 400d. yellow-ochre, black and pale
blue 10 10
2156 400d. reddish lilac, yellow-brown and
black 10 10
2157 2000d. greenish grey, rose and black . . 55 55
2153/2157 *Set of 5* 85 85
Designs:—No. 2154, Dish and bowl; 2155, Swan-shaped
basket; 2156, Deer-shaped basket; 2157, Basket with handle.

471 Mother Tiger with
Cubs

472 Flag, Helmet and
Rifle

(Des Mrs. Hoang Thuy Lieu)

1998 (5 Jan). *New Year. Year of the Tiger. T 471 and similar
square design. Multicoloured.* P 13.
2158 400d. Type **471** 10 10
2159 8000d. Tiger . . . . 1·20 1·20

(Des T. T. Vinh)

1998 (30 Jan). *30th Anniv of Tet Offensive.* P 13.
2160 **472** 400d. multicoloured 25 25

473 Cà Ná Beach, Ninh
Thuân Province

474 Karl Marx and
Freidrich Engels
(authors)

(Des Mrs. Nguyên Thi Sâm)

1998 (2 Feb). *Central Vietnam Landscapes. T 473 and similar
square designs. Multicoloured.* P 13.
2161 400d. Type **473** 10 10
2162 400d. Phong Nha Cave, Quang Binh
Province 10 10
2163 10000d. Hôi An Town, Quang Nam
Province . . . . 1·30 1·30

(Des T. T. Vinh)

1998 (3 Feb). *150th Anniv of Communist Manifesto.* P 13.
2164 **474** 400d. multicoloured 25 25

475 Limonia acidissima

476 Thi Kinh is falsely
accused of killing
Husband

(Des D. L. Tuân)

1998 (2 Mar). *Bonsai Trees. T 475 and similar multicoloured
designs.* P 13.
2165 400d. Type **475** 10 10
2166 400d. *Deeringia polysperma* . . . 10 10
2167 400d. *Pinus merkusii* (*vert*) . . . 10 10
2168 4000d. *Barringtonia acutangula*
(*vert*) 55 55
2169 6000d. India rubber-tree (*Ficus elastica*)
(*vert*) 80 80
2170 10000d. *Wrightia religiosa* (*vert*) . . . 1·30 1·30
2165/2170 *Set of 6* . . . . 2·75 2·75
MS2171 75 × 99 mm. 14000d. Desert rose
(*Adenium obesum*). P 13½ × 14 . . 1·70 1·70

(Des N. M. Lân)

1998 (2 Apr). *Quan Am Thi Kinh (opera). T 476 and similar square
designs. Multicoloured.* P 13.
2172 400d. Type **476** 10 10
a. Sheetlet of 6. Nos. 2172/7 . . 3·00
2173 1000d. Thi Kinh as Buddhist novice and
Thi Mau (with fan) . . . 15 15
2174 2000d. Thi Mau and servant with basket
on head 25 25
2175 4000d. Me Dop (village chief) and Thi
Mau 55 55
2176 6000d. Me Dop, Thi Mau and Thi
Kinh 80 80
2177 9000d. Thi Kinh with Thi Mau's baby
begging for alms . . . 1·20 1·20
2172/2177 *Set of 6* . . . . 2·75 2·75
Nos. 2172/7 were issued together in *se-tenant* sheetlets of six
stamps.

477 Pres. Ho Chi Minh and Nha Rong Wharf

478 Western Honey Buzzard (*Pernis apivorus*)

481 Players competing for Ball

(Des T. T. Vinh)

1998 (30 Apr). *300th Anniv of Ho Chi Minh City (formerly Saigon). T **477** and similar vert design. Multicoloured.* P 13.

2178	400d. Type **477**	10	10
2179	5000d. "Uncle Ho with Children" (sculpture, Diep Minh Chau)	75	75
MS2180	110 × 102 mm. 14000d. Statue of Nguyen Huu Canh (founder of Saigon)	2·00	2·00

(Des Mrs. Nguyên Thi Sâm)

1998 (10 June). *World Cup Football Championship, France. T **481** and similar diamond-shaped designs. Multicoloured.* P 13.

2191	400d. Type **481**	10	10
2192	5000d. Players chasing ball	65	65
2193	7000d. Tackle	1·00	1·00

482 Dragon, Bôi Khê Pagoda

483 Wushu

(Des Mrs. Vo Luong Nhi)

1998 (4 May). *Birds. T **478** and similar square designs. Multicoloured.* P 13.

2181	400d. Type **478**	10	10
2182	400d. Northern goshawk (*Accipter gentilis*)	10	10
2183	400d. Ornate hawk eagle (*Spizaetus ornatus*)	10	10
2184	3000d. Common buzzard (*Buteo buteo*)	40	40
2185	5000d. Pied harrier (*Circus melanoleucus*)	65	65
2186	12000d. White-tailed sea eagle (*Haliaeetus albicilla*)	1·70	1·70
2181/2186 Set of 6		2·75	2·75

(Des Mrs. Vu Liên)

1998 (15 June). *Sculptures from Tran Dynasty. T **482** and similar horiz designs. Multicoloured.* P 13.

2194	400d. Type **482**	10	10
2195	400d. Birds with human heads, Thái Lac Pagoda	10	10
2196	1000d. Dragon's heads, ship's planks and waves (throne back), Thầy Pagoda	15	15
2197	8000d. Fairy offering flower, Hang Pagoda	1·10	1·10
2198	9000d. Kneeling figure, Thái Lac Pagoda	1·30	1·30
2194/2198 Set of 5		2·50	2·50

(Des Mrs. Vu Liên)

1998 (13 July). *13th Asian Games, Bangkok.* P 13.

2199	**483** 2000d. multicoloured	45	45

479 *Paphiopedilum appletonianum*

480 Children going to School (Nguyen Tram)

484 Underwater Scene

485 Alexander Graham Bell's Telephone, 1876

(Des Mrs. Hoang Thuy Lieu)

1998 (18 May). *Orchids. T **479** and similar horiz design. Multicoloured.* P 13½.

2187	400d. Type **479**	10	10
2188	6000d. *Paphiopedilum helenae*	95	95

(Des Mrs. Vu Liên)

1998 (1 Aug). *International Year of the Ocean.* P 13.

2200	**484** 400d. multicoloured	25	25

(Des D. L. Tuân)

1998 (1 June). *Vietnamese Children's Fund. T **480** and similar square designs showing winning paintings in UNICEF contest. Multicoloured.* P 13.

2189	400d. Type **480**	10	10
2190	5000d. Children playing in park (Vu Thi Tuyet)	75	75

(Des Mrs. Vu Liên)

1998 (15 Aug). *Stamp Day. 35th Anniv of Posts and Telecommunications Department.* P 13.
2201 **485** 400d. multicoloured 25 25

486 Tón Dúc Tháng

487 *Antheraea helferi*

(Des Mrs. Vu Liên)

1998 (20 Aug). *110th Birth Anniv of Tón Dúc Tháng (President 1969–80).* P 13.
2202 **486** 400d. multicoloured 25 25

(Des Mrs. Vo Luong Nhi)

1998 (22 Aug). *Moths. T* **487** *and similar multicoloured designs.* P 13.
2203 400d. Type **487** 10 10
2204 400d. Atlas moth (*Attacus atlas*) . . . 10 10
2205 4000d. Tailed comet moth (*Argema mittrei*) (*vert*) 65 65
2206 10000d. *Argema maenas* (*vert*) . . . . 1·50 1·50
2203/2206 Set of 4 . . . . 2·10 2·10

488 "Dragonfly and Lotus"

489 Milan Cathedral and Statue

(Des Mrs. Vu Liên and Mrs. Hoang Thuy Lieu)

1998 (16 Sept). *135th Birth Anniv of Qi Baishi (painter). T* **488** *and similar vert designs.* P 13.
2207 400d. Type **488** 10 10
2208 1000d. "Chickens and Chrysanthemum" 15 15
2209 2000d. "Shrimps" 25 25
2210 4000d. "School of Crabs" 55 55
2211 6000d. "Ducks and Lotus" 80 80
2212 9000d. "Shrimps" (*different*) . . . . 1·20 1·20
2207/2212 Set of 6 . . . . 2·75 2·75

(Des D. L. Tuân)

1998 (6 Oct). *"Italia 98" International Stamp Exhibition, Milan, Italy.* Sheet 100 × 62 *mm.* P 13½ × 14.
MS2213 **489** 16000d. multicoloured . . . . . 2·10 2·10

490 King Le Loi on Boat

(Des T. Q. Thu)

1998 (10 Oct). *Legend of Restored Sword Lake, Hanoi. T* **490** *and similar horiz design. Multicoloured.* P 13.
2214 400d. Type **490** 25 25
2215 400d. Jade Hill Temple and Huc Sunrise bridge 25 25

491 King Le Thang Tong (statue)

(Des Mrs. Hoang Thuy Lieu)

1998 (12 Oct). *500th Death Anniv (1997) of King Le Thang Tong.* P 13.
2216 **491** 400d. multicoloured 25 25

492 Emblem and Couple

(Des Mrs. Nguyên Thi Sâm)

1998 (15 Oct). *Eighth Trade Unions Congress.* P 13.
2217 **492** 400d. multicoloured 25 25

493 King Quang Trung (statue) and Quy Nhon Port

(Des D. L. Tuân)

1998 (20 Oct). *Centenary of Quy Nhon as Binh Dinh Provincial Capital.* P 13.
2218 **493** 400d. multicoloured 25 25

494 Duong Quang Ham (first Vietnamese headmaster) and School

495 Doves around Emblem

498 Cat going to Tet Flower Market

499 Eagle Kite

(Des Mrs. Tran Ngoc Uyên)

1998 (20 Nov). *90th Anniv of Buoi Chu Van An Secondary School, Hanoi. T **494** and similar horiz design. Multicoloured.* P 13.

2219	400d. Type **494**		10	10
2220	5000d. Ho Chi Minh and students		75	75

(Des Mrs. Nguyên Thi Sâm)

1999 (6 Jan). *New Year. Year of the Cat. T **498** and similar square designs. Multicoloured.* P 13½.

2227	400d. Type **498**		10	10
2228	8000d. Cats fighting		1·10	1·10
MS2229	100 × 73 mm. 13000d. Kittens (31 × 42 mm)		1·70	1·70

(Des D. L. Tuân)

1998 (5 Dec). *Sixth Association of South East Asian Nations Summit, Hanoi.* P 13.

2221	**495**	1000d. multicoloured	35	35

(Des Mrs. Hoang Thuy Lieu)

1999 (16 Feb). *Kites. T **499** and similar vert designs. Multicoloured.* P 13.

2230	400d. Type **499**		10	10
2231	5000d. Kite with bamboo flute		65	65
2232	7000d. Peacock		95	95

500 Ha Long Bay Net Boat

(Des D. L. Tuân)

1999 (10 Mar). *"Australia '99" World Stamp Exhibition, Melbourne. Local Craft. T **500** and similar horiz designs. Multicoloured.* P 13.

2233	400d. Type **500**		10	10
2234	400d. Cua Lo bamboo junk		10	10
2235	7000d. Nha Trang bamboo junk		85	85
2236	9000d. Ne Cape junk		1·10	1·10
2233/2236 *Set of 4*			2·00	2·00

497 Spring

501 *Kaempferia galanga*

496 Industrial Symbols, Revolutionary Memorial, Havana and Cuban Flag forming "40"

(Des Mrs. Nguyên Thi Sâm)

1998 (30 Dec). *40th Anniv (1999) of Cuban Revolution.* P 13.

2222	**496**	400d. multicoloured	25	25

(Des Mrs. Vo Luong Nhi)

1999 (15 Mar). *Medicinal Herbs. T **501** and similar multicoloured designs.* P 13.

2237	400d. Type **501**		10	10
2238	400d. *Tacca chantrieri* André (*vert*)		10	10
2239	400d. *Alpinia galanga* Willd (*vert*)		10	10
2240	6000d. *Typhonium trilobatum* Schott (*vert*)		75	75
2241	13000d. *Asarum maximum* Hemsl (*vert*)		1·60	1·60
2237/2241 *Set of 5*			2·40	2·40

(Des Mrs. Hoang Thuy Lieu)

1999 (4 Jan). *Four Seasons Paintings (1st series). T **497** and similar vert designs. Multicoloured.* P 13½ × 13.

2223	400d. Type **497**		10	10
2224	1000d. Summer		15	15
2225	3000d. Autumn		35	35
2226	12000d. Winter		1·50	1·50
2223/2226 *Set of 4*			1·90	1·90

See also Nos. 2390/3.

502 Syringe, Fields, City and Family

(Des D. L. Tuân)

1999 (8 Apr). *International Day Against Drugs.* P 13.
2242 **502** 400d. multicoloured 25 25

506 Emblem, Map and Satellite

(Des Mrs. Nguyên Thi Sâm)

1999 (10 May). *20th Anniv of Asia–Pacific Telecommunity.* P 13.
2256 **506** 400d. multicoloured . . . . 1·30 1·30

503 Van Trong Mask   **504** *Octopus gibertianus*

(Des Mrs. Nguyên Thi Sâm)

1999 (16 Apr). *Tuong Stage Masks.* T **503** *and similar square designs. Multicoloured.* P 13½.
2243	400d. Type **503**	10	10
2244	1000d. Hoang Phi Ho	15	15
2245	2000d. Chau Thuong	25	25
2246	5000d. Tiet Cuong	60	60
2247	6000d. Mao At	75	75
2248	10000d. Tran Long	1·20	1·20
2243/2248 *Set of 6*		2·75	2·75

(Des D. L. Tuân)

1999 (20 Apr). *"iBRA '99" International Stamp Exhibition, Nuremberg, Germany. Octopuses.* T **504** *and similar square designs. Multicoloured.* P 13½.
2249	400d. Type **504**	10	10
2250	400d. *Philonexis catenulata*	10	10
2251	4000d. *Paroctopus yendoi*	55	55
2252	12000d. Common octopus (*Octopus vulgaris*)	1·60	1·60
2249/2252 *Set of 4*		2·10	2·10

505 Cape, Ca Mau Province

(Des Mrs. Vu Lien)

1999 (30 Apr). *Southern Vietnam Landscapes.* T **505** *and similar horiz designs. Multicoloured.* P 13.
2253	400d. Type **505**	10	10
2254	400d. Father and Son Islet, Kien Giang Province	10	10
2255	12000d. Vinh Hung Tower, Bac Lieu Province	1·70	1·70

507 Greater flame-backed Woodpecker (*Chrysocolaptes lucidus*)   **508** Large Hand and Child cowering

(Des D. L. Tuân)

1999 (18 May). *Woodpeckers.* T **507** *and similar vert designs. Multicoloured.* P 13.
2257	400d. Type **507**	10	10
2258	1000d. Speckled piculet (*Picumnus innominatus*)	15	15
2259	3000d. Red-collared woodpecker (*Picus rabieri*)	40	40
2260	13000d. Bay woodpecker (*Blythipicus pyrrhotis*)	1·70	1·70
2257/2260 *Set of 4*		2·10	2·10

(Des Mrs. Vo Luong Nhi)

1999 (1 June). *Vietnamese Children's Fund.* T **508** *and similar vert design.* P 13.
2261	400d. lilac, blue-green and black	10	10
2262	5000d. ultramarine, grey and black	65	65
Design:—5000d. Young man carrying buildings.			

509 Northern Government Office, Hanoi

(Des Mrs. Hoang Thuy Lieu)

1999 (10 June). *Architecture.* T **509** *and similar multicoloured designs.* P 13.
2263	400d. Type **509**	10	10
2264	400d. History Museum, Ho Chi Minh City	10	10
2265	12000d. Duc Ba Cathedral (*vert*)	1·70	1·70
MS2266 96 × 64 mm. 15000d. Big Theatre, Hanoi (42 × 31 *mm*). P 13½ × 14		2·10	2·10

No. **MS**2266 also includes the "Philexfrance 99" International Stamp Exhibition, Paris emblem on the margin.

510 Da Rang Bridge and Nhan Mountains

(Des D. L. Tuân)

1999 (1 July). *Phu Yen Province.* P 13.
2267 **510** 400d. multicoloured 35 35

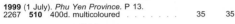

511 Man fighting Tiger, Chay Communal House, Ha Nam Province

(Des Mrs. Vu Lien)

1999 (1 July). *Le Dynasty Sculptures.* T **511** *and similar multicoloured designs.* P 13.
2268 1000d. Type **511** 20 20
2269 1000d. Phoenix, But Thap Pagoda, Bac Ninh Province 20 20
2270 3000d. Playing chess, Ngoc Canh Communal House, Vinh Phuc Province (*vert*) 60 60
2271 7000d. Ostler, Quang Phuc Communal House, Ha Tay Province (*vert*) . . . . 1·50 1·50
2272 9000d. Stone dragon, Kinh Thien Temple, Hanoi . . . . 1·90 1·90
2268/2272 *Set of 5* . . . . 4·00 4·00

512 Globe and Family

513 Van Tho Hill, Di Hoa Park, Peking

(Des T. M. Trang)

1999 (2 Aug). *Birth of World's Six Billionth Inhabitant.* P 13.
2273 **512** 400d. multicoloured 20 20

(Des Mrs. Vu Lien)

1999 (16 Aug). *Chinese Landscapes.* T **513** *and similar horiz designs. Multicoloured.* P 13.
2274 400d. Type **513** 10 10
2275 2000d. Hoang Mountain, An Huy . . . 25 25
2276 3000d. Bong Lai Cap, Dong Hill . . . 40 40
2277 10000d. Di Hoa Park, Peking . . . . 1·30 1·30
2274/2277 *Set of 4* . . . . 1·80 1·80
MS2278 93 × 88 mm. 14000d. Great Wall.
P 13½ × 14. . . . . 1·90 1·90
No. **MS**2278 is inscribed for "China 1999" International Stamp Exhibition, Peking in the margin.

514 Racing Boats, North Vietnam

(Des Mrs. Vo Luong Nhi)

1999 (10 Sept). *Traditional Boat Racing Festivals.* T **514** *and similar horiz designs. Multicoloured.* P 13.
2279 400d. Type **514** 10 10
2280 2000d. Three boats, Central Vietnam 25 25
2281 10000d. Two boats, South Vietnam . . 1·30 1·30

515 Buffaloes fighting

516 Traditional Velvet Dress

(Des Mrs. Hoang Thuy Lieu)

1999 (15 Sept). *Buffalo Festival.* T **515** *and similar horiz design. Multicoloured.* P 13.
2282 400d. Type **515** 10 10
2283 5000d. Buffalo No. 2 goring fallen animal 60 60

(Des Mrs. Vo Luong Nhi)

1999 (10 Oct). *Women's Costumes.* T **516** *and similar vert designs. Multicoloured.* P 13.
2284 400d. Type **516** 10 10
2285 400d. Magenta brocade dress 10 10
2286 12000d. Green dress . . . . 1·50 1·50

517 Ngo Quyen (statue) and Battle of Bach Dang, 938

518 Van Sieu and The Tower of the Pen Brush, Ba Dinh

(Des Mrs. Vu Lien)

1999 (21 Oct). *1100th (1998) Birth Anniv of Ngo Quyen (ruler).* P 13.
2287 **517** 400d. multicoloured 25 25

(Des Mrs. Nguyên Thi Sâm)

1999 (2 Nov). *Birth Bicentenary of Nguyen Van Sieu (scholar).* P 13.
2288 **518** 400d. multicoloured 25 25

519 Tran Xuan Soan

(Des Mrs. Hoang Thuy Lieu)

1999 (24 Nov). *150th Birth Anniv of Tran Xuan Soan (revolutionary).* P 13.
2289 **519** 400d. multicoloured 25 25

520 Fisherwoman, Farmer and Woman carrying Child

521 Hammer and Sickle above Workers (forming of Vietnamese Communist Party, 1930)

(Des N. Du and Mrs. Nguyên Thi Sâm)

1999 (3 Dec). *United Nations Development Programme. Fight Against Poverty. T* **520** *and similar horiz design. Multicoloured.* P 13.
2290 400d. Type **520** 10 10
2291 8000d. Buildings and villagers' meeting 95 95

(Des Mrs. Vu Kim Lien)

2000 (1 Jan). *The Twentieth Century. T* **521** *and similar vert designs. Multicoloured.* P 13.
2292 400d. Type **521** 10 10
2293 400d. Pres. Ho Chi Minh making Independence speech (formation of Democratic Republic, 1945) 10 10
2294 1000d. Flag, tank and people celebrating (liberation of South Vietnam, 1975) 15 15
2295 1000d. Symbols of agriculture and industry (Communist Party's ten year renovation plan) . . . 15 15
2296 8000d. Symbols of industry and communications (industrialization) 95 95
2297 12000d. Emblems (integration into international community) . . . 1·50 1·50
2292/2297 *Set of 6* . . . . 2·75 2·75
MS2298 194 × 124 mm. Nos. 2292/7 . . . . 3·00 3·00

522 Dragon

523 Globe and UNESCO "City for Peace" Prize (Hanoi, 1999)

(Des Mrs. Vu Kim Lien)

2000 (3 Jan). *New Year. Year of the Dragon. T* **522** *and similar square design. Multicoloured.* P 13½.
2299 400d. Type **522** 10 10
2300 8000d. Dragon and One Pillar Pagoda, Hanoi . . . . 1·30 1·30

(Des N. Du)

2000 (18 Jan). *International Year of Culture and Peace.* P 13½.
2301 **523** 400d. multicoloured 25 25

524 Pres. Ho Chí Minh (founder)

(Des N. Du (2302), Mrs. Nguyên Thi Sâm (2303, 2305), Mrs. Vu Liên (2304), L. Tuấn (2306), Mrs. Hoang Thuy Lieu (2307), Mrs. Vo Luong Nhi (2308/9))

2000 (2 Feb). *70th Anniv of Communist Party. T* **524** *and similar horiz designs. Multicoloured.* P 13.
2302 400d. Type **524** 15 15
2303 400d. Tran Phú (first General Secretary, 1930–31) 15 15
2304 400d. Lê Hong Phong (General Secretary, 1935–36) 15 15
2305 400d. Ha Huy Tâp (General Secretary, 1936–38) 15 15
2306 400d. Nguyen Van Cu (General Secretary, 1938–41) 15 15
2307 400d. Truong Chinh (General Secretary, 1941–56 and 1986) 15 15
2308 400d. Lê Duan (General Secretary, 1960–86) 15 15
2309 400d. Nguyen Van Linh (General Secretary, 1986–91) 15 15
2302/2309 *Set of 8* . . . . 1·10 1·10

525 Cocks fighting (Double Cock's Kick)

(Des D. L. Tuấn)

2000 (8 Feb). *Cock Fighting. T* **525** *and similar horiz designs showing cock's fighting. Multicoloured.* P 13.
2310 400d. Type **525** 10 10
2311 400d. "Long vu da dao" posture . . . 10 10

2312	7000d. "Song long phuing hoang" posture	1·10	1·10
2313	9000d. "Nhan o giap chien" posture	1·40	1·40
2310/2313	Set of 4	2·40	2·40

526 Fringed Palanquin

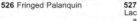

527 Marriage of Lac Long Quan and Âu Co

(Des Mrs. Vu Liên)

2000 (10 Mar). *"Bangkok 2000" International Stamp Exhibition. Processional Litters. T **526** and similar horiz designs. Multicoloured.* P 13.

2314	400d. Type **526**	10	10
2315	7000d. Throne-shaped litter	1·10	1·10
2316	8000d. Palanquin with pagoda-style roof	1·30	13·00
MS2317	95 × 65 mm. 15000d. Palanquin being carried. P 13½ × 14	2·40	2·40

(Des Mrs. Hoang Thuy Lieu)

2000 (4 Apr). *Legend of Lac Long Quan and Âu Co. T **527** and similar vert designs. Multicoloured.* P 13½.

2318	400d. Type **527**	10	10
2319	400d. Âu Co surrounded by sons	10	10
2320	500d. Âu Co and children riding elephants	10	10
2321	3000d. Lac Long Quan and sons by the sea	45	45
2322	4000d. Eldest son Hung Vuong	60	60
2323	11000d. Vietnamese ethnic groups	1·70	1·70
2318/2323	Set of 6	2·75	2·75

528 Iveco Magirus Fire Engine, Germany

529 Sao La

(Des D. L. Tuân)

2000 (15 May). *Fire Engines. Sheet 104 × 89 mm containing T **528** and similar horiz designs. Multicoloured.* P 13.
MS2324 400d. Type **528**; 1000d. Hino, Japan; 5000d. ZIL 130 E, Russia; 12000d. FPS.32 Camiva, France ... 2·75 2·75
No. **MS**2324 also includes "The Stamp Show 2000" International Stamp Exhibition, London emblem on the margin.

(Des Mrs. Vo Luong Nhi)

2000 (18 May). *Endangered Species. Sao La (Pseudoryx nghetinhensis). T **529** and similar horiz designs. Multicoloured.* P 13½.

2325	400d. Type **529**	10	10
	a. Block of 4. Nos. 2325/8	2·50	
2326	400d. Juvenile in grass	10	10
2327	5000d. Beside lake	75	75
2328	10000d. Head of adult	1·50	1·50
2325/2328	Set of 4	2·20	2·20

Nos. 2325/8 were issued either in separate sheets or together in *se-tenant* blocks of four stamps within sheets of eight.

530 Ho Chi Minh and Birthplace

531 Buffon Teu

(Des Mrs. Hoang Thuy Lieu)

2000 (19 May). *110th Birth Anniv of President Ho Chi Minh.* P 13.
| 2329 | **530** | 400d. multicoloured | 25 | 25 |

(Des Mrs. Vu Liên)

2000 (28 June). *"World Stamp Expo 2000", Anaheim, California. Water Puppetry. T **531** and similar square designs showing traditional puppets. Multicoloured.* P 13½.

2330	400d. Type **531**	10	10
2331	400d. Fairy and phoenix	10	10
2332	400d. Ploughman	10	10
2333	3000d. Peasant woman	40	40
2334	9000d. Drummer	1·20	1·20
2335	11000d. Fisherman	1·60	1·60
2330/2335	Set of 6	3·25	3·25

532 Young Girl waving Flag

533 Swimmers and Emblem

(Des Mrs. Hoang Thuy Lieu)

2000 (15 July). *50th Anniv of Youth Volunteers.* P 13.
| 2336 | **532** | 400d. multicoloured | 25 | 25 |

(Des N. Du)

2000 (20 July). *Fifth National Youth Sports Festival, Dong Thap.* P 13.
| 2337 | **533** | 400d. multicoloured | 25 | 25 |

534 Coral Hind (*Cephalopholis miniata*)

(Des D. L. Tuân)

2000 (7 Aug). *Coral Reef Fishes. T **534** and similar multicoloured designs.* P 13.

2338	400d. Type **534**	10	10
2339	400d. Emperor angelfish (*Pomacanthus imperator*)	10	10
2340	400d. Honeycomb grouper (*Epinephelus merra*)	10	10

2341	4000d. Moorish idol (*Zanclus cornutus*)		
	(*vert*)	35	35
2342	6000d. Saddle butterflyfish (*Chaetodon*		
	ephippium) (*vert*)	80	80
2343	12000d. Pennant coralfish (*Heniochus*		
	acuminatus) (*vert*)	1·70	1·70
2338/2343 *Set of 6*		2·75	2·75
MS2344 74 × 99 mm. 15000d. Racoon			
butterflyfish (*Chaetodon lunula*).			
P 13½ × 14		2·00	2·00

535 Postal Workers and Means of Communications

(Des T. M. Trang)

2000 (15 Aug). *55th Anniv of Vietnam Posts and Telecommunications Service.* P 13.

2345	**535**	400d. multicoloured	25	25

536 Ho Chi Minh with Policemen

537 Statue of Nguyen Tri Phuong, Da Nang

(Des N. Du and D. L. Tuân)

2000 (19 Aug). *55th Anniv of National Police Force.* T **536** and similar multicoloured designs. P 13.

2346		400d. Type **536**	10	10
2347		2000d. Police personnel (*vert*)	35	35

(Des Mrs. Vo Luong Nhi)

2000 (31 Aug). *Birth Bicentenary of Nguyen Tri Phuong (provincial Governor).* P 13½.

2348	**537**	400d. multicoloured	25	25

538 Children and Emblem

(Des Mrs. Vu Liên)

2000 (8 Sept). *Tenth Anniv of United Nations Convention on Children's Rights.* T **538** and similar multicoloured design. P 13.

2349		400d. Type **538**	10	10
2350		5000d. Children's faces around emblem		
		(*vert*)	80	80

539 Running

540 Tran Hung Dao Monument, An Phu

(Des Mrs. Vo Luong Nhi)

2000 (15 Sept). *Olympic Games, Sydney.* T **539** and similar multicoloured designs. P 13.

2351		400d. Type **539**	10	10
2352		6000d. Shooting	80	80
2353		7000d. Taekwondo (*vert*)	1·00	1·00

(Des Mrs. Vu Liên)

2000 (15 Sept). *700th Death Anniv of General Tran Hung Dao.* P 13.

2354	**540**	400d. multicoloured	25	25

541 Silver-eared Mesia (*Leiothrix argentauris*)

542 North Vietnam 1976 12x. Stamp, Magnifying Glass and Emblem

(Des Mrs. Vo Luong Nhi)

2000 (28 Sept). *Birds.* T **541** and similar multicoloured designs. P 13½.

2355		400d. Type **541**	10	10
2356		400d. Elliott's pitta (*Pitta ellioti*)	10	10
2357		400d. Coral-billed scimitar babbler		
		(*Pomatorhinus ferruginosus*)		
		(inscr "Pomatorinus")	10	10
2358		5000d. Greater racquet-tailed drongo		
		(*Dicrurus paradiseus*) (inscr		
		"paradiceu") (*vert*)	80	80
2359		7000d. Sultan tit (*Melanochlora*		
		sultanea) (*vert*)	1·00	1·00
2360		10000d. Spot-necked tree babbler		
		(*Stachyris striolata*) (*vert*)	1·30	1·30
2355/2360 *Set of 6*			3·00	3·00
MS2361 106 × 81 mm. 15000d. Blue-backed				
fairy bluebird (*Irena puella*) (42 × 31 *mm*).				
P 13½ × 14			2·00	2·00

No. **MS**2361 is inscribed for "ESPAA 2000" International Stamp Exhibition, Madrid in the margin.

(Des T. M. Trang)

2000 (6 Oct). *40th Anniv of Vietnamese Philatelic Association.* P 13.

2362	**542**	400d. multicoloured	25	25

543 Pigs feeding and Agricultural Workers

(Des Mrs. Nguyên Thi Sâm)

2000 (14 Oct). *70th Anniv of Vietnamese Farmers' Association.* P 13.
2363 **543** 400d. multicoloured 25 25

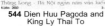

544 Dien Huu Pagoda and King Ly Thai To

545 Harlequin Bat (*Scotomanes ornatus*)

(Des Mrs. Vu Liên)

2000 (15 Oct). *990th Anniv of Hanoi.* T **544** *and similar horiz designs. Multicoloured.* P 13.
2364 400d. Type **544** 10 10
2365 3000d. Van Mieu-Quoc Tu Giam (Confucian temple) and university 45 45
2366 10000d. Hanoi city scene . . . 1·30 1·30
MS2367 97 × 90 mm. 15000d. Women releasing doves (42 × 31 *mm*). P 13½ × 14 . . . 2·00 2·00

(Des Mrs Hoang Thuy Lieu)

2000 (16 Oct). *Bats.* T **545** *and similar vert designs. Multicoloured.* P 13.
2368 400d. Type **545** 10 10
2369 400d. *Pteropus lylei* 10 10
2370 2000d. *Rhinolophus paradoxolophus* 25 25
2371 6000d. Cave fruit bat (*Eonycteris spelaea*) 80 80
2372 11000d. Short-nosed fruit bat (*Cynopterus sphinx*) . . . 1·50 1·50
2368/2372 *Set of 5* . . . . 2·50 2·50

546 "70" and Dove

(Des Mrs. Hoang Thuy Lieu)

2000 (20 Oct). *70th Anniv of Vietnamese Women's Union.* P 13.
2373 **546** 400d. multicoloured 25 25

547 Workers

548 *Oxyspora* sp.

(Des Mrs. Nguyên Thi Sâm and Mrs. Vo Luong Nhi)

2000 (10 Nov). *Sixth National "Heroes of Labour" Congress.* T **547** *and similar multicoloured design.* P 13.
2374 400d. Type **547** 10 10
2375 3000d. Flower and industrial symbols (*vert*) 55 55

(Des Mrs. Nguyên Thi Sâm)

2000 (15 Nov). *Cornflowers.* T **548** *and similar multicoloured design.* P 13½.
2376 400d. Type **548** 10 10
2377 5000d. *Melastoma villosa* 85 85

549 Ho Chi Minh and Crowd

550 Hon Khoai Island and Statue

(Des Mrs. Nguyên Thi Sâm)

2000 (18 Nov). *70th Anniv of Vietnam Fatherland Front.* P 13.
2378 **549** 400d. multicoloured 25 25

(Des Mrs. Hoang Thuy Lieu)

2000 (13 Dec). *60th Anniv of Hon Khoai Uprising.* P 13.
2379 **550** 400d. multicoloured 25 25

551 Banners and Satellite

552 Snake

(Des T. M. Trang)

2001 (1 Jan). *New Millennium.* P 13.
2380 **551** 400d. multicoloured 25 25

(Des T. M. Trang)

2001 (2 Jan). *New Year. Year of the Snake.* T **552** *and similar square design. Multicoloured.* P 13½.
2381 400d. Type **552** 10 10
2382 8000d. Green snake . . . . . 1·30 1·30

553 Archerfish (*Toxotes macrolepis*)

554 Alfred Nobel (founder)

(Des D. L. Tuân)

2001 (18 Jan). *"HONG KONG 2001" International Stamp Exhibition. Freshwater Fish. T 553 and similar horiz designs. Multicoloured.* P 13.

2383	400d.	Type **553**	10	10
2384	800d.	Carp (*Cosmochilus harmandi*) (wrongly inscr "Cosmocheilus")	15	15
2385	2000d.	Indian short-finned eel (*Anguilla bicolor pacifica*)	35	35
2386	3000d.	Chitala ornata	45	45
2387	7000d.	Indo-Pacific tarpon (*Megalops cyprinoids*)	80	80
2388	8000d.	Esok (*Probarbus jullieni*)	95	95
2383/2388		*Set of 6*	2·50	2·50

(Des Mrs. Nguyên Thi Sâm)

2001 (27 Jan). *Centenary of Nobel Prizes.* P 13½.

2389	**554**	400d. greenish blue, orange-yellow and black	25	25

555 Spring

556 *Rubus cochinchinensis*

(Des Mrs. Hoang Thuy Lieu)

2001 (1 Feb). *Four Seasons Paintings (2nd series). T 555 and similar vert designs. Multicoloured.* P 13½ × 13.

2390	400d.	Type **555**	10	10
		a. Sheetlet of 4. Nos. 2390/3	2·00	
2391	800d.	Summer	15	15
2392	4000d.	Autumn	55	55
2393	10000d.	Winter	1·30	1·30
2390/2393		*Set of 4*	1·90	1·90

Nos. 2390/3 were issued in *se-tenant* sheetlets of four stamps.

(Des Mrs. Nguyên Thi Sâm)

2001 (8 Feb). *Forest Fruits. T 556 and similar vert designs. Multicoloured.* P 13½.

2394	400d.	Type **556**	10	10
2395	400d.	Rhizophora mucronata	10	10
2396	400d.	Podocarpus neriifolius	10	10
2397	400d.	Magnolia pumila	10	10
2398	15000d.	Taxus chinensis	1·70	1·70
2394/2398		*Set of 5*	1·90	1·90

557 Co Tien Mountains, Hà Giang Province

(Des Mrs. Vu Liên)

2001 (23 Feb). *Northern Vietnam Landscapes. T 557 and similar horiz designs. Multicoloured.* P 13.

2399	400d.	Type **557**	10	10
2400	400d.	Dong Pagoda, Yen Tu, Quang Ninh Province	10	10
2401	10000d.	King Dinh Temple, Ninh Binh Province	1·30	1·30

558 Medals and Mastheads on "50"

(Des D. L. Tuân)

2001 (11 Mar). *50th Anniv of Nhân Dân (Communist Party newspaper).* P 13.

2402	**558**	400d. multicoloured	25	25

559 Starlight Ruby

560 Youths and Emblem

(Des N. Du)

2001 (20 Mar). *Rubies. T 559 and similar horiz design showing named rubies before and after cutting. Multicoloured.* P 13.

2403	400d.	Type **559**	10	10
2404	6000d.	Vietnam Star	80	80

(Des Mrs. Hoang Thuy Lieu)

2001 (26 Mar). *70th Anniv of Ho Chi Minh Youth Union.* P 13.

2405	**560**	400d. multicoloured	25	25

561 David's Tree Partridge (*Arborophila davidi*)

562 Ho Chi Minh, Flag and Map of Vietnam

(Des Mrs. Vo Luong Nhi)

2001 (3 Apr). *Animals in Cat Tien National Park.* T **561** *and similar horiz designs. Multicoloured.* P 13½.

2406	400d. Type **561**		10	10
2407	800d. Jungle queen butterfly (*Stichophthalma uemurai*)		15	15
2408	3000d. Vietnamese Javan rhino (*Rhinoceros sondaicus annamiticus*)		55	55
2409	5000d. Siamese crocodile (*Crocodylus siamensis*)		95	95
2406/2409 *Set of 4*			1·60	1·60

(Des T. M. Trang and N. Du)

2001 (18 Apr). *Ninth Vietnamese Communist Party Congress.* T **562** *and similar multicoloured design.* P 13.

2410	400d. Type **562**		10	10
2411	3000d. Hammer, sickle and Ngoc Lu drum head (*vert*)		40	40

563 Veiled Stinkhorn (*Phallus indusiatus*)

564 Ho Chi Minh, Girl and Flowers

(Des Mrs. Vu Liên)

2001 (2 May). *Fungi.* T **563** *and similar multicoloured designs.* P 13½.

2412	400d. Type **563**		10	10
2413	400d. *Aseroe arachnoidea*		10	10
2414	400d. *Phallus tenuis*		10	10
2415	2000d. *Phallus impudicus*		25	25
2416	5000d. *Phallus rugulosus*		65	65
2417	6000d. *Simblum periphragmoides*		80	80
2418	7000d. *Mutinus bambusinus*		1·00	1·00
2412/2418 *Set of 7*			2·75	2·75
MS2419 86 × 86 mm. 13000d. *Pseudocolus schellenbergiae* (42 × 31 *mm*)			2·00	2·00

(Des N. Du)

2001 (15 May). *60th Anniv of Vietnam Youth Pioneers.* P 13.

2420	**564** 400d. multicoloured	25	25

565 Ho Chi Minh, Crowd and Flag

566 Cigarette and Flower

(Des Mrs. Vu Liên)

2001 (19 May). *60th Anniv of Vietnam Independence League.* P 13.

2421	**565** 400d. multicoloured	25	25

(Des Mrs. Hoang Thuy Lieu)

2001 (31 May). *World No-Smoking Day.* P 13½.

2422	**566** 800d. multicoloured	40	40

567 Children wearing Protective Clothing

568 Locomotive D18E

(Des Mrs. Hoang Thuy Lieu)

2001 (1 June). *United Nations Children's Fund (400d.) and United Nations General Assembly Special Session on Children (5000d.).* T **567** *and similar square design. Multicoloured.* P 13½.

2423	400d. Type **567**		10	10
2424	5000d. Children of different races and emblem		80	80

(Des D. L. Tuân)

2001 (5 June). *Diesel Locomotives.* T **568** *and similar horiz designs. Multicoloured.* P 13.

2425	400d. Type **568**		10	10
2426	400d. Locomotive D4H		10	10
2427	800d. Locomotive D11H in station		15	15
2428	2000d. Locomotive D5H		35	35
2429	6000d. Locomotive D9E		95	95
2430	7000d. Locomotive D12E		1·10	1·10
2425/2430 *Set of 6*			2·50	2·50
MS2431 96 × 66 mm. 13000d. Locomotive D11H on lakeside track (42 × 31 *mm*). P 13½ × 14			2·00	2·00

569 *Vanda* sp.

570 Golden Birdwing (*Troides aeacus*)

(Des Mrs. Nguyên Thi Sâm)

2001 (5 July). *Orchids.* T **569** *and similar horiz designs. Multicoloured.* P 13½.

2432	800d. Type **569**		15	15
2433	800d. *Dendrobium lowianum*		15	15
2434	800d. *Phajus wallachii*		15	15
2435	800d. *Habenaria medioflexa*		15	15
2436	800d. *Arundina graminifolia* (*vert*)		15	15
2437	12000d. *Calanthe clavata* (*vert*)		1·70	1·70
2432/2437 *Set of 6*			2·20	2·20

(Des Mrs. Vo Luong Nhi)

2001 (16 July). *"PHILA NIPPON '01" International Stamp Exhibition, Tokyo. Butterflies.* T **570** *and similar horiz designs. Multicoloured.* P 13½.

2438	800d. Type **570**		15	15
2439	800d. Peacock (*Inachis io*)		15	15
2440	800d. *Ancyluris formosissima*		15	15
2441	5000d. Red glider (*Cymothoe sangaris*) (wrongly inscr "sanguris")		45	45
2442	7000d. *Taenaris selene*		80	80
2443	10000d. Raja Brooke's birdwing (*Trogonoptera brookiana*)		1·30	1·30
2438/2443 *Set of 6*			2·75	2·75
MS2444 94 × 69 mm. 13000d. *Atrophaneura horishanus* (31 × 42 *mm*)			2·00	2·00

571 Footballer

572 H Gáo

(Des N. Du)

2001 (24 July). *World Cup Football Championship, Japan and South Korea (2002). T* **571** *and similar vert design. Multicoloured.* P 13.
2445	**800d.** Type **571**		15	15
	a. Horiz pair. Nos. 2446/7		75	75
2446	3000d. Footballer and map including			
	Americas		55	55

Nos. 2445/6 were issued together in horizontal *se-tenant* pairs within the sheet, each pair forming a composite design.

(Des Mrs. Hoang Thuy Lieu)

2001 (4 Sept). *Traditional Musical Instruments. T* **572** *and similar multicoloured designs.* P 13.
2447	800d. Type **572**	15	15
2448	800d. Kênh (pan-pipes)	15	15
2449	800d. Dàn Tú (stringed instrument)		
	(*vert*)	15	15
2450	2000d. Dàn T'rung (*vert*)	25	25
2451	6000d. Tróng Kinang (drum) (*vert*)	65	65
2452	9000d. Tính Táu (stringed instrument)		
	(*vert*)	1·20	1·20
2447/2452 Set of 6		2·30	2·30

573 Children encircling Globe

574 Trân Huy Liêu and Books

(Des N. Du)

2001 (9 Oct). *United Nations Year of Dialogue among Civilizations.* P 13½.
2453	**573**	800d. multicoloured	35	35

(Des Mrs. Vo Luong Nhi)

2001 (5 Nov). *Birth Centenary of Trân Huy Liêu (writer and revolutionary).* P 13.
2454	**574**	800d. multicoloured	35	35

575 Nam Cao and Titles of his Works

576 Leaves around Globe

(Des Mrs. Nguyên Thi Sâm)

2001 (30 Nov). *50th Death Anniv of Nam Cao (Trân Hũu Tri) (writer).* P 13.
2455	**575**	800d. multicoloured	35	35

(Des Mrs. Nguyên Thi Sâm)

2001 (27 Dec). *Environment Protection. T* **576** *and similar vert design. Multicoloured.* P 13½.
2456		800d. Type **576**	15	15
2457		3000d. Globe in tree with nesting peace		
		dove	55	55

577 "To He" Horse

578 Giáp Tuóng Nam

(Des N. Du)

2002 (2 Jan). *New Year. Year of the Horse. T* **577** *and similar multicoloured designs.* P 13½.
2458	800d. Type **577**	15	15
2459	8000d. Horse with parasol	80	80
MS2460 76 × 66 mm. 14000d. Flying horse			
(42 × 31 *mm*). P 13½ × 14		2·00	2·00

(Des Mrs. Nguyên Thi Sâm)

2002 (15 Jan). *Tuong (classical opera) Costumes. T* **578** *and similar vert designs showing costumes. Multicoloured.* P 13.
2461	1000d. Type **578**	15	15
2462	1000d. Giáp Tuóng Nu	15	15
2463	2000d. Giáp Tuóng Phán Diên	25	25
2464	3000d. Long Chân	40	40
2465	5000d. Giáp Tuóng Phiên	65	65
2466	9000d. Lung Xiêm Quên Giáp	1·10	1·10
2461/2466 Set of 6		2·40	2·40

579 Vo Thi Sau

580 Symbols of Industry and Communications

(Des Mrs. Hoang Thuy Lieu)

2002 (23 Jan). *50th Death Anniv of Vô Thi Sáu (resistance fighter).* P 13.
2467	**579**	1000d. multicoloured	35	35

(Des T. M. Trang and N. Du)

2002 (1 Feb). *Ninth Communist Party Congress Resolutions. T* **580** *and similar vert design. Multicoloured.* P 13.
2468	800d. Type **580**	15	15
2469	3000d. Thang Long Citadel gate, flag		
	and people	40	40

581 *Echinocereus albatus*

582 Emblem and Woman's Face

(Des Mrs. Vo Luong Nhi and D. L Tuân)

2002 (11 Feb). *Cacti. T* **581** *and similar vert designs. Multicoloured.* P 13 × 13½.
2470	1000d. Type **581**		15	15
2471	1000d. *Echinocereus delaetii*		15	15
2472	1000d. *Cylindropuntia bigelowii*		15	15
2473	5000d. *Echinocereus triglochidatus*		55	55
2474	10000d. *Epiphyllum truncatum*		1·10	1·10
2470/2474 *Set of 5*			1·90	1·90

(Des T. M. Trang)

2002 (21 Feb). *Ninth National Women's Congress.* P 13.
2475	**582**	800d. multicoloured	35	35

583 Hugo and "Liberty Guiding the People" (painting, Eugène Delacroix)

(Des D. L Tuân)

2002 (26 Feb). *Birth Bicentenary of Victor Hugo (writer).* P 13.
2476	**583**	1000d. multicoloured	35	35

584 Black-crowned Barwing (*Actinodura sodangorum*)

585 Gành Son Coast, Binh Thuân Province

(Des Mrs. Vu Liên. Litho)

2002 (15 Mar). *Birds. T* **584** *and similar diamond-shaped designs. Multicoloured.* P 13½.
2477	600d. Type **584**		10	10
2478	800d. Golden-winged Laughing Thrush (*Garrulax ngoclinhensis*)		15	15
2479	800d. Long-billed Scimitar Babbler (*Pomatorhinus hypoleucos*)		15	15
2480	800d. Greater Necklaced Laughing Thrush (*Garrulax pectoralis*)		15	15
2481	5000d. Red-tailed Minla (*Minla ignotincta*)		65	65
2482	8000d. Blue-winged Minla (*Minla cynouroptera*)		1·00	1·00
2477/2482 *Set of 6*			2·00	2·00

(Des Mrs. Nguyên Thi Sâm. Litho)

2002 (23 Mar). *Central Vietnam Landscapes. T* **585** *and similar square designs. Multicoloured.* P 13½.
2483	800d. Type **585**		15	15
2484	800d. Tung Estuary, Quang Tri Province		15	15
2485	10000d. Sa Huynh Harbour, Quang Ngai Province		1·20	1·20

586 Golden-headed Langur (*Trachypithecus poliocephalus*)

587 Bui Thi Xuan riding Elephant

(Des Mrs. Hoang Thuy Lieu. Litho)

2002 (10 Apr). *Primates. T* **586** *and similar vert designs. Multicoloured.* P 13½.
2486	600d. Type **586**		10	10
2487	800d. Delacour's Langur (*Trachypithecus delacouri*)		10	10
2488	1000d. Tonkin Snub-Nosed Monkey (*Rhinopithecus avunculus*)		15	15
2489	2000d. Grey-shanked douc Langur (*Pygathrix cinerea*)		25	25
2490	4000d. Black Crested Gibbon (*Nomascus concolor*)		40	40
2491	5000d. Ha Tinh Langur (*Trachypithecus laotum hatinhensis*)		55	55
2492	7000d. Phayre's Langur (*Trachypithecus phayrei*)		80	80
2493	9000d. Red-shanked douc Langur (*Pygathrix nemaeus nemaeus*)		1·10	1·10
2486/2493 *Set of 8*			3·00	3·00
MS2494 179 × 141 mm. Nos. 2486/93 plus label			3·25	3·25

No. **MS**2494 includes a stamp-sized label showing a primate.

(Des Mrs. Nguyên Thi Sâm. Litho)

2002 (13 Apr). *Death Bicentenary of Commander-in-Chief Bui Thi Xuan.* P 13½.
2495	**587**	1000d. multicoloured	35	35

588 Footballer

589 Yellow Slipper Orchid (*Paphiopedilum concolor*)

(Des T. M. Trang. Litho)

2002 (1 June). *World Cup Football Championships, Japan and South Korea. Sheet* 112 × 100 *mm containing T **588** and similar vert designs. Multicoloured.* P 13.
MS2496 1000d. Type **588**; 2000d. Two players; 5000d. Player with ball; 7000d.
Goalkeeper . . . . 2·00 2·00

(Des L. Tuân and W. Gibbs. Litho)

2002 (5 June). *Flowers of Ha Long Bay. T **589** and similar vert designs. Multicoloured.* P 13½.
2497 600d. Type **589** 10 10
2498 800d. Velvet-pod Tree (*Sterculia lanceolata*) 15 15
2499 1000d. Ha Long Schefflera (*Schefflera alongensis*) 15 15
2500 2000d. Sea Hibiscus (*Hibiscus tiliaceus*) 25 25
2501 3000d. White Butterfly Tree (*Mussaenda glabra*) 40 40
2502 5000d. Puff-fruit Tree (*Boniodendron parviflorum*) 65 65
2503 9000d. Fragrant Bauhinia (*Bauhinia ornata*) . . . . 1·00 1·00
2497/2503 *Set of 7* . . . . 2·40 2·40

590 Châu Van Liêm

591 Winged Envelopes and Globe

(Des L. Tuân. Litho)

2002 (28 June). *Birth Centenary of Châu Van Liêm (revolutionary).* P 13½.
2504 **590** 800d. multicoloured 35 35

(Des T. Q. Thu. Litho)

2002 (1 July). *Stamp Day. 25th Anniv of Vietnam Stamp Company.* P 13.
2505 **591** 800d. multicoloured 35 35
No. 2505 was issued with *se-tenant* half stamp-sized label.

592 Victory Statue, People and Nup (revolutionary)

593 Asian Giant Soft-shelled Turtle (*Pelochelys bibroni*)

(Des Mrs. Nguyên Thi Sâm. Litho)

2002 (10 July). *Tay Nguyen (Western highlands).* P 13.
2506 **592** 800d. multicoloured 35 35

(Des Mrs. Vu Liên. Litho)

2002 (15 July). *Soft-shelled Turtles. T **593** and similar horiz designs showing soft-shelled turtles. Multicoloured.* P 13½.
2507 800d. Type **593** 15 15
2508 2000d. Chinese Turtle (*Pelodiscus sinensis*) 25 25

2509 5000d. Wattle-necked Turtle (*Palea steindachneri*) 55 55
2510 9000d. Black-rayed Turtle (*Trionyx cartilagineus*) . . . . 1·10 1·10
2507/2510 *Set of 4* . . . . 1·80 1·80
MS2511 173 × 100 mm. Nos. 2507/10, each × 2 . . . . 4·00 4·00

594 Khue Van Pavilion, Vietnam and That Luang, Laos

595 Beech 200 Super King Air

(Des Mrs. Vu Liên. Litho)

2002 (18 July). *25th Anniv of Friendship and Co-operation Treaty. 40th Anniv of Vietnam--Laos Diplomatic Relations.* P 13.
2512 **594** 800d. multicoloured 35 35

(Des L. Tuân. Litho)

2002 (1 Aug). *Civilian Aircraft. T **595** and similar horiz designs. Multicoloured.* P 13.
2513 800d. Type **595** 15 15
2514 2000d. Fokker 70 twin-engine jet airliner 25 25
2515 3000d. ATR72-202 twin-turboprop engine aircraft 40 40
2516 8000d. Boeing 767-300 ER . . . . 1·00 1·00
2513/2516 *Set of 4* . . . . 1·60 1·60
MS2517 90 × 60 mm. 14000d. Beech 200 Super King Air (*different*) . . . . 1·90 1·90

596 Ong Sao Lantern

597 Statue, Computer Operators and Satellite

(Des Mrs. Hoang Thuy Lieu. Litho)

2002 (16 Aug). *Mid-Autumn Festival Lanterns. T **596** and similar square designs. Multicoloured.* P 13½.
2518 800d. Type **596** 15 15
2519 800d. Ong Su lantern 15 15
2520 2000d. Con Tho Om Trang lantern . . . 25 25
2521 7000d. Chinese lantern 80 80
2518/2521 *Set of 4* . . . . 1·20 1·20

(Des Mrs. Vu Liên. Litho)

2002 (23 Aug). *55th Anniv of Posts and Telecommunication Worker's Trade Union.* P 13.
2522 **597** 800d. multicoloured 35 35

598 Long Bien Bridge

(Des Mrs. Vo Luong Nhi. Litho)

2002 (27 Sept). *Bridges.* T **598** *and similar horiz designs. Multicoloured.* P 13.

2523	800d. Type **598**	15	15
2524	800d. Song Han bridge	15	15
2525	2000d. Truong Tien bridge	25	25
2526	10000d. My Thuan bridge	1·20	1·20
2523/2526 *Set of 4*		1·60	1·60

599 Open Book and Flowers

(Des Mrs. To Minh Trang and L. Tuân. Litho)

2002 (10 Oct). *72nd Anniv of Ideology and Culture Commission.* P 13.

2527	**599** 800d. multicoloured	25	25

600 Ho Hac Di (first principal) and College Building

601 Teacher and Pupil

599 Open Book and Flowers

(Des Mrs. Vo Luong Nhi and L. Tuân. Litho)

2002 (15 Nov). *Centenary of Hanoi Medical University.* P 13.

2528	**600** 800d. multicoloured	25	25

(Des N. Du. Litho)

2002 (20 Nov). *20th Anniv of Teachers' Day.* P 13.

2529	**601** 800d. multicoloured	25	25

602 Goat

603 One Pillar Pagoda, Hanoi

(Des L. Tuân. Litho)

2002 (15 Dec). *New Year. Year of the Goat.* T **602** *and similar square design. Multicoloured.* P 13½.

2530	800d. Type **602**	15	15
2531	8000d. Goat (*different*)	1·00	1·00

(Des Mrs. Hoang Thuy Lieu, Mrs. Vu Liên and Sejong. Litho)

2002 (21 Dec). *Tenth Anniv of Vietnam–North Korea Diplomatic Relations.* T **603** *and similar vert design. Multicoloured.* P 13.

2532	800d. Type **603**	25	25
2533	800d. Dabotap Pagoda, Bulguksa		
	Temple, North Korea	25	25

STAMP BOOKLETS

The following checklist covers, in simplified form, booklets issued by the Independent State (1951–54) and by South Vietnam. It is intended that it should be used in conjunction with the main listings and details of stamps listed there are not repeated.

Souvenir booklets containing miniature sheets of one stamp are included in the main listing (Nos. **MS**73a and **MS**90a)

Prices are for complete booklets

Booklet No.	Date	Contents and Cover Price	Price
SB1	10.11.52	Red Cross Fund (T **10** surch)	
		1 pane, No. 88 × 20 (40p.)	90·00
SB2	21.12.52	Wounded Soldiers' Relief Fund (T **16**)	
		1 pane, No. 90 × 4 (20p.)	70·00
South Vietnam			
SB3	15.12.67	Mobile Post Office (T **86**)	
		2 panes, No. S302 × 5 (30p.)	£180
SB4	28.1.72	Emperor Quang Trung (T **125**)	
		1 pane, No. S402 × 10 (60p.)	85·00

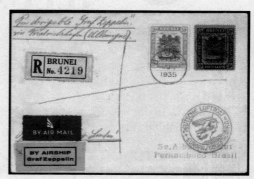

There's a buzz about our auctions

and the reasons are obvious:

- the largest philatelic audience in the UK

- collections selling at 25% over catalogue prices

- unrivalled expertise in the field of philately

- possibly receive 25% of the estimated value of your collection before it goes to auction

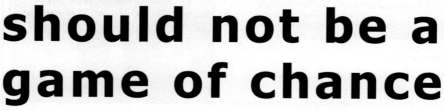

COLLECT SOUTH EAST ASIA STAMPS

Priority order form
Four easy ways to order

Phone:
020 7836 8444

Fax:
020 7557 4499

Email:
stampsales@stanleygibbons.co.uk

Post:
Stamp Mail Order Department
Stanley Gibbons Ltd, 399 Strand
London, WC2R 0LX

Customer details

Account Number ....

Name ....

Address...

.... Postcode ....

Country .... Email ....

Tel no .... Fax no ....

Payment details

Registered Postage & Packaging   £3.60

I enclose my cheque/postal order for £....................
in full payment. Please make cheques/postal orders
payable to Stanley Gibbons Ltd.

Please debit my credit card for £....................in full
payment. I have completed the Credit Card section
below.

Card Number:

Start Date (Switch & Amex)   Expiry Date   Issue No (Switch)

Signature .... Date ....

COLLECT SOUTH EAST ASIA STAMPS

Condition	Country	SG No.	Description	Price
			SUB TOTAL	£
			POSTAGE & PACKAGING	£3.60
			GRAND TOTAL	£

Please complete payment, name and address details overleaf